SECTION OF HARRISBURG QUADRANGLE - HARRISBURG, PA.

GEOGRAPHY IN WORLD SOCIETY

The Lippincott Geography Series
CLARENCE F. JONES, EDITOR
NORTHWESTERN UNIVERSITY

Geography in World Society

A Conceptual Approach

ALFRED H. MEYER

JOHN H. STRIETELMEIER

VALPARAISO UNIVERSITY

J. B. LIPPINCOTT COMPANY

PHILADELPHIA AND NEW YORK

Library of Congress Catalog Card Number: 63-7026
Printed in the United States of America

Preface

This book appears at a time when astronautical man is readying himself for explorations of the sister planets of the earth. It is not surprising that man's attempt at cosmic conquest has produced an impact second to none in transforming our educational system at all levels of instruction. For one thing, the terms *space* and *area* connote new concepts of reality. Despite their importance in cosmic science, particularly as these concepts are implicated in the Cold War of our time, it is an educational paradox that man is motivated towards conquest of other planets before he has learned the significance of space relationships of reality as they apply to the problems of mankind on his own earth. Understanding world reality under man's dominion should be a basic objective of all education; yet this geographic illiteracy has been the chief deficiency in American education. The curricular and instructional systems as a whole have been operating under the illusion that geography consists in merely identifying places on a map and that the study of geography is therefore devoid of disciplinary value requiring professionalized instruction. This book is written with the hope that it may help to dispel this illusion.

Though elements of ancient, medieval, and early modern geography are given integral treatment in this book, emphasis is placed on the twentieth century with its population explosion, economic stress, and political unrest. Moreover, in the interest of motivation, current affairs are featured despite the fact that the geographic pattern with which they are associated today may be changed tomorrow. As with history, to which geography is traditionally most intimately related, it is the *process* of day-by-day event-environment change that is paramount in the study of geography—the former focusing on the element of time, the latter on space (i.e., spatial organization and interaction of phenomena), as both disciplines survey together the affairs of the world.

Geography in World Society is designed as a textbook in introductory college geography, with a spatial-conceptual approach throughout. As here presented, geography is an areal interpretation and evaluation of earth realities, comprehended in the various academic disciplines. In this context, the disciplinary interests and value of geography itself are centered upon *areal association* of the physical, biological, social, economic, and political phenomena of this world, rather than upon the phenomena per se. To this end, the selection and organization of material are designed to assess the *regional* role that natural and human resources play in the creation and solution of world problems. Since geography may be viewed as a land and resource policy-creating subject, process and planning, as well as product and inventory, are stressed. Accordingly, the basic questions to which this text addresses itself are: What is man in terms of *ecesis* (earth-habitat relationship)? What is his *ethos* (earth-steward responsibility)? How do the forms of human occupance reveal areal human behavior? What is the nature of man's control over the nature-conditioning environment? How does the analysis of global phenomena by the unitary "geographic region" method differ from that of the political nation-state approach in the study of world affairs?

Concepts here are focused on two chief spatial factors—areal content (resources) and areal context (region). How have our past cultures evolved? What makes historic changes in areal human occupance come about? Why do we encounter different forms of human occupance in similar natural environments, and similar forms of human occupance in decidedly contrasted natural environments? What geographic criteria and techniques serve us best to understand man–land connections, and effectively assist us in area and resource planning for the future welfare of all mankind?

To facilitate the conceptual approach to the consideration of problems posed by the above questions, all material of this book—textual and illustrative—has been organized on what might be called the "self-tutorial plan." The text is constructed, then, to be teachable as well as readable, with all technical terms italicized and defined, so as to facilitate vocabulary building and the preparation of a geographic glossary by the student.

Insofar as seems practicable, with the little geographic knowledge the student is presumed to have had before coming to college, the *inductive* rather than the deductive approach is used. This is done, for example, particularly in Part IV where periodical "current affairs" topics of limited spatial and chronologic scope introduce chapter material dealing with the larger relevant realms of the world. The accompanying maps specifically drawn for this purpose suggest the close integration of text and map, both of which are to be "studied"—and not simply glanced at.

Joint authorship of any kind inevitably poses the challenge of unity of approach and coherent content. Fortunately, as a result of teaching large classes in social geography in the same institution for many years, the authors have shared experiences and insights conducive to effective co-ordination of subject matter.

"Application of geographic understanding" commits students to class preparation and participation

If thirty-five years of contact with undergraduates in geography have contributed anything at all to our experiences and convictions, it is this:

1. That high school graduates generally are ill-equipped in substantive knowledge in any field directly contributory to the understanding of the basic institutions of society and modern world problems.

2. That secondary school background reflects deficiency particularly in meaningful knowledge of places and peoples in the world in their regional setting, to say nothing of the almost total lack of comprehension of the basic *areal* interacting forces upon which must depend in the last analysis the understanding of the concepts developed in the various disciplines related to geography.

3. That college freshmen and sophomores can benefit most from lectures and discussions when these two procedures are combined, and from a textbook organization designed to insure the necessary background and motivation for intelligent and lively classroom discussion.

4. That entering college freshmen, even some of the best students, have difficulty in expressing themselves, particularly on examinations which involve essay questions, because of lack of experience with such tests on the high school level.

Accordingly, to stimulate the student to do some creative work of his own, before as well as after the reading assignment, a set of questions as an outside work assignment has been carefully worked out to fit every degree of student resourcefulness. Entitled "Application of Geographic Understanding," this section simulates a workbook exercise at the conclusion of each chapter to challenge the student to a reflective review of the facts, concepts, and principles developed in each chapter. Moreover, topics are included for essay work where classroom situations may call for the development of geographic writing suited to examinations of the essay type.

Material is inductively organized

An inductive preview to the organization of each of the six parts of the book, together with a conceptual diagram, is designed to prepare the student to anticipate the kind of concepts he is expected to develop and to point up as well the major unifying elements of the book.

Part I explores historically how the "Geographic Facts of Life" are ordered and how geographic scholars in time have conceived of such facts. Part II reviews the basic classification of natural earth phenomena and basic principles of man–earth relationships. Part III analyzes the systematic processes by which man appraises and appropriates areal resources and emphasizes his responsibilities as conservator of such resources. Part IV reviews the elements considered systematically in Part II and Part III, but in a "regional" context, a critique quite traditionally unique to the geographic profession. But man has his own way of defining domains of control, i.e., areal differentiations by political jurisdictions. It is thus appropriate to analyze geographically, as we do in Part V, the relation of earth occupance, dominated by the nation-state, to the environmental realities of its constituent realms and regions. In Part VI, "The Geographic Way of Life" is portrayed in the combined concept of habitable and resource space in historic time.

Map composition is aimed at expressiveness of geographic concepts and principles rather than cartographic art. Photographs and graphic sketches likewise have been selected for their portrayal of basic landscape composition of interest in land occupance and resource analysis. Recognition of the meaning of areal association of features in any one landscape, and the significance of the varying patterns of the environmental ensemble as they differ from one region to the next, have ever been the goals of the geographer. Accordingly, illustrative media have been selected which seem to lend themselves best towards presenting a unified view of those space and resource relationships most significant in any given context of the text.

Reference material is integral rather than supplemental

Intensive, rather than extensive, readings are here presumed to promote most effectively *geographic* thinking, still seemingly the major problem of beginners in geography. Instead, therefore, of a catalogue of references for the subject of general geography as a whole at the end of the book, or a chapter-by-chapter listing of references representative for each subject division, selected sources are quoted or otherwise referred to in context with each of the concepts and principles introduced in the text. This technique is believed to have significant functional advantages: (1) it contributes a large measure of comprehensive coverage of the various facets of the field; (2) it promotes integration of source ideas with the themes developed in the text; (3) it saves the student the expense of purchasing supplementary reference compendia, or the trouble of going to the library only to find multiple reference works in insufficient supply, particularly of the professional journal type featured here.

As in the case of other works of this character, source selections had to be severely restricted, with high regard for close relevance to textual material. Among other selective criteria were: authoritativeness, diversity of opinion, inclusiveness of divisional subject matter, a focus on both the theoretical and applicational aspects, the use of a geo-historical approach centered on population and resource analysis. World events as reported in current news periodicals are geographically assayed against the more technically presented background provided by the professional journal or other source material. And to give the student an idea of how geographic thinking on world affairs complements the points of view expressed by specialists in other fields, journal sources are cited outside of, but correlative with, geography. In all, some three hundred sources have been cited.

Multiple or single term textbook

Sufficient material is incorporated in this textbook to serve a year's introductory geography curriculum set-up, and this without recourse to supplementary library reading often made difficult by the increasingly large enrollments of beginning classes in college geography. Parts I, II, and III, comprising the first eighteen chapters, each concluded with challenging questions on "Application of Geographic Understanding," may well serve the first semester's assignments for schedules on the semester plan. Similarly, Parts IV, V, and VI provide adequate reading and question material for the second semester. On the three-term quarter basis the sequence might well be: first term

—Parts I and II; second term—Part IV; third term—Parts III, V, and VI.

Flexibility of organization of textual material allows for a single semester or term offering under the selective discretion of the instructor, depending on what feature of the text best serves the individual curricular needs of the institution and the department, as well as the kind of geographic concepts and techniques on which the instructor wishes to focus attention.

Acknowledgments

The writing of any book on any one aspect of human society in global perspective is in itself a most challenging experience. But to embrace total areal reality is nothing short of complex frustration and mortification. Only the intriguing subject matter, the refreshing review of scholarly publications in the field—ancient and modern—and the inspiration that has come from long and regular fraternal association with the most productive research scholars in the field can sustain one in such a prolonged and trying adventure. Accordingly, to all such sources which have lent professional enlightenment we are deeply grateful. Particularly are we indebted to the several hundred sources consulted and cited to strengthen and sharpen the points of view presented here. Quoted sources and reproduced illustrations are duly acknowledged where they appear.

Only long-continued classroom experiences can give one the insights needed to see the problems of teaching geography in true pedagogical perspective. Accordingly, we here gratefully acknowledge such student contacts, especially in such courses as introductory social geography, economic geography, political geography, the philosophy and profession of geography, geography of world affairs, and geographic problems. The latter courses particularly, in developing brief so-called chorograms on current world affairs and term paper projects on some "geo" phase of a societal or national problem, have contributed materially to the development of geographic concepts stimulating to the instructor and student alike.

Also gratefully acknowledged is student participation in executing map and diagram designing as well as typing of the chapter manuscripts. Valuable help in executing maps and diagrams came from Dan Gade, Curtis Iden, Martin Knorr, Janet Koehn, Eugene Kroenke, Marna Tibben, and Richard Wing. Publisher's copy was prepared by Carol Gerlitz, Diane Heidtmann, Janet Severance, Judith Lehrbaummer, and Gretchen Prindle. Mrs. Alfred Meyer assisted in index tabulations.

Gratefully acknowledged are the numerous sources, including editor Clarence Jones, that have supplied courtesy photo material. Arch Gerlach, Chief, Map Division of the Library of Congress, arranged for the reproduction of ancient maps. The following persons were instrumental in providing original or reproduced photos of celebrated geographers: Wilma B. Fairchild, Editor, *The Geographical Review;* P. J. Drewe, Assistant Map Curator of the Royal Geographical Society; Marguerita Oughton, Assistant Editor, *Geography* (The Geographical Association, London); H. Schamp, Wiss. Rat., Institute für Landeskunde; and M. Jean-Brunhes Delamarre.

And finally, our deepest indebtedness is to the helpfulness of the editor and the publisher who have patiently stood by in the protracted preparation of manuscript material. All such material has been critically reviewed by the geography editor, Dr. Clarence F. Jones, on the "installment plan" —several chapters at a time. Preferred this way by Dr. Jones himself, this procedure has signally inspired confidence in the continuity and integrity of the project. Follow-up joint conferences with Dr. Jones and the Lippincott college staff have given the necessary impetus to complete this work.

Valparaiso, Indiana
August, 1962

Alfred H. Meyer
John H. Strietelmeier

Contents

Part I Nature of the Discipline of Geography

Part II Man's Planetary Domain

Part III The Geographic Aspects of Technology and Ethics in Societal and National Life

Part V The Regional and Resource Factors of Nation-States

Part VI Summary Observations on Man's Relations to Space in Time

Chapter 35 Conceptual Geography in Historical Perspective

Chapter 36 The Geographic Way of Life—Planning the Geography of the Future

GEOGRAPHY IN WORLD SOCIETY

Part I

Nature of the discipline of geography

"Geographic Man" is regarded in world affairs geography as *the* being who gives order and meaning to the landscape elements of earth. Epochal experiences of mankind are observed as impressing themselves spatially on each stage of world history. In this sense, geography combines with history in recording and appraising cultural change, the former in a chorographical framework, the latter with a chronological focus.

Like the historian, the geographer must be conversant with institutional phenomena as developed by each of the other academic disciplines which compose the liberal arts curriculum, generalized in the figure at the lower right. And like the historian also, the geographer seeks to unify the concepts which emerge from the study of the separate disciplines. The theme of this book is addressed to this task.

Part I introduces the student to the philosophical base of the geographic discipline as interpreted by celebrated historical scholars of geographic thought. Review of such historical geography reveals that man's behavior and society's institutions must be viewed in terms of the total force of natural-cultural regional reality if man is to control effectively the ever-prevalent conditioning environs.

Chapter 1 considers the basic concepts held by geographers throughout time and how they have evolved. Chapter 2 treats of the modern geographic concepts in the perspective of general and applied education. Chapter 3 illustrates how the historic concepts of earth and of its modern occupance forms by man have been expressed cartographically. And finally, Chapter 4 focuses attention on earth's population potential and man's resource stewardship responsibilities

Chapter 1

The geographic facts of life

What is man, that thou art mindful of him? . . . thou hast put all things under his feet.—Psalm 8: 4-6.

Geography is anthropocentric

The psalmist's query above is typical of the questions mankind has asked of itself throughout the ages. This search for man's origin and destiny, regardless of the stage of culture, religious or scientific views which man may otherwise hold of reality, and of his purpose in it, is universal.

The field of geography bears a unique relationship to this question in two major aspects: (1) the antiquity of the subject—one might term it the mother of sciences and of all secular learning; and (2) the universality of geographic phenomenology which impinges on man's global consciousness in all his world affairs.

At the very outset of our global analysis of reality through the study of areality, three primary factors of earth–man relationships are recognized: (1) the earth was designated by the Creator to be man's domain; (2) the earth was designed in differentiated form, element-wise and space-wise, to function as a unit by what we call natural laws (physical and biological); and (3) man, by the superior order of his creation (intellect, skills, attitude, spirit) was destined to evaluate and appropriate the naturally-differentiated earth and integrate his own variegated culture patterns with those of the natural earth to form the world of reality as we know it. The content and context of global landscapes thus resulting may be said to represent in part the terrestrial base and in part the ideological concepts of man in carrying out the divine injunction to "subdue the earth." Human geography thus is concerned with the earth not simply as the *home* of man but as the *dominion* of man. This distinction is significant in distinguishing man from animal as well as in impressing upon the student that geography is not a static, stereotyped science. He will learn that it is a dynamic field in which we must re-explore each day, so to speak, the geographic patterns of human occupance that are evolving from the unceasing interactions between natural and cultural forces. The dominant philosophy of man's world stewardship is in the best of the Western tradition, as so well stated by Harold Thomas:

¶ Western civilization has been markedly influenced by the idea of man's dominion over the earth put to him in Genesis. Western man has tended to set himself apart from the rest of animate nature, while other and older civilizations and systems of religion have regarded man as being a part of nature. Though very different from the nineteenth-century approach, nevertheless there is today a very real movement in science toward resolution of this duality through studies of the association of mankind with nature.[1]

It thus becomes the chief function of the geographer to describe and explain the nature and meaning of human "dominion" or occupance forms as arranged in space and varied in time. In this connection it is important for the student of geography to recognize the place that the subject occupies in relation to all the other disciplines, which make their own distinctive academic contribution to the study of man and reality, a subject treated more specifically in Chapter 2. Subsequently when we discuss the true nature and methodology of geography, we shall see that geography, unlike the typical systematic science, is not identified by "the kind" of earth phenomena it treats, but rather by "the manner" in which it selects and analyzes in terms of space interrelation the various physical, biotic, and societal features with which it concerns itself either regionally or systematically. In this sense, then, geography is not the study of climate, landforms, soils, minerals, plant and animal life, or even man himself. In the same sense then also, geography is not a study of the cultural establishments by man per se, such

[1] Reprinted from *Man's Role in Changing the Face of the Earth*, edited by William L. Thomas, Jr., by permission of The University of Chicago Press. © The University of Chicago, 1956. Published 1956, composed and printed by The University of Chicago Press, Chicago, Illinois, U.S.A.

as settlement, houses, farms, transportation, communication, and the like. And so we may say that the patterns and processes which inhere in settlement—extractive economies of hunting and fishing, lumbering and mining, clearing land, planting and harvesting of crops, technological procedures of manufacturing, engineering projects of construction and transportation—and in the founding of nation-states, etc., indispensable though they are for regional analysis, are of themselves no more the distinctive province of geography than they are the domain of history, economics, sociology, political science, or any other field. Then, too, though the map, based on the areal differentiation of phenomena, is an indispensable tool of geography, the geographer has no monopoly on either the making or the use of maps.

What, then, is the distinctive core domain of geography? As in the case of every other discipline, rather wide divergences of professional viewpoints are held in this matter, some of which we shall presently explore. But typical core organization of this textbook at least is designed not only to contribute to the understanding of world cultures in their empirical regional settings, but also to learn: (1) how they have come about; (2) what techniques are used by geographers in sharing the responsibility of other social scientists in trying to account for them; and (3) what geographic concepts are significant in regional and interregional analysis.

The over-all significance of our geographic study, then, is to present concepts that will be helpful in analyzing and appraising world affairs in a time-space continuum. In this operation, geography functions conjointly with history, which focuses on the chronology of world events in period sequences, whereas geography is characteristically concerned with the space element in the context of regional sequences (chorography). In partnership, then, the two areas draw on virtually all fields of knowledge and organize them interrelatedly so as to give meaning to reality in place and time.

Geographic man — Who are we? Where are we? Who are our neighbors?

To understand properly any modern field of investigation, one must have at least a glimpse of the major antecedent contributions to the field, and thus see how concepts in science develop. Our review of representative milestones in the history of geographic thought reveals one universal search for the meaning of space, particularly the part which is the place we call "home."

1. Ancient concepts. It soon became apparent to the early Greek philosophers, especially those who were interested in the *ecumene* (the inhabited world), that to understand man–earth relationships, one has to recognize: (1) the different patterns of natural and cultural elements that distinguish one place or region from another, and (2) the cognate relationships that are observable among the several earth–man components of each region. To be sure, such primary observations at first were not always clearly distinguishable one from the other. As a matter of fact, as we shall see later, the nature of the relationships between phenomena themselves and the significance of the arrangement of such phenomena as they occur in any areal study have presented unresolved conflicts and different points of view to this very day. However, since growth in learning is a continuing process, it is well to trace briefly the stages of geographic conceptual development. Regardless of how primitive the ancient concepts may have been, the writings of Herodotus (*ca.* 400 B.C.) show that he realized that event and environment must be considered in relation to one another if one is to understand the significance of the affairs of a people or a nation. Then, as this science, like all others, progressed further, it soon became apparent that environmental features needed to be treated also as an entity. For this purpose, then, Eratosthenes (*ca.* 200 B.C.) proposed the term "geography" for "a description of the earth."

But, as the student should recognize, such differentiation of subject matter in the study of science[1] has both advantages and disadvantages. As is the hallmark of all differentiated areas of knowledge, delimitation or definition of specialized fields is a difficult and often highly arbitrary matter. While certain earth phenomena lend themselves to ready classification into such units as physical, biotic, and human societal categories, their interlocking character in space

[1] Here used in the broadest connotation, as any systematically organized area of knowledge.

(regional) and in interrelationship in functional processes (systematic) challenges the highest ingenuity of man in discovering how elemental and areal diversity of features fits into the whole of reality. Or, to state it perhaps more simply, the meaning that resides in global unity may be obscured or even entirely misinterpreted when sections of areality, or segments of processes, are considered in isolation.

To those generally uninformed of the field and function of modern geography, the central theme of study of "place-to-place differences" may seem prosaic. Indeed, the history of geographic thought reveals that nothing seems to have been more commonplace in the history of mankind than the fact that even unsophisticated man recognized from time immemorial this "difference from place to place" as a universal experience. And so the ancients speculated: Who are we? Where are we? Who are our neighbors? What kind of place do they live in? How and why do they differ from us? Homer's *Odyssey* (*ca.* 800 B.C.) clearly reveals, both fact-wise and fancy-wise, preoccupation with this diversity of far-flung lands in the ancient world. Knowing why one part of the earth was inhabited (*ecumene*) and another was not, was of major concern to the early Greeks. Of significance to the ancients, too, were the recognized facts that one or another place had a more favorable regional situation for commerce, and because of superior skill some nations became more influential than others in the world of commerce, or more powerful in military or political affairs. The people in antiquity probably in the best position to realize this were the Phoenicians (*ca.* 1000 B.C.). Situated at the northeast Mediterranean shore at the crossroads of three continents, these so-called "peddlers of antiquity" commercially exploited with a vengeance the concept of regional differences in both place and product. Though the Phoenicians left little record of their own exploits, the prophet Ezekiel (*ca.* 600 B.C.) in Chapter 27 of the Book of Ezekiel gives us what has been credited to be the most complete account, whether in secular or sacred literature, of a differentiated world. A further exposition of this significant observation on what we call today commercial geography is given in Chapter 15 of our text. The most outstanding contribution to a rather systematic account of general geography of the earlier Mediterranean world is the work of the celebrated Greek scholar Strabo, whose writings at the dawn of the Christian era signify a keen perceptiveness of the significance of "place-to-place" differences in the Roman world. During his extensive travels, he not only visited Rome, where he was in contact with Roman statesmen, but he also spent considerable time in Alexandria, where there was located the greatest library of antiquity. There, Strabo probably did most of his geographic research, in contact with Greek, Roman, and Arabian original source material. His *Geography* in seventeen volumes reflects the first conception of the branches of physical-mathematical, political, and historical geography, and gives us the first comprehensive identification of geography and its evaluation as a hallmark of culture:

¶ The science of Geography . . . is, I think, quite as much as any other science, a concern of the philosopher. . . . Wide learning, which alone makes it possible to undertake a work on geography, is possessed solely by the man who has investigated things both human and divine—knowledge of which, they say, constitutes philosophy. And so, too, the utility of geography—and its utility is manifold, not only as regards the activities of statesmen and commanders but also as regards knowledge both of the heavens and of things on land and sea, animals, plants, fruits, and everything else to be seen in various regions—the utility of geography, I say, presupposes in the geographer the same philosopher, the man who busies himself with the investigation of the art of life, that is, of happiness.[1]

As we might expect in view of the primacy of climates in human affairs, the Greek and Roman geographers primarily stressed the climatic zones (*klimata*). On the human side it is equally understandable that space differentiations were primarily considered in terms of political units because of the importance of the organization of Greek colonies and Roman provinces. Geographical contributions of the classical period may

---

[1] Strabo, *The The Geography of Strabo* (English translation by H. L. Jones), Harvard University Press, Leob Classical Library Edition, Vol. I, pp. 3, 5. Reprinted by permission.

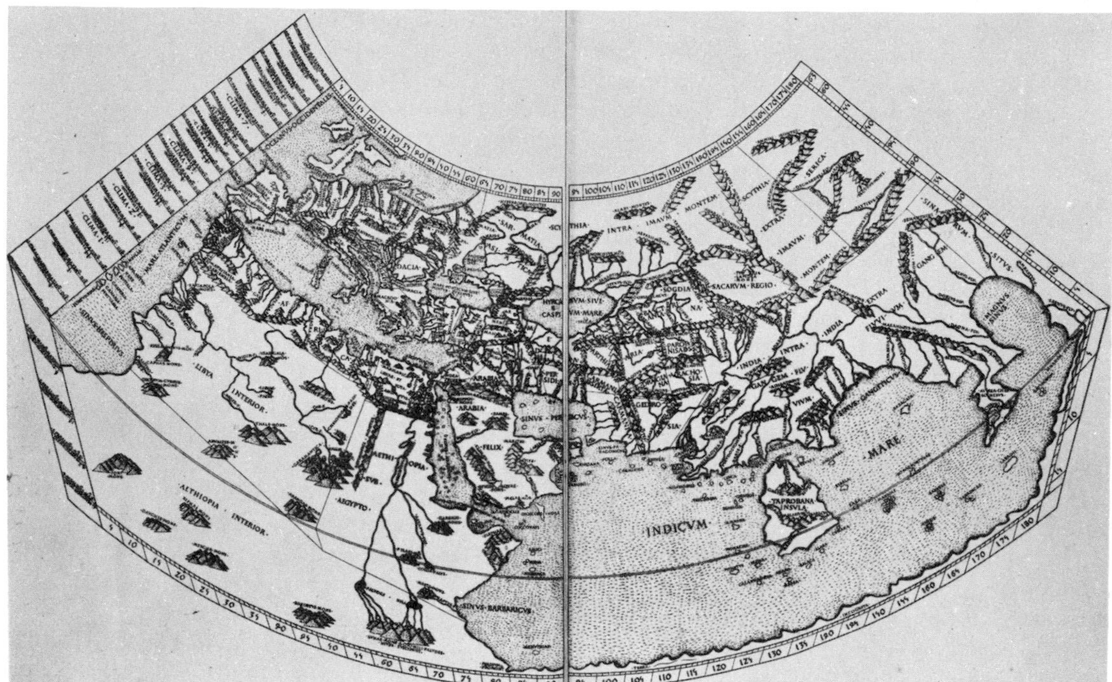

I:1 Reproducing the global surface of the earth on a flat map has always been both a primary concept and challenge in geography. Such representation involves what is known as a projection, either of the perspective type or of the mathematically computed type. Reduced to the simplest terms, we may identify these perspectively with one or another of three types—a plane, cone, or cylinder. Though mathematically determined, to which type does the Ptolemy projection appear related? Also, do you see any evidence of Ptolemy's perception of a basic relationship between latitude and climate? Already in 125 B.C. the Greek astronomer Hipparchus recognized that scientific mapping depends upon determining earth co-ordinates of latitude and longitude; but not until Ptolemy's time (A.D. 150) were there sufficient data to construct a map based on "parallels" and "meridians," terms first used by Ptolemy. Without accurate data, Ptolemy misplaced the Equator by a considerable distance, and, as you see, represented the Indian Ocean as an enclosed sea. Despite such cartographic shortcomings, practically unavoidable at the time, Ptolemy's maps give us our first scientifically drawn projection—a form of conic. Note also the recognition of the "clima" zones, relating climate to latitude. (Reproduced from the Collections of the Library of Congress)

be said to close with the work of Ptolemy whose map of about A.D. 150 (Figure I-1) portrayed not only the extent of the explored world but also projected conceptual outlines of parts of the Old World continents not yet explored.

2. *Medieval concepts.* By contrast, despite the subsequent expansion of knowledge of new lands resulting from extensive travel, the Middle Ages witnessed little of record in the progress of regional geography. As a matter of fact, some prominent travelers and writers actually retarded progress by their archaic observations of the earth and its inhabitants. Thus Cosmas Indicopleustus (*ca.* A.D. 500) in his *Christian Topography* insisted on verifying, by reference to numerous scriptural passages, the flatness of the earth.

To the Arabian, rather than to the European, belongs the chief credit of expanding the frontiers of geographic knowledge during this otherwise dark period. After numerous trading expeditions to the Orient from about the ninth to the fourteenth century, travelers left detailed descriptive accounts of hitherto unvisited countries. Even geographical dictionaries were produced toward the end of that period, such as the one by Jakout, reputed to have been the greatest of the Arab scholars. Moreover, since Arab scholarship in mathematics and astronomy was superior to that of the Greeks, latitudinal and longitudinal distances were more accurately established than was possible in the days of Ptolemy. Determination of accurate co-ordinates in relation to the position of Mecca was prompted by religion so as to synchronize noonday prayers for the widely scattered Moslems. Thus, in the Middle Ages, we have at least two major religious interests toward geography in evidence: The Christian's preoccupation with the implications of the Greek geographical doctrine of the sphericity and antipodal character of the earth, and the Moslem's concern about establishing correct earth co-ordinates to ensure proper chronometry of worship.

Though Moslem geographers did not penetrate Europe in the main, they did preserve for posterity the classic geographical contributions of the ancient Greeks as well as transmit their own geographical lore across northern Africa and the Strait of Gibraltar into the Iberian Peninsula, where at Toledo, Spain, was established the most celebrated library of the time.

*3. **Modern concepts.*** The late fifteenth and early sixteenth century discoveries of transatlantic and transpacific lands, and the circumnavigation of the globe by such explorers as Magellan and Drake, opened up an entirely new area of earth–space evaluation. A new dimension of earth differentiation and man's place in it resulted in a conflict between the claims of the explored regions by the Spanish and those by the Portuguese. The upshot of the dispute was a "Line of Demarcation" drawn to separate the claims of these two countries in the New World. Measurement of differences between places east and west (longitude) also took on a new dimensional significance when in 1675 the spring clock was invented, which for the first time made possible reasonably accurate determination of meridional positions on a global scale. It is significant here to recall that already the early Greeks had invented the *gnomon* which operated somewhat on the order of a sun dial and which, by noting the various shadows, made possible not only the measurement of distances north and south of the Equator (latitude) but also, as indicated before, made possible the approximate determination of the earth's circumference. The Moslem, as indicated above, had achieved comparable competency in longitude determinations, a geo-religious motivation to ensure region-wide synchronous noon worship.

For the first time, an area could be represented regionally with a relatively high degree of accuracy, at least in terms of the globe, since the problem still remained of expressing equal areas comparatively on a flat surface. Despite its high navigational usefulness, the Mercator projection (Figure I-2) did not provide an "equal-area" perspective, and so led to many comparative areal misconceptions which identify much of our basic geographical illiteracy to this very day. This is not the fault, of course, of the map, which Mercator never intended to grace our wall calendars for ready orientation to world affairs. Abused in this connection, its calendar display does serve a purpose: it symbolizes the mediocrity of American standards of education in geography.

The first major attempt to give what we might call a systematic space analysis of man in the world is the *Geographia Generalis* published by Bernard Varen (Varenius) in Amsterdam in 1650. Taking an over-all view of the earth in general, the author set to "describing its various divisions and the phenomena which affect it as a whole." Many of the major geographical concepts of space developed in the succeeding century reflect direct familiarity with the works of Varen.

Systematic search for geographical processes explaining world reality

The two major modern approaches or methods to the study of world geography are commonly recognized as "systematic geography" and "regional geography." Nondualistic in character (both procedures are concerned with analyzing and understanding world areality), the two techniques simply follow a different presentation of subject matter. Systematic geography, as presented in this book primarily in Parts II, III, and VI, focuses its investigation topically on the relationship of world phenomena from one region to the next, seeking to discover geo-

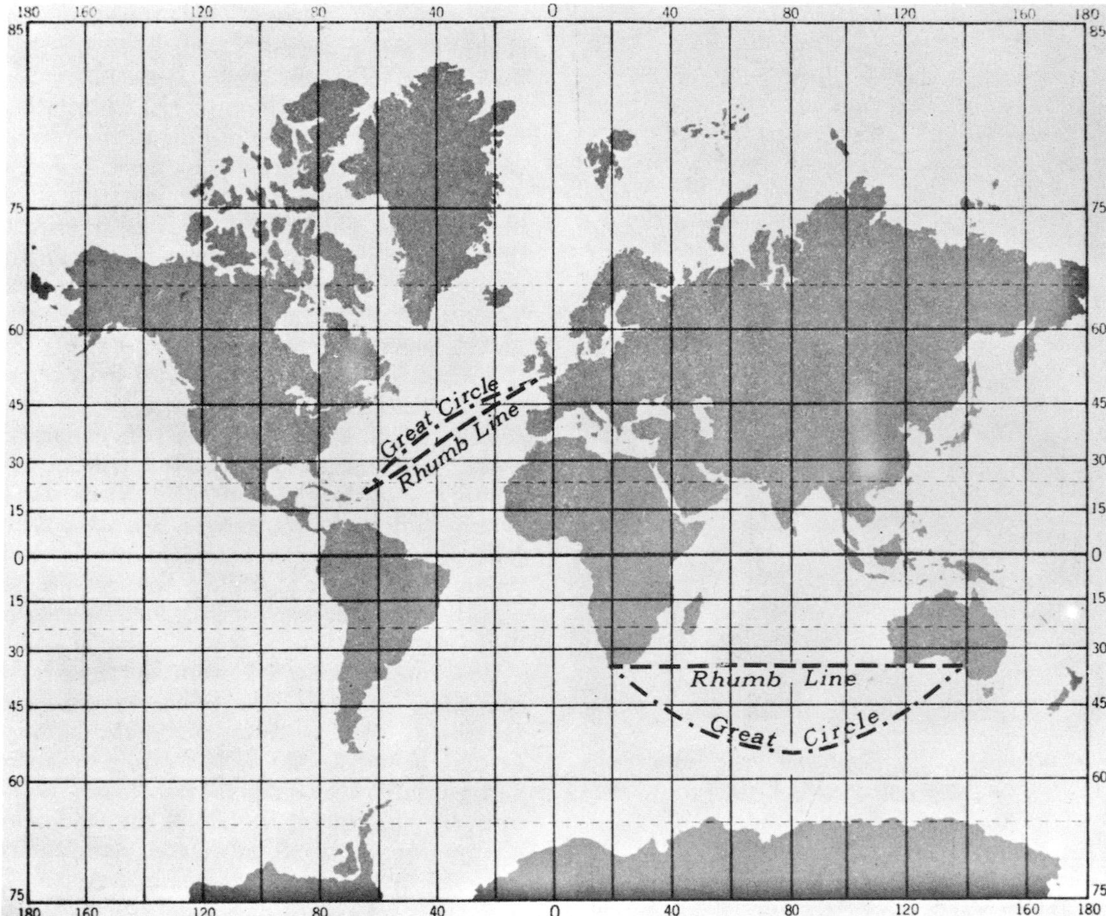

I:2 This shows the Mercator projection (1569) in modern continental perspective. The previous Ptolemy projection (Figure I:1) might be thought of as identified chiefly with land and inland sea earth co-ordinates and their geographic significance to "inland" travel. But when the land-lubber turned sea-navigator incident to the discovery of new seas and continents, another type of projection was called for. As you will note on the chart, the navigator may simply draw a straight line (rhumb line) between his point of departure and his destination, noting the angle to the meridians or parallels (all straight lines also), and set his vessel's course. In actual practice for long voyages the navigator steers his vessel, as far as is practicable, along the shortest route on the globe, the Great Circle. (Courtesy Denoyer-Geppert Company)

graphic relationships throughout the distributions of such phenomena. Thus, in the study of settlement patterns an author may wish to focus his attention on the morphology of urban communities of several or many diverse cultural regions and thus gain an insight into the processes, problems, and planning procedures connected with urbanization. Though regional geography is likewise interested in such an important topic as urbanization, its primary goal is to establish area-differentiating criteria and principles by which *regions* can be identified. The significance of this approach, in both its *homogeneous* and *nodal* settings, will appear later, for it is essentially a twentieth-century development and, in its most recent form—that of the study of the *campage*—a mid-century product of geographic philosophy.

It was logical for geographic methodology

Alexander von Humboldt 1769-1859 (From *Geographischen Taschenbuch* by E. Meynen)

to begin with the systematic (topical) approach, since all science from its earliest development is concerned with the study of reality and, therefore, embraces the processes by which changes are brought about both in the inorganic and in the organic world. In terms of geography, then, causal relationships between the inorganic and organic world are also to be recognized when such can be properly established through adequate data and valid means of measuring the significance of such data. And since the earth is man's domain, the relation of man to nature in both the organic as well as inorganic realms becomes an object of study of total systematic reality.

Varen's *General Geography* was in its own way a systematic treatise and pointed the way to the development of modern systematic geography at the opening of the nineteenth century, the latter half of which geographically came to be known as the classical period. The two great savants of this period are Alexander von Humboldt and Carl Ritter.[1] Though both systematists sought to understand the unity of nature and man as a common goal, Humboldt's researches were primarily directed, both in his field work and in his writings, to the physical aspect of geography (physical geography). Ritter, on the other hand, as geohistorian and philosopher, addressed himself primarily to the role that man played in his own earthly destiny (human geography). Thus, these two contemporaries at the turn of the nineteenth century were largely responsible for developing modern geography on a scientific and philosophical basis. The researches of both are based on extensive travel experiences, Humboldt's travels extending even to the Americas. Both were prolific and profound writers, but since they had altogether different backgrounds and points of view concerning the nature of reality, their objectives and methodologies differed.

The most celebrated work of Humboldt was the *Kosmos* (1793), which reveals that Humboldt felt a close academic kinship existed between the subjects of geography and astronomy, a viewpoint not shared, however, by subsequent leaders in the field. He always sought to discover the connections between the animate and inanimate:

¶ "The great problem of physical geography is to determine . . . the laws of these relationships, the eternal bonds that enchain the phenomena of life with those of inanimate nature." Humboldt appears to have regarded generic studies—the search for general principles that would lead to understanding of the unity of all reality — as a higher level of scientific study than the analysis and interpretation of individual areas[2]

Ritter, in contrast, was distinctly anthropocentric in his outlook on the systematic principles of geography. Like his contemporary, Humboldt, he was also a prodigious worker, seeking principles and laws which reside in the unity of all matter. But Ritter

[1] The pioneering contributions of these world-famous philosopher-scientists were fittingly commemorated in 1959 in numerous centennial observances of their deaths, in acknowledgment of their leadership in world geo-philosophic thought.

[2] Hartshorne, Richard, *Perspective on the Nature of Geography,* published for the Association of American Geographers by Rand McNally & Co., Chicago 1959, pp. 67, 147. Reprinted by permission.

injected a religious note into his philosophical observations when he invoked the teleological concept to help explain systematic phenomenology, thus bringing to the field of geography his own historical and philosophical background. He failed to find in the natural world the total answer to the question of man's relation to the earth and to the universe.[1] He recognized a supernatural force superimposed on the natural as a necessary rationale to explain human phenomenology. Also distinctive was his historical approach.

Ritter was not content to study plants, animals, and man in terms of contemporary relationships one to another as well as to the present-day environment, but also explored these components in their elemental and spatial connections. Thus he has been credited for having influenced subsequent investigations of the domestication of animals. And because he placed the study of man in the continuum of time as well as space, Ritter might be called the father of historical geography. His stature as a pioneer in systematic historical geography is well authenticated by the 21-volume work *Die Erdkunde, Im Verhaltniss Zur Natur Und Zur Geschichte Des Menschen* (Berlin, 1822-1859). Because of his teleological viewpoint of the destiny of man on this earth, it is not surprising to find that in Ritter's works we have the best early exposition of the geography of the Holy Land.

Carl Ritter 1779-1859 (Copyright, Royal Geographical Society, used by permission)

The doctrine of environmentalism is an outgrowth of man's attempt to resolve the riddle of the world's most unique phenomenon — the human habitat

The study of nature and man's part in it became the theme of another historico-geographical study in a combination of fields in the eighteenth and nineteenth centuries. These represented a combination of the evolutionary philosophy of life and environmental determinism. Thus we have the determinist philosophy represented by C. L. De S. Montesquieu (1748) and J. G. Von Herder (1784-1791), and the evolution hypotheses presented by Sir Charles Lyell from a geological viewpoint (1830-1832) and by Charles Darwin in his biologic work, *The Origin of Species* (1859). Contemporary kindred ideas on the geographic side were perhaps best exemplified by Humboldt, the "father of scientific geography," already introduced in the previous section.

As A. H. Clark points out, "This approach presupposed a necessary developmental sequence of culture which was in accord with simply conceived physical principles and, therefore, closely tied to the physical environment." (5).

Paralleling somewhat the ideas of the philosophers and scientists indicated above was the work by a number of geographic writers at the turn of the nineteenth century in the problem of cause and effect relationships between human behavior and forces of the natural environment. The concept that a given element or set of elements of the natural environment produces a certain result in the conduct of human beings has been generally referred to as *environmen-*

[1] As Hartshorne observes: "In Ritter's case, there were three fundamental facts of geography for which science has no explanation—and presumably still has none—namely, the uniqueness of the earth in the universe, so far as we know it; the earth as the home of that unique creature, man; and finally—the fundamental explanation of a host of geographic facts—the differentiation in character among the major land units of the world" (4).

talism, or in its more radical form, as *determinism.* The term "environmentalism," as we shall see later, is semantically confusing, as is often the case with nomenclature of this type. Webster defines it as: "Emphasis on environment, rather than heredity, as the important factor in the development of the individual or race." The philosophy of explaining the present-day cultures of the world, including their social and political institutions, is the result of several historic factors: (1) the cause–effect relationships which were recognized in nature by the several systematic sciences; (2) a recognition also of the strong ecological influences that, as Humboldt had observed, existed in the plant and animal world; (3) a partial dichotomy that came to consider total area study in two compartments—the physical geography on the one hand, and human geography on the other—exhibited in part by the works of Humboldt and Ritter; and (4) the concept of evolution, as in the case of Darwin's "Doctrine of Natural Selection," which is, of course, directly rooted in environmental influences and controls.

Although now largely a matter of history, the "Doctrine of Determinism" should be known to every student of geography, if for no other reason than to point up again the ever-patent fact of the complexity of the geographic discipline. Some of the best minds in the field of geography, in fact, some of its most outstanding scholars, have been among the proponents as well as the opponents of this particular doctrine. The great determinism controversies that raged for almost half a century had a tremendous influence not only on the geographic thought of the geographers themselves, but also on investigators in other fields, such as anthropology, sociology and history. And, as is usual in such great controversies, it is now obvious that much of the disputation resulted from misconceptions of the actual type of concepts held by determinists, or came about through misunderstandings in discussing their points of view when, as so often happens, authorities are quoted directly or indirectly, out of the context of their writings. This viewpoint of studies in determinism should prove exceedingly valuable in teaching that true scholarship not only must employ rigorous methodology in investigating a problem, but must also possess competence to translate and transmit correctly the knowledge of others in a language of common understanding.

To begin then, determinism has meant different things to different people—to some, environment "effects"; to others, environment "affects." In its most extreme form, determinism implied that man is a captive of the natural environment; that he himself is in fact a sort of product of that environment. In the milder form of this philosophy the view is taken that man's attitude and actions are directly, or highly, influenced by the elements of the natural environment. From a review of much of the literature of the environmentalist school, the author must conclude that few prominent writers, if any, held to the extreme form of determinism. But objections have been vigorously voiced even against the modified view that the natural environment "conditions," or the natural environment "influences," "predisposes," "favors," and the like. Other similar statements on the human side of the relationship such as that man "responds to" or "adjusts himself to" the natural environment also have met with local disfavor in expressing man–nature relationships.

Platt gives us a series of categorical gradations of environment-relation terms ranging from strong to weak:

¶ . . . environmental determinism implying absolute cause and effect; environmental control implying less than absolute determinism; environmental influence implying active if not determinative natural force; environmental response implying that nature speaks and man answers; possibilism implying certain inherent possibilities from which to choose; and environmental adjustment implying that man may choose from what he understands to be available.[1]

What the antienvironmentalist, of course, particularly objects to—and justly so—is the attempt to explain a specific occupance form of the landscape by referring it specifically to a natural form of the landscape independent of the areal complex of which both the cultural and the natural forms are a part.

[1] Platt, Robert S., *Field Study in American Geography*, Research Paper No. 61, Department of Geography, The University of Chicago, Chicago, July, 1959. Reprinted by permission.

It should be obvious to the student, for that matter, that a cause–effect relationship cannot be validated by subjectively selecting human and nonhuman features whose significance cannot be properly evaluated out of the total areal complex. In a complex interrelationship of this character, where man's behavior is not functionally separate from nature, the resolution of the factors of both nature and man challenges the highest ingenuity of total analysis and explanation of areal phenomena. Because of this, some geographic writers cautiously avoid using relationship terms of the genetic or generic type even when a genetic process or a generic principle of coherent relationships can quite certainly be demonstrated by field or historical data. The student will observe accordingly that the most characteristic words in geographic writing are "relation," or "relationships," or possibly the equivalent term "connections." Such terms, however convenient they may be, actually carry connotations of only the most general type. All things in this world, including man, necessarily show spatial relationships of one order or another in their distribution over the earth's surface, and so are obviously related one to another. But again we ask, what kind of relationship is it? Is it like "coins in a box," or is man's distribution over the earth a metaphorical equivalent type of relationship suggested rather by a "plant rooted deeply in the sunshine and the soil" (Educator Dewey)? And so, if we are to have "connection" expressions, it will not suffice merely to say that somehow man is related to each and every feature of the natural and biotic environment, but it must be recognized that the moment man enters such an environment he himself becomes an integral part of the environment, though his behavior does not reflect the type of relationship connections found, for example, in ore genesis, or in plant and animal ecology.

Despite the emphases, then, that such writers as Ratzel, Semple, and Huntington placed upon the importance of the natural environment in explaining the social, economic, and political life of peoples, it does not appear that any of these writers actually believed that man had to do certain things because of the outright "dictation" of nature, even when deterministic language might so suggest. It would not be difficult to select (out of context) specific passages from any of the works of these writers which would suggest control of nature over man. On the other hand, it likewise would not be difficult to extract parallel passages from the same works which also would refute this thesis. In other words, all these authors recognized that a very complex relationship exists between the human and the nonhuman phenomena. But on the whole their writings do predominantly feature emphasis, as was the custom of their time, on the natural factor in the human process environmental equation.[1]

Notwithstanding these shortcomings, the writings of these scholars have left us an important legacy in geographic literature. Ratzel's *Anthropogeographie* will always constitute a landmark in geographic writing. Issued in two volumes (1882-1889, 1891-1912), it took into consideration first the impact of the natural environment on man, and second the impact of man on the natural environment. Thus the combined writings quite adequately reflected Ratzel's recognition of natural–cultural interrelationships rather than a one-sided relationship between the human and nonhuman factors of the environment. In fact, the very title of his work indicates the anthropocentric instead of geocentric theme of man's role in this world.

Ellen Semple, as a seminar student of Ratzel, became highly inspired by the anthropological approach of Ratzel in explaining societal and political phenomena. A schol-

[1] Because of the confusion and controversy resulting in part from misunderstandings of both Ratzel's and Semple's works, it is well for the student to note what Hartshorne in his recently abridged revision of his earlier work on *The Nature of Geography* has to say about the environmentalist philosophy held by Ratzel and Semple: "Neither Ratzel nor Semple supposed that the natural environment was all-determinant, as might possibly be inferred from statements in *The Nature of Geography*. . . . In the preface to her most influential work, *Influences of Geographic Environment*, Semple emphasized that 'the writer speaks of geographic factors and influences, shuns the word geographic determinant and speaks with extreme caution of geographic control.' Following Ratzel, she devoted a chapter to the movements of peoples and cultures. . . . She also stressed the importance of past history . . . and of previous habitat . . . , and she emphasized the concept of 'the earth as a unit from earliest human time. . . .' The *Nature of Geography* errs specifically in stating that Semple maintained only the procedure which Ratzel used in his first volume, leading from natural causes to human consequences. . . . Semple also used the procedure Ratzel followed in his second volume studying culture in relation to nature" (3).

Friedrich Ratzel 1844-1904 (Library of Congress)

arly student and a masterful writer, Miss Semple soon adapted Ratzel's philosophy and technique to her own historical training and ideologies and produced a number of unique works which were destined to become the target of deterministic criticism by American writers in the second quarter of the twentieth century. Among these works are *Influences of Geographic Environment, American History and Its Geographic Conditions,* and *Geography of the Mediterranean Region.* All three reveal a keen grasp of historical and geographical facts. The last publication supplies a documentation of sources remarkable for its diversity and aptitudes of application to the development of such principles of environment–event relationships as Miss Semple formulated.

The next celebrated American exponent of environmentalist writing is Ellsworth Huntington. An extensive traveler in Europe and Asia, especially of the innermost parts of Asia, as well as of other parts of the world, Huntington early became a prolific writer, developing his own concepts and formulae for explaining the environmental basis of historic cultures and modern civilization. The philosophy and principles of geography developed by him are expounded in *The Pulse of Asia, Principles of Human Geography, Mainsprings of Civilization,* and other works. His later primary researches, as in the last mentioned case, were largely directed at determining climatological criteria which, in his judgment, were prime factors in promoting or retarding progress; thus his classic studies, reported upon in Chapter 26, on the determination of temperature and rainfall optima for civilization and progress.

Possibilism and probabilism as restrictive environmentalism concepts

French geographers of this period, likewise influenced by the works of Ratzel and other contemporary geographers in Germany, were interested in examining the causal relationship factor between environment and man. But, unlike the American writers just mentioned, they took the view that the causal relationship is a negative (restrictive) rather than a positive one. The *possibilist* held that man, after all, is the sole decisive and deciding element in this relationship,

Ellen Churchill Semple 1863-1932 (American Geographical Society)

and that, while nature is recognized as setting certain limitations at any one time and place upon the exercise of man's volitions, man can and does exercise a wide range of possible choices in making his adaptations "to" and "of" the environment. This philosophy came to be known as *possibilism,* and those who felt that man's responses were often much more directly related to the environmental habitat, suggested the term *probabilism.* Thus Vidal de La Blache and Jean Brunhes in their own respective writings, including in each case a textbook of human geography, were classified as belonging to the possibilist-probabilist school. The influence of their writings soon extended to America, where for several decades geographic writings followed this modified form of environmentalism.

Higher criticism of environmentalism in any form seems often to imply that the exponents of determinism and even possibilism did not recognize that, in the last analysis, man's own attitudes, aptitudes, and activities were of his own making. There is also often the further implication that such scholars failed to realize the significance of place-to-place, time-to-time, and culture-to-culture differences in a changing world. But a reexamination of some of the original writings of the environmentalist school will disabuse us of this historical criticism. At least those of the so-called possibilist school, with which Brunhes has been identified, not only were aware of these factors in time, but also recognized that a basic problem to the understanding of this entire controversial question involves not simply geography but a study of the entire field of psychosomatic processes which are involved in human behavior in the total environmental complex.

P. Vidal de la Blache 1845-1918
(American Geographical Society)

Ellsworth Huntington 1876-1947
(American Geographical Society)

It is of the greatest significance to observe what, for example, Brunhes has to say about this matter:

¶ This habit of seeing realities where they are and as they are has the effect of instilling in the mind a well-founded mistrust of mere labels and giving it a critical sense of the varying value of geographical realities. Thus mountains seem as

Jean Brunhes 1869-1930 (Courtesy of Mme. M. Jean-Brunhes Delamarre)

a general rule to imply the absence of all human life. But it is obviously a mistake to generalize this idea, for in certain latitudes and climates the high regions are the most inhabited ones. . . . So, too, the term "river" will call up very different images . . . .

Between facts of a physical character there are sometimes causal relations, but between facts of human geography there are hardly any relations except those of coexistence. To strain, as it were, the bond that unites phenomena to one another is unscientific, and the critical attitude will be very necessary here if the many cases in which the connexion is by no means the causal one are to be clearly discerned . . .

Hence there arises a complication which sometimes makes it hard to determine the actual bond between man and Nature. This connecting bond is, in fact, variable because it depends on man's wants—both his spontaneous and his considered desires—and these psychological elements, deemed by Nature extremely variable, necessarily cause the relations even between earth and man to vary. Thus we reach a new kind of complication resulting from different phenomena following each other in the course of time in the same place. The geographical setting remains the same, but the men who dwell in it have wants that are constantly growing, changing, and becoming more complex . . . .

Relations between the constant natural factor and the variable human one are continually changing, and it may even happen that in the course of time the relation becomes almost exactly opposite what it was at first . . . .

The human psychological element, therefore, which at the origin of the geographical phenomenon is the necessary intermediary between Nature and man might be called—to use a general phrase that was dear to Henri Bergson—"the direction of attention." And a psychological factor is still the necessary intermediary between Nature and man in respect of the social, historical, and political consequences that follow it . . . .

The power and the means that man has at his disposal are limited, and in the beginning he is up against insurmountable barriers in Nature. So, too, our activity on the earth's surface finds itself stopped by restrictive conditions. Within certain limits it can vary its operations and movements, but it cannot destroy this natural setting: to modify it is often possible but never to eliminate it.

The way in which influential geographical conditions are translated into human facts is what human geography in all its departments must inquire into and elucidate. It must never forget that the facts of human geography find neither their complete explanation nor their single coordinating principle in geographical causes alone. *The psychological repercussions of geographical causes on the human being, within the bounds of his own desires, needs, or fancies,* are indeed the subtle and complex factor that should predominate in all study of human geography. This it is that enables the facts to be classified and coordinated, in regard both to natural forces and to man.

Many geographers, after speaking, not without reason, of the action and reaction of natural and human forces, ask themselves too strictly and in too abstract a manner up to what point the influence of natural force is exerted on human activity and to what extent man reacts to these forces. There are some who ask in addition whether it would not be advisable to start by discriminating between the effects of the first and the second of these two influences, and then to adopt as the basis of a general scientific division these two antithetical terms: "the action of Nature upon man" and "the reaction or action of man upon Nature." Hence arise the phrases "passive or static human geography" and "active or dynamic human geography".[1]

The student must note that these latter two references apparently refer to the two-volume text of the *Anthropogeographie* by Ratzel cited previously. It appears that Brunhes is one of the first modern critics of the dichotomous approach to the study of the nature of areal reality:

¶ "Now, what are we to think of these "chapter headings" that some would propose to adopt? Such a general classification of the facts of anthropo-geography is in our opinion far too artificial to be accepted or even tolerated. On the contrary, even in the most elementary facts there are discernible an action and a reaction that are inextricably intermingled.[2]

Here, indeed, we seem to have a definite foreshadowing of our modern so-called signs of chorography, the essence of modern geography. Here we have a *unitary*, as opposed to a *dualistic*, approach to the understanding of the environmental complex. Brunhes illustrated this unity in reality:

¶ The man who takes refuge by night in a natural cave profits by natural circumstance, and the part he plays in relation to physical Nature is reduced to a minimum. Nevertheless, it is not the cave alone that is the fact of human geography, but the cave as a place of human refuge. Even when man in no way creates or modifies the fact that he makes use of, the mere fact that he does make use of it presents a complex phenomenon in which the man, it is true, submits to what nature suggests, but in which he also shares, if only by a kind of very obscure instinct. The river that man makes use of to journey in a canoe or to float the logs that he has to transport has a place in human geography only because it has been made a highway, so to speak, by the will of man. So the most rudimentary manifestations of our activity on the earth reveal in themselves the close solidarity that exists between that branch of human geography that is wrongly called passive and that which is equally wrongly called active or dynamic.[3]

But, as already previously suggested, Brunhes did recognize nature as having a sort of determinant voice in the man–nature partnership in placing a limit on man's choice at any given state of cultural development:

¶ Human geography is a realm of compromise: nothing is absolute or definite for the human species on the earth except those general laws and fundamental principles that determine the limits beyond which all life is excluded and proscribed. Yet men are capable, if not of pushing back indefinitely those limits—altitude, latitude, depth, and so forth—at all events of stretching or modifying some of them a little . . . .

On the other hand, in the restricted realm wherein man is able to live he is never completely active—i.e. a creator—any more than he is completely passive. When he digs tunnels or cuts through isthmuses he is not eliminating natural facts, but merely altering them, shaping them, interpreting them. These natural facts that have been altered—mountain masses, reclaimed areas, and so forth—still remain, and so strong are they that constant human effort is needed if man's alterations are to continue in existence.[4]

Higher criticism of environmentalism has also often frowned upon the uses of such terms as "response," or "adaptation," or "adjustment" of human activities to the environment, again because of their implied connotations that nature forces man to its terms in an ecological manner. But despite Brunhes' disavowal of this controlling principle, he does not hesitate to use the term "adaptation" repeatedly to illustrate the need of making harmonizable adjustments "to" and "of" the environment so as to realize the

---

[1] Brunhes, Jean, *Human Geography* (Abridged edition by Mme. M. Jean-Brunhes Delamarre and Pierre Deffontaines), translated by Ernest F. Row, Rand McNally & Co., Copyrighted by George C. Harrap & Co., Ltd., Great Britain, 1952. Reprinted by permission. Brunhes is quoted here at some length since his observations and illustrations seem to be among the very best in expounding and resolving the basic controversial issues of what we might call "geographic man." His emphasis on the psychological factor may well be considered a major contribution to the subject.

[2] *Ibid.*

[3] *Ibid.* Reprinted by permission.

[4] *Ibid.* Reprinted by permission.

highest potential of human resource–natural resource relationships:

¶ For mankind on the earth's surface, therefore, everything is a matter of habit, of a sound understanding of physical facts, and of skillful adaptation to those facts. But the adaptation must take effect promptly and at the right moment, as well as being preceded, prepared for, and led up to by precise scientific investigation. The penalty exacted for acting contrary to physical facts is all the more cruel as man's victory over them is great and glorious. . . . Surely it is at least partly an illusion to think that by increasing his power of dominating and conquering the earth man throws off its tyranny and increases his own independence? Is it not the case, on the contrary, that a kind of contract is signed by the civilized people of the world, with more precise and, we might say, more Draconian clauses, just in proportion as the relations with the earth are made more cohesive and more fruitful? . . . It should not be thought, therefore, that as human forces grow and become more concentrated man's dependence on natural conditions has been done away with: all that has happened is that the dependence is of a different kind. And geographical facts are more and more becoming man's supreme masters.[1]

Historical evaluation of environmentalism in all its forms a prerequisite to understanding modern geography

Review of the historical evolution of any theory and the higher criticisms thereof is essential to the understanding of problems concerned with world reality. This is no less true of geography than it is of history, or of any of the other social or natural sciences. Recapitulating the above, therefore, we recognize that the earliest concerns of the study of the earth were cosmological rather than chorographical or chorological.[2]

[1] *Ibid.* Reprinted by permission.

[2] Originally, "chorography" meant regional description, and "chorology" regional explanation. Today they are used synonymously, or even interchangeably, chorography now being used most commonly to include the connotation of explanation as well as description, since, as indicated elsewhere, uninterpretative description has little or no place in scientific geography. Of relevant interest here also in geographic nomenclature is that "chorography" is thought of as a regional study between that of a very small region, "topography" (the conventional topographic quadrangle), and that of "geography" (of a large region, of a country, of a continent, of the world).

The seventeenth century with all its explorations and colonization movements between the Old and New World led to the development of general geography by Varen and his contemporaries. But the systematic search for causal processes underlying areal differentiation in nature and man's relation to them were finally systematically expressed on the physical side by Humboldt and on the human side by Ritter. These works gave Ratzel the impetus to emphasize the two together in reciprocal perspective—now emphasizing the one and then the other, as the focusing element to which to relate the human and nonhuman factors and forces in the environmental complex. This set the stage for environmentalist disciples like Semple and Huntington to select on occasion specific factors of the natural environment (climate, landforms, soils, minerals, plants and animals) and show how each, in turn, exercises a conditioning, if not determining, influence on specific aspects of man's culture. But French geographers like Vidal de la Blache and Brunhes, as we have noted, regarded the natural environment primarily as a permissive, restrictive, or limiting factor in the complex equation of man's milieu.

Now to bring the concepts of environment–man relationships to the current decade, we shall cite an exponent of the modern antienvironmentalist school on the inadequacies of environmentalism.[3] Robert Platt in his *Determinism in Geography* puts the deterministic approach to the test as applied to the understanding of the geography of a particular country—Argentina—an effective expedient in testing the validity of geographic theory, concept, or principle. As Platt indicates, we may set up a list of topical factors such as the fundament, European racial heritage, Spanish cultural heritage, reciprocal trade with Europe, competitive relation with the United States, and military and political affiliations with Fascism in Spain, Italy, and Germany. Now, it is Platt's contention that while these historical and geographical factors are "in effect and of significance" and

[3] The student should realize by now that throughout the treatment of the historical development of the geographic discipline only a representative selection of one or two authorities for each major critique can be presented here.

¶ . . . may help toward an understanding of the country . . . the approach is misleading rather than revealing. The value of the specified factors is unmeasured and immeasurable; multitudes of other factors also are present, many of them different, some of them opposite in effect; countless incidents and decisions of critical value are largely unknown and unknowable; and alternative tendencies are ignored.[1]

Platt then shows how in each of these categories some known and other unknown factors would have to be considered if something better than a mere "rationalization" is to be arrived at to "explain" Argentina.

¶ Determinism is branded as a false guide because it prompts a human pretense of explaining—futile and misleading at least in our present state of knowledge. Conceivably we might hope sometime to explain the present and the past. These have been determined and cannot be changed, all the results are in, all the choices between alternative possibilities have been made. Full explanation is conceivable; practically this may remain impossible. . . . Full explanation . . . involves the whole world and everything that has happened in it.[2]

Predictions of Argentine future would obviously be still more difficult. Such decisions as have been made in the past are definitely determined, but decisions for the future "have not as yet been made, and there is no indication that we shall ever be able to make them in advance for our own future lives, to say nothing of our inability to make them in advance for the future lives of everyone else in the world."

The point which Platt is driving at is that when we are dealing with man we are not only dealing with the environment and its so-called influences, but also the free will of man which enters into the complex change of cause-and-effect relationships. And though the question of free will be "not proven pro or con," it would be, he states

¶ . . . unscientific to reject free will as if it were a closed question, and thus claim to know more about cause and effect than we can know. But if for any reason we wish to make an unscientific practical choice between free will and free determinism, we had better make a consistent and harmless choice. In this case the consistent choice is to believe in free will, and to think and act in accordance with it, because free will is an assumption on which we all live every day—the assumption that we can choose what we do and that our choices are significant, not merely the gestures of puppets or new-born babes . . . . The course of events in our world seems to be like a complex chain reaction into which new directive impulse, imperceptible in most cases, is injected by every human choice.[3]

How areas selected per se for geographic study may affect an author's viewpoint of nature–man relationship is well illustrated in the case of field studies by Griffith Taylor, one of the most prolific geographic writers of all time, and an exponent of the environment–influence philosophy. In defending his position Taylor observes:

¶ I have spent a large part of my life studying the conditions affecting man in the immense areas of Empty Canada, the Sahara, Empty Australia, and Empty Antarctica. No geographer who has this experience could ignore the paramount control exercised by the environment. Granted that all these areas are in a primitive state of civilization where Bacon (unlike some of our geographers) realized "that we must obey Nature," my point is that they will remain in much the same stage of development for many a decade to come, if not forever. A sense of proportion should teach us that the geographer (who should surely study the world as a *whole* in his major conclusions) will err considerably if he bases his philosophy on conditions which obtain in such progressive but restricted areas of the world as Western Europe and much of the United States, and ignores the real, *simple* and *direct* control by Nature in the larger part of the earth.[4]

For developing the student's own perspective it is well at this juncture to anticipate the order of the regional treatment of

[1] Platt, Robert S., "Determinism in Geography," *Annals of the Association of American Geographers,* June, 1948, Vol. 38, pp. 126-131. Reprinted by permission.
[2] *Ibid.* Reprinted by permission.

[3] *Ibid.* Reprinted by permission.
[4] Taylor, Griffith, Editor, *Geography in the Twentieth Century,* Philosophical Library, New York, 1957, p. 13. Reprinted by permission.

our text in Part IV under two general categories: lands *nature-dominated,* and lands *man-dominated,* the former belonging essentially to the category Taylor is talking about.

Regionality the modern geographical core-analysis of world reality

Varied as have been the philosophic concepts of the nature and function of geography ever since man started to think of the earth elements in a space organizational way, there is one universally recognizable feature which runs throughout the entire gamut of time; namely, man's realization that only by some systematic division of earth area can man hope to investigate and comprehend his complex universe. And so we might say the chief goal of geography has been the understanding of areal reality. As a primary step in this direction, some unifying basis for distinguishing and demarking areas is needed. Historically, the initial criterion was no doubt "political," starting with roughly recognized zoned areas which delimited hunting and fishing habitats, followed by a tribal pastoral organization of territorial grazing, and this by successive steps developing into local and country administrative units of government. The systematic geography works of Strabo emphasize this political delineation—and understandably so—for he lived at a time when organization and administration of earth space preoccupied the empire and colonial builders in the Mediterranean world. This "country-based" area treatment of the world, with modifications as to subareality, continued to receive primary attention by Varenius and other geographers of his time. It was a leading feature of the writings of Ritter and his contemporaries, and continues to this present day in our political geography, some of which, however, may be systematically, rather than regionally, organized.

1. The physiographic base of unitary organization. The pioneer work in America of William Morris Davis, "Master of Method," and other geographers in the area of geomorphology in the early twentieth century shifted the emphasis to "structure-process-stage" of regional development of areas. Physiographic diagrams appeared by the late N. M. Fenneman, A. K. Lobeck,

William Morris Davis 1850-1934
(American Geographical Society)

and former President W. W. Atwood of Clark University, which graphically portrayed the physiographic provinces of the United States. First singled out as landform units, these provinces and subdivisions were subsequently used as a basis of correlative land-use studies. Thus was inaugurated the multiple-element feature of combining, within the same areal unit, representation of the works of culture with the works of nature, a practice which is followed in principle, with many variations, to this day.

Because of its primary conditioning worldwide influence, climate has also served as a natural base for areal differentiation for its own sake as well as a framework of correlative distribution patterns of other natural elemental forms such as soils, and particularly vegetation (e.g., the climatic regions by the late British geographer, A. J. Herbertson). Noteworthy is the world-renowned system of climates by Köppen based on broad vegetation types (see map in Appendix). Not only has this system served to delineate the world's great vegetative provinces, but directly or indirectly, it has been

Wallace W. Atwood 1872-1949 (American Geographical Society)

A. J. Herbertson 1865-1915 (By kind permission of the Geographical Association [United Kingdom])

selected more than any other natural element by geographers for human occupance study on a broad world-realm basis. In modified form, it also serves to delineate the global physio-bio-cultural realms of Part IV of our text. This system of climatology leads us to the next step in area–unit sequence analysis: regionalization, the differentiation of earth space in terms of relatively homogeneous units for which the German geographer Sölch has proposed the term "chores" (after the Greek *choros*—place or region).

2. The chorographical unifying concept of modern geography. Like its systematic counterpart, the regional study of space content has various approaches. It is most important for the student to recognize the fact that a "region," as geographers use the term in our present context, does not actually exist, but is a mental construct. Accordingly, significant and useful as is this concept—considered by many the very core of modern geographic thought—selectivity of criteria for area differentiation and the methods used in measuring the relative significance of environmental data in their co-variation with other natural and cultural features, are highly individualistic, subjective, and arbitrary matters. In its broadest connotation, therefore, we may correctly use the term "region" to apply to any homogeneous area of the space categories set up above, as well as others, assuming, of course, that the criteria are significant and meaningful, and that the boundaries are systematically drawn. As defined by the committee appointed by the Association of American Geographers to study all aspects of regionality, a region is:

¶ . . . an area in which accordant areal relations produce some form of cohesion. . . . In geographic study a homogeneous area has meaning when it can be shown to correspond or coincide in its position on the earth with other homogeneous areas. . . . But the identification of an accordant relationship. . . . does not prove a causal relationship. The regional pattern has both meaning and significance when it can be interpreted in terms of systematically related processes, operating through time.[1]

So any human or nonhuman features, whether on global or microcosmic scale, and whether treated separately or conjointly, may be made the basis for regional study. However, where the objective calls for an examination and explanation of areal form and function of a region as compared to those of another region in the attempt to understand continental or world variegated cultures, a multifeature context is used based on the more significant landscape categories that play major roles in establishing patterns of human occupance. A cursory look at the skyline profiles in Figure 2 of Chapter 35 (historical geography) and the accompanying text on the sequent occupance content of the Calumet Region at the head of Lake Michigan will aid the student in grasping this concept of what some may prefer to call a "geographical region," or, as the late Whittlesey proposed to term it, "compage," adapted from the Latin *compages* (a joining together). Homogeneity (essential unity of integral characteristics) is the key for any regionality of this type. But two subtypes are recognized: *uniform* regions, and *nodal* regions.

The physical–cultural realms of Part IV are of the uniform type (landscape features throughout the unit are essentially uniform). The occupance patterns featured in the profile sketches just mentioned place the Calumet study in the nodal category. Nodality, referring to a form of movement or circulation, serves as a unifying regional force, as instanced in the Calumet by the transportation pattern focused on the *cul de sac* of Lake Michigan, the Calumet River–Sag Canal, and metropolitan Chicago, with its commuter service radiating into the Calumet region by numerous road and rail traffic lines.

How well we express the sense of uniformity and nodality, and hence the regionality, of a compage depends in a large measure upon two things: (1) the appropriate number and high relevancy of landscape categories selected, and (2) the temporal and spatial order in which one presents the coherent factors of the landscape so as to simulate as closely as possible the manner in which phenomena occur in the field (the stage) as well as to present an interpretative imagery of the processes by which the spatial arrangement of the phenomena has come into existence (the story).

[1] Whittlesey, Derwent, "The Regional Concept and the Regional Method," from *American Geography—Inventory and Prospect,* Preston E. James and Clarence F. Jones, Editors, The Association of American Geographers, Washington, D.C., 1959. Reprinted by permission.

Geographical processes and principles — The spirit of regional systematic geography

Neither time nor place has any meaning in spatial analysis apart from change. And if regionality, as noted in the previous section, is the heart (core) of geography, then geographic processes and principles by analogy are its lifeblood. If there is to be recognized any new development in the past few years in geographic thought, it is a reactivated interest in stressing the point that scientific chorographic analysis must be framed in systematic chronologic perspective, a principle brought into sharp focus by the sources presently to be cited.

Viewing space content temporally is not a new development. The scholars cited previously, in most cases, held to the *dynamic* landscape point of view. But because of the singular features of regions, they found difficulty in agreeing on principles of evaluating processes and formulating a systematic approach on an interregional basis. And it should be additionally noted that this continues to be a provocative point to this day, albeit in a more critical climate of research than ever before. Modern researchers face the task of resolving and replacing the former environmentalism concept of cause-and-effect land–life relationship between single or several elements of the landscape with a more critically formulated generic set of principles based on man-activated processes operative through time. But even now the traditional cause-and-effect relationship is not ignored where it is felt validated by field or other reliable evidence. Or, as a substitute, adjectives such as "accordant" or "coherent" are used to express genetic or generic types of relationships somewhat reminiscent at times of the former ecological (Barrow's) point of view of man–nature relationships. However this may be, many geographers feel there is nothing wrong about even trying deliberately to establish and expound generic interrelationships between human and nonhuman phenomena, provided, of course, that they are evaluated in their total area complex, and considered, moreover, in the context of time sequences and their technological developments.

As we have seen repeatedly in the context on environmentalism, semantics can compound confusion and controversy. And so here also it is important to have as clear a concept of our terminology as possible when speaking of *processes* and *principles*. Ackerman, in his critique on the geographic discipline, considers process as:

¶ . . . a succession of physical, biotic, or cultural events dependent on characteristic energizing agents. Thus the physical process of erosion is associated with gravity, hydraulic agents, and atmospheric movements; the vegetative process is associated with the still-unfathomed forces of organic life, growth, and decay and technological processes are associated with man's capacity to capture energy from his physical and biotic surroundings and to direct it toward his purposes.[1]

As conceived by James:

¶ A process is a sequence of changes, systematically related as in a chain of cause and effect. There are physical and chemical processes developing the forms of the land surface, the shapes of the ocean basins, the differing characteristics of water and climate. There are biotic processes by which plants and animals spread over the earth in complex areal relation to the physical features and to each other. And there are economic, social, and political processes by which mankind occupies the world's lands.[2]

Historically, the question of whether geography can be classified as a science has been the basis for as much controversy as have been views about the essence of geography itself. Here, again, much depends on semantics—what we mean by science. As already pointed out above, man's behavior is not governed or determined by the same principles or laws as the world of nature, even though man is subject to nature's laws. Yet human behavior involves pattern-making processes which can be classified into spatially related genetic categories, and these in turn used in a comparative study of regions from which may emerge recognizable principles, or even laws. Most of the geographic principles or laws thus far seem to have been formulated in the area of economic geography.[3]

1. Some essential rules for evolving principles.

If geographical principles are to be free from determinism, then it appears necessary that we formulate them in a more accurate frame of reference to total areality than has been customary in the past. In fact, one of the major reasons for misunderstandings, if not actually misstatements, seems to have been a lack of a suitable word in any language to express the very idea of a nondeterministic principle. The term "environment," as most commonly used in geography and even in other social science literature, has usually been taken to mean the natural or physical environment. Consequently, the traditional geographical principle has commonly been so oriented. What we need, then, is a term expressive of the *total content* of area, unitarily inclusive of both the works of nature and the works of man. But, as stated, such a term seems to be lacking in the geographical vernacular. Suggestions such as "geographic milieu," "geographic environment," and "geographic complex" have the disadvantage of dual elements, one of which itself needs defining. And so, to speak of the geographic principles of an area may be variously interpreted. What is important, therefore, is to observe in each instance the context of the principle statement, both in terms

[1] Ackerman, Edward A., *Geography as a Fundamental Research Discipline,* Research Paper No. 53, Department of Geography, The University of Chicago, June, 1958, p. 5. Reprinted by permission.

[2] James, Preston E., "American Geography at Mid-Century," *New Viewpoints in Geography,* Twenty-ninth Yearbook of the National Council for the Social Studies, National Education Assn., 1959, p. 10. Reprinted by permission.

[3] For example: "Price tends to vary geographically directly with Demand Space Potential and Demand Time Potential, and inversely with Product Supply Space Potential and Product Supply Time Potential" (13).

[4] "Principle," as used in geography, is a synonym for "generalization" or "rule" to point up recognizable regional covariance or correlation of human and nonhuman factors in the landscape, and hence is a systematic regional expedient for comparing expressed or implied specific genetic processes from place to place.

of its intent by the writer as well as the range of its applicability to both place and time. Moreover, principles should be recognized in their causal or cognate connotations with respect to the types of category under which they fall, since different degrees of coherence will be recognized as existing between one physical object (mineral lode) and another (parent rock formation); between one organism (plant or animal) and another (animal or plant); between one organic element (plant or animal) and another inorganic element (soil); between man and any element in the realm of nature; and finally between man and his fellow men. Once this is recognized, there should be a more intelligible discernment of the kind of relationship we are dealing with and the conditions of the limitations of the applicability of the principle.

It may be well at this point to emphasize that we should not look for principles of the *absolute* type. It has been said that scientists are not even sure that processes in the natural world, even those with which physics is concerned, operate uniformly in time and space. Thus A. H. Compton, one of America's most celebrated physicists, has been reported as saying that "Natural phenomena do not obey exact laws. . . . The movements of the smallest units of matter and light are unpredictable." This "Theory of Indeterminacy," as it has come to be known, is based on the principle, as pointed out by Ritchie Calder, that the very act of observing the motion of an electron is said to change its course, and, therefore, forever precludes the possibility of predicting its future behavior. To repeat, then, never look for geographic principles to explain fully all phenomena, as Platt pointed out so clearly in the case of Argentina. Rather we should look upon them as generic concepts helpful in understanding certain significant relationships that give character and purposeful meaning to the form and functions of reality at a given time and place.

Viewed in the above context, then, observation, description, and interpretation of geographic phenomena generically not only provide a scientific basis for geography, but also help to relieve the drudgery and monotony of reading an otherwise unstimulating style of geographic writing of a purely descriptive and statistical character. Such inventory and encyclopedic writing not only proves frustrating, but negates the vitalizing spirit of geographic inquiry into the adventurous affairs of this world.

The more widespread a natural phenomenon may be, and the more primitive the culture, the simpler is the basis for generalizations among natural elements, human beings, and natural and human phenomena. We recognize these relationships in studying our cosmological hegemony in which man is utterly dependent upon the order of sunshine, air, and water, and the very earth on which man lives. Indeed such primordial elements at once constitute a predetermining condition of man's existence and the domain over which man is destined to rule. The moment we classify, as geographers customarily do, the cosmic categories of the earth into the various subtypes of climates, of landforms, of soils, of minerals, and of vegetal-animal forms, we enter a complicated hierarchy of factoral interrelationships within which different people at different times will behave in different ways. Yet biological man, psychological man, and spiritual man, in one way or another, finds comfort or discomfort, pain or pleasure, advantage or disadvantage in thinking what he thinks and doing what he does partly in terms of the kind of habitat nature supplies. And so it is one of the commonplaces in geography to speak of regions as "too cold," "too hot," "too dry," and "too humid" for habitable or at least hospitable conditions for settlement. Indeterminate though these classifications may be in "decreeing" future demographic patterns, they indicate differentiated regional analysis. In a similar way, we may categorize the relatively favorable and unfavorable environs of the world with respect to the other chief natural factoral categories. There is nothing wrong with this approach, provided we keep in mind that, as James and others have frequently pointed out, the conditions of facility or difficulty of adjusting to any of these phenomena differ in kind and degree for peoples of different cultures and at different times. Thus, as has been demonstrated time and again, the patterns of culture and the progress of civilization have evolved differently in similar environments, whereas similar cultures may evolve—and have evolved—under quite contrasting types of environment. With modern technological aids, man has learned to live comfortably in the tropics and has learned to survive at least at the "polar regions" of the earth. He has made the deserts (some limited sections at least) to "blossom as the rose" through irrigation; man has drained marshes and swamps to extend further the area of arability and otherwise to improve the conditions of health and habitability. This relation of man to water resources may possibly be thought of as the chief dominant factor.

*2. **Water the tyrant of man.*** To appreciate the extent to which nature is in control and how far man can control nature's controls, one need only consider, for example, the natural controls that account for moisture inadequacy in western United States over an area almost half the size of our country. The subject of water resources in the subhumid, semiarid, and arid sections supplies one of the best topics for developing generic principles, since water, as someone has so well said, is "the tyrant of man." Thus man is challenged to study the causes (natural processes) for the rainfall deficiency and evaluate as well the technological means available to man to overcome, as much as the stage of technology permits, the environmental handicaps imposed by nature. And so man might consider the following remedial measures: (1) remove the mountain ranges to the West, which intercept the moisture to windward; (2) extend the Gulf of Mexico westward so as to permit southerly moisture-bearing winds of a cyclonic storm to transport water vapor into the interior. Now you will say, "But these proposals are preposterous, even under the most fantastic evolution of modern technology." So far, our point is simply to impress upon the student that nature globewise does command an inexorable influence on man. But the story does not stop here. Man can make it rain by seeding the clouds —but only if he has clouds (water vapor). However, as already indicated, mountain barriers and continentality and other meteorological factors generally prevent adequate water vapor from reaching the interior. So technology suggests the digging of more and deeper wells to tap the ground water. But groundwater is also a natural phenomenon and the supply is limited in relation to sources of surface water somewhere, for groundwater, as any other water, in the last analysis must depend upon precipitation in some local area or in more humid lands. Since there is less precipitation than evaporation in drylands (Chapters 20 and 21), the waters have to be for the most part *exotic* (that is, imported from the outside humid areas either by streams or water aquifers, or by man). But this also has its natural and cultural limitations. Headwater streams will normally have their waters tapped by people living in the upper watershed areas. And natural underground aquifer water is available only when the rock meets favorable textural and structural conditions (Chapter 9). Such underground "reservoir" sources are, therefore, not only limited in supply, but also limited in their capacity to transfer water.

Modern technology may suggest that we tap the inexhaustible supply of ocean water, which covers some two-thirds of the earth. This necessitates, of course, the desalting of salt water. Technologically, this has already been proven possible, but as yet generally almost prohibitively expensive. The ultimate harnessing of nuclear energy, or better yet the use of the inexhaustible sun energy for desalinization of sea water by evaporation, freezing, or ionization methods, has already been experimentally tried and proved feasible on a small scale. But even if extensively developed, the utilization of such waters on a large scale would require transportation to the interior, where most of the larger dry areas of the world are located. They will continue to challenge man because of the principle of *continentality*.

Technology must also concern itself with the economics of production and marketing, and so another set of principles arises: Will costs of reclamation, even when administered under the most efficient and economical conditions, justify the raising of crops in competition with areas which have not only marginally sufficient rainfall but copious and dependable water, free and naturally distributed?

But again, you may suggest, man's conquest of the drylands, or at least a partial exploitation of them, can be pursued, as we have done in many cases of our own dry West, by growing crops adapted to semiarid or even arid conditions. That, of course, has also been successfully carried on to a limited degree in nearly all moisture-deficient lands of the world, both in the Old World, as well as in the New World. Agronomists, by observing nature's own patterns and principles of operation have, by crossbreeding of wild dryland plants, produced domesticated varieties highly acclimatized not only to different conditions of meteorological aridity but also to different regional *edaphic* factors of aridity as well. Despite such adaptation practices, physiological controls both as to temperature and moisture are involved, and the question of lower yields and more distant markets additionally poses problems and principles of expediency and economy.

The above example is simply one of many types discussed in our textbook which serve to illustrate the complexities of many principles on the nature of human resources as related to natural resources. It also points to the type of guidelines of thought which the student should incorporate along with his reading of this text. Only then will he fully benefit from the understanding of the complex relationships between man and the natural environment and be in a position to evaluate the future potential of technological processes which not only transform man's own culture through new discoveries and inventions, but also change, to some extent at least, the very forms of the natural environment itself. No less does the example illustrate, however, that natural environment itself has its own resource limitations, and for a season at least extends the effects of those limitations to man's own patterns of cultural development.[1]

And finally, the water resource example illustrates most effectively how geographic processes—both natural and human—leave their impress on human institutions. We have in mind here particularly the three volumes issued by the President's Water Resource Policy Commission, the last of which is exclusively devoted to Water-Resources Law, inclusive of special legislation dealing with geographic problems and principles associated with too much water (floods) and too little water (droughts). This comparative regional review of legislation on the "development, utilization, and conservation of water resources" emphasizes what is perhaps the most important lesson to be learned from the study of geography, namely, that the "Law of Man" must reflect first of all knowledge of the "Law of Nature." The significance of this universal geographic principle is recognized in the aphorism by Francis Bacon, "In order to master Nature, we must first obey her." In this context, legislators, jurists, and judges must be familiar with the behavior of water in all its hydrologic cyclic processes in order to adjudicate properly claims to water appropriation by man.

But imperativeness of geographic intelligence goes even further than that: It points up the universal law that ultimately man's very survival in the case of primitive cultures and man's progressive evolvement of the higher cultures are a function of human behavior directed toward the "harmonization" of all human and nonhuman resources in the regional complex, involving, as it does, an ideological as well as a scientific attitude towards the conservation of all the nation's resources, as pointed up in Chapter 16. Because of its interrelated character, and the need for unified regional treatment, the geographic discipline is best prepared to take on this ethic in citizenship training. Learning how best to live with nature under a rational and ideological stewardship is the chief thesis of the "Geographic Facts of Life."

In the next chapter we shall see how the concepts and principles of this thesis are related to those of other disciplines in form and function to make truly effective the liberal arts and vocational educational process for intelligent citizenship training to meet the complex challenges of our new Atomic and Astronautical Age.

APPLICATION OF GEOGRAPHIC UNDERSTANDING

Except in a most general way, it is practically impossible to give a satisfactory definition of any field of knowlege, because any

[1] Commonplace as is this planetary geographic principle, something extra-mundane seems necessary, like the new science of astronautics, to bring to a focus the importance of resource limitations in their most extreme form.

division thereof for substantive treatment —prescribing precise limits—must be an arbitrary one. This is particularly true of a field such as geography, which, like history, takes a composite view of all elements of societal structure and, therefore, cuts across all disciplines. For the same reason then, a concise definition of the ordinary dictionary type, or even of a special geographic dictionary, cannot be expected to be universally acceptable. Especially is this true when a definition is excerpted (as below) from the related context. Hence we have purposely, up to this point, evaded the issue.

But now having given some of the more basic concepts of the substance and methodology of geography, as held by representative professional geographers in time, we may fittingly conclude this chapter with a presentation of some "definitions" for analysis to determine how well you have perceived the concepts of this chapter:

1. Geography is the science of places.—Vidal de la Blache.
2. Geography is the science of distribution.—Marthe.
3. "Geography as Human Ecology" (title of A.A.G. Presidential address by Barrows).
4. Geography is the correlative science. —Taylor.
5. Geography tells what is where, why and what of it.—Bowman.
6. Geography is the strategy of men, space, and resources.—Spykman.
7. Geography seeks to interpret the significance of likenesses and differences among places in terms of causes and consequences.—James.
8. Geography is that discipline that seeks to describe and interpret the variable character from place to place of the earth as the world of man.—Hartshorne.

I. Determine the school of thought with which each of the above statements seems most closely identified (determinism, possibilism, probabilism, regionalism, or other type).

II. Indicate which approach to the areal study of the earth (systematic or regional) seems by implication to receive the emphasis in the author's philosophy or technique of developing the field.

III. If you had to choose from any of the definitions listed, which one would you select? To validate your choice, compare the virtues of the one chosen with those of the others.

IV. Now test your own comprehension and defining ability by composing a definition of geography which best reflects your understanding of what geography is or what it does to one's thinking about the earth as man's domain.

References

1 Thomas, Harold E., "Man's Tenure of the Earth," *Man's Role in Changing the Face of the Earth* (Thomas, William L., Jr., Editor), International Symposium, published for the Wenner-Gren Foundation for Anthropological Research and the National Science Foundation, by the University of Chicago Press, 1956, p. 401.

2 Strabo, *The Geography of Strabo* (English translation by H. L. Jones), Harvard University Press, Loeb Classical Library Edition, Vol. I, pp. 3, 5.

3 Hartshorne, Richard, *Perspective on the Nature of Geography*, published for the Association of American Geographers by Rand McNally & Co., Chicago, 1959, pp. 57, 67, 147.

4 Hartshorne, Richard, "The Nature of Geography," *Annals of the Association of American Geographers*, Vol. XXIX, Numbers 3 and 4, Derwent Whittlesey, Editor, 1939, p. 60.

5 James, Preston E., and Jones, Clarence F., Editors, *American Geography—Inventory and Prospect*, published for the Association of American Geographers by Syracuse University Press, 1954, p. 77.

6 Platt, Robert S., *Field Study in American Geography*, Research Paper No. 61, Department of Geography, The University of Chicago, July, 1959, pp. 61-62.

7 Brunhes, Jean, *Human Geography* (Abridged edition by Mme. M. Jean-Brunhes Delamarre and Pierre Deffontaines), translated by Ernest F. Row, Rand McNally and Co., pp. 222-228, *passim*. Copyright 1952 by George G. Harrap & Co., Ltd., Great Britain.

8 Platt, Robert S., "Determinism in Geography," *Annals of the Association of American Geographers*, June 1948, Vol. XXXVIII, pp. 126-131, *passim*.

9 Taylor, Griffith, Editor, *Geography in the Twentieth Century*, Philosophical Library, New York, 1957, p. 13.

10 Whittlesey, Derwent, "The Regional Concept and the Regional Method," from *American Geography—Inventory and Prospect,* Preston E. James and Clarence F. Jones, Editors, The Association of American Geographers, Washington, D. C., 1959, pp. 32-33, *passim.*

11 Ackerman, Edward A., *Geography as a Fundamental Research Discipline,* Research Paper No. 53, Department of Geography, The University of Chicago, June, 1958, p. 5.

12 James, Preston E., "American Geography at Mid-Century," *New Viewpoints in Geography,* Twenty-Ninth Yearbook of the National Council for the Social Studies, National Education Association, Washington, D. C., 1959, p. 10.

13 Warntz, William, "Progress in Economic Geography," *New Viewpoints in Geography,* Twenty-Ninth Yearbook of the National Council for the Social Studies, National Education Association, Washington, D. C., 1959, p. 68.

Chapter 2

Geographic education integration

> The frontier where science and philosophy meet and where the conclusions of one are handed across to the premises of the other should be taken as the vital centre in the wide realm of thought. — Lord Samuel

In the sense that areal knowledge cuts across all disciplines of learning, geography, together with history, has a vital stake and responsibility in understanding the frontier alluded to by Lord Samuel. Without facts and concepts of the type developed in the various sciences there can be no synthesis of the major meanings of life; isolated facts in general are sterile. And so in studying the role of geography in education, we would re-emphasize the principle of the preceding chapter that the theme "geographic facts of life" does not connote the facts or objects of the natural or social environment but contemplates rather a set of distinctive space concepts—patterns, processes, principles—of human society. This very literally places geography at the frontier of knowledge "where science and philosophy meet," for the chief aim of geography, may we repeat, is to explain areal reality—our earthly existence and mission—in regionally integrated terms.

It is the purpose of this chapter, then, primarily to see how the principles of geography developed in the preceding chapter find their application in the pursuit of knowledge in general and in specific vocations in particular.

Geographic education in the liberal arts tradition

Education may briefly be defined as all learning processes which inform, liberate, and discipline the mind. The liberal arts concept generally connotes education in the processes and principles of human behavior for the promotion of personal and societal, material and spiritual, welfare. Although educators may variously define or evaluate forms and functions of a liberal arts education, it is within the context stated that we consider the values of geographic education. And parenthetically we must again emphasize that "geographic" as used here and elsewhere throughout the book is defined "conceptually," rather than empirically (i.e., the geography of the "cape and bay," "place and product" type still found regrettably at all levels of geography teaching, especially by nongeographically trained teachers).

Geography, first of all, is one of the most general of all subjects because of its universality of topical subject matter range as well as the regional scope of global inclusiveness of man–milieu relationships. A geographer must at least have some familiarity with practically all the major systematic divisions of knowledge, including the natural sciences, social sciences, and the humanities. Nature-wise he must be conversant with most of the basic facts and processes of climate and weather, of relief and landforms, of soil and water, of vegetation and animal life, of minerals and rocks. And since geography is primarily anthropocentric in character, the geographer must be able not only to inventory landscape content but also to pass value judgments on the sociological, economic, and political institutions and problems of society. Thus he is brought face to face with the study of various cultures of the world in which he must recognize the role that traditions and tabus as well as topography play in the social, economic, and political development of nations. The geographer is expected to know something about demography, especially environmental factors of rural and urban settlements; the principles of economics, particularly those factors that concern the production of farm and factory products; the roles that capital and labor play in affecting the standard of living; the marketing of products, transportation facilities, and the like. On the political side, the geographer is expected to talk intelligently about boundaries, power politics, geopolitics, colonialism, nationalism, world trade, and a host of other subjects concerned primarily with the geographic factors of unity and security of nations. Militarily, a geographer must recognize the geographic implications that are involved in the strategic defenses of a nation, including the changing global concepts incident to the revolutionary atomic and astronautic technology into which we have been catapulted.

Relevant illustrations of the broad background preparation and interest of the geographer may be demonstrated by sampling titles of presidential addresses delivered before the Association of American Geographers, selecting primarily those illustrating the above categories: Geographical Science and Social Philosophy; Geography and Natural Selection: A Preliminary Study of the Origin and Development of Racial Character; The Rise, Decline, and Revival of Malthusianism in Relation to Geography and Character of Soils; Adjustment of Agriculture to its Environment; Rural–Urban Migration and the National Welfare; A Case for Population Geography; Environment, Village and City: A Genetic Approach to Urban Geography, with Some Reference to Possibilism; Planning in Pioneer Settlement; The Increasing Significance of the Geographic Conditions in the Growth of Nation-States; The Michigan-Wisconsin Boundary Case in the Supreme Court of the United States; Grassland and Farmland as Factors in the Cyclic Development of Eurasian History; The Antebellum South: A Geographer's Interpretation (1).

1. Unifying functions. Information alone, of course, is not the end objective of a liberal arts education, however diversely enriching this may be. So here also empirical knowledge of world facts as may be revealed through "objective" population-place-resource tests does not predicate a liberal arts man. In geography particularly, as we have noted in the preceding chapter, it is in discerning the "relationship" of the various phenomena of nature and man in a regional context that we recognize the primary disciplinary value of the subject. The geographer is challenged to select from the host of facts those relevant factors and forces which are most cogent for his particular purposes in organizing a systematic or regional study. The major aspect of his disciplinary training then calls for tying together those natural and cultural elements which most naturally or logically serve to build up units of thought that contribute to a unified understanding of reality, and the making of decisions for better living and a better life.

If modern education, especially as it is known under the term of general education or liberal education, exhibits one common principle, it is to establish a unified view of all knowledge and experience—commonly referred to as integration. While each discipline aims to establish its own form of unitary subject matter, it seems to be the distinctive hallmark of history and geography to treat of all branches of knowledge in a unified way—the former primarily on the basis of chronology, the latter primarily on the basis of chorography. Accordingly, geography offers a unique systematic regional approach to the study of all the world cultures. Besides thus "thinking geographically" of world events and world problems, the student learns to employ a critique not provided by any other discipline. Even the so-called integrated or fusion "social studies," taught as it often is by teachers who are not familiar with the philosophy and technique of geographic thought, commonly reveals that historic and current-events studies are non-environmentally related, and hence lack regional reality and vitality. Numerous concerted attempts have been made institution- and organization-wise to correct this deficiency, especially on the high-school teaching level. One of these proposes specific college training in the "philosophy, science, and art" of geography teaching (2). Several recent yearbooks of *The National Council for the Social Studies* are concerned with better geography teaching (3).

In the same spirit and purpose, the philosophy and art of "geography as an integrating science" has now reached the international level of consideration.

> ¶ Geography is the main means of co-ordinating and integrating the informational aspects of an educational program which includes history and science, in the same way as craft work and architecture are excellent means of integrating mechanical skills and artistry in the field of practical education (4).

Similarly, college teaching of geography is given increasing attention as indicated by numerous geography journal articles and books published here and abroad. A local experiment in developing to "the fullest extent the inherent integrative qualities and functions of the geographic discipline so essential in the Liberal Arts program" supplements a geography staff with guest lecturers from other related social science and humanities disciplines. These lectures show how the various disciplines—each in its own way and yet by co-ordination, one with another—explore man and his culture (5).

2. *Geographic ideologies.* Some refreshing aspects in the development of higher education today, quite irrespective of discipline, is the cultivation of wholesome attitudes, as well as intellectualism, in the molding of human character. Geography has not been exempted from this trend. In fact, as the student will soon observe, nearly every facet of geographic study concludes with some concern as to the moral significance and commitment of regional or resource development. Geography by the very nature of the subject, one might say, is evangelical and ecumenical in its interests in resolving problems related to race discrimination, regional tensions, international strife, and in general all problems which relate to the establishment of good will and world peace. And as already pointed out in Chapter 1, world knowledge presumes a cultivation of citizenship responsibilities, which implies resource stewardship. It is now recognized by many geographers and others, particularly in the area of conservation and planning, that this aspect of a liberal arts education is imperative in a world society increasingly dedicated to the program of uplifting not only economic but ethical standards as well.

3. *"Conservation: more ethics than economics."* In support of this concept as "a way of life, a state of mind, which should pervade every educational process of man," Weaver quotes, for example, the premises of Aldo Leopold to whom conservation "was imbedded in the realm of moral and ethical behavior, or religion itself." Thus, Leopold defined conservation as:

¶ . . . a state of harmony between men and land. . . . All ethics so far evolved rest upon a single premise: That the individual is a member of a community of interdependent parts. . . . That conservation is getting nowhere because it is incompatible with our Abrahamic concept of land. We abuse land because we regard it as a commodity belonging to us. . . . No important change in ethics was ever accomplished without an internal change in our intellectual emphases, loyalties, affections, and convictions.[1]

New developments in geographic writings seem particularly concerned with the aspect of promoting a greater consciousness of this form of world citizenship obligation. Typical of this trend are observations at an international symposium of distinguished scholars representing many disciplines.

Sauer, a leading exponent of anthropological geography, voices the same theme as Weaver in appraising man's "appropriation of habitat by habit":

¶ Thus we come properly also to consider the qualities of his actions as they seem to affect his future well-being. In this proper study of mankind, living out the destiny ascribed in Genesis—"to have dominion over the earth"—the concern is valid as to whether his organized energies (social behavior) have or should have a quality of concern with regard to his posterity. . . . What we need more perhaps is an ethic and aesthetic under which man, practicing the qualities of prudence and moderation, may indeed pass on to posterity a good Earth.[2]

From the introduction of the symposium report from which Sauer's remarks are abstracted, other similar summary observations are noted:

¶ Mark was concerned with man's influence on nature not in an abstract or theoretical sense but in terms of practical changes to improve the lot of mankind. His solution to the problems of Western Europe and the United States was that man could moderate his activities and develop a morality in respect to his use of the earth. . . .

Barlang, in his introductory remarks, emphasizes that Scars's paper has an important effect on "niche" and "role." The occupation of a niche and its maintenance thereafter mean, in our civilization, having a regard for, or obligation to, the

[1] Weaver, John, editorial in *Economic Geography,* Vol. 35, No. 4, October, 1959. Reprinted by permission.

[2] Sauer, Carl O., "The Agency of Man on the Earth," *Man's Role in Changing the Face of the Earth,* Thomas, William L., Jr. (Editor), International Symposium, Wenner-Gren Foundation for Anthropological Research, University of Chicago Press, Chicago, 1956. Copyright 1956 The University of Chicago. Reprinted by permission.

environment in which our niche is located. Developing from that is the new ethic of conservation which may have a great deal more religious consequence than it has had up to the present. Respect for habitat is fundamental in some of the other past and present religions of the world. But in our own it has been foreign to our idea that we have dominion over the earth. . . . There are many interesting approaches to the problem of man and his environment, and all, save perhaps the technological, seem to lead to the same conclusions. With this possible exception, these various approaches indicate that humanity should strive toward a condition of equilibrium with its environment. This is the verdict of ethics, aesthetics, and natural science. . . . Through science, man now has the means to be aware of change and its effects and the ways in which his cultural values and behavior should be modified to insure their own preservation. Whether we consider ethics to be enlightened self-interest, the greatest good for the greatest number, ultimate good rather than present benefit, or Schweitzer's reverence for life, man's obligation toward his environment is equally clear.[1]

Another symposium participant calls man both "creator" and "captive" of our technological civilization and asks:

¶ What effect has man's role in changing the face of the earth had on his aesthetic sensitivity and creativity, his ethical and legal standards for ordering his relations to his fellowmen, his emotive relation to nature itself and its creation, and his moral standards for determining whether his tools are used for good or for bad ends? The last factor suggests that the answer which the evidence and its analysis permit us to give to this question may well determine whether man remains the master or becomes the slave and perhaps even the murdered victim of his tools.[2]

A liberal arts education, too, calls for development of the aesthetic as well as the ethics of life and living. No field offers a better opportunity than geography for cultivating a deep appreciation of the out-of-doors in which man spends much of his life. Modern transportation in a matter of hours or days transports us to any of our national and state parks or other world scenic wonders that excite the curiosity of those prepared to understand the geologic and geographic forces which produced them. Though this is a matter of commonplace observation and experience, it is not by any means uncommon to find Americans cruising their own country and the world without seeing very much. The imbalance in our educational system between educating for economics and educating for the aesthetics and the amenities of life is pointedly illustrated in an address by Stephen B. Jones of Yale delivered at the University of Toronto in 1952:

¶ "Had I two loaves of bread," said Mohammed, "I would sell one and buy white hyacinths to feed my soul." Few in our Occidental world heed this Oriental wisdom. On the contrary, we are ever ready to sell our hyacinths to buy more loaves of bread. We pollute our rivers with industrial waste and call it Enterprise. We destroy a waterfall to generate power, and call it Progress. Even the academic world sells its hyacinths. We force the humanities into the frame of the sciences and call the result Research. Geography has claims to be both a humanity and a science. . . . Geography can be both bread and hyacinths. It can help provide the substantial stuff that supports life, and it can help provide that which makes life worth living. . . . I seem to be buying bread, not hyacinths. But this elementary if somewhat elusive concept can contribute to the greater enjoyment of geography as well as to its theoretical and practical advance. Many years ago I stood on the rim of the Grand Canyon and heard a ranger describe the scene and the origin of the landforms below. At the end of the talk, one visitor said to another, "Isn't it wonderful? To think that bridge down there is 400 feet long!" I do not mean to scoff at the tourist. I earn my living trying to improve the minds of students; I am not going to try to improve the minds of tourists. But for those of us who are not satisfied with knowing the lengths of bridges, there is an intellectual satisfaction in looking upon a part of the world and knowing how it *all* fits together, in knowing how earth and air and water and life have torn and built to produce the scene before our eyes.

. . . . There is more truth than jest in the story of another Grand Canyon tourist, who drove up

[1] *Ibid.* Reprinted by permission.

[2] Northrop, F. S. C., "Man's Relation to the Earth in Its Bearing on His Aesthetic, Ethical, and Legal Values," *op. cit.*, p. 1052. Reprinted by permission.

to the rim, took a look, and drove away, saying sourly, "It looks just like the pictures." For many of us, life is not lived in the real world but in the world of printed paper, television images, and other symbols. We geographers strive to show reality on maps, and then the maps become more real to us than reality.

. . . . Having spoken of reverence, you may think my next step will be to say that God Himself is a geographer. He is, I am sure, a geographile, for we are told that He made the world and saw that it was good.[1]

Geography unifies knowledge

Some years ago a committee appointed by the American Council of Learned Societies dramatically set forth in negative terms the thesis of an ideal education:

¶ Would we not all agree that a person was *not* liberally educated who was illiterate and inarticulate, uninformed and with no knowledge of how to acquire knowledge, insensitive to aesthetic, moral, and religious value, provincial, unintegrated, and enslaved? Does it follow, then, that a person *is* liberally educated in proportion as he is literate and articulate in the "languages" of human intercourse, verbal, symbolic, and expressive; as he is possessed of the basic facts of the world of nature, human nature, and human society, and, in addition, a master of the main techniques of acquiring new knowledge in these realms; . . . as he is freed from the tyranny of provincialism through temporal, spatial, and systematic orientation—in short, as he is an intelligent and responsible agent, able to participate richly in the good life, and ready and eager to contribute all he can to the welfare of his fellow men? Is not this a positive freedom which democracy should cherish and which a liberal education should foster?[2]

With this all-inclusive statement of the nature and objectives of a liberal arts education, few educators as well as subject-matter-specialists would probably disagree. Certainly geographers would recognize in their subject, as pointed out above, the sharing of the points of views of this committee. Of particular geographic relevance are the emphasized sections on integration, knowledge concerning the world of nature, human nature, human society, and freedom from the tyranny of provincialism to temporal, spatial, and systematic orientation. One recalls here a terse summary of this view by the late Isaiah Bowman, one of the most celebrated geographers of all times in academic and government circles, and former president of Johns Hopkins University: "A man is not educated who lacks a sense of time and place."

It is one thing for college administrators and professional educators to outline the aims and objectives of a liberal arts education, but quite another matter to formulate policies and procedures in achieving the purposes so glibly pointed out above. But such disagreement, controversy, and differences of program, including the highly diverse curricula, should not lead to the false impression that school people do not know what they are doing in pursuing their very plan to achieve the goals in liberal arts or what has also been known as general education. In fact, such diverse programs in themselves verify the nature and values of a liberal arts education.

It is understandable, then, that in actual practice educational curricula would be variously organized reflecting diverse philosophies, various emphases on content, methodologies, institutional traditions, and the like.

Whatever the policy, one common feature would seem to apply to all, namely, a system of instruction which attempts in one form or another to unify all learning. Seeking the unity of knowledge has, as a matter of fact, been the common goal of all mankind. It dates back to the curricula in antiquity—the so-called *trivium* (grammar, logic, rhetoric) and *quadrivium* (arithmetic, geometry, astronomy, music).

With the advancement of technology and the proliferation of subject-matter specialties, a unified picture of the world has been all but lost as each specialist pursues the researches in his own field. As evolved products of society, such specialties are not to be deprecated, for it is one of the first principles of education, and particularly geographic

[1] Jones, Stephen B., "The Enjoyment of Geography," *The Geographical Review*, Vol. XLII, No. 4, 1952, *passim*, pp. 543-550. Reprinted by permission.

[2] Greene, Theodore M., *et al.*, *Liberal Education Re-examined—Its Role in a Democracy*, Harper & Bros., New York, 1943, p. 130. Reprinted by permission.

education, to acknowledge that advancements in modern culture and civilization must be attributed to the many scientists who study the behavior and laws of nature and of man, and formulate the principles of interrelationships, characteristically emphasized in the area of geography. Properly considered, then, the formulation of scientific principles and laws which grow out of these considerations is indispensable to the liberal arts program of education.

All generalizations aside, it still behooves the educator to examine continually any educational process in terms of its own contribution to the method by which one may perceive of learning as a basic perception of the unity or totality of reality. Thus each educator regardless of subject matter may well address himself to the question, "How may my subject matter be best presented to establish a unified concept of my field? And how may this unitary concept be related to the unifying concepts of other fields, particularly those that are most closely correlative?" This calls for integrated processes of thought at their best. Here as elsewhere in all forms of education, and especially in general education, we must recognize at the outset two primary principles of learning: (1) That integration of knowledge in the final analysis takes place in the mind of the learner and not in the mind of the instructor. Teachers and textbooks can only stimulate or direct such learning. (2) Whether teacher or student, one cannot integrate anything he does not have. Too often these two principles have been ignored in the so-called unified or integrated educational program of the general education type when neither the teacher nor the students themselves had the necessary background training in the facts and principles of the several disciplines and, therefore, were not in a position to recognize integrating learning processes of such disciplines let alone possess the ability to treat in a unified form the relationship of the learning processes of one discipline or another. This situation is particularly serious in the educational programs of the average American college where neither history nor geography is required to present a unified time-area concept of the world cultural patterns and the socio-economic and political problems related thereto.

Our concern here, of course, is to examine the question, "What part does the discipline of geography play in the integration of knowledge and the liberation of man for world citizenship?" At the very start it may be pointed out that while each subject in the average college curriculum has its own unifying elements, we here submit the proposition that the broadest base for integration of knowledge characteristically inheres in the subjects of history and geography. No historic event can occur *in vacuo,* and knowledge in any form, whether historic, economic, social, political, military, or religious, must be properly time–space integrated to give proper perspective to reality. Effective learning thus must be directed at understanding the significance of an event or human behavior by virtue of its relation to preceding and succeeding events (history), and its relation determined as well to the differentiated areal setting of which the event or behavior is an integral part (geography). Wrong associations in time produce what historians call "anachronisms"; similarily, wrong associations in place (*choros*) result in what we may call "anachorisms." Strange as it may seem, many so-called general education programs operate on the basis that while we cannot get along without correct chronology, we may very well ignore the correct chorographic setting of an event. This no doubt is one basic reason why so many general education or other such types of liberal education programs fail to achieve their unifying objective. They lack reality because they lack systematic areality. And they lack this areality because even in some of the best education circles geography is still understood as dealing merely with a "point on the map" instead of "a point in the head," as someone has so aptly put it. Now it is obvious that space integration of earth phenomena is much more than pinpointing a spot on the globe. In fact such unanalyzed space-dissociated atlas information adds nothing to our knowledge of the history of civilization nor to our understanding of those natural and human forces that differentiate the various cultures of the world. Meaningful learning situations in which the student may fully participate in the process of understanding the interrelationship of world phenomena, therefore, call for keeping things together that belong together or are most closely associated with one another in space and time. This we submit calls for an understanding of the geographic processes which effect areal unity in the study of community, regional, national, and international problems. And as we shall also see later, the geographic methodology co-ordinates the various disciplines in the humanities, the social sciences, and the natural sciences on which it depends for the most part for its basic phenomenology.

With this statement many geographers would indeed agree. However, viewing phenomenology globe-wise or even community-wise with all its heterogeneous components can prove very challenging and frustrating. Even the most discerning person will find it impossible to perceive the entire content of even a local landscape, to say nothing of the bewildering mass of natural and cultural elements which variegate the earth's surface and whose spatial context must be understood. It is in this very challenge that the discipline of geography provides the technique and training needed to rationalize world phenomena and thus make its subject useful in integrating knowledge of human affairs. In this aspect geography is also distinctive from the other sciences. The complex environmental elements, whether physical or cultural, cannot be brought into the laboratory but must be surveyed and analyzed directly in the context of the field. Thus Hartshorne (basing his observations on a review of many other geography works) observes:

¶ In geography, in contrast, [i.e. with other sciences] the interest is focused from the start on the existing integrations of diverse phenomena which, by their existence, determine the variable character of area. It begins, that is, with things as they are actually arranged and interrelated in reality, even as the layman may observe them.[1]

But as already hinted above, the mosaic of earth structure and of man's occupance forms is too complex to provide a synthesis of the impression. And so by way of specialized geographic training the geography student learns to employ certain techniques of selectivity of phenomena and methods by which to analyze the relevance and importance of such phenomena as placed upon the structural and process relationships observed in the landscape. Again quoting Hartshorne:

¶ While the geographer starts at the same level as the observant layman, and each necessarily selects or emphasizes particular features out of all that is observable in an area, in order to analyze the variable character of area, the geographer must use some systematic and purposeful method of selection. In concentrating on one category of features at a time, he will observe the varying manifestations of that particular category, in relation to those of other categories with which the variations are most closely interrelated. By this method he may establish the existence of systems and areal patterns of particular categories which the layman is unable to observe, and by comparison of such areal patterns of different categories induce hypotheses of the process relationships among the different phenomena.[2]

To be sure, as Hartshorne also points out, geographers are not the only investigators to use the principle of integration in scientific work, but it is here also to be noted that geographic integration is on a different level:

¶ Division of the study of that reality into separate sciences may provide explanations of the various parts of these integrations, but it offers no approach to synthetic description or explanation of the total integration of areas. The total reality is there for study, and geography is the name of the section of empirical knowledge which has always been called upon to study that reality.[3]

The degree, then, to which the analyst of geography succeeds in making sound observations and interpretations of societal phenomena depends on his acumen in selecting the chief quantitative and qualitative elements that differentiate landscapes and most significantly play a unifying role in explaining the cultural patterns which man has impressed upon them. Only a few other steps

[1] Hartshorne, Richard, *Perspective on the Nature of Geography,* published for the Association of American Geographers by Rand McNally & Co., Chicago, 1959, p. 33. Reprinted by permission.

[2] *Ibid.* Reprinted by permission.

[3] *Ibid.* Reprinted by permission.

may be considered here, and even these necessarily superficially.

Determining the patterns and principles that survey spatially our "common existence"

Whatever we may think of the natural endowments of a region, whether good or poor, and the ways in which man exercises his stewardship over them, whether apparently wise or unwise, a region presents a logical unitary base for analysis and synthesis. As Vidal de la Blache, one of the world's famous geographers, has so aptly said: "Every region is a domain where many dissimilar things are superficially brought together and subsequently adapted themselves to a common existence." And, as indicated above, in the statement by Hartshorne, it is the distinctive challenge to the geographer to learn the techniques of explaining such unified areal phenomenology.

But even history and geography cannot at any one time treat of the world as a unit. Time and space relationships must obviously be treated regionally, whether by the historian or the geographer, for no human mind in a learning situation can comprehend the whole without understanding its parts. Consequently one of the first challenges that the discriminating student in geography is faced with in any areal study is to delimit such area, however small or large it may be, in accordance with the purpose of his study, and the rationale of the unifying criteria which differentiate the region from those of neighboring regions. The project may deal with a limited local situation, as in the case of community planning. Or it might represent a study of conurban development extending across state boundaries, or deal with a land reclamation and resettlement program, such as the T.V.A. Nearly all such programs call for a rather complete inventory of landscape content for value interpretations and evaluations involving social, economic, and political principles. In a somewhat different category of regional studies would be those that are focused primarily on land occupance of a specialized type—a special form of agriculture, of manufacturing, of commerce, and the like. The geography of political units, such as incorporated cities, counties, states, and countries, calls for still a different set of unifying principles, involving, as they do among other things, jurisdictional differentiations. But whatever the purpose or scope of the areal study may be, the task is to find the common denominator of the "dissimilar things" de la Blache refers to. Unfortunately, since each region is unique, approaches to the techniques must also in a sense be unique. However, several guidelines for unifying areal studies may be indicated:

(1) Thorough familiarity with the area, preferably direct contact with it. Normally there is no substitute for a thoroughgoing field survey based on fairly complete inventory of all relevant phenomena, natural and cultural.

(2) Though difficult at times to predetermine, such relevant phenomena are generally selected, of course, on the basis of their seeming relative importance to the problem at hand. Determine the bonds of relationships that seem most cogent in tying one element to another and note their unifying functions in relation to total areality.

(3) Closely related to the preceding is the recognition of the character-dominating processes operating within each of the physical, biological, and cultural categories. Note, moreover, the role that each plays in establishing systematic unity through its several interconnections.

(4) Not only must the student observe the interrelated patterns of functional processes in the present, but he must also determine how the present spatial distribution patterns have evolved out of the past, which includes consideration of the factor of cultural heritages imported into the area.

(5) And for the most purposive studies, the student will also project the cultural development expected in the future on the basis of the combined history and geography of the area.

The technique of integrating time–space relationships is illustrated by the microregional study described and diagrammatized in Chapter 35. From this the student will observe even in this abridged and cartogramic form that geographic survey and analysis and synthesis of an area can prove to be a very time-consuming process. But it should be kept in mind also that another region many times as large may not necessarily involve proportionately more kinds of geographic processes but may rather simply present higher numerical values in the multiple categories or classes of data recognized in the smaller region.

One of the major academic interests which geographers share with other social scientists is the problem of national security. While this question involves many aspects of technology and diplomacy, there is a common denominator of interests on the part of everyone dealing with this question, focused as it is upon the role which natural resources as well as human resources play in building a strong bulwark for world democracy. And so a geographer may wish to consider the national or world distribution of one or several of the most strategic minerals on which modern atomic warfare is based. This sort of thing would be called a topical study on the distribution of areal phenomena whose integral interest is centered upon the occurrence of a product and its use rather than focused on area as such. On the natural side, the distribution of, let us say, uranium-bearing minerals might be noted in association with the rock formations within which they most commonly occur. Then the technology of exploration and exploitation would be examined, perhaps, in the light of the most favorable geographic factors which enter into the availability and recovery of fissionable and fusionable materials. Such a systematic study necessarily calls for some knowledge of economic, political, and military principles upon which our entire government program on military preparedness operates.

When a political unit is used in geography as a unifying basis for area study, another set of principles obtains. Among the primary considerations in the study of a country, for example, is to see how the several regions of differentiated natural resources and cultures and economies and even political sentiments fit into the federal scheme of central control. Seeking political unity, if for no reason other than defense, under circumstances of regional diversities calls for a study not only of the regions themselves but also of the interregional processes by which the various economies can be co-ordinated to the best advantages for the welfare of the nation-state.

The political approach to the study of world geography by countries and states is still a useful expedient where national and international issues are of primary concern. As a matter of fact, government policies may be of such over-riding importance as to obscure principles of geographic relationships operative between natural and human forces. Thus the politically disunifying elements of two adjacent states or countries may by their diverse interests negate the operation of good planning principles for a geographic region whose social and economic forces call for unit planning across the politically divisive state boundary line.

Extending the level of geographic area study now to a global basis, the "one world" unitary concepts seem to be favored by a combined consideration of the regional, systematic, and political approaches. A major consideration here of world regional differentiation is to keep the number of regions sufficiently small to allow for convenient comprehensive comparisons. But here again in any case the problem arises as to the kind of criteria which best serve areal differentiation. Many textbooks on geography reveal different ideas on this matter, each unquestionably having some virtues to support the basis of textual organization. Long recognized by geographers as significant in land–life relationship studies are the climatological and vegetative patterns. Accordingly, these have often been chosen as unifying global frames of reference. As in the case of other unifying single or multiple feature patterns, any form of regionalized pattern must necessarily be arbitrarily conceived, based upon somewhat artifically separated phenomena that normally belong together.

It should be apparent to the discerning student by this time, then, that no "cut and dried" system of piecemeal unified treatment of world phenomena in a completely satisfactory way has yet suggested itself—nor probably ever will. Only nature is really unified. And the "common existence" of man which de la Blache conceives as a united life with nature can be only an ideological concept, which man will never completely understand. In other words, total reality is incomprehensible; hence, man resorts to all kinds of expedients in classifying knowledge and pursuing its fragmented form as manifested increasingly by the subject proliferation in the academic curriculum. But we repeat that the quest of greatest challenge is

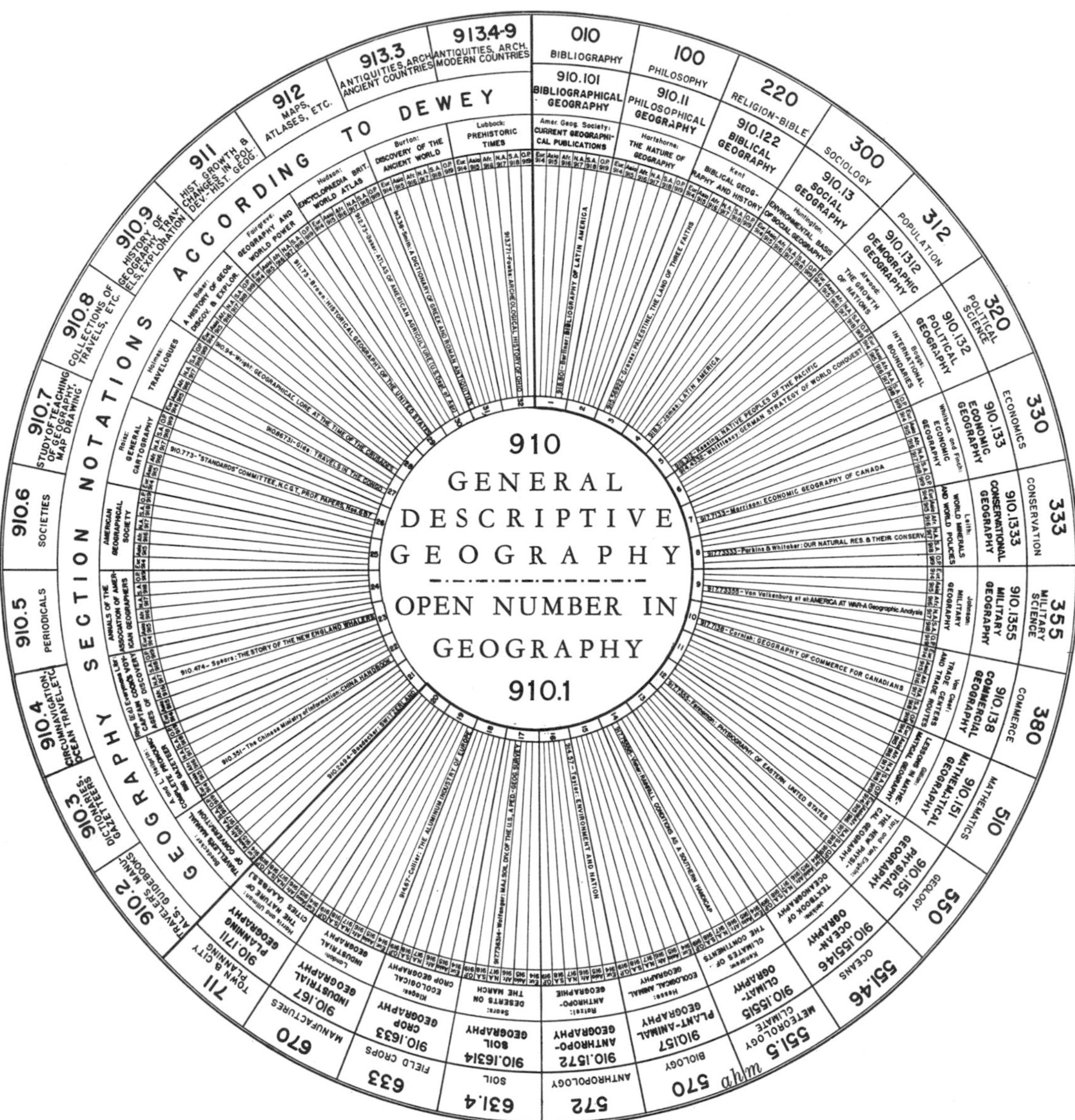

II:1 This wheel chart illustrates the substantive relationships of geography to other cognate disciplines and services as a convenient guide in codifying and classifying all geographic materials within the basic framework of the Dewey Decimal System. The concept of using the basic code 910.1 as a prefix to the index of the cognate field to which the geography subject is systematically related makes possible a unified geographic classification. This system, as reported by the editor of the decimal classification, is now considered functional.

to learn as much as we can of the unitary functions of nature and man's place in it. Thus, in our liberal arts education the student should be at least exposed to as many of the disciplines as possible, not so much for the practical knowledge which they separately provide, but for the specific disciplinary value which each contributes in its own distinctive way to the understanding of earth reality. It is then largely up to the student with the aid of such general education aids as are available to him to see how each topic matter area is related to the other in contributing such knowledge and techniques as we must have in order to make total integration possible.

Geography is a curricular-core subject

The integrative character of genetic geography, as we have seen above, inheres in systematic and regional spatial synthesis of world affairs. But it does not stop here. Integral also are its investigative processes, which systematically cut across virtually all the disciplines. Geography appropriates and adapts their data suited to its needs as it searches for the unifying principles which express the processes by which the various patterns of world occupance have come into being. This continuous alertness to the newly developed ideas and ideologies in the humanities and the social sciences, to the newly found discoveries in the natural sciences, and to history's own time-integration analyses of epochal events, in itself predicates a liberal arts education. At the same time it provides knowledge of the various subject matter areas which gives depth as well as breadth to the understanding of societal problems. Attesting to this "bridge" character of geography are the various systematic organizations of its subject matter — anthropological geography, social geography, economic geography, industrial and commercial geography, planning geography, political geography, historical geography, and military geography—as illustrated in Figure II-1. This wheel chart, designed to unify Dewey classification of geography books, shows: (1) the various systematic fields (outer circle) on which the corresponding or correlative branches of geography (adjacent circle) depend for original investigations, of facts, processes and principles developed in those fields (e.g. political science—political geography); (2) a type of publication (third circle) illustrating the systematic principles of geography which are related closely to political science (e.g., Boggs' *International Boundaries*); and (3) another type of publication (innermost circle) which regionally exemplifies relation of a geography publication to political science (e.g., Whittlesey's *German Strategy of World Conquest*). Such catalog arrangement, then, also serves as an expedient to prevent truly geography works from being scattered all over the library (12).

Figure II-2 reveals why geography has

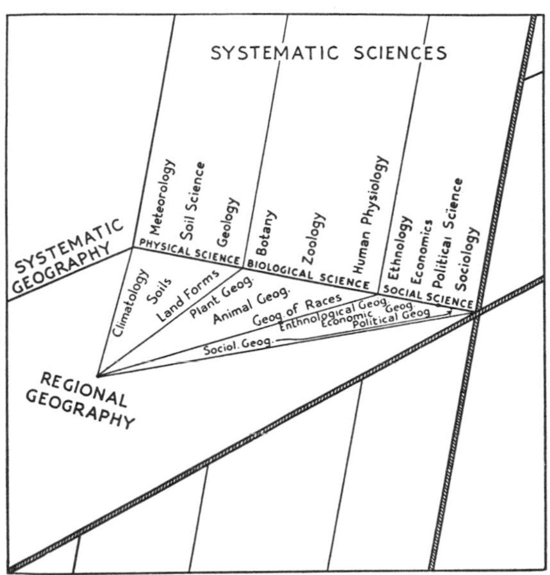

II:2 The nature of the interdisciplinary structure and functions of geography as here diagrammatized can perhaps best be understood by the author's (Hartshorne's) own caption: "The planes are not to be considered literally as plane surfaces, but as representing two opposing points of view in studying reality. The view of reality in terms of areal differentiation of the earth surface is intersected at every point by the view in which reality is considered in terms of phenomena classified by kind. The different systematic sciences that study different phenomena found within the earth surface are intersected by the corresponding branches of systematic geography. The integration of all the branches of systematic geography, focused on a particular place in the earth surface, is regional geography." (From *The Nature of Geography*, by Richard Hartshorne, Annals of the Association of American Geographers, 1939, used by permission)

often been referred to as an "integrating science." Properly understood, this is a fair characterization, for geography is continually correlating or co-ordinating data and integrating ideas from sister fields. This concept of geography in education was pioneered by such celebrated German geographers as Baron F. von Richthofen and Alfred Hettner. As professor of geography at Leipzig and Berlin, Richthofen in his weekly geographic

Baron F. von Richthofen 1833-1905 (Copyright, Royal Geographical Society, used by permission)

Alfred Hettner 1859-1941 (From *Geographischen Taschenbuch* by E. Meynen)

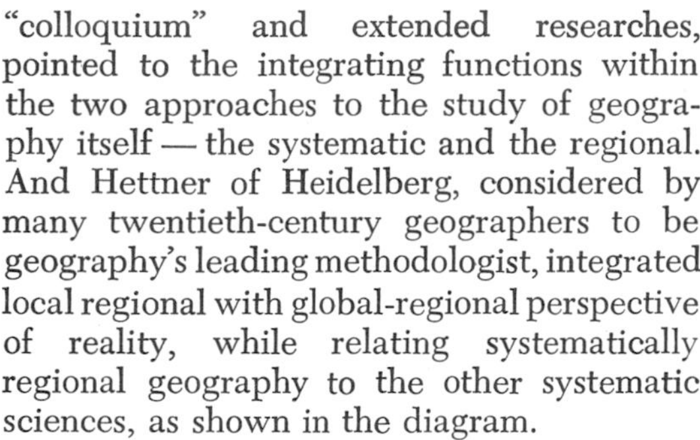

"colloquium" and extended researches, pointed to the integrating functions within the two approaches to the study of geography itself — the systematic and the regional. And Hettner of Heidelberg, considered by many twentieth-century geographers to be geography's leading methodologist, integrated local regional with global-regional perspective of reality, while relating systematically regional geography to the other systematic sciences, as shown in the diagram.

The fact is obvious that conceptual geography must make its own contribution to geographic education if it is not simply to duplicate concepts already supplied by other disciplines. To appreciate the common denominator of interests of geography with the other disciplines with which it is closely identified and at the same time to distinguish the several contributions distinctively made by each towards the understanding of human behavior, it will be well to review some of the "marriage" relationships of geography to other disciplines.

1. ***History and geography.*** As already previously pointed out, time and space are the only two universal terrestrial phenomena to which reality is related. This brings history, an integrator of time, and geography, an integrator of space, into the closest subject matter marriage relationship possible. It is well recognized by geographically informed historians, as well as historically informed geographers, that neither subject can effectively be taught without the other in a meaningful way. To be sure, historians primarily emphasize the past and the geographers primarily the present. But, just as the past holds little meaning apart from our experiences of the present, so our present cannot be understood without the knowledge of past heritages. History is distinguished also by its emphasis on biographical accounts of great men who have made history, and everyone will acknowledge that without the great personages of history and their leadership in the affairs of human society, there would be few milestones of world events to which to relate the story of civilization. Geography, on the other hand, is concerned with showing how the more important historic events are related to coherent areal forces, characteristically cartographically illustrated, as expounded in the next chapter. The technique of synthesizing and graphically portraying event–environment relationships is centuries old, but formal course discipline in the subject of what we call historical geography is a relatively recent development. The subject is of such vital concern for students of combined history and geography that formal courses, such as historical geography of the United States, are now currently offered. A separate chapter—Chapter 35—is designed to expound and illustrate some of the basic concepts and principles of historical geography.

2. ***Political science, military strategy-geography.*** While the geographer is primarily concerned with what is called the "geographic area," the political scientist's materials and ideas are organized in terms of governmental units, whether incorporated cities, townships, counties, states, or nation-states. Man early recognized that some form of order or law was necessary to regulate the affairs of men, having for its purpose the establishment of authority to enact and enforce such laws within given jurisdictional areas. Such matters, then, as systems of government, party organization, nature of laws claimed for various governmental units to regulate the affairs of human society are thus primarily the province of the student interested in government, including problems related to our military defense.

The hard core of geographic interests in jurisdictional organization of areas is focused on topics such as the significance of relative location, size, and shape of a country in the framework of peace and war; the physical and biological structure with which the state has to deal wisely to commandeer its resources; the ownership or otherwise accessibility or position of strategic minerals, particularly in terms of our national defense; the nature of political boundaries as they affect peacetime trade and wartime security. One of the major theoretical concerns of political geography emphasizes the unitary aspect of the diverse regions which operate under one government. Do the several regions beneficially complement each other, or is there a sectional competitiveness which is inimical to the total welfare of the country? Power politics is examined in relation to a nation's resources, geomatical position in the world, and the like.

The science of geography and the science of government enjoy close academic partnership in many items of legislative concern. From the different points of view of political conflict and control both fields are vitally concerned with such problems as sectional race tensions; causes of international friction, such as are expected in colonialism or nationalism; the question of aid to underdeveloped countries, and other political issues and policies.

3. ***Economics and geography.*** The close subject relationship of these two areas is commonly recognized in the curriculum by the fact that economic geography courses of one type or another are taught in some institutions in the economics department, whereas in others they are a part of the geography curriculum. This is readily understandable because of the common denominator of interests in material resources. Again the approach to the study of a community's or nation's wealth is often quite different, however. The economist emphasizes the statistical angle, whereas the geographer commonly reduces statistical values to a cartographic base of space evaluations of such statistics. This is because the distribution pattern of statistical data of any category of values is often far more significant than the numerical values themselves without regional orientation. Thus two countries may statistically show up quite alike in forest and mineral resources, in miles of transportation facilities, in agricultural and industrial production, and the like. Yet the economy and security of the one may be on a much lower level than the other, because the one is not alert towards effecting harmonious environmental or regional distribution patterns or is otherwise in an unfavorable environmental or regional position so as not to be able to keep pace with its competitor. Man-collected statistics and their spatial orientation, then, may tell two entirely different stories.

In pursuit of studies of production, distribution, and consumption of wealth and income, the economist especially investigates resource categories which are normally nongeographic in character, e.g., labor legislation, labor problems, money and banking, taxation, and the like. On the other hand, one of the geographer's primary concerns is to examine a region and discern how the possible standards of living are reflected by the kind of adjustments man has made through the resource potential of the area. Similarly, the geographer is likely to stress the significance of geographic position in the location of industries rather than the problems of capital, labor, and management, however critically important they may be. Such a course as Trade and Transportation may well be found in either department—with a distinctive approach, however. Among the things emphasized by the economist would be a consideration of the monetary values of the several countries and the rates of foreign exchange, while among the geographer's topics would be emphasis on the different environmental bases of natural and human resources in the production of surplus goods which lead to foreign trade.

4. Sociology and geography. Sociologists are interested in the behavior patterns of human society as expressed by various forms of interaction among the various groups of cultures. Thus, sociology surveys the evolution of the various structures and functions of societal institutions established by various human groups. It, together with psychology, is interested in the study of forms of human behavior—sociology primarily from the standpoint of group behavior, and psychology essentially in terms of individual human reaction. Insofar as both these disciplines are related to personality and group experiences as influenced by the milieu of which such experiences are necesarily a part, both share with geography interest in the processes by which humans come "to terms with the natural and cultural forces of the environment." Sociologists and geographers thus often share similar ecological points of interest in explaining human occupance phenomena. And such subjects as Population Problems and Urban–Rural Development are of common academic interest likewise to the sociologist and the geographer. Each has here an important contribution to make, the sociologist primarily from the standpoint of the relation of man to man and group to group, while the geographer emphasizes primarily life–land associations in a regional context. It should be obvious from this also that both fields have a common meeting ground in many facets of community planning.

The geographer as professional consultant and co-ordinator

It may seem paradoxical that while the geographer talks continually about local and world affairs, unlike the lawyer, the doctor, or the engineer, the geographer does not hang his shingle out to announce his professional services. He is rather a "specialized generalist." As a sort of liaison agent, his specialty is to understand how the various contributions of the human social sciences, natural sciences, law, and engineering are interrelated, and to endeavor to find complementary rather than competitive processes in regional resource-use to help ease the tensions that arise among peoples and among nations, and thus to contribute his own part to the betterment of world society.

The professional services of geographers, therefore, outside of teaching as such, are more commonly of the consultant or coordinator type, rather than strictly vocational in character. The moment a geographer qualifies for a technological position, e.g., a meteorologist, or pedologist, he steps essentially out of the field of geography. To be sure, such positions are open to geographically trained people whose background can make distinctive contributions to these specialized fields; however, the person who normally fills this type of position would go under the title of meteorologist, pedologist, agronomist, demographer, statistician, conservationist, cartographer, or such other classification as befits the special assignment.

Our discussion is concerned chiefly with those positions which geographers commonly fill as consultants in connection with their teaching and research and in which they perform essentially "geographic" services of one kind or another.

1. The geography academician as consultant in government. Global geography conceptual service is illustrated in an exemplary way by the personality, position, and philosophy of the late Right Honourable Sir Halford J. Mackinder. Director of the London School of Economics and Political Science and professor of Geography in the

University of London, Mackinder served as Privy Counsellor and one-time Chairman of the Imperial Shipping Committee. Combining academic and political astuteness, Mackinder is probably most noted for his original idea on "The Geographic Pivot of History," first delivered to the Royal Geographic Society—London—in 1904. His "World Island" philosophy was expounded at the Paris Peace Conference in 1919. It expresses a sort of competitive–complementary view of land-water military strategy:

¶ Who rules East Europe commands the Heartland:
Who rules the Heartland commands the World–Island:
Who rules the World–Island commands the World (see Figure II-3).[1]

This unitary concept embracing the inner land power as related to the peripheral sea power of world affairs may now seem largely obsolete in view of our new nuclear age of missiles and rockets. But Mackinder's concept is introduced here to illustrate what an influence historically such a concept may have upon world affairs. A sample of Mackinder's geographic philosophy is reflected in the following quotation from a publication of his in 1918, cautioning the diplomats at the Paris Peace Conference:

¶ The great wars of history—we have had a world war about every hundred years for the last four centuries—are the outcome, direct or indirect, of the unequal growth of nations, and that unequal growth is not wholly due to the greater genius and energy of some nations as compared with others; in large measure it is the result of the uneven distribution of fertility and strategical opportunity upon the face of the globe. In other words, there is in nature no such thing as equality of opportunity for the nations. Unless I wholly misread the facts of geography, I would go further, and say that the grouping of lands and seas, and of fertility and natural pathways, is such as to lend itself to the growth of empires, and in the end of a single world-empire. If we are to realize our ideal of a League of Nations which shall prevent war in the future, we must recognize these geographical realities and take steps to counter their influence. Last century, under the spell of the Darwinian theory, men came to think that those forms of organization should survive which adapted themselves best to their natural environment. To-day we realize, as we emerge from our fiery trial, that human victory consists in our rising superior to such mere fatalism.[2]

Sir Halford J. Mackinder 1861-1947 (Copyright, Royal Geographical Society, used by permission)

An American counterpart of geopolitical world influence was the career of Isaiah Bowman, introduced earlier, whose services were sought in connection with the Paris Peace Conference. Successively enrolled at Harvard and Yale, he subsequently became assistant professor at Yale, and, in 1935, President of Johns Hopkins University. A former Director of the American Geographical Society and one-time President of the Association of American Geographers, Dr. Bowman was the creator of many new political geographic concepts, a leader of many scientific expeditions, chiefly in South

[1] Mackinder, Halford J., *Democratic Ideals and Reality*, Holt, Rinehart and Winston, New York, 1942, p. 150. Reprinted by permission.

[2] *Ibid.*, pp. 1-2. Reprinted by permission.

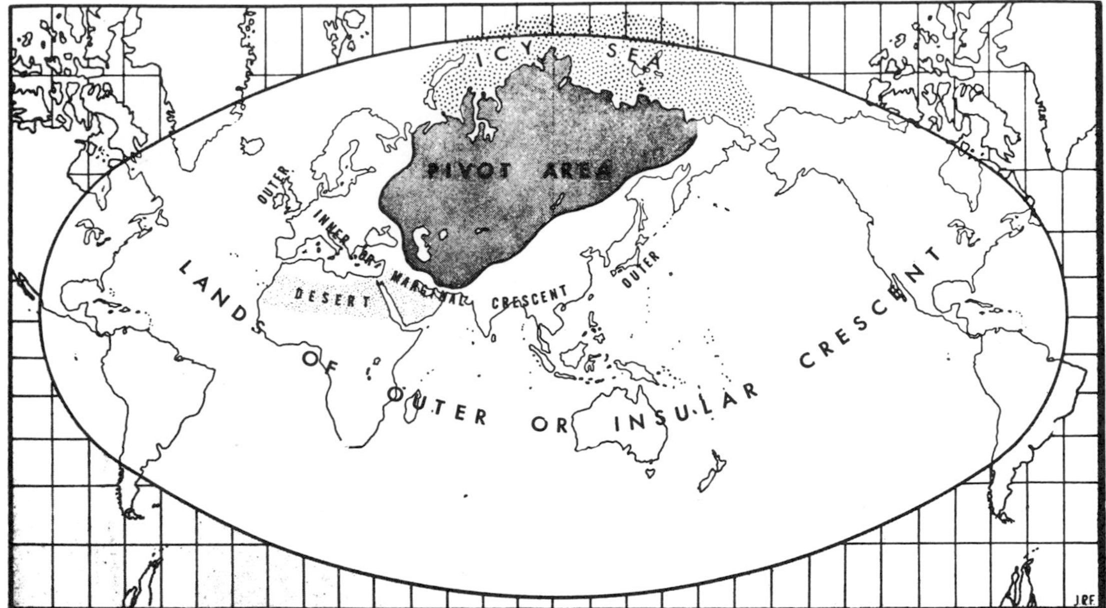

II:3 One of the most publicized and controversial concepts in historical-political geography is Mackinder's Heartland thesis as explained briefly in the text. What spatial geo-strategy is implicit in this map? In the light of mid-twentieth century developments, would you use a different map design to express present-day global relations between the East and the West? (From *Principles of Political Geography* by Hans W. Weigert *et al.* Appleton-Century-Crofts, Inc., New York, 1957, used by permission)

America, and a prolific and vigorous researcher and writer. Literary geographic classics of his include such works as *The New World* (1928) and *The Pioneer Fringe* (1931).

2. ***Military geography.*** It is a peculiar attribute of American geographic education, as attested particularly by the First World War, the Second World War, and the "cold war" of the mid-twentieth century, that when our country is at war or faces an international crisis, academic and governmental demands on geographers' services reach unprecedented heights. It is at such times that geographers are recruited to fill critical positions in government as they did in the Second World War, particularly in the Office of Strategic Services. Such experiences have led to the conviction that better geographic training is needed among our armed forces. For example, as part of the instructional program of the Air Force ROTC, a committee of the Association of American Geographers, with Dr. J. O. M. Broek as chairman, was asked to prepare a manual dealing with the structure, problems, and power potential of nation-states. The motivation and purpose of this project was,

¶ To clarify and increase the student's understanding of these forces and factors (e.g., "excessive nationalism, uncontrolled nuclear power, clashing ideologies, population pressures, inequalities of food supply, natural resources, wealth") as they fit into the physical world in which he lives, and into the political institutions by which man lives. . . . The readings of this text, gathered from many sources, deal with intangible concepts and doctrines and almost imponderable strategic considerations.[1]

3. ***Agricultural geography.*** One of the best examples illustrative of the personal and professional liaison relationship between agriculture and geography is illustrated in connection with the Land Utilization Survey of Britain featuring agricultural land, though also including urbanized and industrial land.

[1] *Military Aspects of World Political Geography,* Air Science 4, Air University Headquarters Air Force ROTC, Montgomery, Ala., September, 1954, p. v. Reprinted by permission.

The purpose of this survey, started in 1930, was to make a complete detailed land-use inventory of every acre of ground in England, Wales, and Scotland. The organizer of this survey was Alfred Dudley Stamp, who continues to serve as its director. One of the most celebrated geographers of all time, in terms of both geographic instruction and in research and publication, Dr. Stamp holds a Professorship of Geography in the University of London—in the London School of Economics and Political Science. He has also served as Chief Advisor in the Rural Land Use program of the British Government. Starting merely as land-use inventory, the LUS has come to be a most exhaustive treatment of the problems and potentialities of land-use in Britain. In his monumental literary and cartographic piece of geographic research, *The Land of Britain: Its Use and Misuse* (Longmans, Green and Co., 1950), Stamp, in addition to giving us a history of the LUS itself, explores and evaluates the complex historic-geographic set of factors "which have determined the very complex and intricate pattern of rural Britain."

A major feature associated with the program is detailed farm studies representative of various types, not only for Britain but for the greater Commonwealth as well. An inquiry to The Association of Agriculture about the relation of the farm type studies to geography teaching brought the following reply in part:

¶ When we selected the farms for study both in Great Britain and the Commonwealth, we made a very careful choice of certain selected regions, realizing that the teacher that was most likely to be interested in this material was the geography expert. . . . Although the Farm Study Scheme was developed independently by the Association, it did so in response to a very definite demand in the teaching world. Over here, particularly in the teaching of geography, sample studies have been increasingly included in the syllabus since the war years and, what was at one time something of a pioneer movement, has now become quite a landslide. Our work has, therefore, been much welcomed by geographers in particular, especially those in charge of teacher training.[1]

[1] Joan Bostock, Editor, Farm Adoption Scheme, Letters, July 19, 1957 and August 18, 1958. Reprinted by permission.

Isaiah Bowman 1878-1950 (American Geographical Society)

The British land-use survey in some ways has its government-geography liaison American counterpart in the land-use mapping of Puerto Rico:

¶ Recognizing the need for current information on the land uses and their distributions throughout the island, Dr. Rafael Picó (Professor of Geography, *ad honorem,* University of Puerto Rico), Chairman of the Puerto Rico Planning Board, in January 1949, invited the Department of Geography of Northwestern University to consider the feasibility of making a land-use map of Puerto Rico on the scale of 1:10,000. Following considerable correspondence with respect to the invitation and discussion by the Staff of the Department of Geography, Dr. G. Donald Hudson, then Chairman of the Department, and Dr. Clarence F. Jones went to Puerto Rico in March 1949 to survey the feasibility of undertaking this assignment.[2]

A unique feature of this program, besides being the most intensive American tropical survey of its kind, is the extensive participation of graduate students in all phases of the

[2] Jones, Clarence F. and Picó, Rafael, Editors, *Symposium on the Geography of Puerto Rico,* University of Puerto Rico Press, Rio Piedras, P.R., 1955, p. vi. Reprinted by permission.

field inventory work as well as follow-up of their own researches, including doctoral dissertations in geography. The published symposium lists eighteen thesis titles, which the student may examine to advantage and thus see in part the kind of work graduate students do in geography.

*4. **Geography careers.*** The number of students inquiring about the functions of geographic education beyond its liberal arts disciplinary values and teaching is increasing. We have already indicated how the geographer as an academician performs "part-time" important consultant services in various government agencies. In other cases geographers are employed by government on a professional career basis. One such geographer reports (as of 1954) that,

¶ Fully 200 are employed by the Department of Defense, most but not all in the Washington area as civilians, a rather small fraction in uniform at domestic bases or overseas. Other Departments and the miscellaneous Independent Offices of the Executive Branch as well as the Legislative Branch employ approximately another two hundred. Relatively large users, employing more than a score each, are the Department of State, the Department of Interior and the Department of Commerce.[1]

The Association of American Geographers has become interested in developing "a more impressive role for geography and geographers in the Federal Government," acting through a "Committee on Geographers in Government Service." This committee has among its objectives publication of "the geographical activities of Federal agencies . . . the establishment and maintenance of a file on geographers in the Federal Government . . . cooperation with the A.A.G. Placement Committee in developing a list of agencies which employ, or might employ, geographers."

While most government geography career positions are on the federal level, there is a rapidly increasing demand for geographers in the area of county and community planning. This is understandable, for while engineers, architects, and various social scientists each play their own distinctive roles in planning, the geographer is best prepared by his special training in regional synthesis to do the job of co-ordinating the work of the other specialist technicians and consultants. A geographer-planner of repute thus reports on this career area:

¶ The Chicago Plan Commission has had at least two geographers on its staff at all times since that Commission was organized as an official agency in 1939. . . . Geographers have headed research divisions of planning agencies in Philadelphia and in Cincinnati. Others have been, and are directors or members of city planning staffs, or with similar official organizations such as housing and redevelopment authorities, from Boston to San Diego. Geographers now head planning agencies in Tennessee and in Puerto Rico, both of which are concerned with urban problems. Among Federal agencies that have used geographers on their planning staffs are the Housing and Home Finance Agency, Department of State, Bureau of the Census, Bureau of the Budget, Tennessee Valley Authority, Bureau of Reclamation, President's Water Resources Commission, and many others. . . . Among communities that have had geographers on their planning commissions are Valparaiso, Indiana; Wellesley, Massachusetts; and University City, Missouri.[2]

Perhaps less definitive but equally challenging are the employment opportunities of combined geography–business majors who integrate their statistical training in business-economics with their chorographical–cartographic skills in geography. The uniqueness of such preparation is attested by the fact that even many of the smaller colleges now graduate each year a dozen or more students with such a double major. Although the industrial and commercial world is still not fully aware of the distinctive value of such a co-ordinated program, executives are soon alerted to the superior training of such students once they have been given the chance to demonstrate their combined statistical-spatial approach to the investigation of busi-

---

[1] Rose, John K., "Opportunities for Geographers in Government Service," *The Professional Geographer,* Vol. VI, May, 1954, p. 1. Reprinted by permission.

[2] Mayer, Harold M., "Geographers in City and Regional Planning," *The Professional Geographer,* Vol. VI, May, 1954, p. 7. Reprinted by permission.

ness and transportation problems. This holds particularly true in marketing: "Every business firm, whether manufacturer, wholesaler, or retailer, is faced with the *where* problem. *Where* will its raw materials come from, *where* should they be produced or stored, *where* can its goods or services be sold?" (18)

The above kind of sources, professional papers, and independent investigation have been made the basis for a study of the entire field of professional geography, a review of which will provide the student with a comprehensive insight into "Geography in Academic Institutions," "Geography in Government," "Geographers Employed in Business and their Work," "Geographical Societies in the United States" (19). It will also aid him to perceive the co-ordinated professional connections between the geographer and other career specialists.

From this and the preceding chapter it should be obvious that the geographic discipline with its emphasis on relationship techniques and man–milieu learning is just as essential in preparing for a business or government career as it is in qualifying for the teaching profession.

APPLICATION OF GEOGRAPHIC UNDERSTANDING

The need of liberal arts and professional academic training in geography is conjointly best illustrated perhaps in the responsibilities of those who exercise governmental power, whether on a local, state, national, or international level. Especially is this true in formulating national and international policies dealing with problems of unity and security which demand integrated regional and interregional considerations of economic, political, and military concepts. Yet this seems to be the very area in which our legislative and executive branches of government show the least proficiency. At no time in history is this ineptitude more critically reflected than in modern commentaries on the "cold war" between the East and the West. Recognizing the dire need for better academically trained diplomats abroad, a United States senator—Mr. Symington—introduced a bill in Congress, in January, 1959, providing for a "Foreign Service Academy," motivated by the responsible thought that:

¶ . . . the ultimate future of the world, whether it be free or slave, will not be settled on the battlefields, but rather in the minds of men . . . dedicated, well-trained representatives are at work for the Communist cause all over the world. We have not matched this effort, either in size or degree of training. . . . Fifty per cent of our entire Foreign Service officers corps does not have a speaking knowledge of any foreign language. . . . Our representatives don't understand other cultures . . . live an isolated life.[1]

By contrast, Symington observes that the "Russian foreign-service personnel are thoroughly grounded in the culture and economy of those countries, are 'experts' before they arrive" (20).

I. As a would-be informed and intelligent citizen and voter, how would you determine the *comparative* national stature of our diplomatic corps?

II. Assuming that we do not rate favorably with other world powers in training career diplomats, how do you account for this in a country which has thus far exercised the greatest political influence in the world generally? Could it be because of our superior natural resources and technological developments? Evaluate these geographic factors in terms of the past, present, and future, taking into consideration the way we have in many instances wasted our natural resources, and the fact that the natural and human resources of the U.S.S.R. have been by comparison belatedly developed.

III. In the light of the geographic concepts and principles developed in this and the preceding chapter, outline a geographic curriculum which you would suggest as a minimum prerequisite for all candidates for the diplomatic service.

IV. Specifically indicate the elements of U.S.S.R. geography with which a U.S. Ambassador to Russia should be especially familiar; similarly the elements with which a Consul should be especially familiar.

---

[1] Symington, Stuart, "Let's Have a West Point for Diplomats," *This Week Magazine,* April 2, 1959, p. 8. Reprinted from *This Week Magazine.* Copyright 1959 by the United Newspapers Magazine Corporation.

References

1 *Handbook Directory,* Association of American Geographers, Washington, D. C., 1956, pp. 24-26.

2 Meyer, Alfred H. (Chairman), "Standards of Certification for the Teaching of Geography in High Schools," Professional Paper No. 6, Committee on Standards of Certification, *National Council of Geography Teachers,* February, 1943.

3 Kohn, Clyde F. (Editor), Nineteenth Yearbook, 1948; James, Preston E. (Editor), Twenty-Ninth Yearbook, 1959, *National Council for the Social Studies.*

4 Scarfe, N. F. (Chairman), "Report of the Commission on the Teaching of Geography in Schools," *International Geographical Union,* August, 1956, p. 5.

5 Meyer, Alfred H., and Strietelmeier, John, "An Attempt at Making Geographers out of students," *The Journal of Geography,* Vol. LIII, No. 5, 1954, pp. 211-214.

6 Weaver, John, Guest Editor, *Economic Geography,* Vol. 35, No. 4, October, 1959, inside front cover.

7 Sauer, Carl O., "The Agency of Man on the Earth," *Man's Role in Changing the Face of the Earth,* Thomas, William L., Jr. (Editor), International Symposium, Wenner-Gren Foundation for Anthropological Research, published by the University of Chicago Press, Chicago, 1956, *passim,* pp. xxix, 49-68, 481.

8 Northrop, F. S. C., "Man's Relation to the Earth in Its Bearing on His Aesthetic, Ethical, and Legal Values," "*Man's Role in Changing the Face of the Earth,* Thomas, William L., Jr. (Editor), International Symposium, Wenner-Gren Foundation for Anthropological Research, published by the University of Chicago Press, Chicago, 1956, p. 1052.

9 Jones, Stephen B., "The Enjoyment of Geography," *The Geographical Review,* Vol. XLII, No. 4, 1952, *passim,* pp. 543-550.

10 Greene, Theodore M., *et al., Liberal Education Re-examined—Its Role in a Democracy,* Harper & Bros., New York, 1943, p. 120.

11 Hartshorne, Richard, *Perspective on the Nature of Geography,* published for the Association of American Geographers by Rand McNally and Co., Chicago, 1959, p. 33.

12 Meyer, Alfred H., "A Geographic Classification of Geography Material Based Upon the Dewey Classification System," *Annals of the Association of American Geographers,* Vol. XXXVII, December, 1947, pp. 209-222.

13 Mackinder, Halford J., *Democratic Ideals and Reality,* Henry Holt & Co., New York, 1942, pp. 1-2, 150.

14 *Military Aspects of World Political Geography,* Air Science 4, Air University Headquarters Air Force ROTC, Montgomery, Alabama, September, 1954, p. v.

15 Jones, Clarence F. and Picó, Rafael, Editors, *Symposium on the Geography of Puerto Rico,* University of Puerto Rico Press, Rio Piedras, P.R., 1955, p. vi.

16 Rose, John K., "Opportunities for Geographers in Government Service," *The Professional Geographer,* Vol. VI, May, 1954, p. 1.

17 Mayer, Harold M., "Geographers in City and Regional Planning," *The Professional Geographer,* Vol. VI, May, 1954, p. 7.

18 *A Career in Geography,* Committee on Careers in Geography, National Research Council and Association of American Geographers, September, 1954, p. 4.

19 Jones, Clarence F., "Status and Trends of Geography in the United States" (Baugh, Ruth E., Editor), *The Professional Geographer,* Vol. XI, Part II, No. 1.

20 Symington, Stuart, "Let's Have a West Point for Diplomats," *This Week Magazine,* April 2, 1959, p. 8.

Chapter 3

Conceiving and conveying geographic concepts graphically

It is just as important to study the proper and effective use of various forms of graphic presentation, as it is to study the values of different methods, treatments, grades, and forms of verbal presentation. — William Morris Davis

Nature and function of cartographs or maps

All of us have had the disconcerting experience at one time or another of being "lost"—losing our sense of direction or orientation in newly visited areas. Almost everyone also has experienced difficulty in directing other people to their destinations. Specifically important as may be the matter of getting our immediate bearings in connection with our movements in unfamiliar territory, much more significant—though generally unobservably so—is cultivating familiarity with the areal concepts of the natural and cultural patterns which portray the distinguishing attributes of landscapes with which we come into contact. As we shall see subsequently, the degree to which we feel "at home" in our community or, more broadly speaking, in the affairs of the world, is dependent upon our imagery of earth terrain patterns and man's land-use designs. Now the most effective way of perceiving land–man relationships on the earth is to see them in some graphic perspective. Such procedure may take essentially one of two forms—a photograph or a map. The photograph, particularly an air photograph taken at the proper altitude, has the advantage of giving detailed, portrait-like fidelity of landscape features which a map cannot supply. On the other hand, though a map does not reveal total content of areas, the selectivity of features to be emphasized adds psychological values to the objective earth features represented. In other words, a map commonly is an interpretative device combining subjective quality with objectivity. But before pursuing the subject of discussion of maps and map-making (cartography) further, let us make certain that we have the proper concept of these terms. Webster defines a map as "a representation (usually on a flat surface) of the surface of the earth, or of some part of it, showing the relative size and position, according to some given scale of projection, of the parts represented." And the term cartography derives from two roots: *carte*, French for "map," and *graphos*, Greek, "to write." Thus cartography is a form of conventional cartograph writing, or map drawing. Distance and direction, properly scaled, are minimal criteria for any true map, and unless map features are self-explanatory, a legend is also necessary.

In order to prepare ourselves for map orientation of subject matter itself, several common illusions should be noted:

1. Aside from such commonplace contacts as the layman has with maps (e.g., with road maps), maps are technical things, not of much use for the layman, and they belong chiefly in the category of the surveyor's art.

2. Aside from representation of road lines, property lines, and other similar boundary delineations, maps have limited usefulness —most concepts of world phenomena such as are discussed in economics, sociology, political science, and history can very well be perceived by description and exposition alone.

3. Cartography is geography and geography is cartography.

To see these illusions and present correct concepts of maps in proper perspective let us review the basic functions of maps: (1) As has been so well stated by Ullman, "A map's basic contribution is to reduce reality to a scale which can be comprehended." Both the indispensibility and limitations of maps can be readily understood by recalling once more the complex content of earth landscapes and the art of interpreting earth features systematically and regionally. As pointed out in the first chapter, only the actual distribution of the natural and cultural phenomena can represent reality, and no amount of qualifying or quantifying verbalization can describe accurately space-relationship-wise the integrated existence of such phenomena. And while description and exposition can supply concepts which a map cannot supply, the significance of relative space relationships of phenomena can nearly always be more effectively presented in cartographic form. To teach multiple-dimensional aspects of phenomena in space without maps would be quite as difficult as trying to teach geometry without diagrams.

1. Lack of carto-concept as a key to failure or success. For lack of a map, or map-reading ability, any of the following experiences may result. Farm yields are below par because the farmer fails to recognize the optimal crop-soil adaptation pattern, although soil maps and descriptive crop-adaptability bulletins are available from the Department of Agriculture. Maladjusted location ruins a business enterprise which disregards such factors as ready accessibility to raw materials, labor, markets, and suitable transportation facilities—all best shown on maps, available from both government and commercial sources.

Urban development suffers from want of community planning, necessarily based on land-use mapping. Consequently, residential areas become blighted; business and industry, for lack of suitable sites, locate elsewhere. One of the very first steps towards correcting the malfunction of a community is to map what we have and then map what we want.

Inaccessibility of, or inexpert use of, land-surface maps showing elevations, relief, and slope, has resulted in enormous waste of money in road-building projects, in loss of precious soil by steep-slope tillage, and in catastrophic floods from accelerated run-off on deforested slopes.

At best, mineral exploration and exploitation are characteristically speculative adventures, but much "wildcat" prospecting for oil and ores could be eliminated by expert interpretation of areal and structural geology maps which are related to a topographic base. Such maps are published by the U. S. Geological Survey in co-operation with various state geological surveys. Of all maps, the topographic quadrangle is the most generally available and useful for correlative mapping and interpretation of physical, biotic, and cultural phenomena. Thus the estimate given by the pioneer American topographic experts Salisbury and Atwood still holds: The topographic map forms "the best basis, and for many regions the only basis, for careful geographic and geologic study."[1]

2. "What" and "how" the map communicates geographically. (1) The map pinpoints the location of the specific phenomena we wish to record and analyze. Mapping calls for a rigorous commitment to accuracy of observation, which in turn creates initial confidence in the objectivity of data we are dealing with. To know specifically what and where phenomena exist is a basic criterion in the study of phenomena geographically.

(2) The areal platting of phenomena gives us a two-dimensional perspective of distribution of the several phenomena and makes possible comparative pattern analysis of areas.

(3) By comparing the several co-varying patterns of phenomena a third-dimensional perspective is introduced. This aids the geographer in determining the processes significant in resolving the evolution of the landscape occupance.

(4) One of the most interesting and instructive features of a map is the attention it draws to the disparity in distribution of phenomena—the various forms of dispersion and concentrations. Thus the mapped phenomena immediately raise questions: Why does concentration occur here? Why is there sparse representation or the complete absence of such phenomena? For example, why do some parts of the world have 500 or 1,000 people per square mile, and others only five or ten, or none at all? Why the concentrations of industry in western Europe and northeastern United States? Many of the principles in geography that we now have, based on the many types of generalizations about phenomena in the world, were made possible only through the coherent analysis of cartographic patterns.

(5) But not only do maps "raise" questions and "answer" questions; they also rather subtly at times suggest the need of exploring for new data and new concepts or values concerning social, economic, political, and military problems.

(6) Maps may reflect "sins of commis-

[1] Salisbury, Rollin D., and Atwood, Wallace W., "The Interpretation of Topographic Maps," Professional Paper 60, *U. S. Geological Survey*, 1908, p. 9.

sion" or "sins of omission" as a result of the kind of data selected or rejected, and the way the map is made to maximize or minimize certain phenomena. This calls for discriminatory map-reading training, if we are going to stay out of trouble.

(7) Probably the most critical graphic art that challenges the geographer today is the designing of maps that portray realistically not only "what is," but what the geographic cartographer "thinks it is" that he wishes to communicate to the map-reader. This may deal with the values of human attributes or resourcefulness (e.g., how well or poorly land is being used). Or it may deal with an ideology (e.g., a country's avowed or conjectured foreign diplomacy as interpreted by the writer, as respects peacetime or wartime relations to friends or enemies). Such "concept" maps recognized in the proper context can be most effective in conveying "value" judgments of social, economic, and political problems.

Graphic, other than cartographic, designs aid conceptual space analysis and synthesis

At times diagrams will more effectively convey geographic relationships than maps. And sometimes it is a good thing for truly geographic thinking to get away from "the thing itself" and its cartographic representation, and do some abstract analysis of space relationship of itself. The type of diagram chosen depends, as does the type of map, upon (1) the kind of environmental structure or function on which we want to focus our attention, or (2) the kind of interpretation we wish to convey of the nature of co-variances between the distribution of several patterns, or (3) the kind of areal principles or generalizations our survey of distributional phenomena warrants. Here is a challenge for imagination in creating correct space imagery—commonly the design combines two or all three of the above elements. Properly composed, a single design, like a single map, will convey in a flash a concept or concepts which otherwise require extended description and exposition. Several types of designs exemplify this concept:

1. The distorted "map." This is an effective device in showing ratio relationship, for example, between size and population of countries of the world (Figure III-1).

2. The schematic diagram. For areal land-use tendencies, the concentric patterns, as shown in Figure III-2, instantly convey significant radial generalizations, and thus roughly portray regional developments about a community.

3. The time-space chart. The greater the number of phenomena we wish to relate spatially, the greater the challenge of depicting space values. This is particularly true when we try to evaluate space phenomenology in time. There are several ways of doing this. We can, of course, simply draw a series of actual maps, one for each period, to portray the kind of landscape that characterized each period of man's occupance of an area (as in the historical atlases). On the other hand, if we want to depict and interpret synthetically the settlement and development of a region both in space and time, we may resort to a series of cross-section skyline silhouettes, as in Figure XXXV-3. Though they represent schematic regional generalizations, the correlations, or co-variances, of natural and cultural forms in this instance were determined percentage-wise from actual field surveys.

Global and continental cartography as featured by historical speculations and explorations

Both literally and figuratively, the universal map-making motivations of mankind are related to two major questions: Where have we come from? And where are we going? Studies in anthropological geography reveal the universal urge of man for earth–space orientation for the purpose of retracing our movements so that we may repeat a certain voyage or visit or have a graphic way of recording such journeys so as to direct other people along the way. The early subsistence economy of primitive man demanded a space frame of reference on the most lucrative hunting and fishing grounds. Living close to nature, such primitive peoples were in many ways especially observant of natural phenomena since earth landmarks, seacoasts, inland rivers, lakes, and mountains served as orientation points which could be fairly readily followed by the traveler. They could also be reasonably well mapped. The clay tablet unearthed at Ga Sur some 200 miles north of Babylon, said to be the world's

A. DISTRIBUTION OF LAND

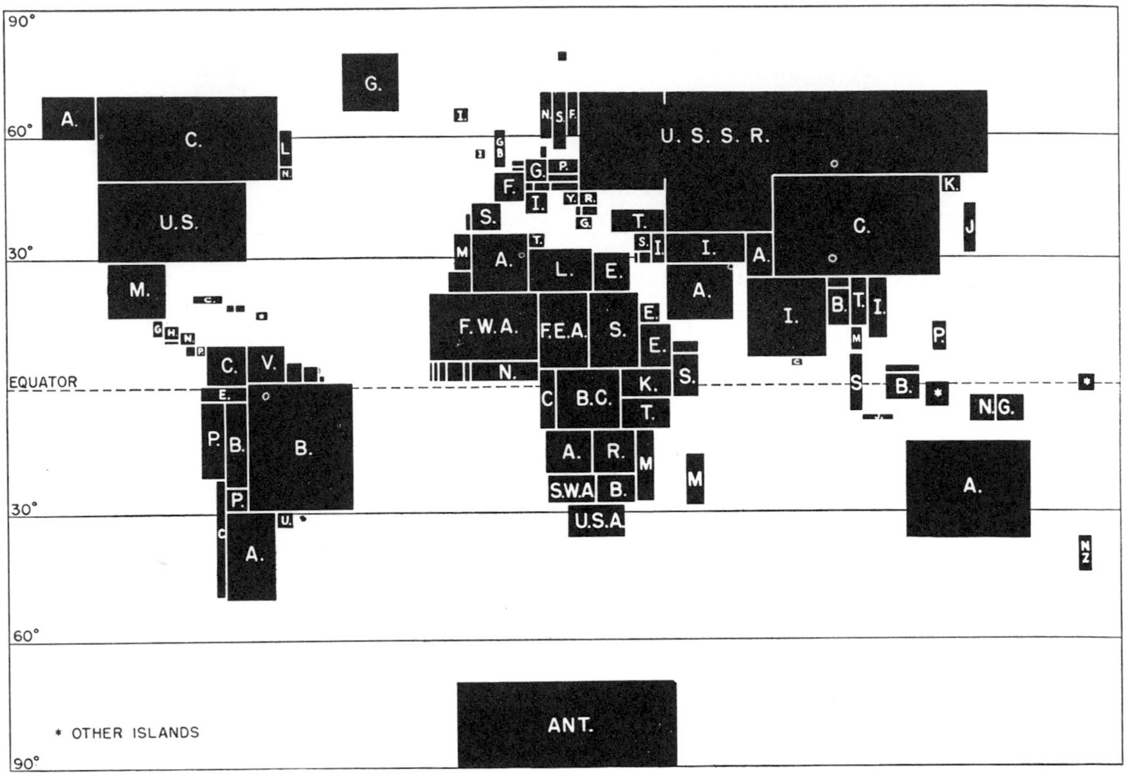

90°
60°
30°
EQUATOR
30°
60°
90°

* OTHER ISLANDS

B. DISTRIBUTION OF POPULATION

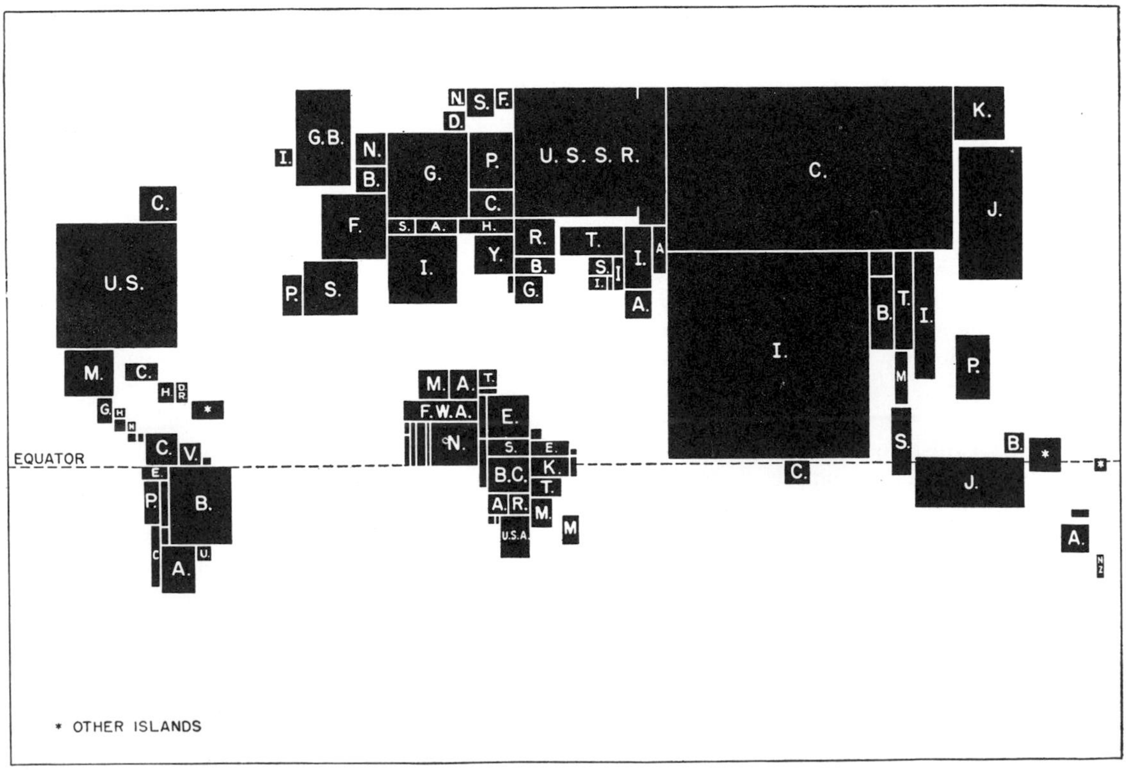

EQUATOR

* OTHER ISLANDS

oldest map (*ca.* 2500 B.C.), thus depicted what is probably the original Euphrates River. Singularly enough this clay tablet, now found in Harvard's library museum, also records north, east, and west points much as our maps do today.

It appears that among the more primitive cultures graphic portrayal of positions related to sea adventures rather than land travel. Perhaps the most elaborate and ingenious design of space orientation without the aid of modern surveying instruments is represented in some of the charts by the South Sea island natives, particularly by the Marshall Islanders. The framework of space reference as shown in Figure III-3 is constructed of the ribs of palm leaves on the "grid" of which islands are shown by attached sea shells. Curved palm ribs are attached to indicate the relative position of wave fronts significant in approaching the islands. Other island and coastal mappers include the Tahitians, the Polynesians, and the Eskimos who have in numerous instances assisted early navigators in exploring the South Pacific and the Arctic regions.

Since travel in antiquity was relatively much easier by water than by land, water features such as rivers, lakes, and particularly sea coasts were charted at an early date. The variegated shoreline features facilitated the outlining of coastal configuration, and this, plus the fact that nearly all the earlier settlement types were established on or near waterfronts, accounts in a great measure for relatively effective mapping by the otherwise crude instruments or measurements then available.

III:1 (Left) These distorted "maps" of the world show comparative land and population distribution by continent and country. Compare, for example, continental Canada with the United States in terms of land (A) with the relative stature in terms of population (B). Similarly, compare India and Australia. Note how comparison of ratio magnitudes of both places and population is facilitated by rectangular representation. One of the chief objectives in geography is to analyze basic conditions of nature and culture which help explain such wide divergences in land–population ratios. Though graphic representations such as these do not of themselves explain anything, they strikingly reveal population density disparities that challenge geographic inquiry. (From *World Population and Production*, by W. S. Woytinsky and E. S. Woytinsky, The Twentieth Century Fund, New York, 1953, used by permission)

The growing emphasis on trading relations towards the end of the thirteenth century further motivated marine charting. Thus the Genoese developed the celebrated portolan charts, the surveys for which apparently, for the first time, had the benefit of compass orientation, and for the first time also, we might say, charted the outlines of the Mediterranean and the Black Sea with great fidelity (Figures III-4 and III-5).

In the ancient world the need for detailed mapping on land, as we would logically expect, was felt by the Romans. Overseeing the economic and administrative affairs of its far-flung colonies or provinces called for an extensive road construction program and hence road surveys. And so by the third century B.C. the so-called *itinerarium scriptum* appeared, which might be thought of as the first "world" road map. Figure III-6 shows a section of this map as reproduced by Conrad Peutinger of Augsburg, who made a copy of one of the twelve sections of the original map in the thirteenth century. As you will observe, various types of landmarks are shown on the road routes. Aside from this extensive road mapping, the Romans contributed relatively little to the science of cartography. And the Phoenicians, the greatest mariners and traders of antiquity, left practically no record, cartographic or otherwise, of their far-flung commercial exploits.

1. Greek cartography. Unlike the "practical" Romans, the classical Greeks showed an entirely different type of cartographic interests and intelligence. Philosophically bent in all his studies, the scholarly Greek was not particularly interested in charting the outlines of sea and land routes of commerce, but projected his imagination and investigation originally to the problem of the characteristics of earth itself—its place in the universe, its shape, its size, and differentiated areas of habitability. This at once suggests that the knowledge of combined astronomy

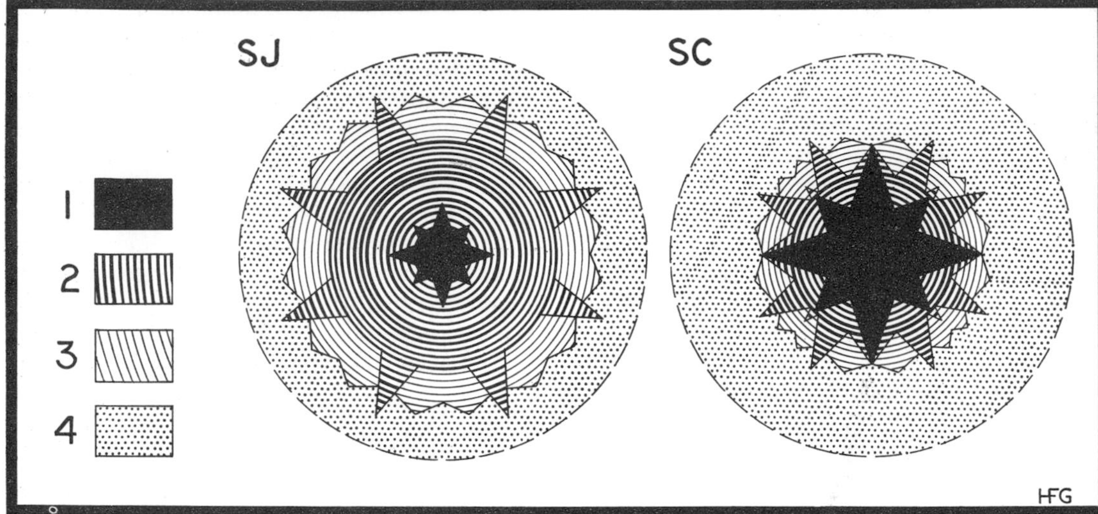

III:2 Schematic diagram of spatial patterns of land-use pressure tendencies illustrated by the San Joaquin Valley (SJ) and Southern California (SC): (1) urban areas; (2) irrigation-farming areas; (3) dry-farming areas; (4) extensive livestock-raising areas (desert). (Diagram by Howard F. Gregor in *Science,* 1959. Reprinted from *Science* by permission)

and mathematics, or what we might call today celestial or mathematical geography, was of foremost consideration. There is evidence that about the seventh century B.C. Ionian Greeks, including among them the celebrated Thales of Miletus (*ca.* 500 B.C.), came in contact with Egyptian and Arabian science. Out of these experiences Anaximander is reputed to have been the first to design a map of the world which recognizes a curved surface of the earth, although in only one direction—a cylindrical concept. But Ptolemy among others not only conceived of the earth as a sphere but also, as shown in his world map (Figure I-1), illustrated significant space relationships between astronomical and geographical phenomena. Thus he indicated the length of the longest day in the various latitudinal belts from the Equator to the Arctic circle—from 12 hours to 24 hours respectively. The term *clima* (from the Greek meaning "incline") thus came not only to have astronomical–latitudinal significance, but to refer to hours of sunshine as well. And though in the original form *clima* did not have the connotation of climatic zones, the parallel belts of varied insolation as we now recognize them were early recognized as having close relationship to length of growing season and other broad climatological criteria.

Following Homer's idea, the habitable world was conceived of in circular or elliptical form, rimmed by a circumfluent river, sometimes called Oceanus. Although this cartographic concept was rejected by the more scientific scholars (e.g., Eratosthenes and Ptolemy), it persisted for a long time. It continued even down into the early part of the fifteenth century (A.D. 1422) in the form of the so-called "T in O" map, so named from the tripartite continent-sea schematic configuration of Asia, Europe, and Africa, with *oriens* (east) at the top (Figure III-7). But the "T in O" cartogram fitted the secular as well as scriptural need of the day also. The concept is probably Babylonian in origin, and the persistence of the flat earth idea as here represented can be attributed in a large manner to such medieval ecclesiastics as Cosmas and St. Beatus who reasoned that this concept of the shape of the earth was in conformity with scriptural teachings.

As *mappae mundi,* hundreds of the "T in O" appeared during the latter medieval period (from the eighth to the fifteenth centuries). Thus the *Orbis Terrarum* (Figure III-8) was designed to represent the Roman Empire as co-terminous with the entire earth.

2. The significance of map projections in the development and transfer of geographic concepts. Not commonly recognized by the layman, or even by the average student, is the impossible task of portraying on the two-dimensional map surface earth phenomena in their true spatial latitudinal and longitudinal perspective. Such spatial representation, as the classical Greek geographer soon recognized, can be reproduced without distortion only on a three-dimensional prototype of the earth itself, namely, the globe. But it did not require a scientist to recognize the impracticability of carrying a globe around in one's pocket, or even trying to record on it any topographic details. If you will examine globes carefully you will find that in nearly all cases the surface consists of a series of "gores" whose outlines follow meridional lines of the globe: When spread out, such gores obviously leave large spaces between them with increasing divergence toward the poles. The globe itself, therefore, is the only means by which to represent true spatial perspective of phenomena without distortion of space, distance, area, or direction. The problem, then, is how to transfer spherical patterns to a flat surface with the least possible distortion of either shape or area, or both, depending on what serves best the particular cartographic concepts we wish to portray.

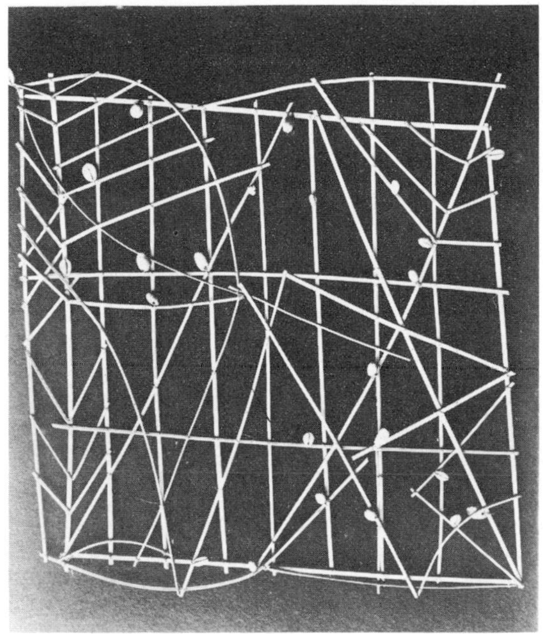

III:3 This sailing chart of the Marshall Islanders shows, with sea shells, the relative geographic positions of islands. Consult the text for aboriginal navigation significance. This clever, if primitive, "mapping" technique is historically associated with the best of craftsmanship in boat-building and most progressive navigational exploits among the Micronesian peoples. (Copyright, Royal Geographical Society, London)

Definitions or mere descriptions of terms can prove quite meaningless and purposeless unless illustrated. So at this point let us discuss, however briefly, the general nature of projections, their derivations, and uses. However, we shall not here be concerned with the technical aspects of the subject. Nor do we need to know the several hundred types of projections in order to understand the primary purposes and functions of projections as related to the understanding of human affairs in earth-space. Though most map projections are of the mathematically derived type, including the historic ones, such as those of Ptolemy and Mercator, it is sufficient and simpler for our purposes to observe projections of the "perspective" type as shown developed in Figure III-9. As you will note, by placing a light in the flask on which hemispheric parallels and meridians are drawn, grid patterns are projected onto tangential surfaces. By using three surfaces—a plane and the developable planes (cylinder and cone)—we can illustrate the three basic classifications of perspective projections—the conical, the cylindrical, and the azimuthal:[1]

(1) First scientific projection—the "Conic." Ptolemy (*ca.* A.D. 150), reputed to be the most influential geographer in cartographic history, met the flat map issue by designing the "grid" shown in Figure I-1. It is a mathematically computed projection of the so-called conic type named after the perspective developed by tracing the global grid onto a cone encircling the globe (see J-I-K, Figure III-9). Ptolemy's objective was to prevent as much distortion of area (equivalency) and

[1] By changing the position of the light, or the point of contact of the several direct and developable planes, innumerable modifications result in the grid pattern.

AFRICA
ASIA
Rey de tunes
Rey de francia
Soldan de babilonia
Rey de polonia

III:5 By the latter part of the seventeenth century the Atlantic and the Americas take on reasonably good outlines thanks to portolan charting extended overseas. Miguel Ferra's portolan (*ca.* 1680) is representative of the mapping artistry of the period. (Reproduced from the original 83 x 61 cm. vellum in the Collections of the Library of Congress)

shape (conformability) as possible. He also adopted the modern principle of achieving highest equivalency and conformability where it counted most. Thus he chose the 40° latitude for the base parallel—a focus on the Mediterranean world. The curved latitude and longitude lines, as you see, did not do too much violence to conformability for the world Ptolemy had to deal with. Since fidelity of scale can exist only at the point of contact, by using two or more cones connecting or intersecting the spherical surface, cumulative distortions can be taken care of at the several latitudes. Such "polyconic" projections, as they have been called, are most excellently adapted for country surveys. The familiar topographic quadrangles issued by the U.S. Geological Survey as well as the larger maps of our country

III:4 (Left) Portolan charts of the type here presented represent the best of classical cartography of the medieval period. The original of this portolan on the Mediterranean (on vellum 96 x 65 cm.) was prepared by Mateua Prunus of Majorca in 1559. Note the remarkable fidelity of coastal configuration and the detailed notations. (Reproduced from the Collections of the Library of Congress)

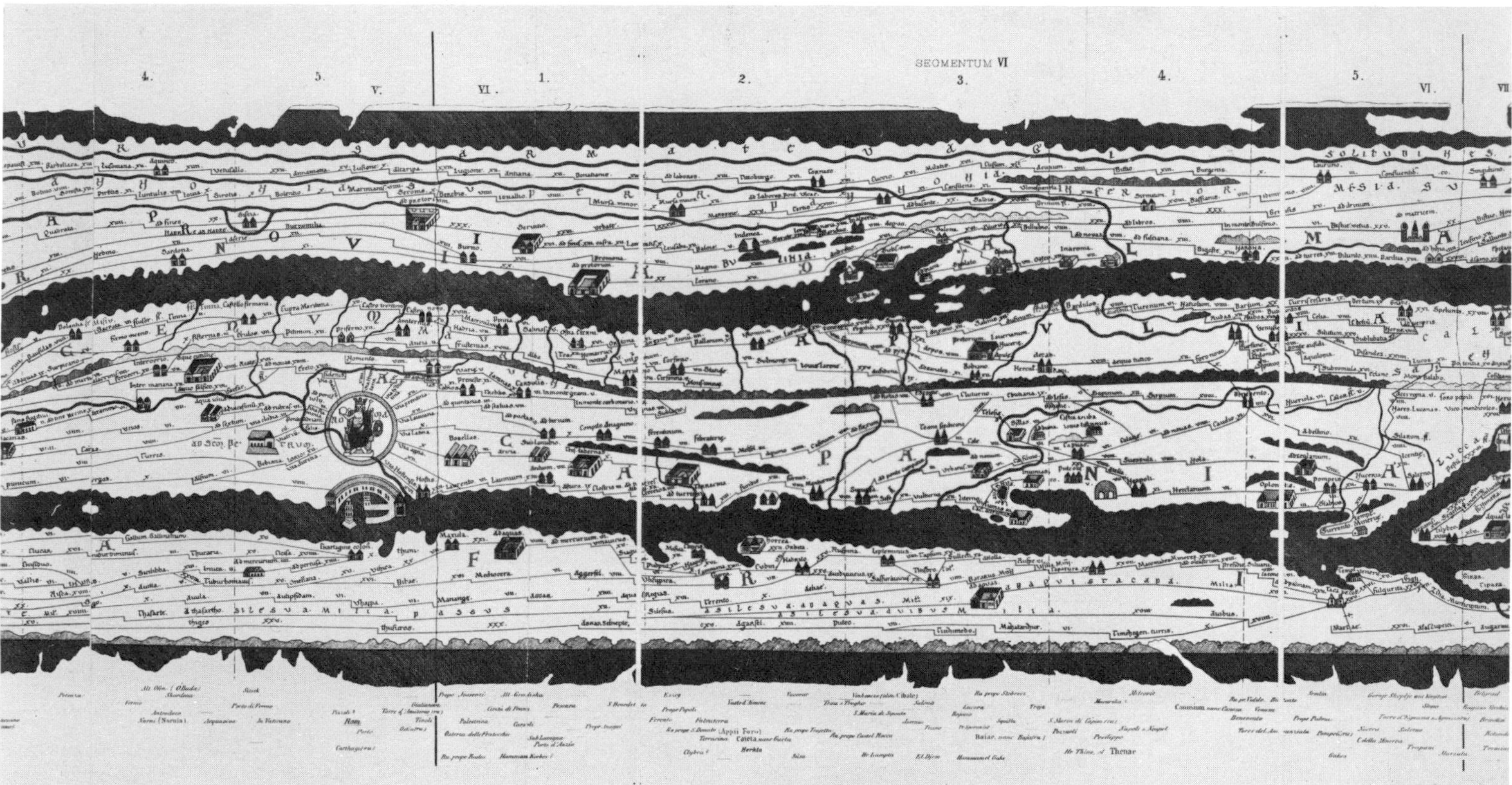
SEGMENTUM VI
4.
5.
V.
VI.
1.
2.
3.
4.
5.
VI.

III:7 This so-called "T in O" map is one of a series of sketches of earth concepts held by early man, the "O" being the circumfluent river or ocean bounding the land, the vertical stem of the "T" representing the Mediterranean and the cross bar diagrammatizing north-south water extensions—Black Sea–Red Sea areas. Note that east was placed at the "top" of the map, with its Edenic setting. (Reproduced from Collections of Library of Congress)

typify this polyconic class. Compared with these more modern polyconic projections, the one by Ptolemy may seem somewhat crude. But, as in the appraisal of any creative work, a product must be viewed in the context of the time and the limitations of the methods and instruments available. Aside from the distortion problem incident to projecting a global surface on a flat map, accurate representation of position of places demands correct co-ordinate data of latitude and longitude. Despite the remarkable progress

III:6 (Left) The Conrad Peutinger *itinerarium scriptum*, a scroll of some twenty feet in length, of which this is a small sectional photo, represents the initial charting of roads, here centered on Rome. Would you call this a map? Why or why not? What surveying and charting equipment was available to the "road mappers" of this period? (Reproduction from Collections of the Library of Congress)

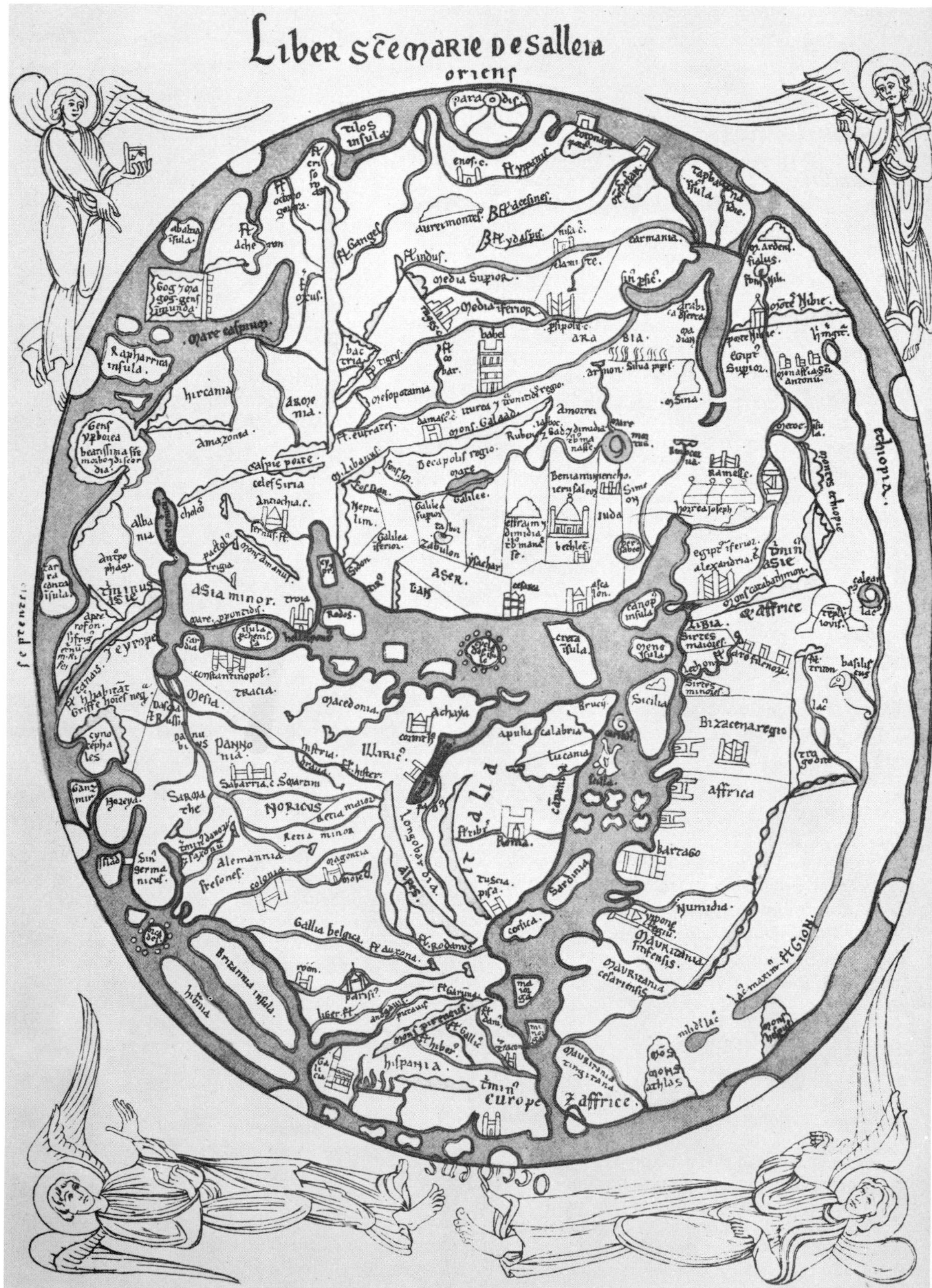

Liber scē marie de salleia
oriens
septentrio
mare caspium
hircania
armenia
mesopotamia
babel
arabia
Decapolis regio
Galilee
Beniamin
iuda
bethlee
Zabulon
Aser
asia minor
troia
Rodos
creta insula
constantinopol.
Tracia
Macedonia
Achaia
Mesia
Pannonia
Histria
Illiric.
Sarmathe
Noricus
Retia minor
Alemannia
colonia
Gallia belgica
Britannia insula
hibernia
parisi.
hispania
Europe
Roma
tuscia
pisa
apulia
calabria
tucania
campania
Sicilia
Sardinia
corsica
Bizacena regio
affrica
kartago
Numidia
alexandria
ethiopia
athlas
affrice

in this direction by the astronomers Marinus and Hipparcus, whose data in part were used by Ptolemy, the means available for determining positions from observations of fixed stars and lunar eclipses could supply only approximate accuracy. Moreover, the ancients had neither the compass nor the chronometer—introduced in the thirteenth and seventeenth centuries, respectively. Accordingly, Ptolemy and the other ancient cartographers had to rely in many instances on distance data as supplied by the itineraries of the period, such as the long marches of Alexander, the Crusades, and the coastal voyages along the Mediterranean. Following Posidonius' rather than Eratosthenes' concept of the size of the earth, Ptolemy projected the ecumene, as shown on his map, through 180 degrees longitude, a distance halfway around the globe. For some undetermined reason he also enclosed the Indian Ocean, as likewise shown on his map. Such errors, excusable as they may seem under the conditions of the time, illustrate effectively how cartography can have a far-reaching influence on historical developments. For example, could the fact that Ptolemy represented the Indian Ocean (*Indicus Oceanus*) as an enclosed sea have been the primary reason for the belated southeast Asia contacts by sea as late as the fifteenth century?[1]

(2) The "Cylindrical" sailing chart. The expanding global maritime enterprises of the sixteenth century called for some type of projection other than the conic whose curved parallels and meridians are poor guidelines for navigation. How easy it is to follow the north-south, east-west grid street pattern of a city having a rectangular orientation! The navigator looks for a similar expedient on the "uncharted" sea. Mercator in 1569 provided such a grid, where both the meridians and the parallels are parallel, making right-angle intersections. Like the Ptolemy projection, it is mathematically derived, and illustrates another class of projections—the "cylindrical." The term derives from the developable cylindrical plane (E-F-G-H). Since its only contact is at the "Equator," the scale is true only at the Equator, and the farther we go from the Equator towards the pole the greater the distortions in shape and area. Mercator equated mathematically the east-west with the north-south discrepancies in the interest of maintaining shape of outlines despite the extra exaggeration it creates in the size of areas. Thus at 60° areas are exaggerated four times; at 80°, thirty-six times! Obviously, it would be altogether the wrong projection to use to convey concepts of relative intensity or density of distribution of phenomena (e.g., population per square mile).

[1] One cannot help speculating also on how the course of history might have been changed had Ptolemy (and after him Columbus) accepted Eratosthenes' circumference figure of the earth (closely approximating the correct one) instead of Posidonius' figure of 18,000 miles. Thus it is understandable that Ptolemy's map, by placing the eastern limits of Asia at 180° longitude, (half way around the earth) instead of approximately at 120°, fitted very well into Columbus' objective of finding a relatively short sea route westward to the Orient. But as you know, it did not turn out that way. Why the Eratosthenes formula was not followed seems to be an unanswered puzzle, for as you will see for yourself, it called for no complicated celestial mechanics or astronomical mathematics.

Eratosthenes conceived the idea that if we had a known dimension between two points on the earth's surface and could determine the degree angle at the earth's center formed by the two radii of the arc of such points, then it would be a simple ratio calculation. His procedure, as shown in diagram (Figure III-10), was simple enough. Noting that the sun's rays at noon on June the 21st registered vertically at the bottom of the well at Syene, Egypt, he proceeded on this date to measure the angle that another parallel ray of the sun made with a staff erected at Alexandria, Egypt. He found this latter degree to be 7-2/10th. By the simple geometric principle, then, "two lines cut by a transversal," the interior earth angle was recognized to be the same as the exterior sun ray angle he had measured at Alexandria, namely, 7-2/10th. The subtended arc—the measured distance between Alexandria and Syene, Egypt—was 5000 stadia (approximately 570 miles). Since the circumference of a circle is 360 degrees, or about 50 times the measured arc, the earth's circumference approximated 50 x 570 miles, or 28,500 miles. Some computations have put this as low as 25,000-26,000, based on a lower stadium equivalent.

III:8 (Left) We might think of this "T in O" map as expressing a form of "national megalomania" at its best—or its worst—depending on one's geographic point of view. This *Orbis Terrarum*, though much more geographically accurate and detailed than the one shown in the previous figure, still clings to the flat-earth concept. But it also reveals that Rome at this time considered itself the center of the world. (From the Collections of the Library of Congress reproduced from *Die Altesten Weltkarten* by Konrad Miller, 1895)

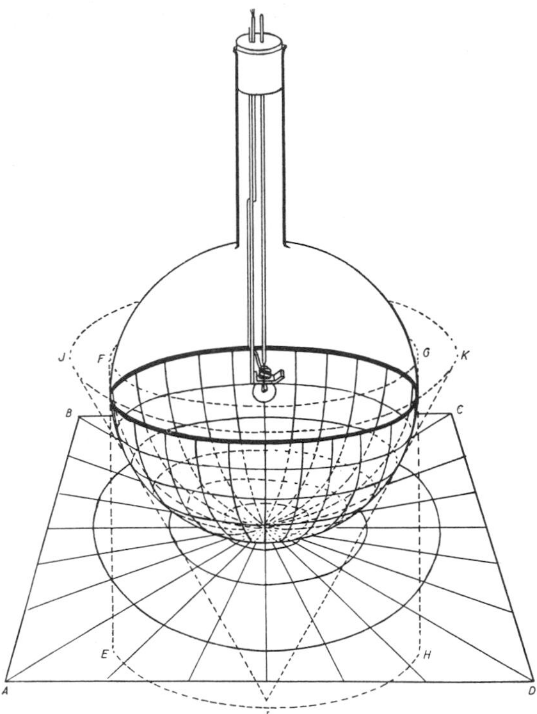

III:9 An illuminated flask with a grid pattern, simulating the parallels of latitude and meridians of longitude projected on a tangent plane, cone, and cylinder, demonstrates the three basic projections of the perspective type. One may observe for oneself how continents or countries take on different sizes and shapes on the several developable tangent planes, by sketching an outline of such on the flask grid. Note that the meridians (great circles–shortest distance) project as straight lines on the basal plane, a great aid in navigation. What kind of grid (straight or curved lines) would you expect on the tangent cylinder? (Diagram by W. B. B. Balchin and A. W. Richards from *Practical and Experimental Geography,* by John Wiley & Sons, Inc., New York, 1952, used by permission)

But Mercator never intended his projection to be used for this purpose. He was looking for a grid which would supply constant angle readings between the north-south trending meridians and any straight line drawn on the world chart, thus making for easier vessel steerage. This unique virtue extends even to directional tracing of the trajectory of our modern satellites, as illustrated in the orbital path for TIROS I (Figure III-11).

(3) *The Azimuthal projection.* While straight lines on the Mercator always give constant meridional angles, the lines normally (unless coinciding with meridians or parallels) do not coincide with "great circle" routes (Figure I-2). And since the shortest distance between two points on the globe necessarily lies on a great circle (the girth of the earth), it is expedient to have a projection on which any straight line connecting navigation points is a great circle guideline. This unique feature is supplied by the "gnomonic" (Figure III: 12D), so-called after the Greek "gnomon," index of the sundial, which it resembles (see A-B-C-D). It is a form of the third class of projections—the "azimuthal" (French *azimut,* direction). In practice today, then, the mariner generally draws a straight line on the gnomonic chart connecting the point of his departure with

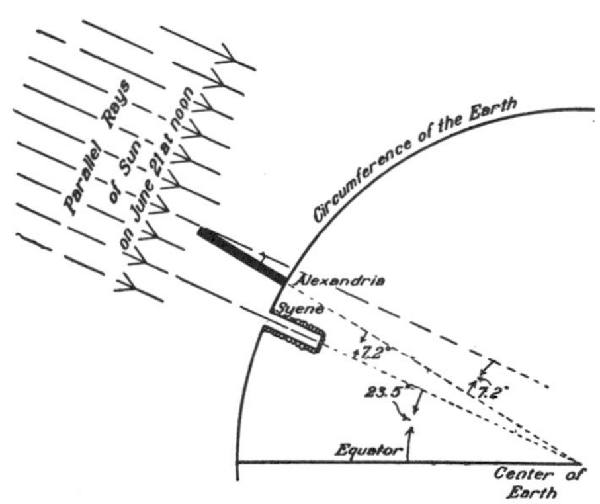

III:10 Columbus did not initiate the concept of earth's sphericity. This had already been done before the dawn of the Christian Era. As a matter of fact, Eratosthenes of Alexandria, over two centuries before Christ, actually calculated by simple elementary sun-angle and survey observations, and by principles of geometry, the approximate circumference of the earth. For the simple mathematical operation see the text. How do you account for the "T in O" flat-earth maps persisting well into the end of the medieval period?

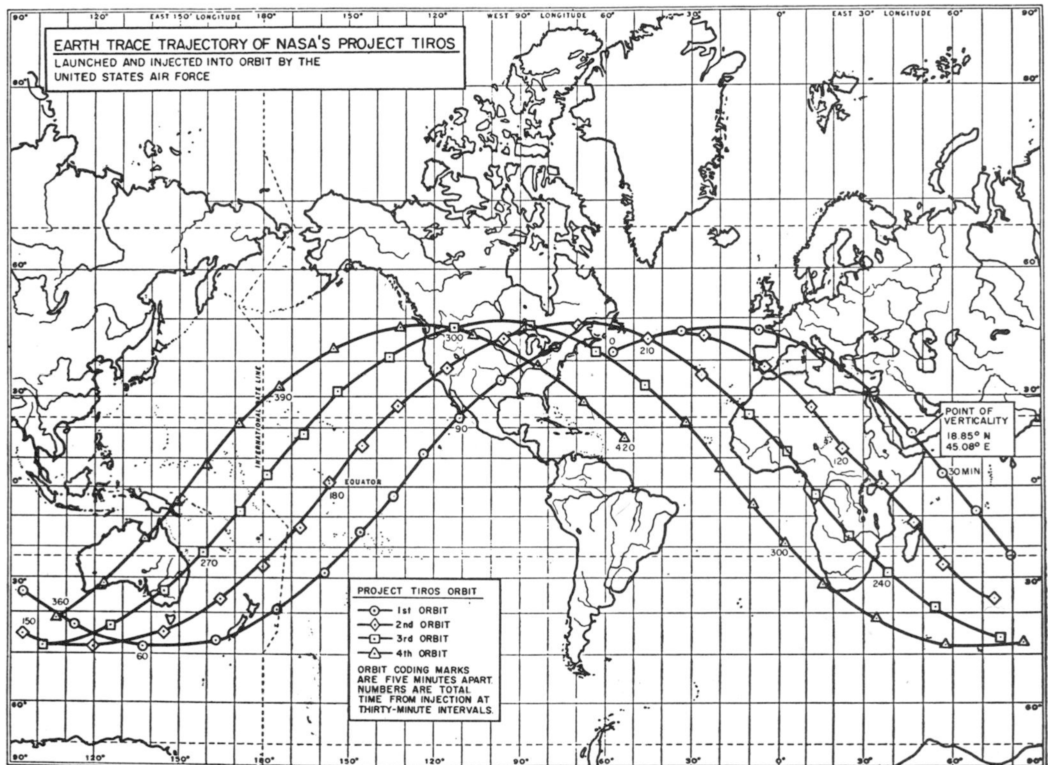

III:11 This figure illustrates that even in our satellite age the Mercator projection has its usefulness apart from sea navigation—here tracing the orbital path for Tiros I for a three-month period between latitudes 48° N and 48° S. (From *Science*, Vol. 131, No. 3406, April 8, 1960, reprinted from *Science* by permission)

the point of disembarkation and then transfers this onto the Mercator.

Other azimuthal projections, like the polar types illustrated in Figure III: 12C are used to convey significant space relationships. For example, in this age of rocketry in the cold war between the East and the West, and most significantly between the United States and the Soviet Union, the eyes of the military are continually focused upon the potential transpolar great circle routes for missile projection. The azimuthal (also sometimes called zenithal) can be centered on any point of the globe (e.g., a particular city) on which we wish to focus our geographic attention.

3. ***Equivalent or equal-area projections.*** To show proper spatial proportions of the distribution of phenomena, whether of climate, people, productions of farm or factory, or of any other quantitative data, equal-area global representations of space are highly desirable. Such projection is indispensable when expressing a ratio value between subject and space (e.g., people per square mile) as in the conventional "dot" map. For narrow latitudinal belts, as we have already noted in connection with the conical projection, spatial representations may be quite equivalent, but the wider the latitude and longitude extend, the greater will be the distributional pattern distortions. Accordingly in modern times many so-called equal-area projections have been invented. The chief problem involved is avoiding as much distortion in direction and shape as possible. Goode's Homolosine Equal Area Quartic Projection is of this type (Figure III-12F). Another approach—the Flat Polar Equal Area Projection, adapted by Robinson—has a major interruption between the Old and the New World. The climate map in the Appendix

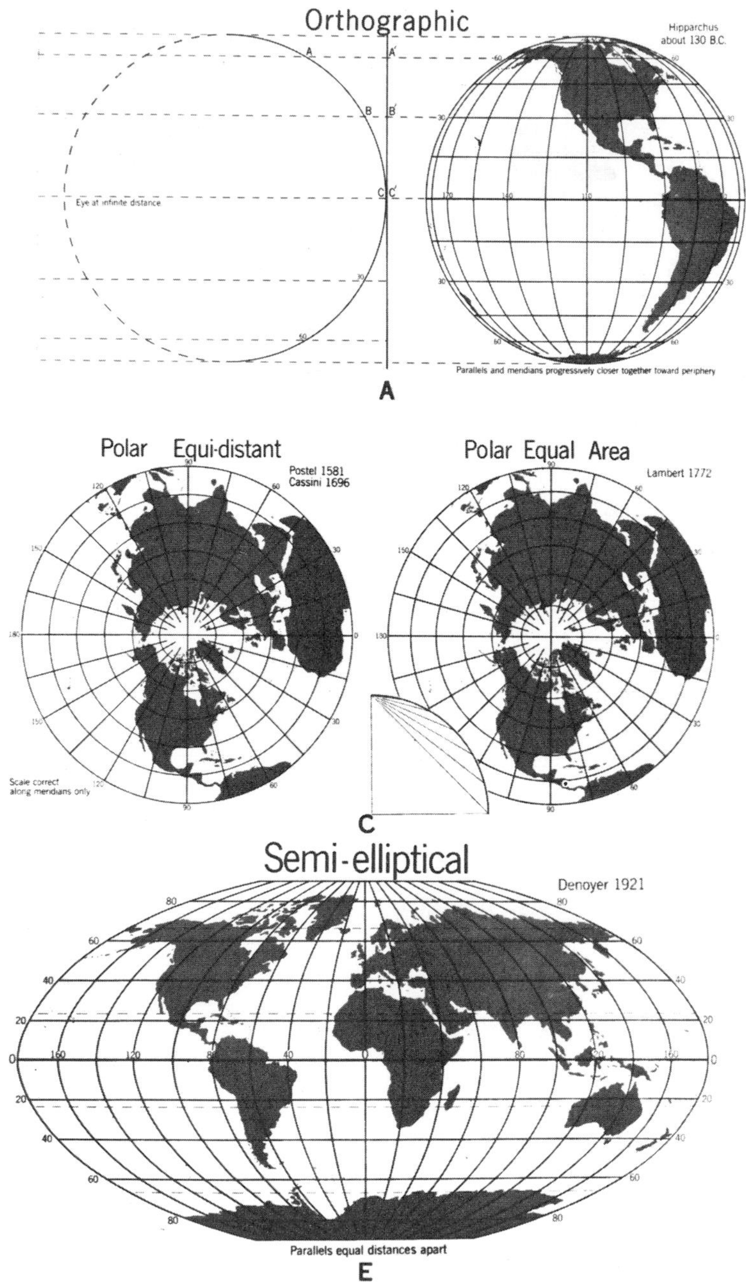

and the regional maps in Part IV are on this base. Thus you can see the correct areal proportions of the several types of climates (and countries), whether they are in the low, middle, or high latitudes. And so (except for comparatively slight distortions in shape, not at all significant at times) we can for all practical purposes produce a "collapsed globe" which we can put into our pocket or in a file or in a book.

*4. **Projection, an indispensable tool.*** The value of a projection as a learning or teaching device for developing geographic concepts has been aptly stated by Robinson: "A map projection should be considered as a valuable device, not as a poor substitute for a globe, regardless of the number of orange peels squashed in the latter's behalf. There is no question that the phrase 'there is no substitute for a globe' is as misleading as it

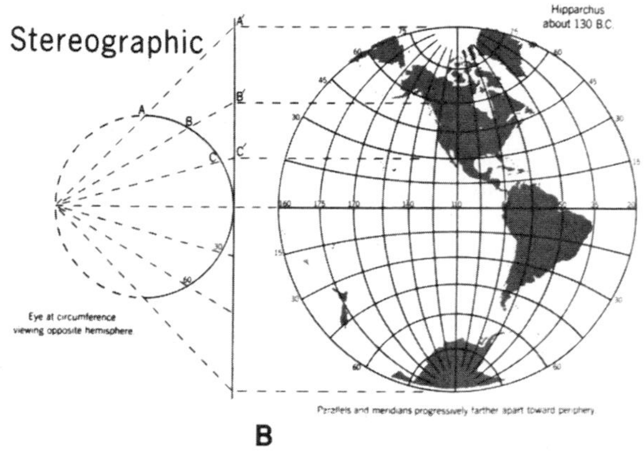

B

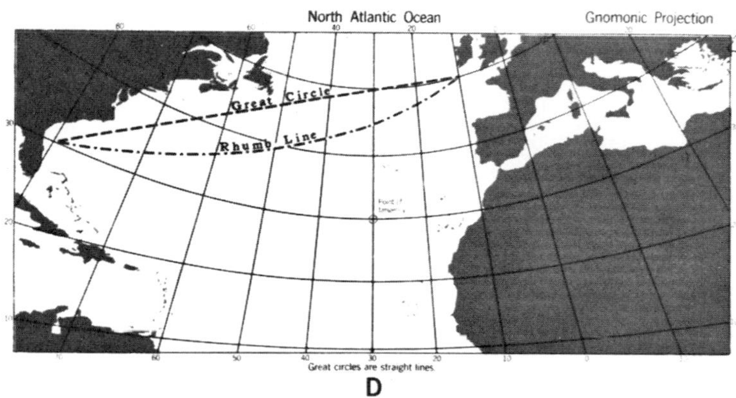

D

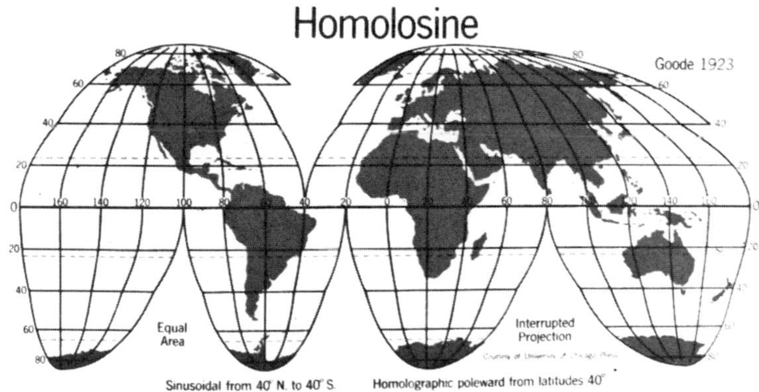

F

III:12 (Above and on left page) As witnessed earlier, projection of a spherical grid onto a flat surface involves distortion—distortion of distance, shape, or area. Thus, which projection is selected depends upon the concept we wish to convey or the use to which we wish to put the map. Sometimes a compromise is sought in combining minimal distortions in all three categories. There are literally hundreds of map projections, a half dozen of which are illustrated above and on page at left. (Courtesy Denoyer-Geppert Company)

is hackneyed. The vast majority of cartographic presentations are of subjects and relationships that would not be nearly so effective if they were actually presented on a spherical surface" (2).

*5. **Filling in the global projections.*** With the founding of the various European empires new demands arose for filling in the global map details for both political and military reasons. A classical example of high correlation between political-military influence and map-making motivation is illustrated in the case of France. Influenced greatly by its position in western Europe and proximate to its traditional rivals of Germany and England, France became involved politically and militarily in practically every major affair of the continents of Europe and Africa, and of the entire world as well. It is not surprising, therefore, that France should have been the first nation to make a systematic survey of its own country and to pioneer in advanced scientific mapping. High correlation between military genius and appreciation of the importance of maps is well illustrated in the case of Napoleon.

¶ Like all great military leaders, Napoleon was an ardent supporter of surveys and mapping. During the Italian campaign he commissioned Dr. Bacler d'Albe to prepare a map of Italy in 1:256,000—one of the most outstanding maps of the age. Napoleon started also a number of important surveys in Germany, Greece, and Egypt. His defeat prevented him from finishing his great project, a 1:100,000 map of Europe.[1]

Peacetime interests in mapping are primarily related to the factors of economic and commercial geography. The earliest map-making and map-marketing stimuli are identified with the first leading maritime nation —the Netherlands. Here in the latter part of the Renaissance, at Antwerp and Amsterdam, converged not only the trunk traffic lines of the European continent but also the maritime exploratory and commerce lanes of the entire world. It is not surprising, therefore, to find the Dutch pioneering the art of good map-making and also exploiting the map-selling business. The navigators, incessantly moving in and out of the ports, were both active contributors and receivers of much needed navigational information at a time when an entirely new concept of global commercial potential was being developed. Raisz observes, "In no other period in the history of cartography can we find such prolific production of high-grade maps as in the *golden age of Dutch cartography,* which began in the middle of the sixteenth century and lasted over a hundred years."[2]

Maritime commerce, again, was the chief motivating factor for cartographic development in the eighteenth century when England superseded the Dutch and the French as the world's leading maritime power.

¶ With the growth of the oversea dominions and the resulting trade and prosperity, maps and charts were more and more in demand, and London became the cartographic center surpassing Amsterdam and rivaling Paris. Indeed, many famous Amsterdam mapmakers established themselves in London, while others came from Paris.[3]

Contributions to and of chronologic cartography illuminate world history. Particularly is this true of the charts and maps of the age of the great maritime and terrestrial discoveries of the fifteenth, sixteenth and seventeenth centuries. Indispensable, therefore, is the "study" of historical atlases.

To fully appreciate cartographic chronology the student must be familiar with the historic events which led to the great epochal discoveries of new lands and new routes to and from such lands. Just as Strabo's work in this respect was the classic of antiquity, so, we might say, Richard Hakluyt's *The Principal Navigations, Voyages, Traffiques, and Discoveries of the English Nation* is a classic of early modern. Characterized as the "prose epic of the modern English nation" (*ca.* 1553-1660), this British geography chronicles all the leading voyages "made by sea or overland to the remote and farthest distant quarters of the earth at any time within the compasse of these 1600 yeares."

Underclassmen often find it difficult, and understandably so, to decide upon a major or minor field of study. A single simple experi-

---

1 Raisz, Erwin, *General Cartography,* McGraw-Hill Book Co., Inc., New York, 1948, p. 39. Reprinted by permission.

2 *Ibid.,* p. 26. Reprinted by permission. While all facts and concepts of history cannot of course, be reduced to map form, a geographically-trained eye scrutinizing artfully conceived and composed maps can "read" more history intelligibly from a few well-selected maps than from textual readings many times as expansive and time-consuming. This area of American academic instruction, whether on lower or higher levels, seems to be particularly poorly exploited; the primary reason again appears to be that teachers generally lack sufficient background in geographic map-making and map-interpretation, and therefore do not fully appreciate the challenges that a good map offers in posing and resolving problems.

3 *Ibid.,* p. 34. Reprinted by permission.

ence may be all it takes to help one make up his mind on career interests. The case of Hakluyt is an example in point: He was educated at Westminster School, subsequently becoming Archdeacon of Westminster.

¶ While on a visit to the Temple his cousin (another Richard Hakluyt) showed him a map of the world, and gave him "a lesson in geography," to such good purpose that the boy, full of "rare delight," resolved, "by good assistance, to prosecute the kind of literature," if ever he should go to the University. In 1570, while Drake was "prospecting" for his Nombre de Dios voyage, he went to Christ Church, Oxford, where he soon acquired five or six languages to help him in his studies. He read all the books of Voyages, and all the mariners' journals, to be obtained at Oxford; and besides this, he studied the arts of map-making and navigation; and began to put together a first collection of Voyages (to America and the West Indies) which was published long after he had taken his degree, in the year 1582.[1]

In the prefatory remarks "to the favourable Reader," Hakluyt, himself, gives thus some insight into the kind of motivation and preparation he had in writing this monumental piece of work in geography:

¶ And to the ende that those men which were the paynefull and personall travellers might reape that good opinion and just commendation which they have deserved, and further, that every man might answere for himselfe, justifie his reports, and stand accountable for his owne doings, I have referred every voyage to his Author, which both in person hath performed, and in writing hath left the same: for I am not ignorant of Ptolomies assertion, that Peregrinationis historia, and not those wearie volumes bearing the titles of universall Cosmographie which some men that I could name have published as their owne, beying in deed most untruly and unprofitablie ramassed and hurled together, is that which must bring us to the certayne and full discoverie of the world. . . .[2]

No original work can prove more enlightening than Hakluyt's, which reveals not only the progressive discoveries of the New World as well as of the Old World but also the motivations of government enterprise and private adventure in the expanding world knowledge and what this implied for a country like Britain with its basic interest in charting world commerce in resource exploitation, and in colonization.

Perusal of navigation chronicles, such as Hakluyt's, gives us the basic insight needed to explore the many problems navigators had not only in finding their way around unexplored regions but also in charting them as well, and this in a day when mapping did not have the benefits of any modern astronomical means of orientation. The exploits of Vasco de Gama around the southern coast of Africa finally removed Ptolemy's error of an enclosed Indian Ocean from the map. Likewise, Magellan's circumnavigation of the globe via the southern tip of South America confirmed not only the existence of the Americas, as determined previously by Amerigo Vespucci, but also indicated the nature of global unity as respects the redistribution of the major ocean and continental areas of the world. Subsequently, such voyages as those particularly of Captain Cook in the eighteenth century, disestablished the illusion of the "fabled Antipodes" of the Southern Hemisphere. The illusionary Antipodes — or, as it also came to be known legendary-wise, Terra Australis — illustrates how instrumental a mythological cartographic conception can be in forging such epoch-making voyages as Cook's. The historical geographer Baker of the University of Oxford considered this of such geo-historical importance that he featured this continental concept in his discussion of the voyages of the Pacific Ocean, 1600-1800:

¶ The first voyage of importance in the Pacific Ocean in the seventeenth century had for its object the discovery of some unknown land in the south of that ocean to which the name Terra Australis was sometimes given. The origin of the belief dates back to classical times. . . . Ptolemy had actually put such a land-mass on the map . . . which stretched along the length of the Southern Ocean. . . . The famous map of Ortelius [Figure III-13] showed it quite clearly; and Mercator not

---

[1] Hakluyt, Richard, *The Principal Voyages of the English Nation*, Everyman's Library, Ernest Rhys, Editor, J. M. Dent and Sons and E. P. Dutton & Co., Inc., New York, Vol. 1, Introduction xiii. Reprinted by permission.

[2] *Ibid.*, p. 6. Reprinted by permission.

III:13 As is to be expected in pioneer mapping with primitive navigational equipment, the original charting of continents was often erratic and sometimes fantastic. Of the latter type was the supposition and subsequent "mapping" of fictitious *Terra Australis,* on a number of maps of the sixteenth and seventeenth centuries, of which this map, *Americae,* by Ortelius (1527-1598) is a type. Despite this imaginary continental profile, this map and others by Ortelius are rated highly for their contribution of the period. Ortelius himself is ranked by some authorities next to Mercator, and his work *Theatrum Orbis Terrarum* is acclaimed as the "first modern atlas." (From the Collections of the Library of Congress)

only put it on his map, but argued that it must be there . . . to balance the land of the Northern Hemisphere. . . . Existence of some such land seemed to be justified by recent discoveries. Magellan had passed through a strait. . . . The discoveries of Quiros and Janszoon seemed to confirm the belief in this land-mass. But not until the "Age of Cook" was this legendary cartographic concept cleared up. Commissioned in 1768 by the Royal Society to observe the transit of Venus, "The observation of the transit of Venus was . . . prefixed to the voyage the real objects of which were the discovery on the southern continent and the annexation of new lands to the British Empire. . . . [Cook] crossed the Pacific to the Society Islands . . . sailing southward, reached New Zealand. . . . This land became the subject of much eager conversation; but the general opinion seemed to be that we had found the Terra Australis Incognita."[1]

Chorographical and topographic cartography as featured by regional and local surveys

1. Abstract regional cartography essentially a modern innovation. The concept of regionality as we understand the term today, especially in its cartographic application, had

[1] Baker, J. N. L., *A History of Geographical Discovery and Exploration*, Houghton Mifflin Co., Boston, 1931, *passim*, pp. 145, 150-162. Reprinted by permission.

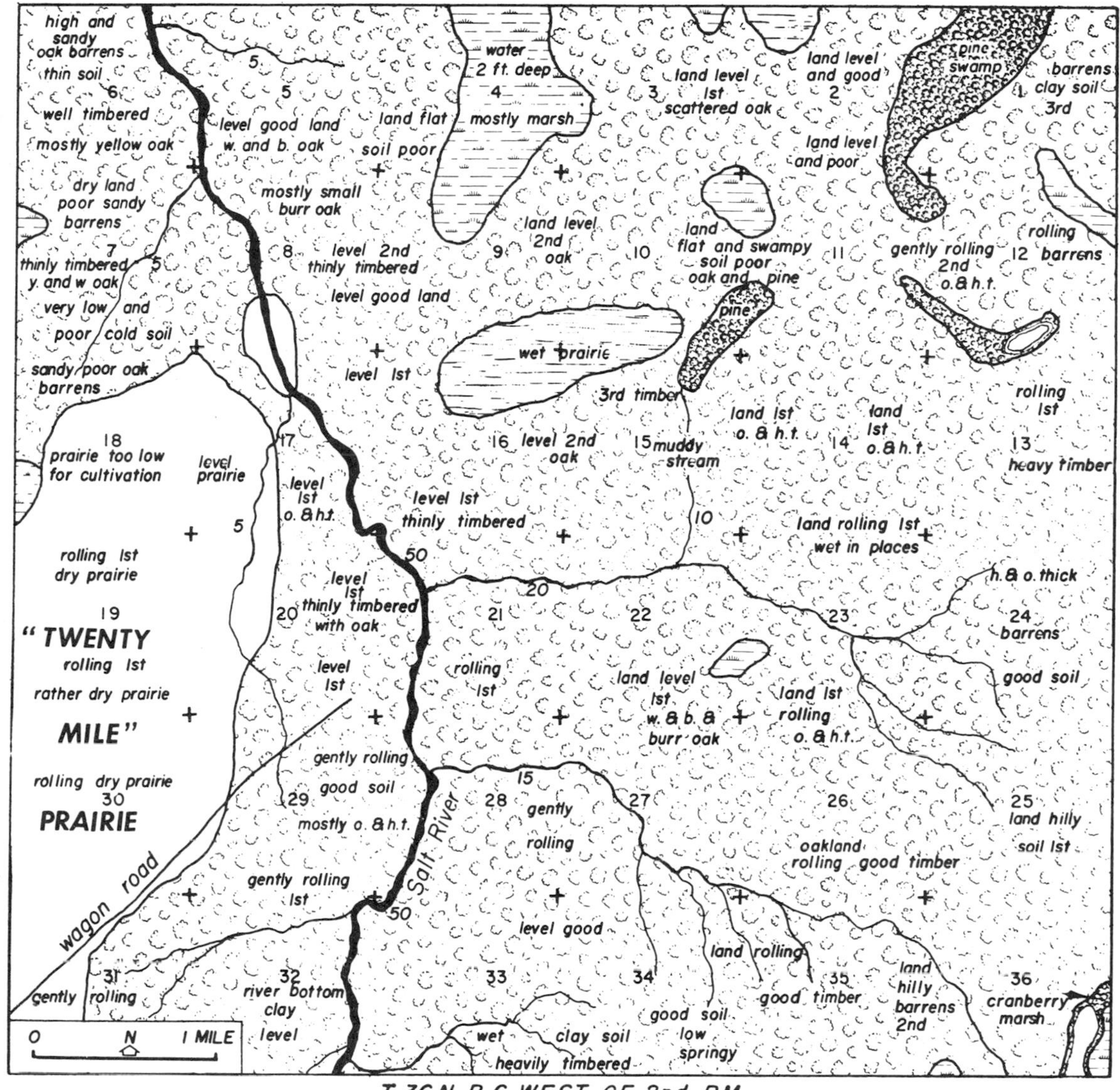

T. 36 N, R. 6 WEST OF 2nd P.M.

III:14 One of the first essentials in regional settlement study is to determine and map, if possible, the "fundament" or aboriginal landscape of an area. The above map was constructed from original composite federal records—of township plat and notebook field data. Though the situations may have been rare where farmers and other settlers took advantage of such records, what advantage might result from studying such topographic features in advance of land purchases? (Map originally published in *Annals of the Association of American Geographers,* Vol. XLVI, September, 1956, used by permission)

really no counterpart in ancient and medieval times. Nor was there the formal recognition of "areal differentiation" as we know it today. But, as already pointed out in Chapter 1, even the most primitive tribes of the world traditionally recognized in a rough form some proprietary interests in the competitive use of land, as by tribes in connection with hunting and fishing. With the more refined and intensive occupance of land, however, there arose the need for surveys—the actual drawing of boundary lines, delimiting areas. An example is ancient Egypt where so-called cadastral surveys

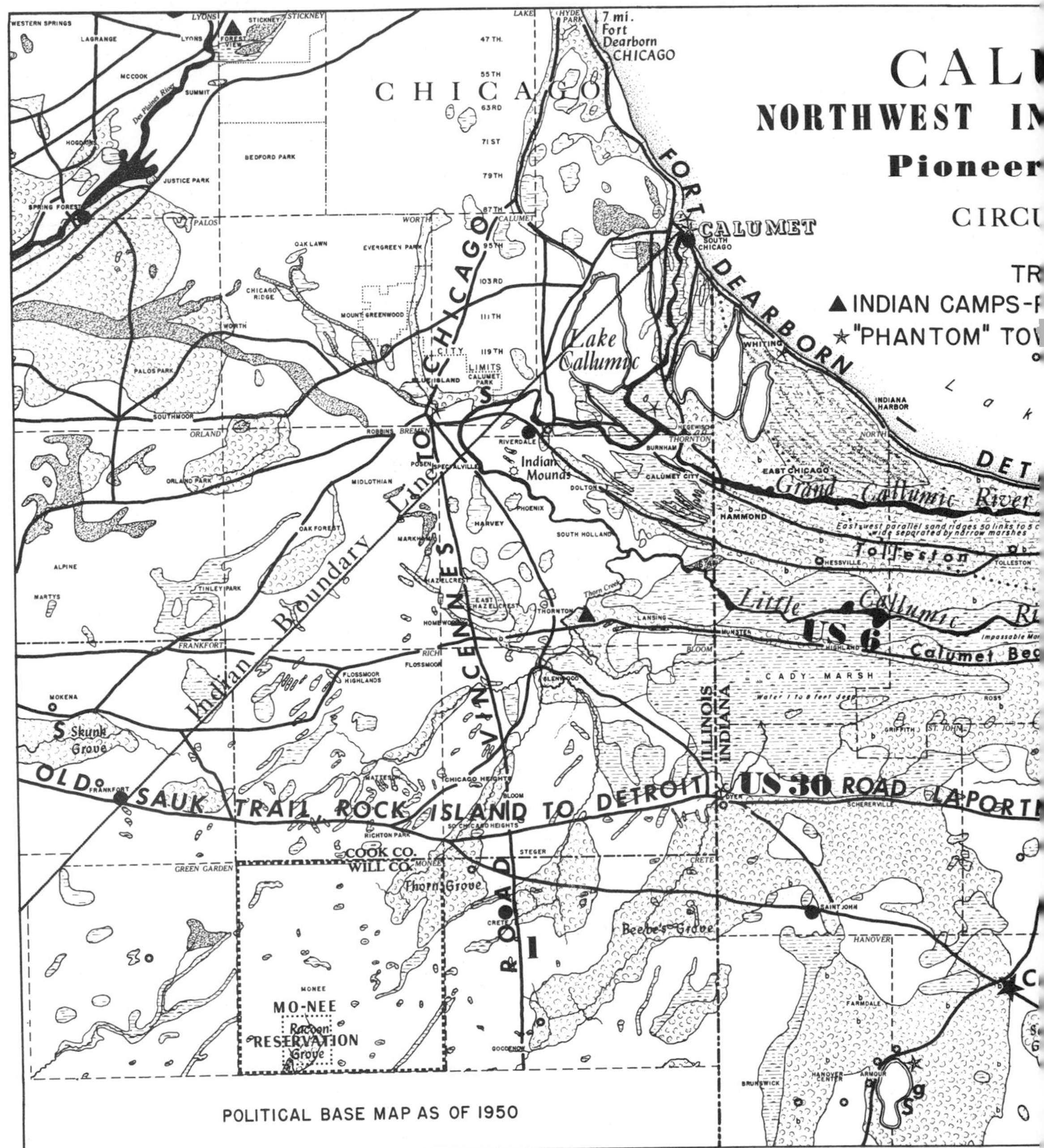

were introduced at an early date not only to systematize field culture along the life-sustaining Nile but also to enable the Pharaoh to assess and collect taxes, in much the same way we do today. For similar reasons, the administration and tax collection procedures made the political unit of areal differentiation the most important in the days of the Roman Empire. And the descriptions of the countries of the Mediterranean by Strabo, abounding as they do in detailed exposition of cities and physical landscape features, do hint at some perception of the regional concept as reflected in such passages as, "Now that I have traversed the region of *Old Italy,*" and "that *part* of the country," and "the whole of *this district.*" Moreover, our own geographical terminology of the several or-

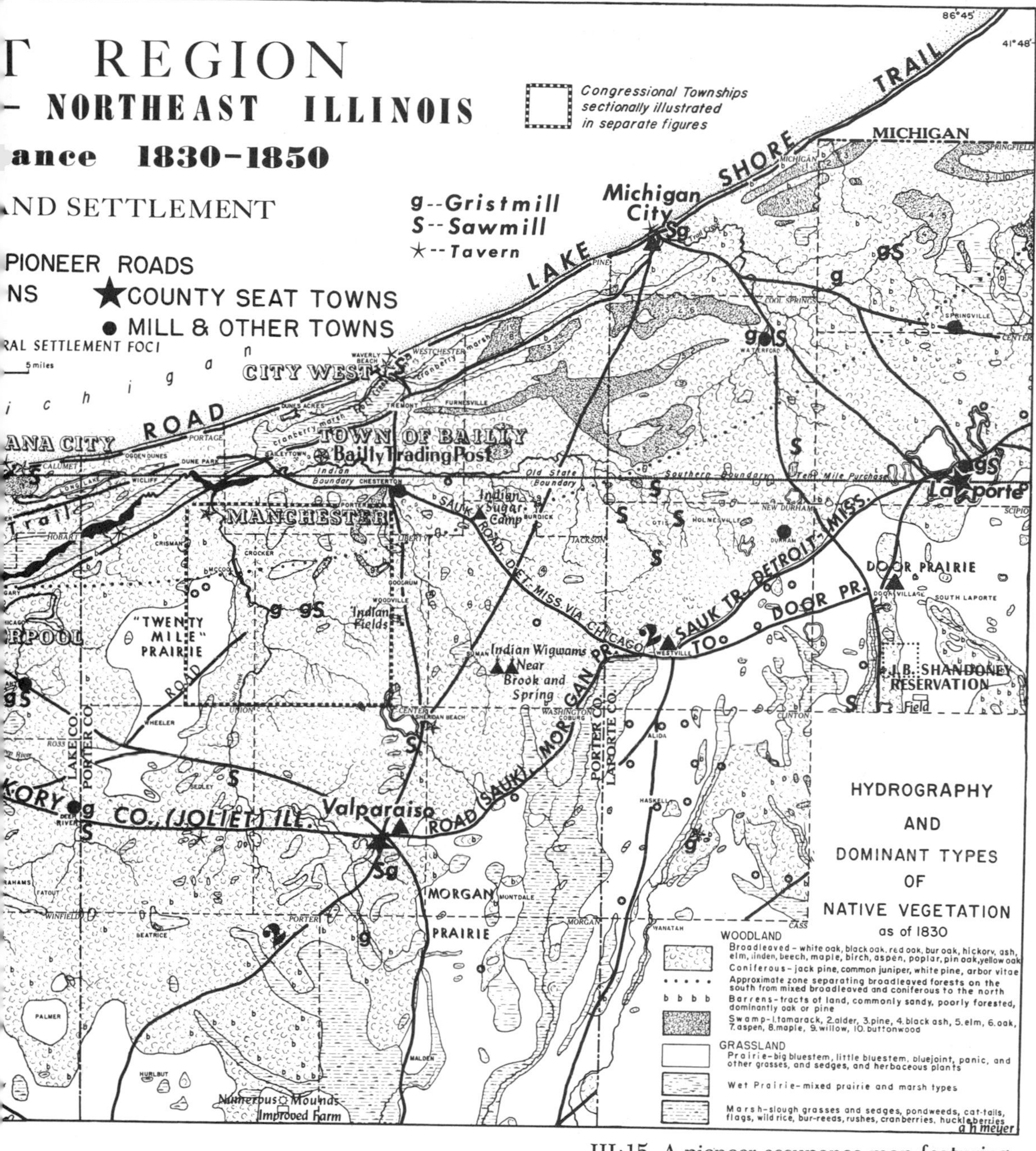

III:15 A pioneer occupance map featuring those landscape elements which point up the life of a midwestern frontiersman as a sequel to Indian occupance. How does this map aid you in answering the questions raised in the text? (Map originally published in *Annals of the Association of American Geographers,* Vol. XLVI, September, 1956, used by permission)

ders of space magnitude derives from the Greek — "ge"-ography of the earth, "chor"-ography of the region, "top"-ography of the local area or site.

A common practice in modern geographic education is to start on the elementary level with field and map studies of the home environment, and move progressively upwards to space areas of higher magnitude in the upper levels. But as indicated above, the historical development of geographic and cartographic art for the most part moved from global or large regional contexts to the smaller topographic units. Thus the earliest philosophically-minded Greek geographer was preoccupied with the shape of the earth and the relations of the ecumene (inhabited part) of it. In the Age of Discovery man was primarily concerned with the major delineations and divisions of land and sea. Once the continents and major countries had received cartographic expression, the motivations for migration and settlement on a regional scale initiated internal surveys. A case in point which effectively illustrates how a land survey "opens up" a frontier for farmer occupance is illustrated in Figure III-14. By the use of the surveyors' township maps and notes of landmarks along section lines we can reconstruct an historic-geographic picture of how the white man determined his occupance forms in relation to the "fundament" — aboriginal landscape and the Indian aborigine (Figure III-15). To what extent, would you say, does the map indicate conformity of the pioneer's circulation and settlement patterns with those of the Indian? How are the Indian's circulation and settlement patterns related to the Lake Michigan shoreline; the inland streams, lakes, and marshes; the upland woodlands, the swamps, and the dry and wet prairies? What differences do you detect here between the behavior of the Indian and the pioneer settler?

This region is part of the historic U.S. Northwest Territory, established by the Ordinance of 1785. Though sectional lines are not shown, the civil township, county, and state lines clearly reveal the quadrate character of the survey pattern designated for the area by Thomas Jefferson. And if you consult a topographic map showing today's pattern of rural and urban land-use, you would find that it, too, bears, in most instances, a striking conformity to the rectilinear outlines of the original survey (See Porter map under "Geographic Understanding"). Whether this is good or bad — good for some purposes; bad, for others — we shall not here explore. The point here is simply to see the cartographic perspective and its relation to the processes of land occupance, which was designed conventionally on a quarter-section basis — 160 acres (or multiples thereof) per farmer. Hildegard Johnson's psycho-geographic analysis of the "quarter-section" aptly illustrates how we may see the significance of geographic form and position in both an abstract and concrete way. But before considering the "models" of Figure III-16, as related to "quarter section" occupance, as does Dr. Johnson, let us apply the several space arrangement of squares first to the building of a home, considering each one of the squares as a room. We are not concerned here with the architectural appointments. We are now dealing with the question of space and positional significance of the different arrangements or patterns which these figures form in the landscape — that is the geography, whether applied to the four rooms of a home, or four "forties" of land, or four sections of an urban community, or four subregions of a larger region, or four provinces or states of a nation, or for that matter any other differentiated natural or cultural or combined natural–cultural landscape units of the earth's surface. The home and the site that it occupies are, of course, geographic phenomena of themselves, but it should be noted that we are primarily interested in the fact that we are dealing here with five different concepts of contiguous-room design. And it is the cartographic expression of this and its occupance implications that is as much geography, or even more significantly geography, than is the "thing of itself" (*Das Ding an Sich*, as the German geographer would say).

Now let us become a little bit more practical and see whether you can figure out how the different house patterns are related in space to things outside of the site which the house itself occupies. For example, how are the five basic room patterns related to sun and shade at different times of the day? How do the seasons and the hemispheres enter the picture?

Now note that, by adding the concept of direction, our four-unit contiguous arrangement presents nineteen geographical possibilities instead of simply five. Again applying the question above, how will sunshine and shade relationships obtain?

The article of which this figure is a part deals with farm occupance, but here also, as Dr. Johnson points out, "the exposure, northern, southern, western, or eastern, makes a difference. Indeed, all nineteen variations of the shape of a quarter section were put on a map and the land by the settlers who entered claims in southeastern Minnesota during 1855."[1] Some practical significances of the several shape and directional variants again may be noted by raising some questions: Which of the quarter sections requires the fewer perimeter fences? Assuming this to be a mixed farming area, as is commonly the case with a combined grain and animal economy, which pattern would seemingly be best adapted to a rotation scheme of field and pasture? Which pattern in general would seem to lend itself best to the administration of farm sales, neighbor–farm relationships, road patterns, and the like?[2]

Simple and effective as is the rectangular farm plat in normal operation, particularly when it is of the compact type, various physical aspects of the land, as the article also points out, often militated against the "ideological" quadrangular setting.

¶ All want a simple, complete, determinative accounting system of the land. But the straight line, so simple to arrive at out of doors with two sticks in the ground and a rope or string stretched between them, is not of nature. It is an expression of control by man. The tiller of the soil has to work with soils, trees, slopes, stones, and creeks, all of which are irregularly distributed. He cannot ignore or control them but must adjust to them, and adjustment means curves and irregular clearings.[3]

It may be well to note here that legislation on geometrical form of land-use preceded the detailed land surveys of the area. But, as the student will observe repeatedly in the text, arbitrariness of legislation often yields — and wisely so — to the "arbitrariness of nature." Hills and valleys, lakes and rivers, diverse natural vegetation, and soil patterns all have their own way of suggesting a

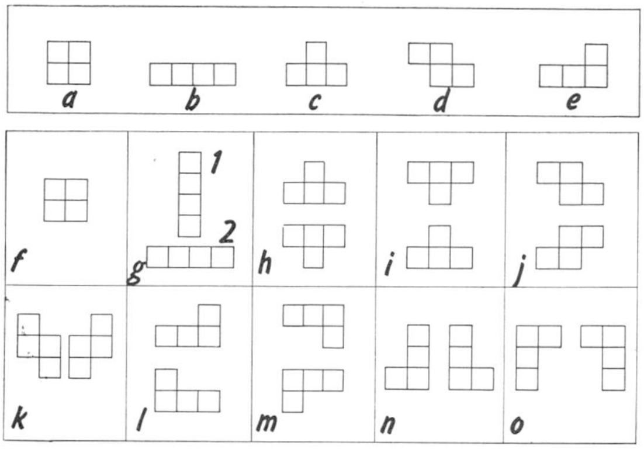

III:16 This diagram shows the spatial perspective of the midwestern farmstead. The Northwest Territory pioneer farmer characteristically settled on what is known as the "Quarter Section" (comprising approximately 160 acres). Though normally a four-forty-acre square, it was not necessarily so. Theoretically, as geographer Johnson here shows (a,b,c,d,e), there are "five mathematical possibilities of combining four squares contiguously," and when to this is added alternate orientation, nineteen geographic possibilities result. For the significance of such, see the text. (Unlettered figure by Dr. Hildegard Johnson in *Geographical Review*, Vol. XLVII, 1957, used by permission)

more rational approach to the use of the land than merely blindly following a conventional survey system. And so the farm patterns, especially in the more rugged regions, often vary widely from the artificial checkerboard design indicated in the figure.

2. *The topographic map.* The pursuit of scientific farming and other orderly occupance of the land soon suggested the need of recording the third dimensional aspect of land — the varying character of landform, relief, and slope. Earlier represented on small scale (large, regional) maps in the form of hachures or shadings, it soon became evident that for most practical purposes the "lay of the land" could be most effectively illustrated by the so-called contour line. Modeling land surface configuration to contour lines, as shown in the accompanying relief illustrations (Figures III-17, 18), is an effective way to introduce the student to the art of topographic map reading. The contour-line idea in mapping relief repre-

[1] Johnson, Hildegard, "The Quarter Section," *The Geographical Review*, Vol. XLVII, No. 3, 1957, p. 340. Used by permission.

[2] The shape factor can have significant geographic implications as well even for a country. In proportion to area, which type—Aa or Ab—has the greater boundary to defend? Consider Romania and Czechoslovakia. Which exhibits the greater variations in climate induced by latitude—Bg 1 or Bg 2? Can you think of two characteristic examples?

[3] *Ibid.*, p. 347. Reprinted by permission.

III:17 This relief model map (vertical exaggeration) shows the Harrisburg, Pennsylvania, area. Compare this "raised" relief with the "flat" contour counterpart on the inside of the front cover of the book. Contrast the relative advantages and disadvantages of each type of map in laboratory work. (Relief map copyright Aero Service Corporation)

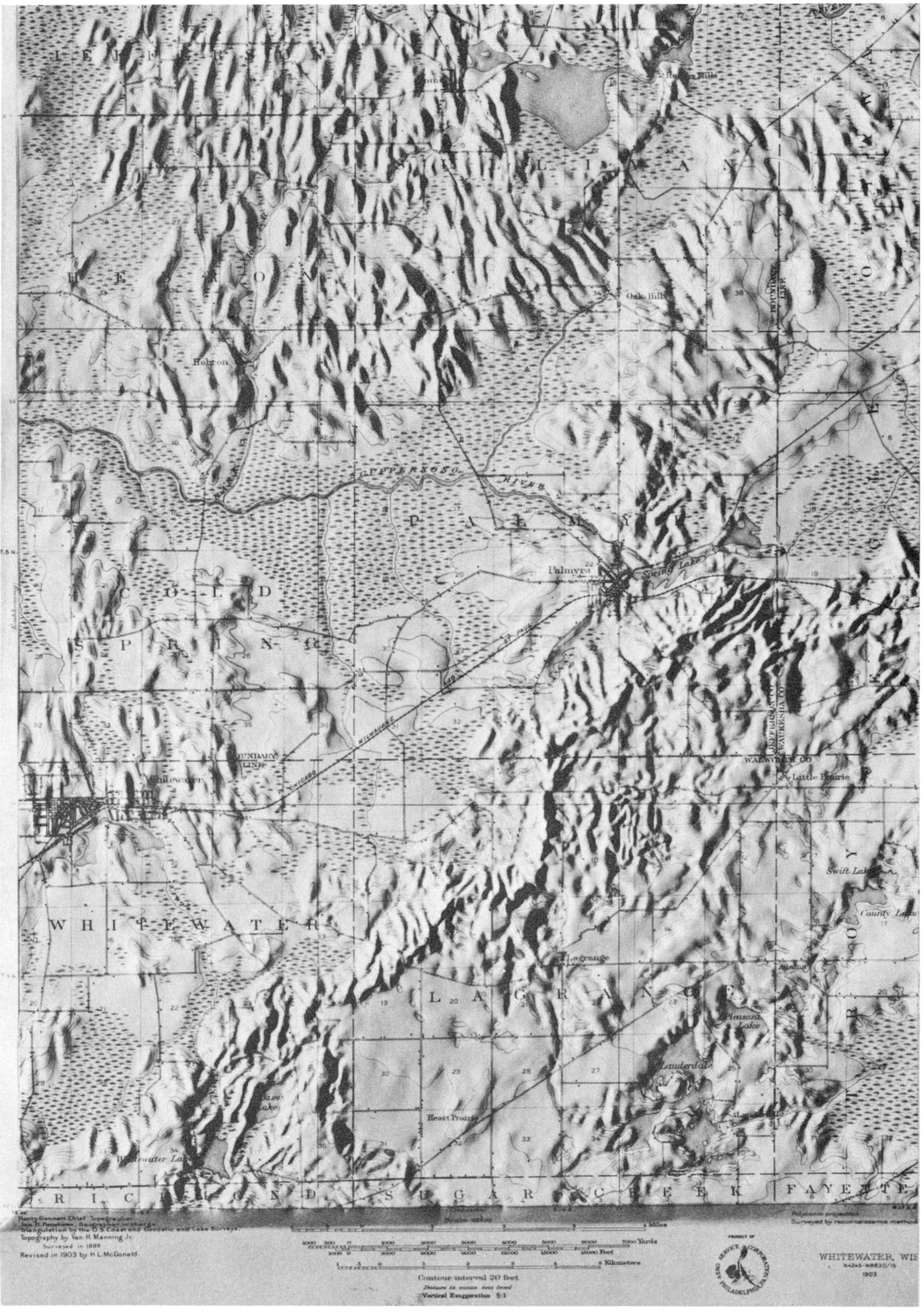

III:18 This relief model map (vertical exaggeration) shows the Whitewater, Wisconsin, area. Why do we need vertical scale exaggerations of "model" maps? Why a different scale here from that of the Harrisburg area (Figure III:17)? (Relief map copyright Aero Service Corporation)

sents a high landmark in cartography; and its counterpart in agriculture — the plowing and sowing of fields contour-fashion — is one of the most advanced soil-conservation practices in modern farming. In fact, so closely is the physical relief and the cultivated crop related contour-wise that one might say no field study can afford to overlook the importance of the degree of correspondence between a contour relief map and a land-use map — to see how the patterns of the latter are related to those of the former. Such practice often elicits major geographic principles of farming methods.[1]

The most common contour map is the type produced by the U. S. Geological Survey, commonly referred to as a topographic quadrangle (inside front and rear covers). No student or teacher of geography, or of the social studies, or of history or of any other field for that matter, can afford to be ignorant of the use of the proverbial "top" sheet. Such a map characteristically shows not only the lay of the land, but also the water features, commonly now also vegetation cover; likewise rural and urban settlements, transportation lines, and generally other special features of resource use (e.g., mines and quarries, national parks and forests, and the like). Of course, one map cannot show everything necessary in understanding human occupance patterns. Accordingly, many other types of topographic maps are made by the geographer in the field which involve such phenomena as crop cover, types of superstructure, and subsurface features (e.g., groundwater table; mineral deposits).

It should also be noted that topographic mapping — even ordinary contour mapping — is still limited to only a small percentage of the land surface of the earth. Less than one-fifth — only a few years ago, less than one-tenth — of the entire earth was so covered.[1] The research student, then, in almost every adventure in field geography, must be prepared to do some mapping of his own, particularly of phenomena which have a direct bearing upon his problem. But before he does any mapping at all, he will familiarize himself with such maps as are available and thus prevent any possible duplication. Moreover, he will want to scrutinize such maps carefully for clues on field data which appear to be most germane to his project, and to sharpen his detection of those processes which have a distinct bearing on formulating valid principles. As we have noted in Chapter 1, principles grow out of processes, and to recognize the dominant processes in the landscape we use our maps and the maps of others — maps of natural attributes, maps of cultural attributes — and focus our eyes on regional co-variances, noting how one phenomenon or several phenomena vary areally in relation to others in the environmental complex. Let us consider again an abstract situation.

Assume that the two topographic quadrangles referred to represent typical (recurring) regional associations between man and the land. What generalizations can you postulate on the relations of the terrain to the selection of farmstead sites? Of sites for orchards? Of sites for cultivated crops? Of sites for permanent pasture? Of sites for towns? Conjecture how the road patterns evolved. In actual practice, to be sure, you will want to verify your postulates based on your own field mapping by consulting historical geography maps and data, and by interviewing experts in the field, and by using any other relevant sources or means available to you.

3. *The chorographic perspective.* Now let us revert to the larger areal consideration of geographical analysis of the "quarter section," namely, its regional position. Assume that the "checkered" farm is transposed from its midlatitude position to the lower or higher latitudes. It should now be obvious

---

[1] The contour line is a form of "isopleth" (Fr. "isos," equal; "pleth," quantity), connecting earth surface points having the same elevation. The isopleth is one of the most expedient and effective cartographic devices used by the geographer to bring out areal differentiation in all significant landscape phenomena (e.g., "isotherms," temperature; "isohyet," rainfall; "isobars," pressure). Conceptual human geography would be greatly aided by techniques measuring human behavior in landscape terms in such a form that it, too, could be regionally recorded "isoplethically." But as noted in Chapter 1, man's behavior is not simply governed by natural laws. Hopefully some pseudo-isoplethic system may yet be perfected which will aid the geographer in giving cartographic expression to at least the broader regional concepts of human occupance.

[1] Accelerated mapping through air photography and photogrammetry, plus the emphasis on cold-war military reconnaissance, are rapidly extending cartographic coverage of the world. Reportedly, with photography by radar we can now map "military targets and other features while flying hundreds of miles away, over friendly territory."

that the latitudinal connotations normally are of a higher order of magnitude than the differences that would result from the shape and directional aspects of the farms located in the same general community. What regional differences would you expect? Also, what major differences in types of farming in the same latitude might be anticipated as between the west coast, interior, and east coast? Even where climate, landforms, soils, and other natural features might be quite identical, you would expect, would you not, major differences in farm types between the Minnesota farm and a farm, let us say, in the Orient? Or even locally? Why?

The moment we move from a lower to a higher hierarchy of land-unit consideration, the more contrasted are land-use differentiations. Processes and principles of increasing complexity are also identified with such major changes.

In sum, then, to comprehend the world cartographically we must have comprehensive chorographical coverage. And to obtain meaningful regional divisions, which lend themselves effectively to comparative continental studies in geography, we must have representative topographic surveys in sufficient number and high quality to produce the kind of generalizations that establish geography as a valid chorologic science.

APPLICATION OF GEOGRAPHIC UNDERSTANDING

Like map projections, geographic concepts may be reduced cartographically to three basic classes — those expressive of relative position, of areal co-variance, and of regionality. Applying these in as simple an environmental context as practicable, let us see what kind of geographic concepts can be "read" directly or inferred from selected sections of the two U.S.G.S. topographical quadrangles — the Harrisburg, Pennsylvania and the Porter, Indiana (inside front and rear covers). Let us be alert as well to the limitations of map data. Examine each map in terms of the following categories:

I. Scale

A. Both are on the same scale. What is it? What does this mean?

B. Contour interval of the Porter map is 10 feet; of Harrisburg, 20 feet. Why was the smaller interval used for the Porter Quadrangle? Or putting it another way, how would the use of a 20-foot interval have adversely affected cartographic configuration?

II. Relative Position of the Area in Space and Time

A. What does the latitude (see maps) suggest as to seasonal–annual temperature scale in the global context? Without changing the latitude, suppose the areas were on the west coast. How would that change the situation?

B. Is the climate dry or humid? Evidence?

C. How is the regional position and survey of the area related to U.S. geo-historical development?

III. Historical-Political Antecedents

What is the difference in the survey patterns of the two areas? How do you account for the diverse delineation and orientation of the two patterns? In the case of Porter (part of Northwest Territory) "congressional" townships were laid out, normally six miles square, embracing 36 sections, each approximating 640 acres. Note the numbering system used for townships and sections. But administrative units, called "civil" townships, such as denoted by the heavy type names (e.g., LIBERTY and PORTAGE), do not normally conform to the size and shape of the "congressional." Can you think of any *geographical* feature — physical, social, economic, or political — which served as guidelines to state and county commissioners in drawing (and at times redrawing) the boundaries of such units?

IV. Terms and Toponymy

Topographic terminology and toponymy often reveal, or at least strongly suggest, significant historic and geographic information. Let us check a few examples to illustrate this often overlooked virtue of the conventional topographic quadrangle. Learn to put the term or name in both local and regional perspective:

Porter Quadrangle

A. Physical—Big Blowout; Waverly Beach

B. Cultural—Tratabas Mill; Burns Ditch

C. Toponymic Nomenclature

Harrisburg Quadrangle

Heckert Gap; White Spring

Heckton Mills; Fort Hunter

Names of counties, townships, towns and cities in many cases give strong clues to the nationality of immigrants into the area. On the basis of this criterion alone, what would you postulate as to the chief sources of pioneer settlement in the two areas? And what does the toponymy of the two major streams suggest?

V. Co-variances, or Correlations, between Physical and Cultural Phenomena

A. Demographic Geography: How does the map give you an approximate idea of the density of population? Compare the two, observing the difference in dates of publication of the two maps. Which is generally more important to know — *statistical* population of towns or townships or *spatial* densities in the diverse geographic regions? Does the map supply any criteria which will aid you in appraising the comparative future potential growth of the two areas?

B. Settlement: How would you describe the pattern of farmstead distribution? Does the change in pattern from one place to the next conform (or co-vary) with the pattern of some other phenomenon (physical or cultural)? For example, do you detect any site preference shown by the average farmer based on the contour of the land (terrain configuration)? What inference can you draw about the size and shape of the average farm? What appear to be "focalizing" forces for urbanization? for suburban and recreational development? for adaptable sites for industrial and commercial use — actual and potential?

C. Circulation: Which of the following factors seem to have been mostly operative in surveyors' designs of the road pattern: (1) original arbitrary survey; (2) construction in conformity with terrain; (3) pattern designed to serve best the needs of the farmer; the urban dweller; the traveler passing through the area? What do the rail and water transport facilities signify?

VI. Regionality

A. For such limited data as are here accessible to you, do you recognize areas distinctive enough one from another, to require separate areal treatment? If so, what criterion or criteria—physical or cultural—would you suggest?

B. Proceed to draw such a line (or lines) on the map (or maps), recalling that such demarcations are intended to represent zonal belts of change rather than sharp-line differentiations. And remember, too, that what you drew is *not* a landscape phenomenon, but a *geographic concept* of yours as to structural or functional relations of the areas.

VII. Comparative Geography

A. On the basis of the mapped data alone, describe the contrasted landscapes of the two areas — combined physical and cultural settings.

B. What additional types of maps do you feel you need in order to form a reasonably accurate perspective of the processes operating in the areas which have produced the diverse cultural impress upon them?

C. Examine the cartography of each of the "chorograms" introducing the chapters of Part IV of this book. See if you can detect some of the "relationship" principles stressed in this and the preceding chapters of this book.

VIII. Geographic Planning

As will be brought out in our last chapter (Chapter 36) on "The Geographic Way of Life," city, county, and regional planning is one of the most promising fields of applying the technique of geographic thinking to practical ends.

IX. The Role of Cartography in Other Fields

As stated earlier, maps alone cannot totally interpret areal man. But what do maps, even these simple topographic maps, tell us?

References

1 Salisbury, Rollin D., and Atwood, Wallace W., "The Interpretation of Topographic Maps," Professional Paper 60, U. S. Geological Survey, 1908, p. 9.

2 Robinson, Arthur H., "An Analytical Approach to Map Projections," *Annals of the Association of American Geographers,* Vol. 39, December, 1949, p. 283.

3. Raisz, Erwin, *General Cartography,* McGraw-Hill Book Co., Inc., New York, 1948, pp. 26, 34, 39.

4 Hakluyt, Richard, *The Principal Voyages of the English Nation,* Everyman's Library, Ernest Rhys, Editor, J. M. Dent and Sons and E. P. Dutton & Co., Inc., New York, Vol. 1, Introduction xiii, p. 6.

5 Baker, J. N. L., *A History of Geographical Discovery and Exploration,* Houghton Mifflin Company, Boston, 1931, *passim,* pp. 145, 150-162.

6 Johnson, Hildegard, "The Quarter Section," *The Geographical Review,* Vol. XLVII, No. 3, 1957, pp. 340, 347.

Chapter 4

Areal man in demographic perspective

In our science, the central theme of which is area differentiation, the dynamic and pivotal element is human life, or population. . . . Population is the point of reference from which all the other elements are observed and from which they all, singly and collectively, derive significance and meaning. It is population which furnishes the focus.—Glenn T. Trewartha

Presidential address before the Association of American Geographers, 1953.

The pre-eminence of population geography

In the concluding topographic map exercise of the preceding chapter, the student will have noticed that the habitation and habitat of man form the focal element of cartographic study. This was so designed in order to impress upon the student that the ultimate goal in cartographic study is not development of skill in contour reading of surface configuration phenomena (essential as that is in all geographic training) but rather visualization—of the way man has decided to place himself in earth space and slope, which we call the demographic pattern. The habitancy of an area, or its population pattern, then, is the pilot principle about which the major structure of our entire textbook has been organized. We agree with Trewartha that all other area elements "derive significance and meaning" from the study of population, and we subscribe to his triad concept of elemental groupings (Figure IV-1). This three-fold grouping in a unitary geography comprises:

¶ (1) Man, the creator and originator of the cultural landscape, as well as the beneficiary of his own production; (2) the natural earth, which provides the environment and the raw materials for the use of man the creator; and (3) the cultural earth, which is the product of man's creation from the natural stuff.[1]

We also consider such demographic study the most important of our time, regardless of subject matter. The "population explosion" problem is viewed by many scientists and statesmen alike today as being of pre-eminent significance. The accelerated rate of increase of world population in the last quarter century preoccupies the attention of the press and the pulpit, of science and government, and of all areas of academic discipline. At the same time, it is one of the most controversial subjects, involving conflicting points of view in areas of the church, government, and science as to the significance and solution of social, economic, and political problems growing out of the race between "man and space" (resources). Thus Fairfield Osborne, President of the Conservation Foundation, in an address before the American Association for the Advancement of Science (1956), observes:

¶ The "Reproductive Potential" of the human race is at last being recognized as perhaps the most basic and certainly one of the most ominous problems facing the world today. . . . In the search for peace, there is mounting evidence that the pressures resulting from rapidly growing population are without question a major cause for the great majority of conflicts between nations. For my own part, I will go a step further and express my belief that the hope for world peace is remote, or even unattainable, until the pressures resulting from population growth are relieved.[2]

Likewise Lord John Boyd-Orr, former Director General of the United Nations Food and Agricultural Organization, recognizes "the upsurge in Asia" as the "most important political event in the world today," a manifestation of "fundamentally a revolt against hunger and poverty." Similarly, scientist Huxley and religionist Fosdick regard population as "the problem of our age" and "the basic problem of the world today." And in

[1] Trewartha, Glenn T., "A Case for Population Geography," *Annals of the Association of American Geographers*, Vol. XLIII, No. 2, June, 1953. Reprinted by permission.

[2] *Population Bulletin*, published by the Population Reference Bureau, Washington 5, D. C., Vol. XIII, No. 1, February, 1957, p. 14. Reprinted by permission.

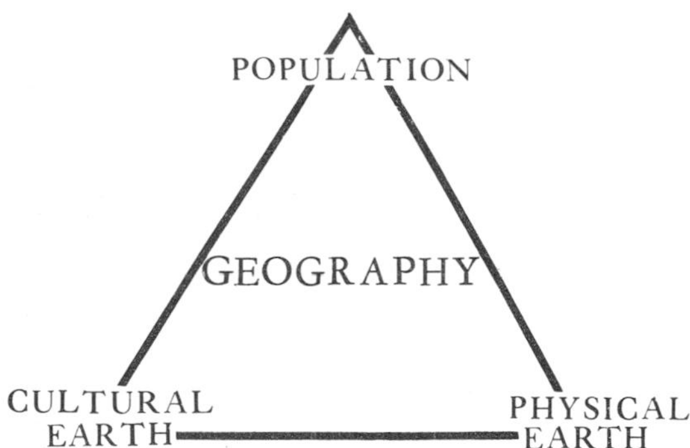

IV:1 This diagram shows a triad concept of geography focused on population. (By Dr. Glenn T. Trewartha from *Annals of the Association of American Geographers,* Vol. XLIII, 1953, used by permission)

view of the fact that there is a marked geographic coincidence between areas of population pressure and areas of resource underdevelopment, President Eisenhower expressed the conviction "that the problem of the underdeveloped nations is more lasting, more important, to Western civilization than Soviet-Western differences."[1]

It is not surprising, therefore, that the population question has received priority attention by the Economic and Social Council of the United Nations in its establishment of the so-called Population Commission with directives to study and advise the Council on: (a) the size and structure of populations and the changes therein; (b) the interplay of demographic factors, and economic and social factors; (c) policies designed to influence the size and structure of populations and the changes therein; (d) any other demographic questions on which either the principal or the subsidiary organs of the United Nations or the Specialized Agencies may seek advice.[2]

The policy of the United States government to render economic assistance to foreign peoples, especially in the so-called undeveloped or underdeveloped countries, is well known to everyone. This, in fact, is the crux of international politics in the cold war as the United States strives to contain communism in Asia, Africa, and Latin America. Though generally directed to the promotion of social and economic welfare and political stability of such nations generally, it is now increasingly recognized that nearly all factors of national prosperity and security and world peace are linked with the population expansion problem. Thus the Third Interim Report of the President's Committee to Study the United States Military Assistance Program, transmitted to the President July 13, 1959, had the following recommendations to make:

¶ That, in order to meet more effectively the problems of economic development, the United States (1) assist those countries with which it is cooperating in economic aid programs, on request, in the formulation of their plans designed to deal with the problem of rapid population growth, (2) increase its assistance to local programs relating to material and child welfare in recognition of the immediate problem created by rapid population growth, and (3) strongly support studies and appropriate research as a part of its own Mutual Security Program, within the United Nations and elsewhere, leading to the availability of relevant information in a form most useful to individual countries in the formulation of practical programs to meet the serious challenge posed by rapidly expanding populations.

Though some demographers view with alarm the accelerated population growth even in our own country[3], there is obviously no concern for a food shortage in the foreseeable future. As everyone so well knows, ours is a problem of excess production, deteriorating surplus storage, and involved economics to keep producer prices up and consumer prices down. Geographically, however, demographic interests at present are concerned largely with the changing patterns of population distribution. Along with absolute differentials in regional increases, there is the phenomenon of migration. For example: Why did 1,580 counties, more than one-

1 "The New Awakening," *Population Bulletin,* published by the Population Reference Bureau, Washington 5, D. C., Vol. XV, No. 8, December, 1959, p. 138. Reprinted by permission.

2 "Population in the United Nations," *Population Bulletin,* published by the Population Reference Bureau, Washington 5, D. C., Vol. XI, No. 7, November, 1955, p. 95.

3 The Bureau of the Census reports an all-time record increase of 27.7 million for the decennium, ending April 1, 1960, and 12.5 million of new housing units, also an all-time record increase (5).

This picture shows census-taking in the continental United States. "Where do the people live?" is the prime question of any area distribution study. The mapping of houses, as part of a rural or urban survey, supplies an answer; and also gives some idea of population density. But if we wish to know just how many people there are in an area, we need a census. In the April 1, 1960, census, information was collected about some 180 million people, distributed among some 55 million dwelling units. In what vital statistics collected by the census taker would a geographer be particularly interested? With what types of data would he be least concerned? (Bureau of the Census, United States Department of Commerce)

half of the nation's 3,072 counties, lose population, as indicated in the preliminary census report of the Census Bureau, despite a national total gain of 28 million population? And why did "nearly two-thirds of the total population increase of the United States since 1950 [occur] in the parts of the Standard Metropolitan Areas outside the central cities"? And how would you go about interpreting Figure IV-2, indicating the per cent changes by states and regions? Consider particularly Florida, Nevada, Arizona, California, and Alaska. Do you think these states might soon experience a population pressure problem? If so, by what geographic standards or criteria? Would the possible national addition of some 60 million people within the next two decades, as has been projected by some students of population growth, produce a food-deficiency problem? Absolute answers may not be forthcoming to such specific questions, but we shall in general concern ourselves here with geographic principles and techniques which presume to throw some light at least on population growth and

The census taker in Alaska rides a dog sled. The first federal census of Alaska was made in 1880, when a population of 33,426 was enumerated. Determine the official census of Alaska for 1960. Do you think this state outpost of ours will ever experience a "population explosion" problem? In answering such a question, what demographic and environmental factors have to be considered? (Bureau of the Census, United States Department of Commerce)

regional shifts and the recurring challenges they present for intelligent appraisal.

The Malthusian principle of population

Foraging for food is probably man's earliest and oldest preoccupation. Thus, Phillips reminds us that it:

¶ Occupied an important place in his thinking long before population curves rose to their present level. To find evidence of this, one has only to turn to the book of Genesis. In the description of the Creation, one finds recurring references to the earth bringing forth grass, herbs, and fruit trees; to the creation of fish, fowl, and cattle; and to man's being given dominion over these things. There is also reference, near the end of the first chapter, to seeds and fruits being "meat" for man and to the green herbs being "meat" for the beast and fowl. It is only in the third chapter of man's history, as described in Genesis, that food of an especially attractive type—fruit of the Tree of Knowledge of Good and Evil—provided the first temptation. As the earth's population grew, and as political organization began to take shape, Nimrod, presumably because of his prowess as a hunter and, therefore, a good provider of food, became the first monarch, according to the Biblical account.[1]

[1] Phillips, Ralph W., "How Adequate Is the World's Food Supply?", *The Scientific Monthly*, Vol. LXXXV, No. 5, November, 1957, pp. 265-266. Reprinted from *The Scientific Monthly* by permission.

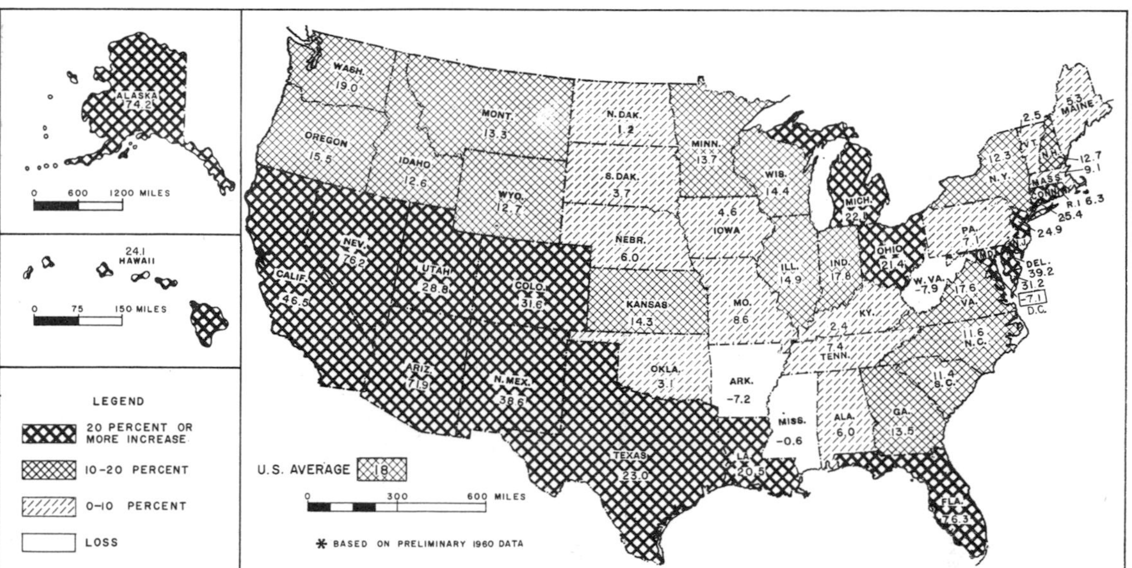

IV:2 This map shows per cent of change in population by state, 1950-1960. What geographic factors do you think should be analyzed to help account for the changes indicated? (Bureau of the Census, United States Department of Commerce)

Even before the new world had been settled to any extent, it became obvious to such economists as Adam Smith and Thomas Malthus that the normal run of population increase would sooner or later outdistance the food supply. At the same time Malthus recognized that any conscious effort on man's part to introduce regulatory measures for controlling population growth would present ideological conflicts. In his own mind and conscience, Malthus met the spiritual conflict by recognizing that man has not only responsibilities as a family procreator but also as family provider. Thus, as he points out, cognizance of this divine order of husbandry places a moral restraint on unlimited procreation against limited sustenance. With the unprecedented acceleration of population growth entitled "population explosion" at mid-twentieth century, ideological considerations of the question are posed. Any design of population control must take into account the fact that widespread major oriental faiths, such as Mohammedanism, Hinduism, and Confucianism, are opposed in principle to population restrictions. And while many leaders in the Roman Catholic Church recognize that certain regions definitely do have a "population problem," the church as such is highly critical of some of the regulatory measures which have been proposed to effect population stability.

Interestingly enough, political ideologies are likewise tied up with the population increase question. Though having nothing in common with the ideological positions taken by religion on this question, one of the basic tenets of Marxism is that population as labor is a form of wealth, and therefore any restrictive measures on population growth result in reduced productivity and hence less means of sustenance. Such regulation, then, it is claimed, would result in a lower instead of a higher standard of living.[1]

Most scientists, including geographers, recognize resource limitations by both nature and man in meeting high standards of sustenance requirements in the face of nonplanned population growth. But despite the lack of immediate realization of a world program of planned parenthood, spiritually ac-

[1] The Communist regimes of both Russia and China at first subscribed to this dialectic of Marxism, but now favor some measure of population control.

ceptable to all, the geographer, along with other scientists, has the moral responsibility to explore every frontier to conserve food, to increase production, and to point the way to better regional distribution of food between areas of overproduction and wasteful storage and the areas of famine. And so the conservation-minded citizen will work for all economic–political programs which are wisely directed to eliminating waste of natural and human resources, and the geographically-trained man will adapt the use of land in every area to its greatest potential productivity regardless of the region or state of culture.

To understand the present-day significance of the world population–food problem, it will be well to go back to the original work of Thomas Robert Malthus entitled, *An Essay on the Principle of Population, or A View of its Past and Present Effects on Human Happiness.* Trained as a clergyman, historian, and political economist, Malthus became interested in the age-old question of the relation of density of population to the welfare of the people and of the state. His thesis may be best expressed by quoting some excerpts from this original work.

¶ The constant tendency in all animated life [is] to increase beyond the nourishment prepared for it. . . . It may safely be pronounced that population, when unchecked, goes on doubling itself every twenty-five years, or increases in a geometrical ratio. The rate according to which the productions of the earth may be supposed to increase, it will not be so easy to determine. Of this, however, we may be perfectly certain, that the ratio of their increase in a limited territory must be of a totally different nature from the ratio of the increase of population. . . . If it be allowed that by the best possible policy, and great encouragements to agriculture, the average produce of the island could be doubled in the first twenty-five years, it will be allowing, probably, a greater increase than could with reason be expected. In the next twenty-five years, it is impossible to suppose that the produce could be quadrupled. It would be contrary to all our knowledge of the properties of land. The improvement of the barren parts would be a work of time and labor; and it must be evident to those who have the slightest acquaintance with agricultural subjects, that in proportion as cultivation extended, the additions that could yearly be made to the former average produce must be gradually and regularly diminishing. . . . It may be fairly pronounced, therefore, that, considering the present average state of the earth, the means of subsistence, under circumstances the most favorable to human industry, could not possibly be made to increase faster than in an arithmetical ratio (7).

Up to this point, Malthus was referring particularly to the growing population and resource conditions of his own country, namely, England, only occasionally referring to population expansion potentials elsewhere, as in Europe and the United States. But then, at the conclusion of his first chapter, Malthus takes a look at the entire earth in summarizing his observation on the relationship between population growth and subsistence.

¶ Taking the whole Earth, instead of this island, emigration would, of course, be excluded; and, supposing the present population equal to a thousand millions, the human species would increase as the numbers 1, 2, 4, 8, 16, 32, 64, 128, 256, and subsistence as 1, 2, 3, 4, 5, 6, 7, 8, 9. In two centuries the population would be to the means of subsistence as 256 to 9; in three centuries as 4,096 to 13, and in two thousand years the difference would be almost incalculable. In this supposition no limits whatever are placed to the produce of the earth. It may increase forever and be greater than any assignable quantity; yet, still the power of population being in every period so much superior, the increase of the human species can only be kept down to the level of the means of subsistence by the constant operation of the strong law of necessity, acting as a check on the greater power (7).

Malthus himself, in subsequent editions of the same work, recognized imperfections of his earlier assumptions concerning the possible increase of food supply, but never disavowed to his dying day the basic principle of his thesis that unrestrained procreation ultimately in any area must result in misery and eventual starvation. Today, with an unprecedented rate of increase of population, interest in the revival of Malthusianism in the form known as neo-Malthusianism has again attracted clerical and scientific attention.

Malthus, being a clergyman as well as a political economist, announced his own principles of morality in dealing with this problem: The Creator's command to "increase and multiply and replenish the earth" implies the responsibility of man as well to keep procreation and means of support in proper balance. Man is therefore committed to study the laws of nature; the birth of a child destined to starve is a violation of man's prudence and divine providence. The basic population control methods suggested by Malthus were: (1) chastity before marriage, (2) postponement of marriage, and (3) relative or restrained continence in marriage. Postponement of marriage was not regarded as an age factor as much as a support factor.

Malthus' views concerning the obligations of marriage in this respect derive from his exegesis of St. Paul's statement on this matter:

¶ If we apply the spirit of St. Paul's declarations respecting marriage to the present state of society and the known constitution of our nature, the natural inference seems to be, that when marriage does not interfere with higher duties it is right; when it does, it is wrong. . . . There are perhaps few actions that tend so directly to diminish the general happiness, as to marry without the means of supporting children. He who commits this act, therefore, clearly offends against the will of God (7).

This in sum, then, expresses Malthus' views of the relationship of the laws of nature to the revealed Word of God as respects the population problem, and man's obligation and opportunity to mitigate widespread suffering and starvation. Despite the controversial questions that it raises in the areas of biology, politics, and religion, if Malthus were alive today, he would no doubt point to the fact that over half of the people of the world are underfed, suffering from dietary deficiencies and maladies resulting therefrom. Actual famines continue to be periodical regional phenomena, while man debates "causes" and "cures." Malthus says in effect, "Hunger is the result of overpopulation," whereas de Castro maintains "Hunger is the cause of overpopulation" (8).

Of course, as we shall see below, there are governmental, scientific, and benevolent agencies which are continuously at work in mitigating this food shortage problem. The crucial question always remains, however: Can an increasing food supply keep pace indefinitely with increasing population growth? Demographic experts tell us that we are today experiencing "the most rapid rate of growth in world history." Of all world geographic phenomena, none is seemingly more difficult to interpret as to areal significance than population. This stems largely from the fact that man is at once a creator as well as a consumer. He not only works with his hands but with his head, changing the geography from day to day. Even Malthus recognized the many potential capacities of man to multiply sources of food production. Therefore, absolute statistics on population in themselves often are relatively meaningless. Nevertheless, a few basic growth statistics will initiate some thinking along the line of growing population pressures. During the time you are reading this chapter (say, three hours), the world population will have increased by some 15,000 — the equivalent size of a typical American county-seat town; tomorrow, at this time, the world will have 120,000 more mouths to feed — a population increment of a good-sized American manufacturing community. On a more extended time basis, say, by the year 2000, at the present rate of increase, the population of the world will have been doubled; and by the year 2050 the population of the United States has been projected to 600 million. The important principle to be derived from this is that population grows like capital whose interest is compounded. The process is one of acceleration, aptly illustrated by the propulsion of a rocket (Figure IV-3). In statistical terms, a one per cent annual increase doubles population in 69 years; a three per cent annual increase (of which there are several regions in the Orient) doubles the population in 23 years. In the United States at the present time the natural increase of population (excess of births over deaths) is 1.7 per cent, a high figure for a country of very high living standards.

In Malthus' day, increasing population as a result of increasing birth rates was the primary concern. Today an added acceleratory factor enters into the picture, namely, "death control." This is effected by the application of modern medical science and surgery in keeping alive babies, who would have died in Malthus' day, and in extending the longevity otherwise through the control of con-

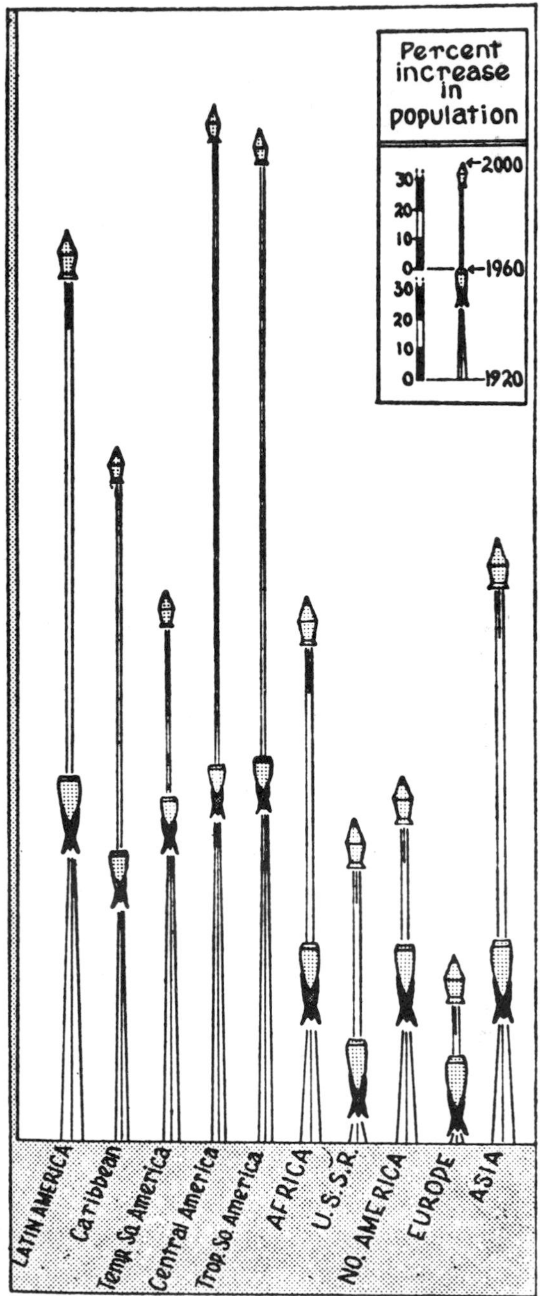

IV:3 Expected percentage increases in regional populations from 1920 to 1960 are shown here, along with increases as projected by the United Nations from 1960. What regions of the world exhibit the greatest acceleration in population increase? What problems are implicit in such regional differential? (From *Population Bulletin*, published by the Population Reference Bureau, Washington, D. C., Vol. XIV, No. 5, August, 1958, used by permission)

tagious, infectious diseases, and of aging processes in general to an age level several decades beyond what it was in pre-Malthusian days. Thus lower death rates combined with higher birth rates, according to demographers, will pose a specially difficult problem for the next two-score years (Figure IV-4).

Another new factor presents itself today. While Malthusians are primarily concerned with survival sustenance with a modicum of happiness, twentieth-century social-economic mores call for "higher standards" of living. Thus it has become the objective of the Population Division of the United Nations social, economic, and health agencies not only to alleviate the sufferings of a people on a near-starvation diet, but also to enhance their total material, medical, and spiritual welfare. This adds then still another variable and indefinite dimension to the world population problem.

Demographic literature has yet to reveal just what "overpopulation" really means. Apparently there is no scientific basis for such a definition inasmuch as it involves values related to "psychic man" as well as values related to "geographic man." Even if we could evolve some formula for an "optimal" geographic adjustment between man and his domain for each region of the world, what is an optimal-sized family in terms of planned parenthood? It is at once clear that we are here faced with incommensurable values. Moreover, the spirit of man lies within the province of the theologian, and not of the geographer. So in this context at least we shall restrict ourselves to the general proposition of examining and evaluating those geographic factors and forces which make for the highest population potential in the foreseeable future consistent with the natural resources and technological advances available to man.

Geographic criteria to appraise population pressure

If all the people in the world were brought together in one place, standing room could be found for them in one of our smaller counties, or even one of our larger townships (approximately 15 miles square). This in itself may sound fantastically incredi-

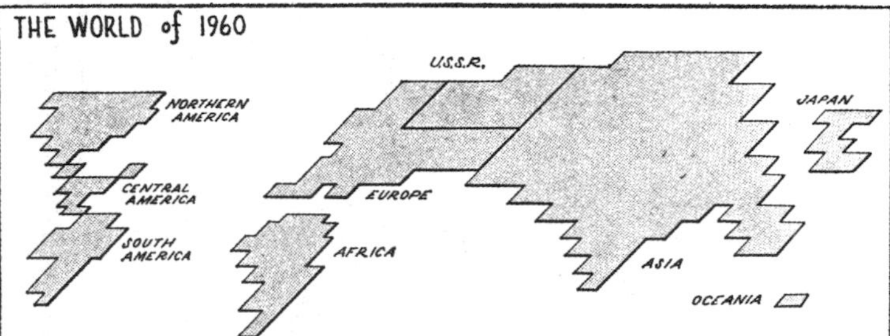

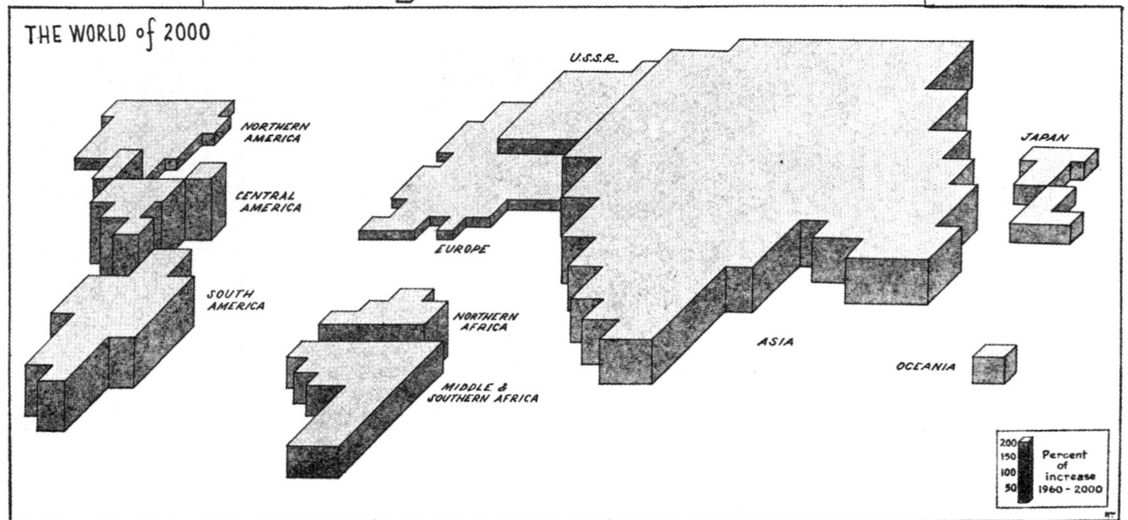

IV: 4 This diagram shows world population distribution as projected from 1960 to 2000. Continental diagrams are drawn proportional to estimated total world population of 6.3 billion by the year 2000. (From *Population Bulletin*, published by the Population Reference Bureau, Washington, D. C., Vol. XV, No. 2, March 1959, used by permission)

ble. Obviously this suggests no concern for overpopulation — or does it? Similarly, the observation that in over one-half of the world the population averages less than one person to four square miles offers no help in understanding the population problem — or does it? Such a figure might be somewhat more meaningful when we equate a square mile into acreage, as is commonly done in the occupance of farm lands. If this were a measure of support, then this would indicate a requirement of 2,560 acres for one individual. Contrast with this the figure of less than three acres per farm family of six in many oriental areas.

But consider still another set of statistics: The populations of the state of Rhode Island and that of Japan average 685 and 622 per square mile respectively. On the face of this simple statistical comparison, Rhode Island should have a population pressure problem more than that of Japan. Such comparisons, however, leave out of account the fact that less than one-sixth of Japan is arable. Moreover, obviously other factors have to be considered as to the relative favorableness or unfavorableness of other resource values that enter into the measurement of the different economies of the two areas. The primary concern of the geographer in dealing with the whole question of world demography, then, is not so much with such academic questions as: How many more people the world can support in view of the possible exploitation of fresh water from the oceans for irrigation; or by the recovery of minerals from the same source for fertilizer material or industrial uses; or by the extension of fisheries, including the recovery of kelps or seaweed for possible human consumption synthetically or otherwise; or by improvement in soil man-

This scene shows settlement and field culture at the foot of Mount Fuji, Japan. Identify all landscape features—natural and cultural—which reveal excessive population pressure in the area. Population density in fertile lowlands, such as shown here on this intermontane topography, may reach more than 3,000 per square mile. Does this picture suggest a predominantly agrarian, commercial, or industrial population, or a combination of these? What evidence is there? (Courtesy Japan Tourist Association)

agement practices extensifying and intensifying land tillage; or by advances in industrial and personal technology which will expand human resources of production and extend transportation; and so forth. Granted that in all these directions phenomenal advances will be made in man's changing processes to enable more people to live on the earth and to live a more abundant life, one can only speculate rather than postulate how such factors are related to potentials of population growth. Beyond all this, the possibility should not be lost sight of, that every technological advancement may also lead to a further upsurge in population expansion. Thus, in the last analysis, we come back to about the same place we started: How many people can the world support comfortably? Or to put it in another form: Is there a geographic population–space optimum of areal living? Absolute density values of themselves are of little or no help in answering these questions.

To be geographically meaningful, then, statistics—whether of demography or other types of data—must be reduced to a spatial-resource base, i.e., they must be "mapped," as emphasized in the preceding chapter. The very term "population" is an areal one, for population means the number of inhabitants within a given area as defined in terms of a survey unit (square mile, or square kilometer), or a politically defined unit such as a town, city, township, county, state, or nation, or of a region as defined by a geographer in a given areal study. "Area" itself to which the number of people is related as an expres-

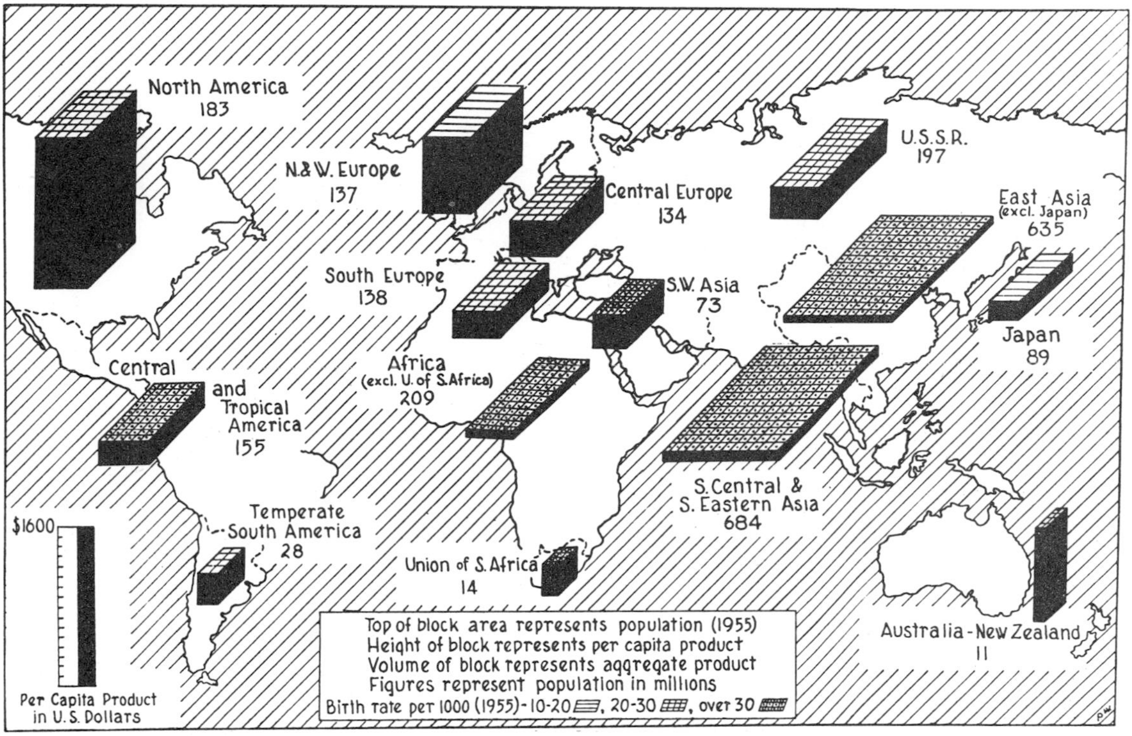

IV:5 The title to this cleverly designed multifunctional diagram in terms of our context might well be, "The Geographic Relationships of Productive Man to Reproductive Man." Actually, it is: Population, Per-Capita Product and Fertility for Major Regions of the World. Study carefully the representation and geographic import of each of the five graphed categories of data. Note, for example, (1) intraregional correlations between low income and high fertility, especially of southeast Asia; (2) interregional comparisons between Asia, Africa, tropical America, northwest Europe, and North America. (From *Population Bulletin*, published by the Population Reference Bureau, Washington, D. C., Vol. XIII ,No. 8, Dec. 1957, P. 146 [modified from *Economic Development: Principles and Patterns*, Prentice-Hall, N. Y., 1954], used by permission)

sion of demographic density is not simply a space abstraction, but implies, as the word "land" always does, a resource value—natural or human. Since, then, neither man nor land geographically have actually any meaning apart from each other, a geographer does not normally attempt to memorize world population statistics per se or land occupance areas per se. Rather, as *the* area specialist, the geographer is trained to analyze population–resource relationships (Figure IV-5). For this purpose he obtains all the demographic data he can relevant to the project or problem he wishes to study. Scores of vital statistics are available for different purposes, but the geographer probably finds the following of primary interest: the rates of birth and death, age composition (which would have a bearing on future rates of reproduction), occupational pursuits, standards of living, educational status, social mores, ethnic and cultural backgrounds, religious affiliation, and the like.

If at all possible the geographer will seek actual distribution pattern data rather than statistical enumeration identified with political or civic divisions. Can you see why? Unfortunately government areal statistics or census enumerations are normally by townships, counties, etc. However, for most regional purposes the plotting of such statistics affords a generalized view of areal variances within regions. For more detailed subregional analysis, the topographic map, which was introduced at the close of the preceding chapter, will aid in relating the relative density of houses (people) to the types of topography with which the varying densities are identified. But, as also pointed out in connection with that map exercise, house distribution densities do not by any means supply all the cultural data we need to know, such as what the quality of population is like. Nor do the "top" sheets provide us with the resource base characteristics other than landform, water resources, and occasionally the type of vegetative cover and locations of such phenomena as local mining and quarrying operations.

Ratio Maps. The one great principle that characterizes all geographic thinking is proportionate or ratio representation of statistical-spatial data. Once we have established the importance of particular relevant data which we think vital to the analysis of the processes by which man has made his particular connections with the environment for better or for worse, it is the geographer's task to select and measure those types of man–land relationships which seemingly best explain how "producer man" is related to "consumer man." And so the geographer asks: What kind of productive square mile are we dealing with? What kind of "productive man" is the statistical inhabitant? Instead, then, of merely being concerned with man–land, he should approach the question of population densities by considering such ratios as: man–arable land; man–total agricultural land; man–total resources (based on all forms of human occupance, e.g., fishing, mining, lumbering, agriculture, industry, commerce, etc.). Ratio area relationships can be most efficiently presented graphically by the "distorted map" (Figure III-1). Area–man evaluation of demographic density is summarily well illustrated on per-capita production and per-capita calorie consumption maps. Thus, the question of whether or not a region or a country is overpopulated can perhaps best be answered by asking the question: Has the region or country areally obtained optimal productivity in terms of the total interplay of natural and human resources? It is in this area, it appears, where lies the greatest challenge to the geographer and other social scientists interested in demographic questions of this character. We shall approach the spatial analysis of this problem in terms of three basic geographic concepts or criteria: (1) space availability, (2) resource capability, and (3) regional appraisal.

Table 4.1 Estimates of Undeveloped Land

1. Food and Agricultural Organization (incomplete)	936,000,000 acres
2. Pearson and Harper	1,070,000,000 acres
3. Robert M. Salter	1,300,000,000 acres
4. O. E. Baker	2,688,000,000 acres
5. Carl Alsberg	2,560,000,000 to 2,880,000,000 acres
6. L. Dudley Stamp	6-7,000,000,000 acres
7. Charles B. Fawcett	7,801,000,000 acres

The criterion of space availability

The geographic facts of the world population–food potential were well presented by Cressey in his address before the Seventeenth International Geographical Congress, Washington, 1952 (9). Utilizing some of the best statistical sources available (e.g., Food and Agricultural Organization yearbooks, United Nations population bulletins, and various individual authoritative publications), Cressey reviewed the classified inventories of geographic factors in terms of present-day major regional variances between production and consumption of food and the estimates of potential land capacity for future population growth. Attention was given to land-use, agricultural limitations, available arable land, and food possibilities. The student is advised to consult this article, if for no other reason than to understand how complex man–resource areal variants are, how little we know of relevant earth data to make dependable geographic regional evaluations of the world population potential, and how a geographer assays what we do know and what we should know concerning the problem. From various sources, Cressey compiled statistics on "Estimates of Undeveloped Land" in the world as indicated in Table 4.1. The student will at once notice the extremes—Fawcett's figure on additional land available for development, for example, being about eight times that given by Pearson and Harper. In view of the varying indexes used by the several authorities in equating man–land potential, it is obvious in the very beginning that we need some standardized methodology as well as better regional inventory of world resources if appraisal of land capacities is to have much meaning. Furthermore, such man–land geographic relationships will have to be reviewed within the framework of each major change in technological development which makes possible both intensification and extensification of land-use.

It should be noted, moreover, that resource inventory is here actually restricted to the land of the earth. Man's habitat with respect to the land has been such a conventional matter that to date little attention has been given to sea resources when discussing the population problem. But with new pressure upon the land, we may rest assured that the term "sea use" may relatively soon enter the geographic vernacular, since already technicians are exploring the "undeveloped" or rather restrictively utilized resources of the water area that comprises two-thirds of the earth—the seas' own indigenous food potential, both animal and vegetable; recovery of various fertilizer minerals; desalinization of sea water for irrigating the many now unproductive drylands that extend from the sea into the interior. Along with these new technological developments, manufacturing is playing an increasing role in food production. The processes of extending them, both land and sea resources, through new factoral utilizations and adaptations of both natural and human resources must be regionally surveyed and measured, and re-surveyed and re-appraised from time to time if we wish to seek a realistic approach to questions that deal with "underpopulation," "overpopulation," "optimal population" of the world, or better, of a region.

Cressey recognizes that "there are few limits to the maximum area which may be cultivated, given labor and capital. . . . The problem of maximum land use is one of agricultural techniques and of economics." However, he is not among geographers and others who are optimistic about widely and richly extending acreages of food production:

¶ There will always be a pioneer fringe, but it seems probable that the major increase of food will come within existing farm areas. . . . The easiest source [for more food] is to increase yields on existing farm land. It is doubtful whether much food can soon or economically come from new land. Agricultural Australia has about reached its limit. Homesteading has essentially ended in the United States. The Peace River Country of Canada offers little more attractive farm land. Siberia has nearly plowed its last virgin prairie. Irrigation projects in the dry parts of the Soviet Union are ambitious but questionable. If the Amazon and Congo or the Arctic have crop potentials of large extent, their exploitation lies well in the future. . . . Until we conquer the arctic and the tropics, it is quite possible that the world is near the peak of total cultivated acreage. We may have already passed it. . . . If added millions are to be fed, the geographer has no new Iowa or Murray Valley or Siberian steppe. The map cannot be stretched much more.[1]

As far as food supplies are concerned for the present century, the author believes that they will be quite adequate, even for the anticipated increases in population; however, there is an important areal problem in that "the areas where production can be increased do not correspond with the present areas of excess people."

As Cressey himself recognizes, many do not agree with this "conservative" view. Recognizing full well that the better lands of the world are already possessed, some of the geographers still see considerable possibilities in the expansion of agriculture of high productivity into areas not now developed. For example, Kimble after noting that "the well-watered pastures of Argentina and Australia have long since been fenced off, and New Zealand, one of the newest of the new countries, seemingly has as many inhabitants as she can readily accommodate," raises the question, "Does this mean that all the good lands have been engrossed, or that, at best, only a few fragments remain? Fortunately, it does not. There are still millions of square miles of potential farm land scattered about the earth."[2]

In another connection, Kimble observes,

¶ Doubtless, white men will continue to reclaim territory in the Tropics with the help of machinery and native labor, and to teach the people of those lands to work more efficiently than at present. As a result, the productivity of these areas

---

1 Cressey, George B., "Land for 2.4 Billion Neighbors," *Economic Geography,* Vol. XXIX, No. 1, January, 1953, p. 7. Reprinted by permission.

2 Kimble, George H. T., *The World's Open Spaces,* Thomas Nelson and Sons, 1939, p. 28. Reprinted by permission.

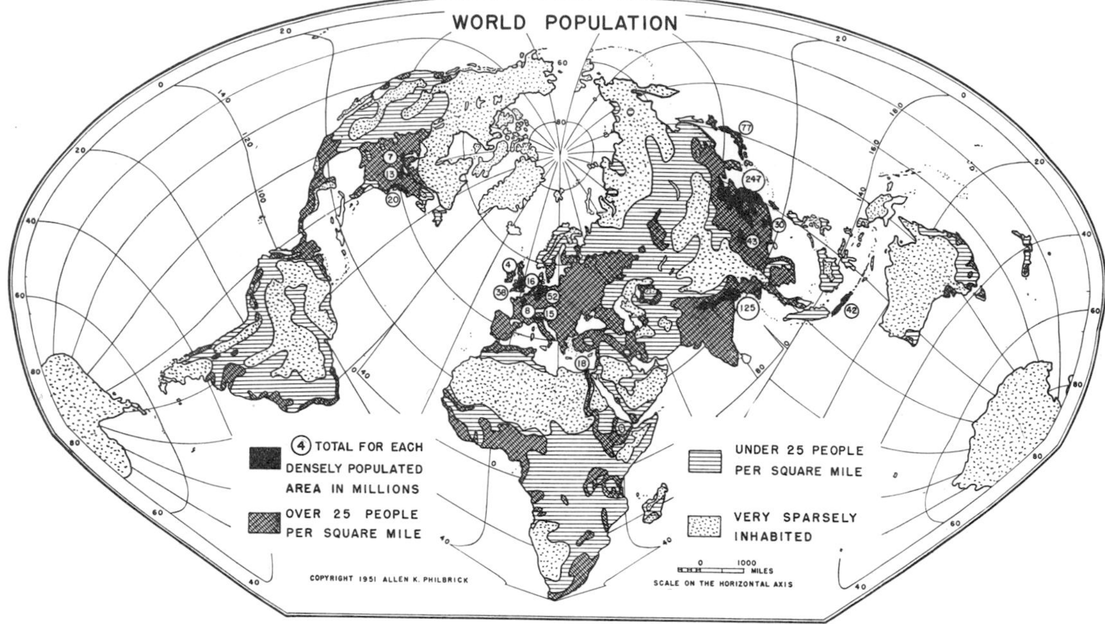

IV:6 Regionalized world population density is shown on this map. A population map—whether of a small locale, a sizeable region, a country, a continent, or of the world—is of premier importance in practically every geographic study. In the last analysis, we want to know where people live and why. Why are there more in some places than in others? Cartographic and other graphic means (such as exemplified in previous "block" diagrams) to express relative densities are almost limitless in design possibilities. The commonplace "dot" distribution map based on an equal-area projection is a very useful expedient to achieve effect of gradational density. On the other hand, where regionalized and simplified patterns of large areas are the chief objectives, the type here presented is effective. (Copyright by Allen K. Philbrick, and published by *Economic Geography*, Vol. XXXIII, No. 4, October 1957, used by permission)

may eventually rival that of the more temperate parts of the world.[1]

But even in these connections, it should be added that the author by no means looks upon the "open spaces" as areas of equal habitability and productivity.

¶ Most of them are essentially marginal zones where there are hazards to face: rain—too much in some cases, too little in others; frost—limiting the range of economic crops and sometimes shrivelling them up; wind—levelling plains and dwellings to the ground; sun—capricious here, scorching there. In other words, there are regions where life is based on slender control of the physical environment.

Criteria of geographic position, resource, and technological capability

As you look at a world population map (Figure IV-6), you will recognize the great disparity in the distribution of mankind. An adequate explanation of the processes which were responsible for the distribution of the several density patterns may be said to be the ultimate goal of geography. In round numbers there are about 3 billion people in the world today, an average of about 55 per square mile, which incidentally is also about the average for the United States. Continent-wise, the density ranges from none in Antarctica to 140 in Europe. Country-wise, we note such disparities as 156 for China, 50 for the United States, 18 for Brazil, 4 for Canada, and 3 for Australia—all countries of approximately the same size. From the view of world power potential, the total population of the United States (approxi-

---

[1] *Ibid.*, p. 82. Reprinted by permission.

mately 180 million) compares quite favorably with the U.S.S.R. (approximately 200 million). However, the density per square mile in the United States is over twice as large as that in the U.S.S.R.

Many complex factors, both historic and geographic, physical as well as cultural, enter into the problem of explaining the disparate ecumene, the unequally inhabited world. Included among the significant genetic factors are the time priority, position, and resource characteristics of place of settlement. Thus, our earliest civilizations are identified with the core ecumene of the Triad continent of Europe, Asia, and Africa—the irrigated Mesopotamian and Nile valleys and the eastern Mediterranean area. Similarly, ancient riverine and alluvial soils in the Ganges and the Brahmaputra of India and the Hwang-Ho and the Sikiang of China attracted at an early date as many as 1,000 persons per square mile. Nearly all these ecumenes are of the agrarian types.

The Industrial Revolution in the eighteenth century in northwest Europe led to a new form of concentration and centralization of settlement of the manufacturing-commercial type. This urban ecumene is centered on what geographers call the world land hemisphere. On the North Sea converged not only the land traffic of Europe but the sea traffic of the world as well. Here today population densities average well over 500 per square mile—England and Wales, 765; Belgium, 751; Netherlands, 819; West Germany, 547; France, 203.

Turning our globe upside down, as it were, or rather looking at the Southern Hemisphere with Australia in the center, we observe that Australia is virtually in the center of the so-called water hemisphere, thus being the most "isolated" of all the continents. Though there are many other factors which must be taken into consideration in explaining the low population of Australia—only 9 million—Australia's geographic position on the globe unquestionably has had much to do with the retarded settlement of the continent.

Another sort of isolation position and its related types of influence, which we may call "continentality" is illustrated by the very low populations of large parts of the heart of Eurasia, inner Africa, and interior South America. Making allowances for other factors to be noted later, Amazonia, for example, over sizable areas is without any population at all, and most of it rates less than 2 persons per square mile. On the other hand, "insularity," under otherwise favorable circumstances, can promote readiness of contact and lead to large populations, as exemplified by Java with some 500 to 1,000 and over per square mile. Contrasted with the commercial accessibility of insular areas are landlocked and mountain-ribbed countries such as Bolivia, which not only are shut off from sea commerce but isolated largely from land-trading countries as well. Thus, the combined upland and inland position in part accounts for a low population of only 8 per square mile.

Population growth and support capacity are not static but change their relative values, as do so many other things, as a result of radical changes in the technology of transportation. Thus, modern air transport as well as the extension of railways and modern highways more and more negates the effects of isolation and insulation processes once so effective in keeping people from emigrating from the areas of the ecumene. It should be noted in this connection that one of the chief causes of human suffering from lack of food —even famines—has been the lack of adequate transportation facilities. Thousands have frequently been reported starving in sections of China and India because of inability to transport food available elsewhere—even in the same country. Such a handicap can, of course, be overcome. Also the entire question of migration of peoples is directly related to the means of circulation. The extension of transport facilities is not only conducive to migration expansion directly, but every new added facility makes possible new frontier resource developments which support trade and to that extent permit population growth of lands hitherto considered unproductive and uninhabitable. With few notable exceptions, low-lying plains skirt most of the coasts of continents with major extensions inland along seas, bays, gulfs, and streams. While again, such low-lying plains and water features promote communicability and accessibility, it is particularly because of the ease with which such land may be occupied and cultivated for food production that they have become the chief nuclei of world population, e.g., the 250 or more per square mile concentrations along the Hwang-Ho, Ganges, Niger, Nile, La Plata, Rhine, and St. Lawrence-Great Lakes.

But now again comparing the density of the population map with the landform map, we observe that, despite the complete explorations now of all continental coastal lands, considerably half of them are nearly uninhabited, and much of the rest rate under 2 per square mile, or otherwise fall in the category between 2 and 25, despite the fact, that by far most of these lands lie within 500 feet above sea level and hence invite both accessibility and communicability. Thus the geography student looks to other map data of regions for evidence of apparent inhospitability of such lands. Turning now to the world climates map he will observe the following co-varying features: In Australia, Arabia, Iran, North Africa, southwest Africa, southwest South America, and southwest North America, drylands and even desert features occur on coasts as well as in the interior. It is obvious also that in the sub-Arctic and far Arctic North where during the warmest month the temperature does not rise above 50°F., plains provide no favorable habitat for vegetation, animal, or man. Similarly, the expansiveness of the plains regions of Canada and Siberia with only two to four months growing season have so far on the whole not been able to attract more than one or two persons per square mile, or along the more favorable lines of river or road communications some five to ten; in most favorable spots perhaps a score.

Moreover, some plains regions in low latitudes have not so far attracted heavy white populations, as illustrated in the big Amazonia region of South America or the Congo in Africa. There the dense rainforests together with high humidity have combined to repel rather than attract white man settlement.

Mountain ranges often rising only within a few miles from coastal plains areas, such as the North American coastal ranges and South American Andes have, because of the steepness of slope and high elevations, frustrated areal man in both circulation and settlement. Only in humid tropical regions will man normally seek out the more elevated areas and thus sacrifice some convenience of arability for the greater comforts of mountain-plateau living conditions. So far, our small-scale world maps have sufficed for discerning broad positive or negative correlations between population density and land quality. Basic as such broad world generalization pattern considerations are in helping to explain how the ecumene came about and what this may signify in analyzing future expansions of populations, the student should realize that this constitutes only a start in population–land resource analysis. And so he must look to other geographic factors, both natural and cultural, for further clues of co-varying areal data which help to explain why people are attracted by some areas and repelled by others. For one thing, he will turn to larger-scale maps capable of portraying diversity of soil types, varying degrees of slope, and fertility; maps which reveal not only local surface water supply but underground water supplies as well; maps which spot mineral resources; and maps which show every form of present-day land utilization.

Useful also in world demographic studies is the comparison of population density distribution with the major classes of human occupance forms (Figure IV-7). If not directly indicating land capability in terms of supporting a certain number of people, such a map does suggest the relative intensity of use of land and thus may indicate a correlative index of the number of people the land is capable of supporting under present conditions of culture. Thus primitive hunting and fishing areas are identified with the most sparsely populated areas; next come usually grazing areas; next farming areas; finally industrial and commercial areas.

An attempt at resource adequacy measurement. Sound as the co-varying analysis of population–resource potential of areas may seem, exact techniques of applying the theory to practice and evaluating a specific regional situation are still wanting. However, one of the professional geographers, Edward Ackerman, has indicated an approach to the problem. Ackerman recognizes, first of all, the need of reducing co-variants to a working number of variables which can then be equated in terms of consumption and production of resources—a "demand" side and "supply" side to form an equation. "On the demand side are population numbers and standards of living; on the supply side, all

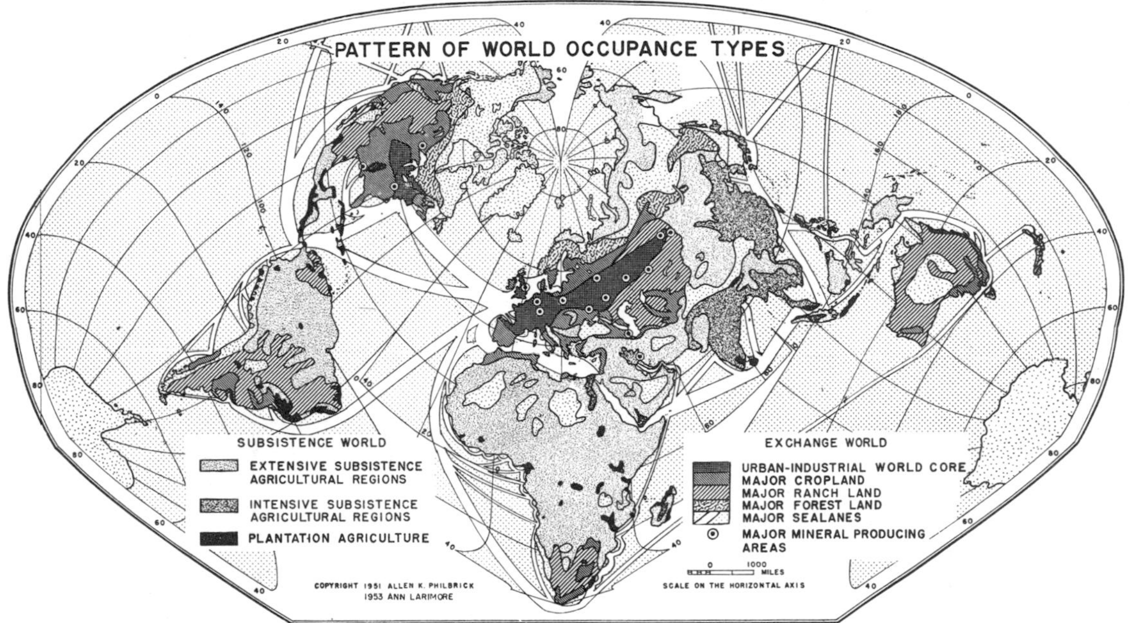

IV:7 If we wish to know why such divergences of population densities exist in the world, as are shown on the previous map, then many other maps showing regionalized distribution of natural and cultural phenomena need to be made and studied. Again, reduced to simple terms a world occupance map of the type here shown is highly useful. Compare, for example, the areas of "extensive subsistence" on this map with the corresponding areas of population density shown on the previous map. Similarly, the population density pattern with "intensive agriculture" or major industrial regions. (Copyright by Allen K. Philbrick, and published by *Economic Geography*, Vol. XXXIII, No. 4 October, 1957, used by permission)

the attributes of resources and all the attributes of culture except for standard of living. The equation might be written:

$$PS = RQ\ (T\ A\ S_t) + E_s + T_r \pm F - W,$$

or

$$P = \frac{RQ\ (T\ A\ S_t) + E_s + T_r \pm F - W}{S},$$

where the symbols have these meanings:

- P numbers of people
- S standard of living
- R amount of resources
- Q factor for natural quality of resources
- T physical technology factor
- A administrative techniques factor
- S_t resource stability factor
- W frugality element (wastage, or intensity of use)
- F institutional advantage and "friction" loss element consequent upon institutional characteristics of the society
- E_s scale economies element (size of territory, etc.)
- T_r resources added in trade"[1]

It appears that this "formula" is offered more as a basis for clarifying our area relationships of demographic factors than to offer precise mathematical calculation of land or resource capability of supporting a specific population. As Dr. Ackerman himself points out: "To most of the elements in this equation one cannot presently attach specific, accurate value in any population study. Nonetheless, the general composition of the relation involved in the resource-adequacy question would seem to be described in the equation."[2]

---

[1] Ackerman, Edward A., "Population and Natural Resources," *The Study of Population*, Hauser, P. M., and Duncan, O. D. (Editors), University of Chicago Press, Chicago, 1959, p. 622. Copyright 1955 by The University of Chicago.

[2] *Ibid.* Reprinted by permission.

Then the author proceeds in the same article to analyze the steps in measuring the role that the component parts of this generalized equation play in a regional study of resource adequacy. After recognizing the possibility and limitations of this type of population-resource relationship, the author proceeds to show how technology further complicates such analysis. Since region-wise we lack sufficient data and attention to this problem, only a broad, world-generalized perspective can be realized at this moment. Thus the author gives us a world regional perspective of the relative population-resource values in relation to advanced and retarded technological developments. Summary evaluations of the five types are reproduced in Table 4.2.

Regional case study in population potential appraisal

It should be apparent by now that any intelligent grasp of population phenomena, whether considered a world problem or not, must be spatially oriented in terms of natural and human resources. And, as with all other world problems, we can best assay the geographic causes and consequences of population pressure when we consider them in a regional context. Thus in Part IV of this textbook, population characteristics and settlement processes form an integral study of each of the climatic realms of the world. A brief preview of one of these, the "controversial" Northlands of Canada and Eurasia, will serve to illustrate some of the basic population principles here expounded and prepare the student to envision in general terms the kind of population-resource-technological analysis the geographer is interested in making.

The Northlands. Both scientific geographic evaluations as well as popular concepts reflect a highly controversial status of the Northlands in economic and demographic potential. However, geographic literature is in general agreement on the geographic forces which have been largely responsible in the past for the retarded penetration of these lands, whose subarctic latitude is identified by marginal agricultural and other resource challenges. Likewise, geographers, along with other social scientists, are in general agreement on the social policies and technological procedures essential toward effecting extensive settlement and effective occupance of this realm.

1. The extractive industries. Exploitation of animal, timber, and mineral resources exercises a dominant role in the economy of the Northlands. In the northernmost and interior sections hunting, trapping, and fishing are generally predominant, with fur as the chief resource. In the southern and coastal parts of the realm the marketing of lumber may spectacularly compete some day with that of the neighboring lands on the southern border. Still uncertain is the relative regional mineral potential, but accelerated prospecting in the last twenty-five years as a result of improved exploratory techniques and transportation reveals many promising productive fields, especially of the fuel minerals, which by themselves may play a major role in the settlement of areas hitherto entirely unoccupied. Important as are the extractive industries, they are not conducive, however, to rapid growth or permanence of settlement, nor do they support dense populations. Therefore, here as elsewhere, stability of settlement and population growth must seek an agricultural, industrial, or commercial base. And in the case of pioneering settlement of a region, agricultural and other pursuits must be realistically dealt with.

The agricultural patterns may be broadly classified into two types: (1) isolated community occupance, perhaps far in the interior, based largely upon some combination of favorable topographic and soil conditions; (2) a gradual "northening" advance into the frontier roughly paralleling the isotherm of the growing season to which commercial as well as subsistence farming may be reasonably well adapted.[1] However striking it may be to the reader that certain vegetables have been very successfully cultivated in gardens within the Arctic Circle based in large measure on the long summer day and highly selective local combination of environmental conditions, spotty and exotic productions cannot ensure and sustain settlements. How-

[1] Such advance must never be thought of, however, as a continuous frontal movement, for agricultural productivity depends also upon factors other than isothermal limitations. It may surprise us, then, to note the observation on Canada by Putnam, a leading Canadian authority: "Canada is a large country, but the area which is suitable for agriculture is surprisingly small. In every province save one, and it the smallest, the nonagricultural land is greater than the present potential farm land" (12).

Table 4.2 Trends affecting resource adequacy in five type areas of the world

Type	*Application of Technology*	*Land Productivity*	*Mineral Productivity*	*Standard of Living*	*Numbers of People*	*Pressure for Use of Foreign Resources*	*Summary Characteristics*
1. United States . . .	U+	U+	U	U+	U	U	Little resource limitation on numbers, some on standard of living; economically strong competition for product of foreign resources
2. European	U+	U–	D	U–	U–	U+	Strong pressure for attachment to foreign resources; where frustrated, crisis possible
3. Brazil	U	U+	U+	U	U+	N	Little resource limitation on numbers; domestic orientation
4. China	U	U	U	U–	U	U	Continued consciousness of impending crisis; increasing pressure for attachment to foreign resources
5. Arctic-desert	U	N	U+	N	N	N	Development by type 1, 2, 4 countries inevitable; strong competition for resources; however, few people

U+ strong upward trend
U, U– } upward trend
D downward trend
N very little or very few

ever, one of the most remarkable phenomena of agricultural geography has been the adaptation in recent years of shorter-season maturing crops, particularly the grains, which made possible pushing the agricultural frontier northwards in some places to as high as the 55°-60° latitude (Figures XXVII-1, XXVII-2). And Canadian and Soviet scientists have recently established institutes to deal with the muskeg problem by determining various commercial uses of muskeg sphagnum. At the same time its exploitation extends the acreage of arable lands, since it has been discovered that the removal of the surface muskeg material and subsequent cultivation of the soil corrects, in part at least, the permafrost problem.

Though still constituting a leading industry of the North American Northland, hunting and trapping as an economic activity is said to have passed its peak. Mink, fox, and muskrat fur-farming has supplanted, in a number of regions, the old-time traditional trapping, and is a form of exploitation which has great extension possibilities. At the present, its highest concentration is on the islands in the Gulf of St. Lawrence where the Newfoundland fisheries provide ample and cheap fish refuse food for the animals as well as ready and cheap transportation of pelts to the leading fur markets of the world, namely, northeastern United States and western Europe. The large inland lakes and the numerous linking rivers readily lend themselves to increased stocking of lake trout, whitefish, and various kinds of game fish, and this, together with other wildlife conservation measures, presages a bright future for the recreation industry.

The timber resources of Canada primarily await better transportation facilities, though it must always be kept in mind that the

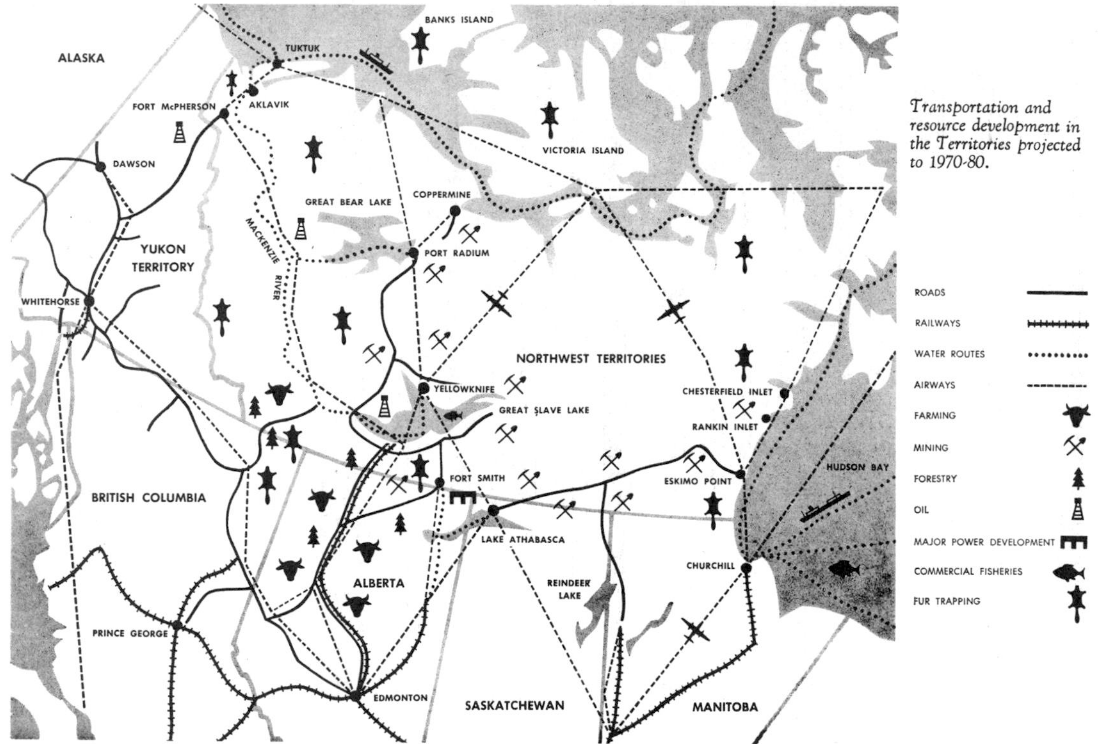

IV:8 Geography is dynamic. Therefore landscapes must be studied with a view of changes—past, present, future. Working in conjunction with other scientists, the geographer's task in part is to appraise the trend of changes in the population patterns and human occupance forms of regions. Here this is done cartographically by R. G. Robertson in illustrating his article "Promise of the Canadian North." What kinds of data seem most useful to a geographer in projecting landscape changes such as is done here? (From *The Beaver,* Hudson's Bay Company, Hudson's Bay House, Winnipeg, Canada, Autumn, 1958, used by permission)

further north we go, the longer become the periods of restocking. The enormous demands for wood pulp for uses in newsprint, shipping cartons, and innumerable other items have made great demands on small pulpwood timber, a type of resource which fits well into the short-season timber growth in the Northlands. But the northernmost taiga must heavily rely in the future on the mineral potential. Thus Keenleyside maintains that:

¶ . . . the real development of the North would depend upon the discovery and development of mineral resources. The Yukon, having lain quiescent for nearly two generations, is experiencing a revival of mining. With cheap power in prospect and easier means of access being developed, the Trail of '98 may again become a road to achievement. Yellowknife, the most exciting town on the continent, is only awaiting the return of a reasonable price for gold as compared with other commodities, or a reduction of the cost of transportation, to develop into a city of considerable size. On the Labrador Boundary there are iron deposits of exceptional quality and of an extent that must be measured in scores of miles. $200,000,000 is to be spent on their exploitation. Base metals on the shores of Great Slave Lake, copper in many places throughout the Territories, oil in the Mackenzie Valley, all give promise of permanent development. Most significant of all are the established radium and uranium deposits at Great Bear Lake, deposits which alone would have made Canada one of the most important countries in the new atomic age.[1]

[1] Keenleyside, H. L., *Canadian Geographical Journal,* Vol. XXXIX, No. 4, October, 1949, pp. 165-167. Reprinted by permission.

The site and situation relationships of the various primary resources and transportation facilities of the least developed section of Canada are well shown in Figure IV-8. In the source from which this figure is taken, Robertson also points to one of the most distinctive personality traits coherent with the type of environment we find in the northlands:

¶ Canada's deep north may prove to be one of the first spots on the face of this earth where the color line is really dropped. . . . Today, throughout northern Canada, communities are growing up—the new Aklavik and Frobisher Bay are prime examples—where Indians and Eskimos, white people, and men and women of mixed blood are living side by side in the same type of house, with their children playing together and going to the same school. And we can increasingly look to the future in which . . . all the countless tasks that make life meaningful and productive will be carried on by individuals who do not inquire whether the man above, below, or alongside him is an Indian or an Eskimo or a white.[1]

2. *Transportation, the key factor in Subarctic development and defense.* It will have been noted repeatedly that transportation is by all odds the chief conditional factor for resource development of any region in the sub-Arctic. Starting with water transportation, we are reminded by Robinson that:

¶ The exciting optimism of the present air age regarding the Northern air routes across the "top of the world" is apt to make one overlook the fact that Northern Canada has two fine navigable water systems, the Mackenzie and Yukon, which have been carrying freight and supplies and opening up the country for over a century. Although new air and land routes will undoubtedly do much to facilitate development in Canada's Northwest, the bulk of heavy imports has always been most economically carried by water transports when available.

Both the Mackenzie and Yukon Rivers are broad and long and rank with the ten greatest river systems in the world. . . . The Mackenzie River system is exceeded in length and drainage area only by the Mississippi-Missouri systems of central United States. . . . For more than 150 years the Mackenzie River and its tributaries have been carrying the traffic of the fur trade, and also, in recent years, that associated with mining and other developments in the Mackenzie district. In the Yukon the story of transportation is inevitably linked with the historic Klondike strike and the gold mining industry of the Territory.[2]

Stimulated by the accelerated national defense program, both highway and railway construction projects are in progress or definitely contemplated. Thus,

¶ Work has already been started by the Department of Northern Affairs and National Resources on major road construction projects in the Yukon and Northwest Territories, involving over 1,200 miles of roads and six major bridges at an estimated cost of over $31,000,000. . . . In the Northwest Territories, the major road project is the 550-mile Great Slave-Great Bear road to provide all-year communication with Yellowknife and to assist exploration and development in the richly mineralized areas lying between Great Slave and Great Bear Lakes. . . . At present the Federal Government and Canadian National and Canadian Pacific railways are studying the possibility of construction of a railway line to Great Slave Lake to tap the very large mineral ore bodies now known to exist in that part of the Northwest Territories bordering on the Province of Alberta.[3]

The belatedness of highway and railway construction in these parts obviously reflects the enormous costs involved in combating permafrost, muskegs, and other adverse hydrographic features. But it is recognized, in the Eurasian as well as the North American divisions of the sub-Arctic, that an extension of spurs of railway lines northward from East-West Trans-Siberian and from the transcontinental Canadian Railway is a prerequisite to a stable settlement and economy. In the Soviet Union, several such trunk lines already reach the open, warm waters of the Scandinavian–Kola Peninsula area; another

[1] Robertson, R. G., "The Promise of the Canadian North," *The Beaver*, Hudson's Bay Company, Winnipeg, August, 1958, p. 5. Reprinted by permission.

[2] Robinson, J. L., "Water Transportation in the Canadian Northwest," *Canadian Geographical Journal*, Vol. XXXI, November, 1945, p. 237. Reprinted by permission.

[3] Van Allen, W. H., "Transportation North of Sixty," *Canadian Geographical Journal*, Vol. LVII, No. 3, September, 1958, pp. 114-115. Reprinted by permission.

major spur projects northeastward to the mouth of the Ob River. In North America, we have a similar railway line linking Winnipeg to the grain exporting port of Churchill on the west side of Hudson Bay, and in Alaska the rail connections from Seward and Anchorage to interior Fairbanks in central Alaska. General review of the transportation literature indicates that the numerous road-building projects, both as highways and railways, have reached the blueprint stage in both Siberia and Canada. At present, these primarily involve consideration of various resource studies now being made on the prospective relative productivity of the different regions.

It would appear that a decided improvement of land transportation facilities is also a prime prerequisite toward combating the psychological factor of isolation and frustration incident to the solitary wilderness life. It has been discovered that even the most adventurous pioneers in time look for a minimum of social amenities, and in small frontier communities such can ordinarily not be supplied. Accordingly, for the more "sophisticated," communication and circulation, in a moderate measure at least, must be provided within the better settled areas if the "outpost" frontier settlements are to survive.

A major transportation transition of incalculable future results is developing in maritime Siberian Arctic. Soviet icebreakers can now maintain an open sea passage, if necessary, along the entire coast. Similar prospects are being entertained in the opening up of Canadian Arctic coastlines to navigation, in the relatively near future, by the possible operation of nuclear-operated icebreakers.

The inherent handicaps of land-sea transportation, despite modern technology, are reflected in the extraordinary sub-Arctic development of air transportation. In no other realm do aircraft seem to play such a major role for local interior or for long distance traffic, for passenger or for light freight, or even for heavy cargoes as in the case of exporting strategic minerals previously indicated. This is even true now also of the northern sections of the more southerly provinces of Canada. "It is not generally realized that in Canada there are nearly 120 airports, water ports, and landing strips in that area of Canada lying north of the sixtieth parallel. Of these, one-third are located north of the Arctic Circle" (16). In Alaska, transport by plane of both man and freight is reported as having attained the highest per capita figure in the world, a factor significant even in considering the very low population.

The above regional inventory and evaluations of geographic phenomena are neither definitive nor complete. But they do suggest the type of research that must be done—on a more intensive and extensive scale—for each world realm to appreciate any phase of demographic study, particularly where there is an "underpopulated" or an "overpopulated" region.

Summary observations on man as a geographic phenomenon

The density and distribution of people in the world, geographically assayed against global resource sustenance, have been of universal concern in time and space. Accordingly, demographic studies are of interdisciplinary concern, related as they are to all aspects of social, economic, political, and religious institutions of man. Each specialist, then, in the several subjects of the humanities, the social sciences, and the natural sciences has his own distinctive contribution to make to the understanding of the philosophical and practical implications of man's destiny to occupy the earth "fruitfully" as procreator, producer, and provider. These academic challenges pose many questions, such as: What are man's responsibilities in these several stewardship commitments? How is each to be evaluated over against the others? When do we attain the total "optimal" regional balance between food production and food consumption? What ideological, spiritual, and technological principles are paramount to ensure the proper diffusion of food from areas of waste to areas of want? And what have all these questions to do with the so-called world "population explosion" problem? Ultimately, which agency is best prepared to co-ordinate attempts in dealing with this problem?

If one learns anything from demographic literature, such as here referred to, it is that we cannot hope fully to understand the interrelated psychological and environmental complex questions such as the above involve. But an academic pursuit of the subject can and should be made by all agencies—church, government, science—to explore all conscionable and constructive means to attain a spiritual and material standard of living the world over befitting the dignity of man. Where does the geographer come into the picture?

In this section, we have tried to explore the problem and its partial solution in the perspective of space, resource, and region—the cardinal points of the geographic compass: (1) The geographer wants to know, first of all, where the people of the world live? We still do not have accurate population maps (present ones contain many "voids"). (2) Then we want to know why we have the various ecumene (ordinary population maps simply show statistical spread—so many dots, so many people). (3) Next, we must know the nature of the ecesis: What field evidence points to accordant and discordant man–land relationships? Do the geographic processes of life reflect wise adjustments? (4) Since we cannot assay the entire world at one time, what shall be the regional basis for areal resource analysis? (5) By what criteria and formula are we to weigh the different variables in such spatial analysis?

In sum, it is clear that what is needed above all is a systematic world survey of natural and human resources from which data maps can be made of the "geographical relationship" type. In a word, we need to understand better "geographic man," before we can intelligently talk about world population (or any regional population) and its significance in our world society and economy. The International Geographical Union would seem to be best equipped to project the global one-scale inventory mapping task. It, too, with the assistance of the various national geographic societies, might arrange for some uniform procedure and formulae for composing "ratio" maps revealing regional differentiations in present man–land productivity and future potential capability. Such findings then could very well be used by such an agency as the Economic and Social Council of the United Nations, working in conjunction with the International Geographical Union, in effectuating policies which will equate world potential food production and diffusion with world population potential.

APPLICATION OF GEOGRAPHIC UNDERSTANDING

Write a brief essay on a population problem of a selected region of the world, employing the concepts, principles, techniques, and terminology that a geographer uses, as illustrated in Part I of this text. Then construct one or two maps to illustrate the basic problem, featuring the core environmental elements involved in an intelligent attack on the problem. Review particularly the chapter on cartography, Chapter 3.

References

1 Trewartha, Glenn T., "A Case for Population Geography," *Annals of the Association of American Geographers,* Vol. XLIII, No. 2, June, 1953, p. 81.

2 *Population Bulletin,* published by the Population Reference Bureau, Washington 5, D. C., Vol. XIII, No. 1, February, 1957, p. 14.

3 "The New Awakening," *Population Bulletin,* Vol. XV, No. 8, December, 1959, p. 138.

4 "Population in the United Nations," *Population Bulletin,* Vol. XI, No. 7, November, 1955, p. 95.

5 Preliminary Reports, 1960 Census of Population, U. S. Department of Commerce, August-September, 1960.

6 Phillips, Ralph W., "How Adequate Is the World's Food Supply?" *The Scientific Monthly,* Vol. LXXXV, No. 5, November, 1957, pp. 265-266.

7 Malthus, The Reverend Thomas R., *An Essay on the Principle of Population, or a View of its Past and Present Effects on Human Happiness,* Ward, Lock and Co. Limited, 1890, pp. 2-6, *passim,* 7, 454.

8 DeCastro, Josué de, *The Geography of Hunger,* Little, Brown & Co., Boston, 1952, p. 25.

9 Cressey, George B., "Land for 2.4 Billion Neighbors," *Economic Geography,* Vol. XXIX, No. 1, January, 1953, pp. 1-9, *passim.*

10 Kimble, George H. T., *The World's Open Spaces,* Thomas Nelson and Sons, 1939, pp. 28, 82.

11 Ackerman, Edward A., "Population and Natural Resources," *The Study of Population,* Hauser, P. M., and Duncan, O. D. (Editors), University of Chicago Press, Chicago, 1959, p. 622.

12 Putnam, Donald, Editor, "Canadian Production," *Canadian Regions,* J. M. Dent & Sons (Canada) Ltd., Toronto, 1952, p. 510.

13 Keenleyside, H. L., *Canadian Geographical Journal,* Vol. XXXIX, October, 1949, pp. 165-167.

14 Robertson, R. G., "The Promise of the Canadian North," *The Beaver,* Hudson's Bay Company, August, 1958, p. 5.

15 Robinson, J. L., "Water Transportation in the Canadian Northwest," *Canadian Geographical Journal,* Vol. XXXI, November, 1945, p. 237.

16 Van Allen, W. H., "Transportation North of Sixty," *Canadian Geographical Journal,* Vol. LVII, No. 3, September, 1958, pp. 113, 114-115.

Part II

Man's planetary domain

If man is to exercise intelligent and dedicated dominion over the earth, as expounded in Part I, then he must learn to live in harmony with the milieu of which he and his fellow men are an integral part. First of all, this calls for a knowledge of the physical and biological components of earth structure, broadly categorized in the figure at the lower right. But despite their intrinsic indispensability, even the most thorough mastery of earth elements *per se* does not constitute "geographic" understanding. Geographic instruction and understanding, as emphasized in the conclusion of each chapter of our book, ensue only when concepts and principles are formulated that relate these elements to the *ecumene* — man's habitation and the man-created occupance patterns.

Central to the organization of this line of thought then, as indicated in the core of the diagram, is that here in Part II we treat *earth elements* as *regional resources.* And so, in successive chapters, man's global relations are viewed with a focus on climate and culture, landform and land-use, soils and their relation to the nation's economy, inland waters and their impact on man, man's habitat as affected by vegetal and animal life; and minerals as strategic resources.

Elemental classified man–land relationships such as these, it must be conceded, are made in the interest of simplicity but not without the acknowledged risk of oversimplifying regional rationale, necessarily based as it is not on one, nor even several, but all existing natural and cultural phenomena interrelated. Keeping this reservation in the forefront of our minds as we deal with the separate elemental focus in each chapter, we learn the lesson that each earth element, despite its operation in unison with all the others, has its own role to play in setting the stage for life's complex drama.

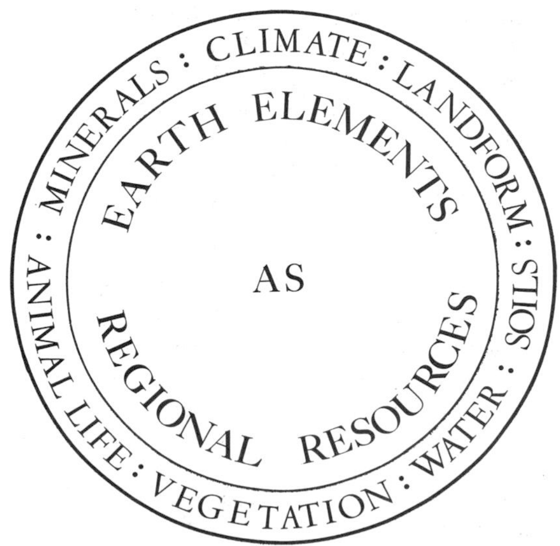

Chapter 5

Man's global relations

It is rather embarrassing for the geographer to admit that he does not know precisely the size, shape, or weight of the object he must describe. When one bears in mind, however, that the object is the earth, the geographer's difficulty may be appreciated. For, after all, our planet is a very large object and the systematic, scientific study of its features and processes dates back only a little more than a century and a half.

At a very early date, Greek philosophers, proceeding from the argument that the circle is the perfect geometrical form, concluded that the world is round. Pythagoras (*ca.* 500 B.C.) developed this idea further. He postulated a universe made up of layers, like an onion. Pythagoras had discovered that music is a form of applied mathematics, and he suggested that as the earth and other heavenly bodies revolved about each other they produced harmonies, "the music of the spheres." Three hundred years later, Eratosthenes estimated that the circumference of the earth was 25,000 miles.

In the second century after Christ, the great Claudius Ptolemy of Alexandria wrote a famous geography which incorporated all of the generally accepted Greek ideas of the form and size of the world. Among these ideas was the mistaken notion that the earth is the center of the universe. This Ptolemaic concept of the universe went unchallenged for more than 1200 years, until Nicolaus Copernicus (1473-1543) of Poland suggested that the earth was just another planet revolving around the sun. This idea was taken up by the Italian philosopher Giordano Bruno (1548?-1600) who insisted that our whole solar system was only a very small part of the universe. For teaching this so-called heretical notion, Bruno was burned at the stake. However, a contemporary of Bruno's, Galileo Galilei (1564-1642), found new evidence to support the Copernican theory. Galileo built the first astronomical telescope. With it he became the first man to see the moon as it really is. From his observations he concluded that Copernicus had been right: the earth does move around the sun. Threatened with the same fate that Bruno had suffered, Galileo recanted his theories, although he adhered to his observation that "it [the earth] does move!"

Today, the Copernican theory is universally accepted. We know that our earth is only one planet (and a rather small one at that) in one of the smaller solar systems in one of the smaller galaxies of the universe. We know also that, by the laws of probability, there could be thousands of worlds like our own, blanketed in atmosphere and capable of supporting intelligent life. But so far as our direct observation is concerned, our world is unique. Whatever the probabilities may be, we know of no other planet in the vastnesses of the universe which supports any form of life that is capable of examining, understanding, and appreciating itself and its environment. This uniqueness of our planet, along with other considerations, prompted the nineteeth-century geographer, Carl Ritter, to "ask the earth for its answers" as to the nature, purpose, and destiny of man. In the process, he built a framework for the scientific study of geography.

A sphere with middle-age spread

For all practical purposes a twelve-inch desk globe represents the shape of the earth and the configuration of its surface. Actually, the equatorial diameter of the earth is twenty-seven miles greater than its axial diameter. This difference, however, is so slight that it cannot be shown to accurate scale on any globe. This is true also of surface differences. Mount Everest, the highest mountain on earth, rises only 29,028 feet above sea level. The Swire Deep, east of the Philippines, the deepest place yet sounded, is only 34,218 feet deep. If one were to attempt to show these extreme differences to scale on a twelve-inch globe, the resulting globe would be as smooth as a highly polished ball bearing. It is important to remember, however, that the earth is not a true sphere. It is a sphere in the very earliest stages of becoming a disc. Properly speaking, the form of the earth is that of an oblate spheroid or ellipsoid; that is, a spherical body bulged at its

Equator and foreshortened along its axis. The bulge is the result of the spin or rotation of the earth.

Few today doubt the sphericity of the earth. However, until the Renaissance, intelligent men had good reason to doubt that the earth was anything but what it appeared to be: a flat surface enclosed by the vault of the heavens. It is therefore all the more remarkable that the ancient Greeks already had concluded that the earth was a sphere. In fact, three of the classic proofs that are offered in modern textbooks for the sphericity of the earth were first stated by Aristotle:

1. The tendency of matter to fall toward a common center.
2. The circular shape of the shadow which appears on the moon during an eclipse.
3. The constant shifting of the horizon and the appearance of new stars as one travels from north to south.

Later, three strong lines of proof were added to Aristotle's three:

1. The fact that the weight of any given body is very nearly the same everywhere on earth, indicating that at every point on the surface of the earth the body is approximately the same distance from the earth's center.
2. The fact that, as ships at sea pass over the horizon, the tips of their masts disappear from view last, rather than their bodies.
3. The fact that ships which have circumnavigated the earth (and there have been many such voyages in the past four hundred years) report an essentially uniform length of voyage.

In the past decade or so, we have been able to add still another proof of the sphericity of the earth. Photographs taken at very high altitudes depict, beyond all doubt, the curvature of the earth. To this proof we may hope, within the next generation, to add the ultimate proof: a photograph of the earth taken from the moon or another planet.

The need for more precise measurements. One of the chief purposes of the 1957 International Geophysical Year was to remeasure the earth. For most purposes, the measurements found in standard reference works are perfectly adequate. But as man's science becomes more sophisticated, precise measurements of distance and area become absolutely essential. To take just one example, the value of unmanned intercontinental vehicles and missiles depends very largely upon our ability to set them down on very narrowly defined targets several thousand miles from their launching points. Before we can do this, we must know the size of the earth even more precisely than we do now.

Subject to whatever corrections may be made necessary as data from the Geophysical Year studies become available, the critical dimensions of the earth are as follows.

Equatorial Diameter	7,926.68 mi.
Axial Diameter	7,899.98 mi.
Equatorial Circumference	24,902.39 mi.
Meridional Circumference	24,860.49 mi.
Area	196,950,284 sq. mi.
	of which three-fourths are water.

An indication of the kind of correction that may be necessary in these figures is provided by the report of results of a computation by the United States Army Map Service in 1956. This report suggests that the actual equatorial diameter of the earth is approximately 840 feet short of the figure which had been accepted up until that time.

The weight that Atlas carried. The earth is composed of a great variety of materials, all of which have different densities. In general, the lightest materials seem to lie at or near the surface, while the heaviest materials seem to be collected in the core of the earth. The average density of the materials of the earth has been deduced by comparing its gravitational attraction on a small sphere at the surface with that of a large sphere of known mass upon the same small sphere. The weight of the earth, according to this experiment, is 5.52 times as great as that of a body of water equal to the earth in volume. Since the average density of the surface rocks is only 2.7, and assuming that the weight of the materials of the earth increases at a uniform rate toward its core, the materials at the core would have a density of 11.0. The gross weight of the earth is estimated to be approximately 6,594,000,000,000,000,000,000 short tons.

How earth movements affect man's life

A rather impressive body of evidence suggests that the various heavenly bodies are rushing away from each other and from some

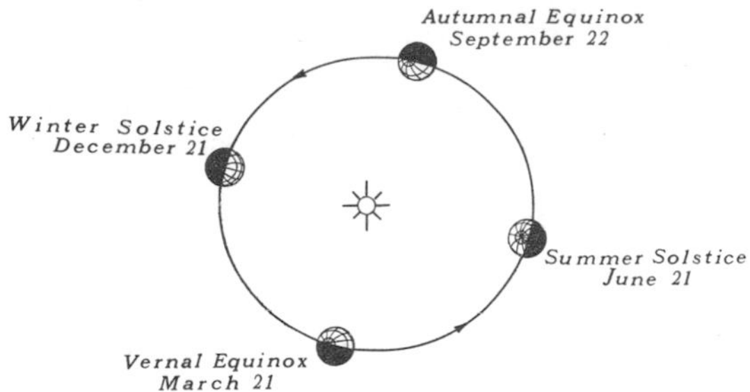

V:1 The change of seasons as a reflection of earth-sun relationships is shown here. (From a drawing by Marie Bohrn in *Fundamentals of Earth Science,* by Henry Dewey Thompson. Second edition, copyright © 1960, Appleton-Century-Crofts, Inc. Reproduced by permission.

common center. Our sun, as it continues to fly outward from this center, carries its satellites, including our earth, with it. And so, however sedentary our lives may otherwise be, we find ourselves riding outward toward the margins of the universe at a speed of about 43,000 miles per hour.

Seasons and the year. This trip is not, however, a straight-line journey. As the earth moves outward through space it also moves in an elliptical orbit about the sun at an average speed of 68,000 miles per hour. The orbit is an eccentric one so that the earth is nearest the sun (91,500,000 miles; at perihelion) on January 8 and farthest from the sun (94,500,000 miles; at aphelion) on July 8. The entire journey around the sun takes 365 days, 6 hours, 9 minutes, and 9.54 seconds. This interval of time is called a sidereal year.

If the earth stood erect upon its axis in its passage around the sun, days and nights would be of the same length all over the world; the amount of radiant energy received from the sun would be more nearly the same in all parts of the world; and there would be little or no distinct seasonality. The earth does not, however, stand erect upon its axis. Instead, it is tilted almost 23½° toward the ecliptic, the plane which is bounded by the earth's orbit. Moreover, the axis maintains a constant position (parallelism) so that every day the apparent position of the sun in the sky is slightly different from what it was the previous day and from what it will be the next day (see Figure V-1). The combination of the inclined axis and the parallelism of the axis accounts for the change of seasons.

The vernal equinox in the Northern Hemisphere is the day, usually March 21, when the rays of the sun strike the earth vertically along the Equator as the sun appears to move into the Northern Hemisphere. The autumnal equinox is the day, usually September 23, when the rays of the sun strike the earth vertically along the Equator as the sun seems to move into the Southern Hemisphere. The summer solstice in the Northern Hemisphere is the day, usually June 21, when the rays of the sun strike the earth vertically along the Tropic of Cancer and the winter solstice is the day, usually December 22, when the rays of the sun strike the earth vertically along the Tropic of Capricorn. In the Southern Hemisphere, obviously, the seasons are the reverse of those in the Northern Hemisphere.

So completely do most people of the world take for granted the changing of the seasons, that it would be almost impossible for them to imagine a world without climatic change. Outside the tropics the whole rhythm of life and activity is closely related to the changes of the seasons. To an extent perhaps considerably greater than we realize, human civilization has been nurtured by the necessity of anticipating and preparing for these changes. Certainly there is also, in the seasonal changes of the landscape, a powerful stimulus to man's aesthetic sensibilities and to his capacity for appreciating and learning from new experiences.

Day and night. The rotation of the earth on its axis sets the length of the day, or rather the lengths of the days, since there are at least three kinds of day. The sidereal or apparent equinoctial day is the period of the earth's rotation measured with respect to a point in the sky called the vernal equinox. The apparent solar day is the period of the earth's rotation measured with respect to the sun. Since both the apparent solar and sidereal days are of variable length (the longest apparent solar day, about December 23, is thirty seconds longer than the average solar day) mean solar time has been devised and has come to be the universal referent for the expression of time.

Until very recently in man's history, "the time" was a purely local consideration. Every community had its own time, the standard usually being the clock in the tower of the town hall or the cathedral. With the rise of the modern national states, individual countries computed time from some more or less arbitrarily designated prime meridian. In the United States the lack of any uniform way of measuring time became a nuisance as railroad networks began to span the continent. In 1883, the railroads of the United States and Canada agreed upon standards of time for the operation of their services. Finally, in October, 1884, The International Meridian Conference convened in Washington on invitation of the United States government. At that time was reached a substantial measure of agreement on "a meridian proper to be employed as a common zero of longitude and standard of time reckoned throughout the globe." (1)

The system proposed by that conference is, with numerous modifications, the system that is still used for the delimitation of standard time zones. Starting with the Greenwich meridian as the zero meridian, standard time zones are laid out so that their boundaries fall 7½° on either side of each meridian divisible by fifteen. Since the sun, in its apparent passage around the earth, seems to move 15° per hour, the time zones correspond to actual time intervals stated in terms of mean solar time. Zonal boundaries are, in many cases, quite irregular, as they tend to skirt areas where their presence would constitute a serious inconvenience (e.g., between a city and its suburbs, between an offshore island and the mainland, or within a relatively small political unit).

Time belts are, in essence, generalizations, and like all generalizations they fail to satisfy everybody. Along the margins of the standard time belts there is more or less constant agitation to shift from one belt to another. This agitation can be observed in its most acute form in Indiana which lies on the easternmost boundary of the Central Standard Time belt and yet is due south of Michigan, which has Eastern Standard Time. Urban interests, desiring an extension of daylight into the evening hours, favor either year-round Daylight Saving Time or adoption of Eastern Standard Time. Rural interests, influenced by the stubborn insistence of their livestock upon adhering to solar time, favor year-round Central Standard Time because it allows them to perform their morning chores in daylight. Attempts by the state legislature to regulate time have led to all sorts of local evasions and subterfuges. Discontent of this sort would naturally be expected along zonal boundaries where the discrepancy between standard time and solar time is greatest.

Daylight Saving Time. Daylight Saving Time is, in effect, a device to make us creatures of habit get up an hour earlier than usual in the morning and retire an hour earlier than usual in the evening. Put another way, Daylight Saving Time is the adoption, for the time being, of the standard time of the neighboring time zone to the east.

We have become so accustomed to time zones that many of us suppose that they are not only necessary, but somehow written into the very structure of the earth. One of the objections raised against Daylight Saving Time is that it violates "God's time." But measurements of time are purely human inventions, and in an interesting little article one geographer has raised the question: "Why have time belts?" In that article he notes that:

¶ Men who served in the Pacific during the war have told me that, when at sea for long periods, their ship operated on Greenwich civil time, the time used in the Nautical Almanac. Only when they returned to a land base was the ship's time synchronized with the standard time of the locality. (Of course the crew, being slaves to the clock and so unable to enjoy their meals without the clock's approval, set their watches as best they could to local time by figuring the longitude from Greenwich.) Why should not the whole world use Greenwich civil time or some other universal time? No! No! I can hear you say. Of course it would never do unless we could emancipate ourselves from the tyranny of the clock. Here in Wisconsin we would eat our breakfast at 1:00, quit work at 11:00, and go to bed at 16:00. So what? We would, at least, get rid of all time belts. Furthermore, the same date would prevail all over the world and would change to the following date at the same instant all over the world. Freed from enslavement to the clock, each community could more effectively utilize the hours of daylight.[1]

A proposal of this sort should appeal to students if for no other reason than that it would make the International Date Line unnecessary and thus spare the student the trouble of trying to remember what happens when one crosses the Date Line.

Actually, the logic behind the Date Line is quite self-evident. Any time one travels 15° west of the time zone from which he started, he "gains" an hour. Thus, if he leaves New York City Sunday at noon and arrives in St. Louis twenty-four hours later, he will find that it is only 11:00 A.M. Monday. If he were to continue westward until he had gone completely around the world, he would "gain" twenty-four hours, a full day. Conversely, if he had gone eastward around the world he would have "lost" a full day. This being the case, it is convenient to have some starting line at which the new day may be assumed to begin. The 180th meridian, running through the Pacific Ocean, crosses hardly any occupied land areas, so it was chosen as that starting line. In order to avoid placing portions of the same political unit on opposite sides of the line, the Date Line deviates from the 180th meridian between Alaska and the U.S.S.R. and runs east of Fiji and New Zealand. Service personnel on their way home from Far Eastern duty who were fortunate enough to arrive at the Date Line on Christmas have no difficulty remembering what happens when one crosses the Date Line going east. It meant for them two Christmases in the same year. If they had been unlucky enough to come to the Date Line on Christmas going west, they would have missed Christmas altogether.

The simplest way for the student to visualize the consequences of the earth's revolution around the sun is to reconstruct the earth–sun relationship by conceiving of himself as the sun and causing an ordinary desk globe to pass around him in a counterclockwise direction. The globe must, of course, be kept tilted at an angle of 23½° from horizontal and the North Pole must be kept pointed in the direction toward which the student is looking at the beginning of the experiment. With the globe thus situated, its initial position will be that of the Northern Hemisphere winter solstice. As the globe moves to a place directly to the left of the student, it stands in the position of the Northern Hemisphere vernal, or spring, equinox. Directly behind the student, the globe stands in the position of the Northern Hemisphere summer solstice, and directly to the right of the student it stands in the position of the Northern Hemisphere autumnal equinox. The student will observe that if he were the sun, the North Pole would receive no light at the time of the winter solstice, that both poles would receive some light at the equinoxes, and that the North Pole would receive the maximum amount of light at the summer solstice. Evident also will be the fact that while the tropical latitudes receive almost the same amount of sunlight throughout the year, the amount of direct sunlight received shows greater seasonal variability as latitude increases toward the poles. Thus, when middle-latitude or high-latitude people speak of seasons, they usually mean seasons of warmth and cold. Tropical people, who experience little change in temperature, usually define seasons in terms of rain and drought.

How seasons affect life. The recurring cycle of change within the year which we call seasonality has interesting and far-reaching consequences for all forms of life, including man. Recent studies in photoperiodism have shown, for instance, that the turning of the leaves in fall is primarily the result of the shortening of the period of sunlight rather than the lowering of temperatures. Plant ecologists have discovered ways of speeding up or slowing down the life cycles of plants by varying the amounts of sunlight which they receive.

On a world scale, spore plants are more common in the tropics and in the oceans, where there is comparatively little variation in temperature, rather than in the temperate and cold latitudes, where temperatures run to extremes. In these more extreme latitudes, seed plants are more common, the seed providing a form of "clothing" for the spores. Animals also adapt themselves to local conditions. Sheep in the tropics, for instance, develop a coat of hair rather than wool.

---

[1] Stratton, C. G., "Slaves of the Time Belts," *The Journal of Geography*, Vol. 46, No. 7, October, 1947, p. 270. Reprinted by permission.

Within the cold-winter latitudes, many animals are capable of conception only at times of the year which will enable their offspring to be born at the season most favorable for their survival. Other animals develop heavier coats during the winter or go into hibernation.

Man, too, responds biologically to seasonal changes. Throughout the middle latitudes, the death rate is higher in late winter than it is in summer. Birth rates show seasonal peaks in spring and fall. Distress from peptic ulcers is most noticeable during periods of changeable weather such as occur in spring and fall. Within limits man can, however, create his own climatic environment and thus he is less immediately subject to climatic influences than are nonhuman forms of life.

How we locate places on the earth sphere

Properly speaking, a sphere has neither length nor breadth. However, the first attempts to locate places mathematically on the surface of the earth were made by people living along the margins of the Mediterranean Sea. They were not interested in locating places all over the world, but were satisfied to plot locations in the relatively small segment of the world of which they had firsthand knowledge. And this world—essentially the basin of the Mediterranean Sea—was longer than it was wide. Its length *(longitudo)* could be measured from approximately the Strait of Gibraltar to the Mesopotamian lowland; its breadth (*latitudo*) from the Alps to the margins of the Sahara. Despite later broadening of horizons, the terms were retained.

Latitude is measured north and south from the Equator and is marked off by parallels, lines running east and west parallel to the Equator. Longitude is measured east and west from the prime or Greenwich meridian. Both latitude and longitude are measured in degrees, minutes, and seconds. A minute of longitude at the Equator is one nautical mile. A degree, therefore, is 60 nautical miles and a second is 1/60 of a nautical mile. The location of the office in which this paragraph is being written is 41°30″18.3′ N—87°3″3.6′ W. While this location hardly constitutes a claim to fame, it is the only such location on earth and is, therefore, unique.

The length of a degree of latitude is approximately the same in all parts of the world, although it increases slightly near the poles because of the flattening of the earth sphere in the polar regions. The length of a degree of longitude varies from 69.17 miles at the Equator to zero at the poles.

The earth as a magnet

The earth behaves like a spherical magnet and is enveloped in a magnetic field which varies both in direction and in intensity. One pole of the earth-magnet is in northern Canada; the other in the Antarctic northwest of Ross Sea. At each of these poles, the needle of a compass, if it were supported on a horizontal axis, would point straight down.

Useful as the compass is, certain geomagnetic anomalies and disturbances may throw it off. Magnetic metals or materials in the rocks may do so. In earthquake zones the compass needle may be deflected by faults. Magnetic storms in the atmosphere will also throw the needle off direction.

¶ There are many manifestations of magnetic storms. In polar and subpolar regions, the aurora is the most apparent as well as the most beautiful effect. At times the luminous streamers come as low in Norway as 65 kilometers of the earth's surface. Some American reports record yet lower altitudes. The compass may not be dependable during intense auroral activity. . . .

There are constantly small electrical currents in the earth (earth-currents), which fluctuate in different rocks, soils, metals, oil, and water. The strength of the electrical current is modified by the structure and composition of the materials. Because of this variation, measured changes of resistance to passage of a known current between separated points have been used in locating oil and economically valuable minerals without the expense and difficulty of prospecting blindly. During intense geomagnetic storms the normal earth-currents are greatly increased, so much so, that at times instruments and telegraph lines are fused and prevent wire and cable communication. . . .

Certain regions of the upper atmosphere are ionized, that is to say, they are electrically conducting regions. The ion-formations in the layer-like regions give rise to geomagnetic changes, to

ARCTIC OCEAN
BERING SEA
ALEUTIAN ISLANDS
BEAUFORT SEA
HUDSON BAY
GREENLAN
PACIFIC OCEAN
HAWAII
GULF OF MEXICO
CARIBBEAN SEA
NEW YORK
PHILADELPHIA
WASHINGTON
SAN FRANCISCO
LOS ANGELES
RIO DE JANEIRO
SANTIAGO
NEW ZEALAND
LEGEND
LAND ELEVATIONS
GEOGRAPHICAL EQUIVALENTS
ALPS
LAPLAND
TRUE RAISED RELIEF MAPS
AERO SERVICE CORPORATION
210 EAST COURTLAND STREET
PHILADELPHIA 20, PA., U.S.A.

(Courtesy, Aero Service Corporation)

auroral displays, and to earth-current effects. They also turn back transmitted radio waves, and thus make possible wireless communication over great distances by reflecting the radio waves back to earth.

During geomagnetic storms, there is interference with normal ionization, at times so great that we experience "fade-outs" in radio communication. These fade-outs appear only in the sun-lit hemisphere and are usually of short duration—more than 60 per cent do not last 15 minutes. Radio is only one of many electrical instruments affected by magnetic storms. Telephone and telegraph are others.[1]

The island homes of man

If the earth ever should be visited by an intelligent being from another planet, we would be interested in seeing how he would describe it. One thing that might impress him forcefully is the very small percentage of the total surface of the earth which is inhabited or which, indeed, seems capable of being inhabited.

Our space man might be as surprised as are some of us earth men by the fact that the Creator chose to "waste" three-fourths of the world on water—water which the vast majority of the world's inhabitants have found not only uninhabitable but undrinkable. However, it is a gross oversimplification of the facts to write the oceans off as waste space. First, though, let us look at the nature and pattern of the solid portions of the earth on which men live.

Four great land masses stand up like islands in the watery surface of the earth. By far the largest of these land masses is the Afro-Eurasian continent which Sir Halford Mackinder called "the World Island" and which other geographers have called "the Continental Triad." Traditionally we have applied three names to various parts of this land mass. Geologically, and to a constantly greater extent, geographically, it is one land mass, almost but not quite severed by the Red Sea. Historically, Mediterranean Africa has always been more closely related to the peoples and cultures of the Mediterranean Basin than to the Negro tribes of trans-Saharan Africa. Indeed, geographically speaking the boundary between Europe and Africa lies somewhere in the Sahara rather than in the Mediterranean Sea. And even geologically, rock formations and fault lines continue from southwestern Asia into eastern Africa. Europe itself is only a complex of peninsulas which, taken together, form a kind of "super-peninsula" of the Eurasian continent. No meaningful geological, climatic, or cultural division has yet been found to serve as a boundary between Europe and Asia. In our own day the attempt to draw such a line is not only futile but potentially dangerous. Much of the strength of the Soviet Union lies in the fact that it occupies a central position in the one great land mass of Eurasia.

Much smaller than the so-called World Island, but still of immense size is the land mass of the Americas: two great blocks of land connected at the Isthmus of Panama. The block which we call South America could just as properly be called East America, for practically all of it lies to the east of the North American block. Buenos Aires is, thus, closer to the western ports of Europe than it is to New York City, a fact which tends to be overlooked by some who think of the Americas or "the Western Hemisphere" as an entity which enjoys some kind of inherent unity and a "natural" isolation from the World Island. Considerations of distance, no less than community of culture, draw the Argentine toward Europe more strongly than he is drawn toward the United States. Regional economic differences and potentials tend to magnify the strength of this attraction, for the economies of western Europe and the Argentine are supplementary while those of the Argentine and the United States tend to be competitive.

The next land mass in size is the Antarctic continent, probably some 6 million square miles in area. Its exact size will not be known until we are more certain of what lies beneath the vast south polar icecap.[2] Antarctica is the only continent which, at this time, is uninhabitable. Even if the ice were removed and temperatures greatly moderated

---

[1] Mears, Eliot G., *Pacific Ocean Handbook*, Published and Copyrighted by James Ladd Delkin, 1944, pp. 169-170. Reprinted by permission.

[2] Soviet scientists who took part in Antarctic exploration during the International Geophysical Year have questioned whether Antarctica is a continent or an archipelago.

there would be no soil to support agriculture except perhaps along the very fringe of the continent.

The smallest land mass is Oceania, the continent of Australia plus a great many islands which are detached from the continent by shallow seas and straits. The boundary between Oceania and Asia is not a sharp one, for the two continental masses are connected by a number of large and small islands. These have varied greatly in number and size during geological time so that through the ages land bridges have been established only to disappear later. The most generally accepted boundary is Wallace's Line, a biological boundary which divides the continental fauna of Asia from the insular fauna of Oceania. This line lies east of Bali, west of the Celebes, and south of the Philippines. The Australian continent, the largest block of land in Oceania, is believed to be one of the world's oldest existing land masses.

The islands. Most of the world's islands are actually detached segments of continental masses cut off, as in the case of Great Britain, by waves cutting away peninsulas of soft rock or, as in the case of Madagascar, isolated by the sinking of lowlands which once lay between the present island and the mainland. Some small islands are the products of deltaic deposition upon the continental shelf; others the results of shoreline submergences which left only peaks and ridges standing above water. Pelagic islands, those which arise from the ocean basins rather than the continental shelf, are almost without exception of volcanic origin. They may be either volcanic cones (high islands such as Fiji), or coral formations around the rims of collapsed cones (atolls), or eroded complexes of cones and flows (the Hawaiian Islands).

Islands tend to be favored sites for settlement because their climates are commonly more moderate than are the climates of the mainland. Ocean waters warm up more slowly and cool more slowly than do land masses, and winds that have blown across the ocean thus tend to reduce temperature extremes on those islands which lie in the paths of the winds. Such winds are also likely to bring abundant precipitation. Very large islands, such as New Guinea and Borneo, are too large to enjoy this marine influence throughout their areas and thus tend, in their interiors, to be continental in climate. Many other large islands such as Greenland and Baffin Island lie too close to the poles to enjoy anything describable as a moderate climate.

How did the continents originate? The arrangement of the continents and the configuration of their coast lines have given rise to a great deal of speculation about their origins. The following news article and its accompanying map will serve to illustrate one line of speculation:

¶ Startling changes are being considered in the outlook of American geology toward current theories explaining how the continents got their form and structure. . . .

Several generations of school children now are familiar with the exercise of fitting continental cutouts together so the nose of South America nestles into the Gulf of Guinea; North America swings over to match up with Europe; and Australia, New Zealand, and Antarctica fit in at the south in the Indian Ocean.

This was the supercontinent of Gondwana, or Gondwanaland, insofar as many overseas geomorphologists are concerned. But the geography seldom led much farther on this side of the Atlantic where geologists Schuchert, Bailey Willis, and J. W. Gregory gave the "continental drift" theory short shrift.

Lecturing before various groups of researchers of the American Association of Petroleum Geologists in 1951 and 1952, Dr. Lester C. King, University of Natal geologist from Durban, South Africa, noted "a new spirit of impartial inquiry and broad outlook" in his United States audiences. As a result, the AAPG, which now is finding room in its Journal for up-to-the-minute reports on South American geology, especially in Peru and Venezuela, is also running a series on "The Necessity for Continental Drift," by Dr. King. . . .

He traces Africa's Great Karroo Basin from a western beginning in Brazil, Paraguay, and Uruguay across a sizable area of South Africa to Queen Maud Land in Antarctica.

Both driftists and nondriftists agree that at some time in the past there must have been land beyond the boundaries of the present continents. But it is in the manner of deriving these lands that the cleavage of opinion has come about.

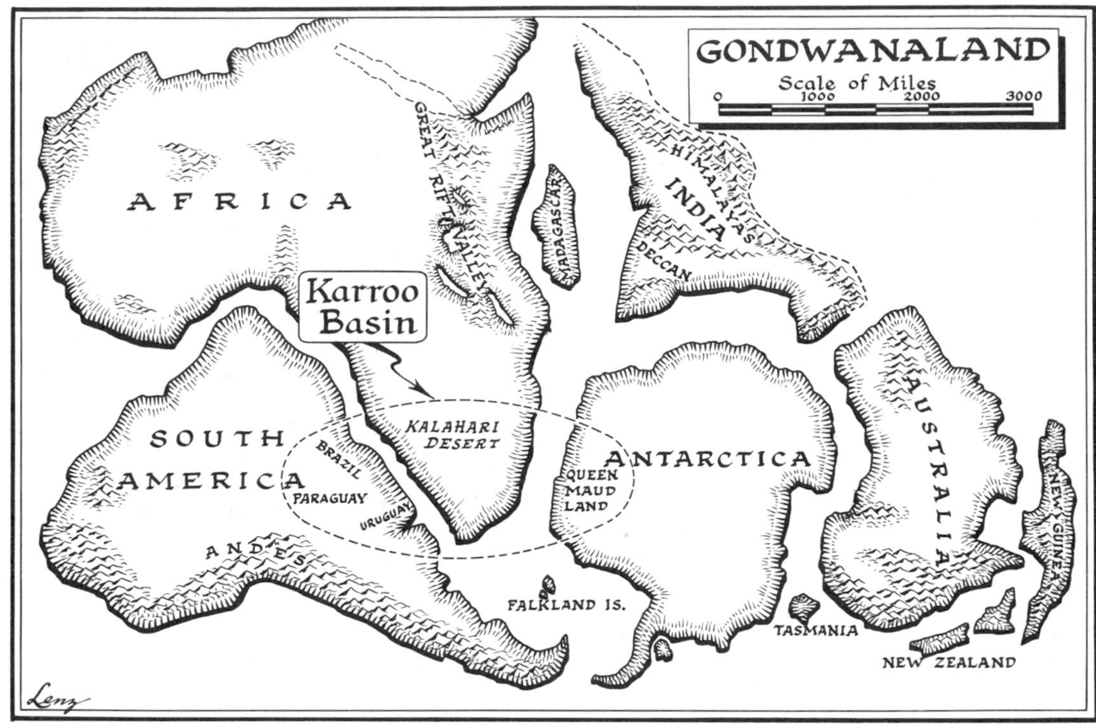

V:2 Geologists have reconstructed the supercontinent of Gondwanaland, and believe it looked something like this. (Map by Russell H. Lenz in *The Christian Science Monitor*, December 3, 1953, used by permission)

Some geologists backcast a time when deep ocean floors were elevated as land masses. Driftists say the movement was not vertical but horizontal. They point out that the continents are built of light material that cannot sink and disappear in the ocean depths; that all evidence from earthquake measurements of the constitution of the oceanic floors indicates (in the main) only heavy magmatic material.

The lighter (sial) continents thus float above the heavier material (sima) of the oceanic floors; just as a raft floats on water. Like rafts the continents are seen capable of drifting horizontally.

In 1911 Howard Baker presented his "displacement globe" postulating a single supercontinent or pangaea which split from Alaska across the Arctic and down the full length of the Atlantic to the Antarctic, the unequal parts drifting off in opposite directions toward the Pacific region. Later, Alfred Wegener, German geophysicist, put prevailing theories to test and assembled the parts in the working hypothesis that bears his name. He quoted astronomical observations to support a claim that the continents still are drifting. . . .

Dr. King expressed amazement that "so useful an hypothesis should have been allowed to fall into neglect or provoke such violent opposition in other quarters. . . .

The conception of drift harmonizes completely with what is known of the physical condition of the earth's crust: high-standing lighter continents, deeper, heavier oceanic sectors, isostasy (general equilibrium in the earth's crust) involving horizontal transfer of material at depth, the existence of at least one level of no strain."[1]

The thinking of most American geographers and geologists at the present time seems to be that there is still insufficient evidence to allow a judgment on the value of the "continental drift" theory. Worth noting, however, is the fact that like all respectable scientific theories, this one proceeds from the observation of facts to attempts to syn-

[1] "Single Land Mass? U. S. Geologists Re-examine Continental Drift Theory," *Christian Science Monitor*, December 3, 1953, p. 3 (Map by Russell H. Lenz). Reprinted by permission.

thesize them into a pattern. Whether these attempts result in a generally accepted theory or not, the attempt itself furnishes a framework for investigation. This in turn will encourage the uncovering of facts which may lead to conclusions quite different from any that we can now anticipate. This is the present-day study method of the earth sciences: to be constantly asking the earth for its own answers.

The seven seas

If the importance of environmental factors were dependent only upon size, man would be far more interested in oceanography than in geography, for the oceans constitute almost three quarters (72 per cent) of the surface of the earth. The comparatively little interest which man has shown in the oceans in the past is ascribable chiefly to his very limited knowledge of the resources and potential uses of the ocean. Then, too, water has always been a foreign element to man.

Unlike the continents, the oceans constitute a single unit, portions of which are interconnected. So vast is the largest single portion of this unit, the Pacific Ocean, that if all of the earth's land above sea level were dumped into it there would still be a rim of water 430 miles wide surrounding it. There is even a theory that the moon may be a mass of material drawn out of the earth from the present basin of the Pacific. If a globe is positioned in such a way that one's eyes are fixed upon the midpoint of the Pacific Ocean, only a narrow fringe of land will lie within the observer's field of vision. For this reason the Pacific Ocean Basin is sometimes called "the water hemisphere." The Pacific Ocean contains 69,400,000 of the earth's 140 million square miles of ocean water—almost half.

Next largest of the oceans is the Atlantic Ocean, 35,400,000 square miles in extent, much narrower than the Pacific and only half as large in terms of total area. Actually, the Atlantic is two large basins, one north of the Equator and one south of the Equator, joined by a relatively narrow passage between the nose of Brazil and the bulge of Africa. Third in order of size is the Indian Ocean, 29,500,000 square miles; and smallest of all is the Arctic Ocean with 5,300,000 square miles. Although it is the smallest of the oceans, it is still one and three-quarter times larger than Australia, the smallest of the continents. Because it is almost completely surrounded by land, the Arctic is sometimes classified as a sea rather than an ocean; and because it lies between the two great world power centers of the modern world it is sometimes called "the world Mediterranean."

1. The ocean floor. Only in very recent times have we begun to get even the merest inkling of the depths of the ocean and the character of the ocean floor. We do know that the average depth of the ocean floor below sea level is far greater than the average elevation of the continents above sea level, and that the extreme depths of the ocean are far greater than the heights of the highest mountains. The Swire Deep is deep enough that if Mount Everest were dropped into it, the mountain peak would be hidden under a mile of water.

We happen to be living in a period of earth history when the waters of the ocean have overflowed the ocean basins onto the rims of the continents. The submerged portion of a continent is called the continental shelf. From the seaward edge of the continental shelf there is a steep drop-off to the ocean floor or the abyssal plain called the continental slope. The ocean floor is far smoother and much less varied than are the continental surfaces because there is little erosive action upon it, and irregularities tend to be leveled off by deposition. One would be mistaken, however, to think of the ocean floor as a flat, featureless plain. Actually its surface rises to immense, broad swells and to narrow, relatively sharp ridges. Then it descends to broad troughs and precipitous deeps.

2. The ocean waters. The waters of the ocean vary greatly from place to place in salinity, largely because the degree of salinity depends upon rainfall–evaporation ratios, and upon supplies of minerals washed into the oceans by rivers. On an average, though, 100 pounds of ocean water contains about 3.5 pounds of dissolved minerals. Three billion tons of minerals are carried into the oceans each year. Of this mineral content almost 78 per cent is sodium chloride, common salt. (In many countries the extraction of salt from sea water is a government monopoly.) The next most common mineral is magnesium chloride, which in recent years has become the chief source of magnesium. Three other very common minerals in sea water are magnesium sulphate (Epsom salts), calcium sulphate, and potassium sulphate. More than forty of the chemical elements have been found in sea water, although some occur only in very minute quantities. In addition to these solid materials, sea water also contains oxygen, nitrogen, and carbon dioxide.

Sunlight is effective as a warming and illuminating agent in the ocean, only within a very shallow layer at the surface. Below 200 to 300 feet from the surface the temperature of the water is little affected by insolation and below about 600 feet there is no effect. By 2,000 feet the light is too faint to permit normal visibility and at depths of a mile there is no light except that of phosphorescent animals.

Temperatures of ocean water therefore vary both horizontally and vertically. At the Equator, surface temperatures average around 80°; in the polar seas they average around 30°. Since the oceans are interconnected and since temperature differences bring about differences in the density of the water, there are large-scale interchanges of warm and cold water. The warm water tends to expand outward on the surface over the cold-water currents, and cold water tends to settle and expand outward beneath the warm-water surface. This interchange of water, plus the fact that water cools and warms more slowly than land, accounts for the low seasonal range of temperature over the oceans. Therefore winds blowing off the ocean onto land would tend to warm the lands in the winter and to cool them in the summer.

There is even less seasonality in the temperatures of the deep waters. In general, temperatures decrease with depth to readings of from 32° to 40°. Probably about 80 per cent of the water in the ocean is below 40°F. At temperatures below 28.6°F., sea water of normal salinity freezes. The polar seas are covered in winter by ice which has been buffeted by wind and wave, creating a rough, jagged surface. This high-latitude marine ice is called pack ice. Ships caught while pack ice is forming may be literally crushed.

3. ***Movements of the waters.*** In almost every language, the word for sea is of the feminine gender. "A thing of moods and changes is woman always," Virgil wrote in the *Aeneid,* and he might have been writing about the ocean. Earth knows no fury like the fury of a winter storm in the North Atlantic, and there is no calm like the calm of the tropical waters of the Pacific on a windless day. But even the calms of the ocean are calms of activity. Its waters are forever in motion.

The most regular and most universal movement of ocean water is the ebb and flow of the tides. Tides are produced by the centrifugal force of the earth's spin and by the gravitational pull of the sun and the moon upon the earth. In the open ocean, they are hardly noticeable, rising only about two feet. Along shorelines, however, the height of the tide increases because of the shallowness of the water, and where tidal movements enter constricted bays the tidal range may be very great. In the Bay of Fundy, in Nova Scotia, the range may exceed fifty feet. Tides occur also in the lands but because of the greater rigidity of the land they are not nearly so noticeable as in water.

The tidal range is greatest at those times, twice in each lunar month, when the sun and the moon pull upon the earth in the same plane. This maximum tidal range is called *spring* tide. The tidal range is least at those times when the sun and moon pull upon the earth in perpendicular planes. This minimum range is called *neap* tide. Although the gravitational pull of the sun is far greater than that of the moon, the nearness of the moon to earth makes it the more effective tide-producing agent.

Ocean currents appear to be caused chiefly by two factors: (1) the friction of the winds upon the waters, particularly in those wind zones where the direction of the wind is relatively constant; and (2) the exchange of warm and cold water masses. The direction which these currents take is largely determined by (a) the rotation of the earth, which tends to deflect moving bodies to the right in the Northern Hemisphere and to the left in the Southern Hemisphere; and (b) the location and configuration of the coast lines toward which the currents flow.

The general circulation pattern in the

North Pacific Ocean is typical of the eddy-like patterns that are found in all of the world's oceans. A warm current flows westward along the Equator until it reaches the Philippine Islands, at which point some of its waters return and flow eastward in the Equatorial Countercurrent. The rest of its waters are deflected still farther to the right as they come up against the shoreline obstacles of the Japanese Islands and the Aleutians. As this North Pacific Drift flows through cooler waters, it receives the cold waters of currents originating in the Arctic Ocean. Thus chilled, it flows southward along the North American coast as the California Current. This current, in turn, flows into the North Equatorial Current, completing the circle of flow.

Ocean currents are of inestimable importance to lands which are situated so as to be able to receive winds that blow across the currents. The most heavily-populated parts of Europe lie in latitudes comparable to those of Hudson Bay and Labrador. Yet the inhabitants enjoy moderate temperatures both in summer and in winter, thanks to westerly winds blowing across the North Atlantic Drift (Gulf Stream). In earlier days, when ships were driven by the wind, mariners sought out the great ocean currents to carry them to their destinations. Many of the early voyages of discovery to the New World followed the Canary Current and the North Equatorial Current from Spain to Middle America and the Antilles. Even today, the major shipping route from North America to northwestern Europe follows the North Atlantic Drift.

Ocean waves are produced chiefly by the friction of wind against water. Therefore, in a general way, the stronger the wind the rougher becomes the water surface. In a violent storm, waves may measure as much as sixty feet from trough to crest. A special kind of wave, the so-called tidal wave, is set in motion by undersea volcanic activity or earthquakes. Since tidal waves are not related in any way to tidal activity, they are

Tides, waves, and currents cause the more properly called sea waves. oceans to constitute nature's amazingly efficient garbage-disposal unit. The wastes of erosion and of human living are washed into the oceans by streams. There they are ground up by waves, scoured out by the tides, and scattered by the currents. Our generation has the dubious distinction of being the first to find a way to pollute large areas of the ocean—with radioactive fall-out from atomic test explosions.

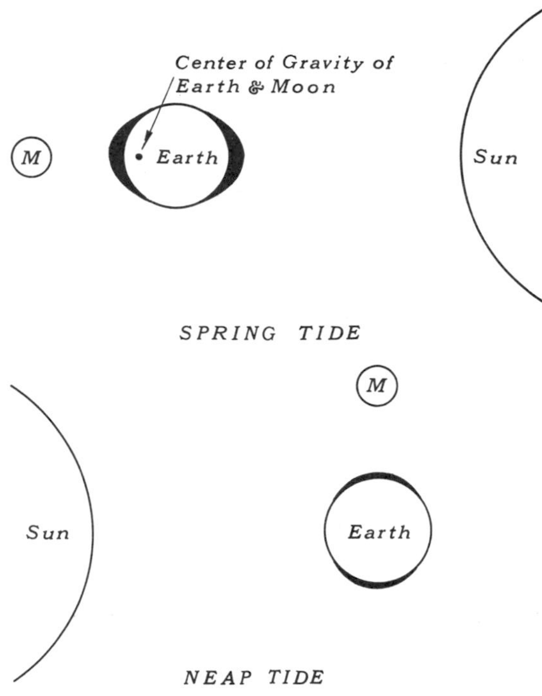

V:3 Relative positions of the sun, the moon, and the earth at spring tide and at neap tide are shown in this diagram. The solid black represents, at much exaggerated scale, the tidal bulges. Note that at spring tide the sun and the moon exert a gravitational "pull" upon the earth in the same plane. At neap tide, the sun and the moon "pull" upon the earth in perpendicular planes, thus offsetting each other's gravitational attraction. (Drawing by Marie Bohrn from *Fundamentals of Earth Science*, by Henry Dewey Thompson. Second edition, copyright © 1960, Appleton-Century-Crafts, Inc. Reproduced by permission).

4. The life of the oceans. Marine species far outnumber terrestrial and fresh-water species. The study of marine life is a vast field in itself, but the following generalizations suggest something of its nature and complexity:

¶ 1. In the sea we find life, both plant and animal, far more primitive and simple than that which we find on land.
2. Most of the life in the oceans, most of the species, and bulk of the weight of all living material, is microscopic and near-microscopic drifting life, unobserved and unknown even to those who live by the sea.
3. The pyramid of life in the ocean is based upon the utilization of inorganic compounds by microscopic, one-celled plants drifting in the sunlight zone. The large animals of the sea are not herbivores, as they are on land, but carnivores, because the plant life is entirely microscopic and cannot be caught directly by large animals.
4. There is no uniformity in distribution of marine organisms throughout the oceans either horizontally or bathymetrically; there is no depth of water without life.
5. The fixed algae along the shore contribute to the food of the sea in a most minor way, the principal food production being carried on by microscopic, one-celled algae drifting in the water.
6. The production of lush plant and fish life in the oceans is dependent on the restoration to the photic areas of fertilizers which have sunk either into lower strata or to the sea bottom.
7. Life in the oceans is delicately adjusted to conditions of temperature, movement of the waters, availability of certain kinds of food supply, sunlight, and the presence of dissolved gases.
8. The area available for food production in the oceans is some three hundred times as large as the area available on land.[1]

This last point has intrigued many students of world affairs who are concerned about the growing inability of the earth to feed its increasing population. Countries such as Japan have already learned to supplement their food supplies with seaweed. Might it not be possible, by systematic cultivation of the "ocean meadows," to double or triple man's food supply? Many conservative scholars think that it is.

5. The oceans and man. If this were to happen, one more item would be added to the long list of benefits which the oceans have conferred upon man. For centuries they have served him as highways, cheaper than any roads or railroads that he has been able to build. Along their margins man has built his greatest cities, gathering points not only for merchandise, but for ideas. For many men, the ocean has meant a living, either directly from fishing or commerce, or indirectly from shipbuilding and port activity. In the future, we may expect to see the energy latent in waves and tides harnessed to produce electricity to power homes and factories.

Historically, the oceans and seas have played a major role in establishing cultural and political patterns. Seacoast people often differ from inland dwellers not only culturally but also ethnically. This is true even on such small islands as the Admiralties, where the coastal Melanesians (the "salt-water boys") are taller, more vigorous, and much more highly civilized than are the more ancient tribes of the mountainous interior. South America is a vast mosaic of aboriginal tribes in a very primitive stage of culture surrounded by a coastal rim of European settlers. Even Europe shows a greater diversity of people and a generally higher level of civilization along its margins than in its interior.

For well over a century a basic consideration in the foreign policies of our own country was the presence of a broad watery moat around most of our national territory. Then when the width of that moat was exaggerated by the distortions of the Mercator map, it was easy to suppose that Europe was much farther away than it actually was. And in an age of surface warfare the mistake was not too important. Air warfare has changed all that. Now as the narrowing width of the oceans has impressed itself upon the thinking of our people and their leaders, our policies have undergone gradual but very significant transformations. Wherever the frontiers of our interest may lie today, they lie far beyond our shorelines.

Summary and conclusions

Such, then, in a very general way is the sort of earth we inhabit. We are creatures of the land, living in a world which is mostly water. We are creatures of a planet which experiences day and night. Most of us live in latitudes which know summer and winter,

[1] Haan, Aubrey, "Oceanography in General Education," *The Journal of Geography*, Vol. 50, No. 7, October, 1951, pp. 299-300. Reprinted by permission.

seedtime and harvest, cold and heat. Whether or not we are conscious of the great cyclical changes which confront us day by day with subtle changes in our environment, we are at every moment influenced by them and must, whether we like it or not, respond to them. The degree to which we can hope to master our environment depends, in the first instance, upon our knowledge of its nature. If it is true that civilization is man's conscious and systematic mastery of his environment, the study of geography must be considered an essential prerequisite for civilization.

APPLICATION OF GEOGRAPHIC UNDERSTANDING

I. What reasons might there be for the fact that migrations of people tend to move latitudinally while the exchange of raw materials tends to take place longitudinally?

II. If the captain of a ship at sea knew that he was 135° west of Greenwich and that it was 3:00 P.M. Greenwich mean time, how could he find out the correct solar time for his ship?

III. It is believed that during most of geological time the climates of the earth were relatively uniform and relatively mild. Develop a theory to account for this.

IV. How does the location of the earth's magnetic poles complicate the problems of polar exploration?

V. Evaluate the significance of the location of the State of Israel in the light of what this chapter has to say about the unity of the World Island.

VI. It has been said that the North Atlantic Treaty Organization represents a present-day application of the geographic principles that gave birth to the Monroe Doctrine. Do you agree? Why or why not?

VII. Can you suggest any reasons why Australia should have become a sanctuary for primitive peoples and primitive animals in the days before it was discovered by Europeans?

VIII. In the light of the arrangement of the world's great oceans and seas, appraise the strategic importance of the following places:

a) Pearl Harbor
b) Gibraltar
c) Dakar
d) Cyprus
e) Thule, Greenland

IX. What consequences might be expected if the Greenland and Antarctica ice caps were to melt?

X. The annual average temperature in Great Britain is higher than that of North Dakota. Corn needs warm temperatures to mature. Farmers in North Dakota are able to raise corn. Why does Great Britain raise no corn?

References

1 *International Conference Held at Washington for the Purpose of Fixing a Prime Meridian and Universal Day*, 1884, p. 1.

2 Stratton, C. G., "Slaves of the Time Belts," *The Journal of Geography*, Vol 46, No. 7, Oct., 1947.

3 Mears, Eliot G., *Pacific Ocean Handbook*, Published and Copyrighted by James Ladd Delkin, 1944, pp. 169-170.

4 "Single Land Mass? U. S. Geologists Re-examine Continental Drift Theory," *Christian Science Monitor*, December 3, 1953, p. 3.

5 Haan, Aubrey, "Oceanography in General Education," *The Journal of Geography*, Vol. 50, No. 7, October, 1951, pp. 299-300.

Chapter 6

Climate and culture

The narcotic of civilization makes us forget many of the realities of the natural world. But with all our smugness and ingenuity, we remain acutely conscious of the power of climate and its tangible expression, the weather. Climate still shapes the broad pattern of human activity over the earth, while weather may turn the tide of battle and affect, not only the comfort, but the fortunes of mankind. However much we plague and ridicule the efforts of the weather bureau, its prognostications are standard front page news, the first item to be scanned by millions of readers.

Paul B. Sears, "The Atmosphere at Work," *This is Our World,* University of Oklahoma Press, 1937, pp. 41-42. Reprinted by permission.

Context connotations

Climate may be defined as composite weather more or less seasonally evaluated in terms of temperature and precipitation. Weather itself is the state of the atmosphere at any one time, usually considered on a day-by-day basis. The analysis of the components of the atmosphere, and the study of the meteorological elements and principles basic to the understanding of the controls of weather and climate are certainly important. Yet scientific consideration of such phenomena would seem to have greater relevance in a textbook on meteorology and climatology or in a treatment of physical geography. May it suffice here, then, to introduce only those basic climatological principles the knowledge of which will aid in the understanding of the primary concepts of land—life relationships which distinguish the major occupance patterns of the world — the "works of culture."

Wherever climatic controls have a particular bearing on a significant cultural-environmental relationship, they are generally introduced in connection with the region with which they are most characteristically identified. Such references occur primarily in Part IV of this text.

Culture, as Webster defines it, is "a particular state or stage of the advancement of civilization or the characteristics of such a state or stage." As used in a geographic sense, and particularly in this context, culture connotes the forms of human occupance of landscapes by which regional distinctions of patterns of civilization may be recognized. In the above semantic connotations, then, the connections between culture and climate will be discussed and illustrated. Even the intellectual, aesthetic, and spiritual content of a civilization is partially revealed in the cultural complex of houses, schools, churches, rural and urban settlement patterns, field cultures, factories, forms of communication, transportation, recreation, and the like. Practically all these forms of land-use reflect in one form or another the major climatic region of which they are an integral part. As a test, then, preliminary to the further reading of this chapter, view the photographic illustrations of Part IV and jot down the geographic evidences exhibiting or subtly suggesting culture–climate relationships. One of the objectives of this text is to refine the art of interpreting the social order of a society by its physical-cultural landmarks.

Climate a time-space universal in life–land relationships

Ever since the days of Herodotus geographers have recognized climate as the leading element of the natural environment affecting man and his behavior. An axiomatic fact is that climate, particularly weather, is a subject of universal conversation. But, as is the case with so many other common experiences of mankind, this element of the created order is generally taken for granted. Very little attention seems to be given to the systematic relationships existing between climate and other environmental elements of earth and man. Though climate may not predestine man's culture at any time or place, the benefits of certain climates, as well as the limitations placed on man by certain aspects of temperature and precipitation, are incontrovertible facts of history. The exact evaluation of the influences of climate on man in any one region or at any one time, however, is difficult to assess, since man is the active agent in determining his environmental relationships. These, of course, include many other physical factors of the environment besides climate. Furthermore, by the very nature of his creation man, unlike animals, is influenced by many nonphysical factors — psychological, ethical, and spiritual — which may or may not bear a relationship to factors of the natural environment. This culture-climate relationship is succinctly stated by Whitbeck:

¶ Of all the geographical influences to which man is subjected, climate seems to be the most potent. It is an influence that no individual or race can escape. On land or sea, on plain or mountain, in savagery or civilization, man must meet the climate virtually on its own terms. Those terms are sometimes easy and generous, and sometimes extremely rigorous. The great continent of Antarctica, larger than Europe, has not a single human inhabitant, for the rule of its icy climate is complete and relentless. Greenland, three times the size of Germany or France, holds but a handful of impoverished people and counts for little in the world's affairs. The vast Sahara, the valley of the Amazon, the Siberian tundra, and many other lands are under the blight of unfriendly climates, and man's wisest adjustment may be to avoid them.

In large measure climate determines where man may live and thrive, what crops he may raise, what type of home he may appropriately build, what sort of clothing he needs, and what pests and diseases he must combat. The influence of climate reaches into the social, political, and religious life of mankind. There is a direct connection between climate and the type and degree of civilization which characterizes the different zones. No one believes it to be an accident that the progressive and energetic peoples who dominate the world are found in the intermediate zones.

Truly, through his intelligence and inventiveness, man overcomes some of the handicaps of an unfavorable climate; by means of clothing and heated houses, by irrigation, by medical knowledge, and by guarded habits of life, he may, in effect, modify his climate, but only to a degree. Man's rise in civilization is due in large measure to his victorious struggle against natural difficulties, including especially the difficulties imposed by climate. In the progress of mankind it is evident that that climate is best which forces man to match his wits against nature, to devise and invent, but which, in return, rewards him for his struggle. This favorable condition is found mainly in the agricultural lands of the temperate zones, between the stern, uncompromising regions of perpetual cold, and the languorous and enervating blandishments of the tropics. It is an oft-told tale and need not be repeated. It is a notable fact that neither the tropics nor the lands of perpetual cold have ever produced a masterful people. No great nation exists outside the temperate zones.[1]

Visher gives cartographic expression to these and related concepts in his *Climatic Atlas of the United States.* (2) In *isopleth* pattern are shown: (1) the number of days by which the length of the vegetative season exceeds that of the frost-free season; (2) *isotherms* of special correspondence significant to the limits of "extensive" and "chief" production of specific crops; (3) similarly, *isohyet* representation of rainfall correspondences to limits of commercial crop productivity; (4) the usual seasonal dates for planting and harvesting staple agricultural commodities. Again, in isopleth fashion, relative climate–health correspondences are noted under such criteria as: climatic efficiency-contrasts in human health; seasonal variations-death rates; and climatic energy-output of factory worker. The concluding maps of the United States reveal regional contrasts of death rates based on life-insurance statistics, and composite scale "civilization" ratings (e.g. Figure VI-1).

In this chapter we will first concern ourselves with the demonstrable effects climate has on the physical, biological, and human world. Then we will consider some theories or observations which have been made concerning the effect of climate on human culture. Climate as a world phenomenon is difficult to visualize. The precipitation factor, however, is ingeniously portrayed in Figure IX-1, which schematically illustrates the operation of the hydrologic cycle, involving as it does the complex elements of the hydrosphere, the atmosphere, the lithosphere, and the biosphere.

*1. **Landform relationships.*** Configuration of the earth's surface, as we will see in

[1] *The Geographic Factor,* by Ray H. Whitbeck and Olive J. Thomas. Copyright, 1932, Ray H. Whitbeck and Olive J. Thomas. By permission of Appleton-Century-Crofts, Inc., New York, pp. 87-88.

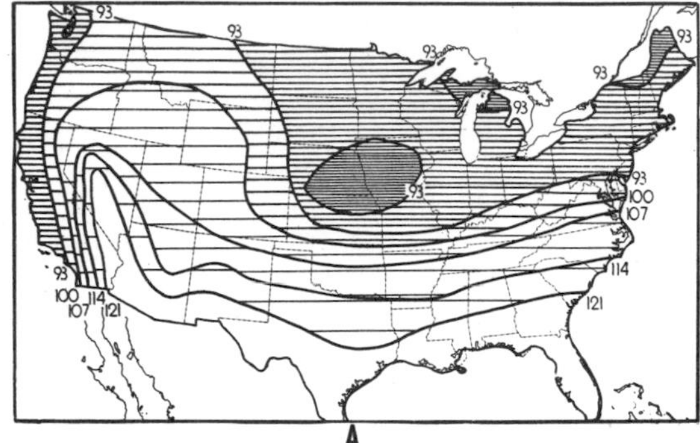

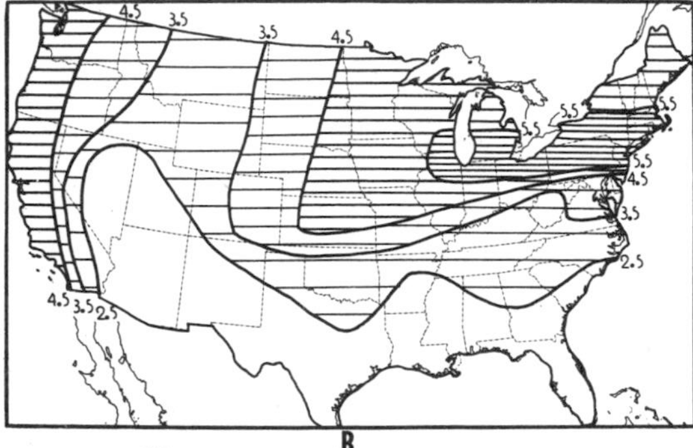

VI:1 Many geographic concepts based on correlations between natural and human phenomena can be developed by employing the *isopleth* principle and noting regional co-variances in quantitative-qualitative relationships. The types here selected from a prolific assemblage of maps by Stephen S. Visher feature relations between climate and health and progress:
A. Climate and health as suggested by difference in human death rates. (The numbers are percentages of the average death rate for the entire country, according to life insurance statistics.) B. Civilization contrasts. (Each of twenty-three Americans on a scale of 1 to 6, 6 being the highest. The numbers shown are the averages of the ratings.) (From *Climatic Atlas of the United States*, Harvard University Press, 1954, used by permission)

Chapter 7, results from a number of geologic and geographic factors — the nature of bedrock and surface materials; tectonic forces and vulcanism; erosional and depositional forms by water, wind, and ice; vegetative cover; and modification of the terrain by man himself as a result of his manifold activities. But certain expressions of landform are sculpturally related to climate. If you travel to a dry region you will observe, for example, sharp angular profiles of bedrock outcrops such as we find spectacularly developed on dry intermontane plateaus. In the more humid sections changing slopes are less articulated. Such type of topography has been referred to as the *cliff and platform* type. Dunes, consisting of wind-blown sand, may be found in humid lands, but dune formation is much more extensively developed and more migratory in dry regions, as in the desert *erg* regions of northern Africa and southwestern Asia. (See photos in Chapters 20 and 21.)

Typically, the larger deserts of the earth have only interior drainage, whereas in humid regions drainage systems on land connect finally with the sea. It should also be noted that mechanical rather than chemical weathering is dominant in drylands. This accounts in a great measure for the different landscape profiles and drainage patterns indicated above. Culturally related to these in turn are the settlement patterns and field cultures. Thus, there are concentrated and radial forms of occupance on the naturally irrigated *alluvial fans* on the foothills of the *mountain and bolson* provinces of the drylands, and there are in the humid highlands, zonation and contour configuration of land-use, including the seasonal migration of man and his flock, known as *transhumance* (Figure XXIV-5).

*2. **Soils.*** As we shall see in Chapter 8, soils result from an interplay of a number of environmental factors such as climate, vegetation, topography, and parent material. Of these, climate is by far the most significant when classifying differentiated soil types over broad regions of the earth. It affects most of the other environmental factors which together produce our varied regional soil types (Figure VI-2C). As a result of high temperature and heavy rainfall, chemical weathering is predominant in low latitude regions. In colder climates, such as in high latitudes and at high altitudes, the major type of weathering is mechanical. Consequently, tropical soils in rainy climates have deep profiles and are fine-textured; by contrast, soils of high latitude are thin and coarse-textured. (A soil profile is illustrated in Figure VIII-1.) Another major difference is found between the *pedocal* soils developed

Schematic representation of:

A. The distribution of climatic types;

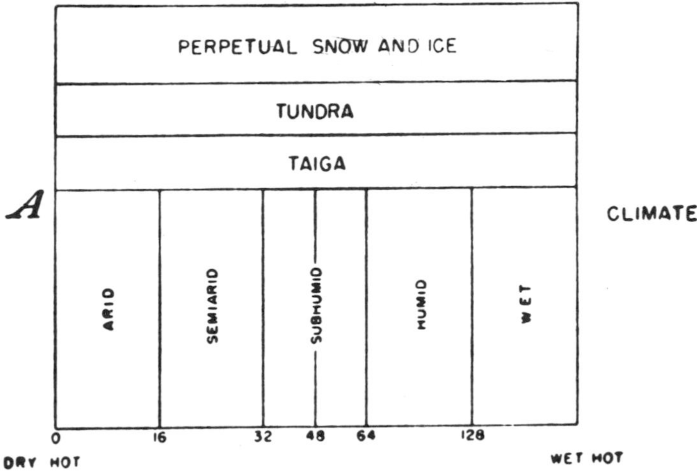

B. The distribution of vegetative formations, on a climatic base;

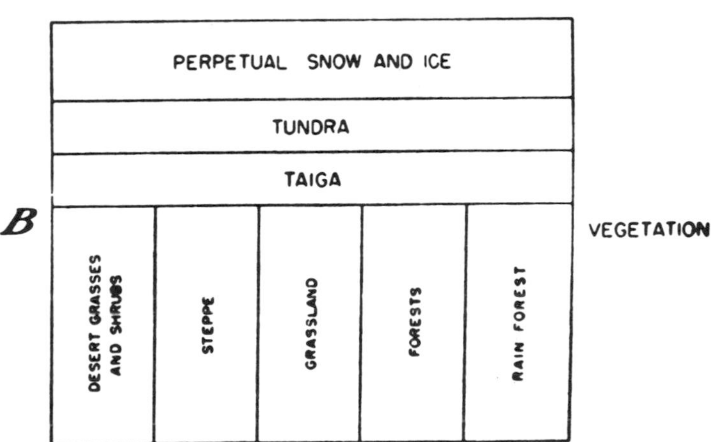

C. The distribution of the major zonal soil groups on a climatic base.

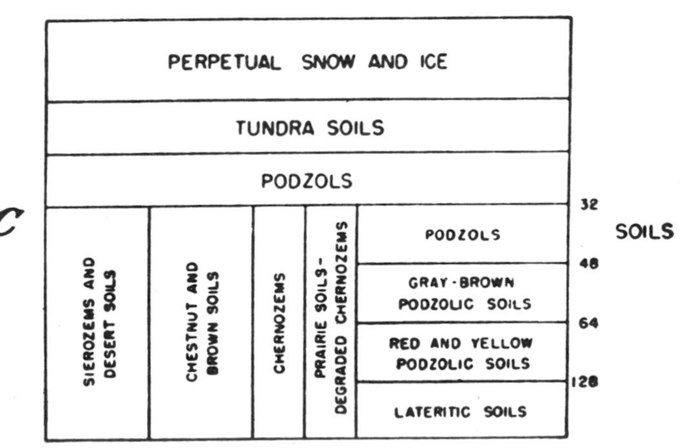

VI:2 This diagram shows the generalized climatic relationships to vegetation and soils. For example: Note the correlation between semihumid climate, steppe vegetation, and chestnut and brown soils. (From C. Warren Thornthwaite, in *Climate and Man, Yearbook of Agriculture*, 1941, United States Department of Agriculture)

in a dry climate, as distinct from the *pedalfers* which form in humid low and mid-latitude climates. Because of the low amount of rainfall, the pedocals are only slightly leached. As a matter of fact, the excess evaporation may result in a considerable amount of concentration of calcium and other mineral products. Such soils are frequently referred to as alkaline. By contrast, the heavily leached tropical soils—*laterites*—are characteristically acid and infertile. Their red color results from excessive oxidation and hydration of iron and other minerals. The cultural implication of this linking of soils to climate becomes obvious when we recognize the close relationship of agriculture to a soil fertility which is determined and regionally differentiated in a major way by climate.

*3. **Biotic relationships.*** Again, of all the factors of the environment influencing plant and animal life, climate is by far the most significant. Especially is this true in the case of vegetation (Figure VI-2B). So close is the association between climate and vegetation that a geography student familiar with the ecology of plant forms, as found related to the broader climatic types, can usually distinguish the type of climate of an area by the consociation of plants existing within it. As a result, various climatic classifications have been based largely upon the natural vegetation. Animals are less sensitive to slight changes in temperature and rainfall and, because of their mobility, express a lower degree of correlation to climatic areal differences.

Also of the greatest significance in the distribution of plants is the fact that while they tolerate a rather wide range of temperature and moisture conditions, there is a definite species optimum of temperature and moisture for each. This is particularly significant in the cultivation of crops. Optimal weather conditions are far more important than soil fertility. Thus Whitbeck observes:

¶ There is an optimum for every crop, and many crops are extremely sensitive to particular climatic conditions. For example, wheat and corn are grown mainly in a belt of mean annual temperature between 39° and 68° F.; oats between 28° and 68° F.; potatoes between 35° and 61° F., and rice between 68° and 86° F. Most crop plants attain little or no growth in temperatures below 42.8° F. The date palm shows little or no growth below 64° F. Most soil bacteria do not become active until the soil temperature reaches 45° to 50° F. Even slight differences in some element of climate may determine the commercial success or failure of a given crop.[1]

Whitbeck in his further discussion of "Special Climates for Special Crops" then shows how the successful commercial development of each major cereal is climatologically controlled and regionally exploited. Its significant relevance to this chapter is premised on the principle that the evaluation of the culture of any region cannot leave out of account the basic agricultural resources upon which that culture rests. In turn, this resource base cannot be understood without a knowledge of the "optimal" and "limiting" climatic factors that help determine on the natural side the regional capacity for profitable commercial agriculture. A further application of this principle is found in the development of new varieties of crops to ranges beyond the early limits of production. Various grains such as corn and wheat and oats are now found in northern Canada and the U.S.S.R. Similarly, there is a wider range in the development of crops which tolerate semiarid conditions. Such extensions of cultures have greatly augmented the food supply of the world.

The basic involvement of climate in the total environmental complex is schematically portrayed in Figure VI-2.

Climatic conditioning of land surface, soils, and biota and its integral role in cultural regional perspective

Let us now see briefly how the climatically-linked environmental factors enter into the cultural-climatic context on a regional chainlike basis: The cultural pattern of a typical rainforest (*Af-Am*)[2] (Chapter 23) native is low. It is low in part because of a poor diet; the nutritional deficiency consists

[1] Whitbeck and Thomas, *Op. cit.*, p. 121. Reprinted by permission.

[2] For the significance of the letter symbols see Köppen climates map and key in the Appendix.

to a large extent of a concentrated carbohydrate diet, deficient in minerals; the low mineral content of the food results from low percentage of minerals in the soil; the soil is deficient in minerals because of excessive leaching; and the excessive leaching is the direct result of two climatic factors—heavy rains the year round combined with twelve months of open (nonfrozen) ground, thus producing an almost uninterrupted solution and removal of minerals by the continually percolating ground water.

Now, the poorly balanced, mineral- and vitamin-deficient diet lowers man's resistance to disease. Endemic to the tropics are epidemics resulting from the transfer of pathological micro-organisms or viruses from one person to another by animals, chiefly insects. Examples are the malaria-spreading Anopheles, and the yellow fever-transmitting Aedes, mosquitoes. Such insects commonly breed in standing water. The copious rains and high temperatures of the tropical rainforest thus contribute to the ideal habitat. Much of the medical geography is perhaps related to this area of germ and virus infections, as is revealed in the chapter on hunger and disease (Chapter 17).

The home as well as the health of the rainforest inhabitant has a cultural pattern strongly influenced by his climatic milieu. There is not much point for the average native to build a permanent house, even if he had services and material of the midlatitude architect and contractor available, or possessed enough skill to do the job himself. Normally he lives close to his food supply. But infertility shows up in the native garden after it has been cropped for only a few years. This is primarily because accelerated tropical erosion and leaching leave the ground exhausted after the removal of several crops. Thus the rainfall-temperature pattern conduces to a migratory type of agriculture — a settlement type known natively as *chena* or *milpa*.[1]

All this does not mean that the health and occupance patterns have to stay this way. In fact, they may be radically transformed by newly superimposed regimes—remedial measures, including terracing; fertilization and other soil conservation practices to cope with erosion and leaching; drainage wherever possible of malaria-infested swamps; establishment of hygienic living and health clinics; erection of well-ventilated and screened dwellings, and the like. Whatever adjustments make possible the improvements of health, energy, and progress, the point to be remembered here is that we are not eliminating the influence of climate or its potential effects on the environment or culture. Man is simply reacting in another manner to the same climatic influences. He will exploit in his own interest such climatic elements as may be favorable. Then he will amend the adverse factors by some technological means to make them less unfavorable. To re-emphasize the principle, the influence of climate persists, but the human response to it simply takes on a different form.

As a contrast with the year-round unfrozen *laterites* of the equatorial belt, let us consider the *permafrost podsol* belt of the 60° latitude. The American, in his readiness to discredit everything Russian, because of its Communist connotations, is quick to point out, for example, that the five-year agricultural programs of the Soviets have been unsuccessful. Even the most dedicated Communist is ready to admit that they have not yielded all the results planned for, and the agrarian system itself is recognized by the Soviet leaders as far from perfect in its operation. But the point of relevance here is that the problem of Russian agriculture is not simply one to be evaluated in terms of a particular political philosophy. We must consider that here is a challenging soil-management program not found on a comparable scale among any of the world powers. We must take into consideration the generally thin and poor siliceous podsols which cover the major portions of northern Europe and Asia. Poor drainage induced by permafrost in the subsoil, and high acidity from the surface raw humus of the *taiga* (itself a climatic product) further complicate the soil-management situation. Add to this the fact that the five-year programs of agri-

[1] For a discussion of this form of migratory primitive agriculture, consult *Economic Geography* by Clarence F. Jones and Gordon G. Darkenwald. The Macmillan Company, New York, 1954, pp. 133-139.

cultural extension into these areas have to cope with the problem of developing quick maturing crops for the short two-to-three-months growing season, (*Cfc*).[1]

The chain linking "permafrost to politics" at first may not seem to present a regional rationale of much national or international significance. But, as with other major resource considerations, it cannot be left out of account if one would accurately appraise the influence of natural resources on the governmental functions or political stature of any state. Examine a globe and note the latitudinal position of our forty-ninth state. For the first time in our history, Congress is faced with novel legislative programs to meet the challenges of resource development of a taiga-tundra (*Dfc — ET*) region larger than our national "breadbasket"—the historic Northwest Territory (states north of the Ohio River). Such legislation, to be directed intelligently, must take into consideration the fact that nearly three-fifths of Alaska has only a two-to-three-months growing season, and that permafrost in this region renders unstable nearly all construction work.

Historic climate-culture patterns reflect significant elements of regional consequence

Perhaps the most significant climatic relations are with respect to man himself. One does not have to be told by experts that how we feel, or how clearly we think, or how hard we work, or how well we succeed is often charged or credited to weather or climate. We all know people who suffer from respiratory and rheumatic ailments, and others who migrate or retire to other sections of the country because of climate. Although we cannot set prescribed optimal climatic criteria for all-time energy, health, and progress potential, we can prove that, except for a few local cultures of which we have only limited archeological or anthropological records, highly cultured civilizations have not developed in very low or very high latitudes, nor in non-irrigable areas, nor in excessively damp non-drainable marsh or swamp regions. Furthermore, climate is only one influential factor in man's milieu. The forces of cultural heredity and modern technology can and do modify the environment of which man himself is a part, so we must recognize that what may constitute optimal climatic conditions for one culture at one period in earth's history or at a particular place in present-day geography may not provide the optimal cultural circumstances for another time or another place.

Some of our early civilizations developed in arid and semiarid lands, such as Egypt and Arabia; but these were of the distinctly oasis-irrigation type. In time we had the development of the Mediterranean Sea cultures. First came those around the Aegean Sea: the Phoenician, Palestinian, and Minoan cultures. Subsequently came those of ancient Greece and Rome. Unquestionably, the lower temperatures of the so-called Mediterranean climate proved much more favorable than the excessive heat of the subtropical deserts. Even more favorable was the rainfall adequate for general agriculture without the aid of irrigation, excepting for cultivated crops during the dry summer season. The subsequent migration of man from Mediterranean areas into central and northwestern Europe led to new settlement experiences. Here man encountered marked seasons on a lower temperature level, with a wider seasonal temperature range, and having adequate precipitation all year. It is in this west coast, marine type of climate (*Cfb* in the Köppen system) that modern man developed Western culture.

Though geographers differ very much in their opinions as to the effect which climate has on man in contributing to a certain type of culture or civilization, it would be difficult to ignore the striking areal coherence that exists between the areas of highest culture today and the types of climate which are identified with western Europe and the northeastern part of United States. Here the temperatures and amounts of precipitation approximate the optimal health and energy criteria determined by Ellsworth Huntington. On the basis of his researches, Huntington postulated that the approximate optimum climate for man is found where the summer month temperatures range between 60° and 68°F., and the winter temperatures

---

[1] What is also not generally known is the fact that Russia has truly desert lands (*BW*) over twice the extent of those of the United States.

between 36° and 44°F.; precipitation between 2-4 inches for the average summer month, and 1½-2½ inches for the average winter month.

Such specific climatic optima for man may sound too definite and deterministic. In fact, Huntington has been very generally criticized for his emphasis on the role of climates in culture and civilization. It is believed, however, that much of this criticism stems from a lack of complete familiarity with the published works on the subject. Huntington himself has frequently acknowledged the fact that climate is only one factor which needs to be considered in the evaluation of any culture or the progress that man has made through the ages. Heredity, for example, is recognized by him as one of such important factors.[1]

New settlement patterns. The histories of major migrations also throw light on climatic influences on man and possibly even indicate climatic changes. For example, nearly two thousand years ago the historic *Völkerwanderung* radiated from the Dry Heart of Asia, displacing or assimilating the peoples of eastern and central Europe. The impact of their invasion extended to Rome on the south, and to England on the northwest. Thus, Prince Kropotkin, the celebrated Russian geographer of the nineteenth century, and an early pioneer of geographic expeditions in central Asia, observed:

¶ Traces of desiccation which have been going on with great rapidity during historic times abound everywhere in central Asia. . . . Altogether it is quite certain that within historical times East Turkestan and Central Mongolia have not been the deserts they are now. It must have been the rapid desiccation of this region which compelled its inhabitants . . . to produce those great migrations and invasions of Europe which took place during the first centuries of our era.[2]

Following the discovery and exploration of the New World, from the sixteenth to the nineteenth century, settlement extended to all continents and climes of the earth. In the latter part of the nineteenth century new areas were opened to pioneer settlement. Although these climatic realms were quite suited to settlement, they were poorly equipped with transportation facilities. At the middle of the twentieth century we find man probing environmental areas for prospective settlement in lands hitherto considered either too hot, or too cold, too dry, or too wet for comfortable human habitation. Lands in such regions usually have been designated as marginal in their human habitability and productivity. Such, for example, are the desert fringes of the steppe world, much of the equatorial rainforest region, and the high-latitude zones where the growing season is restricted to the three or four months during which the temperature remains above 50°F.

Unfavorable climatic conditions, then, may not preclude settlement. Although man as yet exerts very little direct control over climate and weather, modern technology, especially in the field of agriculture, has made it possible to extend the limits of crop and animal productivity through sound practices of adaptation and conservation. Hundreds of millions of acres may thus eventually be opened to human settlement in areas hitherto repellent to man.

Some of the questions asked about the extension of settlement into these "nature dominated" regions are: Can man fully acclimatize himself to the extremes of climate? Will he be capable of establishing standards of living comparable to those of the climes of middle latitudes with their moderate ranges of temperature and adequate precipitation? Will he be able to conquer fully the virulent diseases indigenous to the tropical world? What effect will native population have on white man's cultures, socially and economically, in view of the natives' lower standard of living? Just how far will man be able to develop the sciences of pedology, agronomy, and animal husbandry in the *Dfc* or even *ET* lands of the world? The exploitation of forests, minerals, and fisheries in such high latitude climes is definitely possible, but these economies do not contribute much to major and long-term settlement.

---

1 Huntington's philosophy on the role that climate plays in civilization can perhaps best be expounded when applied to particular regions of his historic investigations, and is therefore reserved for Chapter 26 on the marine type of climate.

2 Kropotkin, Peter A., "The Desiccation of Asia," *Geographical Journal*, Vol. XXIII, 1904, pp. 722-723. Reprinted by Permission of the Royal Geographical Society.

Consideration of such regional problems and answers to some of the questions raised above will be found in an interesting article by Broek, "Climate and Future Settlement."[1]

¶ There are large areas still potentially available for human settlement. But it must be kept in mind that migration is essentially not a flow from densely populated areas to sparsely populated ones, but from areas of lesser to those of better opportunities. For some 400 years the European peoples have swarmed out into nearly empty lands, which were at the same time—broadly speaking—good lands. The situation is different now; land that has not yet been taken is mainly of a marginal nature, often because of its climate.

Controlling a new environment requires learning the laws of its behavior and devising ways to use them to the greatest advantage. No doubt science and technology will find further means of overcoming the present obstacles; even so, the border lands with unfavorable climates can be won only with considerable effort and at high cost. This imposes a heavy burden on the modern pioneer, diminishing his chances of gaining a better living than he had in his home country.

This is not to say that the frontiers have become stagnant. At present there is an intensive search for lands suitable for European refugees. This need may well give new impetus to colonization of hitherto neglected territories. Nevertheless, it seems beyond doubt that the advance would take place more slowly than before. But just because expansion will be slower, it may be more substantial and may lead to a more secure grip on the climatic problem areas (4).

Of the three climate-challenging regions considered — tropical lands, drylands, and polar lands — Broek believes the equatorial lowlands to be the "least repellent to human settlement." While acclimatization in the drylands on the whole may be better than in the rainy tropics, productivity or sustenance is very uncertain, and "successful occupation depends upon how well the farming methods are adapted to these special conditions. . . . Clearly it is not production per acre that counts here, but production per man. Settlement, therefore, will always be sparse." Although Broek recognizes that the taiga conditions "are not adverse to the production of well-selected crops . . . the demands for foodstuffs in areas of forest and mineral exploitation" supply only a meager market for agricultural products and hence do not contribute to intense settlement (4). One might observe also that future development of transportation in large areas of *Dfc* Canada and Eurasia may well solve part of this problem.

Climate is the major regional attraction

Modern transportation by auto and airplane, and extended vacations, have given tourism a major commercial and industrial rank. As one glances at the attractive scenes featured on promotional literature for tourists, one notes that almost every outdoor attraction is related to some distinctive climatic factor. Moreover, the increased span of life of man and his relatively early retirement have led many retired people in middle latitude countries to move to climatic areas actually or apparently better suited for spending a more comfortable, pleasurable, and healthful life. Hence the migration within the United States to the mild winter climates of the South, the marine-tempered winters and cool summers of the west coast, or the dry atmosphere of the Southwest. Obviously these locales have attractions other than climate, such as sports and other forms of entertainment and the sharing of an all-round sybaritic life. Climate, however, although desirable in itself also makes possible other environmental attractions which are exploited for comfortable and pleasurable living. Regional amenities, as Ullman concludes, have played a significant role in "the growth of California, with a 53 per cent increase, Arizona, 50 per cent, and Florida, 46 per cent, followed by Oregon, 39 per cent, and Washington, 37 per cent" during the 1940-50 decennium:

¶ For the first time in the world's history pleasant living conditions—amenities—instead of more narrowly defined economic advantages are be-

[1] Incidentally, the *U.S. Department of Agriculture Yearbook, 1941,* which contains this article, is one of the most comprehensive and authoritative treatments on the many-faceted relations of man to climate. It includes contributions from some of the leading geographers in the country. This 1,248-page volume comprises some two-score articles, most of which analyze regional relationships of climate to settlement in the various climatic regions of the United States, and the systematic relationships of climatic factors to the various types of crop culture.

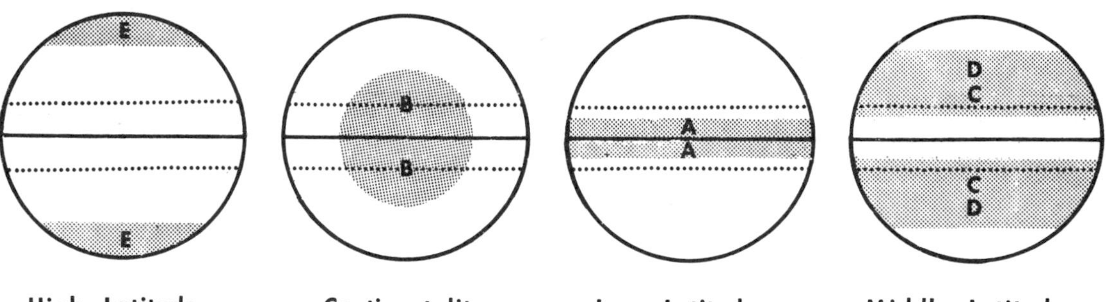

VI:3 A schematic representation of major types of climate in planetary perspective is shown here. The letters A, B, C, D, E, as shown are not to suggest pattern distribution of climates as represented in the Köppen system used later in this text, but rather a generalized concept of effects of varied zonal insolation and continentality.

coming sparks that generate significant population increase, particularly in the United States. In spite of the handicaps of remote location and economic isolation, the fastest-growing states are California, Arizona, and Florida. The new "frontier" of America is thus a frontier of comfort, in contrast with the traditional frontier of hardship. . . . Climate is probably the most important regional amenity, because it can be combined with other amenities, especially within the continental United States, where there is a fairly even spread of culture, education, sanitation, and creature comforts of all sorts.[1]

Though major migrations, such as the above, also involve recognized economic factors, Bright and Thomas in a sociological study of interstate migration concluded: "We are of the opinion that an important part of the migration to California has been of a hedonistic rather than a primarily economic character and has been motivated more by climate and legend than by superior job opportunities" (6).

The atmosphere and the anthroposphere

Since climate, then, is the dominating factor of the world of nature as well as the dominant natural factor considered in anthropogeography, it behooves us to take a glimpse at the major atmospheric and other earth controls that determine the differentiating temperature and precipitation criteria used in the classification presently to be considered, and leave their impress on the works of culture. Although climatic types (even the major ones) do not occur zonally, the schematic diagram (Figure VI-3) expresses a broad basic planetary concept of global relationships of the major types.

The atmosphere. The basic planetary circulation of the atmosphere is shown hypothetically in Figure VI-4. Weather phenomena are identified with the *troposphere,* the lowermost level of the earth's atmosphere. Here take place the changes in temperature, atmospheric pressure, wind direction, cloudiness, relative humidity, precipitation, and other weather-producing phenomena. As weather is concerned with those conditions of the atmosphere which are primarily of local and temporary significance, the functions of the various regional weather-creating elements will be considered in connection with their particular climatic realms.

We are now primarily concerned with the basic structure and behavior of the atmosphere on the planetary level. You may have wondered, for example, why the television weather forecaster almost always moves his symbols of high and low pressure areas from left to right (west to east) on the map of the United States. This is one of the most fundamental bases for forecasting the progressive weather eastward. Then, have you ever questioned why some climes like the rainforest (area of *Equatorial Calms*) are continuously humid, whereas in the latitudes from 25° to 30° North and 25° to 30° South appear the

[1] Ullman, Edward L., "Amenities as a Factor in Regional Growth," *Geographical Review,* Vol. XLIV, No. 1, January, 1954, pp. 119-123, *passim.* Reprinted by permission.

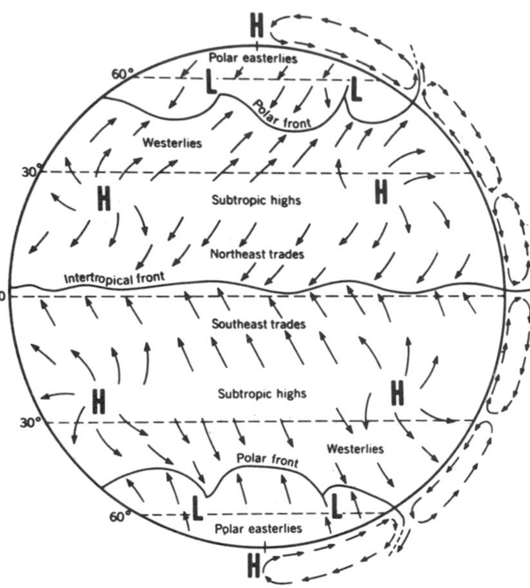

VI:4 This illustration shows a hypothetical arrangement of planetary winds and pressure belts. Note the general horizontal and vertical circulation at the different latitudinal zones (land–water influences here are disregarded). (By Howard J. Critchfield, from *General Climatology,* Prentice-Hall, Inc., Englewood Cliffs, 1960, used by permission)

great deserts or semiarid regions of the world (e.g., the Sahara, and the Great Australian Desert); why we have winter-dry climates in some regions and summer-dry climates in others; and why we have differentiated climates in the first place? An examination of Figure VI-4 reveals some of the basic patterns and principles of atmospheric structure and behavior necessary to the understanding of some of these phenomena. Revealed in a generalized way are some of the basic climatic controls, chief among which perhaps is the insolation feature; that is, the intensity of the radiant energy from the sun at different latitudes. Since the sun's rays strike the curved earth's surface most directly in the equatorial area, this belt will have the greatest amount of heat absorption, radiation, and convection. The highest degree of evaporation and relative humidity, then, will also be in this zone. The rising convection currents in this low pressure belt (the *Doldrums*) carry the vapor aloft. Precipitation results when sufficiently low temperatures are encountered to increase the *relative humidity* to the so-called *dew point,* the saturation limits of the air.

You will note, again by examining the diagram, that at about the 30° latitude air descends, producing a high pressure girdle around the globe (the *Horse Latitudes*). The increased pressure results in *adiabatic* heating. The warmer the air is, the more moisture it can hold; hence such atmosphere is evaporative, rather than precipitative of moisture. Note the major spread of the deserts and steppes of the world at this general latitude (Figures XX-7 and XXI-2).

Such differences as are indicated between the low pressure area of the equatorial regions and the high pressure areas of the subtropics account for air movements which we call winds or air currents. Regardless of how wind may vary in direction or intensity, air always moves from high to low pressures; hence in this instance the movement of air currents on the earth's surface is from the *Subtropical Calms* to the *Equatorial Calms.*

The diagram also shows that the arrows pointing in the direction of the wind flow do not head directly for the Equator but are deflected rightward in the Northern Hemisphere and leftward in the Southern Hemisphere. This illustrates another basically important planetary phenomenon. It is an expression of the *Coriolis Force* by which all moving bodies in the Northern Hemisphere, such as air and ocean currents, are deflected to the right of their general line of movement, whereas in the Southern Hemisphere all moving bodies are deflected to the left. This phenomenon results from the combined factors of the sphericity and rotation of the earth. Thus we have the belts of the *Northeast Trades* in the Northern Hemisphere and of the *Southeast Trades* in the Southern Hemisphere. These are onshore winds which bring cooling sea breezes and heavy rains to the east coasts at these low latitudes. Since in latitudes 30°–60° air currents move to the *Subpolar Lows,* their rightward deflection in the Northern Hemisphere and leftward deflection in the Southern Hemisphere result in the *Prevailing Westerlies,* whose onshore tempering air currents bring warm winters, cool summers, and ample to heavy rainfall. When such west coasts come under the influence of the high pressure *Tropical Calms* as these calms shift poleward with the high sun in the summer season, the coasts experience a dry season (*Cs*). The student will now also understand why *Lows* and *Highs* with their variable weather-producing elements should be moving from west to east across the United States, and why the weatherman should be looking to the west so to speak to give him clues for weather prognostications.

Another climatic control of planetary significance is the 23½° inclination of the earth's axis. This position maintained throughout the revolution of the earth in its orbit around the sun in approximately 365¼ days is responsible for the various seasons differentiated by temperature and rainfall. With a vertical polar axis there would be no seasons. The sun would remain directly overhead on the Equator throughout the year. Since all latitudes between 0° and 23½° N. and S. come progressively under the influence of the vertical rays of the sun, the wind belt system just discussed migrates in synchronism with the changing vertical sunray position. And since, as explained above, low and high pressure belts are significant, respectively, in explaining wet and dry conditions of the atmosphere, we would expect resulting seasonal differences in the different zones.

Differentiated heating of the earth's surface, a primary factor in accounting for the planetary atmospheric circulation, is also a function of the distribution patterns of oceans and continents, landforms, and vegetation. Thus the greater expanses of water in the Southern Hemisphere increase the effects of oceanity in that hemisphere. The greatest continental landmass — Asia, or rather Eurasia — produces, on the other hand, the greatest extremes of high and low pressures and, therefore, also of temperature and seasonal rainfall. Accordingly, we have the accentuated summer-wet and winter-dry monsoon climates of southeast Asia (*Aw, Cw,* and *Dw*) with their associated summer floods.

The varying altitudes and exposures of mountains affect climatic zonation. If they are sufficiently high, they will intercept moisture to windward, thus producing *rainshadow*, semiaridity or even deserts on the leeward side. The lower temperatures at the higher altitudes not only increase the relative humidity, favoring *orographic* rains, but in general add to the comfort of high altitude living in tropical climates. (There are, however, some people who suffer from mountain illnesses induced by the low atmospheric pressure at high altitudes.) People in tropical highland settlements may thus enjoy temperatures as much as 20°–30° lower than those at sea level. Temperatures drop approximately at the rate of 10°F. with each 3,500-foot rise in elevation.

Forests and other vegetation play a reciprocal role in climate. By transpiring moisture they return vapor to the atmosphere and thus serve as an important link in the hydrographic chain.

The global interplay of the above described factors and forces results in seasonal planetary pressure, temperature, and rainfall patterns.

The anthroposphere. In the preceding section we learned that atmospheric pressure, airmass, wind, temperature, and precipitation are the primary components of weather. As we have also noted, these meteorological elements are conditionally related to the shape and movements of the earth and to the patterns of its water bodies, landforms, and vegetational forms. Accordingly, synthesized weather, or climates, may be variously identified according to the geographic connotation which we wish to attach to them. Thus we may speak of a low, middle, or high latitude climate (0°–30°, 30°–60°, 60°–90°, respectively), with their broad global implications of zonal temperature differentiations. A low or high altitude climate has similar zonal connotation, particularly in the tropics where high altitudes neutralize the effect of high temperatures at low latitudes. Differences of exposure and slope, as well as rapid changes in elevation in many places, often make it difficult to characterize systematically the climate of a mountain area. We then simply call it mountain complex.

The Western world does not normally associate winds with climate identification. Yet the Oriental's pattern of life might be said to be almost completely regimented by his *monsoon climate,* with its threat of famine from either winter drought or summer flood. To the mariner of sailing ships, especially in exploratory days, the climate of the *Doldrums* (equatorial calms) held the uncomfortable

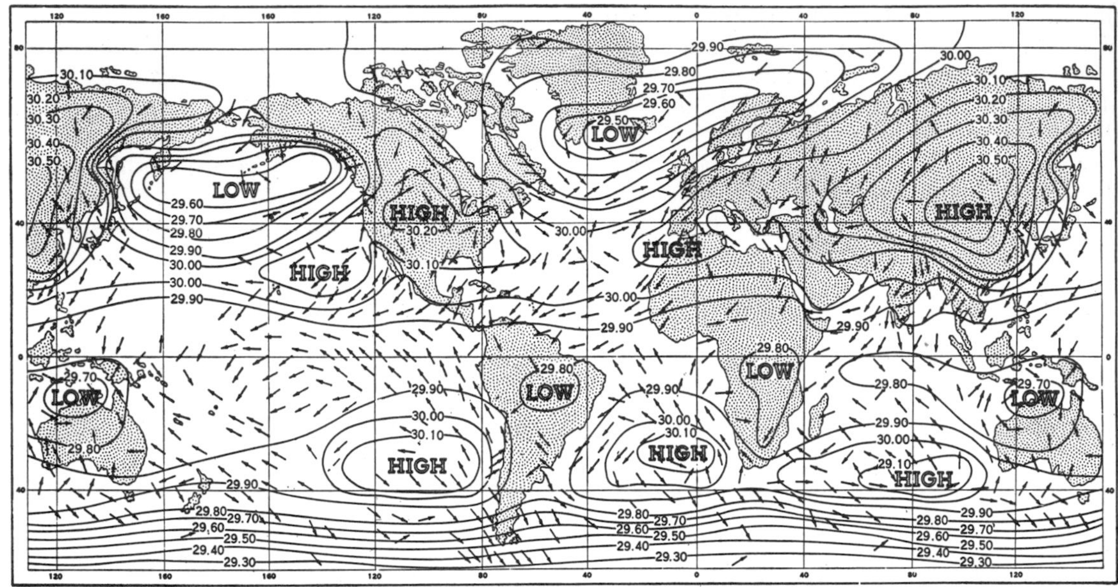

VI:5 The average distribution of pressure and wind over the earth in January is shown on this map. Note the relation of the air flow from HIGH to LOW, as well as the general planetary wind circulation. Understanding of seasonal and daily regional weather phenomena predicates a general knowledge of such planetary climatological phenomena as here shown. (From *Weather Forecasting*, United States Department of Commerce, 1952)

climatic connotation of immobility. So, today, "in the doldrums" is another way of saying "in the dumps" when expressing our depressed spirits or physical indisposition. "Air mass source regions and circulation systems," as the basis of winds, form a useful frame of global climatic reference when attention is focused on the "genesis" of weather and climate, as is illustrated in Figure VI-5. The various airmasses are graphically portrayed and designated by symbols, such as maritime polar air *(mPw)*, and maritime tropical warm air (*mTw*). Airmasses such as these are significant in spawning our major cyclonic storms and anticyclonic masses in the Pacific. As they move across our country from west to east, they bring us our highly variable weather. Airmass movements are related to planetary "Low" and "High" pressure systems as illustrated in Figure VI-6.

From climatic relations induced by coastal or interior position emerge such characterizations as *marine climate, littoral climate,* and *continental climate.* In each case are carried specific connotations as to relative differences in range of temperature and amount of rainfall. In association with different latitudes, there are seasonal implications as well.

As indicated, the vegetative cover of a region virtually mirrors its climate; hence such derivative denotations as the *rainforest climate* of the deep tropics, the *steppe climate* of the semiarid regions, the *tundra climate* of the subpolar realm. The cultivated counterpart of the plant world — the crops which man grows — may similarly serve as an ecological basis for climatic nomenclature in such associations as *corn climate* (e.g., our famous Corn Belt), or the *olive climate,* geographically synonymous with the Mediterranean world.

Since the various climatological phenomena — whatever their origin or form may be — occupy a definite geographic area such as a country or a region, place identification also serves a useful purpose in climatic classification. This identification is especially instructive when a climatic type is typical of a certain area, such as the *South China climate;* or plays a world leading role in regional association like the *Mediterranean climate.* Our *California climate* is an analogue of the latter.

In popular parlance such terse terms as

"dry" and "hot," "damp" and "cool," seem to serve us best, especially when we have some pronounced predilection for a certain type of weather or climate. And interestingly enough, when given definitive expression, such characterizations also have scientific recognition. Thus the Climatology Unit of the Research and Development Branch of the Office of the Quartermaster General has published a series of maps of all continents in which three quantitative categories of precipitation — dry, humid, and wet — and eight of temperature ranges — hot, warm, mild, cool, cold, very cold, extreme cold, and ultra cold — are interrelatedly classified. These maps, as indicated in a communication, "were constructed primarily for use in determining military clothing requirements."

In sum, then, it would appear that any classification which enables us to bring together as many of the above generic geographic associations as possible, is best for our purposes. We may then focus these in a conceptual global framework without resort to undue technical treatment of the physical and mathematical bases of weather and climate. The Köppen Classification of Climates, as adapted in Fahrenheit degree temperature and inches of rainfall criteria, and organized in taxonomic form, is designed to fill this function. This system was developed by Wladimir Köppen, a leading German meteorologist, whose researches in climatology extended from 1868 to almost the time of his death in 1940. Today, this system, either in the original or a slightly modified form, is probably used in more college textbooks than any other system. Ackerman observes:

¶ In spite of its shortcomings, the Köppen system thus has met with wide acceptance among climatologists and geographers. Those who criticise it for its emphasis on the quantitative side in reality endorse it; for nearly all the purely empirical classifications are based on Köppen's and differ from it in only minor ways. Its simplicity makes it pre-eminent among the quantitative systems, a position it is likely to retain until our knowledge of plant physiology and physiographic processes has advanced far beyond its present state.[1]

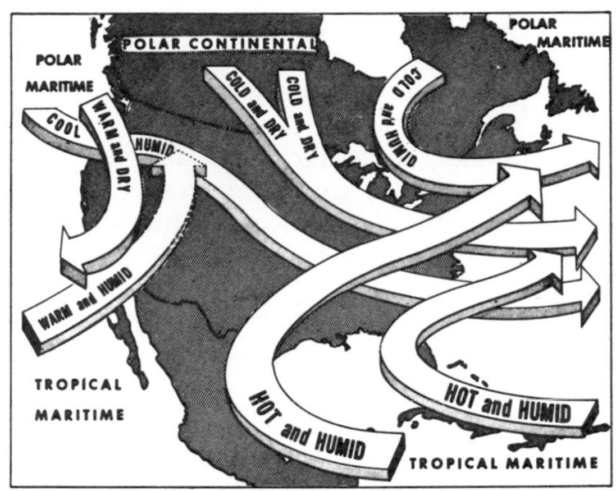

VI:6 Sources and paths of airmasses entering the United States are shown here. Highly schematic, this diagram does convey useful concepts of the complex system of airmasses, the general pattern of the origin, movement, and destination of the more typical airmasses, and the kind of atmospheric conditions related to them. In meteorological-climatological literature such airmasses are identified by symbolisms, such as *c P k* (continental—polar—colder than earth surface over which it moves). *(A Pilot's Weather Handbook,* Technical Manual No. 104, Federal Aviation Agency, Dec., 1955)

The key to Köppen

Ready understanding and application of the Köppen system suggest immediate reference to a number of charts and cartographic guidelines: (1) a map showing the global distribution pattern; (2) a *synoptic* diagram *synthesizing* the climatic types on a hypothetical continent without relief; (3) the vegetative schematic complement on which Köppen is initially based; (4) a "key" whose "wards" establish the guideposts that differentiate the numerous climatic types and subtypes; and (5) a "choro-climograph" which serves as a sort of conceptual prop for "viewing" and "evaluating" comparatively the several climatic types in relation to both nature and man.

The Köppen climate map shown in the Appendix is based on the more recent revi-

[1] Ackerman, Edward A., "The Köppen Classification of Climates in North America," *The Geographical Review,* Vol. XXXI, No. 1, January, 1941, p. 106. Reprinted by permission.

sions by Geiger of the original Köppen and is charted on an excellently-shaped equal-area projection by American cartographers. This makes it lend itself readily to "per square-mile" equatings of natural and cultural phenomena correlative with the various climatic realms at all latitudes. The student will want to refer continually to this map, particularly when he is reading the chapters in Part III and Part IV. At this introductory point you will note that, as is true of most global maps based on natural phenomena, certain mapped elements represented by symbolic letter nomenclature, repeat themselves. These, which will be defined shortly, suggest genetic, or at least, generic associations. Since this absorbing principle pervades the entire discipline of geography, the student should be continuously conscious of it as he discovers for himself new geographic principles and concepts connoting significant space relationships of physical and cultural phenomena.

The synoptic diagram. This diagrammatic device (Figure VI-7) is used to pose a number of conceptual generalizations:

(1) It shows the way the Köppen types would be distributed on a continent, as we now have them (top-shaped), but positioned at the Equator and of uniform land surface near sea level. Such a pattern when related to the latitude, to the pressure and wind belt system, and to the relative position of sea and land, affords not only an empirical representation of the generalized distribution of the world climatic realms, but also gives an elemental picture of the meteorological basis or controls for such climates. The *Tropical Rainforest (Af)* in the equatorial zone occurs where the rising (low pressure) convections result generally in year-round heavy rains. Similarly, the *Desert (BW)* and *Steppe (BS)* areas of rainfall deficiency are associated with the descending (high pressure) subtropical calms. Likewise genetically reflected are the "dry heart" of the continental interiors and the monsoonic *(Aw-Cw-Dw)* influences on east coasts of the bulging "continent."

(2) This type of idealized diagram lends itself equally well to a world patternization of natural vegetation. In fact, such a schematic arrangement of the major regional plant formations by A. de Candolle was the basis for Köppen's original climatic classification. Thus the tundra mosses, lichens, and other herbaceous vegetation of the *ET* may be differentiated; the xerophytic shrubs and grasses of the desert *(BW);* the steppe short succulent grass and shrub *(BS);* the Rainforest of the *Af-Am;* the tall and reedy grasses of the Savannahs *(Aw);* the mesothermal broadleaf and needleleaf evergreen forests of the summer dry *Cs* and the broadleaf deciduous and needleleaf evergreen forests of the *Cf-Cw;* and the evergreen and deciduous needleleaf and broadleaf deciduous of the *microthermal* realms *(Df-Dw).*

(3) Though Köppen did not profess to be a geographer (he was a meteorologist), he did in later years discern not only a regional correspondence between the broad patterns of plant formations and the climatic realms, but recognized them as guidelines to the understanding of man's culture.

The Köppen key opens door to recognizing basic geographic principles, systematic and regional

A French geographer once said, "All generalizations are false, including ours." But kept in proper perspective, generalizations or principles of both the systematic and regional type are fundamental in developing conceptual geography. In geography, cultural generalizations particularly cannot be reduced to universal terms. Moreover, the greater the number of variables in the landscape, the more difficult it is to "regionalize" such areas. Our cultural heritage and human behavior, complex as they are of themselves, cannot, therefore, be delimited by any natural bounds. It is surprising, then, that in the Köppen framework of the major climatic types (sequentially, *E, B, A, C,* and *D*) and

VI:7 (Right) This is a synoptic diagram of the Köppen climatic system projected on a hypothetical continent. Featured are the generalized patterns of distribution of major types of climate, the basic temperature and rainfall criteria on which the types are based, and the major planetary air circulation at the low, middle, and high latitudes. For the significance of the symbolism consult Köppen key in the Appendix.

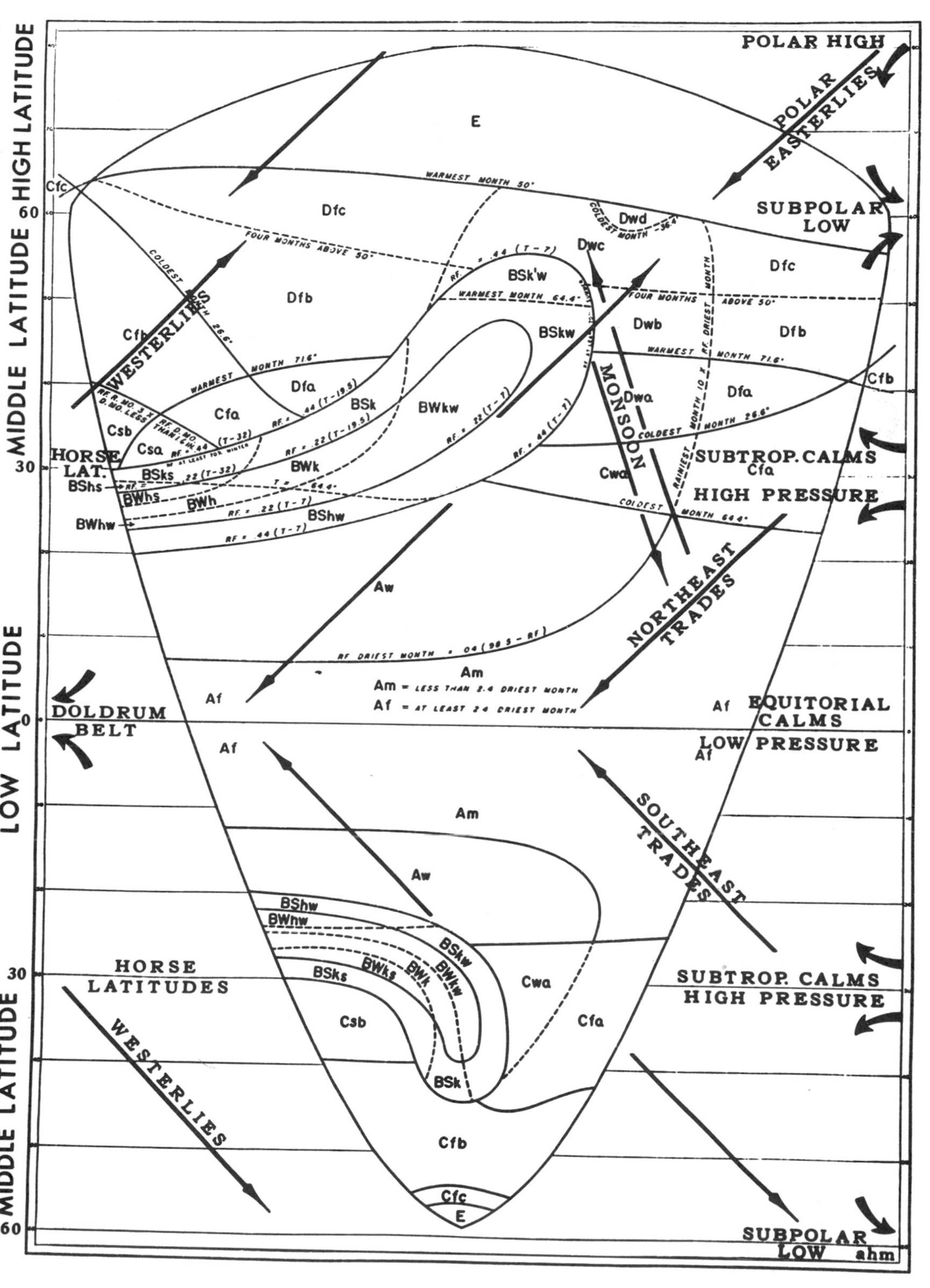

POLAR HIGH
POLAR EASTERLIES
E
WARMEST MONTH 50°
Cfc
60
Dfc
SUBPOLAR LOW
Dwd
COLDEST MONTH -36.4°
FOUR MONTHS ABOVE 50°
Dwc
Dfc
BSk'w
WARMEST MONTH 64.4°
FOUR MONTHS ABOVE 50°
Dfb
Dfb
Dwb
BSkw
Cfb
WESTERLIES
WARMEST MONTH 71.6°
WARMEST MONTH 71.6°
Cfb
Dfa
Dwa
Dfa
BSk
BWkw
Cfa
Csb
COLDEST MONTH 26.6°
MONSOON
HORSE LAT.
Csa
30
BSks
BWk
Cwa
SUBTROP. CALMS
Cfa
HIGH PRESSURE
BShs
BWhs
BWh
COLDEST MONTH 64.4°
BShw
BWhw
NORTHEAST TRADES
Aw
Am
Am = LESS THAN 2.4 DRIEST MONTH
Af = AT LEAST 2.4 DRIEST MONTH
Af
Af
EQUITORIAL CALMS LOW PRESSURE
DOLDRUM BELT
0
Af
Af
LOW LATITUDE
SOUTHEAST TRADES
Am
Aw
BShw
BWhw
BSkw
BWkw
BWk
BWks
BSks
Cwa
HORSE LATITUDES
30
SUBTROP. CALMS HIGH PRESSURE
Csb
Cfa
WESTERLIES
BSk
Cfb
Cfc
E
60
SUBPOLAR LOW
ahm
MIDDLE LATITUDE
HIGH LATITUDE
MIDDLE LATITUDE

their subtypes, generalizations between the natural setting and the cultural impress of the various regions designated by these climatic symbols are capable of meaningful coherent analysis. And it is this principle of study, and not the mere memorization of temperature and rainfall criteria and meteorological formulae in order to classify stations, that we are here interested in developing. However, to do this we should become intimately familiar with the Köppen key of classification.

The key as here organized (see Appendix) follows the taxonomic plan commonly used in identifying plants and animals. It shows at a glance the classification principles upon which the Köppen system is based, the types of climate recognized, and the taxonomic position of each climatic type in relation to every other type. It aids in the systematic identification of the several climatic types from station data and, by substituting formulae, eliminates the necessity of consulting lengthy tables of temperature and rainfall. From a geographic point of view, however, the identification and classification index serves only as a means to an end. Gradually introduced, part by part, as needed with reference to particular geographic principles or regions, the key has been found a helpful device in simplifying and clarifying the Köppen system. Experience shows that the key in time becomes automatic in readily integrating the elements of climate with the facts and principles of world and regional geography (8).

Thus we don't think of "50°F. for the warmest month" as simply the equatorward boundary of *E* lands, but rather conceive of it as dividing the world initially into two realms — the polar and the nonpolar (or the high latitude as distinguished from the middle-low latitudes). The contrast of such parallelisms (1-1) as "below 50" and "above 50" (and other similar parallelisms throughout the key), besides serving as a sort of mnemonic aid or psychological prop to the quick mastery of the technique of station classification, accents the comparative regional aspect of global classification. It sets the combined Frigid *(EF)* and Tundra *(ET)* apart from all the rest of the world *(B, A, C, D)*. Certain concepts follow: A growing season so short that even near the equatorward margin only frost-resistant herbaceous vegetation can thrive. Such sparse population as manages to eke out a migratory existence cannot subsist here, either on wild or cultivated products of the plant world but must rely on animal food — also in scant supply. In other words, the almost year-round frost is predicated by the 50° "life-critical" figure. So critical in fact is this temperature value that it takes top priority in testing for the classification of any climatic station data, again the virtue of a sequential key arrangement of criteria definitions. The first question, then, in classifying any station is not, "How much rainfall does it have?" or "How cold is it?" but rather "How warm does it get in the growing season?" For upon the sun's energy depends the plant-food supply, and upon this in turn herbivorous animals must subsist. Forage too limited for even the best acclimated animals, wild or domestic, often decimates the herd, and man then must rely for food almost exclusively on land carnivora or marine forms of life.

But, let us say, the station has a warmest month mean of over 50°F. In that case we move into the second or *B* category of parallel testing (2-2). Its basic concern is moisture availability. However, the critical vegetational value between dry grasslands and humid forest lands cannot be validated in terms of a single annual rainfall figure, since the rate of evaporation is also a function of the rainfall effectiveness in plant growth. For example, in the "h" subtype where the annual mean temperature is 85°F. and the rainfall is about evenly distributed throughout the year, 28 inches might be deficient for a good stand of forest. Also if the rainfall came mostly in the summer, when evaporation is most excessive, then even 33 inches might not suffice. If, on the other hand, the rainfall came mostly in the cool season when evaporation is low, then 24 inches might well be sufficient. By the same token, if the station annual mean temperature rated a "k," say 60°F., the critical grass–forest boundary values would approximate 18, 24, and 13 inches, respectively, on the basis of the "even" distribution, and the "summer" and "winter" concentrations. To take care of the evaporative factor, then, we must determine by formulae the rainfall "effectivity" value, beneath which the climate is "dry" and above which, it is "humid."[1]

Assuming that we have found that our station is a *B*, the next sequential step, as you will see by the key code 3-3, is to distinguish the degree of dryness — *BW*, Desert, when less than half of formula rainfall; *BS*, Semi-arid Steppe, if more than half. In the same systematic parallel procedure the classification proceeds for differentiating the hot, cool, and cold deserts *(h, k, k')*, and the even rainfall, winter *(s)*, and summer *(w)* concentration types; likewise for the Steppe.

Illuminating concepts. The student may now have been disillusioned about the validity of the simple 20-inch rainfall figure often used to differentiate dry and humid lands. If he were doing research in this area he would discover that this matter is even more complicated than these relatively simple formulae suggest.[2]

A further disillusionment may come from the fact that the simple concept of at most two types of dry region has now to be displaced by the idea of a score or more. The student may determine the number for himself by combining the *BW* and *BS* subtypes in all the different orders possible. Then he should check the map for their actual regional occurrences, and try to figure out why the several subtypes occur where they do. This, too, is not to be merely a perfunctory performance. We should associate therewith the possible vegetation cover characteristics and contemplate the probable type of human occupance forms best adapted to each situation. Where would the better grazing areas be found? annually? seasonally? Which do you think presents the greater problems for settlement and land-use rehabilitation programs — the *BW* or the *BS*? And which of the subtypes?

Now, collectively the tundra, desert, and steppe may be spoken of as the herb and shrub lands. The remaining categories, then, *A*, *C*, and *D*, are dominated by forests with some significant areal components of grass. And immediately this should suggest to the student that in the first group (tundra, desert, and steppe) grazing is a dominant economy, whereas in the other uncleared areas, lumbering is of substantive importance. However, one should not expect low, middle, and high latitude forest stands to be alike, nor even necessarily similar in the same latitude. Climatic differences may arise as a result of west coast, east coast, or interior position, or from changing altitudes with their zonal implications of climate.

The next step a classifier has to take is to differentiate among the forest areas. In the Köppen system this was done, first of all, by singling out the tropical forest. It was noted, for example, that a tropical plant like the date palm did not thrive, if it survived at all, when the temperature mean of the coldest month was much below 64°F. You will recall that in the case of determining the equatorward boundary of the *E* lands, the critical principle was not how cold the winter is but rather how warm the summer becomes, which roughly sets the poleward limits of forest growth in the neighboring *D* lands. But now in the case of tropical vegetation it becomes a question, not of how hot it gets, but how "cold." Of course, winter never comes to the tropics, but, strange as it may seem to midlatitude people, the minimum mean isotherm of 64°F. is critical for a large number of tropical plants which collectively form the rainforest, and whose products concern not only the native, but midlatitude peoples as well. For this the letter *A* is used with "f" *(feucht)* denoting heavy, or ample, year-round rainfall, and with "m" to indicate a somewhat dry monsoon period, not differentiated lineally on the map. Where this monsoon characteristic becomes so marked that there is truly a dry season, symbolized by *Aw*, then the evergreen rainforest gives way to the savannah broadleaf deciduous

---

1 Simply select the appropriate rainfall distribution formula, and work it out empirically, as instructed in the key. There is no purpose here to belabor the point of its derivation, a matter of meteorological physics.

2 Another factor that enters into the problem of arriving at a more accurate figure for moisture effectiveness, is *transpiration*, or rather the combination of evaporation and transpiration as Thornthwaite, a specialist in this area, points out: "We must know whether precipitation is greater or less than the water needed for evaporation and transpiration"(9). And so Thornthwaite addresses his research towards determining possible techniques of measuring what he calls "evapotranspiration." In the Thornthwaite system climatic boundaries are determined rationally by comparing precipitation and evapotranspiration, a classification based on climatic data *per se* instead of empirically on vegetation. This system, however, has not been completely developed. As Thornthwaite himself observes, we need to develop "better means of determining potential evapotranspiration" which await more extensive observation of data in the tropics and in high latitude regions.

landscape. This in turn changes steppeward to the dominant savannah grass. Obviously we need, therefore, to recognize this new cover type — and all its concomitant associations: the rich herbivore population and the carnivores which feed upon them, providing the best game hunting in the world. The warm and wet tropics belong to the most fascinating areas of geographic studies, but these concepts will be described in Part IV.

Having considered the more plant-critical and man-challenging temperature and precipitation conditions of the world, the student should be prepared to seek further differentiations. Even in midlatitudes and the lower high latitudes, there are great differences in the length of winter, marked differences in seasonal rainfall with corresponding contrasts in forest and prairie cover, and, of course, the expected difference in patterns of human occupance. Only one isopleth determination remains to be considered — the one to divide the *C* and *D* lands. Köppen originally decided again in favor of a coldest month isotherm, namely, —3°C., or approximately 27°F. Why not 32°F., the freezing temperature, you may ask? Geiger, formerly a collaborator with Köppen, points out that the first figure was considered more significant when related to lasting winter snow cover. But this position has been challenged by a number of geographers, such as Russell, Trewartha, Van Royen, and Ackerman. They all contend that better correspondences with plant life and soils and even cultural landscapes are observed when the freezing temperature isotherm is used.[1] This controversy on Köppen definitive criteria and others, as in connection with the dry-humid land boundary and major global differences in *Cfb* regions, is reviewed and evaluated in Part IV, which is oriented regionally on the Köppen system. The matter is introduced here to show that probably no classification can be simple enough, yet sufficiently "correct" scientifically to satisfy all authorities and all purposes. It also re-emphasizes the principle that nature recognizes no boundaries such as are here represented. Therefore, these, as well as any other man-conceived definitions and delimitations, are devices of convenience mainly for organizing principles and concepts for educational, disciplinary, and philosophical objectives. Moreover, the student should also recognize the principle that a classification map reduced so far that the entire globe is shown within the compass of a double-page spread — or even a large wall map for that matter — is not intended to be "correct" in detail. In fact, as Köppen himself contended, such a map is intended to portray only "general features."

In returning, then, to the key classification, the student will note that it was decided to

VI:8 (Right) Visualizing climatic types seasonally and comparing one type with another regionally are basic to the analysis of human occupance. For this purpose, a graph connecting co-ordinately monthly temperature and rainfall data of a station is effective. As earlier initiated by Ellsworth Huntington, Griffith Taylor, and others, this has now become a commonplace device to picture a climatic pattern. By placing such a graph in the framework of Köppen classification criteria and symbolism, as is done here, a synoptic view may be had of both seasonal characteristics and classification type. Note the "comfort core." How does Hamburg, Germany, fit into this frame of reference? The temperature classification (ultra cold-hot) appears on maps prepared by the Office of the Quartermaster General during the Second World War. Infer the army service value of such classification. Each climatic realm in this part of the textbook will be illustrated in turn by several climo-chorograms to help develop insights of regional differences in human as well as natural factors in which climate exercises a perceptible measure of climatic control.

[1] "Plant associations in the central United States extend to, or end somewhere near, the 0° January isotherm; changes in the distribution of domesticated plants correspond very closely to it; and the cultural landscapes of 'Midwest' and 'South' are conveniently divided by it. The 0°C. isotherm also closely approximates the boundary between the gray soils of the North and the yellow and red soils of the South. The C/D boundary drawn according to the criteria given in the 'Grundriss der Klimakunde,' on the other hand, shows very little correspondence to the natural landscape. It is based on the period of lasting snow cover alone—a division of questionable importance in the regions where modern agriculture dominates the landscape. Russell also has proved that the 0°C. January isotherm is a more significant h/k boundary in American dry climates than the 18° mean yearly temperature established by Köppen"—Edward A. Ackerman, "The Köppen Classification of Climates in North America," *The Geographical Review*, Vol. XXXI, No. 1, January, 1941, p. 109.

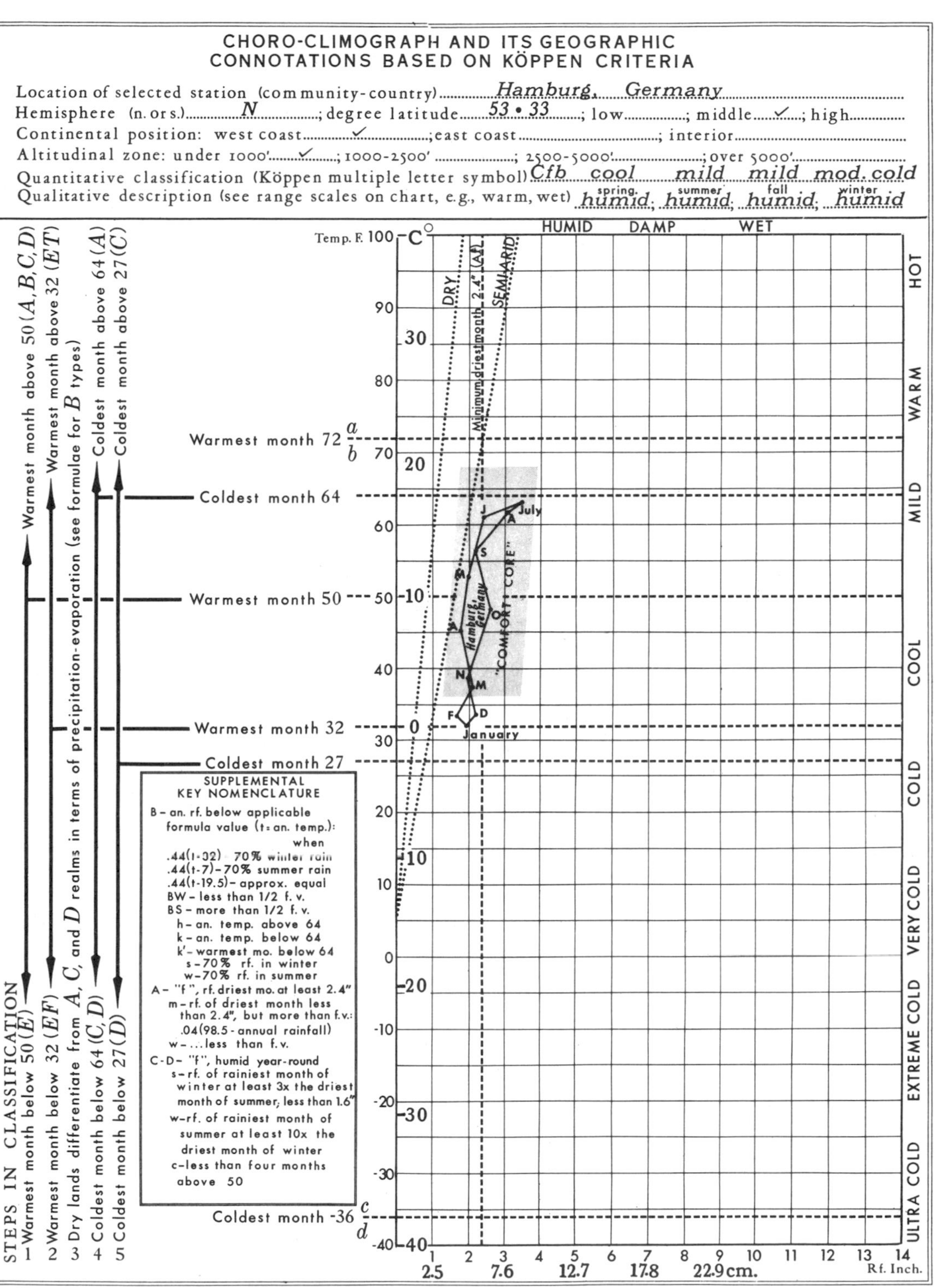
CHORO-CLIMOGRAPH AND ITS GEOGRAPHIC
CONNOTATIONS BASED ON KÖPPEN CRITERIA
Location of selected station (community-country) Hamburg, Germany
Hemisphere (n. or s.) N; degree latitude 53 • 33; low; middle ✓; high
Continental position: west coast ✓; east coast; interior
Altitudinal zone: under 1000' ✓; 1000-2500'; 2500-5000'; over 5000'
Quantitative classification (Köppen multiple letter symbol) Cfb cool mild mild mod. cold
Qualitative description (see range scales on chart, e.g., warm, wet) spring. humid; summer humid; fall humid; winter humid
STEPS IN CLASSIFICATION
1 Warmest month below 50 (E) — Warmest month above 50 (A, B, C, D)
2 Warmest month below 32 (EF) — Warmest month above 32 (ET)
3 Dry lands differentiate from A, C, and D realms in terms of precipitation-evaporation (see formulae for B types)
4 Coldest month below 64 (C, D) — Coldest month above 64 (A)
5 Coldest month below 27 (D) — Coldest month above 27 (C)
Warmest month 72 a b
Coldest month 64
Warmest month 50
Warmest month 32
Coldest month 27
Coldest month -36 c d
SUPPLEMENTAL KEY NOMENCLATURE
B – an. rf. below applicable formula value (t = an. temp.): when
.44(t-32) 70% winter rain
.44(t-7)-70% summer rain
.44(t-19.5)- approx. equal
BW – less than 1/2 f. v.
BS – more than 1/2 f. v.
h – an. temp. above 64
k – an. temp. below 64
k' – warmest mo. below 64
s – 70% rf. in winter
w – 70% rf. in summer
A – "f", rf. driest mo. at least 2.4"
m – rf. of driest month less than 2.4", but more than f.v.: .04(98.5 - annual rainfall)
w – ...less than f.v.
C-D – "f", humid year-round
s – rf. of rainiest month of winter at least 3x the driest month of summer; less than 1.6"
w – rf. of rainiest month of summer at least 10x the driest month of winter
c – less than four months above 50
Temp. F. 100 C°
90 80 70 60 50 40 30 20 10 0 -10 -20 -30 -40
30 20 10 0 -10 -20 -30 -40
HUMID DAMP WET
DRY
Minimum driest month 2.4" (Af)
SEMIARID
Hamburg, Germany
"COMFORT CORE"
July
January
J A S O N D F M
HOT WARM MILD COOL COLD VERY COLD EXTREME COLD ULTRA COLD
1 2 3 4 5 6 7 8 9 10 11 12 13 14
2.5 7.6 12.7 17.8 22.9 cm.
Rf. Inch.

retain the original Köppen −3°C., or its Fahrenheit equivalent of 27°, as the *C-D* boundary. But for regional considerations we should perhaps conceive of two subregional categories separated by the 200-day frost-free season isopleth. Thus we differentiate the equatorward "cotton-belt" clime from the poleward "winter-wheat" zone.

The *C* is normally referred to as the mild-winter type; the *D*, as severe winter. The forests of the former are predominantly broadleaf deciduous; *D*, primarily needleleaf evergreen and deciduous. A major base for concepts in geography is length of growing season, a critical key to agricultural productivity. The frost-free season in the *D* realm ranges from about six months to one-month poleward; whereas in the *C* the season ranges from about six months to virtually ten — or even eleven — months on the equatorward *A* boundary.

The next categorical key consideration, you will observe, is seasonal distribution of rainfall for both *C* and *D*—the markedly summer-dry *Cs* and *Ds*, spelling droughts; the monsoonic winter-dry *Cw* and *Dw*, with commonly flood-producing rains in the summer; and the *Cf* and *Df* of a more even distribution pattern of precipitation, and hence less conducive to soil erosion. Each moisture subclass is in turn subdivided by thermal criteria again significant in natural and cultural landscape analysis. Thus are recognized the hot and long summer, *a;* the cool and shorter summer, *b;* the still cooler and very short (less than four months) growing season, *c;* and the *d*, expressive of the winter frigidity of the type we find in *ET* lands but having temperatures in summer comparable to those of other high-latitude *D* lands — in other words, marked by extreme annual ranges. Though occupying tertiary categorical ranking, these thermal distinctions, it should be noted, can have more than secondary significance in regional evaluations. For example, a *Cfa* and a *Cfb* may very well be much more dissimilar in natural endowments and land-use forms than a *Cfa* and a *Dfa*. Comparative systematic and regional analysis of types and subtypes, such as this, rather than the mere memorization of definitions and the classifications of stations, determines how much the student actually profits from the mastery of the Köppen Key. The concluding exercise, based on the choro-climograph, Figure VI-8, may serve to summarize graphically the climatological criteria and principles of the Köppen classification and to view them evaluatingly in the global cultural frame of reference.

APPLICATION OF GEOGRAPHIC UNDERSTANDING

I. From the list of climatological station data in Appendix, select a station representative of each of the following: *ET, BWks, BShw, Aw.* Collectively, these might be called "problem climes." Now, using a distinctive color for each, plot on the choro-climograph the monthly temperature-rainfall polygon, as was done for Hamburg, Germany. Number and label each with the appropriate symbol. In each case point out how the type departs from the illustrated *Cfb* (Hamburg), held by many geographers to be one of the most favorable climates for modern man. Your comparative analysis should include: (1) warmest month mean; (2) coldest month mean; (3) annual temperature range; (4) number of months above 50°F.; (5) total annual rainfall; (6) seasonal "max" and "min" rainfall, and their relation to the temperature.

II. Why is each of the above criteria significant in life–land analysis?

III. Now on the basis of your reflections envison some of the problems in each case which apparently derive from such specific climatic conditions as you have pointed out in I. Aspects of adjustments or culture to be considered are: (1) comparative density of population; (2) patterns of settlement; (3) general types of houses; (4) systems of transportation; (5) forms of occupation; (6) integration in world affairs.

IV. Naturally, climate is only one, and sometimes the least important, of definitive natural factors related to a specific pattern of culture.

A. What other factors of the natural environment have to be considered for any one area?

B. Since neither climate (nor any other natural factor) actually can "determine" a cultural pattern, how, then, may be properly expressed the significant relation of the former to the latter?

V. Do you think man has the inherent

capacity to surmount most, if not all, climatic limitations? Illustrate, by example from your travel or readings, how man in each case has had to cope with such temperature-rainfall adversities as indicated in the climographs drawn.

VI. To what extent has man tried to "change" or rather ameliorate adverse climatic conditions? How? Geographically evaluate the statement: "In the not too distant future, man will no longer be the slave of weather and climate." — *U. S. News and World Report,* January 10, 1958. This journal and others, like *Newsweek* (January 13, 1958), call attention to such man-made "controls" as: hurricane-busting, cloud-seeding, sprinkling of sunlight-absorbing coal dust or soot, and dam-construction across Bering Strait. What objectives, potentialities, and problems do each of these present? H. Wexler in *Science* (Vol. 128, No. 3331, Oct. 31, 1958) under the title "Modifying Weather on a Large Scale," has this to say: "Current proposals are either impractical or likely to produce cures that are worse than the ailment." What "worsened cures," for example?

VII. Examine the Köppen Key of Classification in Appendix for climatic "challenges" to man other than those indicated above, adding these to the list:

A. What would you conclude as to the comparative areas in the world which annually or seasonally are either too hot or too cold, too dry or too damp, for "optimal" or comfortable living?

B. Which seems to offer the most promise in improving man's relation to climate — change the climate of a region, or change to the patterns of cultural geography best adapted to the climate?

C. How may the exploitation of sun power and atomic power eventually transform the habitability factor of certain regions? To which categorical environmental factors are these two aspects of cultural development most coherently related?

D. Classify by relevant key sequential statements, as illustrated in Appendix, a *BWhs* station; a *Dwd* station. In classifying stations by the key, why are sequential steps significant? For example: Why test first for *E* and then *B* before finally deciding upon the *D* category of the *Dwd* station?

VIII. Illustrate how a quantitative system of climatic classification like Köppen's sharpens one's geographic thinking about the relations between climate and culture, as distinct from a qualitative one.

References

1 Whitbeck, Ray H., and Thomas, Olive J., *The Geographic Factor,* Appleton-Century-Crofts, Inc., New York, 1932, pp. 87-88, 121.

2 Visher, Stephen Sargent, "Some Consequences of Climate and Weather on Agriculture and Health," *Climatic Atlas of the United States,* Harvard University Press, Cambridge, Mass., 1954, pp. 344-348; 354-355.

3 Kropotkin, Peter A., "The Desiccation of Asia," *Geographical Journal,* Vol. XXIII, 1904, pp. 722-723.

4 Broek, Jan O. M., "Climate and Future Settlement," *Climate and Man, Yearbook of Agriculture,* U. S. Department of Agriculture, 1941, pp. 233-235, *passim.*

5 Ullman, Edward L., "Amenities as a Factor in Regional Growth," *Geographical Review,* Vol. XLIV, No. 1, January, 1954, pp. 119-123, *passim.*

6 Bright, M. L., and Thomas, D. S., "Interstate Migration and Intervening Opportunities," *American Sociological Review,* Vol. 6, 1941, p. 773.

7 Ackerman, Edward A., "The Köppen Classification of Climates in North America," *The Geographical Review,* Vol. XXXI, No. 1, January, 1941, p. 106.

8 Meyer, Alfred H., "An American Adaptation of the Köppen Classification of Climates," Papers of the Michigan Academy of Science, Arts, and Letters, Vol. XXIII, 1937 (pub. 1938), pp. 362-366.

9 Ackerman, Edward A., "Problems in the Classification of Climates," *Geographical Review,* Vol. XXXIII, No. 2, April, 1943, pp. 233-255; and "An Approach Toward a Rational Classification of Climate," *Geographical Review,* Vol. XXXVIII, No. 1, January, 1948, pp. 55-94.

Chapter 7

Landform and land-use

Geographers are concerned about differences in the configuration of the earth from place to place because these differences help to account for the different uses to which people put the various regions which they occupy. These regional differences in land-use produce, in turn, different landscapes; and it is by differentiating one landscape from another that the geographer is able to organize the world into those logically coherent units which he calls regions.

Most geographers have some background in geology and are, therefore, interested also in how landscapes originated and developed. Many geographers also have an intense aesthetic interest in landscapes and may become as excited as any artist or poet at the beauty of a landscape. But the geographer operating as a geographer sees whatever portion of the earth he happens to be studying as a part of the answer to the riddle of why people live and work and think as they do in a particular place. Irrespective of how a plateau, for instance, got there, and irrespective of whether it is beautiful or ugly, the plateau is there; and if there are people living on it they are living rather differently than they would live on a mountain side or on a coastal plain or on a glacial moraine. The visible evidences of their way of living are comprehended under the term "land-use." Land-use, imposed upon landforms, yields landscape.

Geologists and geomorphologists differentiate landforms on at least three levels of magnitude. The first-order landforms are the continents and the ocean basins. Second-order landforms are plains, plateaus, mountains, and volcanoes. Third-order landforms are those various features of the earth's surface which are produced by the agents of erosion working on the first-order and second-order landforms; examples of third-order landforms would be such features as sand dunes, deltas, drumlins, beaches, and geyser cones. This chapter will be organized around the second-order landforms with one modification: since man's use of the land is generally affected more by the configuration of the surface than by its actual elevation, we shall consider the hill landscape as a condition intermediate between the generally rugged mountain landscape and the relatively level plateau and plain landscapes, and we shall not give separate consideration to the volcanic landscape.

Museums of social antiquities

What is a mountain? To the religious mind mountains have long been objects of mystery and majesty. In the Old Testament Mount Ararat was the site on which the ark of Noah came to rest, Mount Sinai was the mountain of fire and smoke and thunder from which Moses descended with the Law, Mount Zion was the holy mountain upon which Solomon built his temple. To the ancient Greeks, Mount Olympus was the home of the gods from which Zeus, the king of the gods, hurled his thunderbolts. To the Japanese Fujiyama is a sacred mountain, the very symbol of their country. To the fervent nationalist, mountains have often been the visible limits of the area which they believed to be theirs by some divine or natural dispensation. Thus the Frenchman sees the Pyrenees as the natural boundary between his country and Spain, and the German sees the Alps as a kind of divinely-appointed fence between Teutonic Europe and Mediterranean Europe. To the highway or railway engineer, mountains are obstacles that have to be tunneled through or negotiated by winding routes at enormous cost. Partly because of this, in our own country prices are "slightly higher west of the Rockies." To the mountain-climber mountains are challenges which nature has thrown into the face of puny men; they have to be climbed just because they are there. To the climatologist, mountains are great obstacles in the way of winds and air masses. Winds which have to cross them are often drained of their moisture as they rise to the chilly summits and descend as dry, evaporating winds. To the tourist, mountains are scenery, a relief from the tamed, overcrowded environment of his lowland home

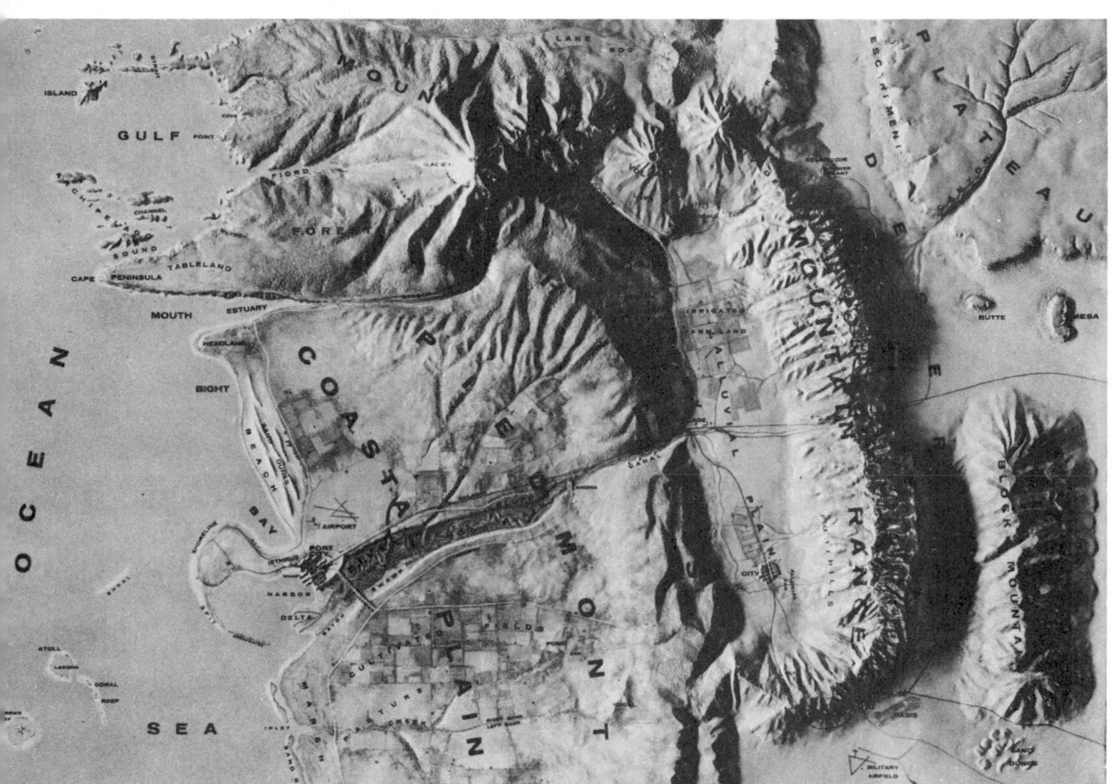

VII:1 This diagram of a hypothetical landscape illustrates some of the more common physiographic features of the earth. (Copyright Aero Service Corporation, used by permission)

and a refuge for fish, birds, and animal life which could not survive close association with man.

The geologist, while not disputing any of these other definitions of mountains, is content with a more precise and less subjective definition. He sees mountains as elevated portions of the earth's surface characterized by summit areas which are very small in proportion to their slopes, resulting from large-scale disturbance or deformation of the surface rocks. He classifies mountains on the basis of the type of deformation which produced them. Thus dome mountains are, as their name implies, strata which have bulged up in the form of a dome; folded mountains are great wrinkles of rock, usually quite long in proportion to their width; block mountains are produced by the uptilting of a block of rock along a break, or fault, in the earth's surface; and complex mountains are the results of a number of disturbed structures (1).

Popular usage has given the title of mountain to many elevated landforms which would not qualify for the title under the geologist's definition. In general, the flatter the surrounding landscape, the less elevated a feature need be in order to be called a mountain. In the very flat Midwest, mere erosional remnants or dunal hills may be called mountains. In much-dissected plateau country, remnants of the original plateau surface are often called mountains. The discrepancy between scientific and popular usage of the term need not bother us greatly. Man's use of landforms is related to the landform as it actually is, not to the name which, perhaps quite improperly, he has attached to it. Road patterns, field layouts, and crop choices in hill country reflect a hill environment, even though it may be called mountain country. For our purposes, therefore, we shall consider mountains features which, by reason of their elevation and ruggedness, do not merely modify but actually interrupt the occupance patterns of the level land that surrounds them. Some very low, eroded mountains (in the geological sense) we shall, therefore, demote to the category of hills; and some high, rugged erosional remnants in badly dissected plateaus we shall call mountains.

To the geographer, the essential thing about mountains is that they represent major exceptions to the normal habitat of man. The overwhelming majority of men live on relatively level surfaces below 1,000 feet above sea level. Smaller numbers live on rolling surfaces below this level and on relatively level surfaces above this level. But very few live on slopeland above 1,000 feet. When we find groups living in these unusual settings, we therefore ask immediately: Why?

In most cases the answer, if traced far enough back, resolves itself into one of necessity. Historically, mountain areas have been places of refuge into which people fled before invaders more numerous, more advanced, or more bloodthirsty. The ancient Celts were driven into the mountains of Wales and Scotland by the Angles and Saxons. Pigmy tribes in the Philippines were dispossessed of the lowlands by more advanced invaders and withdrew into the mountains. In the Caucasus Mountains between Turkey and the U.S.S.R. more than forty different national groups have found refuge from succeeding waves of Arabs, Turks, nomadic tribes from the north, and Cossacks (2). Conscious of their descent from ancestors who once chose the hard life of the mountains in preference to death, slavery, or absorption in the easier lowlands, these mountain tribes tend to be fiercely independent, proud of their own kind and correspondingly contemptuous of "outsiders," and jealous of their heritage of language, religion, music, and literature. This tenacious loyalty to the past and its institutions has resulted in the preservation, among mountain peoples, of cultural institutions and folkways which justifies Dr. Ellen Churchill Semple's statement that mountain areas are "museums of social antiquities."

The price which the mountain dweller pays for his independence and particularism is, in most cases, a heavy one. Except in the occasional small intermontane valley he finds agriculture difficult or impossible unless he is willing to rebuild the mountain slopes with terraces. Cattle, with their large bodies and fragile legs, are poorly adapted to the rugged terrain. Sheep and goats have, therefore, claimed the slopes, leaving such cattle as there are to compete with crops for the more level land. Isolated by a topography which makes any kind of surface transportation route difficult (and therefore costly) to build and maintain, the mountain dweller suffers from a limited market for the few things he can produce, and from high prices for the things which he must import. The Ifugao of Luzon attempts to overcome the limitations of his mountain home by terracing his slopes and raising rice. The Swiss mountaineer combines lowland agriculture with stock-pasturage on the slopes. The German Schwarzwalder develops his skill in manufacturing small, high-value products from the forest trees of the Black Forest. The enterprising Andorran runs a prosperous smuggling operation between France and Spain. Before strong national governments came into the picture, hill tribes used to make periodic hit-and-run forays upon their more prosperous lowland neighbors. Thus in many ways mountain people have sought to compensate for the paucity of their resources.

Since mountain populations tend to live in small clusters isolated from each other and from the outside world, inbreeding takes a heavy toll of the physical and mental vigor of the people. The "queer 'un" is a stock figure in our own hillbilly humor, just as the "wild Welshman" is in British humor.

How much longer the mountaineer will be able or willing to maintain his apartness from the world around him is a question which intrigues the cultural anthropologist. Arrayed against him, especially in Europe and in North America, are all the great contemporary levelers of culture: the airplane, radio, state and national tax laws (and the revenue agents who seek out the delinquent taxpayer), universal military conscription, and compulsory education. Physical barriers are no longer sufficient to create either a refuge or a prison, and as the barriers give

way, the mountain people tend to leave the mountains for the easier life and the greater opportunities of the lowlands. In our country, we have seen the "hillbilly" deserting his worn-out slope farms for a factory job in the new industries of the South or for the unskilled jobs of the North. In the British Isles, mountain districts have been taken over by tourists and water-power developments. In the Soviet Union, promising young mountain

This picture shows a mountain landscape in the Swiss Alps. The road seems to be an intrusion—as, indeed, it is. On the slope to the left, rocks lie poised to descend upon the road in winter avalanches. The bare rock slopes show no signs of human occupance. Obviously only a wealthy people could afford to build a road like this through such a forbidding landscape. But most mountainous countries are not wealthy. (Courtesy Swiss National Tourist Office)

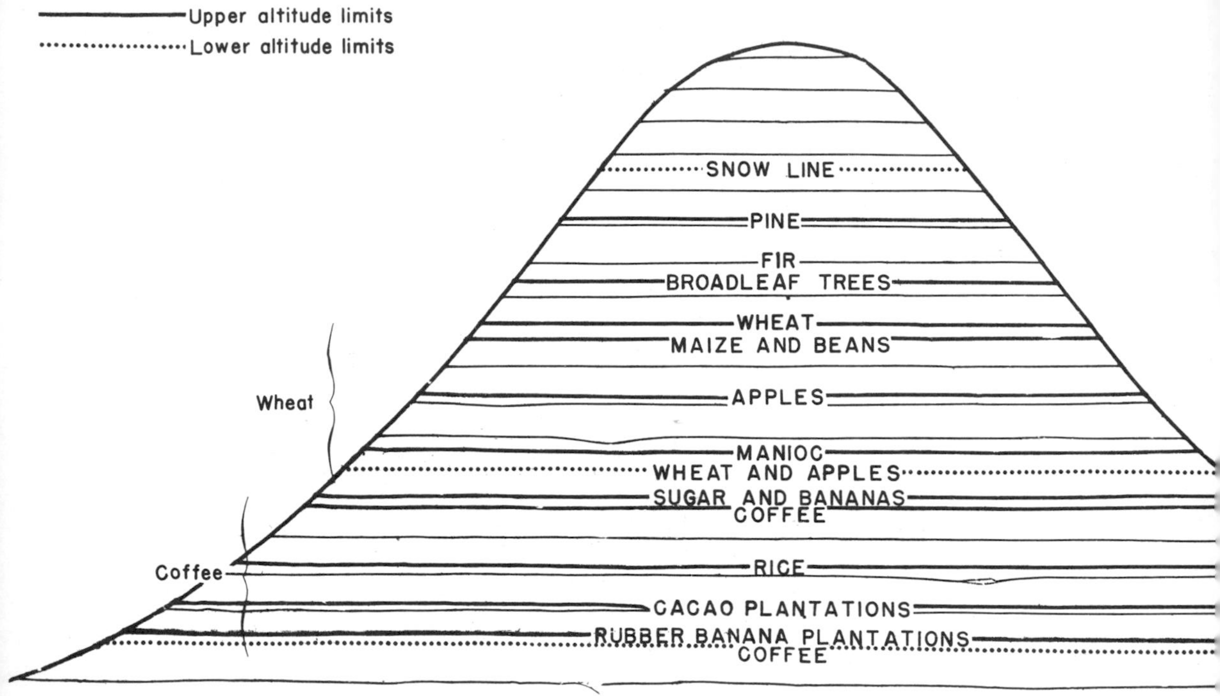

boys are sent off to schools in the big cities from which they return to serve as architects of change among their people.

Meanwhile, others move in to replace those who have left. Where the mineral-rich cores of mountains have been exposed by erosion, as in the Urals, or where streams have cut down through coal formations, as in the Appalachians and in the Ruhr Valley, miners have come in to exploit resources which the older settlers neither knew about nor could have used if they had known about them. Where mountains stand adjacent to or between industrial regions, as in Wales or the Franco-Italian border area or Japan, the upper reaches of their perennial, swift-flowing streams have become favorite sites for water-power development. For many a city-dweller in Europe or North America, a hotel or a small cabin in the mountains has become a retreat from the smog and noise and artificiality of the urban environment. Thus one might say that there has been a tendency for poverty to migrate out of the mountains and for wealth to migrate toward them.

It would be unfortunate if what we have said up to this time in the way of broad generalizations were to leave the impression that all mountain areas are impassable wildernesses and all mountain people poverty-striken goatherds. Mountains grade all the way from the wild, inaccessible Himalayas to such "tame" mountains as the English Pennines, the Russian Urals, or the American Blue Ridge. Geologists speak of "old" mountains and "young" mountains. These terms do not refer to calendar age but to stage of development, young mountains being those which have been eroded little or not at all, and old mountains being those which have been greatly reduced and much-smoothed-off by erosion. In general, the older the mountains are, the more useful they are likely to be to man. Old mountains in regions of moderate temperatures and dependable rainfall may, indeed, offer certain advantages to man which are not present in adjacent lowlands.

Some of these advantages derive from the fact that altitudinal differences reproduce many of the climatic and vegetational patterns that result from differences in latitude. Temperatures drop at the rate of approximately one degree for every 300 feet of elevation. This decline in temperatures produces a pattern of climatic and vegetational zones arranged like horizontal bands on the mountain slopes. Climatic and vegetational zoning, in turn, tends to produce zonation of

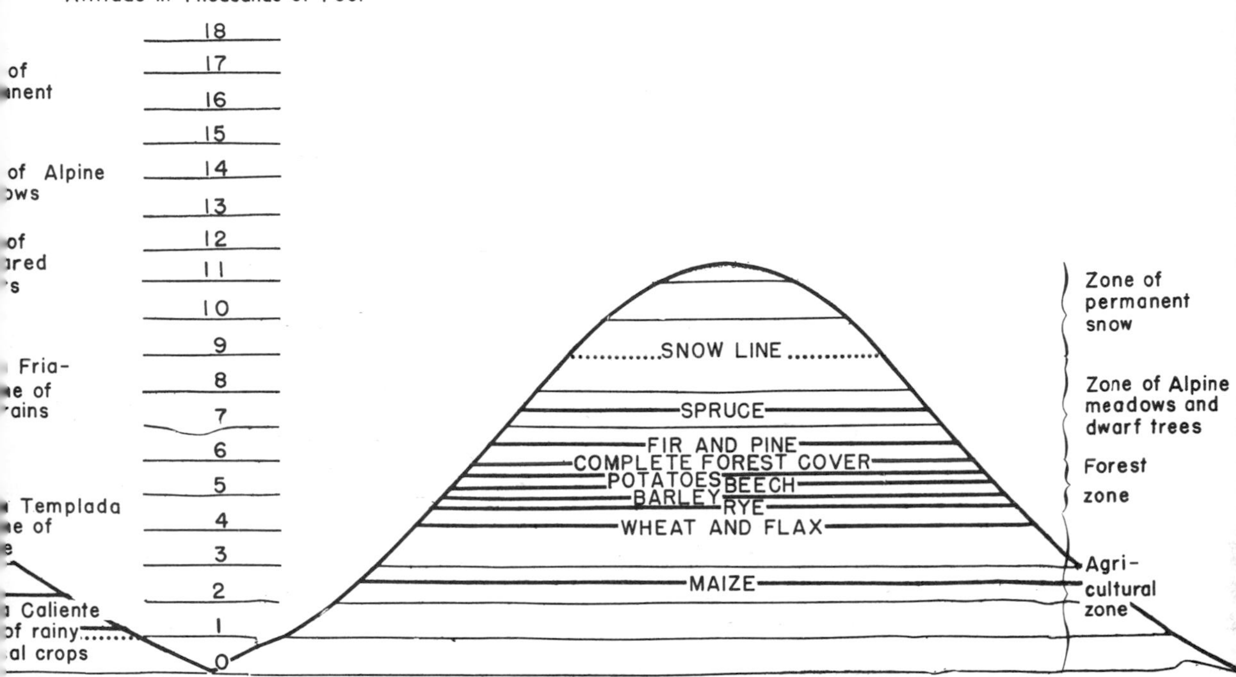

VII:2 Temperature zones and crop limits on Mount Orizaba (left) and in the Otztaler Alps (right) illustrate how zonation of crops reflects zonation of climates which, in turn, reflect differences in elevation. (After Karl Sapper, *Allgemeine Wirtschafts- und Verkehrsgeographie,* Berlin, 1930)

man's activities and settlements as intensive use of the mountain sides develops. The actual use of the various levels differs from place to place but the zonation itself is characteristic of practically all mountain areas. The implications of this zonation are indicated by the diagram (Figure VII-2) which shows temperature zones and associated crop limits on a tropical mountain (Mount Orizaba) and a middle-latitude mountain (one of the Ötztaler Alps in Austria).

Another advantage of mountain terrain derives from the fact that the sunward mountain slopes receive the rays of the sun more directly than do the adjoining lowlands. Particularly in the middle latitudes, therefore, certain types of agriculture, notably vineyards, thrive on slopeland. Often the greater warmth resulting from more direct heating is reinforced by air drainage, the flow of air down the slope, which reduces frost hazard. In the tropics, the more rapid runoff of rain water from mountain slopes may, locally, make the mountains more advantageous for agriculture than the wet lowlands.

Finally, it would have to be noted that throughout the tropics mountains and high plateaus are the preferred areas of settlement, especially for people of European descent. In countries such as India and the Philippines, where the large cities and the bulk of the population live in the warm lowlands, Europeans and the more fortunate nationals of these nations characteristically spend the warmest months of the year at hill stations which are often, in effect, summer capitals (Simla in India, Baguio in the Philippines).

In some parts of the world, mountain passes have served as great funnels through which travel and trade found their way from one lowland region to the other. In our own country, the Cumberland Pass was one of the great avenues of migration from the coastal lowland into the interior plains. In Europe the Brenner Pass, the St. Gotthard Pass, the Simplon Pass, and the St. Bernard Pass were early highways between Mediterranean Europe and the North European Plain. Milan and Venice profited from their strategic locations near the southern ends of the routes through these passes, as did Munich and Zurich at their northern ends. In Asia three of the most famous passes are the Khyber Pass, between Afghanistan and India; the Nankow Pass, between Mongolia and the Peking region; and the Jade Gate, which connects the basin of the Wei Ho with the Tarim Basin.

The destructible hills

There is, perhaps, no more imprecise word in the vocabulary of the geographer than the word "hill." Its connotations are clear enough: a hill signifies a surface eminence less prominent than a mountain, but there is no precise set of criteria which distinguishes hills from mountains. Some hills are steeper than some mountains. Some hills rise to higher elevations than do some mountains. Some mountains, in the geological sense, are called hills, and some hills are popularly called mountains.

Perhaps the best way to define hills is by example. The transition from plains to mountains often takes place in a belt of rolling country characterized by peaks or ridges set off from each other by valleys; these are foothills. Plains and plateaus, in many cases, have been very much cut into (dissected) by stream erosion; the resulting topography is often described as hilly. Some old mountains have been so badly worn down by erosion that they no longer seem deserving of the name of mountains; they may be called hills. In regions where continental glaciers were once active, the material accumulated at their ends may form a ridge conspicuously higher than the surrounding topography; these ridges (moraines) may be called hills. In other areas, the wind has piled up great mounds of sand (dunes); these are quite commonly called sand hills.

Because hills represent a condition transitional between level topography and mountain topography, it is difficult, and dangerous, to generalize about their significance for human occupance. The higher and more rugged hills invite much the same occupance patterns as do mountains. Low, gently-undulating hills may take on the occupance patterns of the surrounding plains. And it is just because of this transitional nature of hill country that, in so many places, hills have tempted men to use them unwisely. Failing to recognize the subtle, but neverthless important, differences between flatland and slopeland, men have carried crops, field patterns, and farming practices up with them from the plains into the hills. The result, in many cases, has been loss of the soil to the speeded-up processes of erosion acting on surfaces that have been stripped of their soil-holding vegetation. It would be fair to say that the most dangerous hill areas have been those which could have been, under wise systems of use, the most valuable.

This fact need not surprise us. Man is little tempted to settle in hills where slopes are obviously too steep for cultivation or where temperatures are uncomfortably low or where there is little rainfall or where the soil (as in the case of dunes) is obviously infertile. But he has been sorely tempted to settle in rolling country. Indeed, he has often preferred hill country with its good natural drainage to the poorly-drained, often malarial lowlands.

¶ Any considerable rain or melting of snow removes soil from all exposed areas having a slope in excess of about 0.5 per cent.[1] . . . No land anywhere in the United States having a slope in excess of about 25 per cent can be cultivated safely without protection against erosion. Generally, all land steeper than about 15 per cent is doomed to eventual severe impoverishment or destruction if cultivated without protection. Most land so steep should be maintained in forest, grass, or some other protective cover of vegetation.[2]

Ignorance of these elementary facts of life, or failure to act in conformity to them, has left a trail of worn-out land, worn-out economies, and worn-out people in the hill lands not only of our own country but of the world.

Indeed, the worst poverty to be found in rugged country is not usually to be found in the mountains but in the hills. High, rugged mountains actively discourage attempts at any kind of agriculture except tree agriculture and most mountain dwellers look for their livelihoods to resources other than the

---

1 A slope of 45° is considered a 100% slope.

2 Reprinted with permission from H. H. Bennett "Soil Erosion and Its Prevention," *Our Natural Resources and Their Conservation*, 1939, John Wiley & Sons, Inc., New York, pp. 68-69.

soil. Hill people have often foolishly destroyed the resources which might have sustained them in an effort to open up more land to cultivation. Thus they have cut down or burnt out trees; destroyed game, including potentially-profitable fur-bearing forms; and replaced unspoiled scenic beauty, which might have lured the tourist, with a landscape of row-cropped fields and ramshackle farmsteads.

But let us not sit in judgment on the hill-dweller. He discovered his mistakes the way man has usually discovered his mistakes, the hard way, by experience. Some more recent settlers in the hills have profited from the expensive experience of early settlers and have adapted their use of the land to the character of its topography and to the nature of its resources. This is most noticeably true in parts of Europe and Asia where the cycle of misuse and destruction was completed generations or even centuries ago. It is becoming true of many parts of the New World.

The principle of successful occupance of hill country is, basically, a very simple one: man need only work with the topography and the resources, rather than against them. Farming is possible if the type of agriculture and the choice of crops takes into account the ever-present danger of erosion. Crops planted in rows up and down slopes create, in effect, channels which speed up the run-off of water and greatly increase its erosive power. If such crops are to be planted at all, it is, therefore, advisable to plant them in rows perpendicular to the direction of the slope. Better still, the land can be given to grass and used for some form of animal husbandry, or planted to forests and orchards. Locally, as in mountains, there may be mineral wealth which can be profitably exploited or water-power sites which can be developed. And, of course, there are scenic resources which often require nothing more for their development than that they be made accessible.

In connection with the 17th International Geographical Congress, which was held in Washington in 1952, several field trips were arranged for the delegates. One of these led from Washington down through Kentucky, Tennessee, and Alabama and back through the Carolinas and Virginia. The guidebook for this trip provides several notable vignettes of the hill-country occupance. The following notes, digested from a much more detailed section of the itinerary, give not only an idea of the nature of one section of the Kentucky hill country but also an insight into the variations in occupance patterns that can be found within fairly short distances:

¶ Five miles west of Lexington is the famous Calumet Farm. Besides the estate house and cottages there are 18 barns, including the air-conditioned stallion barn with cork floors, pine-panelled walls, and a classic portico. White-washed wooden fences wind across the karst topography between the lush bluegrass pastures.

A mile past the Calumet Farm, and on the same side of the road, is the Keeneland Race Track, which seats 2,500 people and is considered one of the fastest in the United States. A fine four-lane highway continues to Versailles.

West of Versailles the route crosses the deeply entrenched meanders of the Kentucky River, here some 350 feet below the general level of the surrounding country. The railroad bridge on the left, 1,655 feet long, crosses the deep valley at a level 265 feet above the stream.

Lawrenceburg (population 2,379), a local market town and county seat, is near the eastern edge of the shale belt of yellow soils. The surface is much more dissected here, and abandoned land and woods are more common, and to the southwest the landscape appears increasingly unkempt.

Bardstown (population 4,135), a county seat and local trade center, is one of Kentucky's oldest towns. In it are several buildings that were constructed about a century and a half ago, when the town was one of the leading social and educational centers of the state. Bardstown is at the eastern edge of the rounded Knobs, known here as Muldrough's Hills. These conical sandstone-capped hills are largely forested. Some mixed livestock and semi-subsistence farming is practical, but the Knobs are of no notable agricultural importance.

Elizabethtown (population 5,793), a county seat, is the market center for the livestock, tobacco, and grain of a large rural area. As in most of the Southeast, Saturday is the busiest market day, and on that day the town is crowded with farmers.

The section of the Interior Low Plateaus between the Knobs and the Tennessee-Kentucky boundary is known locally as the "Pennyrile," after the pennyroyal, an aromatic herb of the mint family, which grows profusely along the streams of the area. The underlying rocks are dominantly limestones and shaly limestones whose fertility has been greatly increased by the application of phosphate fertilizers. Pastures and livestock assume local importance. Nevertheless, the dominant economy of the Pennyroyal is based on tobacco as a cash crop and on corn raised for human consumption and for feeding a few hogs and chickens, or possibly even cattle. This is one of the most extensive areas of karst topography in the eastern United States. Since Indian days it has served as a corridor for travel between the Bluegrass Basin and the Ohio River to the North and the Nashville Basin to the south.

South of Elizabethtown, the gently rolling topography supports corn and tobacco, with frequent poor pastures and wooded hills. South of the Nolin River is a small but prosperous livestock farming area, which gives way to wooded hills around Upton. Beyond Upton the landscape becomes more desolate, farms are smaller and shabbier, and some of the fields are cultivated by hand instead of by plow. Frequent gullies and bare red hillsides attest the severity of soil erosion. Farther from the main road live those "transgressors, nonconformists only in regard to that item of the legal order as to the manner in which they shall not market their corn," for in this area, as in many of the remoter parts of the Southeast, the farmers are either unable or unwilling to carry their corn to market. Instead they operate illicit distilleries, or "stills," to convert their surplus grain into "corn whiskey," which is much simpler and easier, albeit illegal, to transport.

South of Bonnieville the making of baskets and chairs from split white oak has become a rather important rural industry, and many kinds of basket work are displayed beside the road or on the porches of the houses.

In Cave City (population 1,114) the route turns northwest to Mammoth Cave, in a region of amazing karst features.

After leaving Cave City the route climbs the Dripping Springs Escarpment and follows a ridge capped with Cypress Sandstone. Farmers in the area are relatively prosperous, despite the unpainted barns and houses. Tobacco is the economic mainstay although corn and hay crops occupy much more of the land. Cattle, horses, mules, and sheep are common on the pastures, and practically every farm has a few hogs. Here sinkholes are used for livestock watering ponds.

Bowling Green (population 17,427) is a hilly town. The town has some importance as a warehouse center and market for both dark and burley tobacco. The production of strawberries has assumed significance in the surrounding area, and Bowling Green is crowded with migrant workers during the two-week picking season, which usually begins in early June. The Western Kentucky State Teachers College occupies a hilltop position on the site of a Civil War fort, built to command the Pennyroyal corridor between Louisville and Nashville (4).

One of the first things a geographer must learn is not to generalize from limited observation. This particular passage was chosen, though, because it points up a number of distinctive features of the hill-country occupance, notably the following:

1. The striking contrasts in land-use and apparent farm prosperity within very short distances, contrasts resulting both from natural opportunities and limitations and from man's capitalizing or failing to capitalize upon the opportunities presented to him.

2. The generally small size of the towns. Lexington (1950 population 55,534) is the regional capital. Market centers fall into the 5,000-or-under class except for Bowling Green. Hill-country towns are typically small, chiefly because they have restricted and often impoverished hinterlands to draw upon.

3. The relation of roads and other routes of travel to ridge tops and valleys. Typically, the roads avoid the slopes. Railroads also usually avoid the ridge-tops and funnel through the stream valleys.

4. An atmosphere of glory departed. Towns like Bardstown have failed to realize the promise of their early days when they were centers of wealth and culture. Fine old homes have fallen into decay or been preserved as museums, their one-time owners or their descendants having found it impossible to maintain their wealth in the limited economic environment of the region or having left for places of greater opportunity.

5. New wealth resulting from specialization of land-use. Calumet Farm, the Keeneland Race Track, livestock farming, basket and chair manufacturing, strawberry

culture are examples of such specialization.

6. The breakdown of law enforcement in areas which are difficult of access. In such situations, local mores determine conduct and the outside law enforcement officer may be regarded less as a conservator of the peace than a disturber of local social order, customs, and traditions.

7. The association of woodlands with hill tops. So common is this association that hill districts in Europe are often called forests (German *Wälder*) even when, as in some cases, the forest has been removed. England, for instance, has its New Forest, Germany its Black Forest—both of them hill areas.

8. The flight from the hills to the lowlands or even to other regions. Abandoned lands, woods, and farmsteads are characteristic of hill districts which have been worn out by unwise cultivation.

In the tropics, hills, like mountains, may offer advantageous sites for settlement and for certain high-value types of farming. Coffee culture and tea culture, for instance, are typically associated with hill sites, partly because of the cooler temperatures, partly because of the better drainage, and partly because of air drainage. But erosion is even more of a threat in the tropics than it is in the middle latitudes, and the lush forest cover may make hill areas very difficult of access.

Along the mountainous margins of drylands, foothill zones, often built up by the deposition of streams debouching from the mountains, may provide prime settlement sites. The alluvial soils, dependably supplied with waters, often support specialized crops grown under irrigation. These are, properly speaking, oasis sites, natural or man-made. In the Old World, especially in the dry heart of Asia, settlements in these belts of rolling alluvial deposits are connected by trails, some of which have been used as major highways since prehistoric days.

But it is in the Mediterranean world, with its dearth of level land, that the hill environment truly comes into its own. Here, by way of exception to the general rule, the great cities are typically built on hills: Jerusalem, Athens, Rome, Toledo are only the most famous of numerous such cities. It would appear that their sites were originally chosen for defensive reasons: defense against invaders who swept across the narrow, almost tideless Mediterranean, defense against the mosquito that dominated the wet coastal lowlands. As these cities grew in numbers and power, they commonly spread out over the intervening valleys, but even so their cores remained fixed on the hills. The heart of Athens was the Acropolis (the "high city") and the heart of Jerusalem was Mt. Zion. Rome, greatest of all ancient cities, spread itself across seven hills. In the New World Mediterranean lands, the pattern has repeated itself, although perhaps less perfectly, in such hill metropolises as San Francisco and Santiago. But even these great cities have had to pay for the charm of their settings. Their sites do not favor the establishment of industries such as steel mills and metal fabricating plants which require large areas of flat land for economical operation. They have had to turn, instead, to commerce or light industry for an economic base, leaving heavy industry and major transportational facilities to satellite towns located in the coastal lowlands (Jaffa-Tel Aviv, Piraeus, Ostia, Oakland, Valparaiso de Chile).

The high and dry plateau habitat

Distinguishing plains from plateaus presents some of the same difficulties that are encountered in attempting to distinguish mountains from hills. Both plains and plateaus are, normally, regions of horizontal or only very slightly tilted rock. Both tend to be flat and featureless in the youthful and old-age phases of their erosion cycle and both may be so badly dissected in the mature stage that they are described as hilly or even mountainous (Figure VII-3). Some plateaus stand at lower elevations than some plains, and traditional nomenclature serves only to confuse the matter.

Geologists differentiate plains from plateaus primarily on the basis of relief. River valleys in a plain are typically shallow, and broad in proportion to their depth. River valleys in plateaus are typically canyon-like, narrow in proportion to their depth. Since plateaus are often found in association with mountains, they are often affected by a "rain shadow" condition and are, therefore, dry. Arid plateaus typically have little or no vegetational cover, and the absence of such a cover, taken with the general flatness of the surface, gives free course to the winds. The

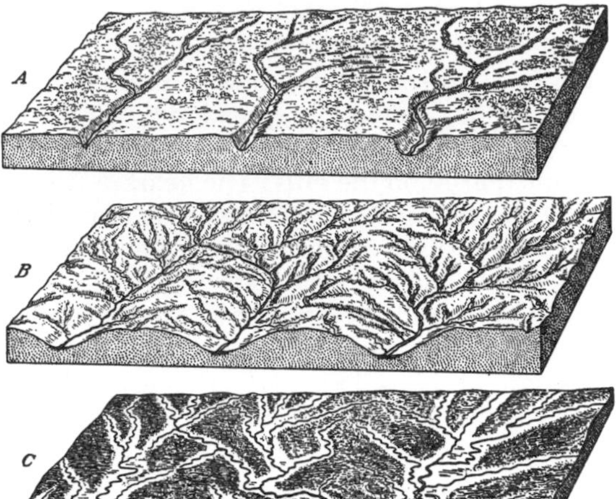

VII:3 The erosion cycle of a plain in a region of uniform rock and humid climate is shown here. From top to bottom: the level, almost featureless landscape of youth; the strongly dissected, "hilly" landscape of maturity; the gently rolling landscape of old age. (Reprinted with permission of The Macmillan Company from *New Physical Geography* by Ralph S. Tarr and O. D. von Engeln. Copyright 1947 by The Macmillan Company.)

dryness of the air over most plateaus also encourages extremes of temperature since there is no insulating layer of moisture to absorb the heat of the sun's rays during the daytime or to prevent heat loss from the surface at night. Finally, since plateaus typically stand at high elevations, the temperature level tends to be significantly lower than in lowlands of the same latitude.

So far as man's occupance is concerned, plateaus may be divided into three classes: middle-latitude humid plateaus, middle-latitude dry plateaus, and low-latitude plateaus. Most middle-latitude humid plateaus are in the mature (maximally-dissected) stage of the erosion cycle and fall, accordingly, into the category of hill country. To this class belong the plateaus associated with the Appalachian system, the Ozark "Mountains," the Laurentian Highlands of Canada, the Massif Central of France, the Bavarian Plateau of Germany, and the South China hill country.

Middle-latitude dry plateaus, on the other hand, present a singular environment associated with distinct occupance forms. These forms are described at length in Chapters 21 and 22. For our present purposes it is necessary only to summarize some of the major characteristics of this environment, such as:

1. The dominance of animal husbandry in the economy. The American dry plateaus provided the locale for the cowboy legends which have been elaborated into countless television westerns. Similar legends have grown up around the Argentine gaucho and the Australian sheep drover.

2. The importance, locally, of irrigated agriculture. Western man, especially, has seen the dry plateaus as a kind of challenge to his ingenuity. His response can best be seen from the air: ribbons of rich green winding through the brownish, yellowish landscape of the plateau, nurtured by the waters of streams, many of which are fed by the rains and melted snow of the adjacent mountains. Closer inspection would show that the green color is the color of hay crops or wheat or sugar beets.

3. The sparsity of population, and its concentration along such local sources of water as streams, wells, and springs.

4. The relative scarcity of roads and railroads. Plateaus, typically, are difficult of access because their margins are fringed by steep escarpments or high mountains. The surface of the plateau itself is transected by steep-sided canyons, often too wide and too deep for successful bridging. To cross from the south rim of the Grand Canyon to the north rim, for example, one must drive 252 miles, although the straight-line distance across the canyon is only twelve miles.

5. The isolating effect of plateaus upon local populations. One of the best examples of this effect, historically, is to be found in the Old Testament in the divergent destinies of the kingdoms of Israel and Judah after the division of the Solomonic kingdom. Highland Judah maintained the ancient language, the ancient religion, and the integrity of its ethnic inheritance. Lowland Israel was quickly absorbed into the linguistic, religious, and ethnic melting-pot of the near-eastern culture. In our own country, Mormonism is found in the Snake River and Great Basin plateaus, a haven within which it could develop its own particularism.

A recent writer has captured the "feel" of

the dry plateaus in a passage which deserves to be quoted at length:

¶ In the western parts of Kansas and Nebraska in 1870 there were not two persons to the square mile. In all Montana there were 20,000 people; in the whole Dakota territory fewer than that; in Wyoming only 9,000. The South Dakota gold rush and the Colorado silver rush ushered in, in the seventies, the expansive decades. The railroads were built, and the boom was on.

After two centuries of underestimation and neglect, the plains within two decades became overestimated and abused. This was the vastest area in the world to be settled so swiftly and so late in history—so late that the ruts of the wagon trains of the pioneers still lie clear in the earth of North Dakota. In the 20 years that ended the century Kansas multiplied its population by 3, Wyoming by 6, Nebraska by 8, and South Dakota by 24.

The bonanza of ranching, one of the events leading up to the tragedy, roused cupidities as far off as Canada, Scotland, and Australia. In England newspapers reported that yearlings purchasable for $5 a head could be fattened on the free grass of the plains at a cost of $1 and sold for $60. The story was told of a servant girl who received 15 cows from her employer in payment of $150 in wages, and who ten years later sold them and their progeny for $25,000. A book entitled *Brisbin's Beef Bonanza* proved with mathematical precision that an investment of $25,000 would produce $51,278 in six years. English and Scotch syndicates poured money and representatives onto the plains. Twenty mammoth cattle companies were formed in Wyoming in a single year, six for $50,000 each, two for $1,000,000, one for $2,000,000. American swindlers in Europe sold "range rights" to the unskeptical.

It was fascinating to reflect that cattle could be put out on an inexhaustible range and forgotten till they were fat and ready for market. No one gave a thought to winter feed. As long as the grass held out there was year-round forage. Investors were "betting against God Almighty and a sub-Arctic winter." It took sometimes as little as two or three years of wet weather and good prices to convince a plainsman, against all the evidence of history, that there would be nothing but grey skies from then on.

The cattle bonanza lasted until the test of the 'eighties. Then drouth came by summer and blizzard by winter, and when they were over the bonanza was over. Cattle had gone blind in the dazzling snow and plunged to death over the canyon cliffs; they had wandered into the streets of towns by night, bellowing with hunger, had starved and frozen in snowdrifts up to their buttocks, the grass locked away from them by snow and ice. Half to three quarters of herds perished. Many cattlemen, disgusted, resigned the land to the coyotes and the grasshoppers, quit business, and moved out. Those who stayed had learned a lesson: ranchers must produce their own feed, to weather out drouth and blizzard.

Meanwhile the bonanza of farming, another event leading up to the tragedy, had begun. Free land! Rich land! A fortune for the making! Step right up, folks! Step up a little closer!

The land rush was on. Anyone could have 160 acres, a quarter of a section, under the Homestead Act of 1862. The railroads became the ballyhooers-in-chief, selling off the land they had received free, to settlers who would swell their traffic. They plastered the North American continent and a good part of Europe with advertisements of quick riches.

Tenderfoot settlers came by every train, people who, if they knew farming at all, knew a kind that was practicable in the humid climates they had come from but useless in the semi-arid land to which they were coming. But come one, come all! Congress will give you each and every one a tract of land too small to make a living on, and laid out without any regard to water supply! If you will only step a little closer, please!

The farmers fenced their land, the first barriers that had ever been laid across the one great rolling sea of grass, thousands of square miles of it. The cattlemen resisted, with violence. "I wish," said Charlie Russell, the famous Montana cowboy artist, "the coyotes would get big enough to eat the damn farmers!" But when the shooting was over the cattlemen had lost. Unable to beat the game of fencing, they joined it. They fenced the land they owned and they bought more and fenced that.

The cattlemen were defeated by the farmers, and the farmers were defeated by themselves. They starved out, wave after wave of them. All that was needed to put the finishing touch to the bonanza of farming was the customary drouth, and it came in the early 'nineties. Thousands of heartsick settlers moved out, for-

NORTH AMERICA
ARCTIC OCEAN
QUEEN ELIZABETH ISLANDS
GREENLAND
BEAUFORT SEA
HUDSON BAY
CANADA
PACIFIC OCEAN
GULF OF MEXICO
ALEUTIAN ISLANDS
HAWAII
THE AERO RELIEF MAP OF NORTH AMERICA
LEGEND
CHICAGO
TORONTO
Sacramento
CASCADE RANGE
BELCHER ISLANDS
Cape Cod
YUCATÁN
LAND ELEVATIONS & OCEAN DEPTHS
GEOGRAPHICAL EQUIVALENTS
AERO SERVICE CORPORATION

ever. In 50 counties one third of the population left. The loss was 60 per cent in six counties of southwestern Kansas. Bonanza farming, like bonanza ranching, was a bubble popped.

Farming did not gain a toehold on the plains until immigrants from Europe brought to the region their skill at farming in a subhumid climate, and beet seed from Germany, Red Fife, Turkey Red, Turkey, Kharkov, and Crimean wheats from Turkey and the Russian steppes—strains adapted to lands of little water.

Farming did not gain a foothold until irrigation—begun in Montana and Colorado in the 'fifties, promoted by Horace Greeley, editor of the *New York Tribune* and enunciator of the westward-ho, at Greeley, Colo., in the 'seventies—came into widespread use after the turn of the century.

Farmers were not told the facts of living on the Great Plains till Maj. John Wesley Powell, of the United States Geographical and Geological Survey, in 1878 wrote a preface to understanding of this region, a report which has become a classic. He took these truths to be fundamental:

Deficiencies of water, and acute drouth, are normal conditions.

The only kind of farming that is safe in the semi-arid and arid zones is irrigated farming.

Aside from farming, the only use of the land should be for ranching.

The land should be laid out in tracts large enough to afford a livelihood: for an irrigated farm, 80 acres; for unirrigated pasture, 2,560 acres.

But many chose to remain strangers to the land despite Major Powell's wise counsel—gambling on the one good year when they would strike it rich, but exposed meanwhile to the inexorable mathematic of the plains: more than half the time, failure.

The first World War brought back the old mad cycle of boom and bust. Prices went sky high: wheat $2 a bushel, corn $1.50. At those prices, farmers couldn't get enough land to put to wheat and corn, though land sold for as much as $300 an acre. They plowed up and planted grassland that should have stayed grassland.

VII:4 (Left) This relief map of North America shows the comparative elevations. (Relief map copyright Aero Service Corporation, used by permission)

The years immediately after the war brought, along with high prices, new machinery specially adapted to the plains, which made it possible to raise wheat there 50 per cent cheaper than on the smaller, rougher farms of the east. Here, where a furrow could be plowed 100 miles long, the huge machines were at home. Grasslands were put to the plow by the millions of acres. In the five years starting in 1924, in the whole of the Great Plains (including the Texas and Oklahoma portions as well as those of the Missouri Valley) cropland increased almost 15 million acres, the equivalent of half the State of Ohio.

As the soil was made progressively finer by cropping, it began to blow, and in 1934 began the black hurricane, the dust storms that were a pestilence in the middle and late 'thirties, winds full of irreplaceable soil which turned day into night. In all the plains the dust storms robbed soil from 19 million acres.

But the farmers came as strangers to the valley, and strangers they stayed. In what had been the worst part of the Dust Bowl barely ten years earlier, around Huron, S. Dak., farmers in 1944 raised 75 bushels of corn to the acre on unirrigated land. They were in the money. They would plant corn again, and so would their neighbors. And the Huron area is semi-arid; corn can be successfully grown there less than half the time, and should never be attempted without irrigation. But once again prices were high and the land was wet.

Powell had learned the lesson more than half a century before and had given it to the plains; he had found few takers. A little rain, a few high prices, and everybody is hell-bending it for the old cycle that comes rhyming back:

Boom and bust,
Plague of dust (5).[1]

Low-latitude plateaus are not the world's best habitats for man, either, but by comparison with the tropical lowlands even a dry, inaccessible, wind-swept plateau looks quite inviting. Climatically, plateaus are the temperate zones of the tropics and preferred regions of settlement. Four of the fourteen cities within the tropics that have populations in excess of one million stand at ele-

[1] Terral, Rufus, *The Missouri Valley: Land of Drouth, Flood, and Promise,* Yale University Press, New Haven, Conn., 1947, pp. 3-8. Reprinted by permission.

vations higher than 1,000 feet, a very high percentage when one takes into account the fact that of the 56 one-million class cities outside the tropics only three (Santiago, Madrid, and Tehran) stand at elevations above 1,000 feet. Of the 32 self-governing countries which lie wholly or mostly within the tropics, almost half (15) are governed from capital cities located above the 1,000-foot level. When Brazil's new capital at Brasilia is completed, the number of capitals thus located will be exactly half the total.

It should not be necessary to belabor the reasons for this concentration of population in the tropical highlands. What should perhaps be emphasized is that these people are here in spite of an impressive number of natural handicaps which the middle-latitude plains dweller would find discouraging. Until the advent of air travel, for instance, it took eight days to reach Bogotá, the capital of Colombia, by river and rail from the coast. The average temperature for the warmest month at Quito, the capital of Ecuador, is 58° F., approximately the same as the July temperature of the Yukon valley. The air is so thin and the night winds so chilly over Bolivia that the huts of the poorer folk (who cannot afford glass) have no windows in them, and visitors from the lowlands find the least exertion wearying.

In spite of these handicaps, however, some tropical plateaus have become not only centers of population but also of civilization and culture. Mexico City is the intellectual, social, political, and economic capital of a nation which has experienced what can only be called a rebirth in the twentieth century. Bogotá calls itself, and with considerable justification, the "Athens of the New World" and has produced a surprising number of intellectuals whose influence has been felt throughout the Spanish-speaking world. São Paulo, the self-styled "Chicago of South America," has all the vigor and bustle of its North America counterpart and is one of the fastest-growing cities in the world. Air travel, which has already done so much to relieve the isolation of the tropical plateaus, will undoubtedly open up an even more promising future to them. It may well be that the tropical plateau will be the great frontier of the future.

The key to the future of the tropical plateau is transportation. Until very recently the plateau dweller had little economic opportunity. For the masses the only possible means of livelihood was a primitive kind of subsistence agriculture. Such commercial agriculture as there was (e.g., the coffee of Brazil and Colombia) was at the mercy of middle-latitude markets. Mineral wealth lay hidden in vast unmapped and even unvisited areas and, when discovered, was hardly worth exploiting unless, like the tin of Bolivia, it consisted of some rather rare mineral which could stand heavy transportation costs. Manufacturing was ruled out by a limited domestic market, difficulty of assembling raw materials, and the high cost of transportation to foreign markets. Not surprisingly, therefore, far-seeing governments in these lands are attempting, above all else, to open up the land by means of roads, railroads, and airlines. Unfortunately, the limited resources of these governments, coupled often with conditions of political instability, make this a painfully slow process.

The gravitational pull of the plains

"Man—", Ellen Semple once wrote, "like air and water—feels always the pull of gravity." This is only a graphic way of saying that, by and large, man is a creature of the lowlands, congregating in largest numbers at or near sea level and thinning out rapidly above levels of about 1,000 feet.

But while man has shown a great affinity for plains, not all plains have shown any great affinity for man. The Arctic lowlands offer him no inducement to settle there, the tropical lowlands plague him with humidity and swamp and mosquito, many deltas and coastal plains offer him no dry ground on which to set his foot, and some otherwise suitable plains get too little water to nourish his crops and flocks. Even large areas of the plains which he now occupies had to be wrested from marshland and swamp, from forbidding forest and from grass too thick for his accustomed plows. Like a rich and at-

VII:5 (Right) This relief map of South America shows its comparative elevations. (Relief map copyright Aero Service Corporation, used by permission)

SOUTH AMERICA
RELIEF MAP OF SOUTH AMERICA
LAND ELEVATIONS & OCEAN DEPTHS
ANDES
PAMPAS
RIO DE JANEIRO
FALKLAND ISLANDS

VII:6 This relief map of Europe shows its comparative elevations. (Relief map copyright Aero Service Corporation, used by permission)

tractive woman, the plains took much wooing (involving, at times, some cave-man techniques), but they have made man a good wife.

The basic reason for man's concentration in the lowlands is to be found in the gregarious nature of man and in the communal nature of most of his enterprises. Man is most truly man only in association with other people. Robinson Crusoe was well along toward insanity until Friday appeared upon the scene. "Civilization" comes from a Latin root (*civis*) which meant the voting resident of a town. Involvement, not isolation, produces civilization and culture.

Of all of the environments discussed in this chapter, the plains environment is most conducive to man-to-man and group-to-group contacts. Few obstacles oppose man's free movement. Of those obstacles which do stand in his way, some, like forests, can be fairly easily removed; others, like hills, can be circumvented; and others, like rivers, can be bridged or forded or even converted into highways. Only climate has set obstacles which, at least until now, man has been unable to overcome, bypass, or convert to his own advantage.

In a sense, the greater part of this book is the story of man's occupance of the plains, for most of man's activities are carried on in the plains environment. Therefore, instead of attempting what could only be, at best, a superficial analysis of the plains occupance, we shall look at some of the more common types of plains and indicate, in a very general way, their possibilities and limitations in terms of land-use.

*1. **Coastal plains.*** Fringing the continents are strips of lowland, sometimes quite wide, sometimes very narrow. These plains are actually unsubmerged portions of the continental shelf, raised above sea level either by a slight uplift of the continental margin or by a drop in the level of the ocean. On such plains there is usually a drainage problem because the slope to the sea is not great enough to encourage the rapid and efficient runoff of water. Along the coast itself, there are likely to be extensive areas of swamp. Soils in many cases are relatively poor, consisting of sands which were accumulated when the present plains were still submerged under the shallow waters of the coastal zone and were receiving alluvial wash from the continent. In some cases, subsidence of the plain after its initial uplift caused the "drowning" of river mouths, producing wide, but usually shallow, embayments.

The combination of poor drainage and poor soils tends to limit the value of coastal plains for agriculture. Along our own Atlantic Coastal Plain in the Carolinas, surprisingly large areas have remained in forest or have been bought up as hunting estates by wealthy sportsmen. But where coastal lowlands fringe a rich hinterland, wilderness tends to give way to commercial development, especially at good natural harbor sites, and this kind of development tends, in turn, to lead to more intensive use of the land for agriculture. Often such agriculture can be carried on only by radically altering the face of the land. As a general rule, though, coastal plains are areas of fairly limited opportunity. Except for the port cities themselves, population along the margins of the land masses tends to settle somewhat inland from the coastal plain, on the higher ground which, because it is higher and has had a longer time to develop a normal drainage pattern, is more adaptable both to settlement and to agriculture. In some places, especially along our own east coast, the dividing line between the older plain and the younger one is a very sharp one. We call our dividing line "the fall line" because streams passing from the older plains to the younger ones do so by means of falls or rapids. In days when water power was the chief source of energy for industry, fall line sites were favored sites for industrial development and its concomitant urbanization. Examples of fall line cities are Philadelphia, Baltimore, Washington, Richmond, Raleigh, Columbia, Augusta, and Macon.

*2. **Deltas.*** A special type of coastal lowland is the delta. Deltas form where streams enter bodies of fairly motionless water and drop the materials which they had eroded from the land. Since deltas are formed by river deposition, they can be built no higher than the flood level of the river which builds them. They are, therefore, characteristically very low-lying, their outstanding surface feature being natural levees which are built up during flood periods along the channels of the stream and its distributaries.

Deltas tend to be very poorly drained. Their soils are typically fine and unconsolidated. The distributaries which branch off from the main stream wind sluggishly and apparently purposelessly about, often abandoning their channels for new ones. On the delta margins, the waves often deposit infertile sands.

Most deltas are sparsely settled, settlements concentrating along the natural levees. Typically, roads and homesites are placed on the levee, and farm units extend in long, narrow bands away from the levee downslope to the swamplands. But some deltas are heavily populated, notable examples being the Ganges Delta of India; the coastal section of the Netherlands which consists of the combined deltas of the Rhine, the Meuse, and the Scheldt Rivers; the great delta of North China which was built by the Hwang Ho and a number of smaller streams; the Po Delta with its great city, Venice; and the Nile Delta. Populations such as those found in these areas have been made possible only by superhuman effort and eternal vigilance. The following excerpts from an article on the Netherlands gives some idea of what delta people are up against:

¶ Saturday evening, January 31, 1953. I remember listening to the radio with that sense of disaster that both fascinates and appalls. Gale warnings, tide warnings—all the coasts of the

This is a view of the northeast polder of the Zuiderzee works in the Netherlands. Here is a plains landscape in its ultimate expression. Contrast it with the mountain landscape pictured on page 143. Man is the active agent in this landscape; in fact, he is its "creator," inasmuch as this is land reclaimed from the sea. The flat, featureless surface of such a landscape allows for the imposition of ordered patterns—straight-line roads, rectangular fields, regularly dispersed farmsteads. (Courtesy Netherlands Information Service)

North Sea were threatened. It was a time of spring tides, when sun and moon pull together to raise the level of the sea, and for days there had been strong northerlies, blocking the escape northward of each ebbing tide. Now it was full gale right on top of one of the year's biggest tides, and Holland stood in the direct path of the storm. Wind force a hundred miles an hour plus, and almost one quarter of that country lay below sea level—five million people, half the population, with no protection against the elements but the dikes they themselves had erected over the centuries. . . .

Fatal it was. In that first onslaught the sea did not breach the protecting dikes; it swept in over the top of them. In places a twelve-foot wall of water rampaged through farm and village. And in that and succeeding nights 1,800 people lost their lives; 10,000 farms and houses were destroyed, a further 40,000 damaged. Three hundred miles of dike were swamped, and successive tides tore sixty-seven major breaches in the dikes, attacking them often from the rear.

. . . Holland has had 140 recorded disasters, going back as far as December 14, 1287, when all the land between the old Zuider Zee and the River Ems was inundated and 50,000 people drowned.

Holland as a country is unique, and to anybody who knows the sea and its destructive power, utterly fascinating, for geologically it has no right to exist. Half the population is living in what should be water or swamp. As one Frenchman put it: "God created the world except Holland, which the Dutch created themselves."

. . . We sailed up to Rotterdam, past oil refineries and cranes and miles of warehouses; it was hard to realize that this, the second-greatest port in the world, was all built on piles in a quaking land of bog. And then down through the rivers and canals to Flushing—locks and bridges and barges everywhere, and from the deck no land visible except the dikes on either side, their green tops in silhouette against the cloud-spattered sky. But when I climbed the mast, then I could see all the rich land of Holland laid out below the level of the water on which we sailed —way, way below it, as much as twenty feet.

. . . I left Schiedam for Kinderdijk—to look at windmills. I have always loved windmills, though for years I thought of them as corn grinders and actually made several visits to Holland before I realized that the Dutch used them mainly to drain the polders (reclaimed areas of former sea bottom) of excess rain water. At one time they had over seven thousand mills, the wind in their whirling sails providing the power to lift the water, step by step, to the canals.

At Kinderdijk, some ten miles east of Rotterdam, you can find the biggest cluster of the remaining twelve hundred; mill after mill, one behind the other, standing in the sunken polder lands with their big sails spread like dumb giants in perpetual conclave. They are still working, these mills—still lifting the water above the roofs of the little thatched houses snugged against the dike. . . .

There is a scheme now to convert these old windmills to the production of electricity and so give them a chance to earn their keep, for as water lifters their days are numbered. In the new polders of the Zuider Zee, two or three big diesel pumping stations suffice to keep the water level down in a hundred thousand acres.

To learn about these new polders, I went to The Hague. . . . I found the man I had come to see in an office in the Binnenhof. . . .

"Every year," he told me, "there are 60,000 more people in Holland. We must have more land—much more land. Look!" Maps were spread, books, illustrations—all the future was flung at me in a rush of words. "First the Zuider Zee. We reclaim half a million acres there. That will take another ten years, maybe more.

"Meanwhile, we commence work on the Delta Plan. That is the second stage. It is essential. That was shown by the disaster of '53. Look! We make enclosing dams there and there and there." He drew swift pencil marks across all the main outlets of the Rhine north of Flushing. "It means giant sluices, secondary dams—and the tides are stronger in the south. Maybe it takes twenty-five years. I don't know."

He looked up at me quickly, intent on his dream. "Then we will begin the third stage." More pencil marks, short lines linking the offshore islands to the north. . . . "All the northern flats enclosed. Then we have reduced our coastline to three hundred miles. Then we are safe, even though we know the land is sinking by almost one foot every century. Or maybe it is the tides that are rising. Whatever it is, this threat must be met or there is no more Holland. And this is how we do it."

They were planning for the year 2000 *and beyond.*[1]

*3. **Floodplains.*** Floodplains are typically associated with streams found in mature or old-age landscapes. They are what their name suggests: plains formed by stream deposition at times when the stream rose out of its bed and transgressed the adjoining lowlands. Since the first check on the movement of the flood water is at the stream's bank, the heaviest deposition takes place here, in the form of natural levees. But beyond the levees the flooding stream deposits a layer of silt as far as the floodwaters reach.

Thanks to this periodic renewal of the soil, floodplains are usually excellent agricultural regions when properly drained. But drainage may present quite a problem since there is very little slope down toward the stream. Ditching and tiling and sometimes the gathering of water into shallow ponds are devices for draining the land. In a typical floodplain landscape, the floodplain itself is given to crops. Roads run either along the inner and higher margin of the floodplain, or in some cases along the top of the levees. Farmsteads and towns are located either on higher ground inland from the floodplain or, if there are high terraces intruding into the floodplain, on such terraces.

The width and surface appearance of floodplains depend on the age, size, and

[1] Innes, Hammond, "Holland," *Holiday,* Vol. 21, No. 3, pp. 51-57 *passim.* Reprinted by special permission from *Holiday,* copyright March, 1957, by the Curtis Publishing Company.

VII:7 This relief map of Asia shows its comparative elevations. (Relief map copyright Aero Service Corporation, used by permission)

nature of the streams which form them. In general, there is a close correlation between the size of a stream and its floodplain, but this rule is subject to some exceptions. The floodplain of the Lower Amazon, for instance, averages less than thirty miles wide (7), while the floodplain of the Mississippi at Cairo, Illinois, is at some points as much as seventy-five miles wide. The age and the nature of the stream have much to do with the appearance of the floodplain surface. Old, sluggish, meandering streams, rejuvenated during periods of flood by the enormously greater volume of water, often reshape their channels, leaving abandoned meanders, called oxbow lakes, which after a while become silted up. Tributaries to the main stream, blocked by natural levees from entering it, may follow an aimless course of least resistance through the floodplain until eventually they discover a break through which they can escape into the main stream. Associated with these Yazoo tributaries will be swamps, often grown up in tangled woods.

4. Piedmont plains. At the foot of mountains or high hills, material eroded from the highlands may accumulate where streams suddenly lose velocity as they drop from the highlands onto the adjoining lowlands. As the channeled water spreads out at the foot of such highlands, it spreads alluvium out in a kind of fan shape with the "handle" of the fan extending up the stream valley into the highlands. Materials deposited in such situations follow a fairly orderly pattern of gradation: the coarsest and heaviest materials form at the "handle" of the fan and progressively finer materials are deposited out toward its margins.

If a number of streams debouch along the same highland front, their fans may coalesce into an "alluvial piedmont plain." Sometimes these deposits are sufficiently rolling to be classified as hill country, but often they are quite smooth, sloping gently away from the highlands. Plentifully supplied with water and oftentimes enriched by fine dust blown onto them by winds from the (usually dry) lowlands, these piedmont plains are, in many cases, first-rate agricultural areas. Since they are often located in a rain shadow condition, irrigation may be necessary for successful cultivation. In such situations, the combination of ample water and long periods of sunlight makes these plains especially desirable for the raising of sugar-rich crops since sunlight is essential to fixing the sucrose (sweetness) content of plants.

5. Glacial plains. Much of the upper Midwest and a very large part of the great North European Plain display features that were developed by continental glaciation. These features are far too numerous and too complex to discuss in detail in a general survey. In general, though, it may be said that glaciation tends, near its source, to scrape off surface irregularities, often taking all soil with it, as in the Laurentian Upland of Canada, and to pile up material toward its terminus. Ridges of material piled up at the end or along the sides of a glacial lobe are called moraines. They may run from a few feet to two or three hundred feet higher than the surrounding countryside. Beyond the moraines (away from the ice), glacial melt waters lay down relatively smooth deposits of sand and silt which, if they happen to lie between morainic ridges, may be very swampy. Behind the moraines, shallow bodies of meltwater may develop if there is no outlet to carry away the waters that flow from the wasting face of the glacier. Under such waters, other silt- or sand-covered lowlands may develop.

Where glacial plains are well drained, their soils are typically very good, for they tend to contain a greater variety of minerals than do soils developed from the necessarily limited varieties of rock found in any one place. But on most glacial plains, drainage is a vexing problem. Usually, the morainic ridges were first settled and put under cultivation. Often the major settlements remain there even today. Later on, ditching, tiling, and river-straightening speed the runoff from the lowlands, but even so, considerable areas of unusable peat and muck may remain to baffle the agriculturist, and floods remain a threat. Nevertheless, both in our country and in Europe glacial plains account for a large percentage of the agricultural land, and the morainic areas tend more and more to support livestock and dairying activities. In the upper Midwest, which is generally rather unscenic because of the flat topography, morainic areas are also coveted residential and recreational sites.

Typical of the sequence of occupance patterns in a glacial lowland is the Kankakee reclaimed marsh of northern Indiana and Illinois. The four stages in this occupance have been identified and described by the senior author of this book as follows:

¶ THE POTTAWATOMIE'S KANKAKEE (—1840) generally represents a wild morass of aquatic vegetation, a haven of wild life, a seasonal habitat and hunting quarters for the northwestern Indiana Indian.

Though some Indians occupied the marsh the year round, a certain number in the summer would contact the French at fur-trading posts on Lake Michigan or select as their summer habitat the more desirable moraine bordering the marsh. In thc fall thc aboriginc migratcd into the marsh or swamp and established his winter encampment on one of the numerous high and dry dunal knobs or ridges interspersed throughout the wet marshes or marking the elevated sites along the river-swamp margin. Black oak and white oak constituted the chief cover; pin oaks, conspicuous for their dead lower branches, invariably marked the boundary between "island" and marsh, a phenomenon still very noticeable. These oak-covered "islands" afforded shelter, fuel, and game, and served as a refuge against the ferocious Iroquois of the East.

The surrounding higher marshes of sedge and grass grazed the Indian ponies, which "kept fat and wallowed in nature's choicest luxuries." The lower and wetter marshes of wild rice attracted countless numbers of wild fowl; the flag-, cattail-, and reed-filled shallow ponds of the marsh and the forest-rimmed bayous of the river in the swamp marked the sites of widespread colonies

VII:8 This relief map of Africa shows its comparative elevations. (Relief map copyright Aero Service Corporation, used by permission)

of muskrats; the meandering lacustral "The-a-ki-ki" teemed with fish.

From the standpoint of interregional communication between points north and south the marsh, which trended generally east-west for a hundred miles across northwest Indiana, proved to be a real barrier except where it could be crossed by three naturally favored routes. . . . These routes, together with wigwam sites, are shown on the original century-old Federal surveyors' plats. . . .

Land travel definitely was oriented in accordance with the distribution of the elevated sand ridges, the trails utilizing these to the utmost extent as they wended their way riverward or crossed any part of the marshes or swamp. Conditions of internal circulation otherwise generally favored rather than hindered the primitive mode of travel of the redskin, who, during three fourths of the year or more, could push, if not paddle, his way by canoe, in practically any direction he chose to go. The river served as a more special artery of travel and trade, by which, as in the case of Lake Michigan, the Pottawatomie was brought into contact with the French explorer and trader of the 17th and 18th centuries, who portaged into the headwaters of the "Siegnelay" (the undifferentiated upper Kankakee-Illinois) at what is now South Bend, and by this route penetrated into the Land of the Setting Sun, the "Illini" Prairies, and the Father of Waters to the west. . . .

THE PIONEER'S KANKAKEE (1840-1880) presents practically unchanged the condition of the environment of the preceding period. Not unlike the Indians they displaced, the Danes, Swedes, English, and Germans, who migrated hither from the East, adjusted themselves most closely to their surroundings. Theirs, too, was the simple economy of "fur, fowl, and fin," supplemented commonly by gardening and occasionally by subsistence farming. Wild huckleberries, blueberries, blackberries, and locally cranberries grew in profusion, and contributed their seasonal offerings for home use and the market. Like the Indian, the marsh frontiersman practiced a form of transhumance, his movements synchronizing with the seasonal migration of geese and ducks.

Occupying a hastily constructed shanty or, less commonly, a more substantial log cabin, on one of the marsh or swamp "islands," the squatter passed the winter hunting and trapping the ubiquitous muskrat and other fur-bearing animals. "Claims" to trapping territory were of specified width and extended strip-fashion from the river bank into the marsh on either side. In summer the trapper might find employment in one of the towns growing up on the edge of the marsh or be hired out as a "hand" to one of the settlers cultivating a small clearing on the margin of the marsh, or possibly on one of the "islands" near it.

Crop lands on the marsh margin or "islands" usually were devoted to a little corn, wheat, and oats. These were fenced to keep out livestock, which grazed at will on the upper wet prairies of rank grass and sedge. Cut by scythe or sickle, marsh hay was transferred from the wet places, usually by a specially constructed sled, and stacked on one of the "islands" for winter forage.

Sink-tubs, dugouts, and pushboats, expressive of the hunter's economy, were marks of culture of the lower and wetter marshes and of the swamp.

Logs of black ash and white ash, water elm, silver maple, pin oak, and other swamp species denote lumbering operations in the swamp, while clearings on the oak knolls of the smaller upland oak timber signify the cutting of trees for firewood, fence posts, props, and ties, the latter chiefly of white oak, an exportable product of "legal tender" reputation.

Travel by foot, horseback, or vehicle, as in the previous epoch, generally followed the line of least wetness, while cattle seemed instinctively to be able to pick out the more elevated though frequently submerged pathways.

By 1880, it is reported, most of the old-time hunters had left the marsh, and townships could vote out the free range. Nels Morris, the famous Chicago packer, and others became interested in the Kankakee grazing and potentially grain-producing lands, and sportsmen's clubs recognized in the Kankakee "the hunter's paradise."

THE RANCHER'S AND THE RECREATIONIST'S KANKAKEE (1880-1910) presents a double ensemble of landscape characteristics: a cattle economy on the higher, drier, and artificially drained lands side by side with public shooting and trapping grounds of wild fowl and other game on the ill-drained marshes and swamps. It expresses a conflict of two sets of forces contesting for the use of the land, that of the reclamationist in competition with that of the conservationist.

The axe encroaching on the swamp, the barbed-wire fence enclosing the mile-square ranges, the sickle mowing its swath in the wild-hay marsh, the plow breaking the prairie stubby sod where the steam dredge had dug deep and wide drainage ditches riverward bound—these are the animated aspects of a "country which God forgot to finish." Yet finished, indeed, from the naturalist's and the sportsman's viewpoint was this "Edenic playground" with its pristine vegetal and animal life providing scenery and sport reputed to be among the most alluring in the Central West.

In spite of the reclamationist's steam dredge, which made cultivable and habitable the surrounding prairies, the dunal island continued to hold its former power of attraction as a site of

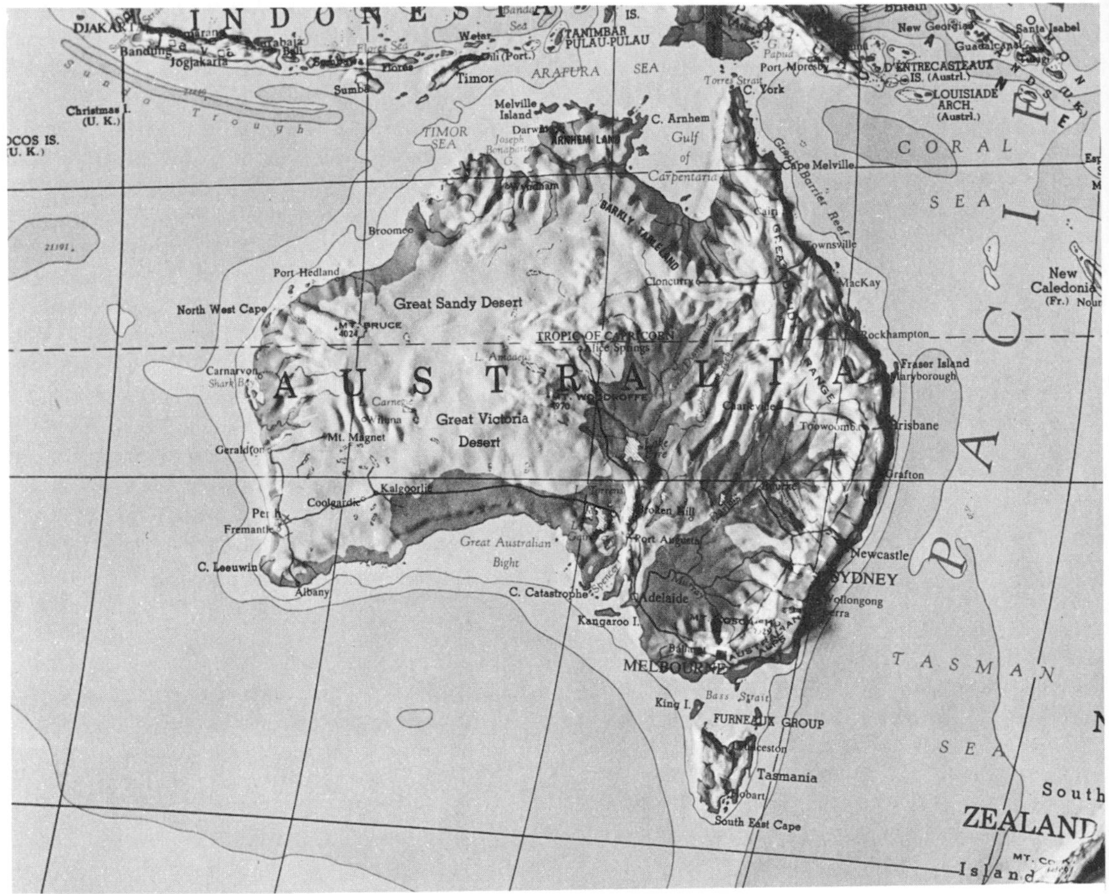

VII:9 This relief map of Australia shows its comparative elevations. (Relief map copyright Aero Service Corporation, used by permission)

the human habitat, whether of farmer, fowler, or fisherman. Especially imposing were the double-story frame clubhouses, whose sites were a function of the river situation. Here were established organized hunting and fishing clubs from Chicago, Indianapolis, Louisville, Pittsburgh, and other large cities; also a number of resorts. Towns on the edge of the marsh and hotels along the river shared the activities of the recreational industry.

Cultivation, formerly confined almost exclusively to the upland light sandier tracts, now came to be extended onto the lower reclaimed prairies, on loams subsequently classified as Maumee. The staples corn and oats complemented the natural resource of marsh hay in supporting a livestock industry, and supplemented locally by wheat, foreboded a grain culture on a cash-crop basis. Wild hay also furnished a cash income, from the exportation of bales for feeding, bedding, or packing, according to quality. The swamp continued to supply lumber, and professional hunters engaged in shooting and trapping as a business and as a sport.

Ditch digging and road building went hand in hand, the spoil-bank gravel and the sand of the ditch often being utilized as roadbed material. Railroads, which transected the marsh in the previous period, now figured in the agricultural and the recreational development of the Kankakee, while small-craft river navigation assumed an importance never exceeded before or since. The straightening of the main river channel, begun in 1906, may be said practically to mark the culmination of this period. . . .

THE RECLAMATIONIST'S AND THE RESORTER'S KANKAKEE of the twentieth century (1910-) continues to express a dual occupance of the landscape, but by the straightening of the lower Indiana Kankakee in 1917 agricul ture pushed the recreational interests clear out of the marsh and confined them to the river front, where they take the form of single or grouped cottage resorts.

The former wild hay of the upper marshes and the wild rice of the lower marshes or sloughs have given way to cultivated grasses and grains. Roads, drainage ditches, spoil banks, and fences demarcate 40-, 80-, and 160-acre rectangular field units, reflective of the far-flung flattish terrain and the ease with which it may be cultivated by the modern tractor. Irregularities of size and shape are now and then introduced by the oval or sinuous, oak-covered or pastured ridges, or by the drainage lines directed diagonally riverward.

The sandy "barrens" . . . [are] subject to "blowing" when the native cover is removed. Accordingly, many of these upland timber tracts show only local cutting for fence posts and firewood. Except on the heavier phases of this type, soybeans, cowpeas, rye, and certain truck products are practically the only crops grown. Although a characteristic woodlot-pasture formation, [these "barrens"] are noteworthy chiefly for their farmstead site quality. Considerable tracts represent true barrens, with only a cover of acid-tolerant plants, and therefore idle lands of no agricultural utility. . . .

The former wild-hay stock ranches and wild-rice duck-feeding grounds have by drainage been converted into the main crop lands of the Kankakee. . . . Corn is King in Kankakee . . . except locally, as in the East, where mint may assume a position of first importance on Muck areas.

The river Swamp . . . represents an almost unmappable mixture of relict timber, of "burns," clearings, sprouting stumps, and reproduction stands. It has little merchantable timber or pasture value. Once reputed to be the most beautiful river in Indiana, the meandering Kankakee has been obliterated by the deep, wide, and highly banked ditches. . . . Only remnants of the original winding channel, with its bayous, are still found.

The transformed river-ditch shows a most marked effect on resort developments. Only one half as many resort cottages occur along the lengthy straightened channel in Indiana, as along the few miles on the Illinois side, where the river has been left in essentially its natural condition. . . .[1]

This case study has been quoted at some length because it illustrates a point which was made at the beginning of this chapter and which is of basic significance to the geographer; land-use, imposed upon landforms, produces a landscape. Since landforms change very slowly, by far most of the changes in the appearance of any landscape are the products of human wisdom, foolishness, ingenuity, or carelessness. Whether, therefore, by effort or by neglect, man is forever altering the face of the land. And these alterations make the study of geography a dynamic study—never the study of what is, but always the study of what is becoming.

APPLICATION OF GEOGRAPHIC UNDERSTANDING

I. If middle-latitude mountain areas tend to be relatively backward "museums of social antiquities," how do you account for the fact that we got our religion from the uplands of Judah, our systems of logic and philosophy from Greece, and many of our basic political and legal concepts from Italy—all of which are mountainous or hilly countries?

II. Consult an atlas of the United States showing county boundaries in the various states. Note that the counties of the eastern seaboard states are, generally, more irregular in form than are the generally-rectangular counties of the Middle West. How do you account for this difference? Can you find any rational explanation of the boundaries in either case? Why should so many counties in the Rocky Mountain area conform to the Midwestern pattern when the topography is mountainous?

III. Would it have been possible for the Mississippi River to have carved a valley like the Grand Canyon? Why or why not? Why is it easier to bridge the Mississippi than to bridge the Colorado at Grand Canyon?

IV. Why might the Spaniards have made better settlers of the Great Plains than did the Northern Europeans who did settle there? What difference might it have made in the land-use of the Great Plains if our country had been settled from the west coast rather than the east coast?

---

[1] Meyer, Alfred H., "The Kankakee 'Marsh' of Northern Indiana and Illinois." Reproduced by permission of the University of Michigan from *Papers of the Michigan Academy of Science, Arts, and Letters* XXI (1935), p. 366.

V. Why are our dry plains and plateaus especially susceptible to speculative types of farming? What relation might there be between the boom-and-bust cycle in these regions and such "radical" political movements as Populism?

VI. What good reason can you suggest for the Brazilians' wanting to build a new capital city up on the plateau when they already have one of the world's most beautiful capital cities in Rio de Janeiro?

VII. In *American History and Its Geographic Conditions,* Dr. Ellen Churchill Semple wrote: "Everywhere one notices a certain largeness of view in the ordinary Westerner. Even when uncultured and crude from lack of opportunity, he never takes a contracted view of things. He measures things with a big yardstick. The nomadic instinct is still in him, handed down by his emigrant forebears. Wherever he is found he has always come there from somewhere else. Hence he is never provincial, and he is intensely, broadly American." Would you agree or disagree with this analysis of the Westerner? Why? Could the converse, then, be said about the Kentucky mountaineer?

VIII. If deltas are such difficult regions to bring and keep under control, why should a great city such as Venice ever have been founded in a delta, and how could it have become such an important commercial and political center?

IX. If alluvial fans are preferred sites for specialized types of agriculture, why is so little of this kind of agriculture found in underdeveloped areas, such as central Asia, where local populations badly need the additional income that comes from specialization of agriculture?

X. Bearing in mind the growth, both in area and population, of the Chicago metropolitan area, and remembering that the Kankakee River is only about forty miles south of the Chicago city limits, what suggestions can you offer for a possible fifth stage of occupance in the Kankakee region? If you do not feel that you have sufficient information to offer an intelligent opinion, what further information would you want?

References

1 Thompson, Henry Dewey, *Fundamentals of Earth Science,* D. Appleton-Century, New York, 1947, p. 396.

2 Gregory, James S., and Shave, D. W., *The U.S.S.R., A Geographical Survey,* John Wiley & Sons, Inc., New York, 1944, pp. 483-484.

3 Bennett, H. H., "Soil Erosion and Its Prevention," *Our Natural Resources and Their Conservation,* John Wiley & Sons, Inc., New York, 1939, pp. 68-69.

4 Mather, Eugene, and Hart, J. Fraser, *Southeastern Excursion Guidebook,* U.S. Committee of the International Geographical Union, 1952, pp. 71-77.

5 Terral, Rufus, *The Missouri Valley: Land of Drouth, Flood, and Promise,* Yale University Press, New Haven, Conn., 1947, pp. 3-8.

6 Innes, Hammond, "Holland," *Holiday,* Vol. 21, No. 3, March, 1957, pp. 51-57, *passim.*

7 Marbut, C. F., and Manifold, C. B., "The Topography of the Amazon Valley," *Geographical Review,* Vol. 15, 1925, p. 617.

8 Meyer, Alfred H., "The Kankakee 'Marsh' of Northern Indiana and Illinois," from *Papers of the Michigan Academy of Science, Arts and Letters,* Vol. XXI, 1935, insert following p. 366.

Chapter 8

Soils and their relation to a nation's economy

The typical undergraduate geography student approaches a chapter on soils with all the enthusiasm of a taxpayer sitting down to his income tax blank, and this is understandable. The overwhelming majority of young men and women today have spent all or most of their lives in metropolitan areas and thus have had little contact with, or knowledge of, the land. Moreover, the soil is a rather passive element in the environment, displaying none of the day-to-day changeability of weather or the inescapably obvious place-to-place variations of landforms. Little wonder, therefore, that to most of us soil is simply dirt, and soil classification an apparently dull job for the specialist.

As with so many other things, however, interest in the soil grows in direct proportion to one's knowledge of it. Perhaps this is especially true of soils, for lifeless as soil may appear to the casual observer, it is a kind of little universe within which billions of living organisms, great and small, live and work and reproduce and die, changing the nature of their environment even as man changes his environment. Under the microscope, much of this activity is visible. To most of us the labors of these bacteria are visible only in their effects. After a while, we learn to recognize some of the more obvious differences among soils, but we miss out on how and why these differences occur.

The soil: animal, vegetable, or mineral?

What is soil? Perhaps the briefest and most concise definition is one suggested by Dr. Louis M. Thompson of Iowa State College: "Soil is the mixture of mineral and organic material at the land surface of the earth that is capable of sustaining plant life" (1). The mineral material is very finely divided rock. Over very large areas of the earth's surface, the soil is classified as residual soil, that is, soil formed from the decay of local rocks. In other places, the soils are classified as transported soils, that is, soils formed from materials brought into the region by running water, or winds, or glaciers. The mineral content of any given soil is, therefore, a reflection of the mineral composition of the rocks from which it was formed. Since any given rock is likely to contain only a limited variety of minerals, residual soils are likely to display less variety of minerals than do transported soils, although this is not always the case.

The organic material in soils comes from debris, chiefly vegetational, created by local plants or washed in by water or blown in by winds. So important is the vegetational cover to the nature of any given soil that soils are often classified by the kind of vegetation which they support and which, in turn, has done so much to shape their character. Thus we speak of tundra soils, or grassland soils, or taiga soils, or deciduous forest soils.

The mere mechanical mixture of mineral material and organic material does not, however, create a soil. Micro-organisms in the soil break down the complex organic compounds of plant tissue into simple inorganic compounds which feed the growing plants. Energy flows toward the earth's surface from two different sources: solar radiation and the slow atomic decay of radioactive elements inside the crust. The ceaseless excitation of the surface by these extraneous sources of energy transforms the relatively inert crust of the earth into a thermodynamic system which has functioned throughout geological history. The study of such a soil system is called soil dynamics (2).

Fully-developed soils exhibit a series of layers, or horizons, which, taken together, constitute the soil profile (see Figure VIII-1). The process of soil formation begins with the breaking down of rock under the elements of weathering into a layer of "rotten" rock called regolith. Plants and microorganisms establish themselves in this regolith and, as they die and decay, contribute organic matter to it, gradually transforming its outermost layer into a weakly-developed A horizon. A and C horizons, as defined in Figure VIII-1, are, therefore, common to all soils except very new regoliths. The B hori-

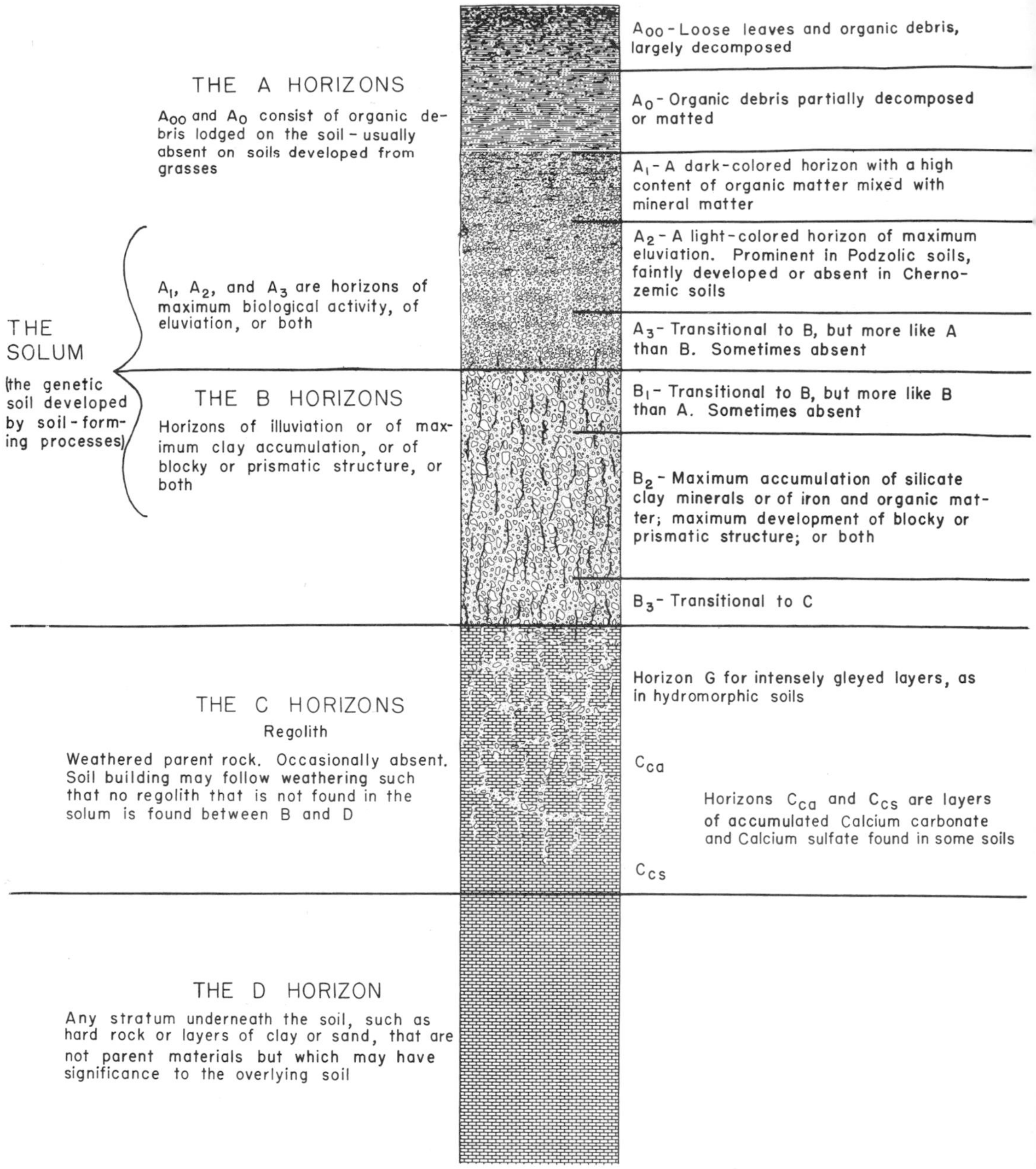

THE A HORIZONS

A_{00} and A_0 consist of organic debris lodged on the soil – usually absent on soils developed from grasses

A_{00} – Loose leaves and organic debris, largely decomposed

A_0 – Organic debris partially decomposed or matted

A_1 – A dark-colored horizon with a high content of organic matter mixed with mineral matter

A_1, A_2, and A_3 are horizons of maximum biological activity, of eluviation, or both

A_2 – A light-colored horizon of maximum eluviation. Prominent in Podzolic soils, faintly developed or absent in Chernozemic soils

A_3 – Transitional to B, but more like A than B. Sometimes absent

THE SOLUM

(the genetic soil developed by soil-forming processes)

THE B HORIZONS

Horizons of illuviation or of maximum clay accumulation, or of blocky or prismatic structure, or both

B_1 – Transitional to B, but more like B than A. Sometimes absent

B_2 – Maximum accumulation of silicate clay minerals or of iron and organic matter; maximum development of blocky or prismatic structure; or both

B_3 – Transitional to C

THE C HORIZONS

Regolith

Weathered parent rock. Occasionally absent. Soil building may follow weathering such that no regolith that is not found in the solum is found between B and D

Horizon G for intensely gleyed layers, as in hydromorphic soils

C_{ca}

Horizons C_{ca} and C_{cs} are layers of accumulated Calcium carbonate and Calcium sulfate found in some soils

C_{cs}

THE D HORIZON

Any stratum underneath the soil, such as hard rock or layers of clay or sand, that are not parent materials but which may have significance to the overlying soil

VIII:1 This hypothetical soil profile shows all the principal horizons. Not all of these horizons would be present in any actual profile, but every profile has some of them. (Adapted from *Soil, The 1957 Yearbook of Agriculture,* United States Department of Agriculture)

zon generally develops later, although it may be formed at the same time as the A horizon.

The final test of whether loose crustal materials actually are a soil is their capacity to sustain plant life. It should be noted that capacity can not always be determined merely by looking, for a potentially-productive soil may be inhibited from producing

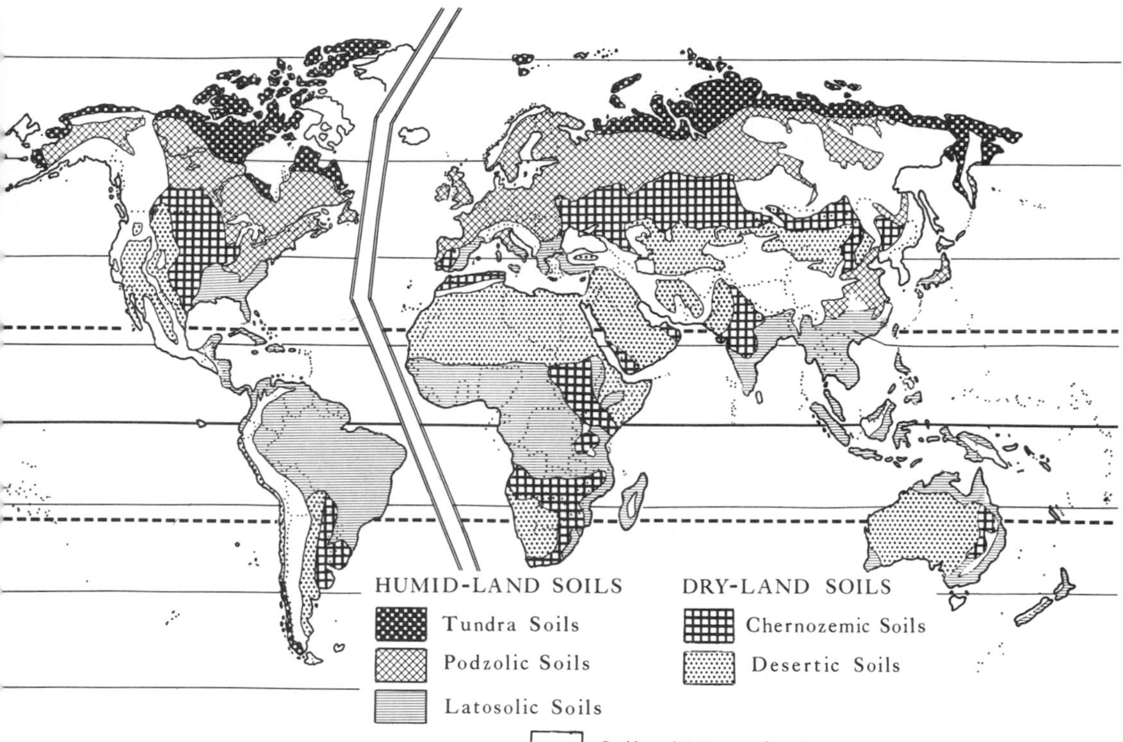

VIII:2 This map is a generalized soil map of the world. (Redrawn from *Soils, The 1957 Yearbook of Agriculture,* United States Department of Agriculture)

by some extraneous condition, for example, lack of water. Or its true capacity may be concealed by inferior vegetation's reflecting some correctable condition, for example, poor drainage. Natural plant life is not, therefore, a foolproof index to the capacity of any given soil. But it is perhaps the best single index that we have, and our forefathers were not too far off (except in the one notable case of the prairies) when they said that a soil that would not grow trees would not grow crops.

Soil realities vs. soil classifications

More than a thousand different types of soil have been identified just within the boundaries of the United States. No one knows how many types might be identified by a careful world survey, for no such survey has ever been made. One of the major difficulties of soil classification is the fact that any one major type of soil is capable of almost infinite subclassification—not as a mere academic exercise but as a desirable prerequisite to efficient use. The most successful farmers in our country recognize and appreciate very subtle differences in the soil within small areas and adapt their crops and cultivation techniques to the differences in soil capabilities revealed by the soil map.

The geographer works with many kinds of soil maps, ranging from very detailed ones for the study of small regions to very generalized ones for introducing the beginning student to basic world patterns. The map used in this chapter (Figure VIII-2), portraying the great soil groups of the world, is very generalized—comparable, in its lack of detail, to a photograph of the earth taken from an orbiting satellite. Its value is that it illuminates the broadest soil patterns and permits some correlation of these patterns with other meaningful earth realities.

How soils differ from each other on a world scale

As one looks at this map, perhaps the first impression that strikes the observer is the remarkably large amount of the earth's surface which, simply from the standpoint of soils, must be written off as unusable under any presently-known systems of cultivation. This is most obviously true of the large areas of mountain soils, only infinitesimally small patches of which are cultivable. Soil and climate combine to make the icecaps of Greenland and Antarctica and the tundra soils of the Far North and of southern Chile useless for agriculture except, perhaps, for local experiments in agriculture. The vast majority of desertic soils must also be placed in the useless category, although locally large areas may be made cultivable by irrigation. (It is a mistake, though, to suppose that irrigation can make every desert bloom as the rose. Vast areas of desert are mantled by bare rock or a coarse regolith which no amount of water can make productive.) Finally, large areas of podsolic soils and latosolic soils are of little or no agricultural value for reasons which will become apparent from a discussion of these soil groups.

Most of the productive or potentially-productive agricultural areas of the world must, therefore, be sought in portions of the podsolic, chernozemic, and latosolic regions. Each of these will be examined in turn.

Podsolic soils, as the map shows, are found characteristically in temperate to cool humid regions (the *D* climates and some of the cooler phases of the *C* climate in Köppen's classification). They are forest-land soils, associated with the coniferous evergreen and mixed evergreen-deciduous forests. The larger the percentage of conifers in the forest, the smaller the amount of humus in the soil normally tends to be, for conifer needles make poor humus. By the same token, the cooler the climate the smaller the humic content of the soil normally tends to be because cool temperatures inhibit the decay of vegetation and generally cause it to accumulate on the surface as a soggy, semidecomposed layer of infertile material. The best podsolic soils are those along the southern margins of the regions where warmer temperatures and deciduous trees encourage the accumulation of humus in the soil. But even the best podsolic soils tend to be acid, low in bases, such as calcium, and low in organic matter. "Liming," that is, the addition of calcium to the soil, is essential in podsolic regions, and a crop system which adds humus to the soil is necessary to maintain and improve the fertility of the soil.

Chernozemic soils are found in subhumid or semiarid regions where the natural cover is grass or prairie. Most chernozems are found in the so-called temperate zones, but there are also significant areas of them in the tropics. The temperate-zone chernozems are among the world's most fertile soils, but their fertility is at least partly a reflection of a deficiency of water—water which would have dissolved out the soluble plant nutrients but which is also necessary for agriculture. Chernozems are closely associated with grain farming; indeed, they produce about 90 per cent of the grain that enters world trade. But commercial grain farming, also, is a reflection of dryness since only in dry areas are the relatively low-value grain crops secure against competition with more valuable crops requiring greater amounts of water. Tropical and subtropical chernozemic soils tend to be problem soils for they are high in clay, plastic, and subject to great swelling and shrinkage. The usually primitive cultivation practices of the peoples who work these soils do little to improve their quality. Chernozemic soils thus support a wide range of agriculture, from the extensive, commercial, winter-wheat culture of North America and the Soviet Union to the simple, subsistence culture of the low latitudes—but often under a shortage of water, and always under the threat of a shortage.

Latosols are characteristically associated with tropical *A* climates and subtropical *Ca* climates. They are typically red, orange, or yellow in color, the color deriving from the high concentration of iron oxides in the soil as a result of year-round oxidation and hydration of iron and other minerals. In fact, the latosols are the most strongly weathered of all soils. They are also typically severely leached; that is, their soluble minerals have been dissolved by the seepage of water through the upper horizons of the soil and deposited in a "hardpan" layer of mineral accumulation at considerable distance below the surface. Latosols tend, therefore, to be quite infertile. The most fertile latosols are found on the coldward margins of the latosol belts where weathering and leaching are

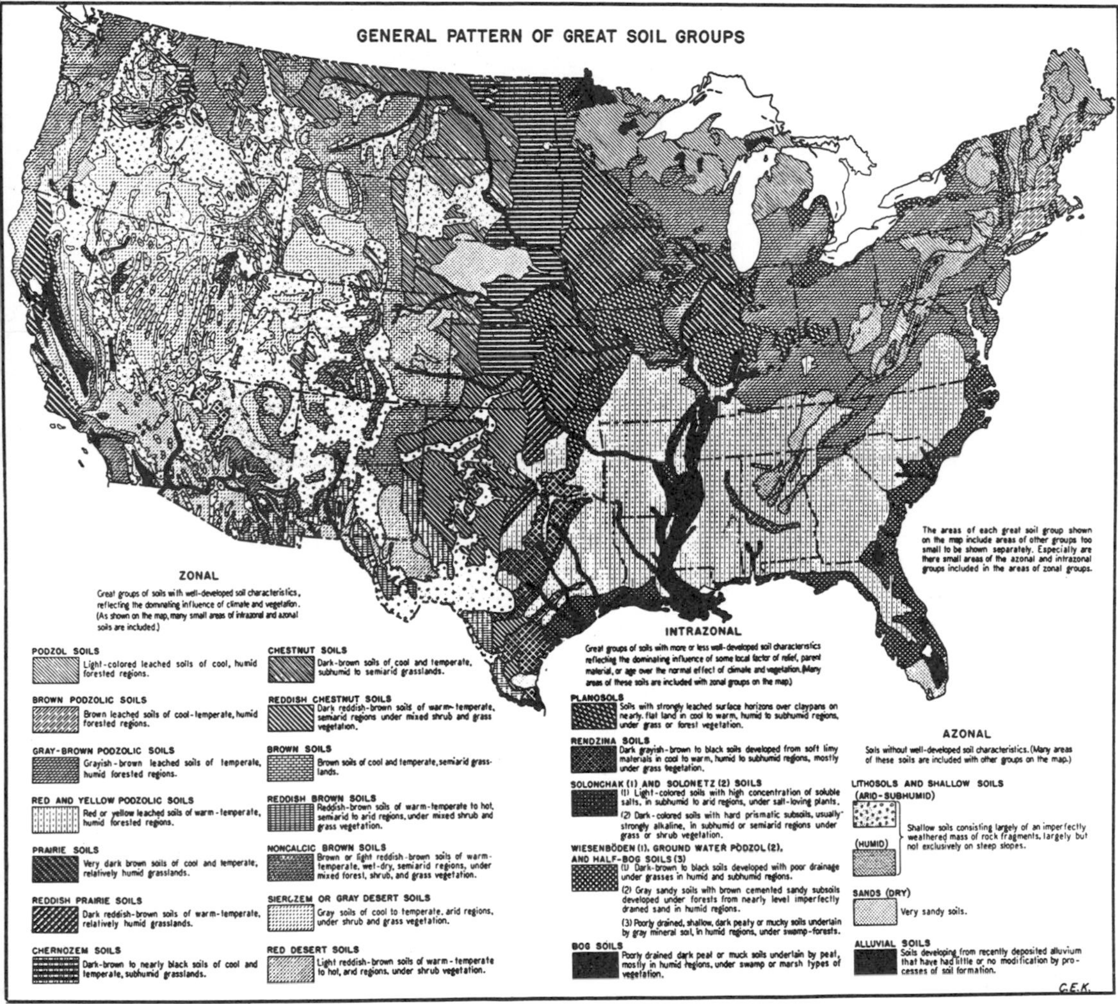

VIII:3 The great soil groups of the United States are shown on this map. (From *The Agricultural Regions of the United States* by Ladd Haystead and Gilbert C. Fite, The University of Oklahoma Press, 1955, used by permission)

somewhat less effective than they are toward the centers of these belts.

It should be borne in mind that the soil types which have just been described are very broad types, and that the map is a very generalized map. At any given place within any of the zones shown on the map, the actual soil might be quite different from the type indicated by the symbolism of the map. It should be noted also that this map does not show bands of alluvial (water-deposited) soils along the great rivers, or areas of lava flows. Such local exceptions to the general pattern are often of major importance in explaining regional distributions of agriculture. Characteristically, such exceptional soil areas are devoted to specialized crops which are particularly valuable because they can not be raised widely elsewhere in the region or, perhaps, in the world.

The great soil groups of the United States

The next map (Figure VIII-3), since it deals with a smaller area, presents a somewhat more refined classification of soils than does the world map. On this map, the podsolic soils, for instance, are broken down into podsols, brown podsolics, gray-brown podsolics, and red-yellow podsolics. The heavy

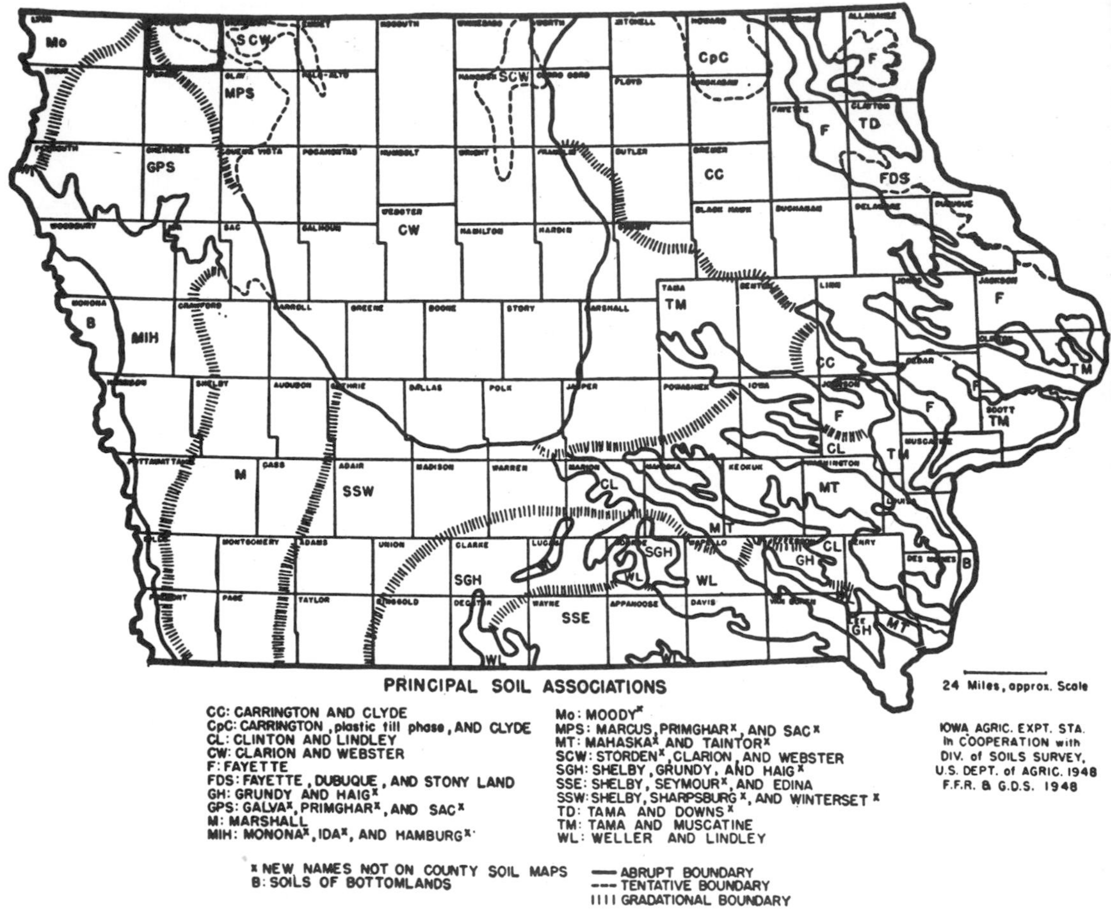

VIII:4 This map shows the principal soil association areas in Iowa. (From *Soils and Soil Fertility* by Louis M. Thompson, McGraw-Hill Book Co., Inc., New York, 1952, used by permission)

lines indicate the boundaries previously shown on the world map. Although both these maps are from the United States Department of Agriculture, note that there are certain apparent discrepancies in terminology, most notably in the southeastern part of the United States where the soils indicated on the world map as latosols are classified chiefly as red-yellow podsolic soils. The discrepancy is, however, more apparent than real. Lying as it does between the tropics and the typically cyclonic belt, the American Southeast is a transitional area climatically and vegetationally, and one might expect to find that its soils, also, are of an "in-between" kind. The reddish-yellow color testifies to their relation to the latosols and the gradation as one moves southward toward the Gulf of Mexico is toward more distinctly lateritic soils.

Soil differences within a state. Observe now the soils of Iowa as shown on the soil map of the United States (Figure VIII-3), and then look at Figure VIII-4, which is a map of the principal soil-association areas of the state as mapped by the Iowa Agricultural Experiment Station in co-operation with the Division of Soil Surveys of the United States Department of Agriculture. On the soil map of the United States, Iowa contains areas of three great soil groups: prairie soils, planosols, and brown podsolics. The more detailed map of Iowa shows twenty soil associations. Notice that these associations are most broadly developed over he drier, more level western portion of the tate, while in the more humid, more disected eastern part of the state the associaions are arranged in linear patterns related ery largely to drainage lines. It is not too asy to correlate the associations on the Iowa nap with the groups on the United States nap, but in general it may be said that the rea of linear associations on the Iowa map ie within the region of brown podsols; the ssociations labeled SSW, SGH, and SSE lie vithin the region of planosols, and the rest of the state's associations are subdivisions of he prairie soils.

Local differences in soils. Finally, on the owa map, find Osceola County, which is utlined in heavy black lines along the orthernmost tier of counties. Notice that hree soil associations are indicated within he boundaries of the county. Now look at Figure VIII-5, which is a soil map of eight quare miles within Osceola County. Note hat six soil types have been mapped within hese eight square miles. Note also that there ppears to be a very close correlation beween soil types and topography; certain gradations appear obvious as one descends rom uplands into stream valleys. Thus, in he left-hand third of the figure, the upland Marshall silty clay loam passes into a tillubstratum phase which, in turn, gives way o the Afton silty clay loam in the valley ottom.[1] To the beginning student, these re merely names. To the farmer, these are asic considerations to be taken into account

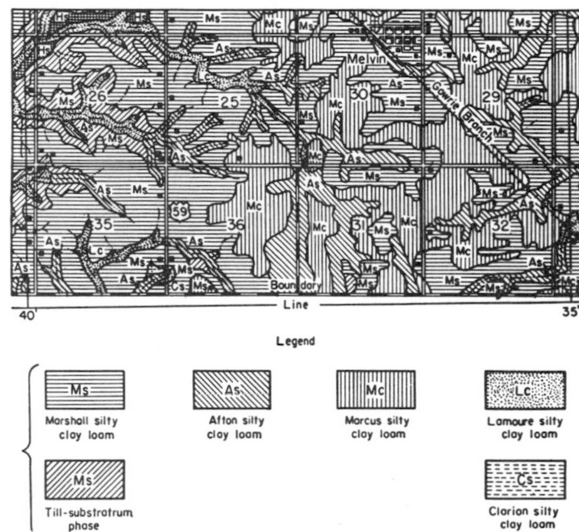

VIII:5 This is a soils map of eight sections of Osceola County, Iowa. (From *Soils and Soil Fertility* by Louis M. Thompson, McGraw-Hill Book Co., Inc., New York, 1952, used by permission)

when he chooses what crops he will plant, how he will lay out his fields, what special precautions he must take to preserve the land, and what special machinery he may use.

Civilization and man's "uncountable millions of fields"

The great German political geographer, Friedrich Ratzel, once defined the state as *"ein Stück Boden und Menschheit"*—a bit of soil and of mankind. The Old Testament goes further and pictures man himself as a creature formed of the dust of the ground —"dust thou art, and unto dust shalt thou return."

For the political or economic geographer, statements such as these are neither mystical nor poetic. Rather, they are basic statements of fact, far-reaching in their implications. Dr. Louis A. Wolfanger, one of our country's foremost authorities on soils, has written:

¶ The soil of a nation is its most valuable material heritage. It nurtures the ever-flowing stream of vegetation from which men and their animals must derive their food. It absorbs the groundwater which relieves their thirst, and the floodwater which would deluge them. It generates

---

[1] The name of a soil, such as *Marshall*, is called the *series* ame. The *series* name is generally given to a soil where it vas first mapped. *Afton* is also a series name. As these two oils are similar and related, they are called a soil *association*. The series name, Marshall, is like *Acer*, the genus name for maple trees. The texture of the surface soil (A horizon), such s *silty clay loam*, is the *type* designation. It is like *saccharum*, he species name of sugar maple. *Acer saccharum* is the full ame of the sugar maple. Soil *texture* refers to the proportions of clay, silt, and sand in a soil. A loam is a soil which is a nixture of all three. Loam soils contain 7 to 27 per cent clay, 28 to 50 per cent silt, and less than 52 per cent sand. Soils vhich contain somewhat more clay are called clay loams; those nade up predominantly of silt are silt loams. Sands and clays re soils that do not contain enough silt to warrant the use of he term *loam*. Soil texture, which means fineness or coarseess of the soil, is perhaps the most important characteristic in a general scheme of classification. Gravel particles are larger han 8 hundreds of an inch in diameter; sand particles measure rom 2 thousandths to 8 hundreds of an inch across; silt particles are 8 hundred-thousandths to 2 thousandths of an inch in liameter; and clay particles are still smaller across.

the organic raw materials so vital to shelter, clothing, and comfort, such as wood, cotton, and rubber. Small groups of people here and there may exist for a time on the free gifts of nature, but the great civilizations of the centuries have rested fundamentally upon uncountable millions of fields planted and tended by man.[1]

It is always a gross oversimplification to explain the decline and fall of civilizations in terms of any one cause, and yet there would appear to be more than a germ of truth in the statement that "the glory that was Greece and the grandeur that was Rome were washed away by the winter rains." It was, after all, the independent small farmer, fighting in defense of his ancestral acres, who formed the hard core of the Roman and Greek armies. The erosion of soil from hillside farms, left powder-dry after deforestation, by the long summer drought and then attacked by the torrential rains of winter, ruined the small farmer and drove him to the city where he became just another member of the demoralized and dispirited mob which had to be appeased with bread and circuses. It was apparently the Greek and Roman experiences which led Thomas Jefferson to conclude that freedom in our country could survive only so long as it was based on a strong and independent class of small farmers.

Ironically, however, it is the small farmer who has been most responsible for the rapid destruction of our country's soils. Lacking anything like precise knowledge of the potentials and limitations of his land, limited in the resources that he could invest in the land, uncritically committed to crop choices and cultivation practices ill-suited to his new home, and beguiled by the promise of rich new land on a constantly advancing frontier, the American small farmer until very recently followed a policy of "use up and move on," and the paths of our great migrations are strewn with abandoned farms and decaying towns prematurely aged by the wearing out of their economic hinterlands.

Only in the past fifty years or so have we begun to take seriously the fact that man is never more than a few inches from catastrophe—the few inches of life-producing soil which separates him from sterile rock. And the realization has brought with it a new concern for preserving the soil.

Soil must be understood to be preserved

Wisely used, soil is a preservable and even improvable resource. Much of the agricultural land of China has been continuously cultivated for more than four thousand years. The Nile Valley and Mesopotamia have been farmed for at least as long. Much of the most valuable agricultural land of the Netherlands, Germany, and Denmark has been created over the centuries from what was originally wet and sandy wasteland. Even in our own Midwest, some of the most productive farmland has been built up from marshlands and wet river bottoms. The wise use of the soil requires essentially three things: (1) specific knowledge of the nature of the soil; (2) the employment of tillage methods best adapted to the nature of the land being cultivated; and (3) the adaptation of crops to the potentials, needs, and limitations of the soil.

Chemical properties of soils. Specific knowledge of the soil means principally an understanding of its chemical composition and of the areal distribution of types of soil. Chemically, one of the most significant distinctions among soils is the distinction between acid and alkaline soils, expressed in terms of pH. The value of pH is arrived at by a rather complicated equation but the actual pH of any given soil can be determined and the value expressed as a figure. Soils range from a pH of about 4 for strongly acid soils to about 10 for strongly alkaline soils. A pH of 7 indicates a neutral soil. Most agricultural soils range from about 5 to 8.5. The type of fertilization advisable for any given type of soil depends very largely upon the pH of the soil.

But it is not enough to know merely whether a soil is acid or alkaline. Some seventeen chemical elements have been shown to be necessary for the growth of plants or for the development of microorganisms. Elements which must be present in considerable quantity include calcium (lime), magnesium, sulfur, nitrogen, potassium, phosphorus, carbon, hydrogen, and oxygen. These are called macronutrients. In

[1] Reprinted with permission from "The Soils of the United States," *Our Natural Resources and Their Conservation*, A. E. Parkins and J. R. Whitaker, Editors, 1939, John Wiley & Sons, Inc., New York, p. 35.

addition to these macronutrients, fertile soils must contain at least twelve elements in small quantities. These are called micronutrients. Seven of these micronutrients—iron, manganese, boron, zinc, copper, molybdenum, and chlorine—have been shown to be essential for the growth of the higher plants. Another five—cobalt, iodine, vanadium, fluorine, and sodium—are necessary for the growth of the lower plants and such microorganisms as the fungi and the algae. These micronutrients were formerly called "trace elements." More recent usage prefers the term micronutrients for those elements which are known to be essential to soil fertility, and "trace elements" for other minerals which may be present in small quantities in the soil but which have not been proved to be essential to soil fertility.

The identification of the mineral constituents and the mineral deficiencies in any particular soil is, obviously, a matter of chemical analysis. The correction of deficiencies is usually a matter of fertilization, although it may sometimes be managed through changed tillage practices.

Soils vary in capability from place to place. The second aspect of specific knowledge of the soil is a reasonably precise understanding of the areal distribution of types of soil, especially from the standpoint of capability. The United States Department of Agriculture groups soils into eight capability classes which are further subdivided into subclasses and units. Of the eight classes, those numbered I through IV are considered suited to cultivated crops, pasture or range, woodland, and wildlife. Classes V through VIII are considered suited to pasture or woodland and wildlife, but not generally suited to cultivation. The descriptions of the individual classes which follow are based for the most part on *Soil, The Yearbook of Agriculture for 1957*, published by the Department of Agriculture, pages 402-408, *passim:*

Class I is very good land from all points of view. It is nearly level and does not wash or blow readily. The soil is deep and friable, holds water well, and is at least fairly well supplied with plant food. It can be safely used for almost any purpose.

Class II has some limitations that reduce the choice of use or require some conservation practices to keep it productive, but the limitations are not great or the practices difficult.

Class III has more natural features that restrict its use or require more careful management than Class II. Its limitations are more severe and problems more difficult to overcome.

Class IV has definite restrictions that limit the choice of use or require very careful management. Often the number of years favorable for cultivation is limited. It therefore requires careful use and, often, special conservation practices.

Class V has natural features that generally restrict its use to pasture, woodland, or wildlife. The soils in this class are nearly level and often wet, overflowed, or stony, or have a climatic limitation. Pastures can be renovated. The major limitation is the kind of plants that can be grown.

Class VI has pronounced features such as steep slopes, severe erosion, a stony or shallow or wet condition, or low water-holding capacity, any one of which may make it unsuitable for cultivation. Such land may, however, support pasture or woodland or wildlife. The soils usually can be renovated, and good pastures are obtained with careful management.

Classes VII and VIII include those soils which are of least commercial use to man—indeed, of no use without special care and treatment.

Land capability maps are, in effect, resource inventories. They tell what the landuser has to work with. By adapting crops and tillage methods to the different types of soil and terrain shown on these maps, he can use the land much more profitably than he could ever hope to do by a process of trial and error. It should be noted that especially in the first four classes, and even to a lesser extent in Classes V through VIII, numerous alternative uses of the land are possible, and the choice of the most profitable of these various alternatives at any given time may depend upon economic factors as much as upon the nature of the soil or the topography of the surface. Compare Figure VIII-6, which is a capability map, with Figure VIII-7, a conservation plan map for the same farm.

Tillage must be determined by its purposes. Tillage methods vary, or should vary,

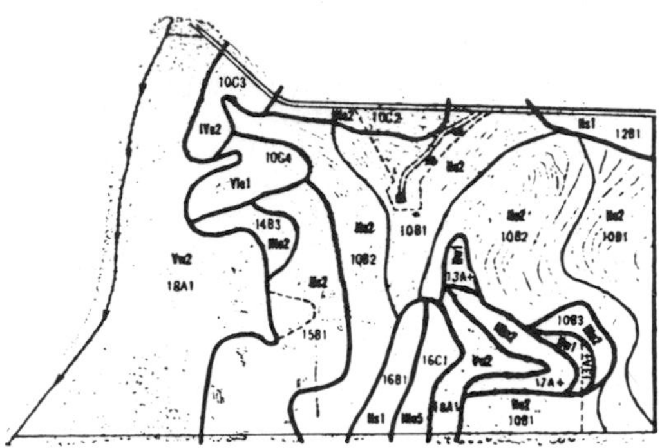

VIII:6 This map of a farm shows soil types and their capabilities. For our purposes, the meanings of the symbols are not important. Note, however, how the boundaries on this map become boundaries for the land-use map in Figure VIII:7. (From *Soils, The 1957 Yearbook of Agriculture,* United States Department of Agriculture)

from place to place because soils vary from place to place. The purposes of tillage are (1) to change the structure of the soil; (2) to kill weeds, and (3) to manage crop residues.

The structure of a soil is a matter of the arrangement of the soil particles. Since the structure of the soil largely determines its ability to absorb, store, and transmit water, the structure may need to be modified so as to increase or diminish the amount of water absorbed, stored, or transmitted. Cultivated soils which have not been plowed for some time tend to compact and, thus, to prohibit the entry of water. Rainfall which cannot enter such a soil will run off the surface, cutting channels as it flows. Plowing at appropriate intervals is, therefore, an essential element in an erosion-control program. Overplowing, on the other hand, can do severe and lasting damage to the soil.

Weeds absorb water, nutrients, and sometimes light, which are needed by cultivated plants. Overcultivation of the land with the laudable purpose of getting rid of weeds may, however, do more harm than the weeds would do because excessive tillage breaks down the structure of the soil and leaves it susceptible to crusting, which impedes water intake, increases runoff, and reduces the amount of water stored for plant use. How much tillage is advisable depends chiefly on the nature of the soil. Some soils, as for example the loessial soils of the lower Mississippi Valley, are best managed under a system of minimum tillage.

Crop residues must be managed in order to provide suitable conditions for seeding and managing a crop. Often it is advisable, by plowing, to bury residue. In other cases, the burial of residues is not advisable.

Crop adaptation: a practical application of geography

The adaptation of crops to the potentials, needs, and limitations of the soil would seem to be a self-evidently advisable practice, but in the past it has been honored almost as much in the breach as in the observance. Traditions die hard, and the farmer whose family has, perhaps for several generations, raised corn, tobacco, and beans may resist suggestions of a change in his accustomed way of doing things.

Crop adaptation is, in its essence, the practical application, usually on a comparatively small scale, of basic geographic understandings. It is an awareness of place-to-place differences and an adjustment to these differences. The adjustment may take the form of devoting specific types of land to specific crops, as for example in the cranberry bogs of New Jersey, or it may take the form of establishing crop rotations designed to restore to the soil, by way of one crop, what is taken from it by another crop; for example, a rotation system such as that in the Middle West, of corn, a small grain, and legume crops, the last serving to add nitrogen and humus to the soil.

¶ The choice of a cropping system that will provide for the longtime maintenance of soil productivity involves many factors.

The pattern of different kinds of soil on the farm must be considered. If the soil on the farm is quite uniform and is subject to hazard from erosion, a cropping system that involves fairly regular use of grass-legume sods, rotated over all the cropland on the farm, should be given serious consideration.

On the other hand, if the farmer has several different kinds of soil, a monoculture system with each crop grown continuously on the soil where it is best adapted may be most satisfactory.

The agronomic characteristics of the forage crops to be grown are also important in determining the cropping system. Forage crops which are relatively easy to establish by seeding but which tend to decline in yield as time goes on are best used as a component of fairly short sod-based rotations. Red clover and timothy mixture, are a good example. If the preferred forage crop is rather slow or difficult to establish, but when once established remains productive over a long period, continuous use of the same field for this crop may be desirable. . . .

Every plan of a cropping system should provide for flexibility, in order to permit changing the acreage of crops from year to year to adjust to changes in demand and farm organization. Provision for alternate crops for use on areas where the intended crop is destroyed by weather, insects, or diseases early in its growing season is also needed. As a general rule, regular rotations are best adapted to regions where annual rainfall is less subject to extreme variations (4).

From this it will be seen that crop adaptation is not a simple one-to-one matter of devoting a given type of soil to a given type of crop or a given series of crops in rotation. The best information that can be supplied by scientists and government agencies does not relieve the individual farmer or rancher of the necessity of making his own decisions, based not only on his knowledge of his soils but also upon many other physical and cultural factors. The intelligent and responsible land manager today is a geographer, whether he realizes it or not, for land management is nothing more than the practical application of insights derived from a knowledge of the interrelationship of a complex of physical and cultural conditions in a given time and place.

Society: the marriage of man and the land

This is not a textbook on agronomy, and certainly this chapter does not pretend to exhaust the knowledge that has been gained on the subject of soils as a physical phenomenon. The above brief overview of the chemical and physical properties of soils is designed only to set the stage for a consideration of some of the social consequences of soil fertility and soil depletion. The maps (Figures VIII-8, VIII-9, and VIII-10) are re-

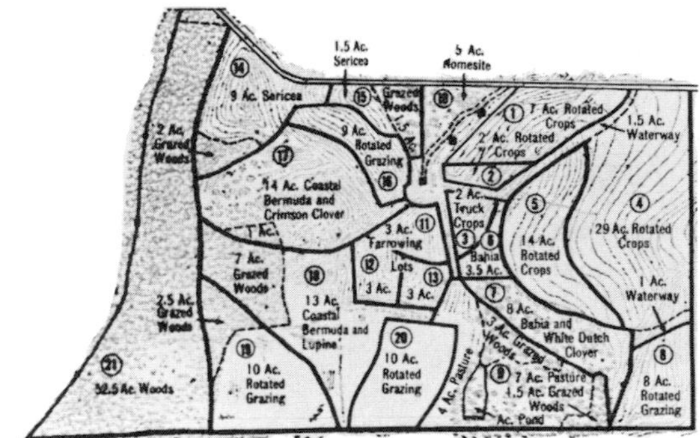

VIII:7 This is a conservation plan map for the farm illustrated in Figure VIII:6. Note that while the boundaries on this map show some striking similarities to the boundaries in Figure VIII:6 there are also some striking dissimilarities. The reason for this is that the wishes and needs of the farmer are taken into account along with the soil capability in preparing a conservation plan. (From *Soils, The 1957 Yearbook of Agriculture,* United States Department of Agriculture)

printed from a recent issue of a professional journal. Commenting on these maps, the author notes that:

¶ Patterns of human ailments are suggestive. Statistics of draftees' health, profusely recorded in the late wars, deserve careful study. In Missouri, statistics suggest that the better bodies of boys going into the Army for that state are related to better soil. Our national health pattern in terms of dental caries likewise relates this human anatomical segment of biotic geography to soil fertility. A map of the number of caries of teeth per mouth shows a minimum in the mid-continent and increasing numbers eastward and westward from that area of moderate soil development and maximum production of natural proteins.[1]

These correlations should not surprise us. There is an old German proverb that says that "*Man ist was er iszt,*" that is, "One is what one eats." Oversimplified this may be as an explanation of the complexity of man, but it contains a large measure of truth. And

[1] Albrecht, William A., "Soil Fertility and Biotic Geography," *The Geographical Review,* January, 1957, pp. 102-103. Reprinted by permission. (The maps of Missouri are from an unpublished doctoral dissertation submitted to the graduate school of the University of Missouri by L. M. Hepple.)

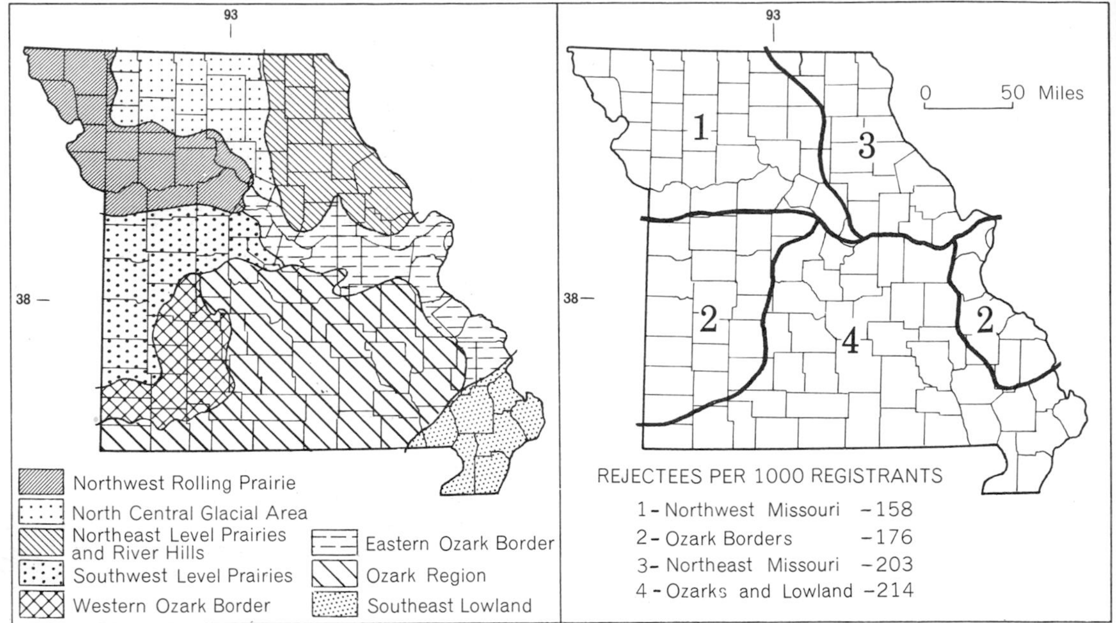

VIII:8 This map shows the major soil regions of Missouri. (From "Soil Fertility and Biotic Geography" by William A. Albrecht, *The Geographical Review*, January, 1957, used by permission)

VIII:9 This map shows army rejectees in Missouri per thousand registrants. (From "Soil Fertility and Biotic Geography" by William A. Albrecht, *The Geographical Review*, January, 1957, used by permission)

what man eats derives ultimately from the soil which produces his food. The health of any given population is, therefore, inextricably bound to the "health" of the soil which supplies its foodstuffs. Perhaps this is one reason why populations that must depend wholly or primarily upon local food resources are characteristically less well nourished than are those which have developed exchange economies that permit them to bring in food from many parts of the world.

Another author has suggested a correlation between fertile soils and political freedom:

¶ Food is the basic resource. So it is that man or groups of men who in any particular period of the history of a nation control the supply and are in possession of the basic foods are supreme in power. A government is stable and supreme only if it has control or can take over the rationing of food. In frontier countries where there is adequate food in the hands of those who produce it, plenty of good land, then the government cannot effectively control the food supply. Our "Land of the Free" tradition stems directly from plenty of good land.

As acres become too few and people too many, the government steps in and regulates the distribution of food. Egyptian history back to 2830 B.C. *records governmental agents as overseers of the grains.* The story of Joseph in the Bible shows how *government can reduce a people to slavery by control of the food.* In China, two sets of interest—the consumers and the producers—were recognized and controls designed to regulate the supply and demand by price fixing. About 1122 B.C. it was recognized that if the price of grain were too high it would hurt the consumer and if too low it would hurt the producer. High prices caused emigration and low prices for the farmers made the nation poor. Either extreme, with prices high or low, produced final bad results.

In Athens the history records that Xenophon in 404 B.C. counted it an important quality of a statesman to have knowledge of the grain business. A century later, 303 B.C., Rome was experiencing the problems of man-land ratio, and *price controls* were listed for more than eight-hundred articles of commerce. England tried in 1199 to control both retail and wholesale prices and again in 1815, but these as well as other arbitrary measures failed. Belgium failed in 1584 and 1585 to regulate prices by government at Antwerp. India, following rice failures in 1770, in which one-third of the population died, passed laws designed to prohibit speculation in food.

On December 20, 1777, Sir Henry Clinton in charge of the collection of taxes for the British at New York, proclaimed the legal rate for the sale of wheat, corn, and other foods. The proclamation specified that the farmer's supply would be confiscated if he refused to sell at the specified price as set by the government agent. But because there was plenty of good land the controls proved fruitless and were discontinued after six months. In France at this time price-fixing became a major factor in the Reign of Terror.

The lesson of history here is that first population increases overtake the productive ability of the declining fertility of the soils and that governmental efforts to limit the price artificially are doomed to failure.

After the government takes over the controls of the food supply—when acres divided by people is less than two acres per person—we recognize a trend in type of government to be socialistic, fascist or communistic. Democracy as we know it was created by and grew out of the independent food supply of farmers. We still live under the benefits of personal and political freedom fruiting from plenty of good land, land of the free. But our days as a democracy as we know it will reach the critical day when we shall no longer have the two acres per person.[1]

If the soil is one of the defenses which a free people have against the encroachment of governments upon their liberties, it is also one of the resources to which government must look for the taxes which support the proper functions of government. Since the assessed valuation of land is, in the final analysis, an estimate of its capacity to produce wealth, this valuation depends very largely upon the nature of the soil.

Several years ago, the junior author made a study of the correlations between landforms and the assessed valuation of farmland in a township in southeastern Wisconsin. The landforms, in turn, were related to certain soil types. It happened that in this area the four major landform types were terminal moraine, ground moraine, kamy moraine, and old lake plain. Assessed valuations showed an orderly progression of values downward from the terminal moraine through the ground moraine and the kamy moraine to the lake plain (7). Since the topographical differences among these landform types were not in themselves great enough to have major effects on land-use, it would appear that the different types of soil which had developed in relationship to the different landforms accounted for the notable differences in assessed valuation.

In a federal republic such as ours, in which many of the most significant functions of government are still carried on primarily by state and local units, differences in the productive capacity of the land may have important consequences. Poor land means a low tax base, which burdens the people with inferior schools that may produce a citizenry unable or unwilling to carry its proper share of political and economic responsibility. And since our Constitution guarantees to all of our people unlimited freedom of movement within the boundaries of our country, the problems created in such impoverished areas cannot be contained there but will spread to other areas by way of migrants. This being the case, the loss of soil by erosion or its damage by unwise farming methods can never be considered a purely local or regional problem. It is at least a national problem and, in view of the growing interdependence of man throughout the world, ought to be considered an international problem.

The interrelationships between soils, on the one hand, and socio-economic factors on the other would make a whole volume in itself, for the soils and what man does to them or with them set off a chain reaction which works its way through the whole of a society. Many years ago, one of the greatest of American geographers had this to say about the influence of soils upon the cultural and economic patterns of two of our states:

¶ Iowa and Alabama afford typical examples of the influence of the soil. There is no contradiction between them. The only difference is that other factors have led to different degrees of exhaustion. In both places the first effect of good soil was to give a large yield of crops per acre, and thus promote prosperity. Prosperous people

[1] Fink, Ollie E., "Soil and Democracy," *The Land*, Vol. II, No. 1, Spring 1952, pp. 34-39. Reprinted by permission.

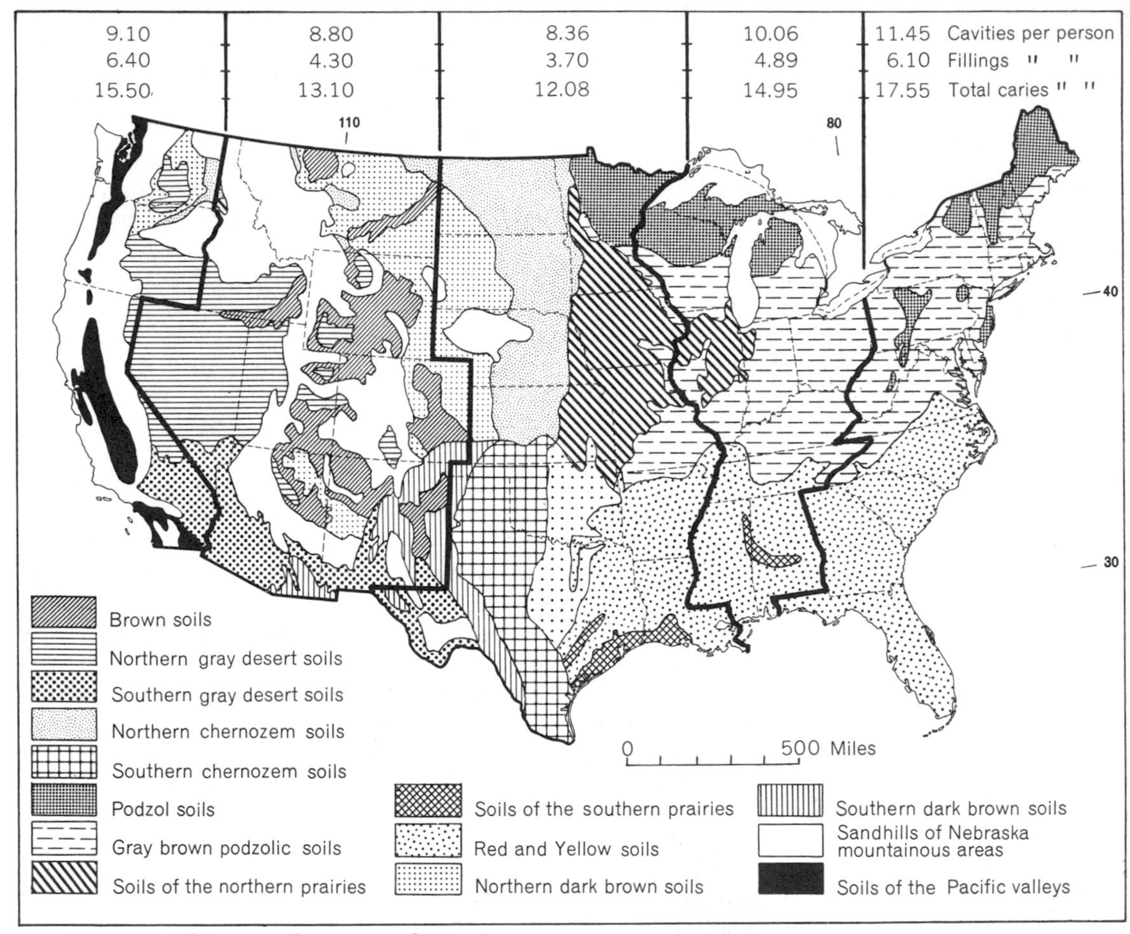

VIII:10 This map shows correlation between the incidence of dental caries among Navy inductees, 1942, and major soil groups. (From "Soil Fertility and Biotic Geography" by William A. Albrecht, *The Geographical Review*, January, 1957, used by permission)

can afford better houses, better roads, and more luxuries than people on poorer soils. Hence in the prosperous communities many people engage in occupations other than farming, business is active, and the non-farming population tends to be relatively dense. Such conditions, as well as the ability of the farmers to hire helpers, brings laborers into the community. Frequently these belong to a different social class from the farmers, being foreigners in Iowa and Negroes in Alabama. Still another important economic situation, namely, tenancy, arises from the presence of such people, and from the fact that good soil often makes it possible for a man's work to support not only himself and his family, but also a landlord. Thus where the soil is especially good, there is a strong tendency toward a division of the population into an upper land-owning class, which has considerable wealth and education, and a lower class of tenants and laborers. In Iowa this tendency is slight; in Alabama it reached its greatest extreme in the days of slavery, and is still strong.

The present contrast between the best soils of Iowa and the Black Belt [of Alabama] illustrates the fact that the human factor alters the economic geography of any particular region from one period to another. The effect of good soil in the two states has been the same, but other factors have been different. One of these factors is the length of time that the soil has been used. Alabama was settled before Iowa, and there has been more time in which to exhaust the soil. More important than this is the climate. In warm climates . . . the soil deteriorates faster than in cooler ones. Also in such climates people have less energy and are more likely to be careless in their farm work. This has tended to make the Alabama farmers take poor care of their land. Again, the social system and the nature of the laboring class have a great effect upon the use and care of the soil. Where labor is despised, as it was in the South during the days of slavery, the landowners have little to do with the actual cultivation of the soil. Hence many of them take little personal interest in seeing that fertility is preserved. Still other conditions, such as the habits of the farmers as to keeping animals, enter into the matter. The outstanding fact is that the value of even the best soil can be temporarily destroyed by cultivation of a single crop without proper fertilization and rotation. When that happens, a soil which was originally of the best quality, and which still has great potentialities, may become of little value, and the economic geography of a region is greatly changed (8).[1]

Will our children get enough to eat?

Since soils are so fundamentally important to a nation, and since it takes on an average 1,000 years for an inch of soil to form, it would seem that the proper care of soils would be one of the major concerns of a people. Unfortunately, this has not been the case in the past, and there is no strong evidence to suggest that we are even now as concerned about the conservation of our soil resources as we should be.

We cannot, of course, prevent the kind of soil destruction which nature normally carries on as a part of the process of tearing down and building up and which is everywhere operative on the face of the earth, nor, perhaps, should we want to do so. We can and must prevent that acceleration of natural destruction which results from man's thoughtless or rapacious use of soil resources. Some of the means by which this destruction may be prevented have already been hinted at. We can restore nutrients to the soil, and at the same time in many cases preserve or improve its structure by the use of fertilizers, by adapting crops to the kinds of soil to which they are best suited, and by rotating crops. We can even improve some low-value land by irrigation or by drainage. But our first and most urgent job is to reduce the amount of physical loss of the soil which results from soil erosion.

Cultivated land is likely to erode more rapidly than uncultivated land chiefly for two reasons: (1) the removal of the natural vegetational cover tends to speed up the runoff from the land, and as runoff is accelerated its erosive power increases; and (2) the loosening of the soil by cultivation allows it to be carried away more easily by running water or blown away by the winds.

The first point that must be made with respect to soil conservation is, therefore, that cultivation in and of itself increases the hazard of soil erosion. But in a country as large and as diverse as ours, the second point is equally important: that the degree of the hazard varies notably from one region to another, depending upon such factors as the quantity and nature of the precipitation, the amount and degree of slope, the structure of the soil, and the amount and character of the local vegetational cover. Methods of cultivation which might do little or no injury to the soil on the relatively flat prairies with their fairly even and gentle rainfall would probably result in severe erosion in a region of steep slopes and torrential rainfall. Conservation practices are not, therefore, absolutes to be applied indiscriminately to any region, but adaptations to be worked out in response to the peculiar conditions of the region.

Fundamentally, the prevention of soil erosion is a matter of preventing or at least slowing down the runoff of water. This can be accomplished in many ways. On very steep slopes, the only possible way may be to leave the land under its native vegetational cover or to rebuild the slope by terracing, as is done in parts of south China and the Philippines. On less steep slopes, runoff may be inhibited by putting the land under grass, by contour plowing, or by strip farming.

Grass reduces runoff by imposing innumerable obstacles to the flow of water and by giving the surface a sponge-like quality that encourages the seepage of water into the ground. Unfortunately, except in favored situations where other factors encourage a stock or dairy industry, grass is usually less

[1] Reprinted with permission from *Principles of Economic Geography*, Ellsworth Huntington, 1940, John Wiley & Sons, Inc., New York, pp. 147-148.

profitable than other crops and therefore tends to give way to them. However, it is interesting to note that in some of the badly eroded hill areas of our South, once abandoned land has been placed under grass and is slowly beginning to recover its fertility.

Contour plowing, as its name suggests, is simply plowing slopeland along points of equal elevation and perpendicularly to the direction of slope. It makes such obvious sense that one might wonder why anyone would ever have plowed slopeland any other way; and yet many did, cutting their furrows up and down the slope and, in the process, creating ready-made channels for runoff. Contour plowing arrests the flow of water down a slope and encourages it to seep into the loose soil of the furrows.

Strip farming involves laying out the fields in strips of different kinds of crops, typically one of the cereal grains or legumes in one field and corn in another. Strip farming also tends to capture more of the water in the ground and inhibit runoff. A variant of strip cropping, called patch farming, is practiced in some areas where primitive farming methods are still used. In patch farming, small patches of cultivated land are dispersed through areas of grass or bush. The grass or bush captures the debris which the water carries along as cutting tools and slows down the rate of flow so that, upon entering the cleared patch, the water can do comparatively little in the way of erosion.

While most soil erosion is the result of the work of running water, certain areas suffer considerable damage from wind erosion, or deflation. This kind of erosion is most typically found in drylands or, even more commonly, along the margins of drylands. In such situations, the very dryness of the soil gives it a powdery quality which makes it particularly susceptible to wind action. Our American Dust Bowl is one of the best examples of a region which has suffered intensive deflation. When one considers the climatic hazards under which cultivation is carried on in such areas, it would seem reasonable to suggest that perhaps the best solution to the problem of wind deflation is to withdraw such areas from cultivation. Such a policy would seem to be especially advisable for a nation which finds itself embarrassed by surplus agricultural production.

Dr. Charles R. Van Hise, one of our country's foremost authorities on soil conservation, once said that "of all our duties to our descendants, that of maintaining our soil unimpaired in thickness and richness is the most serious." In a day of nuclear bomb testing and its attendant pollution of the air, Dr. Van Hise might be inclined to give higher priority to maintaining the purity of the atmosphere, but certainly no one could quarrel with the importance which he attaches to the maintenance of our soil resources. Short of some catastrophe greater than any hitherto known in man's history, the human race may be expected to continue to increase in numbers and needs. Soil, as we have seen, develops so slowly that, for all practical purposes, we may say that man's soil resources do not really increase at all. We shall have to feed ourselves in the future on essentially the same soils that are now sustaining us. Whether we shall actually be able to do so will depend on how intelligently and how responsibly we use these resources.

APPLICATION OF GEOGRAPHIC UNDERSTANDING

I. Some writers have suggested that the soil should be considered a part of the animal kingdom. What do you suppose prompts such a suggestion? What arguments can you present for or against it?

II. Two of the most important agricultural trends in our country are (1) the trend toward more and more mechanization and (2) the trend toward larger units of ownership. Do these trends promise better or poorer treatment of the soil? Why?

III. Minute quantities of gold, silver, and lead are found in most soils. Should they be considered micronutrients or trace elements? Could a trace element ever be reclassified as a micronutrient? Would the opposite ever be possible?

IV. Corn and cotton are two crops that are particularly dangerous to the soils of the rainy tropics. Why? If they are so dangerous, why do tropical peoples persist in raising them?

V. Does it seem probable to you that, as our knowledge of soil capabilities and crop requirements grows, we will someday be able to say that some one crop is the one best possible use of a particular field? Why or why not?

VI. What grounds does this chapter suggest for the hope that, in the long run, technological aid to underdeveloped countries may be more in the interests of the United States than military aid?

VII. What practical consequences does soil erosion in the South have for the Chicago or Detroit taxpayer?

VIII. What are the practical reasons for saying that a truly effective program of soil conservation must be directed by the federal government rather than by state or local governments?

IX. Certain soils developed from volcanic flows are among the richest and most productive soils in the world. Would this be generally true of volcanic soils? Why or why not?

X. If populations continue to increase at their present dramatic rate, and if on the average two acres of productive land are needed to feed each one of us, what suggestions do you have to offer for maintaining a reasonably satisfactory man-land ratio in the future?

References

1 Thompson, Louis M., *Soils and Their Fertility,* McGraw-Hill Book Co., Inc., New York, 1952, p. 3.

2 Nikiforoff, C. C., "Reappraisal of the Soil," *Science,* Vol. 129, 22 January, 1959, pp. 187-188.

3 "The Soils of the United States," *Our Natural Resources and Their Conservation,* A. E. Parkins and J. R. Whitaker, Editors, John Wiley and Sons, Inc., New York, 1939, p. 35.

4 Allaway, W. H., "Cropping Systems and Soil," *Soil, The 1957 Yearbook of Agriculture,* United States Department of Agriculture, 1957, p. 395.

5 Albrecht, William A., "Soil Fertility and Biotic Geography," *The Geographical Review,* January, 1957, pp. 102-103. (The maps of Missouri are from an unpublished doctoral dissertation submitted to the graduate school of the University of Missouri by L. M. Hepple).

6 Fink, Ollie E., "Soil and Democracy," *The Land,* Vol. II, No. 1, Spring, 1952, pp. 34-39.

7 Strietelmeier, John, "The Relationships Between Certain Landforms and the Assessed Values of Farmlands: A Case Study," 1947, an unpublished study.

8 Huntington, Ellsworth, *Principles of Economic Geography,* John Wiley and Sons, Inc., New York, 1940, pp. 147-148.

Chapter 9

Inland waters and their importance to man

Water is and has been many things to many people. To the physical scientist it is not only one of the most common but also one of the most remarkable of substances: a substance that expands when it reaches a critical point in the process of cooling; one of the most nearly universal of solvents, although it is practically inert; next to mercury, the liquid which possesses the highest surface tension; an almost transparent liquid which differentially absorbs the light rays within the range of the visible spectrum; a substance rivaled by hardly any other in its capacity to split or ionize dissolved material; a remarkable absorber of heat, with a uniquely high latent heat of evaporation (1). To the earth scientist, "running water is by far the most important agent of gradation that modifies the greater part of the land surface of the earth" (2), the sculptor of the Grand Canyon and the builder of the Mississippi floodplain and delta. To the industrialist, water is an absolute essential in the manufacturing process: it takes 65,000 to 80,000 gallons of water to produce a ton of steel, seven to ten gallons to produce a gallon of gasoline, 70,000 gallons to produce one ton of newsprint by the sulphate process, 200,000 to produce a ton of viscose rayon, and 600,000 in fermenting a thousand bushels of industrial grain (3). Crops require enormous quantities of water. Carhart cites the results of experiments conducted at Akron, Colorado, which showed that 334 tons of water were involved in growing one ton of dry matter in a crop of barley. Beans required 738 tons of water to a ton of dry matter produced, clover 797 tons of water, oats 599, peas 788, potatoes 636, and wheat 544 (3). While no experimental data are available for the amount of water required for meat production, it has been estimated that a dairy cow consumes about 500 pounds of water to produce 100 pounds of milk.

Man himself is mostly water, seventy per cent or more. His blood is mostly water and he must have water for his digestive processes. Under normal activity, he must have six to eight pints of water per day to replace body losses—about a ton a year.

But water is more than a curious phenomenon or a practical necessity. In its various surface forms it has long evoked emotional responses which have nothing to do with science or technology. The undergraduate singing of an alma mater that stands "far above Cayuga's water," the homesick Hoosier dreaming about "the moonlight on the Wabash," the German nationalist standing his "watch on the Rhine"—each of these in his own way testifies to the almost mystical attachments that men have felt to certain water features which seem to give identity or definition to those parts of the earth which they consider their own.

This chapter is concerned with those water features which are found on the earth's land masses: rivers, lakes, swamps, marshes, ground water and its surface manifestations. These features collect or drain the water which falls onto the surface as rain, snow, sleet, or hail and eventually return it to the ocean from which it comes back by way of evaporation to the atmosphere. This ceaseless round of evaporation, precipitation, and drainage comprises one of the great natural cycles, the hydrologic cycle, which is shown in diagrammatic form in Figure IX-1.

The water cycle

There is something awe-inspiring about the operations of all the great natural cycles, not least of them the hydrologic cycle. One writer, a Netherlander whose country has known water as friend and foe for centuries, has described the workings of the hydrologic cycle with just the right mixture of wonder and scientific objectivity:

¶ If it were possible to trace the careers of all the water-molecules on earth from the earliest times, it would be found that no two were alike. The opportunities for adventure open to such a molecule are circumscribed; but just as writings of limitless variety result from the different groupings of a very small number of letters and symbols, so are the life-histories of all water-molecules composed of a very restricted range of possible episodes.

Thus one will evaporate from the surface of the sea and rain back into it many times in succession before it is engulfed at the Pole in a submerging stream and drifts through the dark depths of the ocean, year upon year, until it eventually emerges at the Equator or at the opposite Pole. Meanwhile, a neighbour molecule, which had also taken a few turns at rising from and falling back into the sea, has been wafted higher into the atmosphere and, now transformed into the constituent of a snowflake, has landed on a glacier. Years later it may sweep towards the valley in the glacier stream or evaporate from the tongue of ice, only to return to earth again, this time, maybe, flung down in heavy rain upon a desert, from which it may evaporate at sunrise and return as dew at night again and again.

Elsewhere, water penetrates many hundreds of feet into the earth's crust and follows long, tortuous paths until it spurts upward in a hot spring or unobtrusively makes its appearance in the bed of a river, flowing with the latter towards the ocean. Most water that goes underground, however, eventually evaporates at the surface again, or else is absorbed by vegetation and is thus returned to the atmosphere. Another considerable contingent may have travelled only a little way between sand and particles of clay before oozing into a brook and sweeping rapidly out to sea.

There are, again, prisons, as it were, in which the molecules of water may be trapped. They may be held between grains of sand at the bottom of the sea and smothered there under growing accumulations of deposits. If such be their fate . . . not until the sea-bed has been raised up to mountains and these in turn have been worn down by the teeth of time [will they be released]. Then, carried along by the creeping groundwater, a few of those drops of water . . . will at last make good their escape. Molecules which are caught up as crystal water in weathering minerals are imprisoned in far smaller but no less escape-proof cells. Their liberation will not come until mountain-forming forces have pushed them deep down into the earth's crust, whence the heat will drive them out once more. Then again there is stagnant water deep down in Norwegian fjords or the Black Sea which, through lack of circulation, becomes foul and saturated with hydrogen sulphide and semi-decayed organic remains.

Most of the water absorbed by plants and animals is set free again within twenty-four hours, but those particles which are pressed into service for the building of cells have a much longer period of enforced rest.[1]

Rivers and their valleys

Interesting as the hydrologic cycle is for its own sake, however, our interest in this chapter is in what happens between the time water reaches the surface of the earth in the form of precipitation and returns either to the atmosphere by evaporation or to the ocean by runoff. To the geographer, probably the most significant features which are formed by water on the earth's surface are streams and their associated valleys.

¶ Rivers . . . have characteristics that derive from their basic function as conveyors of the surplus water of precipitation from land to sea. These are: (1) the continuous *one-directional movement* of the waters, with flow in the longer rivers even from one climatic zone to another; (2) notable *variations in velocity* with changes in volume; (3) extreme *fluctuation in level, or stage, and in width,* according to conditions of precipitation and run-off; (4) conditions, not ordinarily of stratification as in lakes, but rather of *continual mixing* or *turbulence,* it being understood that the term "turbulence," as used in discussion of natural waters, does not imply violence of movement, but applies to all sorts of movements that involve mixing—in a stream turbulence prevails always, its degree varying with the velocity of flow and with the shape of sides and bottom; (5) continued or occasional *turbidity* . . . ; and (6) following from the changes in velocity, a relative *instability of bottom;* and (7) the most significant fact that the river is an *open system,* i.e., it continually receives new water and nutritive substances from without and passes them from one potential home of organisms to another.[2]

The term "river" is usually restricted to streams having a considerable volume of water. Smaller streams go by a great variety

[1] Reprinted with permission from P. H. Kuehnen, *Realms of Water,* 1955, John Wiley & Sons, Inc., New York, pp. 11-12.
[2] Coker, Robert E., *Streams, Lakes, and Ponds,* The University of North Carolina Press, Chapel Hill, 1954, pp. 123-124, 127 Reprinted by permission.

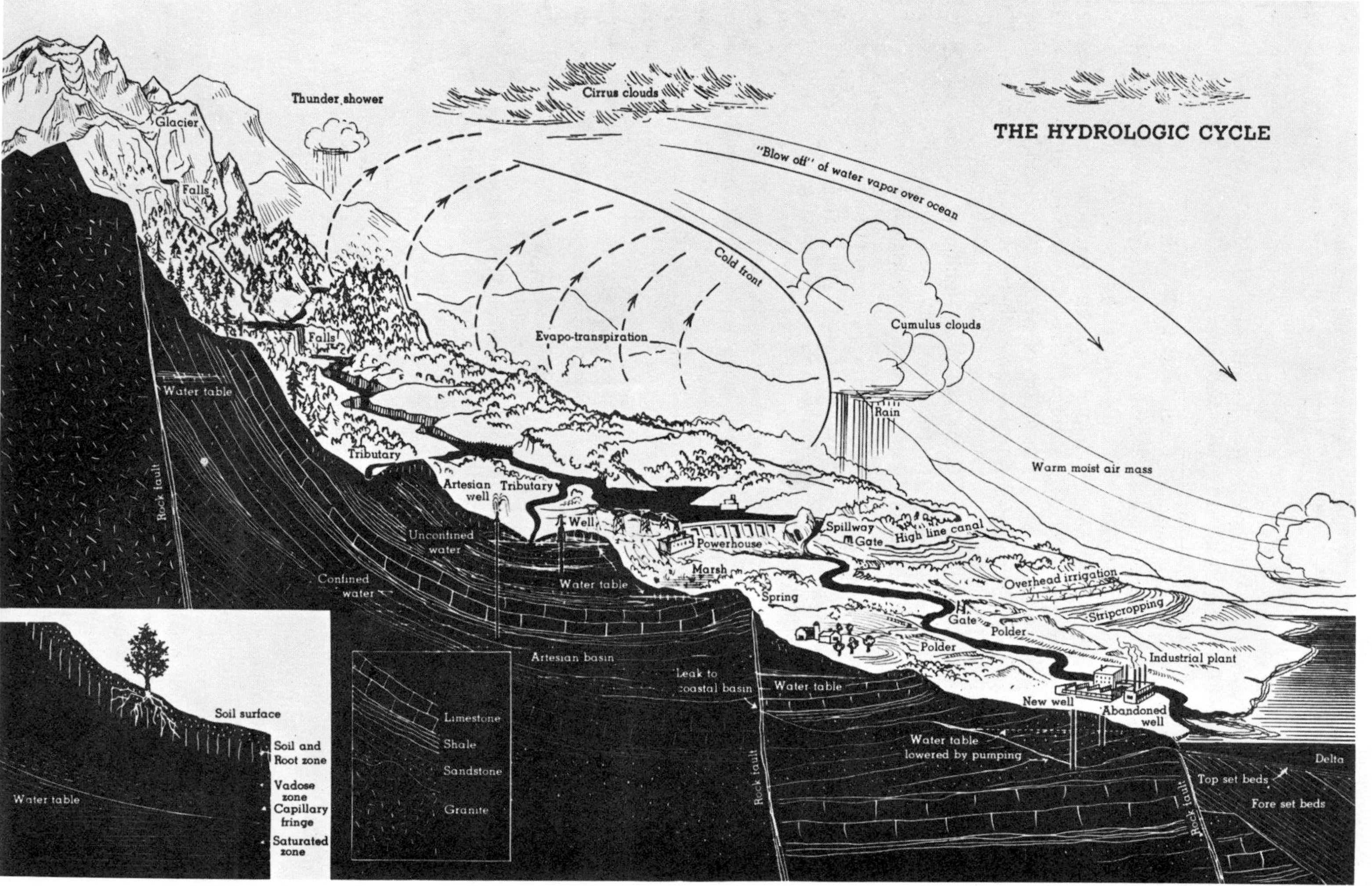
THE HYDROLOGIC CYCLE
Thunder shower
Cirrus clouds
Glacier
Falls
"Blow off" of water vapor over ocean
Cold front
Evapo-transpiration
Cumulus clouds
Rain
Warm moist air mass
Falls
Water table
Rock fault
Tributary
Artesian well
Tributary
Well
Unconfined water
Confined water
Water table
Powerhouse
Spillway
Gate
High line canal
Marsh
Spring
Overhead irrigation
Stripcropping
Gate
Polder
Polder
Industrial plant
Artesian basin
Leak to coastal basin
Water table
New well
Abandoned well
Water table lowered by pumping
Rock fault
Rock fault
Delta
Top set beds
Fore set beds
Limestone
Shale
Sandstone
Granite
Soil surface
Soil and Root zone
Vadose zone
Capillary fringe
Saturated zone
Water table

of names, among them creek, brook, run, and rill. Major streams and their tributaries form a river system which may be as large as the great Mississippi-Missouri-Ohio system of the American midcontinent or as small as the river system on some small island. The pattern, or "layout," of streams in a system is very largely determined by the nature of the geological structures upon which the local topography has been developed. The seven drainage patterns generally recognized by geomorphologists are diagrammed in Figure IX-2. These patterns are significant to the geographer because they are very largely responsible for giving landscapes their distinctive appearance or characteristics, and because such works of man as roads, railroads, field patterns, and settlements are closely related to them.

Rivers as sources of water supplies. The importance of rivers to man was suggested by the statistics cited at the beginning of this chapter. Let us look now in more detail at the eight chief functions which rivers historically have performed for man. These are the water supply, waste disposal, industrial water, irrigation, highway, boundary, regional bond, and recreational functions.

It is no accident that man's earliest civilizations arose in river valleys—the Nile Valley of Egypt and the Tigris-Euphrates Valley of Mesopotamia. For the great cities of these early civilizations, as for many of the great cities of the modern world, the rivers were quite literally the water of life for the close-packed populations that inhabited them. But in these ancient settlements, and down through the ages to our own times, the function of the river as a source of drinking water came into conflict with its function as a sewage disposal system. The result has been that, wherever men have lived for any length of time, they have converted their rivers into open sewers—foul smelling, foul tasting, and often toxic. The consequences of our mistreatment of our great rivers is perhaps best illustrated by the much-publicized water problem of New York City. "The irony of that was, the Hudson River, with an average volume of water sufficient to supply the city nine times over, flows past Manhattan. It couldn't be used; it is a great sewer for up-country communities" (3).

Pollution is not, however, the whole story behind our avoidance of rivers as drinking water supplies. After mapping the pattern of surface-water-using communities and superimposing this pattern on a map showing the practical availability of subsurface water, Borchert found that "most of the municipalities that use surface-water supplies are located in regions where ground-water condi-

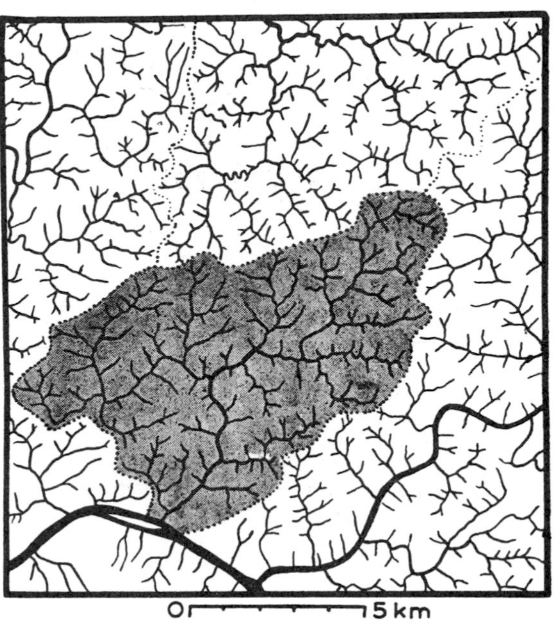

IX:2a This is a diagram of a dendritic drainage pattern. It resembles the branch system of a tree or the ramifications of the human nervous system. It develops where neither topography nor rock structure exercises any significant control over drainage, and water follows the "path of least resistance." Roads tend to follow the valleys or the tops of the divides. Field units are usually small and irregularly laid out. Towns may begin in the valleys and climb the slopes as they grow larger. Because of the large amount of slope land, soil erosion is always a threat, often a problem. The land is uniformly well-drained with little or no standing water. (From *Realms of Water* by P. H. Kuehnen, John Wiley & Sons, Inc., New York, 1955, used by permission)

IX:1 (Left) This is a diagram of the hydrologic cycle. (From *A Water Policy for the American People,* The Report of the President's Water Resources Policy Commission, Volume I)

IX:2b This is a diagram of a pinnate drainage pattern. It is similar to the dendritic pattern but develops where there is a pronounced regional slope. Human use of it is similar to use of the dendritic pattern. (From *Realms of Water* by P. H. Kuehnen, John Wiley & Sons, Inc., New York, 1955, used by permission)

tions are poor as a result of high salinity or low permeability of the underlying rock," and he concluded that "where ground-water conditions are suitable to meet local demands, surface water is a second choice, usually because of its greater seasonal fluctuation in temperature and hardness together with its comparatively high content of sediment and organic matter."[1] The map (Figure IX-3) strikingly illustrates the data from which Dr. Borchert drew his conclusion.

Unfortunately, while groundwater may be more desirable than surface water for drinking purposes, there is nothing to compare with a convenient stream for the disposal of sewage and industrial wastes. And in so using our streams, we are only imitating nature, for one of the chief natural functions of streams is to carry away surplus water and the rock waste resulting from erosion. However, the wastes which man adds to the rivers are not of a kind which fit naturally into the ecology of a stream and, as a result, they create havoc in the life of the stream. Left to themselves, the problems growing out of stream pollution tend to grow more serious with growth in population and increasing industrialization but, happily, the problems are not insoluble. At reasonable cost, sewage can be treated so that its residue may be emptied safely into streams without contaminating them. Increasingly, municipalities are establishing sewage disposal plants, and many more would undoubtedly do so were it not for the fact that most of our cities have been practically bankrupt for decades and cannot afford the initial cost of such a plant.

As sources of industrial water, most rivers leave a great deal to be desired. In general, river water is in many places warmer than either lake water or ground water and, therefore, less satisfactory for cooling purposes, which are among the most important uses of industrial water. Silt, offensive odors, unpleasant taste, or undesirable minerals may further limit the suitability of river water for industrial purposes. In spite of these limitations, however, in every part of the United States except the dry West and the Great Lakes area the bulk of the water used for industrial purposes comes from streams.

Rivers as sources of power. It may be argued whether the use of water for the generation of hydroelectric power should be considered an industrial use or should be classified separately. For our purposes, we shall consider it an industrial use inasmuch as the power generated at hydroelectric power sites often undergirds the entire industrial development of a whole region.

The growing importance of hydroelectric power, not only for industry but also as an economic support for other types of water use, has been indicated by Dr. Peveril Meigs:

¶ The inclusion of hydroelectric power in a water development program often makes the difference between a self-liquidating and a tax-supported project. During the depression of the thirties scores of irrigation districts depending for revenue solely on sales of water to farmers were forced to default on their obligations; the farms could not produce enough income to pay all water production costs. Sales of electricity, however, can cover part of the cost of development and thus permit irrigation water to be sold at reasonable rates. Aside from its role in cost apportionment, the growth of diversified industries in the Tennessee River Basin and, more recently, the development of large aluminum industries in the Columbia Basin show how availability of low-priced power stimulates the

[1] Borchert, John R., "The Surface Water Supply of American Municipalities," *Annals of the Association of American Geographers,* Vol. XLIV, No. 1, March, 1954, p. 19. (Map from p. 18.) Reprinted by permission.

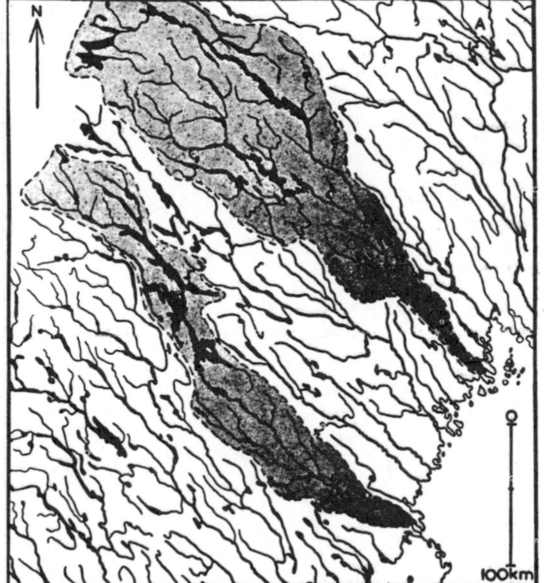

IX:2c This is a diagram of a parallel drainage pattern. It tends to develop where there is a very pronounced regional slope or where there is strong subsurface rock control or where glaciers have carved out parallel valleys which are now occupied by streams. There is a strong tendency for the valleys to become avenues of transportation and for towns to develop at their ends, claiming the inland valleys for their hinterlands. Where this kind of pattern is found along a coastline, traffic is more likely to move by water along the coast than to move up hill and down dale inland, unless the relief is very subdued. Political boundaries often follow along stream channels. (From *Realms of Water* by P. H. Kuehnen, John Wiley & Sons, Inc., New York, 1955, used by permission)

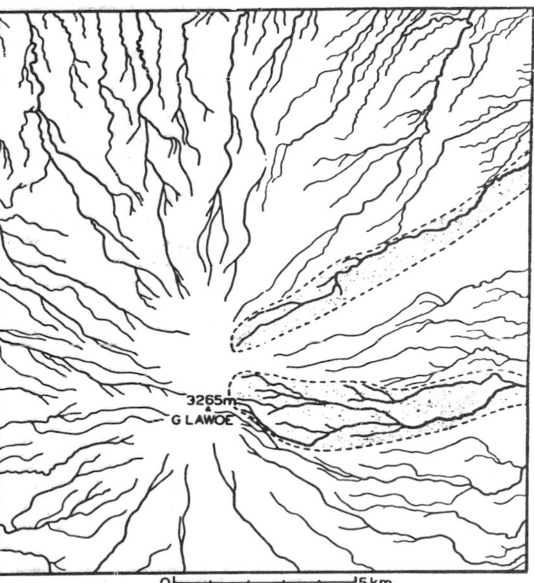

IX:2d This is a diagram of a radial drainage pattern. It is associated with prominent surface features such as volcanoes or with the earliest stages of dissection in a region where the rocks have been thrust up in the form of a dome. As the radiating streams cut their valleys, tributaries may form on the secondary slopes, flowing into the radiating streams so as to form an annular pattern reminiscent of the "rings" of a tree. (From *Realms of Water*, by P. H. Kuehnen, John Wiley & Sons, Inc., New York, 1955, used by permission)

development of private industries in areas where other fuels are lacking or uneconomical. . . .

Since initiation of the Tennessee Valley Authority in 1933, much thought has been given to coordinated development of entire river basins and discussion of water problems has acquired a broader view.[1]

Rivers and irrigation. One of the most ancient uses of water has been for irrigation. Not only in the dry world, but also in many parts of the Mediterranean and Far Eastern worlds, archeologists have uncovered irrigation works dating back to or beyond the beginnings of recorded history. And even today, vast areas that would otherwise be too dry for agriculture have been made productive by irrigation.

In drylands particularly, a kind of mystique has grown up around irrigation which makes it difficult to discuss irrigation objectively, particularly if such a discussion involves pointing up some of the limitations and hazards of irrigation. It is nevertheless necessary to point out that irrigation is not the cure-all for every problem of a dry region, and that even as a remedy it carries certain hazards which have to be reckoned with.

The nature of this hazard has been de-

[1] Meigs, Peveril, "Water Problems in the United States," *Geographical Review*, Vol. 42, 1952, pp. 353-354. Reprinted by permission.

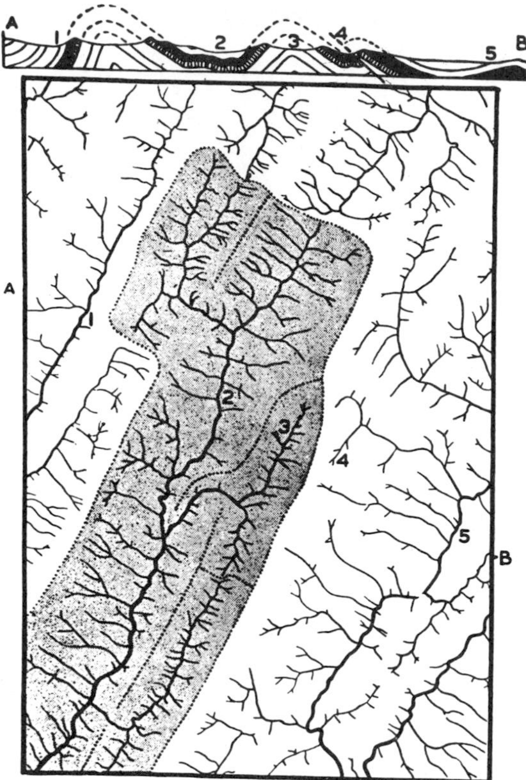

IX:2e This is a diagram of a trellis drainage pattern. It is characteristically found in regions where the subsurface rocks lie in parallel folds. As the folds are eroded, the larger streams cut trenches into the softer rock, and tributaries flow down into them from the folds of more resistant rock. The larger streams become the highways of the region, and other forms of transportation tend to funnel through their valleys. Settlement is mostly in the valleys and on the divides, with comparatively little on the slopes. (From *Realms of Water,* by P. H. Kuehnen, John Wiley & Sons, Inc., New York, 1955, used by permission)

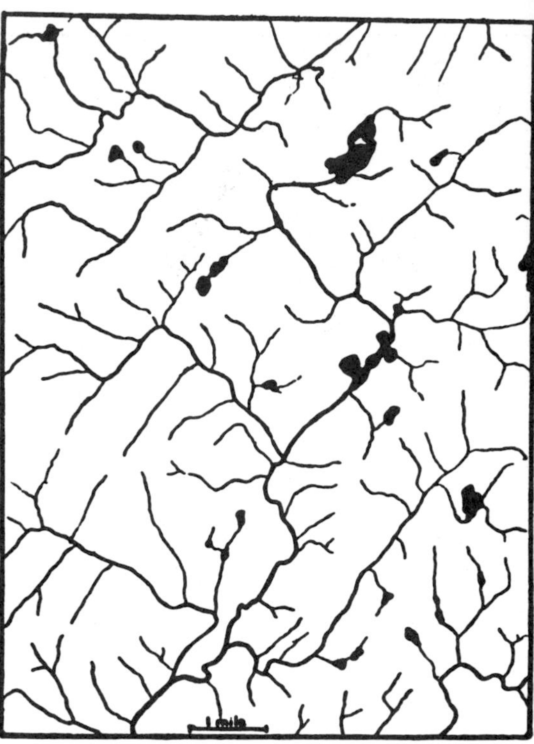

IX:2f This is a diagram of a rectangular drainage pattern. It is typically found in regions where large cracks (faults) have developed in the rocks, the lines of breakage running more or less perpendicular to each other. Streams carve their channels along the faults, often abruptly changing direction to follow another fault line. Unless very maturely dissected, this drainage pattern exercises comparatively little control over settlement patterns. (From *Realms of Water,* by P. H. Kuehnen, John Wiley & Sons, Inc., New York, 1955, used by permission)

scribed by one of the great figures of American geography, Dr. J. Russell Smith:

¶ Every schoolboy knows of the annual Nile flood and its automatic fertilization and the long continued productivity of the Nile Valley. The people of Egypt have had great cause for thankfulness because of the kind favors that geology has bestowed upon them. The head waters of the Nile coming down from the mountains of Ethiopia load themselves with mud as is the habit of such streams in flood, but the upper Nile flows through wide areas in which great blocks of the earth's crust have sunk, making depressions like the one of which the Dead Sea occupies the bottom. This area is storing the mud, the heavy silt loosened by the Nile floods, so that the water that finally reaches Egypt carries only very fine sediments and has built up the valley at the rate of about an inch a century, and fertilized as it built. For some six thousand years man has utilized this flood and its resulting thin layer of slime—this marvelous gift of nature. As the flood waters receded, the man of the Nile has walked through the shallow waters and sowed grain broadcast. The seeds settled in the mud, planted themselves, sprouted, and there was enough moisture and enough fertility to bring the grains through to a ripened crop—automatic fertilization—no plowing—a crop every year—manna couldn't touch that!

But in recent years Egypt has entered into a new era. This one crop system did not produce enough for the population that is now increasing rapidly under the influence of our new knowledge of preventable diseases, sanitation, and public health, accompanied by uncontrolled birth rate. To meet this new emergency the Egyptians are cutting out the flood system, have built a huge reservoir at Assuan and are using the water to irrigate two crops a year. A new problem enters, soil exhaustion; and the Egyptians are beginning to buy fertilizer almost as recklessly as the cotton growers of our South. Thus Egypt has lost its automatic source of wealth, and its economic independence. That country has given hostage to fortune by this new dependence upon foreign supplies and therefore upon foreign markets to get the wherewithall to meet its food needs. Incidentally, also, they are getting the irrigation problems of salt and alkali which did not exist with the ancient flood system. By that automatic and benign donation of Providence, the ground dried deeply in the dry season, it cracked open, the salt settled on the insides of the cracks and sometimes on the surface, but the oncoming flood dissolved it and carried it on down to the sea. Now the Egyptians have begun to find they must fight the alkali problem as we do in our own West, where it is said we destroy almost as much land by alkali as we add by reclamation (7).

IX:2g This is a diagram of an anastomosing drainage pattern. It is found in very flat plains, on deltas, and on tidal marshes. The channels wander apparently aimlessly about on the surface, threading into and out of each other. The streams often abandon their bends (meanders), leaving the former channel as a meander scar or as an oxbow lake. Drainage is very poor, the region is likely to remain in a very primitive condition, and there is very sparse settlement. (From *Realms of Water* by P. H. Kuehnen, John Wiley & Sons, Inc., New York, 1955, used by permission)

There is no way of knowing whether any responsible official of the Egyptian government ever read these observations of Dr. Smith. At any rate, by 1956, the Egyptian government was prepared to give more "hostages to fortune" in the form of a proposed high dam at Aswan which it hoped to finance with loans from the United States. When the American government did not come through, the Egyptians retaliated by nationalizing the Suez Canal, thereby provoking a short but bitter war with Great Britain and France which threatened the whole precarious peace of the Middle East.

Since the one side of the irrigation story in Egypt has been told, perhaps we should in fairness look at the other side. If nothing else, a comparison of the two views will serve to illustrate the complexities of the arguments which characteristically develop over proposals for specific irrigation projects.

¶ The Sadd Eli Ali (High Dam) is a scheme for harnessing the Nile River at Aswan. This dam is supposed to insure the storage of 70 billion meters of water, thus guaranteeing the discharge of 60 billion cubic meters required yearly for irrigation and compensating, as well, for any

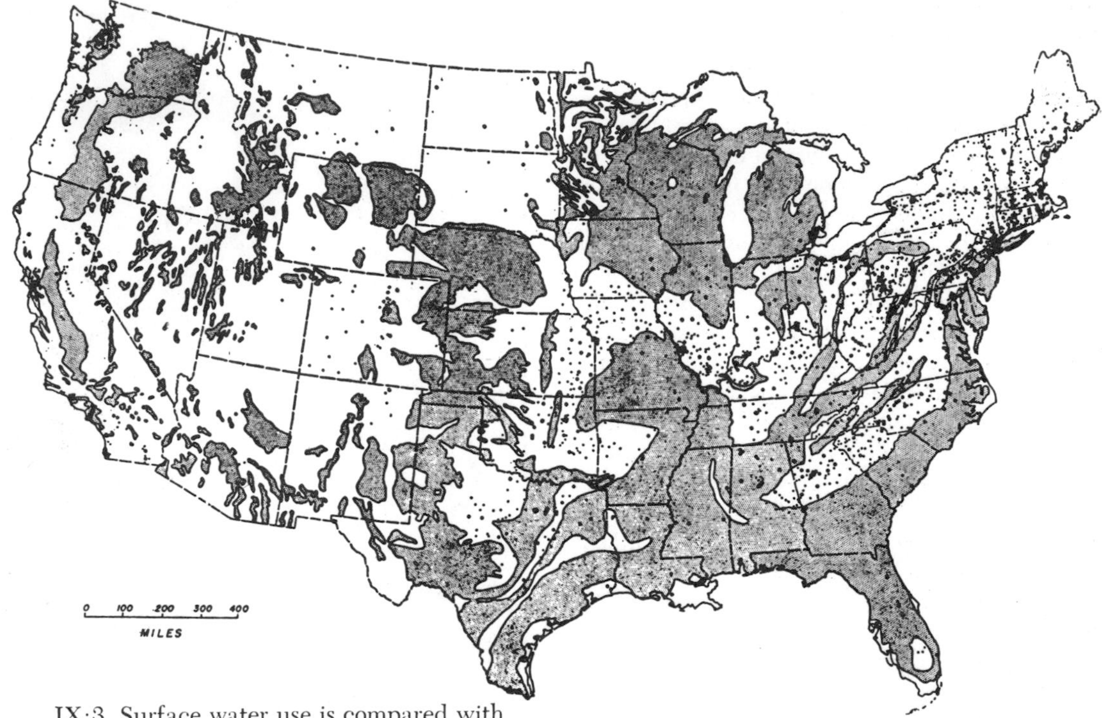

IX:3 Surface water use is compared with surface water availability on this map. Dots represent surface-water-using communities. Shaded areas indicate areas where ground water containing less than 2,000 parts per million of dissolved solids is available at rates exceeding approximately 72,000 gallons per day; i.e., enough for a town of about 1,000 people. (From "Surface Water Supply of American Municipalities" by John R. Borchert, *Annals of the Association of American Geographers,* March, 1954. The subsurface pattern was adapted from a map prepared by Harold E. Thomas for the Conservation Foundation, Figure 17 *United States Geological Survey Circular 114,* 1951, used by permission)

deficiency incurred by low floods. Since an acre of land required 8,000 cubic meters of water yearly, it is hoped that if this dam is built, it will be possible to expand the cultivation area in Egypt by roughly 2 million acres to a total of 7½ million acres and convert basin irrigation in upper Egypt to perennial irrigation. The Aswan Dam and the projects attached to it may also:

1. Protect the country against the damage of high floods and the necessity of raising and strengthening the existing embankments along the Nile. Egypt, with 95 per cent of its land unsuitable for cultivation needs to look to the desert and the Nile for a greater source of income.

2. Permit the installation of powerful hydro-electric generating plants capable of producing 10 billion kilowatt hours per year. The building of the power plant is necessary to utilize whatever iron and other minerals may be found in upper Egypt. The hydro-electric plant at Aswan could increase the country's power capacity about 200 per cent.

3. Permit expansion of the fertilizer industry to produce about 500,000 tons of fertilizer per year. The artificial fertilizer can be made from air, limestone, and Nile water at a plant operated from the hydro-electric plant. The fertilizer plant alone could employ more than seven hundred persons.

4. Help relieve the population pressure for agricultural land of this heavily-populated country. Egypt's population is growing faster than any scheme for making available more land to the farmers. Yet, the Aswan project is a step in the right direction.

Many persons will be gainfully employed because of these enterprises in mining, fertilizer production, hydro-electric power production, transporting and selling of farm products and raw materials. One gratifying fact is that the establishment of "secondary" industries may be possible. Ultimately, the cumulative effect of the Aswan Development Scheme on the economy of Egypt as a whole can be great. An increased national income and an expanding industrial capacity could usher in a new era for Egypt.[1]

On one point, at least, our two authorities agree: irrigation has opened a new era for Egypt. The disagreement is over the question whether this is a bright new day or the beginning of the end. If only a river were not such a useful thing! If only a river were not such a potentially destructive thing!

Rivers as transportation routes. It is difficult for us to comprehend in our day of jet planes, fast trains, and superhighways that through all of man's history, until as recently as two centuries ago, water routes were man's chief highways. Land journeys were tedious, time-consuming, and often perilous. Travelers moved therefore across the seas or along the seacoasts and up the rivers. Most of the great cities of the Old World are either seaports (Copenhagen, Lisbon, Barcelona, for example) or river ports located at the head of navigation on great rivers (London, Paris, Hamburg). Still other great cities grew up at river confluences (Lyon, Frankfurt), or on sites which controlled passage from one river system into another (Milan, Munich).

In our own country, settlement threaded its way through river valleys and along the Great Lakes from the east coast into the interior of the continent. The oldest cities of the American midcontinent are river towns, St. Louis and New Orleans and Cincinnati being examples that come immediately to mind. But, especially in our own country, the quasi-monopoly of water routes on commerce and travel disappeared rapidly in the face of the advancing railroads, and with each new development in the field of transport the role of the river has declined.

Strangely, though, while river transport as a whole has been declining, certain rivers have been increasing in importance as carriers of commerce, among them the Rhine, the St. Lawrence, and the Ohio. Water is still the cheapest form of transport and is, therefore, the preferred carrier for bulky goods that have little time value. Coal, petroleum, and iron ore are examples of such commodities.

One of the most spectacular river renaissances has been that of the Ohio River, whose valley some people are beginning to call "the American Ruhr."

¶ Today the Ohio River carries far more inland waterway commerce than any other river in the United States and about twice the paid commerce of the Panama Canal. Yet 25 years ago many people questioned its potentialities and many are still unaware of its present significance. After a stormy debate as to the feasibility and need of providing a minimum 9-foot constant navigation channel in the Ohio, such a project was authorized in 1910, and construction completed in 1929. . . .

The assurance of a 9-foot channel throughout the year has encouraged the location of industry in the valley. After the first experimental dams to provide a 9-foot channel below Pittsburgh were approved and before they could be constructed, industry began buying riparian factory sites. By 1907, even before canalization of the entire river was approved, practically all industrial sites on the Ohio for a distance of 30 miles below Pittsburgh had been purchased. Since then, industry has continued to buy and develop industrial sites up and down this river and some of its navigable tributaries, particularly the Monongahela, Allegheny, and Kanawha.

Industrial location along the river following the economic stalemate of the 1930's has been especially rapid. It is estimated that more than 2500 factories have been located in the basin since the end of the Second World War. In a lecture in Toledo, Major General Sturgis, Jr., reported that during the second quarter of 1953 alone 75 sites for plants, each costing more than a million dollars, were located in the Ohio valley, along with hundreds of others costing less.

Recent industrial expansion is exemplified by the atomic and chemicals industries. Within a 250-mile radius of Cincinnati alone is almost 70 per cent of the Atomic Energy Commission's planned development east of the Mississippi River. Government-owned atomic plants will represent an investment of over four billion dollars.

Also, the Ohio watershed is well known for its

---

[1] Jackson, Eureal Grant, "Economic-Geographic Philosophy Behind the Proposed Aswan Valley Project in Egypt," *Journal of Geography*, Vol. LVI, No. 7, October, 1957, p. 337. Reprinted by permission.

rapidly expanding chemical industry with its larger centers in the upper Ohio and its tributaries and in the Kanawha valley and with smaller areas at Cincinnati and Louisville. Several other recently developed and expanding centers have started, such as Calvert City.

While additional investigations need to be made and published as to why the new factories have located in the valley, a detailed investigation has been made of the chemical industry along the midwestern river and intra-coastal canal routes. This study substantiates the vital role that barge transportation has made in encouraging factory location here. Undoubtedly, some of the factories located in the valley have no relation to the availability of water transportation. However, as the years go by and larger dams are constructed and bigger pools of water created, fewer industries can escape being influenced directly or indirectly by navigation improvements. These big pools of water will not only improve water transportation facilities but the water can be used in other ways.

In summary, some of the important factors influencing the rapid location of industry in the valley are: (1) an abundance of coal, petroleum, and other minerals and materials moved by efficient barge transportation; (2) an abundant water supply from the second largest river in the United States, and (3) the possibility of using the river for ultimate waste disposal.[1]

No one expects the success story of the Ohio to be repeated on any considerable number of the major rivers of our country, but the development of the multi-purpose water-control project, typically including some provision for improving the navigability of the streams, has again focused attention upon rivers as commercial carriers. The Illinois Waterway, linking the St. Lawrence Seaway with the Mississippi Valley, could be the next river to experience such a commercial rebirth.

Rivers as boundaries. One function which rivers have long been called upon to perform is one for which they are not especially well suited. This is the boundary function.

It is difficult to give more than two good reasons why rivers should ever have been designated as boundaries between states or countries. In a new or poorly-explored country the major rivers may be the only landscape features that have been located with any degree of precision and, therefore, the only features along which a boundary can be drawn. And second, since it is desirable that a boundary be highly visible, rivers, as perhaps the most visible feature in a landscape, best fulfill this requirement of the boundary-maker.

Offsetting these relatively unimportant advantages are two over-riding disadvantages which make rivers not only undesirable, but often unworkable, as boundaries. First, a river is constantly changing. Anyone who has read *Life on the Mississippi* knows how prone that river is to change its navigable channel, and this is true of most large rivers. Indeed, rivers are continually altering not only their navigable channels but even their beds, abandoning meanders or creating new ones, seasonally expanding and contracting their beds, creating and destroying islands in their channels. What happens to the boundary when these changes take place? Generally a boundary, once fixed, is presumed to be a permanent thing, however impermanent the feature upon which it was originally based. This can create problems. Between Indiana and Kentucky, for instance, the boundary was originally drawn along the north bank of the Ohio River. But in the century and a half since the boundary was drawn changes in the course of the Ohio have left small patches of Kentucky stranded on the Indiana side of the river. "No man's lands" of this sort raise irritating problems of taxation and law enforcement and sometimes spell opportunity to the enterprising operator who prefers to conduct his business in places where there is doubt as to the jurisdiction of the law.

The second disadvantage of rivers as boundaries is an even greater one, for it involves the negation of some of the most basic geographic principles. A river—almost any river—is one of nature's great unifying forces, and its basin is a basic geographic unity. The Rhine is a good example. Germans and Frenchmen alike recognize that there is such a thing as the Rhineland, a cultural entity which is neither quite German nor quite French. And so, despite attempts to make it so, the Rhine has never served as

---

[1] Barton, Thomas F., "Twenty-Five Years' Use of the 9-Foot Ohio River Channel," *Economic Geography*, Vol. 33, No. 1, January, 1957, pp. 41, 46-48. Reprinted by permission.

a satisfactory boundary between Germany and France. Rather, each country has attempted to incorporate the whole Rhineland into its own boundaries.

Rivers have served us reasonably well as state boundaries simply because state boundaries are not particularly important in a nation whose constitution guarantees freedom of movement for both people and goods within its national territory, and which gives the federal government control of navigable rivers. It would not be hard to imagine the confusion and even hostility that would develop, though, if the state of Missouri were free to control all shipping passing through her territorial waters in the Mississippi River. As it is, we have enough trouble controlling, improving, and bridging rivers which serve as state boundaries.

The comments which have just been made on the role of rivers in unifying regions need to be refined now by noting that under some circumstances rivers are regional bonds and in other circumstances their presence may be divisive. Taking the Columbia–Snake River system as an example, Dr. Edward Ullman has illustrated these opposite effects of streams in a particular setting:

¶ The Columbia-Snake river system probably crosses more markedly defined mountains and deserts combined than any other river system in the world. Two mountain ranges and two deserts are crossed within the United States; thus there are two *dioric* [mountain-crossing] and two *exotic* [desert-crossing] stretches, and also some minor transitional reaches.

The lower Columbia, crossing the Cascades and the Coast Ranges, is an all-important transport route and regional bond, surpassing even the Potomac. The deep-cut Columbia Gorge provides the only water-level route through the entire Cascade Range. Its easy gradients are followed by two transcontinental railroads and two highways. Its low elevations and openness to the mild west coast give it a warmer winter climate than that of the snow-covered mountain passes, a vital factor in keeping its transport lines open in winter. It also serves (1) as a passageway for weather from the East—because of pressure differences, easterly gales sometimes blow down the gorge in winter and reduce ground fog at Portland to shorter duration than at Salem or Seattle—(2) as a flyway for birds and airplanes; and (3) as a watercourse for vessels drawing 26 feet as far as The Dalles, 188 miles from the mouth, and for barges drawing five to seven feet as far as the Yakima River, 139 miles above The Dalles at Pasco. Above Portland, however, little traffic is carried except inbound petroleum products. Below Portland the channel is 35 feet deep and is a much-used water route to the sea, though only one railroad and one highway parallel the river across the Coast Ranges.

In contrast, the upper Columbia, crossing the relatively level desert of central Washington, is of little importance as a bond, because its water has not yet been used for irrigation. At present, only tributaries of the Columbia, such as the Yakima and the Wenatchee, are used significantly for irrigation, creating populous valleys extending out into the desert from the eastern flank of the Cascades. The Columbia itself is intrenched in a gorge a few hundred feet deep, which requires construction of large dams or expensive pumping before water can be diverted from it. As a result, central Washington is empty desert between the Cascades and the relatively populous wheat-farming belt of eastern Washington and northern Idaho, where precipitation is greater.

The effect of the Snake is just the reverse. So precipitous are the banks of its canyon that only a pack-animal trail has been built along this dioric section. The gorge is a barrier forcing transportation into the adjoining mountains. Hells Canyon on the Snake is more than 7000 feet deep, the deepest canyon in the United States, exceeding even the Grand Canyon of the Colorado. It has not attracted attention because it can be reached only by trail or by a combination of an 18- to 25-hour motorboat trip up the rapids from Lewiston to Johnson Bar and a trail trip for some 20 miles up from this head of so-called "navigation." In the deeper parts of the canyon a few scattered ranches are based on the occasional alluvial fans debouching into the gorge. These are practically the only level areas where readily available water on which alfalfa or other fodder needed to carry stock through the winter can be raised; feed cannot be imported because of lack of transportation. The number of cattle is a direct function of the limited area of the alluvial fans, an almost inconceivable situation in a modern transportation corridor.

The fourth section, the exotic upper Snake, resembles the Nile in its effects: in contrast with the upper Columbia, it supports a chain of irrigation settlements along its banks. Although the upper Snake is slightly intrenched, its gorge is much shallower than the gorge of the Columbia across the desert of central Washington; consequently, dams have been built at some places, such as American Falls. Elsewhere, as at Boise, the water of tributaries is used, but the land irrigated is a part of the Snake River Plain.

Thus one dioric stretch of river, the lower Columbia, is an all-important bond, and the other dioric stretch, the Snake Canyon, is a barrier; conversely, one exotic stretch, the Snake in southern Idaho, is a significant bond, and the other exotic stretch, the upper Columbia, is not now a bond.[1]

Where rivers serve as regional bonds, it is not only desirable but usually necessary to handle such problems as flood control, soil erosion, improvement of navigation, watershed protection, and a great variety of economic problems on a regional basis, using the river basin as the planning unit. Where rivers are barriers, this would obviously not be the case.

Rivers for recreation. Let us conclude this discussion of the geography of rivers on a lighter note — although perhaps as our country becomes more and more heavily settled and the pace of life grows daily more hectic recreation ceases to be a light matter and becomes more and more one of the essentials of life.

Popular mythology cherishes the memory of the "old swimming hole," but unfortunately the memory is about all that is left of it. As a people, we have been much too "practical" to recognize or be concerned with the refreshment of body and mind and spirit that we might have obtained from our rivers and their banks. With a few notable exceptions, the urban river fronts which might have been given over to parks and outdoor cafes have been crowded with commercial buildings, and in many towns "the riverfront" is synonymous with the most blighted part of the city. The fish life which once thrived in even our largest rivers has largely disappeared, choked out by oxygen-destroying pollution. As for swimming, it takes a sturdy stomach even to go near some of our rivers, let alone go into them.

These things should not be. Insofar as we can determine any of the Creator's purposes, it would appear that He intended the rivers of the earth as much for racing sculls as for coal barges; as much for water-loving youngsters as for manufacturing corporations; as much for the development of the mind as for the irrigation of the land. This is not mere sentimentalism. The more vigorous a society, the greater its need for recreation, and water resources — whether they be rivers or lakes or the ocean — have long been among man's most valued recreational resources. Their destruction is a real loss — also in the economic sense.

Lakes and their uses

Lakes are confined bodies of water occupying depressions on the land. Some very large lakes, particularly if they are quite salty, may be called seas, as, for example, the Caspian Sea. Very small lakes are often called ponds. Some lakes, so-called, are actually widened-out portions of river channels.

How lakes are formed. Natural lakes may be formed in any one of five ways. (1) Tectonic lakes, occupying structural basins, are the product of the action of mountain building forces such as the warping of rock strata or the breaking (faulting) of the strata. Several of the large lakes of eastern Africa are of tectonic origin, occupying portions of a long, deep, down-dropped block of the earth's crust, called a rift. Lake Superior is probably partly of tectonic origin. (2) Lakes formed by erosion are among the largest and most common lakes in the modern world. This is particularly true of those formed by glacial erosion. All of our American Great Lakes, except Lake Superior, are believed to have been given their present sizes and shapes by glacial excavation, although the glaciers themselves may have been attracted to the present lake basins by the presence there of preglacial stream valleys. In many places in mountain country, chains of small glacial lakes or tarns *(cirques)* mark the path of a former glacier's descent down the slope. In morainic areas, uneven deposition of the glacial waste in many places left small basins

[1] Ullman, Edward L., "Rivers as Regional Bonds: The Columbia-Snake Example," *Geographical Review*, Vol. 41, 1951, pp. 212-217. Reprinted by permission.

IX:4 This is a schematic representation of a multiple-purpose river basin development. (From *Water Policy for the American People,* The Report of the President's Water Resources Policy Commission, Volume I)

which later became filled with runoff or groundwater, as in the Kettle Moraine region of southern Wisconsin. (3) Barrier lakes, as their name suggests, are formed when some obstruction is laid across a natural drainage channel. Landslides or rockslides are common agents for the construction of barrier lakes, and in glaciated areas terminal moraines built across preglacial drainage lines may also produce barrier lakes. The Finger Lakes of upstate New York are a good example. Generally barrier lakes are ephemeral features of the landscape, draining very rapidly once the barrier has been cut through by erosion. (4) Lakes formed by volcanic action may be considered a special type of barrier lake. To this class would belong crater lakes, bodies of water (such as Oregon's famous Crater Lake) occupying the craters of dormant or extinct volcanoes, and also lakes formed by the establishment of a lava dam across an earlier drainage line. (5) Another special form of barrier lake is the lake formed by the action of plants and animals. An example that comes immediately to mind is the work of beavers. But vegetation, either by growing so as to block the flow of water, or by falling across watercourses, can be a very effective agent of lake building also.

To this classification of natural lakes should be added man-made lakes. The largest and best-known of these lakes are usually found in drylands where they are associated with irrigation or multipurpose water-control projects. One of the best examples is Lake Mead, behind Hoover Dam. However, there has been, especially in recent years, a great deal of lake or reservoir building in the northeastern part of our country, most of it associated with flood control, power developments, or the development of premium residential sites.

The value of lakes. The value of lakes to man depends largely upon their size and their fresh or salt water content. Depending on local circumstances, lakes may be valuable as (1) sources of water for irrigation; (2) sources of municipal water; (3) attractions to resort and recreational development; (4) attractions to high-value residential development; (5) highways of commerce; or (6) factors in the creation of microclimates.

In drylands, natural lakes are almost always associated with regions of interior drainage, that is, basins into which water flows and from which there is no outlet; for example, Great Salt Lake. Lakes formed in such circumstances would, of course, be salt lakes and would be unusable for irrigation. Man-made lakes in drylands, on the other hand, commonly serve as reservoirs of irrigation water or hydroelectric power.

As sources of municipal water, lakes follow the general rule that the larger the lake the more satisfactory it is as a source of industrial or drinking water. Very small lakes tend to shoal during dry seasons, are easily polluted, respond rapidly to temperature changes, and often pick up offensive tastes or odors from decaying vegetation. Any one of the Great Lakes, on the other hand, makes a prime source of water both for industry and for human consumption. Indeed, nowhere else in the world is so much fresh, clear, cool, odorless water available as in the Great Lakes area. For that reason, if for no other, we could predict that this area will experience a disproportionately great increase both in population and in industrialization during the remainder of this century.

As attractions to resort and recreational development, it is possible that most of our smaller lakes, at least, have reached the point of diminishing returns. Many of our smaller lakes have distressingly become centers of rural slum development. Their shores are lined with flimsily built shacks, originally meant for summer "cottages" but now occupied the year around. Their waters are polluted by raw sewage or by the overflow from improperly-constructed septic tanks. The stillness that once rewarded the fisherman even when he wasn't catching any fish has been shattered by the outboard motor. And to the margins of the lakes, like moths to flame, have come the souvenir hunters and the operators of amusement devices and the roller-rink people and all the other natural enemies of silence and natural order.

And so, having allowed our lakes to be overbuilt, commercialized, and vulgarized, we have, at considerable expense, had to develop artificial lakes to provide us with the spaciousness and peace and quiet that some of us still crave. Especially in the lower Midwest, where there is neither ocean nor unspoiled natural lake, the artificial lake is becoming the local equivalent of Knob Hill or Beacon Street. Bordered by fine homes and a golf course, policed by a Property Owners Association, inhabited by the leaders of the local business and professional community, it attempts to conserve for private groups those values which we were not farsighted enough to conserve for the whole community along the shores of our natural lakes.

Very large lakes rank among the most important of the world's natural highways. Lake Victoria, in eastern Africa; the Caspian Sea, connecting the Middle Eastern oil fields with the Volga River system; the Lake of Constance and Lake Geneva in Switzerland — all of these carry a large percentage of the traffic of their regions. But the lake highway *par excellence* is, of course, the North American Great Lake Route which reaches into the iron- and wheat-rich heart of the continent and serves as a kind of Main Street for the most heavily industrialized region in the world.

The importance of this highway has been enhanced enormously by the completion, in 1958, of the St. Lawrence Seaway, a project carried out jointly by the governments of the United States and Canada. So much has been written on this project in recent years that there is no need to go into details on it here. Essentially, what it does is convert the Great Lakes into a new Mediterranean, and the lake cities into actual or potential ocean ports. American geographers can take considerable pride in the fact that one of the most vigorous and persuasive exponents of the seaway idea was one of their colleagues, Dr. Harold M. Mayer, whose studies of traffic and harbor facilities on the Great Lakes helped to establish the economic feasibility of the seaway proposal.

Finally, something should be said of the role that lakes may play in the development of microclimates. Lake water, like all water, warms more slowly and cools more slowly under the effects of seasonal variations in insolation than does land. Winds blowing off a lake onto the land in the summertime would, therefore, tend to have a cooling effect, while in the wintertime they would have a warming effect. The climate of the area thus affected would, therefore, be an exception to the general climate of the region, a microclimate, and it might permit uses of the land which would not be possible elsewhere in the region. Thus, along the southeast shore of Lake Michigan and along the southern shore of Lake Ontario, orchards thrive in regions which are essentially marine exceptions to the general pattern of continental climates. The highly localized area of microclimate makes possible a specialized (and therefore very profitable) use of the land.

Underground water and its surface manifestations

Until now, this chapter has been dealing with surface water forms which are largely the results of runoff. It will be remembered from our description of the hydrologic cycle that a very considerable portion of the water which reaches the earth in the form of precipitation is captured and held in the ground for greater or shorter periods of time. This *cutoff* water is called groundwater. In most parts of the world — and the United States is no exception — it constitutes the larger part of the total fresh water reserve.

¶ The water beneath the land surface is not all ground water. . . . Ground water is only the part of the subterranean water that occurs where all pores in the containing rock materials are saturated. The "zone of saturation" may extend up to the land surface in some places, notably in seep areas and in some stream channels, lakes, and marshes. At all other places, above the ground-water zone, "a zone of aeration" exists that may range in thickness from a few inches to hundreds of feet. Some water is in the zone of aeration at all times, held there by molecular attraction—in particular, soils may hold significant volumes of water against the downward pull of gravity. Wells cannot extract any of this water; they must be drilled through the zone of aeration and obtain their supplies from ground water.

The normal field of operations of the ground-water hydrologist is delimited only approximately by such a definition of ground water. Thus the top of the zone of saturation cannot readily be identified from the land surface. The hydrologist, therefore, measures the water levels in shallow wells. From the measurements he constructs a map of the "water table," which is thus a phreatic surface—that is, pertaining to a well—where the water is at atmospheric pressure. The water table may coincide approximately with the top of the zone of saturation in coarse gravel but is likely to be several inches or even several feet below it in finer grained materials, because capillary rise results in the saturation of a zone above the water table (the capillary fringe).

Often it is hard to identify or classify subterranean water on the basis of the definition above. There may be saturated flow, at least temporarily, in parts of the soil zone. A well driller may encounter a saturated zone and then continue down into dry materials, obviously in the zone of aeration. Or he may find saturated materials that yield no water to his well, so that there is no water table. And he may drill through materials that yield no water, and then encounter a stratum from which water rises in the well to a level high in the zone of aeration, and the water may even overflow. All these are typical of the wide range in conditions of occurrence of ground water. They reflect the great variations in porosity and permeability of the solid components of the earth's crust (11).

Once water has gotten into the ground, it percolates very slowly through pores and crevices in the rock, following paths of least resistance and, ordinarily, seeping always farther downward into the rock. Eventually, most of it returns to the surface — a great deal by way of transpiration from the plants which have absorbed it; some of it by the upward attraction of capillarity; a very considerable amount by way of wells; and most of the rest by way of springs and seepages into rivers, lakes, and the ocean.

Springs are classified in a number of ways. Those which have a continuous flow are called permanent springs; those which dry up seasonally are called intermittent springs. Those which result from water seeping down until it encounters impervious rock which it then follows to some place of outcrop are called gravity springs; those which result from the forcing up of water by pressure along cracks or fissures in the rock are called fissure springs. Thermal springs send forth water which has been heated by contact with hot rock benearth the surface. Mineral springs contain an unusually large amount of mineral material or some unusual (and usually smellable) mineral. Springs which intermittently erupt boiling water are called geysers — remarkable, among other things, for the fact that they are found in only three parts of the world: Iceland, Yellowstone Park, and New Zealand.

Artesian springs are in a class by themselves because they develop only where certain definite subsurface conditions prevail. These conditions are shown in the diagram (Figure IX-1) and include: (1) an aquifer, or water-bearing layer of rock, porous so that water can enter and seep through it; (2) an intake point where water can enter the aquifer in sufficient quantity to build up pressure; (3) an impervious "capping" layer to prevent water from escaping from the aquifer; and (4) enough rainfall to keep the aquifer supplied with water. Given these conditions, artesian structures can develop on a very large scale. There is, for instance, a huge artesian basin in Australia between the Great Dividing Range and the desert. Similarly, in the United States, there is a great artesian basin which includes the western halves of the Dakotas and the eastern portions of Montana and Wyoming. There is growing evidence that a huge artesian structure lies deep under the Sahara Desert. Where artesian water is available, it may come to the surface in the form of springs, or it may have to be brought to the surface by wells. In either case, once the capping layer has been breached so that the water in the aquifer can get through to the surface, hydraulic pressure is great enough to cause it to discharge freely at the surface without pumping.

Groundwater has long been one of the prime sources of water for irrigation, not only because there is generally a shortage of surface water in areas which require irrigation, but also because wells can be strategically located within the area to be irrigated and, thus, may be more convenient sources of water than are surface water features. The great danger in using groundwater for irrigation — or, indeed, for any other purpose — is that it is easy to forget that the water in the ground, like the water at the surface, came originally from regional precipitation; that it is, therefore, distinctly limited in quantity, however abundant it may seem when first tapped; and that man is technologically capable of taking water out of the ground many times faster than nature replaces it. Overpumping of groundwater supplies leads inevitably not only to exhaustion of the water source, but also in many places to serious slumping of the surface as the water is drained from beneath it.

One other aspect of groundwater which is locally important is its role in the development of certain very striking types of features and landscapes. Especially in country which is underlain by limestone, water under the surface may dissolve the rock along certain channels of movement, creating such curious phenomena as underground rivers, caves, and caverns. Sometimes the "roofs" of these underground hollows will collapse, creating sinkholes which may fill up with water and form small, deep lakes with circular outlines. Landscapes which are pitted with such sinkholes and exhibit other characteristics of erosion by underground water are called *karst* landscapes.[1] In the United States, two fair-sized karst areas are in northern Florida and in a belt extending from western Kentucky into southwestern Indiana.

Water and the law

Essential as water is to life, it is not surprising that water rights are a subject of frequent and often very bitter litigation, especially in subhumid and arid regions. Nor should it be surprising to anyone who realizes that laws grow out of the quest for justice in concrete situations that laws respecting the ownership and use of water differ from place to place.

In the United States, the two basic doctrines of surface water law are the Riparian Doctrine of Water Use, an essentially *laissez-faire* concept embedded in the common law which was developed in England, where water has never been any great problem; and the Doctrine of the Prior Appropriation of Water, an essentially "first come, first served" concept which was developed in the arid American southwest. Under the riparian doctrine, every landowner along a watercourse was considered entitled to equal and undiminished flow and quantity of water and any one landowner was entitled to use only a reasonable amount of water for artificial needs, such as irrigation. In case of serious disagreement over any particular question of reasonable use, the only recourse was to litigation and the judgment of a jury. The Doctrine of Prior Appropriation, developed in dry areas where it was obvious that one of the principal uses of water had to be for irrigation, recognized the prior right of the first person to make productive use of the water.

Groundwater, also, is variously regulated from one state to another. In general, its use is governed either by the (1) "strict rule" which states that the only limitation on the nature and extent of use is the water supply itself or the cost of recovery and replenishment or (2) "the rule of reasonable use" which differs from the strict rule by providing that the court may restrain an owner who develops and uses the groundwater in a way that wilfully, negligently, or maliciously injures his neighbor's water supply.

Experts agree that laws respecting the use of both surface water and groundwater require rethinking and rewriting. In many states, the actual statutory law represents an accretion of piecemeal rules and regulations around common law principles which were themselves based upon conditions not characteristic of twentieth-century America. And the statutory law has been further modified by court decisions so that the average citizen is not sure just what the law really is. In such a situation of legal uncertainty, the citizen must sometimes choose either to sacrifice a right or to accept the possibly ruinous costs of litigation.

APPLICATION OF GEOGRAPHIC UNDERSTANDING

I. In the limited space of one chapter, it is obviously impossible to deal with every aspect of water. What are the most pressing water problems of your own state and what, if anything, is being done to solve them?

II. If Dr. Borchert is correct in saying that surface water is a second choice for drinking water supplies where groundwater conditions are suitable to meet local demands, why do few of our major cities rely on ground water?

III. Is it possible for groundwater to be polluted? If so, how? If not, why not?

IV. What possible consequences may the opening of the St. Lawrence Seaway have for the Illinois River Valley? For the St. Louis area? For the long stretches of primitive sand dunes along the southern and eastern shores of Lake Michigan?

V. Under what circumstances do rivers tend to be unifying bonds? Under what cir-

---

[1] After the Karst limestone region in the Dinaric Alps of Yugoslavia.

cumstances do they tend to be barriers? To what extent is it possible for man to transform a river from a barrier into a bond?

VI. Much has been made — and properly so — of the Great Lakes as natural highways of commerce. What significant handicaps do they have as commercial routes?

VII. In northwestern Europe, a very elaborate system of canals still carries a considerable portion of the area's commerce. Why have we shown so little interest in or dependence on canals?

VIII. Health resorts have developed around a number of thermal and mineral springs both in the United States and in Europe. Can you think of any practical reasons why these resorts should have been beneficial to anyone's health?

IX. Can you think of any basic principles of water use that would be as valid as a basis of water law in Arizona as in New York? Can you think of any specific details of the law that would be equally valid for both states?

X. If you were a member of the United States Senate, called upon to vote on a bill to establish a particular regional irrigation district, what questions would you ask of the bill's sponsors and supporters? What principles — economic, geographical, ethical, and moral — would finally determine your vote?

References

1 Coker, Robert E., *Streams, Lakes, and Ponds,* The University of North Carolina Press, Chapel Hill, 1954, pp. 4-8, *passim,* 123-124, 127.

2 Thompson, Henry D., *Fundamentals of Earth Science,* D. Appleton-Century, Inc., New York, 1947, p. 142.

3 Carhart, Albert H., "Our Nation's Water Wealth," *The Land,* Vol. X, No. 4, Winter, 1951-52, pp. 441, 442.

4 Kuehnen, P. H., *Realms of Water,* John Wiley & Sons, Inc., New York, 1955, pp. 11-12.

5 Borchert, John R., "The Surface Water Supply of American Municipalities," *Annals of the Association of American Geographers,* Vol. XLIV, No. 1, March, 1954, p. 19. (Map from p. 18.)

6 Meigs, Peveril, "Water Problems in the United States," *Geographical Review,* Vol. XLII, 1952, pp. 353-354.

7 Smith, J. Russell, "Regional Suicide," *The Land,* Vol. VIII, No. 3, Autumn, 1949, pp. 316-317.

8 Jackson, Eureal Grant, "Economic-Geographic Philosophy Behind the Proposed Aswan Valley Project in Egypt," *Journal of Geography,* Vol. LVI, No. 7, October, 1957, p. 337.

9 Barton, Thomas F., "Twenty-Five Years' Use of the 9-Foot Ohio River Channel," *Economic Geography,* Vol. XXXIII, No. 1, January, 1957, pp. 41, 46-48.

10 Ullman, Edward L., "Rivers as Regional Bonds: The Columbia-Snake Example," *Geographical Review,* Vol. XLI, 1951, pp. 212-217.

11 Thomas, Harold E., "Underground Sources of Our Water," *Water, The Yearbook of Agriculture,* 1955, U. S. Department of Agriculture, pp. 64-65.

Chapter 10

Man's habitat as affected by vegetal and animal life

"All of nature," Dean Inge once wrote, "is a conjugation of the verb to eat, in the active and passive." This is one way — perhaps a rather cynical one — of saying that nature forms a closed and interdependent system within which every kind of life has not only its own purposes but its significance for other forms of life. This is as true of man as any other creature. Western man, cut off from nature in his artificial world of concrete and structural steel, may be little aware of his kinship to the oak tree and the beaver, but the relationship is there, nonetheless, and now and then, even in the very heart of his great cities, man receives sudden, surprising reminders that he has not, after all, managed to divorce himself completely from the community of nature. The wanton destruction of trees in a watershed area means flooded streets and stores in cities downstream. The extermination of fur-bearing animals gives the mink coat social significance.

Man has domesticated many plants and animals for his use. These accultural forms will be discussed in the chapter on the geography of agriculture (Chapter 13). In this chapter we are interested in natural vegetation and wild animal life. Our interest in these forms is not that of the botanist or the zoologist, but that of the geographer. We are interested in their major distributional patterns and in the way these patterns correlate with other significant distributional patterns.

The distribution of plants

Biogeography is one of the newer fields of geographic specialization and, as a result, it has not yet developed a universally accepted vocabulary. For vegetation, one of the simplest and most useful systems of biogeographical classification so far suggested is that of Dansereau (1) which correlates vegetational units with environmental units on a scale of descending magnitude (Table 10.1).

A classification of this kind permits us to regionalize on any of six different levels. We shall do so in this chapter primarily on the levels of the biochore and the climax area.

The four great biochores are related to major climatic types. The desert biochore is essentially the *BW* world in the Köppen classification. The grassland biochore is associated with subhumid to semiarid climates, the *BS* world and some of its *C* and *D* margins. The savannah biochore correlates most closely with the *Aw* world, extending in places beyond the *Aw* into *Ca* lands. And the forest biochore takes in what is left — generally speaking, the *Af*, most of the *C* lands, and the *D* lands. The most important climatic factor in the creation of a biochore is rainfall, or rather rainfall effectivity, by which we mean the amount of water that is actually available to the plants after evaporation has taken its toll. Since the evaporation rate itself is very largely the result of temperature, we may say that biochores are primarily determined by rainfall and secondarily by temperatures operating as determinants of evaporation. The vegetational unit associated with the biochore is the formation, one or more of which will be found in every biochore. Thus, in the North American forest biochore, there are four formations: the tropical rainforest, the temperate rainforest, the temperate deciduous forest, and the needleleaf evergreen forest.

Climax areas are also the products primarily of climate. The vegetational associations of the climax areas represent, in many cases, very fine adaptations to rather subtle climatic differences. The map (Figure X-1) shows nine such associations within the temperate deciduous forest formation of North America. Several interesting correlations are suggested by this map:

1. The mixed mesophytic forest covers essentially the Appalachian plateau, the northwestern boundary of which is a portion of the boundary of that part of North America which was glaciated.

2. The oak-chestnut forest corresponds almost perfectly to the main ranges of the Appalachians and might be considered a product of the cooler temperatures which are associated with the mountains.

3. The oak-pine forest correlates closely

Table 10.1 The division of the biosphere into units of generally decreasing magnitude, and the vegetation units which they harbor (Adapted from Dansereau).

Area Covered	*Designation of the Environmental Unit*	*Designation of the Vegetation Unit*	*Major Control*
The World	Biocycle	Various Designations	Type of medium (e.g., salt water, fresh water, land)
A continent or a province	Biochore	Formation — Class	Climate
A region	Climax Area	Climax Association and Subordinate Seres	Climate
A particular landform	Habitat	Association	Edaphic Factors (topography and soil)
A layer or stratum of vegetation	Synusia	Union	Microclimate
A niche	Biotope	Microsociety or Aggregation	Microclimate

SOURCE: Pierre Dansereau, *Biogeography, An Ecological Perspective.* Copyright 1957, The Ronald Press Company, p. 127. Reprinted by permission.

with the Appalachian piedmont, its eastern boundary lying almost exactly along the Fall Line from the Potomac River southward.

4. The softwoods of hemlock and white pine, the northern hardwoods, such as the beech maple, and the southern evergreen forests show striking east-west orientations on a topography which is generally quite flat. It might be supposed, therefore, that their boundaries are set primarily by earth-sun relations having to do with temperatures and intensity and duration of sunlight.

5. By contrast, the oak-hickory forest trends southwest-northeast, running generally perpendicular to the trend of the associations to the east of it. This orientation would strongly indicate a relationship to subhumid climates which begin to manifest themselves within this general area.

A warning observation is called for at this point. Actual correlations in nature are never simple or precise. The boundaries of vegetational associations are set along lines of compromise reflecting the influences of many natural factors of which climate is only one, even though it may be the most important single one. Moreover, the effects of climate itself would be difficult to assess precisely, because vegetational boundary lines reflect not only present climatic conditions but also past climatic conditions. This would be particularly true in such parts of the world as eastern North America and western Europe, where recent glaciation disorganized vegetational patterns and left many anomalies which have not yet disappeared from the vegetational scene.

With this by way of introduction, let us turn now to a consideration of each of the four great biochores.

1. The desert biochore. Deserts are found wherever and for whatever reason there is insufficient water to support normal plant processes. Usually, when we think of deserts, we think of regions where the deficiency is meteorological, that is, where there just isn't enough rain or other precipitation. But there are large areas of what are sometimes called high-latitude deserts where the deficiency is not meteorological but physiological, that is, the result of factors which make what would otherwise be a sufficiency of water unavailable for plant growth. In the Köppen classification, the meteorological deserts are the *Bw* lands. The physiological deserts are the *E* lands. In the *EF* lands, physiological drought results from the accumulation of precipitation as ice in the form of immense glaciers. In the *ET* lands, physiological drought results from permafrost and summer

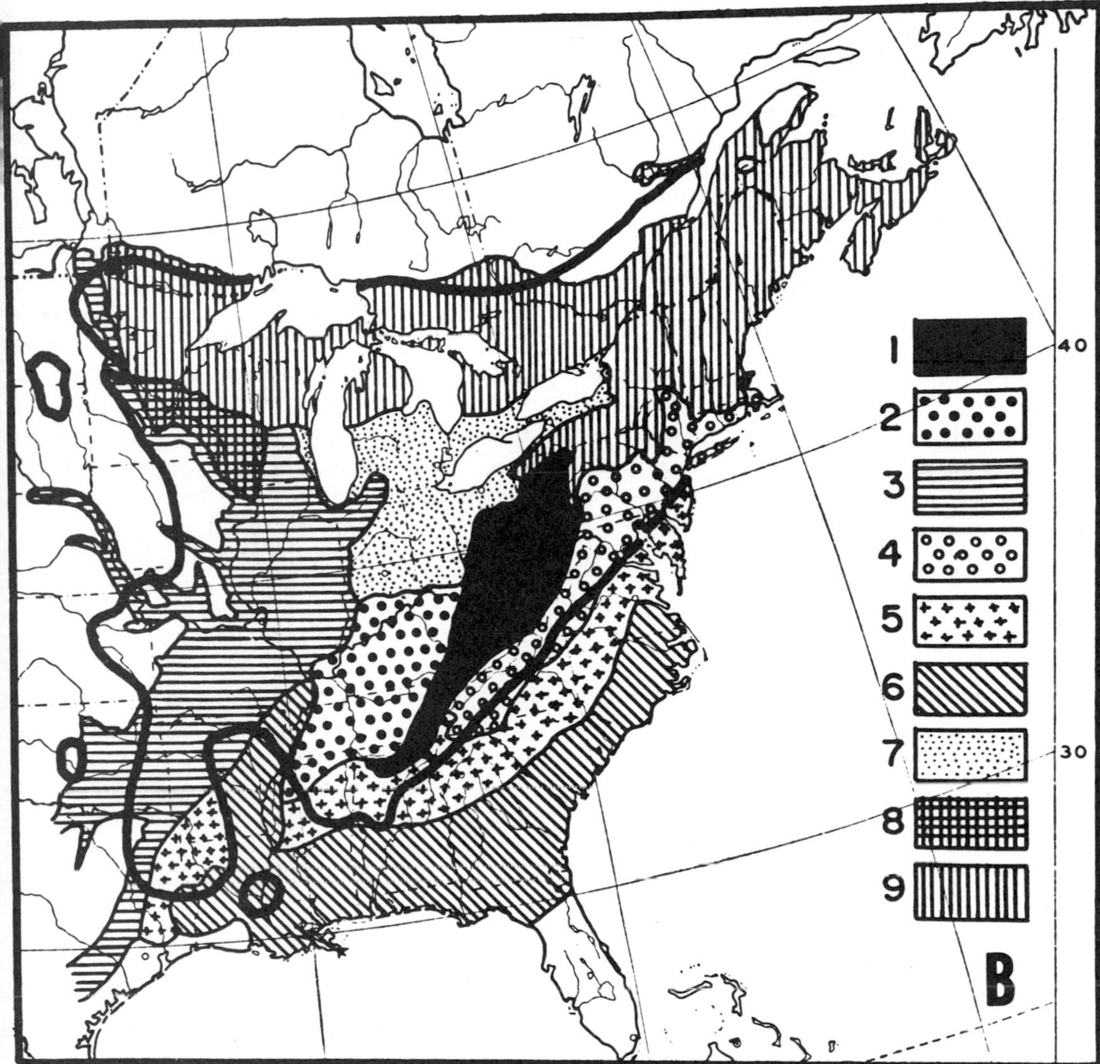

X:1 This map illustrates vegetational associations within the temperate deciduous forest formation of North America. The symbols indicate: (1) mixed mesophytic; (2) western mesophytic; (3) oak-hickory; (4) oak-chestnut; (5) oak-pine; (6) southeastern evergreen; (7) beech-maple; (8) maple-basswood; (9) hemlock-white pine-northern hardwoods. The heavy line indicates the bioclimatic limits of the sugar maple. (From *Biogeography* by Pierre Dansereau, The Ronald Press Company, New York, 1957, used by permission)

bog conditions which produce alternate conditions of drought and waterlogging.

Plants are, of course, unacquainted with the Köppen classification of climates and therefore make little distinction between meteorological and physiological drought. Their adaptations are to the simple fact of drought, whatever its cause. As a result, strikingly similar gradations are apparent in the vegetational profile of the *E* lands and the *BW* lands as one approaches the extreme condition of each. In the *E* lands, the trees which occur along the inland border of the tundra, where it adjoins the taiga or high-latitude evergreen forest, give way to gnarled and twisted shrub forms which, in turn, yield to rocky barrens covered with patches of moss or lichen, which finally give way either to barren rock surface or to lifeless glacial ice. In the *B* lands, the trees which occur in the boundary zone between *BS* and *Aw* or *Cs* give way to shrub forms and grass in the *BS* which, in turn, yield to isolated patches of scrub or dry grass, which finally give way to barren rock surface or to lifeless basins of sand. Here, if anywhere, is substantiation of Huntington's dictum: "Any environmental condition tends to become fatal if it is either too intense or too weak."

The plants of the desert biochore have managed to survive their hostile environment because they have developed special means of trapping and retaining water, the ability to remain dormant during long periods of drought, and certain qualities which attract fertilizing insects. A writer in a popular magazine has summed up the resulting vegetational landscapes of deserts as follows:

¶ One acre of a well-watered region may easily have more vegetation, more plants, than twenty acres of desert. And yet . . . deserts are botanists' paradises. Well-watered regions tend simply to multiply endlessly a limited number of species of plants. Deserts multiply the number and variety of species themselves. By imposing difficulties they have stimulated their plants into developing character, individuality. Desert species are numbered well into the thousands. A single desert may have hundreds of species, distinctly its own, found only within its borders.

They are xerophytes, which is simply Greek for "dry plants"; plants that have learned to live in dry climates. Some endure the dry seasons by becoming dormant or remaining in seed form. Others modify their leaves, against evaporation, reduce breathing pores in size and put them on the undersides, develop thick and waxy skins, twist them edgewise to the sun or curl them up in the hottest hours. They often give up leaves altogether, modifying stems to perform leaf functions as in the innumerable cacti, those stout independent Americans, native only to the western hemisphere. They devise amazing root systems. They seize water when it is available and hold it for future use, storing it in ingenious reservoirs in leaves, in stems, in roots, in tubers. They even, as do the wild buckwheats, extract moisture from the cooling air at night.

They exhaust the possibilities, go to what seem absolute extremes. Some are in a hurry, apprehensive about the next generation. Rain falls and they spring up, reach maturity, flower, seed, in a matter of days. Others take it slow, like the saguaro cactus which in time may tower fifty feet, yet after three or four years is still a seedling and after ten years may be all of one inch high. Some are incredibly patient, like a gourd which inhabits the driest of areas, content to wait in the form of an apparently dead knot of wood until there *ought* to be a little rain; then it experimentally puts forth a few small shoots and a few small roots and if there is no rain patiently dries up again and waits for another year—and will do that year after year until there *is* rain. Others are unabashed opportunists, like the jaunty creosote bush, adapting to almost all desert situations, retaining the perky dark green of its tiny effiicent leaves as long as there is the faintest trace of moisture within reach, flowering gaily in season—and quite willing to forget seasonal punctuality and bloom whenever rain happens to fall.

And out of adversity—beauty. In our deserts are found the nation's most extensive and most beautiful wildflower gardens. The few rains come and out of the seemingly barren land spring acres and acres, often miles and miles of blooms, the swift-springing ephemeral colorful wildflowers of the arid regions. Our deserts cradle more than 6,000 species. Not to be outdone, the other plants leap into bloom in their own seasons. There is no period of flower. The stranger the plant, the more twisted and gnarled and spiny, the more lovely is likely to be the blossom, deep and rich in colors, delicate and perfect in modeling.

The cacti, ugliest of plants, make amends with the loveliest flowers of all. The bush yuccas, dagger-leaved, send up tall single stems to wave their blooms aloft like banners. To please man? No. To attract the yucca moth which, in return for egg-nurturing hospitality, deliberately performs the pollen-fertilizing rite. Watch carefully that tall, thin, apparently dead stalk; there will come the evening when it will suddenly offer huge pure-white flowers, claiming its old Mexican title, *La Reina de la Noche,* the Queen of the Night.[1]

This is the desert. Or, perhaps more accurately, this is the subtropical desert such as our Nevada desert. The tropical deserts *(BWh)*, such as the Sahara or the Great Australian Desert, are much more sparsely vegetated, and within these there are large areas

[1] Schaefer, Jack, "Our Challenging Deserts," *Holiday,* Vol. 24, No. 1. Reprinted by special permission from *Holiday,* copyright July, 1958, by the Curtis Publishing Company, pp. 91-92.

(tanezroufts) which appear to be altogether lifeless. Even in such areas, though, the occasional shower quickens life which had lain dormant in crevices or under the sands of the desert floor.

By and large, man has avoided the desert and thus has had little occasion to make use of the desert plants. The typically small local populations of desert lands have, however, relied heavily upon native plants for food, for forage, for textile fibers, for building materials, and for medicines. In a study of the vegetation of the Great American Desert, Dr. Jonas W. Hoover notes, for example, that the beans of the mesquite were a very important item in the diet of all the southern Indian tribes and, since they were fattening, produced a marked tendency to obesity and indolence among these tribes; that the white man used the desert perennials, especially the nutritious grama grass, for the grazing of cattle; that the Apache wove the yucca leaf fibers into textiles which were used in the making of clothing and ropes and saddle bags; that Mexican and American settlers, in the days before the importation of building materials became easy, used many desert trees, especially the mesquite and the cottonwood, for supporting uprights, roof beams and poles; and that the Indian medicine man made use of a considerable variety of healing herbs (3). But let us not labor the point. However useful desert vegetation may be to local populations, the most significant thing that we can know about deserts is that the 19 per cent of the earth's land surface which is desert supports only 5 per cent of its population.

2. *The grassland biochore.* Natural grasslands are characteristically found in regions where the upper layers of soil are moist the year round or most of it but the deeper layers are too dry to support deep-rooted plants such as trees. Regions of this sort are commonly transitional areas, climatically, between true drylands (*BW*) and true humid lands (*A*, *C*, or *D*). The typical grassland climates would, therefore, be the *BS* and the drier margins of the *C* and *D*. Grasslands may also be found in the very heart of humid regions — in swamps and on recently uplifted coastal plains—for grass will grow not only in drier but also in wetter land than trees.

Many geographers recognize three kinds of grassland: the short-grass lands (steppes); the tall-grass lands (prairie); and the sparsely-forested tropical grasslands (savannah). We shall follow Dansereau in considering the savannah a separate biochore and including the grassy tundra in the grassland biochore.

Steppe vegetation is very closely associated with the *BS* climate, particularly with its *k* subclassification. This type of climate is characterized not only by an over-all insufficiency of rainfall but by great fluctuations from year to year so that in one year the actual rainfall may be no more than that of a desert climate, while in another year it may be as great as that of a truly humid land. As a result, there is enough water to keep the upper layers of the soil moist during the summer growing season most years, but not enough to moisten the soil down to the groundwater. And so a permanent dry layer lies beneath the moist surface layer.

The largest and best known of the world's steppe lands are the Great Plains of North America and the steppes of Russian Eurasia. The word "steppe" itself is from the Russian "stiep" and was originally applied to the short-grass lands which lie between the Russian forests and the deserts of central Asia.

¶ The zone of true steppe occupies about 12 per cent of the territory of the Soviet Union and corresponds to the fertile zone of black earth. The climate of the steppe is characterized by great annual variation in temperature and rainfall. The rainfall is about 16 inches in the west (near Odessa), but decreases rapidly toward the east. It falls mainly in the spring or early summer. Tree-growth is therefore limited both by drought and great heat in summer, when dry winds parch the soil, and by the fact that in winter, owing to severe frosts, the ground is physiologically dry. Trees, therefore, are found only near lakes and rivers, and it is in the valleys that human settlement is most dense.

The country is generally level or rolling, open, and treeless, often lying on a plateau surface from 600 to 1,000 feet above sea-level. . . . The level surface, however, is often dissected by gullies and ravine-like valleys, along which, as also along the sides of the valleys of the main rivers, the trees of the wooded steppe zone penetrate.

The present open steppe country was never forested, although it is probable that forest growth has extended over the northern parts of the original steppe zone since the end of the Ice Age.

The vegetation of the steppe responds very closely to the change of the seasons. The spring thaw comes suddenly; the warm sun and showers of rain which fall at intervals favour the growth of flowers, and before the shade of the tall grasses is established the soil is carpeted with the hyacinth, the purple and yellow iris, the crocus, and red and yellow tulips. The song of birds fills the air. At night the nightingale breaks the silence with its song.

The spring flowers gradually give way to the growth of various types of grasses, the exact types varying with local conditions. In late spring the colour of the landscape is fresh and green, but with the commencement of summer it changes to grey. By the middle of July the grasses have reached their full growth. Feather-grass, greyish-silver in colour, gives the steppe its characteristic appearance of a sea upon which the breeze stirs up gentle waves. Among this waving sea of grass there stand out spots of cornflower, bluebells, and sage, or the dull green of steppe bushes.

During the second half of the summer the sea of grass begins to fade under the scorching rays of the hot sun. New types of growth appear, dull and insignificant in appearance, but well able to withstand the heat and drought. The steppe becomes cheerless. Under the dull blue sky the birds are silent, and only the chirp of the grasshopper can be heard. A whirlwind may sweep across the plains, twisting and turning as it carries earth and dried grass high into the sky, only to scatter them again over the land. The streams shrink and dry. Rain seldom falls, except in occasional thunderstorms, which rapidly change the landscape into a sea of mud but give little moisture to the parched earth, since the water runs off the slopes very quickly.

To-day there remain very few large expanses of virgin steppe. The fertile black earth has been ploughed up.[1]

With some modification here and there, these paragraphs describe the American Great Plains as well as they do the Russian steppes. Both are areas of capricious rainfall and often violent weather, of hot summers and cold winters and strong winds. Both are areas of rich, black soil. And both have been largely denuded of their original grass cover and planted to wheat.

Historically, the steppes have been the range of the nomadic herdsman, the preserve of the hard-riding cavalryman. In North America, it was the plains Indian who controlled the steppe and gave the United States Cavalry a rough time of it. In the Eurasian Steppe, wave after wave of horsemen found a nature-made avenue between the highland basins of central Asia and the lowlands of central and coastal Europe. Huns, Bulgars, Mongols, Tatars, Turks thundered through these grasslands, driven often by grass-killing droughts in central Asia which left their herds and families starving. And the man who survived the rigors of this dangerous life came to be, over the centuries, a special kind of man. As Huntington puts it:

¶ The successful nomad must have innate qualities such that he can arouse himself to intense exertion if need be, endure great privation and weariness when animals stray for mile after mile, when wild beasts attack the flock, when he himself goes on a raid, or when other tribesmen attempt to drive off his animals. It is even more important that he possess the power of leadership, ability to make quick decisions in an emergency, and the capacity to obey his leaders unquestioningly and to cooperate fully with his comrades. Lack of these qualities spells failure in the great crises of life. Hence the social ideal of pastoral nomads is the man who is a good raider, no matter how idle he may be ordinarily. Young men who fall too far below the ideal—cowards or those whose comrades cannot rely on them—have for ages been expelled by public opinion and forced to go to the oases or other agricultural regions. The youth who approaches the ideal, on the contrary, gets the prettiest, healthiest girl for a wife. He later gets other wives, and has many children. Thus a drastic selective process tends to produce a certain definite innate type of temperament wherein self-reliance, boldness, versatility, military capacity, and power of leadership are well combined.[2]

The nomad has long since disappeared

[1] Reprinted with permission from Gregory, James S., and Shave, D. W., *The U.S.S.R.: A Geographical Survey,* John Wiley & Sons, 1944, pp. 130-132.

[2] Huntington, Ellsworth, "The Influence of Geography and Climate Upon History." Reprinted with permission of The Macmillan Company from *Compass of the World,* edited by Hans W. Weigert and Vilhjalmur Stefansson, pp. 175-176. Copyright 1945 by The Macmillan Company.

from the North American grasslands and is in the process of disappearing from the Eurasian grasslands, victim of that pacific weapon, the rifle. The steppes today are, typically, the lands of the wheat farmer and the rancher, and the nomadic legend lives on only in certain industries, such as television and the movies which are devoted to providing vicarious experiences of self-reliance, boldness, versatility, military capacity, and power of leadership to routinized urban man.

Prairies are something of a conundrum to the biogeographer. Typically they are tall-grass invasions into regions which would seem to be climatically intended for forest lands. At one time it was widely surmised that the hunting practices of the Indians, involving as they did the use of fire, might have been responsible for the destruction of original forest cover which was succeeded by grass. This theory has now been discarded. The depth of the prairie soil, quite obviously developed under a grass cover, is such that it must have been in the process of formation much longer than the Indians have been in North America.

Dansereau defines prairies as grasslands that are "found mostly in temperate regions where precipitation is reduced towards the end of summer" (1). The *1948 Yearbook of Agriculture,* on the other hand, comes to no such definite conclusion. Noting that prairies occupy both humid and subhumid lands and that in the United States particularly, prairies extend into humid regions where trees grow perfectly well when planted, the Yearbook says:

¶ Why prairies should be found in such a climate has long been a matter of speculation. Given prairie to start with, it is not hard to imagine that the dense, vigorous grass, with the help of fire, could have kept trees from invading. A good prairie fire would destroy any tree seedlings that might have come up, with no permanent injury to the grass. There is some evidence that the central prairie region has somewhat more dry years and perhaps less actual moisture than the forested regions adjoining it.

But this fact obviously cannot explain the absence of trees in the wet swales that, before they were drained, covered a great acreage in northern Illinois and northern Iowa. These wet places in the prairies were grass-covered, while in the forested parts of Indiana and Ohio some of the correspondingly wet places had become timbered. It seems possible, then, that forest might in time have occupied the humid prairie, if the white man had not intervened.

Some prairies are found in humid climates where soils have developed from chalk, marl, or other highly calcareous material. The Black Prairies of Texas and Alabama are examples. Most trees seem to be less tolerant of salts, including calcium carbonate, than grasses are. This may explain these humid, calcareous prairies, the soils of which are known as Rendzinas.

Some tall-grass prairies are marshlands. Some of these wet prairies, as I have noted, occur within general prairie regions; others occur in forested or even in desert regions. Some, like the Everglades, occur in fresh water; others, like the tidal marshes, grow in salt water. Marshlands generally occur in environments too wet for most trees—yet mangrove woodlands grow with roots submerged by sea water. The most we can say by way of general explanation of marshland is that tree species tolerant enough of the soil and moisture conditions of the particular marshland to compete with grasses have not existed near enough to invade the marsh. This can be said about any grassland near the transition zone between woodland and grassland (6).

The three great prairie areas of the world are found in the North American Midwest, in European Russia, and in the Argentine Pampa region, extending into nearby Uruguay and southern Brazil. Whatever the origin of these grasslands, they have become some of the most highly productive agricultural regions of the world, largely because of the high quality of the rich black soils that developed under a grass cover. The typical prairie crops are the grain crops, our cultivated grains being essentially domesticated grasses which are very much at home in a natural grassland environment. Indeed, so intensively used are these prairie areas that there are few places anywhere in the world today where natural prairie can be seen.

3. The savannah biochore. Traditionally the term savannah has been restricted to the open forest–grassland association of the wet-dry tropics, and it is in this sense that the term is still used in most geography textbooks. Dansereau has suggested a broader usage of the term, applying it to vegetational landscapes intermediate between forests and grasslands wherein trees are widely spaced and commonly low; lower layers of vegetation develop variously, and consist of tall grasses, shrubs, bunchgrasses, tufts of annuals, and even patches of lichens; the soil remains dry at the surface, water accumulating lower down; and fires are a regular, if not necessary, feature (1). Thus defined, savannahs include not only the tropical forest-grasslands but also (1) the subtropical or temperate savannah woodland, sometimes called the park grassland; (2) the thorn forest and scrub; (3) the semidesert; (4) the high-latitude heath; and (5) the cold woodland.

The tropical forest-grasslands (savannah in the narrower sense) are closely associated with the *Aw* type of climate, the identifying characteristic of which is a pronounced dry season during the low-sun period. This dry season, combined with high temperatures and the resulting high rate of evaporation, hinders the growth of trees and causes those which do grow to take on a stunted and scrubby appearance. Savannah trees in most places grow singly or in groups except in specially favored areas where there is greater rainfall or where the soils collect and hold more moisture or where streams flow across the savannah. In such situations the trees may grow close enough together to form an actual woodland. Typically, though, the savannah cover is grass: tall grasses in the more humid areas, shorter grasses in the drier areas. These grasses generally do not form a continuous cover, and the soils formed under them are much less fertile than are those of the steppe or the prairie but commonly more fertile than rainforest soils *(Af)*. Savannahs are particularly vulnerable to fire, and it is believed that fires originating in the savannah and extending into the forest margins may, in the past, have enlarged the area of savannah at the expense of the forest.

The largest areas of savannah are in Africa and in Brazil. In Africa and in southeastern Asia the savannahs are still great natural preserves of game, although advancing agricultural settlement yearly reduces the area of open rangeland. To what extent the hitherto little-used savannahs will be occupied and used by man in the future is difficult to say. The soils are generally poor-grade laterites; the dry season is a major obstacle both to agriculture and to animal husbandry; the native grasses are, for all practical purposes, useless for domesticated animals and difficult to clear; and in some areas insects, such as the African tsetse fly, carry diseases which have, until now, stubbornly resisted eradication.

Savannah woodlands are found in subtropical and even temperate areas where the problem is not so much one of a dry season as of unreliable precipitation. In some of them, there is a thick covering of grass and in others a layer of shrubs beneath the level of the forest foliage. Soils tend to develop a prairie profile. Relatively large areas of savannah woodland are found in northern Australia, on the Deccan plateau of India, in a band between the forests and steppe of China, on the Ethiopian plateau and on parts of the Brazilian plateau. Climatically, the savannah woodland is associated with the *Aw* type, especially with higher-altitude *Aw* situations where the rate of evaporation is lower than in the warmer lowlands, but the park grasslands of *BS* Manitoba also fall into Dansereau's classification of savannah woodlands. In the tropics, savannah woodland is so much preferable to the forests and the ordinary savannah for agriculture and stockraising that it tends to attract not only heavier populations but also more advanced cultures. In places, as in Kenya in recent years, the struggle for possession of the savannah woodlands has led to violence.

Thorn forest and scrub are found typically along the *Aw-BS* boundary where the dry period is longer than the period of active vegetation. As its name implies, this formation consists mostly of deciduous thorny trees and shrubs, smooth-barked and generally short in height. In tropical Africa many species of the acacia are represented.

¶ Some of these are fine trees that may reach 12 to 15 meters [forty to fifty feet] in height, with crowns typically outspread in parasols and a delicate foliage that casts little shade. In certain places these trees are spaced fairly far apart and form open forests on grassy steppe land. Elsewhere, the thorny shrubs draw close together in dense or even impenetrable thickets. Most commonly, however, the formation is of savannah or of thorny steppe type. The drier the climate becomes, the more open become the thorny steppes, and, as true desert is approached, the shrub stands become extremely scattered.[1]

A rather small but very interesting vegetational landscape called the *caatinga*, found in the small *BS* area of northeastern Brazil, belongs to the thorn forest formation.

¶ The *caatinga* . . . displays a remarkable contrast in aspect between the dry season and rainy season. During the pronounced drought of the former period, the thick brush covers the plateaus with an apparently dead growth of whitish wood, broken only by the small areas of mountain tropical rain forest on the serra heights of the north. With the advent of the rains all plant life quickens with astonishing vigor and soon a leafy mantle of fresh green is produced. In the drier parts or those deficient in soils, the change is less abrupt owing to the dominance of cacti.

Mimosas in great variety preponderate over most of the area. Prominent also are plants reflecting rain and drought by their water-storing organs: especially various *Bombacaceae* of smaller trunk and many fleshy cacti. In the west, the *manicoba (Manihot glaziovii)* is an important growth in that it furnishes a not inconsiderable quantity of rubber, while along the moist bottoms of the valleys grows the valuable wax-producing *carnauba* palm *(Copernicia cerifera)*. The several trees and shrubs have much aggregate importance, but of greater significance to the average inhabitant are the herbaceous forms which quickly rise in profusion following the rains and provide forage for the region's livestock.[2]

Semidesert savannah is typically found at high altitudes within deserts, or along the *BWks-BSks* boundary. The vegetation is shrub-form, mostly deciduous and very scattered. There may or may not be trees. Some 90 million acres of rangeland in our country fall within this category, and the semidesert landscape is one of the most familiar of all landscapes to those television viewers who are addicted to stories of the early West. Sagebrush and grama grass are typical plants, and the forage supports a limited grazing industry. Sheep are perhaps better adapted than are cattle to the rather low-quality forage available, but they are more destructive of the range because of their ability to graze more closely than cattle can. Partly for this reason there is a long-standing hostility between sheepmen and cattlemen.

Heath vegetation develops characteristically at relatively high altitudes or in high latitudes where strong winds check the growth of coniferous forest or where the soil, because of dryness or shallowness or acidity, prevents the growth of forest trees (9). Characteristic plants of this association are the heather, the bog birch, cottongrass and other sedges, and sphagnum moss. Heath is often either confused with moor or lumped in together with it. True moors, or "wet moors," are poorly drained areas developed over a great thickness of peat. Heath generally grows on gravelly or relatively coarse sandy soil, one layer of which is a compact stratum of hard moorpan.

¶ The moorpan may be only a few inches but perhaps several feet below the surface, but it is this which prevents the invasion of heathland by trees, and heathland in which the hard pan is present cannot be afforested unless the pan is broken up or holes made in it for the roots of young trees to penetrate.[3]

Even in such otherwise densely populated countries as Great Britain and Germany, heathlands are still sparsely populated. In this they are true to their history. Centuries ago, when Christianity was first spreading over western Europe, the isolated, backward heath-dwellers were the last to be reached by the missionaries, and in both England and Germany the word for heath-dweller (heath-en; Heide-(e)n) came to stand for a non-Christian. In more recent times, the heath and moor country has come to connote sport, as in the grouse lands of the Scottish moors.

Last of the savannah formations is the cold woodland, actually a kind of transitional type between polar barrens and the Boreal

---

[1] *A World Geography of Forest Resources*, Edited by Stephen Haden-Guest, John K. Wright, and Eileen M. Teclaff, for the American Geographical Society. Copyright 1956 The Ronald Press Company, New York, pp. 381-382. Reprinted by permission.

[2] Jones, Clarence F., *South America*, Holt, Rinehart and Winston, New York, 1947, pp. 62-63. Reprinted by permission.

[3] Stamp, L. Dudley, and Beaver, Stanley H., *The British Isles*, Longmans, Green and Co., Inc., New York, 1954, p. 143. Reprinted by permission.

coniferous forest (Taiga). This formation is typically associated with *glei* soils, characterized by poor drainage and peat accumulation at the surface. The trees of the cold woodland are low and poorly developed laterally but well spaced; the shrub layer has a better development. Muskeg is abundant on poorly drained sites and tends to expand onto the uplands. Mosses and lichens are also common. The cold woodland has hitherto proved inhospitable to human settlement except in isolated instances where valuable mineral supplies have made it worth man's while to put up with the discomforts of such regions and made it economically feasible to import food and other necessities.

4. The forest biochore. Forests are vegetational communities in which the individual trees grow so closely together that their crowns meet and form a canopy which shades the ground. The shade thus produced creates a microclimate condition on the forest floor very different from that of open land in the same region and, therefore, differently vegetated.

The factors which set boundaries to forest growth have been summarized by Dr. Newbigin as follows:

¶ 1. Bearing in mind that bulky permanent tissues have to be built up, and that the shoots formed each season have to be ripened sufficiently to withstand the following unfavourable season, it is clear that there must be a long growing period. Apparently, herbaceous growth can often go on under conditions of temperature below the limit for woody growth; for example, a mean July temperature of not less than 50° F. is needed for formation of dense stands of even the hardiest northern conifers. Low temperatures thus limit forest range both in high latitudes and at greater altitudes.

2. The deeper layers of the soil must be permanently moist and the moisture present must be in a readily available form. The actual rainfall necessary to ensure adequate reserves of soil moisture varies greatly both with local temperatures as affecting evaporation and with tree type. Certain general points are, nevertheless, clear. Since trees are long-lived, the long-period fluctuations in the total fall must not be such as to lead to exhaustion of soil reserves; regions of highly variable rainfall are therefore unsuitable. Demands on soil moisture are greatest during the growing season; therefore, other things being equal, areas of warm-season rainfall will be more favourable to forest than those with cold-season precipitation. Since some moisture must be absorbed even during the 'dead' season, a low total, markedly seasonal in character, inhibits forest development.

3. Where very low winter temperatures occur, the air must be relatively calm. Winds, especially dry winds, are indeed a notable limiting factor, particularly in high latitudes and at great elevations, where they tend to lead to a loss of moisture which cannot be made good by absorption from the chilled soil.[1]

The major forest types are treated at considerable length in other chapters of this book. Briefly summarized, the distribution of forests shapes up somewhat along the following lines.

In the far northerly regions of the northern hemisphere where summers are mild, winters cold and long, and precipitation abundant, the characteristic forest cover is needleleaf evergreen. The Russian word for this kind of forest is *taiga*, and this term is often applied to all forests of this kind, including the great evergreen forests of Canada. Taiga soils are podsols, having a surface dotted with bogs. Many parts of the forest are poorly drained, a condition which leads to the accumulation of peat. The taiga and the tropical forests, to be discussed later, represent the last large stands of virgin forest left in the world, and in both cases the reason for survival is essentially the same: physical conditions, primarily climatic, discourage settlement and make movement through the forests difficult. Logging and lumbering operations, therefore, take place almost exclusively along the warmer margins of the forest. It should be noted, however, that since the best trees of the taiga are found along these warmer margins, the consumption of useful timber is much greater than one would suppose from relating consumption figures to total forest area.

Going southward from the taiga in the northern hemisphere, the next type of forest which typically appears is the temperate deciduous forest. The two largest areas of

[1] Newbigin, Marion I., *Plant and Animal Geography*, E. P. Dutton and Co., Inc., N.Y., 1948, pp. 113-114. Reprinted by permission.

temperate deciduous forest are found in the North European Plain and in the interior lowland of the United States. Both of these areas have a distinct cold season and plentiful precipitation with no marked dry season. The deciduous nature of the forest derives not, however, from the low winter temperatures but from the low intensity and short duration of sunlight during the winter season. Very few examples of virgin temperate deciduous forest are still to be found, and even these are very problematical. Most of the trees found within this formation represent recent plantings, most of them after a long period of forest denudation associated with the establishment of agriculture.

Still proceeding equatorward, in North America one comes to another belt of needleleaf forest along the east and gulf coasts of the United States. In Europe only a very narrow band of needleleaf forest lies equatorward from the deciduous forest, and this band is associated with the high, cool slopes of the Pyrenees and the Alps. There is evidence to suggest that the needleleaf forests of the eastern and southern coastal districts of the United States are not "climax,"[1] that they represent the persistence of vegetational associations developed under formerly cooler climates, probably associated with continental glaciation. The needleleaf forests of the North American Pacific region, on the other hand, are well adapted to their cool, high-elevation, superhumid environments.

As one approaches the subtropics in the northern hemisphere, notable differences become apparent between west-coast and east-coast climatic types, and forest associations mirror these differences. In regions of Mediterranean climate (*Cs*), typically developed along the west coasts of the continents, the forest is an evergreen hardwood forest and locally conifers, drought-resistant (xerophytic) in nature, consisting of small trees and secondary brush formations (chaparral or garigue). The brush formations often include many spiny shrubs *(maquis)*. Since the Mediterranean world is a mountainous world, Mediterranean forests display zonation patterns which vary from place to place. In Italy, for instance, the vegetation in the lowlands is largely evergreen, consisting of forms such as the ilex oak, the stone-pine, the olive, and the cypress. On the moderately high slopes, deciduous trees are found such as elms and poplars and especially the chestnut. In the highest mountains, most of the trees typical of central Europe are found. Since the Mediterranean world is a transitional region between temperate and tropical, humid and dry, numerous exotic forms appear in the vegetational pattern. Examples include various types of palm and bougainvillea from the tropics, cacti and century plants from the drylands.

The east-coast counterpart of the Mediterranean climate is the *Cw* climate, found most typically in eastern and southeastern China and representing a poleward extension of the monsoonal *Aw* climate. The vegetational types associated with this climate are the temperate and subtropical rainforests. Both are luxuriant forest characterized by a great variety of tree types. The winter-dry period produces a visible life cycle in the vegetation, more evident in the temperate rainforests than in the subtropical.

Finally, within the tropics there are two great, broadly-developed forest types: the tropical rainforest and the monsoon forest.

"The Tropical Rainforest," Dr. Wendell H. Camp has declared, "is perhaps our least understood vegetation type." He then goes on to point out that:

¶ Many forest areas in the tropics classed as "rain forest" actually are *Light Tropical Forest.* A further complication is the presence of large forest tracts on mountain slopes in the tropics which, because of the terrain and wind pattern, are well watered. These are *Tropical Montane Rain Forests;* on the middle slopes where the precipitation is usually highest, they have a composition considerably different from that of the rain forests of the lowlands. Where they are adjacent, both lowland rainforest and light forest pass into the montane rain-forest type. . . .

[Dr. Camp then calls attention to a diagram which is reproduced in this chapter as Figure X-2.]

[This figure] indicates in a diagrammatic manner the seasonal pattern of rainfall in this region. It is immediately obvious that there is only a narrow strip along the equator in which rain can be expected to fall at almost all times of the

---

[1] This term expresses a stabilized form of vegetation-association, as an ultimate adjustment to the environment.

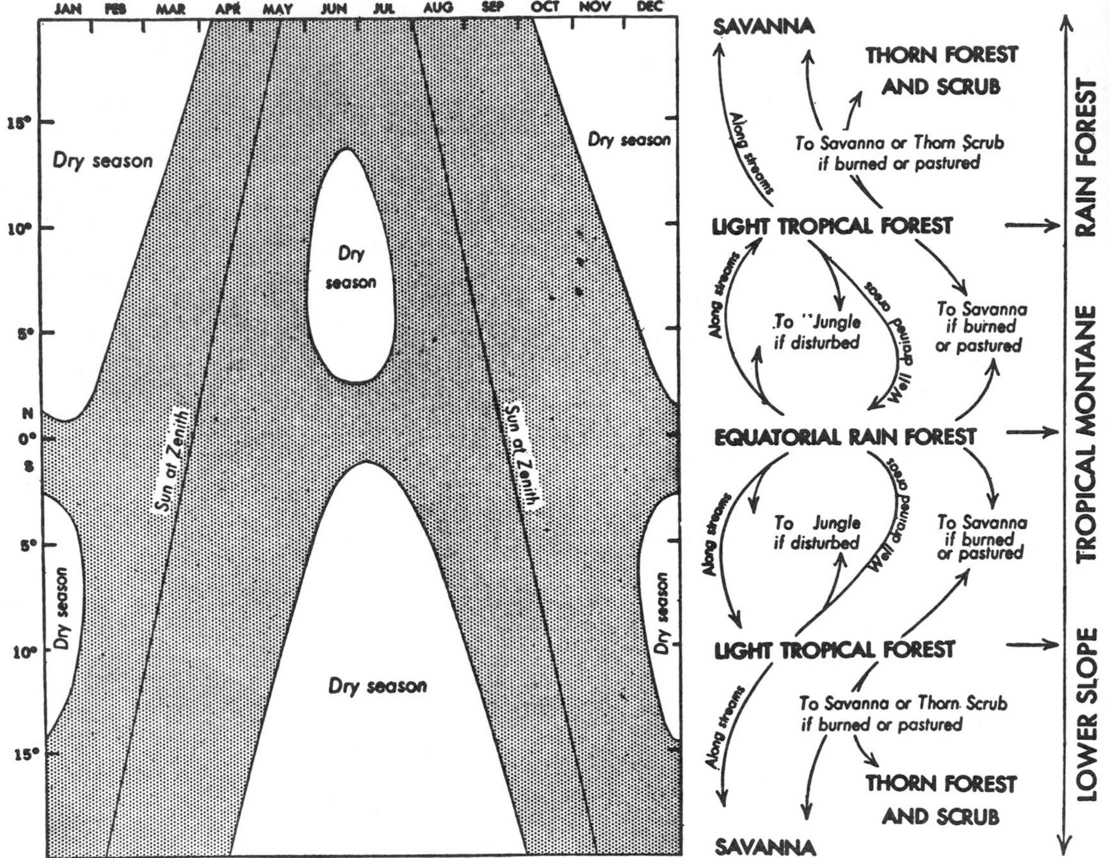

X:2 This pattern of wet and dry seasons in equatorial regions, is shown correlated with the main forest types. (From *A World Geography of Forest Resources*, edited by Stephen Haden-Guest, John K. Wright, and Eileen M. Teclaff for the American Geographical Society. Copyright, 1956, by The Ronald Press Company, New York, used by permission)

year. Here seasonal maxima may occur, but only exceptionally does any long period pass without rain. This relatively narrow equatorial band is the locale of the true rainforest, although local conditions in some places produce equivalent conditions that enlarge the occurrence of this forest type. . . .

Light forest is found in those regions near the equator where there are two yearly maxima of rain, with one of the dry seasons of about three months in length. . . .

After abandonment, . . . cleared and briefly cultivated areas [in the tropical forests] return to vegetation natural to the area, but not to the original forest type. Such tropical "weed forest" is the most rampantly growing sort of vegetation known. But remarkable as is this secondary forest, with its dense undergrowth and tangle of lianas, it is characteristic only of the disturbed areas of the region. Descriptions of these "impenetrable jungles," usually written in awed and somewhat lurid phrases by early travelers, who necessarily had to stay close to the rivers, have become the classic texts from which we have taken our concepts of tropical vegetation for much too long a time.[1]

The tropical rainforest is characterized by a great variety of trees standing individually in the forest rather than in pure stands; by "layering" of the vegetation; by the presence of many and various climbers and air plants (epiphytes), such as the orchid; and by the

[1] *A World Geography of Forest Resources*, edited for The American Geographical Society by Stephen Haden-Guest, John K. Wright, and Eileen M. Teclaff. Copyright 1956 The Ronald Press Company.

absence of any noticeable seasonal rhythm of plant or animal life.

Monsoon forest, on the other hand, is largely deciduous in response to a more or less prolonged drier, and colder, period. In those monsoonal areas where the total annual rainfall is great, the monsoonal forest may be hardly distinguishable, especially during the rainy season, from tropical rainforest although there would be fewer epiphytes and lianas and the trees would not be so tall as those of the rainforest. The distinguishing characteristic of the monsoonal forest is its loss of leaves during the dry season. Dr. Newbigin suggests that the monsoonal forest is rarely due wholly to natural causes, but has been largely influenced by the activities of man. Noting that certain very common kinds of monsoonal forest tend to run back to rainforest when protected from fire, she suggests that this kind of forest may not be a "climax" cover but rather one of a successional series resulting from fires set by man to extend cultivation or assist hunting or encourage the growth of grass for pasture (9).

Many years ago, a fascinating article on the influence of forests on man's history appeared in one of the professional geographic magazines. The author recognized three stages in the relation of man to forest: (1) civilization dominated by forests; (2) civilization overcoming the forest; and (3) civilization dominating the forest.

After noting that the first great nuclei of civilization — the Egyptian, Babylonian, Assyrian, Phoenician, Aztec, and Inca — originated in dry, unforested regions, this writer goes on to point out that:

¶ Forests have acted as barriers to human colonization in all parts of the world. In the Alleghenies as well as in tropical West Africa the forest for many decades delayed the penetration of the white man into the interior of the continent. It took the American colonists about 200 years to reach the crest of the Alleghenies. It prevented the spread of the Hamites from North Africa southward and stopped the movement into the Congo region of the cattle-keeping aristocracies such as the Bahima which had a social, political, and military organization superior to other tribes. In the heart of the Congo forest no traces of an ancient population have been found. The expansion of the Inca Empire from the high plateaus of Peru and Bolivia eastward was limited by the impenetrable forests of the headwaters of the Amazon River. . . . The history of the Spanish conquest is similar: the forest continued to mark the boundary of effective control. Indeed much the same is true today.

The Romans, the greatest colonizers of olden times, were forced to stop in their expansion and Empire building at the boundaries of the dense, virgin German forests. . . . The more recent European historians, such as Gradmann for instance, consider the boundary of the Roman Empire as coinciding with the western boundary of the coniferous forests of southern Germany. . . .

Just as the Romans were compelled to stop in their colonizing activities at the boundary of the virgin forests of central Europe, so the successive later waves of the nomadic tribes which moved from the eastern prairies westward—Huns, Magyars, Avars, and the like—broke up when they reached the barrier of primeval forests. The routes of migration in western and central Europe were largely determined by the openings in the primeval forest.

The difficulty with which primeval forests could be penetrated made them always an obstacle to all great historic migrations of man. On the grasslands pack animals could be used, and here the wheeled cart originated. In the primeval forest where a path must be hacked out with the aid of ax and knife man must be his own burden bearer. Three or four miles a day is the average rate of travel in such forests. Not infrequently man depends here on the animal trails. Mammoth and rhinoceros in the ages past were the first trail builders in the forests of central Europe, just as the elephants are breaking trails now in Africa and eastern Asiatic forests to be later followed by man. The bear trails served as roads for the Teutons in the primeval forests of Europe, just as they are now doing in the forests of Kamchatka and Siberia for the hunters of fur animals. In North America, as Humboldt remarks, the "bison pointed out to man the best roads through the Cumberland Mountains." In medieval Europe the wild cattle broke the first trails in the forests, just as in our own western forests the cattle trails were the first which many of us traveled.[1]

Man's first significant moves toward over-

[1] Zon, Raphael, "Forests and Human Progress," *Geographical Review*, Vol. 10, 1920, pp. 140-142. Reprinted by permission.

The koala bear, living model of the teddy bear, is the classic example of the close adjustment of a creature to an environment. Clumsy on the ground, the koala is an expert climber. His diet consists exclusively of the young, tender leaves of certain species of eucalyptus or gum trees. Only the protection of the Australian government prevents his extinction. (News and Information Bureau, Department of the Interior, Commonwealth of Australia)

coming the forest, the writer points out, were made in localities where the forest existed under adverse conditions of climate or soil and where it was, therefore, particularly vulnerable to his simple tools. He cites the Mediterranean forest as an example of such easily-cleared forests. But the great thick forest of central Europe did not yield to man's encroachment until the Middle Ages when it was vigorously and systematically attacked by the religious and knightly orders.

Men attack forests for many reasons: to provide homesites for themselves and their families in areas where the cleared land has already been appropriated; to provide supplementary sources of food in a pattern of primitive agriculture; to provide fuel for domestic heating and for manufactural purposes; and to provide raw materials for their industries. In the process of conquering the forest, it is possible that man develops certain personality characteristics which even today we associate with the backwoodsman. Dr. Zon says:

¶ Many of the specific pioneer traits of our own original settlers in this country may be traced to their battle against the forest on the slopes of the Alleghenies to provide a place for settlement. The hazardous work of hewing farms out of the virgin forest has bred a race of men of sturdy character and of enormous enterprise and self-reliance. It is true that life in the forest was not conducive to the cultivation of the graces of life characteristic of high culture. The virtues of the backwoodsman were those of a strong animal nature—courage, pertinacity, resourcefulness. . . .

In spite, however, of coarsenses and even brutality, these people were undeniably men. No weaklings were produced by the life of the forest. The boundless woods with the long stretches of swamp land, the rough trails, the isolated homesteads sometimes miles away from the nearest neighbor bred unwillingness to co-operate with others for common purposes or to submit to any kind of discipline. . . .

If of all the present nations, the Anglo-Saxons, the Teutons, and the Russians display the great colonizing capacity, may it not be attributed largely to their original impenetrable forests, in the struggle with which they have developed the persistence and unrelenting energy required for pioneer work?[1]

Except, as we have noted, for the taiga and the tropical forests, the modern world is one in which civilization dominates the forest. For years, even centuries, man asserted his mastery over the forest by its destruction. More recently he has been asserting his mastery more intelligently by controlled cutting and even a certain amount of reforestation. But an unprecedented demand for forest products threatens to revive the old practices of exploitative forestry. In our own country, according to the Paley Report of 1952, the cubic-foot requirement of wood for all purposes is expected to increase by 17 per cent between 1950 and 1975. Meanwhile competing land-uses may be expected to continue to

[1] *Ibid.*, pp. 158-159. Reprinted by permission.

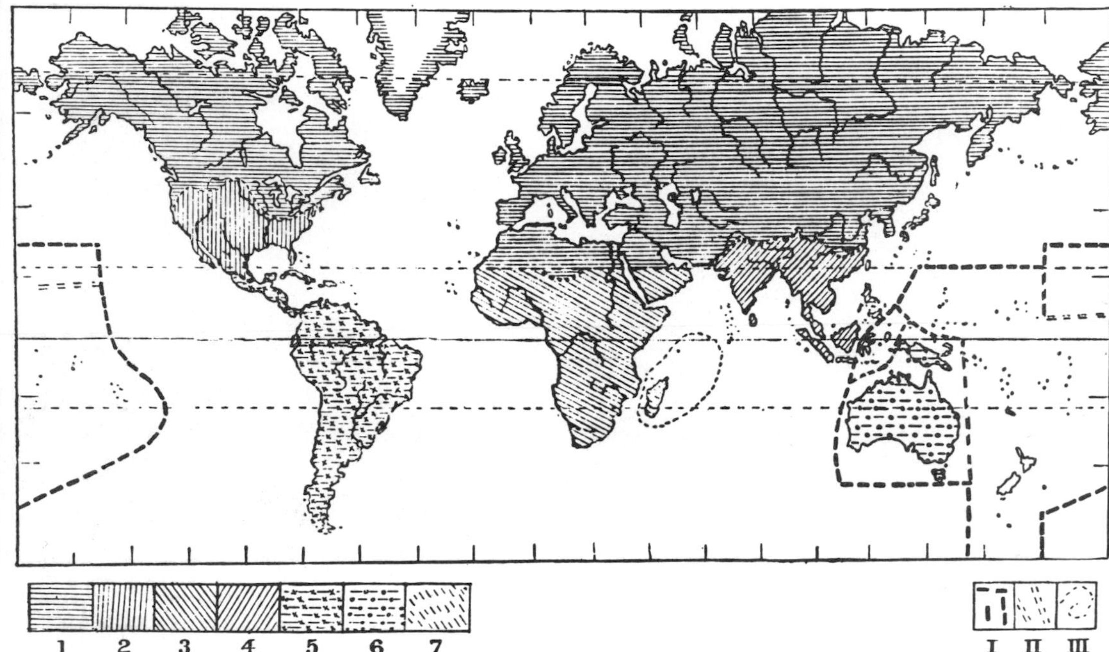

X:3 This map shows the major animal realms of the world.

I. Outer limit of the Notogaeic Realm
II. a) Inner limits of regions within the Notogaeic realm
b) Boundary between the Oriental and the Holarctic
c) Boundary of the Ethiopian in the middle of the Sahara Desert (outside the Sahara this boundary is the Tropic of Cancer)
III. a) Northern boundary of the Sonoran
b) Boundary of the Malagasy
(1) The Holarctic Region; (2) the Sonoran; (3) The Ethiopian; (4) the Oriental; (5) the Neotropical; (6) the Australian; (7) the Malagasian. (From *Plant and Animal Geography,* by Marion I. Newbigin, E. P. Dutton & Co., Inc., New York, 1948, used by permission)

threaten the forest, and perhaps more seriously than ever before as increasing population and the space-consuming accoutrements of high civilization demand more and more open space.

The regional geography of animal life

Animal life is much more difficult to regionalize than is plant life because animals are quite mobile and are, in varying degrees, capable of adjusting to environments other than those to which they are native. Nevertheless, attempts have been made to construct major animal realms. One of the most acceptable of these attempts is shown in Figure X-3, which is based upon a map drawn by Dr. Newbigin.

The regionalization suggested by Dr. Newbigin divides the world into three great faunal realms, eight regions, and one major subregion, as follows:

A. The Arctogaeic realm
1. *The Holarctic Region*
2. *The Sonoran Region*
3. *The Ethiopian Region*
a) *The Malagasay Subregion*
4. *The Oriental Region*

B. The Neogaeic realm
5. *The Neotropical Region*

C. The Notogaeic realm
6. *The Australian Region*
7. *The Polynesian Region*
8. *The Hawaiian Region*

The Notogaeic realm. The most clearly defined of these realms — although even its boundaries are a subject of continuing controversy — is the Notogaeic whose typical fauna may perhaps be best described as living fossils. Here, isolated from the placental

Kangaroos leap toward their camping ground in Australia. Typical of Notogaeic animal forms, the kangaroo has survived largely because geographic isolation protected him from competition with carnivores which, in other parts of the world, seem to have nearly exterminated the gentle and relatively defenseless marsupials. The landscape in this picture is typical of the kangaroo's habitat—grassy hills and plains. (News and Information Bureau, Department of the Interior, Commonwealth of Australia)

mammals which everywhere else dominate the life scene, marsupials (pouched animals) abound, and alongside them such biological curiosities as flightless birds and insects. One might almost describe the fauna as a refugee fauna — gentle and relatively defenseless forms which perhaps escaped to these end-of-the-line landmasses from the encroachments of the mammalian carnivores and were sealed off by the drowning of former land bridges between Australasia and southeast Asia. Representative examples of Notogaeic forms would include the kangaroo and his tree-dwelling New Guinea cousin; the koala with his monomania for eucalyptus leaves; that sadly disorganized egg-laying mammal, the duckbill platypus; the great, awkward, flightless emu of Australia and the equally flightless, almost extinct kiwi of New Zealand; and a very primitive fish, found only in the rivers of Queensland, called ceratodus.

Of placental forms, the only representatives are some types of bats, a few mice, the dingo or native dog, and the pig of New Guinea. The fact that the placental mammals and the more highly developed marsupials are generally found in the northern part of the realm suggests that the great animal migrations into Australia in the past may have been from the south from the general direction of South America, rather than from the north as has been generally supposed. Whichever route it was, the primitiveness of the life indicates that this realm has long been isolated from other parts of the world.

The Neogaeic Realm. The Neogaeic Realm, which includes South and Central America, is coterminous with the Neotropical Region. Its fauna are much less strikingly differentiated than are the fauna of the Notogaeic Realm, and no one group of animals is dominant as are the marsupials of Australia. It is interesting to note, though, that in the steppelands of South America, "within the human period, but prior to the immigration of the white, large ungulates were almost absent. No horse, no relative of cattle or sheep or antelope cropped the herbage of the great plains, but their place in nature was taken by enormous numbers of rodents, which reached here a size not attained elsewhere" (12). To this peculiarity of the fauna might be added the general absence of insectivores and the fact that all of the carnivores are obviously fairly recent immigrants, as are, of course, the domesticated animals.

Four major environmental situations can be identified in this realm, each of them with a fairly characteristic fauna. Over much of the realm there is still unbroken tropical forest and in the forest there is an abundance of arboreal life, including marmosets, a form of monkey believed to have originated in South America, perhaps from lemur ancestors which somehow made the long journey from Africa; sloths and some anteaters, representatives of the edentates which are more commonly found in this realm than in any other; rodents, such as the tree porcupine; opossums; and monkeys. Down the spine of the continent runs the Andean Cordillera, a natural line of migration and, particularly in its upper slopes, a habitat notably different from anything around it. Here are found the llama-like guanaco, the ruminant vicuña, and the little rodent, the chinchilla — all three of them peculiar to South America. The deserts of the west coast and Patagonia also have their peculiar forms of life, largely rodent. Finally, the grasslands, most notably the Argentine pampas, constitute a differentiated habitat which, in former times, supported an abundance of ungulate and rodent life. The ungulates included the guanaco, the llama, and the pampas deer; the most common rodent was the viscacha. By comparison with the Arctogaeic Realm, mammalian forms in the Neogaeic Realm were few, but each form was represented by an abundance of individuals. With the entry of the European into the grasslands, native forms were destroyed unmercifully and replaced by domesticated animals.

¶ The bats are very peculiar. Here only (with a slight extension into North America) do we find the vampire bats, while the fruit-bats of the Old World are completely absent, as well as another family called the horse-shoe bats. . . .

The birds of South America are almost as peculiar as the mammals, though, as was to be expected, many of the characteristic forms extend also into North America. Among the important families are the hummingbirds, the macaws (Conurinae), the toucans, the jacamars, the motmots, the chatterers, the tanagers, the tinamus, the curassows, &c. The so-called American ostrich (genus Rhea) is characteristic, and is represented by several species. Among the negative characteristics we may note the absence of crows and ravens, which do not extend south of Guatemala. As in Australia there are many parrots. Among the reptiles interesting forms are the rattlesnakes, the boas and anacondas, and the lizards of the family Iguanidae, while there is a large number of toads and frogs, especially tree-frogs (Hylidae).[1]

The Arctogaeic Realm. Largest and least clearly defined of all the faunal realms is the Arctogaeic Realm, which includes all of North America north of the Tropic of Cancer, all of Eurasia, and all of Africa. This is the realm of the highest mammals and the most specialized birds, of the highest and most specialized of the hoofed mammals (ungulates) and the most advanced primates. Negatively, within this realm few primitive forms have managed to survive the competition with the higher forms. No marsupial except for one North American opossum, no monotreme, no primitive reptile is found within this realm.

The remarkable homogeneity of animal life throughout this vast area points back to an earlier age when a land bridge connected Asia and North America across what is now Bering Strait and when there were as yet no great desert barriers to inhibit movement within the Afro-Eurasian land mass. The re-

---

[1] Newbigin, Marion I., *Animal Geography*, Oxford University Press, 1938, pp. 222-223. Reprinted by permission.

This scene is from the high Andes, inland from Lima, Peru. The herbivorous llama is to the Andean Indian all that the camel is to the desert Bedouin—burden-bearer, symbol of wealth and status, source of milk and fiber. Sure-footed and capable of tolerating the rarefied air of the high mountain slopes, the llama can take man where no other means of transportation can take him. Like the camel, the llama works well but grudgingly. (Canadian Pacific Railway)

gionalization of faunas within this realm is very largely the product of recent events in geological history, such as the glaciation of large parts of Europe and North America, the splitting of landmasses by crustal movements, and the development of great deserts in North Africa and central Asia.

The largest of the faunal regions of the Arctogaeic Realm — and indeed the largest faunal region in the world — is the Holarctic Region which covers all of northern North America from the Arctic Ocean to the Ohio and the Missouri, all of Europe, all of Asia north of the Himalayas and the Tropic of Cancer, and all of Africa north of the Tropic of Cancer. The unifying fact around which this region is organized is its occupation throughout by animals well adapted to conditions that developed as the great ice sheets of North America and Europe retreated. There are no toothless mammals (edentates) in this region, no marsupials, and no primates except a few on the southern border of its eastern section.

The Holarctic Region is sometimes divided into an eastern (Palaearctic) section embracing Eurasia and North Africa, and a western (Nearctic) section covering the North American portion of the region. Certain differences may be noted between these two sections. Although both sections have oxen, the Palaearctic section has quite a number of sheep and goats while the Nearctic has few. The Palaearctic has camels and horses; the Nearctic does not (except, of course, for the horses that were re-introduced into the Nearctic by white immigrants). The badger is characteristic of the Old World, whereas skunks and raccoons are found in the New World. There are also significant dissimilarities in bird life. Both subregions are rich in carnivores and rodents and tailed amphibians, and both are poor in antelopes and reptiles.

In North America, the Holarctic Region gives way to the Sonoran Region, although there are no significant physical features to mark the boundary. The distinction between the two regions lies in the fact that the fauna of the Holarctic are essentially the same as those of temperate Eurasia, while the Sonoran fauna include the peccary, the armadillo, and the opossum—which are not found in the Old World but which are found in Neogaea. The Sonoran may thus be considered a kind of transitional region between the Holarctic and the Neogaeic Realm — a region, moreover, which served as an escape route for mammals fleeing before the advancing ice of the Glacial Age. Thus within it there is an intermingling of North American preglacial faunas and some forms from Neogaea.

The similarities between the Oriental and Ethiopian Regions are so striking that the two regions are sometimes lumped together in one. There is value, however, in keeping them separate since the differences that do exist between them are significant enough to warrant attention. Some of the more important of these differences are indicated on the following table (Table 10.2).

A subregion of the Ethiopian Region is the Malagasy, which includes the large island of Madagascar and some very small land masses to the north and east. Among the characteristics of its fauna which serve to distinguish it from the Ethiopian fauna are the absence of anthropoid apes and monkeys, the great number (36) of species of lemur and the abundance of insectivores, the absence of members of the cat family and of characteristic African birds, and the presence of reptiles which seem to be more closely related to those of South America than to those of Africa. It might also be noted that of the various forms which this subregion does share with the Ethiopian Region, a great many represent peculiar genera.

Our age of extinction. The discerning student may have noted, in this description of the world's wild life, a slightly antiquarian note. Throughout the world's natural habitats, the undomesticated species are disappearing before the incursion of the grazer, the farmer, the miner, and the settler. The general rule would seem to be that "the bigger they are, the faster they disappear," partly because the large animals are fewest in number and therefore easiest to exterminate and partly because they are the first to feel the effects of a diminished food supply. Recalling Dean Inge's comment about the interdependence of living things upon each other for food, it will be evident that the removal of any one living form from an animal community must affect the nature of the whole community. Usually these effects are unfortunate for the community. Certain forms die out while others increase beyond safe limits.

With human populations increasing as they are, it is probable that people now living will see the extinction of some of the great carnivores, or at least their reduction to zoological rareties. It is probable that, with the destruction of these large forms, the smaller forms will thrive as never before, becoming nuisances in areas where their numbers have hitherto been controlled.

It will also be noted that our description of the world's wildlife has omitted the life of the sea. Actually, the overwhelming majority of living things dwell in the sea, but at least until now man has had comparatively little to do with the sea forms except in a rather direct exploitative way. What the future may hold, when the sea becomes better known to man and its life becomes a major supplement to the food which man gets from terrestrial life, is still too problematical for anything like scientific discussion. All that is obvious at this time is that man must become increasingly dependent upon the plant and animal life of the sea if his numbers continue to increase at their present rate.

The systematic geography of animal life

The geography of world fauna lends itself well to a study of the relative values of the regional and systematic approaches to the study of areal phenomena, as introduced in Chapter 1. Having considered the regional patterns of animal types, let us now briefly focus upon some of the more salient geo-

Table 10.2 Similarities and Differences in the Fauna of the Oriental and Ethiopian Regions (Compiled from Newbigin, Marion I., *Animal Geography*, Oxford University Press, 1938.)

Oriental Region	*Life Form*	*Ethiopian Region*
Orangutan Gibbon	Anthropoid Apes	Gorilla Chimpanzee
Many kinds	Monkeys	Five peculiar genera with many species
Four species, including two of the very peculiar genus Tarsius	Lemurs	Two genera, eight species
Many, including representatives of both the insect-eating and fruit-eating forms	Bats	Fewer than in oriental region
Include the peculiar flying lemurs of the Philippines, also tree shrews, both of which are confined to this region	Insectivores	Peculiar and primitive. Include jumping shrews, potamogale, and golden mole
Bears (which probably originated in this region) Tigers Many civets Numerous Felidae (cats)	Carnivores	No bears No tigers Two peculiar dogs having very primitive teeth Lions
Oxen Deer Many Pigs Rhinoceros Tapir Elephant (smaller than Ethiopian) Few antelopes	Ungulates	Goats and sheep practically absent Only one true pig Wart hogs Bush pigs River hogs Hippopotamus No Tapir or camel Rhinoceros Elephant (larger than oriental) Several kinds of horses Giraffe Okapi Antelopes abundant
Abundant, including squirrels and mice, some of peculiar genera	Rodents	Plentiful, but no flying squirrels
Pangolin (scaly anteater)	Edentates	Pangolin (scaly anteater) Aardvark
Many and beautiful	Birds	Not so abundant or so beautiful as those of oriental region. Ostrich
Many, including flying lizards and crocodiles	Reptiles	Numerous, including crocodiles

graphic principles of man–animal relationships. These are presented here in summary fashion, since the significance of human geography as related to animal life can be made more apparent when animals are discussed anthropocentrically than when they are regionalized faunally. This systematic treatment thus develops man–animal concepts in the several chapter contexts where such geographic principles can be most effectively illustrated in the total environmental complex. Such a systematic approach not only envisions particular forms of fauna in their own ecological habitat, but it also aids one in better understanding why some animals figure more prominently than others in certain stages of man's culture. Thus in connection with "Hunger and Disease" (Chapter 17), and "The Tropical Rainforest Lands" (Chapter 23), the tropical and subtropical disease-spreading insects are featured. In other chapters (e.g., 19, 20, 21, 22, dealing with lands of more primitive and difficult life) the use of regionally diverse animal forms for draft or pack is an important means of transportation. The student should likewise recognize that such animal forms as fish and the fur-bearers have their greatest geographic significance when discussed in areal contexts where nature and culture together best favor their exploitation, as, for example, in the *Cfb* and *Db-c* regions, respectively. Equally pedagogically sound would be to treat such a subject as "Conservation of Wildlife" in close conjunction with the natural vegetation forms which also need to be conserved if we wish desirable forms of animals to survive, as is pointed out in Chapter 16.

The faunal forms mentioned above (except the disease-producing insects) deal with the beneficial phases of modern man–animal relationships. Man has for the most part given many native animals "the choice of domestication or death," or otherwise learned to control the spread of destructive forms. Typical examples of the former are the draft animals or beasts of burden, such as the Indian buffalo, the Lapland reindeer, the Canadian caribou, and the Andean llama. Any student of anthropo-geography would have to consider this all-important animal element of the natural environment if he would understand how the various native cultures have developed in the several regions of the world.

But extermination, or at least control, of the pests which plague man is also of major geographic consequence. This is effectively exemplified in Taylor's account of the historic agricultural pests of Australia. Here in connection with the pastoral economy, he traces cartographically (Figure X-4) and textually the spread of plagues produced by the rabbit, the wild dog, and the cattle tick.

1. The rabbit pest. "Since the latter part of the nineteenth century, Australia has been menaced with agricultural pests. Of these the rabbit has been much the more costly, for one rabbit is said to consume and destroy 2 lbs. of feed every 24 hours." Continuing, Taylor points out that the rabbit was introduced to Australia by the First Fleet; the rabbit was subsequently reported in Sydney in 1788. Kept at first in fence enclosures in Victoria, the rabbits escaped as a result of destruction of fences by fire which permitted them to spread northward and westward, invading all the states and eventually covering almost two-thirds of the continent (see accompanying figure). Fences hundreds of miles long (e.g., the 648-mile fence between New South Wales and Queensland, which cost 11,000 pounds to maintain) proved ineffective. "Since 40 rabbits are said to eat as much as a sheep, the damage done by the millions of rodents can readily be imagined. Upon three stations (aggregating 1 million acres) in New South Wales the carrying capacity between 1880 and 1890 was reduced by 120,000 sheep."

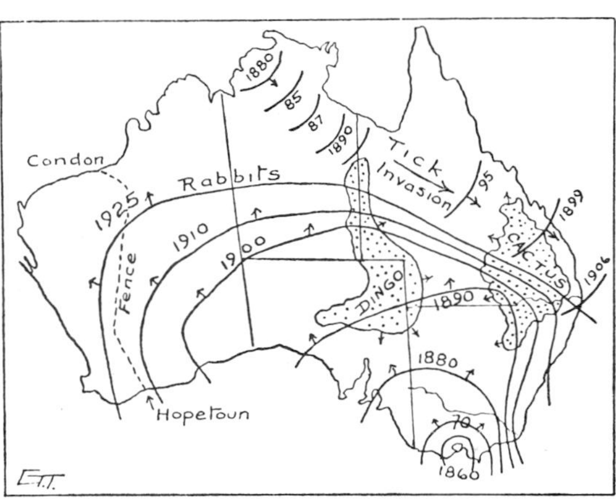

X:4 This map shows the spread of various agricultural pests across Australia. These pests have all, by now, been brought under control. (Redrawn from *Australia*, by Griffith Taylor, E. P. Dutton & Co., Inc., New York, 1940.)

2. The wild dog pest. While the rabbit threatened the supply of forage for sheep, the "dingo" directly preyed upon the sheep. Native of the wilds of innermost Australia, the dogs at first fared on rabbits in their own arid and semiarid haunts, then moved into the sheeplands eastward and southward, where they killed lambs by the thousands (e.g., two stations at Broken Hill losing 22,000 and 45,000 respectively).

3. The cattle tick. Tropical Australia, like other tropical regions, has had its share of parasites. Thus Taylor reports that "This pest has caused grave losses in northern Australia, especially during the period from 1894 to 1900, when cattle worth 3½ million sterling died. Many herds lost 90 per cent of their numbers" (13).

All these one-time pests have now been rather effectively controlled. Better fencing and trapping have kept the rabbit population within bounds; rabbits are now even reared in some sections for food and pelt. Placing a bonus on the dingo's scalp and shifting regionally to cattle culture have reduced the dingo hazard; the dipping of cattle is likewise controlling the tick infestation.

Thus, the study of the pastoral economy of Australia reveals a number of most interesting and instructive interacting geographic forces, natural and cultural: domestic animals competing with wild animals for forage; wild animals preying on domestic animals; and man's ultimate control of the "ecological balance." Thinking of Australia still as a "frontier continent," one nevertheless cannot help wondering how much longer the strikingly distinctive wildlife of the continent island can survive domestication, once again pointing up the geographic principle of the general environmental incompatibility of wildlife and civilized man.

APPLICATION OF GEOGRAPHIC UNDERSTANDING

I. When a mountainous area is stripped of its forest cover, what chain of consequences is begun? Try to carry these consequences through as far as you can, ending up, if possible, with effects upon your own life.

II. How do you explain the considerable concentration of population in the western part of the Russian steppe area in the Ukraine, when no part of our Great Plains is particularly heavily populated?

III. What reasons can you suggest for the fact that the savannah lands are the big-game hunting lands of the modern world?

IV. Can you suggest any reasons why prairie regions are never found on the west coasts of continents?

V. When one considers how many millions of trees are still left in the world, why should there be all this talk about forest conservation and restoration?

VI. If there is comparatively little jungle in the tropical world, why do so many people have the impression that tropical lands are mostly covered by jungle?

VII. Can you think of any possible connections between forest depletion and changes in architectural styles in our country? Between forest depletion and choice of building materials?

VIII. This chapter does not go into detail on specific adaptations of animals to their environments. But knowing what you do of the desert environment, what kinds of adaptation would you expect to find in desert animals?

IX. Why would you not expect to find great numbers of large carnivores in the true tropical rainforest?

X. One of the popular themes of scientific thriller fiction is the prospect of insects taking over and dominating life on earth, perhaps eventually even eliminating human life. Is there any solid basis in fact for such speculations?

References

1 Dansereau, Pierre, *Biogeography, An Ecological Perspective,* Ronald Press Company, New York, 1957, pp. 92, 95, 127.

2 Schaefer, Jack, "Our Challenging Deserts," *Holiday,* Vol. XXIV, No. 1, July, 1958, pp. 91-92.

3 Hoover, Jonas W., "Southwestern Desert Vegetation: Its Adaptations and Utilization," *Journal of Geography,* Vol. XXXI, April, 1935, pp. 151-155, *passim.*

4 Gregory, James S., and Shave, D. W., *The U.S.S.R.: A Geographical Survey,* John Wiley & Sons, Inc., New York, 1944, pp. 130-132.

5 Huntington, Ellsworth, "The Influence of Geography and Climate Upon History," *Compass of the World,* Edited by Hans W. Weigert and Vilhjalmur Stefansson, The Macmillan Company, New York, 1945, pp. 175-176.

6 Barnes, C. P., "Environment of Natural Grassland," *Grass: The Yearbook of Agriculture, 1948,* United States Department of Agriculture, 1948, pp. 47-49.

7 *A World Geography of Forest Resources,* Edited by Stephen Haden-Guest, John K. Wright, and Eileen M. Teclaff, The Ronald Press Company, New York, 1956, pp. 41-43, *passim,* 381-382.

8 Jones, Clarence F., *South America,* Henry Holt and Company, New York, 1947, pp. 62-63.

9 Newbigin, Marion I., *Plant and Animal Geography,* E. P. Dutton and Co., Inc., N.Y., 1948, pp. 113-114, 127-128, 286.

10 Stamp, L. Dudley, and Beaver, Stanley H., *The British Isles,* Longmans, Green and Co., Inc., New York, 1954, p. 143.

11 Zon, Raphael, "Forests and Human Progress," *Geographical Review,* Vol. X, 1920, pp. 140-142, 158-159.

12 Newbigin, Marion I., *Animal Geography,* Oxford University Press, 1938, pp. 56, 222-223.

13 Taylor, Griffith, *Australia,* E. P. Dutton and Co., Inc., New York, 1940, pp. 317-319, *passim.*

Chapter 11

Minerals as strategic resources

Minerals are chemical elements or compounds which occur naturally in the earth. Although some minerals may be found in a pure state, they are much more commonly dispersed through heterogeneous masses of rock, called ores. Properly speaking, an ore is any mass of rocky or earthy material which contains an economically usable mineral in quantities sufficient to justify exploitation. Since minerals vary greatly in value, and since some minerals can be much more cheaply separated from their ores than can others, it is not possible to state what percentage of mineral a mass of material must contain before it can be classified as an ore. Gold-bearing material may be classified as an ore when the gold content runs less than one per cent. For such common minerals as iron or aluminum, the percentage would have to be much higher for the materials to be classified as an ore. But even with iron and aluminum, new and cheaper methods of extraction may greatly increase the amount of presently unusable material to be classed as ores.

If the surface of the earth to a depth of ten or fifteen miles were homogeneous in composition, there would be no ores, for nowhere would there be a sufficient concentration of any one mineral to permit its extraction and utilization. Fortunately, however, the surface of the earth is not homogeneous, and minerals are not evenly distributed through the crustal materials. Typically, minerals are found highly concentrated in relatively small areas. Most of the world's nickel, for instance, comes from a very small district around Sudbury, Ontario, and a large part of the world's manganese comes from the Georgian Republic of the Soviet Union.

Concentration of minerals in small areas

Minerals are not fortuitously scattered about in the earth. Their presence in any given place is the result of the operation of geological processes which, while still operative, add only very slowly to the total mineral supply — so slowly that it would be accurate to say that, for all practical purposes, there is no observable increase in the total supply.

The geological processes chiefly responsible for the formation and location of mineral deposits are (1) sedimentation, (2) movements within the crust of the earth (diastrophism), (3) volcanism, (4) metamorphism, and (5) fossilization. A general understanding of how these processes operate helps to explain why certain kinds of minerals are found in certain typical situations and not elsewhere.

Sedimentation in the geological sense means the accumulation of rock waste and organic remains, most of which has been transported from its point of origin by wind, or water, or ice. The most important single agent of erosion and transportation is running water. Since running water loses its power to transport material when its velocity is reduced, deposition typically takes place along the margins of bodies of standing water, such as lakes and oceans, or in basins which have no outlet, such as swamps and marshes. The salt flats adjacent to Great Salt Lake are a classic example of mineral accumulation in a lake basin. In this particular case, the salt deposits have been exposed by the later shrinkage of the lake. In other places, salt deposits thus formed were later covered by other sediments, producing the types of geological structure in which most of the world's supply of salt, potash, and gypsum are now found. In certain places where heavy and insoluble minerals such as gold and platinum are dispersed through the local rocks, the streams which are eroding these rocks build up accumulations of sand or gravel which contain high concentrations of these minerals. Such deposits are called placer deposits. The image they call to mind is that of the perennially optimistic sourdough panning for gold. Some ancient swamp areas supported a particular type of vegetation which, as its remains accumulated under water, formed layers of carbon-rich material. From these, coal was later formed by processes which applied heat and pressure to them. And, of course, minerals of many kinds are found dispersed through sedimentary rocks, usually too finely to permit exploitation, but sometimes in great enough quantity to allow them to be classified as ores. Red hematite and limonite, both iron ores, sometimes occur in large enough masses to be classified as sedimentary rocks.

Diastrophism, or movements of the crustal rocks of the earth, has played a part in mineral formation by subjecting mineral strata to pressures which caused them to harden, as in the case of anthracite coal, or to take on a layered or banded appearance as in the case of some of the metallic minerals. But perhaps the major effect of diastrophism upon the distribution of mineral resources has been that of making otherwise unavailable resources available to man. Many minerals, especially the metallic ones, were apparently concentrated originally at very deep levels in the crust. Later diastrophism in the form of upthrusting or upfolding of the rocks, followed by intensive erosion, has brought these minerals to the surface or to shallow depths below the surface. The Appalachian coals and the great mineral treasures of the Ural Mountains were thus made available to man.

Volcanism has to do with the formation and movement of molten materials in the earth's crust. Such material, when it is contained within the crust, is known as magma. When it seeps or erupts to the surface, it is called lava. In either case, magma or lava may be thought of as a kind of "rock soup" in which a great variety of minerals are boiled together. Since the various minerals in the "soup" harden at different temperatures in the cooling process, many lavas or magmas contain bands or layers of relatively pure minerals. Among the first minerals to crystallize during the cooling process are the iron and magnesia minerals. The last to solidify are those which contain significant quantities of silica, alumina, potash, and soda. Many minerals of volcanic origin remain buried at considerable distances below the surface and can be reached only by deep shafts, if at all. Other volcanic deposits have been lifted to the surface by diastrophism and can be mined by open-pit methods. Still other volcanic deposits, after diastrophism had brought them to the surface, were carried away by erosive agents and re-deposited in alluvial materials or glacial tills.

Metamorphism is the changing of originally igneous or sedimentary rock into metamorphic rock under conditions of high temperature and great pressure. Metamorphism often accompanies diastrophism or volcanism, but it may result simply from the weight of surface rocks upon rocks that are more deepseated. Metamorphic rocks are most commonly found in areas of great crustal deformation such as folded mountains. Among the minerals which are found almost exclusively in association with metamorphic rocks are graphite, garnet, and talc.

Fossilization is the process by which certain ancient forms of organic life have been buried, consolidated, and carbonized. Coal may be considered a sedimentary deposit, later fossilized and hardened by diastrophism and metamorphism. Petroleum is believed to be the product of accumulations of plant and animal remains, chiefly plankton, buried in and under sands and clays that settled to the bottoms of shallow seas. While a reasonable degree of diastrophism and metamorphism apparently improves the quality of coal by driving out the volatile materials in it, it is obvious that any considerable amount of heat would consume either coal or petroleum. For this reason the fossil fuels are not found in regions which have experienced either volcanism or intense diastrophism.

Since mineral occurrence is so intimately related to geological forces and processes, modern-day mineral exploration is a highly technical activity requiring specialized knowledge of regional geological conditions and, often, specialized equipment. The day of the sourdough prospector and the lucky adventurer would appear to be almost a thing of the past in mineral exploration, for the surface of the earth has been so carefully combed for minerals that it is extremely unlikely that any major surface deposits have been overlooked. The search now has gone underground and underwater, adding both to the difficulty and the expense of mineral exploration.

Man has relied heavily on a few mineral deposits

In our mineral-hungry world there are very few known mineral deposits that are not being actively exploited. Indeed, our generation has seen the exhaustion of one famous mineral area after another. But until as recently as half a century ago, some of the largest and most important mineral deposits in the world were either unknown or unused, and the bulk of man's mineral supply came from a few famous and intensively-worked regions such as the coal fields of the Ruhr, the Pennine flanks, and the Appalachians; the iron ore regions of northern Minnesota and Lorraine; the petroleum fields of Texas and Pennsylvania; and the tin mines of Malaya. Why this concentration on certain deposits and avoidance of others?

The answer to this question is partly cultural and partly economic. Underlying both aspects of the answer are certain geographical facts and considerations.

It must be reiterated that a resource has no power to compel its use. Whether a given resource will be used by a given people in a given place and at a given time depends upon the entire cultural setting within which the question is asked. A tribe of nomadic herdsmen obviously has little use for bauxite, and a nation whose people cannot afford automobiles will have little use for gasoline. Even peoples of advanced culture, if they lack such basic resources as iron and the mineral fuels, may find their industrial development so seriously inhibited that they may have little use for such ferroalloys and nonferrous metals as they may have. Even in the great industrial countries, minerals do not achieve the status of resources until some use is found for them.

So dependent is twentieth-century industrial man upon minerals that it is hard for him to realize how little his ancestors of the not-too-remote past depended on minerals, and how few minerals were known to them or used by them. Only since the beginnings of the Industrial Revolution have minerals played their present dominant role in the world economy, and even today some seven countries (the United States, the Soviet Union, the United Kingdom, Germany, Japan, France, and Canada) containing only a quarter of the world's population account for more than 90 per cent of the world's annual mineral consumption. Among the peoples who have been little affected by the Industrial Revolution are not only so-called primitive folk but also such peoples of advanced culture as the Spanish, the Portuguese, the Greeks, the Magyars, and the Latin Americans. Some of these peoples have been handicapped in industrializing by the absence of the basic iron and fuel resources. Others still, it would appear, seem to be almost temperamentally disinclined toward the factory system. If any general principle can be stated regarding the relationship of cultural factors to mineral exploitation, it would be that those nations which, for whatever reason, have not developed the factory system of manufacturing tend either not to use such minerals as they have or to work them for export to the great industrial countries. Examples which come immediately to mind are the tin resources of Bolivia, the petroleum of the Persian Gulf region, the iron ores of northern Spain, the diamonds and gold of South Africa.

The economic answer to the question posed in the first paragraph of this section is, basically, a practical application of certain geographical considerations. Dr. Alan N. Bateman, one of our country's most distinguished economic geologists, lists twelve geographical factors which bear upon the utilization of mineral deposits: location, transportation, topography, water supply, power resources, climate, the availability of timber, labor supply, food supplies, problems of health and sanitation, the availability close at hand of complementary and supplementary resources, and markets for by-products (1). Dr. Bateman notes that "the geographical situation of a mineral deposit is perhaps the most important single item that determines whether it may be utilized." In other words, the question is one of cost. Only in the case of rare or precious minerals is it economically profitable to struggle against hostile terrain or harsh weather, to bring in food and water, and to recruit labor at premium wages to work under conditions of hardship. Renner's dictum that "man is as lazy as he can afford to be" applies also to his exploitation of minerals.

This being the case, man has historically worked the richest and most easily exploitable resources to exhaustion, then moved on to the next easiest, and so forth, each generation scraping off the "cream" and leaving the residue to its posterity. The marks of this "use up and run out" policy are by now familiar to most of us: ghost towns or towns that have "died on their feet," unsightly piles of overburden and rock waste, abandoned diggings, rust-eaten railroad tracks.

The pattern of man's use of mineral resources has been summarized by Renner in two "laws": (1) *The Law of Primacy in Resource Use* which states that "in all primitive economies, and in present-day local economies not yet fully invaded by modern means of transportation, those resources possessing the greatest richness of fertility tend to be exploited first"; and (2) *The Law of Accessibility* which states that "Under an exchange economy, lower-grade resources, if readily accessible to a large market, can be utilized profitably, while richer grades of resources, less accessible, remain unexploited."[1]

The idea of "Have" and "Have-Not" nations

A generation ago, discussions of the distribution of minerals were often organized around the concepts of "Have" and "Have-Not" nations. The "Have" nations—the United States, the U.S.S.R., the then British Empire, and the French Empire—were those which, allegedly, had achieved a kind of monopoly of mineral reserves and production and were, therefore, inclined to be peaceful, i.e., content with the international political status quo. The "Have-Not" nations, on the other hand—Germany, Italy, Japan—were those which lacked the mineral resource base for secure status as first-rank military and economic powers and might, therefore, be expected to disturb the peace in order to improve, by force if necessary, their resource situation.

This idea of "Have" and "Have-Not" nations was, as might be expected, eagerly embraced by German, Japanese, and Italian theoreticians who were anxious to find plausible justification for the expansionist policies of their governments. It appealed strongly also to scholars and students of public affairs in other countries, our own included, for when men of reason are confronted with irrational conduct they tend to devise rational explanations for it. And what could be a more rational reason for war than the justification, under the laws of economic self-survival, of going out to seize the apparent necessities of national health and strength?

To the extent that people believe an idea to be true—whether it actually is or not—they are likely to act in accord with it. In a world where ownership or control of minerals is considered a prerequisite of national power, nations may go to war for control of a larger proportion of the world's mineral resources. But it is extremely unlikely that any major power would venture into a war today for such narrowly economic reasons because:

1. The weapons of modern warfare altogether preclude the possibility of economic profit, even for the victor.

2. It is apparent to anyone who is acquainted with the world geonomic[2] situation that the physical ownership and control of minerals often creates more problems than it solves.

This second point requires some elaboration. No nation possesses, or even comes close to possessing, adequate supplies of all the minerals required by modern industrial technology. The great industrial countries typically possess large and high-grade resources of the "basic" industrial minerals: coal, iron, perhaps petroleum. But these basic minerals are largely useless without other, rarer minerals which may have to be brought in from every corner of the earth. In a sense, therefore, the more industrialized a nation becomes, the more vulnerable it becomes, for its economic health and its military strength are, to a considerable degree, at the mercy of many suppliers, some of them capricious. And the nineteenth-century solution of ensuring supplies by establishing political control over the sources of supply is no longer a live option; colonialism is as dead as feudalism. What this means in practice is that the great, mineral-hungry, industrial nations must take extraordinary pains to stay on the good side of those countries, often small, which can supply them with critically-needed minerals. No major power has denounced the policies of the govern-

[1] Renner, George T., "Some Principles and Laws of Economic Geography," *Journal of Geography*, Vol. XLIX, No. 1, January, 1950, pp. 16-17. Reprinted by permission.

[2] A term coined by the geographer to express an economic-earth relationship of the type commonly considered in the area of Economic Geography.

ment of Saudi Arabia in the United Nations —nor is any major power likely to do so as long as the Arabian oil holds out.

Minerals in peace and war

The mining and movement of minerals in peacetime are governed primarily by considerations of cost and profit, subject to numerous political interferences in the way of subsidies, taxes, currency and trade restrictions, tariffs, embargoes, and the like. Because of their scarcity and their exhaustibility, minerals have never enjoyed complete freedom to move about in the world economy. To a greater or lesser degree, their movement has been directed or inhibited by governments. In spite of this, however, economic laws have been operative in the minerals industry. Thus, primarily for reasons of relative cost, Canada in 1949 imported 18 million tons of bituminous coal from the United States and, in the same year, exported 319,360 tons of bituminous to the United States. This two-way movement of the same commodity across an international border would be a common and unremarkable phenomenon in the world where the trade in minerals was governed by economics rather than political considerations.

Unfortunately, for at least the past three decades the world economy has been, even in times of so-called peace, a war economy, and mineral geonomics has been governed not so much by considerations of price and profit as by considerations of national defense and security. In general, governments have attempted to ensure safe and dependable sources of minerals for themselves and their allies and to deny minerals to possible enemies.

During the Second World War, for example, the Army and Navy Munitions Board drew up a long list of minerals that were deemed essential to national defense. Certain minerals on this list (e.g., nickel, manganese, chromium, tungsten, antimony, mercury, tin, mica, and quartz crystal) were classified as strategic materials, i.e., materials essential to the national defense, for the supply of which, in war, dependence must be placed, in whole or in substantial part, on sources outside the continental limits of the United States, and for which strict conservation and distribution controls would be necessary. During the war, these minerals were, for all practical purposes, unobtainable for any uses other than those directly related to the war effort. Other minerals (e.g., vanadium, platinum, iodine, aluminum, graphite, toluol, and phenol) were classified as critical materials, i.e., materials essential to the national defense, the procurement of which in war would be less difficult than the procurement of the strategic materials either because they are less essential or are obtainable in more adequate quantities from domestic sources; but for which some degree of conservation and distribution control would be necessary (3). In the later stages of the war, these minerals also were, for all practical purposes, treated as strategic. For our purposes, what is significant is not the fact that these minerals were tightly controlled in a war which each year fades into a more remote past but that any new period of imminent national peril would undoubtedly bring a similar cycle of mineral inventory, classification, and control.

The actual outbreak of war would no doubt be accompanied by thrusts at certain strategic mineral areas. Several years ago, Dr. William S. McGovern predicted that if war were to break out between the United States and the Soviet Union, the first overt act of war might be a Soviet drive into the oil-rich Persian Gulf area. Without concurring in any specific prediction along this line, we find ourselves in complete agreement with the principle which underlies Dr. McGovern's prediction: that, in the event war were known to be imminent, the major powers could be expected to take action as drastic as the situation might dictate in order to ensure adequate fuel supplies for their own use and to deny them to the enemy. Indeed, the strategy of the "Cold War" has been influenced on both sides very largely by the need to have adequate supplies of minerals more or less immediately available in case the cold war warmed up. In general, the Soviet way of assuring these supplies has been to bring supplying areas under its military and political control behind the so-called Iron Curtain. The American way has been to attempt to win the good will of the supplying nations through various types of economic and military aid.

Distributional patterns of the important minerals

At some point in his education, the student must master the basic distributional patterns of the more significant mineral deposits. There is little point, however, in memorizing regional or even national production figures because these rapidly become obsolete. Even the production of a particular mine or well may fluctuate significantly from year to year because of fluctuations in demand and price or because of government intervention on the side of greater or smaller production. There may be some value in memorizing producing areas in order of their rank in terms of the amount of mineral available (reserves), but such figures can never be, at best, more than estimates.

Coal. Figure XIV-1 (Chapter 14), showing the location of the world's major bituminous coal deposits, may very well be one of the most significant maps in this book. We might, without undue exaggeration, call it a map of the world's industrial potential, for despite the importance of other sources of power, bituminous coal, in the form of coke, is still the prime metallurgical fuel, and almost every one of the world's most important industrial districts is on or quite near a bituminous coal field.

The map suggests some interesting correlations:

1. With three or four minor exceptions, all of the world's major coal fields are to be found in the Northern Hemisphere between latitudes 30° and 60°. (In 1959, the total coal production of the Southern Hemisphere was less than that of Japan.)

2. Coal is a resource of the lowlands—low plains, low plateaus, low mountains. It is not found on any high plateau or in regions of high and rugged mountains.

3. Coal is a humid-land resource. It is not found in any of the great deserts, and it is a rarity in steppe lands and savannahs. Allowing for a few relatively unimportant exceptions, coal is found in Köppen's *Cf* and *Df* lands.

Within this general pattern, four countries stand out as near-monopolists of the world's most valuable coal reserves. These are, in order of their 1959 production, the United States, the U.S.S.R., the United Kingdom, and West Germany. Most of the production of the United States comes from the Appalachian coal field which extends along the western side of the Appalachian Range from Pennsylvania into central Alabama. In the U.S.S.R., the bulk of the coal is in central Siberia, but for geonomic reasons the greater part of the production has come from the Donets Basin of the Ukraine. British coal fields include those of central Scotland and a series of Midland fields following the flanks of the Pennine Range; the Cardiff district of south Wales is the world's most important exporter of coal. Germany has several small fields and one very important field, the Ruhr Valley.

The English and German coal fields represent individual units in a band of coal deposits extending through northern Europe from the Irish Sea into the Ukraine. France, Belgium, and especially Poland include significantly large areas of this coal within their boundaries. It is interesting, and probably quite significant for an understanding of recent European history, that neither Scandinavia nor Mediterranean Europe has much coal.

One of the striking and distressing facts of economic geography is the virtual absence of high-grade coal in Asia outside the Soviet Union. There is a considerable quantity of coal in northern China and Manchuria, but comparatively little of it appears to be of coking grade. Japan has only a few scattered, low-grade, hard-to-work deposits. There is easily accessible coal of excellent quality in central India, but reserves seem to be very small, even by comparison with so depleted a country as Great Britain. Lacking coal, hungry Asia, which so badly needs to enlarge the base of its economy through industrialization, finds itself frustrated at the very outset.

It has already been noted that the Southern Hemisphere is almost totally lacking in coal. The two major exceptions to this statement are the Newcastle-Sydney area of Australia and the Upper Vaal field of the Union of South Africa. South America has only small coal deposits; the nearest thing to a significant deposit is the small coal field of middle Chile.

This is a view of a coal preparation plant in Pennsylvania. Coal enters the plant over the suspension bridge (center), and is cleaned and prepared for use at the Jones and Laughlin Aliquippa and Pittsburgh Works, traveling by barge down the Monongahela River. The mines from which the coal comes stretch five to ten miles beyond the town. The town itself is a typical mining town—row upon row of standardized houses built on a hillside. The river helped to make this a mining area by eroding the surface and thus making the coal seams more accessible. Today it continues to assist mining by providing a highway for barges and a pass. (Photograph by Russell Lee for Jones and Laughlin Steel Corporation. Courtesy National Coal Association)

Petroleum and natural gas. Petroleum is one of the most versatile of all minerals and, for that reason, one of the most essential in peace and in war. The range of materials which derive from crude oil is indicated in the diagram (Figure XI-1). But by far the chief use of petroleum is as a source of energy. It has been estimated that for the world at large petroleum supplies almost a third of the total energy used. For the United States, the figure is considerably higher, around one-half.

Petroleum is found characteristically in marine sedimentary rocks where crustal disturbances have produced oil "traps." Examples of some of the more common of these traps are shown in the diagram (Figure XI-2). The regions of marine sedimentary rocks within which oil might be found are shown on the map (Figure XI-3). It is important to note that these "resource regions" may or may not actually have oil; they are merely regions where oil might be found. Not until the oil is actually discovered do these "resources" become "reserves."

Actual producing areas are very small by comparison with reserves and resources. At the present time, the bulk of the world's petroleum production comes from three

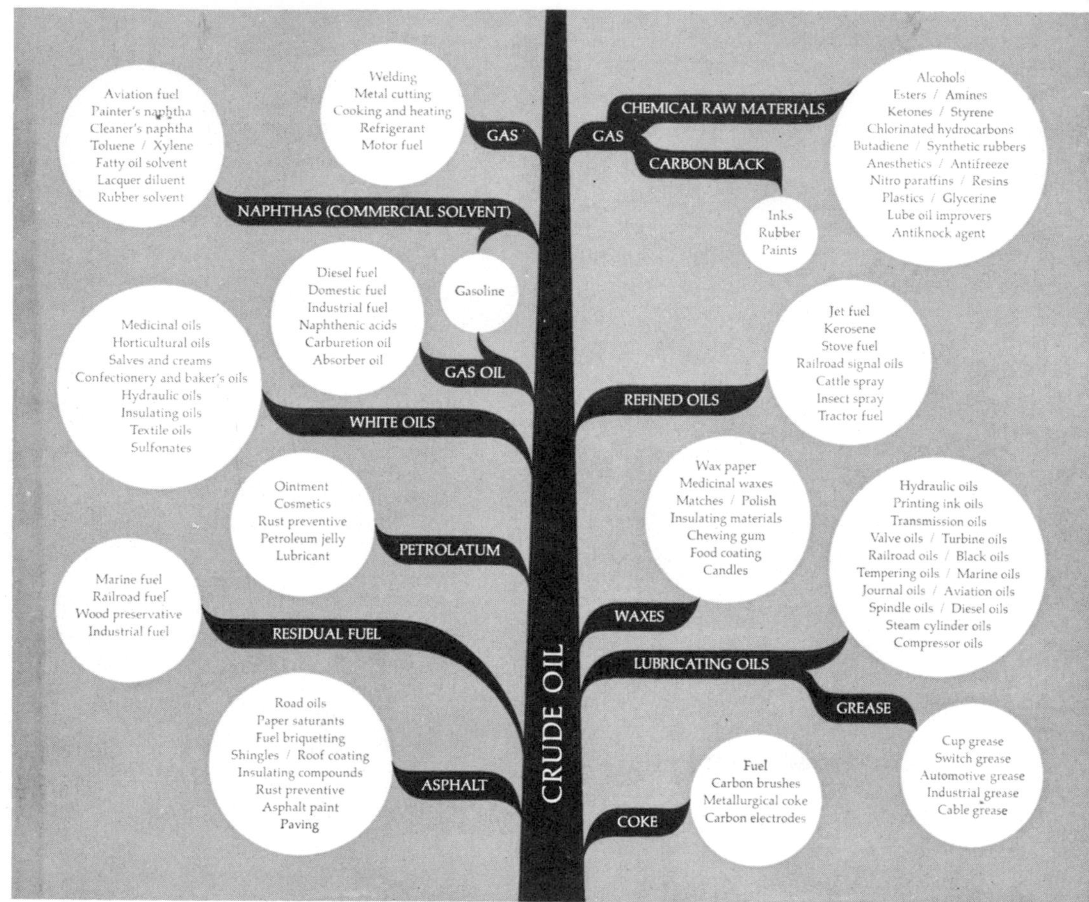

XI:1 This diagram, "The Crude Oil Tree," illustrates the wide range of materials that are derived from crude oil. (From *Oil for the World* by Stewart Schnacke and N. D'Arcy Drake. Copyright 1950, © 1955, 1960 by Standard Oil Company [New Jersey]. Reprinted by permission of Harper & Brothers)

regions: the southwestern United States, northern South America, and the Middle East (including portions of the U.S.S.R.). The major fields in the southwestern United States are in Texas and along the Gulf Coast of Louisiana (including some important tidelands deposits), Oklahoma, and southern California. The center of production in northern South America is Lake Maracaibo in Venezuela where most of the oil is pumped up from beneath the shallow waters of the lake. In the Middle East, there are two centers: the one fringing the Persian Gulf in Iran, Iraq, Saudi Arabia, and some small semi-independent territories; the other in the Soviet Union in an area bounded by the Caspian Sea, the southern Urals, the Volga River, and the Black Sea.

Almost from the very beginnings of the petroleum industry there has been considerable public concern over the possibility of exhaustion of the petroleum supplies. And, indeed, a comparison of any year's production with published reserve figures for that year seemed to give good grounds for concern. But such simple mathematics failed to give sufficient weight to what we now know to be the most significant factor involved in the prediction of resource life: the discovery rate. For petroleum, this rate is, for all practical purposes, impossible to predict. In the past, however, it has consistently exceeded the rate of consumption so that at the end of every year, in spite of the

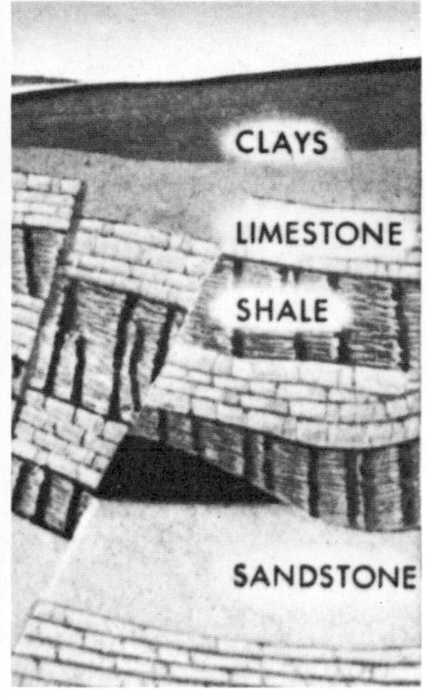

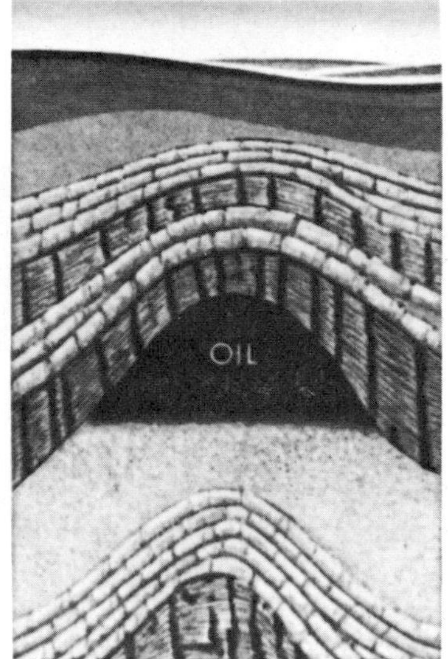

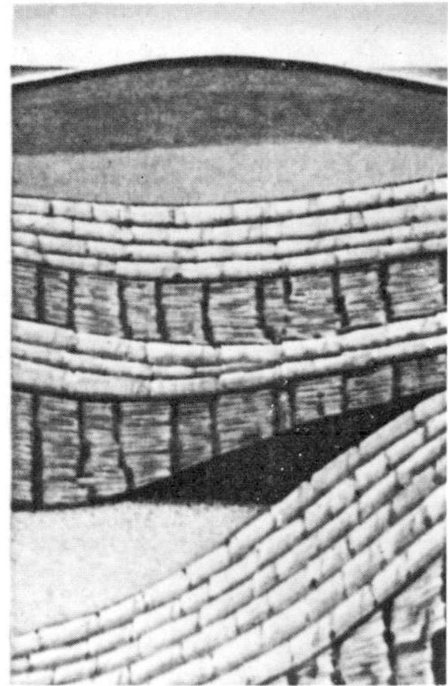

XI:2 This diagram illustrates three kinds of oil traps. In the one at the left a trap has been created by the faulting of sedimentary rock so that the oil, as it seeps through the sandstone, is blocked when it encounters the harder (less porous) limestone and shale. In the center diagram the same result is accomplished by the encounter of the oil with shale folded up into an anticline. In the one to the right, the sandstone stratum "gives out" and the seeping oil is trapped between strata of shale and limestone. (From *Oil for the World* by Stewart Schnacke and N. D'Arcy Drake, Harper & Brothers, New York, 1950, used by permission)

continual and dramatic increase in the consumption of petroleum products, proved reserves of petroleum have stood at record highs. And these reserves do not include the almost untapped riches of petroleum in oil shale. This favorable trend cannot go on forever, obviously, but with huge areas of possibly petroliferous rock still to be explored there is no reason to suppose that the rate of discovery will soon decline significantly.

Natural gas is a by-product of petroleum production. For many years it was wasted or destroyed because of the difficulty of transporting and storing it. More recently, and especially since the Second World War, there has been a great increase in demand for natural gas, especially in home heating, and several notable advances in transportation (by high-pressure, large-diameter pipeline) and in storage.

Iron. Iron is one of the commonest of the earth's minerals but its presence in economically workable concentrations is highly localized. The four most important ores of iron are hematite, limonite, magnetite, and siderite. All of these except magnetite are associated with sedimentary deposits. The most widely used of the ores is hematite, which is widely distributed and easily reduced.

All iron ores contain minerals other than iron. The value of any given ore depends, therefore, at least in part on the nature of the "impurities" which it contains. Arsenic, copper, and especially titanium and phosphorus weaken the iron and, therefore, greatly reduce the value of the ores containing them. In fact, ore containing any amount of phosphorus in excess of one thousandth of one per cent of the metallic iron is not considered usable.

The production of iron ore is not closely related to the size of the ore reserves. India and Brazil are credited with the largest reserves, between them about one-half of the known reserves of the world. But neither country has yet become an important producer. For large-scale production there must be not only a large quantity of ore but also high quality (high iron content, low content of impurities); easy access (e.g., open-pit mining as opposed to shaft and tunnel

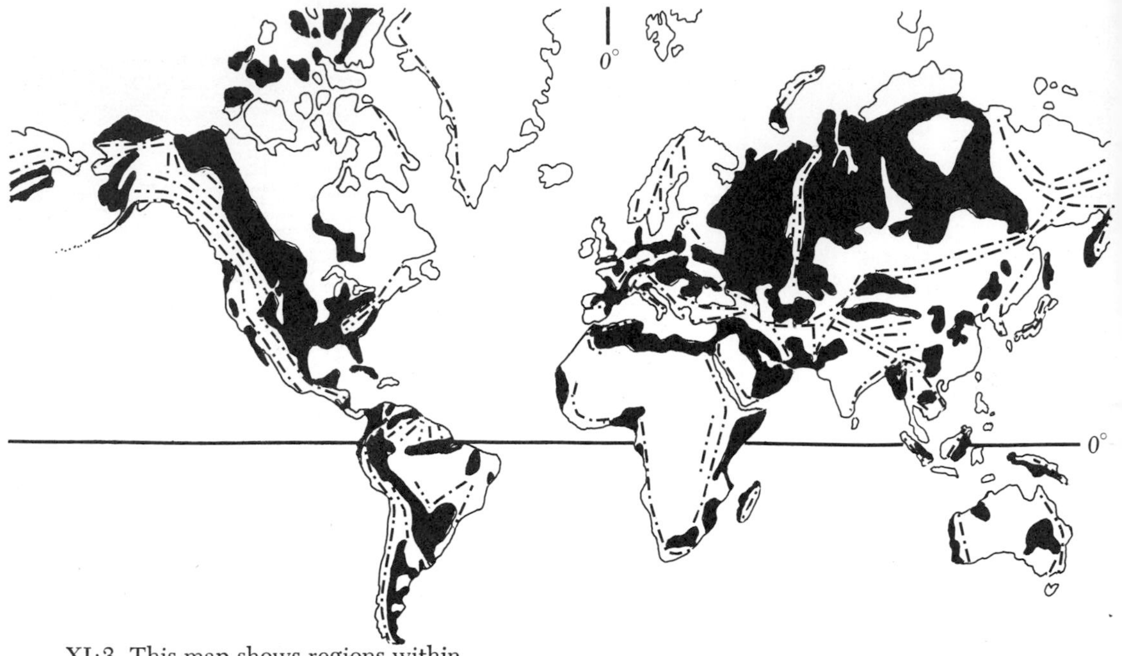

XI:3 This map shows regions within which oil might be found. These are typically regions of marine sedimentary rock (shown here in solid black) forming basins within or alongside mountain ranges (shown here by broken lines). The fact that marine sedimentary rocks underlie an area is not, of course, any assurance that oil will be found there. (Adapted from *Oil for the World* by Stewart Schackne and N. D'Arcy Drake, Harper & Brothers, New York, 1950, used by permission)

mining); propinquity to industrial areas and metallurgical coal; and convenient, low-cost transportation. These conditions are found in such industrial countries as the United States, France, Sweden, and the Soviet Union, and these are, accordingly, the major iron-ore producing countries in spite of the fact that, of these four, only the United States and France have more than five per cent of the world's estimated iron ore reserves.

Certain places and regions have long been famous iron-mining centers. (Figure XIV-1.) In North America, for decades the chief source of ore for the great American iron and steel industry was the Lake Superior district, often referred to as the Mesabi range because of the early prominence of this section of the district. Actually the ore occurred along the margins of Lake Superior from the Marquette district of upper Michigan, through the Gogebic and Menominee districts of northern Wisconsin, the Cuyuna and Mesabi and Vermilion districts of northeastern Minnesota, and into the Steep Rock district on the Ontario side of the Minnesota-Ontario boundary. Despite the heavy demands that have been made upon these ores for decades, this is still the single most important producing region in North America. However, with these ores facing the prospect of exhaustion, new sources have been brought into production. Two of the most important of these are the Wabana district of southeastern Newfoundland and the Burnt Creek district along the Quebec-Labrador boundary. All of these districts are associated with the great mass of much-eroded crystalline rock known as the Laurentian Shield. Outside the Laurentian area the only major producing area on the North American mainland is the Red Mountain district near Birmingham, Alabama. Here the ore is close to coal and limestone, almost necessitating the establishment of an iron and steel industry. Other significant North American deposits are in the Mayari district of eastern Cuba and in the Durango district of Northern Mexico.

Europe west of the Iron Curtain is literally dotted with iron mines and districts, three of which have long been of special significance. These are the Pennine flanks of England, including the rich Cleveland district of Yorkshire; the Lorraine district of northeastern France, long a bone of contention between Germany and France; and the Kiruna district of northern Sweden. In the U.S.S.R., there is the old, rich, and important district of Krivoi Rog in the Ukraine, just north of the Black Sea, well located with respect to coal and transportation facilities; and the smaller but strategically located ores of the southern Urals.

In Asia, the largest known reserves and the most important producing area is in India, southwest of Calcutta, at Singhbhum in the state of Orissa. These ores have been a major factor in the industrialization of India, particularly since the attainment of independence. Outside India, there are numerous relatively small mines in China and Malaya and some rather large, good-quality reserves in the Philippines.

In the Southern Hemisphere, only South America has any great wealth of iron ore. There are a couple of small mining districts in Australia, but the reserves are not believed to be large. In the Union of South Africa, there are major reserves at Rustenburg and some momentarily important producing mines in Algeria, but otherwise the continent is believed to be quite poor in iron. South America, on the other hand, has at least four prime producing areas, each with very large reserves. These are the Cerro Bolívar district in the Orinoco River valley of Venezuela; the Tofo district of central Chile; the great new Itabira district, one of the richest yet discovered, in the Brazilian state of Minas Geraes, and the Marcona deposits of the Peruvian coastal desert.

The ferroalloys. Properly speaking, ferroalloys are alloys of iron and some other metal or metals. In common usage, however, the term is often applied to the associated metal itself. The most important of the metals thus employed are boron, chromium, cobalt, manganese, molybdenum, nickel, tungsten, and vanadium. Their uses, and the principal producing districts, are summarized in Table 11.1. Major producing districts are also shown on the map, Figure XI-4.

What should chiefly impress the student as he studies the ferroalloy situation is that, while the United States still has large supplies of iron and the mineral fuels, it is seriously deficient or altogether lacking in many of the ferroalloys. For these, we must depend upon foreign sources. Without access to these foreign supplies, it would literally be impossible for the United States to produce steel, despite our abundance of coal and iron and limestone. One of the concerns of those who direct our foreign relations is, therefore, to guarantee the security of our sources of the ferroalloys.

Like everything else in nature, the ferroalloys show an intelligible geographic distribution pattern. Chromium, cobalt, and nickel are characteristically associated with the ferromagnesian (mafic), dark-colored igneous rocks or with metamorphics derived from such rocks. Molybdenum, which is also found in association with igneous rocks, is almost invariably associated with quartz. Manganese and tungsten are commonly found in sediments derived from such rocks. Manganese is, in addition, almost always confined to a zone lying above the water table, or generally less than 150 feet below the surface. Moreover, since manganese is so typically a surface deposit, it is not likely to be found in glaciated areas where the original surface materials have been removed. Vanadium, while it is often found in igneous rock, may also be found in sedimentary iron ores, in phosphate deposits, and in petroleum. The soot from the oils of Lake Maracaibo runs between 35 and 40 per cent vanadium oxide. Finally, boron, especially in its familiar form as borax, is associated with salt lakes and regions of interior drainage such as Death Valley and the Caspian depression of the Soviet Union.

In recent years, it has become necessary to add to the list of ferroalloys three metals whose function is that of a carbide stabilizing element in some of the stainless and heat-resisting grades of steel. These metals are titanium, columbium, and cerium. Titanium is produced in New York, Florida, North Carolina, and Virginia, the United States being the world's largest producer followed by India, Norway, Australia, Malaya, and Brazil. The principal sources of columbium are Nigeria, the Congo, and Belgium-Luxemburg. Cerium, in the form of monazite sand, is found chiefly in Brazil but there

50°E
0°
Chromium
Cobalt
Manganese
Molybdenum
Nickel
Tungsten
Vanadium

Table 11.1 Summary of significant information about the ferroalloys

Metal	*Principal Sources*	*Special Properties Which It Imparts to Steel*	*Typical Uses of the Alloy Steel*
Boron	The United States (southern California); the U.S.S.R. (Caspian Sea area)	great hardness; minute quantities permit reduction by one-half or more of amounts of scarcer alloys such as nickel, chromium, molybdenum, manganese, and vanadium in "hard" steels	stainless and heat-resisting steels
Chromium	Black Sea and Aegean Sea area (Turkey, Greece, Yugoslavia); the Urals; Southern Rhodesia (Selukwe); the Union of South Africa; central and southern India; New Caledonia	hardness and strength; more than ten per cent prevents rust	armor-plate; projectiles; guns; safes; ball-bearings; ornamentation on automobiles
Cobalt	Congo (Katanga Region) and adjacent portion of Northern Rhodesia; Morocco; Canada (Cobalt-Gowganda District of Ontario); Burma	ability to hold cutting edge at high temperatures	high-speed cutting tools; permanent magnet steel
Manganese	The U.S.S.R. (Georgian and Ukrainian Republics); central India; Union of South Africa (Postmasburg); Ghana; Brazil (Ouro, Preto, and Amapá)	toughness and resistance to abrasion; serves also as a deoxidizer and desulphurizer; some manganese needed in all steel	mining machinery; safes; rails for curves; frogs; switches; dredge-bucket teeth; road-working machinery
Molybdenum	The United States (Climax, Colorado); Mexico (northern Sonora); southern Norway	strength; toughness; resistance to repeated shock	tools; automobile parts; tubing for airplane fuselage
Nickel	Canada (Sudbury, Ontario); New Caledonia; the U.S.S.R. (central Urals); Norway; Greece	toughness; stiffness; strength; ductility	tools; machinery parts; stainless steels; heat and acid-resisting steels
Tungsten	South China; Burma and the Malay Peninsula; the United States (Bishop, California); Bolivia; Portugal	hardness at high temperatures; high-speed steel	high-speed cutting tools; magnets
Vanadium	Peru (Minas Ragra); the United States (western Colorado); Mexico (Chihuahua); Northern Rhodesia; South-west Africa	strength; toughness; resistance to repeated shock	tools; automobile parts and gears; springs

SOURCE: *Steel Facts*, February, 1947, page 4. Information on boron from Zimmerman, R. E., *Materials for the Production of Steel* (United States Steel Corporation, 1951), pp. 27-28. This table includes, of course, only the most important ferroalloys.

XI:4 (Left) This map shows the major world sources of the ferroalloys. Note especially the close correlation between the producing districts shown on this map and the location of such major mountain ranges as the Rockies, the Andes, and the Urals.

is a small production in Idaho and Florida.

The nonferrous metals. Copper, lead, zinc, tin, aluminum, and antimony are the principal nonferrous industrial metals. The distribution of the principal centers of production of these metals is shown in Figure XI-5.

As long ago as 1945 it was pointed out

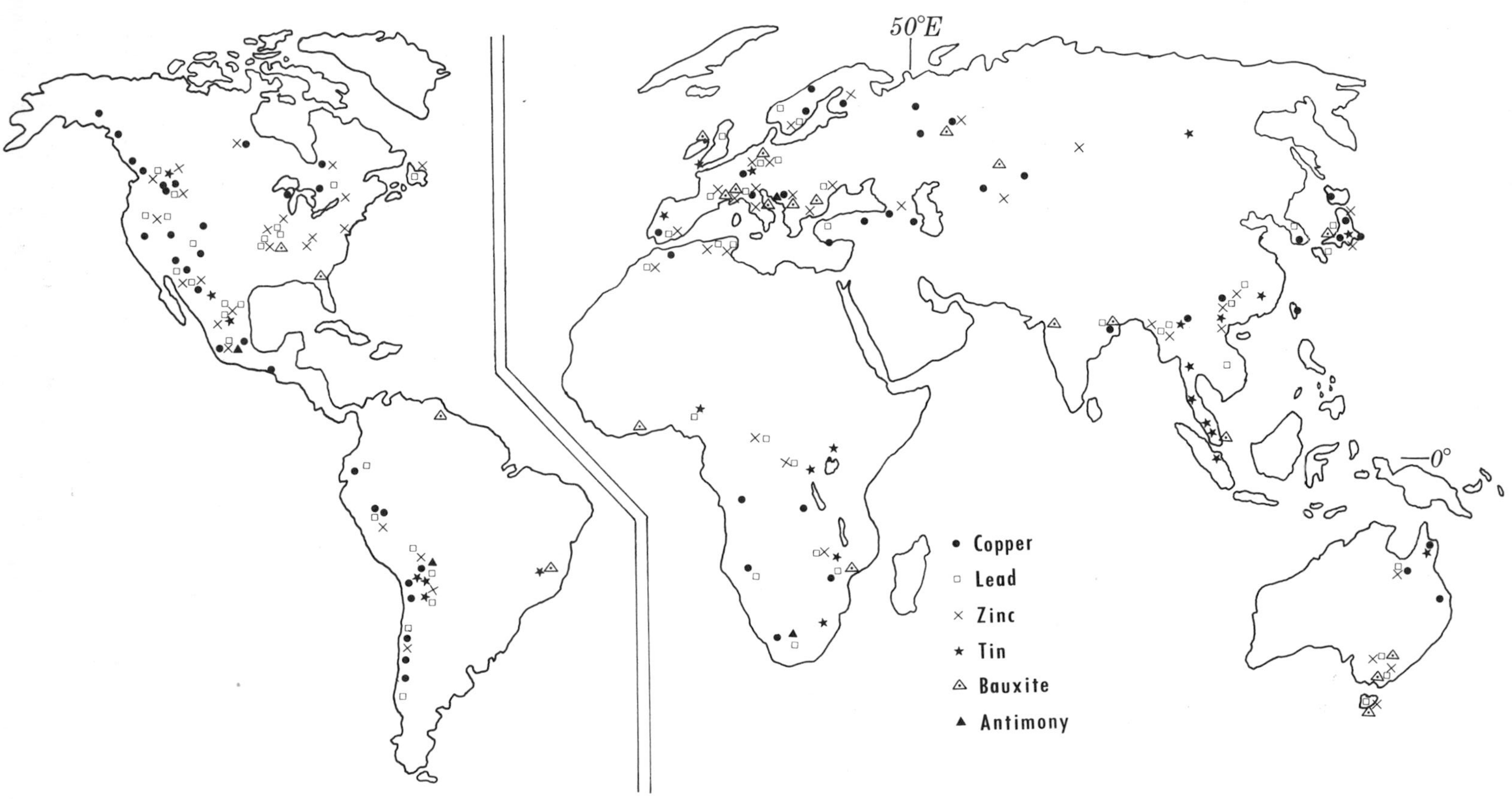
50°E
0°
Copper
Lead
Zinc
Tin
Bauxite
Antimony

that the United States had to prepare itself for serious shortages of these metals. In terms of our consumption over the period 1935-1939, it was estimated that our commercial reserves of the nonferrous metals were of the following order: copper, 34 years; zinc, 19 years; lead, 12 years; bauxite (aluminum), 9 years; antimony, 4 years; and tin, one year (4). The accuracy of this prediction has been demonstrated by experience since it was made. We have managed to postpone the day of exhaustion by increasing imports, by finding substitutes for some of these metals for certain uses, and by relying more heavily upon scrap. But the approaching depletion of domestic supplies has led us to scour the earth, and particularly the Western Hemisphere, for supplementary supplies. Fortunately, we have been able to find large and dependable supplies of most of these metals among our sister nations of the Americas.

Especially in our country, regions which have staked their economic health on the mining of nonferrous metals have had occasion to regret it. The demand for these metals fluctuates notably from year to year, being especially high in times of crisis and very limited in "normal" times. The amount of scrap available also plays a major role in determining demand, as does the amount of by-product production from other types of mining. The tendency, therefore, is for many marginal mines to produce in times of high demand and to close up when the demand drops.

Precious metals and diamonds. There is an aura of romance which still attaches to the precious metals and diamonds but which, unfortunately, is belied by their present importance in the world economy. Of the three best-known precious metals—gold, silver, and platinum—only silver allows any large-scale industrial application; it is used in the manufacture of plated and sterling silver, certain types of photographic equipment, chemicals, and money. Gold still has some importance as a means of international exchange and in the manufacture of jewelry, but the great bulk of the world's gold today is held by governments, much of it in depositories such as our government's Fort Knox. Platinum, too rare and too expensive to be used as a means of exchange, is also of only limited usefulness for jewelry because of its cost. It does, however, have a number of important industrial uses and is included on the list of critical metals.

Most of the world's silver (about 40 per cent) comes from Mexico, followed by the United States (Idaho, Utah, and Montana), Peru, Canada, and Australia. More than half of the world's gold today comes from the Witwatersrand at Johannesburg in the Union of South Africa; it has been said that gold nowadays is mined in the U. of S.A. to be reburied in the U.S.A. Other important producing regions are the Laurentian Highlands of Canada and the basin of the Lena River in the Soviet Union. Platinum comes from these same three countries, plus Colombia.

The decline in the significance of the precious metals can be ascribed to the Western world's shift, over a period of the past three or four centuries, from an economy of hoarded wealth to an economy of productive wealth. There is not much that one can do with gold except wear it or look at it or exchange it for something of equal value. Iron and petroleum, aluminum, and even lowly zinc can be used to make things which have greater value than they possess in themselves. The Spanish found, in gratifying measure, what they had come to the New World to seek: gold and silver; their descendants in our day, at home and in the Americas, are either fantastically rich in hoarded wealth or bitterly poor. The English, as hungry for gold as the Spanish, came late upon the scene and were forced to be content with the chill lands of North America where there was little but coal and iron and petroleum and vast areas of agricultural land; they and their descendants for generations have become wealthier with each new use of these unglamorous resources.

The production of diamonds in the world is controlled, to the extent of 95 per cent, by the Diamond Trading Corporation of London. The principal producing area today is the Kasai Province of the Congo, which

XI:5 (Left) This map shows the major world sources of the nonferrous metals. Here also a close correlation is obvious between these producing districts and mountain systems.

Table 11.2 Summary of significant information about the nonferrous metals

Metal	*Principal Sources*	*Uses*
Copper	The United States (Butte, Montana; Bingham, Utah; several localities in Arizona and Nevada); the Katanga district of the Congo and Northern Rhodesia; Chile (Chuquicamata); Canada (Sudbury, Ontario; northwest Quebec; British Columbia).	Over half the copper used in the United States is used to conduct electricity. Other uses: utensils, roofing, ornaments, munitions, manufacture of brass and bronze.
Lead and Zinc	The United States (the Ozark Plateau and Coeur d'Alene, Idaho; zinc only in Sussex County, New Jersey); Australia (Broken Hill); Canada (Kimberly, B.C.); Germany (Harz Mountains and the Rhineland); Mexico (Taxco, San Luis Potosi, Chihuahua).	Lead: storage batteries, cable coverings, pigments, ammunition, solder. Zinc: galvanizing material, brass, castings, photo-engraving sheets, pharmaceuticals, battery cans, pigments, glass jar tops.
Tin	Southeast Asia (Malaya, Indonesia, Siam, Burma); Bolivia; Nigeria; China (Yunnan Province).	Tin plate, solder, bearing (Babbitt) metal, bronze, tin foil, chemicals.
Aluminum (bauxite)	Surinam; British Guiana; Jamaica; the United States (central Arkansas); France (the Rhone Valley); Hungary (southwest of Budapest).	Transportation equipment, especially aircraft; electrical equipment, especially cable; building materials; cooking utensils; chemicals; aluminum foil.
Antimony	Bolivia; Mexico (especially the states of San Luis Potosi, Oaxaca, and Sonora); southwest China (especially the province of Hunan).	"Hard lead"; bearing metal; type metal; pewter; pigments; lead pipe; lead foil.

only recently took over the lead from the famous "pipe" deposits of Kimberley in the Union of South Africa. Brazil, the earliest major supplier of diamonds, is still important, and there is increasing production from Angola, Ghana, and Sierra Leone. Although the highest prices are paid for those diamonds which can be profitably cut as gemstones, the great majority of diamonds which enter the world market do so as industrial diamonds. Being the hardest known natural substance, the diamond is very useful in industrial operations requiring the cutting of hard materials.

The radioactive minerals. It is, for all practical purposes, impossible to get any reliable information on the production of the ores of uranium or radium, the two most important radioactive materials. Their critical importance in the manufacture of the weapons of war makes even the location of producing mines a matter of military secrecy in those countries which are able to enforce a close censorship. We do know, however, that among the most important producing areas are the Shinkolobwe mine in the Congo; the Great Bear Lake and the Lake Athabaska districts of Canada; the Erz Mountains between East Germany and Czechoslovakia; the Colorado Plateau in Utah, Colorado, New Mexico, and Arizona; and several places within a radius of about 250 miles from Tashkent in Soviet central Asia.

The mineral fertilizers. Successful farming over any extended period of time requires that minerals taken out of the soil by growing plants be replaced. In the Far East, this replacement is accomplished primarily by returning every recoverable bit of organic waste to the soil. In Europe and the Americas the replacement usually takes the form of mineral fertilizers, the most important of which are those containing nitrogen, phosphorus, and potassium. In recent years calcium, magnesium, and sulfur have also been found wanting in soils and have been added to the list of elements to be replaced.

Three of these elements—nitrogen, magnesium, and calcium—are, fortunately, so abundant as to be, for all practical purposes, inexhaustible. Nitrogen, formerly recovered almost entirely from the caliche deposits of the Atacama Desert in Chile, is now extracted from the air under one or more of three processes, the best-known of which is

Chuquicamata, Chile, is the site of the world's largest single deposit of copper ore. Narrow-gauge rail lines encircle the excavation on each of the terrace levels. The depth of the excavation can be judged by comparing it with the height of the ore cars (almost invisible) on the far slope. At such a depth as this, why has this mine not filled up with groundwater? (Courtesy The Anaconda Company)

the Haber-Bosch process, which was developed by German scientists just before the outbreak of the First World War. Every nation today can, then, be said to have adequate "raw material" sources for nitrogen. Actual production is greatest in nations such as the United States and Germany, which are simultaneously major industrial and agricultural nations. Magnesium is one of the elements recovered from ocean water. The recovery process was invented by German scientists, but the most important producers today are the United States, the U.S.S.R., and the United Kingdom. The chief center of production in the United States is the Gulf Coast of Texas. Calcium, or lime, is abundant in every part of the world which is mantled by limestones or dolomites. Because of its low value per unit of weight and consequent inability to absorb high transportation costs, lime tends to be produced within its market areas, and these are principally the pedalfer soil areas of the humid middle latitudes.

The most important source of phosphorus is phosphate rock, of which the United States is believed to have about 40 per cent of the world's high-grade supply, chiefly in the Rocky Mountain states with secondary reserves in Tennessee and Florida. Interestingly, these secondary supplies furnish most of the phosphate used in our country. This is because of their nearness to the major agricultural regions of our country, especially the one-crop Cotton Belt and the intensively-cultivated Corn Belt. Major producers outside the United States are Morocco and Tunisia in northern Africa, and the U.S.S.R. The phosphates of the U.S.S.R. are chiefly in the Moscow region and the Kazakh Republic, and are believed to be at least as large as those of the United States.

Potassium salts (potash) are very highly soluble, and need therefore to be constantly replaced in lands of humid climate. Fortunately, the most important potash resources are found in those very parts of the world that need them most. In Europe the oldest and still most important producing areas are in West and East Germany (38 per cent of world production in 1958). There are important producing districts in eastern France, the U.S.S.R., and northeastern Spain. The United States stands second in production of potash (25 per cent of the world total in 1958). The center of American production is in Carlsbad, New Mexico. The reserves are limited however, and it has been suggested that they be set aside for emergency use in time of war, and that for normal peacetime uses we should again rely upon imports from West Germany and France, as we did prior to the early 1930's.

No such suggestion has been made, or need be made, with regard to sulfur. The United States accounts for more than 78 per cent (1958) of the world's total production of native sulfur. Our resources occur in the form of cap rocks overlying salt domes along the Gulf Coast in Louisiana and Texas. Mining is easy and inexpensive, involving the use of hot water forced through a perforated pipe into the sulfur which, upon melting, is brought by air-lift to the surface, where it is pumped into bins to cool and dry. After it has solidified, it is blasted for loading into railway cars. Another source of sulfur is pyrites or iron sulfides, the most important producers of which are Mediterranean Europe (Spain and Portugal, Italy, and Cyprus) and Japan. The United States has abundant resources of pyrites and despite competition from native sulfur, produced about 7 per cent of the world's sulfur derived from pyrites.

The life and death of a mining town

The announcement of an important mineral find anywhere in the world acts as a lure to draw the high-spirited, the adventurous, and the rambunctious to the area.[1] It is mostly men who come; those who have families expect either to return to them after they have made their fortune, or to send for them after settling permanently. The majority of the men are young, and of course, a few women also appear on the scene whose roles are more properly the concern of the sociologist than the geographer.

There are two characteristics these first settlers have in common: they all expect, one way or another, to strike it rich; and they all expect to stay for only a short time. Boom towns are, therefore, jerry-built, usually of unpainted wood. The streets are unpaved dirt tracks. There are few municipal services and no amenities. Often there are only the rudiments of law and order.

Nevertheless, in its heyday, the boom town may be something of a cultural center. In the days when fortunes were being made and lost in Virginia City, Nevada, for instance, the great Melba sang there, Paderewski played, and Mark Twain was a reporter for the local newspaper. But the glitter and the excitement are ephemeral, as ephemeral as the gold or silver or whatever it is that occasioned the rush. And unless the town finds new interests, new activities to sustain it, it is doomed.

In our own western states, there are a number of such ghost towns. In the iron range country of northern Minnesota, much more solidly established communities have for two or three decades anticipated the exhaustion of the iron ores and have attempted to find alternative bases for their economies. Whether they will succeed or not, we shall not know until the ores are further along

[1] This section does not, of course, characterize such large modern mining developments as the Marcona iron mines of Peru, the Chuquicamata copper mines of Chile, or the Amapá manganese mines of Brazil. In these and other modern mining areas companies typically provide modern housing for the families of managers, technicians, and even laborers, many of whom are married and have children.

toward exhaustion. It is possible for mining communities to survive the exhaustion of the resources around which they were built; the fair-sized industrial towns of the old Gas Belt in north central Indiana are examples of towns which have done so. Ultimately, the hope of the mining community lies in finding some other set of geographical advantages which it can exploit, but to do so it needs a cadre of "solid citizens" who trust to forethought and labor more than to luck for their livelihood.

APPLICATION OF GEOGRAPHIC UNDERSTANDING

I. So many minerals are found in mountainous areas. Can you suggest any reasons why this should be so?

II. At the same time, many reasonably large deposits of the commoner minerals lie largely untouched in mountain and plateau country. Why should this be so?

III. Which comes first—the "chicken" of industrialization or the "egg" of mineral exploitation?

IV. Does this chapter suggest any reasons why, after several decades of delay, the United States finally agreed to join Canada in the development of the St. Lawrence Seaway?

V. Would you classify the United States as a "Have" or "Have-Not" nation? Why? What arguments might be adduced in defense of the opposite point of view?

VI. What has been the historical significance of the fact that most of the iron of western Europe lies west of the Rhine while most of the coal lies east of the Rhine? What steps have been taken since the end of the Second World War to minimize the effects of these geographical phenomena?

VII. In several places in this chapter reference is made to the considerable mineral wealth of the Congo. Why, if the Congo is so wealthy, has it not developed manufacturing industries based on these minerals?

VIII. Is future technological development likely to make the United States more free or less free of dependence on minerals brought in from other countries? Give reasons for your answer.

IX. What are the arguments for and against nationalizing the mineral wealth of the United States? For a system of private ownership under rigid public controls? For a system of private ownership with no significant public controls?

X. If you were living in a community which depended primarily upon the iron mining industry, what suggestions would you have for your fellow-citizens in the way of keeping the town alive and economically healthy after the ore gave out?

References

1 Bateman, Alan N., "Geographic Factors in the Utilization of Mineral Deposits," *Proceedings of the United Nations Scientific Conference on the Conservation and Utilization of Resources,* United Nations, Department of Economic Affairs, 1951.

2 Renner, George T., "Some Principles and Laws of Economic Geography," *The Journal of Geography,* Vol. XLIX, No. 1, January, 1950, pp. 16-17.

3 *The Strategic and Critical Materials,* The Army and Navy Munitions Board, Washington, March, 1940, p. 3.

4 Pearson, Elmer W., "The Mineral Position of the United States and the Outlook for the Future," *Mining and Metallurgy,* April, 1945, p. 4.

The geographic aspects of technology and ethics in societal and national life

In Part II the geographic focus was on natural resources of man's habitat. In Part III the organizational theme shifts to the human enterprises which regionally emerge as man tries to effect, in terms of the existing stage of culture and technology, a harmonious adjustment of his own resources to those provided by nature. The interplay of provident nature and creative man thus forms the drama of life in which both the techniques and the ethics of our enterprises become matters of daily concern. Basically what we as geographers like to know is by what types of geographic processes in any given region man can use to the best advantage, for himself and for his fellowman, the resources available to him and developable by him. Complex as are such man–land and man–man interrelationships, insights into the principles operative in the geographic process and the resolution of life's issues are clarified when the broad area of geography is broken down into more manageable units as is shown in the figure at lower right.

Thus, treatment of the extractive industries (e.g., hunting and fishing, lumbering, mining) explores the treasures of nature. In this area of Economic Geography we want to know in what regions and countries these resources are concentrated, and how they are being exploited.

In Agricultural Geography, we are interested in such regional forces as determine the extensiveness or intensiveness with which land is being used for the production of food and fiber staples.

Manufactural Geography assays the bases for the localization of industry. Why are some regions and countries almost entirely without manufacturing enterprises?

In Commercial Geography we seek to discover the basic principles that promote intercity, interregional, and international trade, considered by geographers a leading beneficent force in the social, economic, and political life of nations.

As another significant contribution to man's physical welfare, Medical Geography (Epidemiology) examines the distribution of diseases and conditions of health throughout the world. Areal associations of such factors as climate, terrain, hydrography, as well as areal social factors, are studied in their regional patterns as correlated with states of sanitation and health. Of particular relevance here is the geographic distribution of infectious diseases and epidemics strongly environment-conditioned, as in the tropics.

And finally, in the chapters on Geography of Resource Use and the Geography of Religions the ethic of man is treated in terms of his earth stewardship commitments.

Chapter 12

An introduction to economic geography

Of all the branches of human geography, the one which has undoubtedly received the greatest amount of attention in the United States is economic geography. So many are the facets of this field, and so voluminous is its literature, that it is difficult to develop a sufficiently inclusive definition. Perhaps the best approach is to say that the economic geographer is interested (1) in the relationships between *how* men make their livings and *where* they make them; and (2) in the patterns of structure and movement that result from man's economic exploitation of the earth.

The underlying assumption of the economic geographer is that man, being a reasonable creature, tends, at least in the long run, to capitalize on the opportunities and to avoid or minimize the handicaps which he finds in his environment. As a result, both the patterns of man's economic activities and the landscape patterns that these activities produce differ strikingly from place to place. Differentiated landscapes arising out of differences of economic use permit the drawing of boundaries around geonomic regions or districts or belts. Thus economic geography is both systematic and regional in nature.

Some economic geographers believe that enough evidence has been accumulated over a long enough period of time in their field to permit the statement of certain geonomic principles and laws. It is to be understood, of course, that these principles and laws are not presumed to have the degree of universal validity that the physical or biological scientist might properly claim for the most basic laws of his discipline. Man is, after all, capable of irrational, whimsical, and even suicidal behavior, so that what man would normally or generally do in a particular situation is not necessarily what he will be found doing in such a situation. He may, indeed, be doing the very opposite.

It is the purpose of this chapter to bring together some of the more significant geonomic laws and principles as a prelude to a closer examination of the major classes of man's economic activities. We hope to conclude with a very general understanding of why people make their livings differently in various parts of the world.

Limitations of environment

One of the most obvious and, at the same time, most significant laws of economic geography is the *Law of Limits.* As formulated by Huntington, this law states that "physical environment sets limits to the area within which any living creature can survive, or can successfully carry on its various activities such as growth or reproduction. An environmental condition sets limits if it is either too intense or too weak"[1]. One may object that there is nothing very profound about this law; that it is, as a matter of fact, a laboring of the obvious. It is only fair to point out that the same might be said for almost everything that the geographer or any other scholar has to say. Certainly it is true of everything that this chapter deals with. But it must also be said that a very large number of man's troubles have derived from his persistent inability or unwillingness to see those geographical facts of life which, in Li'l Abner's words, "any fool kin plainly see," but which it is the continuing task of high scholarship to identify and formulate.

Let us look at some of the implications of the Law of Limits. The more specialized a life form is, the more restricted is the range permitted to it by the physical environment. For most cultivated plants it is possible to draw up quite precise statements of limits — climatic, topographic, and edaphic. For such highly specialized animals as coral, the limits of survival and reproduction are equally easy to define with a high degree of precision. But the less specialized a life form is, the less easily definable are its limits. By the time one reaches the least specialized of all life forms — man — there seem to be unlimited

[1] Reprinted with permission from Ellsworth Huntington, *Principles of Economic Geography,* 1940, John Wiley & Sons, Inc., New York, p. 18.

possibilities as to where he can live, survive, and reproduce.

And yet, any map of world population distribution will show that man lives in very unevenly distributed areas across the face of the earth. And those areas where he is most rarely found are, in almost every case, areas where the physical environment is, by his definition of the term, hostile. The best examples are deserts, icecaps, very high and rugged mountains, and regions where the soil has been removed by erosion. This fact is of significance to the economic geographer in two ways. First, to a greater extent than we may wish to admit, what man does in any given place is a matter of his choice among alternatives proposed to him by the environment. These alternatives, in turn, reflect the operation of the Law of Limits. Second, resources in and of themselves do not create economic activity. For all we know, there may be vast quantities of coal under the Antarctic ice. So long as climate and the presence of the ice limit man's ability to live and survive in Antarctica, the coal might just as well not be there.

The Law of Limits sets physical boundaries to man's activities. The next law we shall discuss puts man into the picture and explains his role in the choice-making process. This is the *Principle of Geonomic Relationship*, which states that:

¶ Every industry represents the capitalization by man of some element or combination of elements in the natural environment. The choice of industry and the success with which it is prosecuted depend upon the quality of the local resources balanced against the level and effectiveness of the available technology.[1]

For our present purposes, the operative words in this statement are "the capitalization by man" and "the level and effectiveness of the available technology." These two expressions point toward the same all-important consideration; the decisive role that human skill and intelligence play in the determination of geonomic patterns. Someone has said that "Europe is what the Europeans have made it" and it could be said with equal accuracy that China is what the Chinese have made it or the Congo what the Congolese have made it. That still leaves unanswered the question of how the European or the Chinese or the Congolese developed as he did, and the attempt to answer the question has, in the past, presented even the most objective scholars with the very attractive temptation to explain the economic accomplishments of their own people as products of some innate, natural superiority — German *Kultur* or English craftsmanship or French skill or American "know-how." Perhaps just to avoid such implications of jingoism, geographers have tended to steer clear of the apparent "built-in" aptitudes of certain peoples and the apparent mental sluggishness of others. Certain programs of our government, however — most notably the Point 4 program — have taken cognizance of the practical fact that in certain countries economic development has been inhibited by the generally low level and effectiveness of the available technology. We have attempted to buttress it with technical assistance.

The choice of industry in any given place depends not only upon the physical limits and the available technology, but also upon the size of the population. As Renner puts it:

¶ As population increases, any human society tends to shift its geonomic dependence from one set of environmental elements toward a more productive set of elements. Conversely, where population decreases, human society tends to shift its geonomic dependence to a less productive set of elements.[2]

Renner calls this statement the *Principle of Geonomic Succession.*

This principle can be observed in operation, either historically or as a contemporary phenomenon, in any part of the world where there have been significant increases or decreases in human population. Thus, in several islands of the Caribbean area where sugar plantations were one of the earliest uses of the land, steadily mounting population eventually forced the commercial sugar economy out of the picture and replaced it by an intensive subsistence economy. In Ireland, on the other hand, and in some of the

[1] Renner, George T., "Some Principles and Laws of Economic Geography," *The Journal of Geography*, Vol. XLIX, No. 1, January, 1950, p. 16. Reprinted by permission.

[2] *Ibid.*, p. 20. Reprinted by permission.

This scene shows the modern way of rubber gathering. The rubber plantations shown here are typical of an industry which, not too long ago, involved scouting through the tropical rainforest for isolated trees. The tree is the *hevea brasiliensis*—as its name implies a native of the Amazonian forests of Brazil. This plantation is a new one in the Madre de Dios section of Peru. (United States Department of Agriculture, Office of Foreign Agricultural Relations)

hill districts of our own Southeast, emigration has resulted in the return of agricultural land to economically less productive uses such as grazing land and forests.

There would appear to be some relationship between size of population and the level of technological progress. This relationship itself seems to substantiate certain implications of the Law of Limits. That is to say, as human populations increase up to a certain point, the greater demand for goods and services seems to furnish an incentive to invent new commodities and new ways of doing things. But beyond this point the "dead weight" of population pressure seems to put a premium upon security at the expense of the risk that goes along with inventiveness.

Man's ways of living are patternized

Traditionally we have described the economic and technological status of human groups in terms of "stages" of development. Such a descriptive framework is not altogether satisfactory because it implies a kind of necessary progression from one stage to another, which is not, actually, the case; and because it suggests that certain stages are necessarily more "advanced" than others — which, again, is not necessarily the case. Nevertheless, this framework is very useful, particularly for the beginning student, because it permits of a very broad kind of economic regionalization.

Within this framework, the most primitive type of economy is that of the gathering stage. In few places in the world today could peoples be found in a pure version of this stage. There are a few tribes in Amazonia which live by gathering nuts and berries and other forest products, but even these people supplement their diets with foodstuffs typically associated with the next stage, the hunting and fishing stage.

Hunting and fishing still supply the essentials of life for a surprisingly large part of the world's population. On many a small Pacific island a very large part of life is a ritual designed to ensure good fishing, and in the polar lands, almost the whole of life is a search for meat. The intimate relationships among occupation, environment, and culture exhibited in these societies will serve to illustrate one of the weaknesses of this particular way of categorizing geonomic patterns. It will not do to suggest that people who have so closely and so carefully related their ways of living and their whole pattern of culture to the limitations and opportunities of their environments are "primitive" or "backward." The hunting and fishing economy is primitive in the sense that it does not allow for any considerable increase in population. As populations increase in such an economy, a more productive set of environmental elements must be found to sustain it.

Historically, one of the great landmarks of man's progress was the discovery that animals did not have to be hunted down as needed but could be stored up (domesticated) for future use. This discovery established the grazing industry, and down to our own day grazing has been an important and profitable way of making a living. The grazing stage is actually two stages in one: a nomadic phase, which is found most typically in the Eurasian semidry lands, and a sedentary, ranch-type phase, which is found typically in the American and Australian semidry lands. While grazing represents a more sophisticated use of resources than does either gathering or hunting and fishing, it is universally associated with light population densities. Any environmental change which brings with it heavier population — such as the introduction of mining or the establishment of irrigation projects — proves almost immediately fatal to grazing. (It should be noted that dairy farming and the fattening of animals for market, while both forms of animal husbandry, are not considered branches of the grazing industry.)

The agricultural stage represented, until quite recently, the most advanced stage of resource use — at least in the thinking of the major nations of Europe and Asia. Wherever agriculture entered the picture, it all but destroyed the gathering, hunting and fishing, and grazing industries, and imposed its own occupance patterns upon the landscape. So completely did agriculture "take over" when it appeared upon the scene that it soon came to be generally accepted that agriculture represented a kind of absolute best use of the land, and that any land which was not agricultural, or could not be made agricultural, was somehow inferior. The result of this kind of thinking was that considerable land which should never have been put under crops was planted, with results disastrous both to the land and to those who attempted to farm it. We know now that just as individuals vary in tastes and abilities and aptitudes, so regions vary in resources and capacities. And just as some parents would rather have their son become a first-rate locksmith than a second-rate lawyer, so geographers today judge land-use not on some scale of intrinsic prestige but on the basis of its congruity with the whole environmental ensemble.

Agriculture has supported — and still does support — some of the heaviest population densities known to man. But agriculture in itself has never supported large numbers of people at a high level of comfort. The peasant or serf of preindustrial Europe wore himself out at back-breaking labor at an early age, just as the Indian or Chinese peasant does today. And as populations increase, the choice becomes one of either finding more productive bases for the economy, or reducing the population.

In the modern world, the stage at which the greatest number of people has achieved the highest level of physical comfort is the industrial stage. Actually, it is an oversimplification to call this stage "industrial," for actually it is a very complicated thing marked by two dominant characteristics: the

These Spanish fishermen pursue one of mankind's most ancient trades, but with modern equipment which makes them many times more efficient than fishermen of the past. In spite of such improvements, however, fishing is still a primitive industry in the sense that it is immediately dependent on the free resources of nature. It is a type of gathering, carried on at sea, rather than in the forests. (Courtesy Consulate General of Spain)

specialized use of resources, and the specialized use of people. Thus, within this stage there is not only the development of factory industry on a large scale but also a notable intensification of agriculture, allocation of nonagricultural land to grazing and forestry, rapid and efficient exploitation of minerals, the development of complicated networks of trade and exchange, and an almost infinite reduction of labor to an increasing number of specialized jobs. Associated with this stage are such unique modern phenomena as the assembly line, the corporate form of enterprise, the conurbation, the mechanized farm, scientific forestry, and rapid transportation.

Unlike the other stages we have discussed, which tend to prove inadequate to the needs of rising population densities, the industrial stage seems to require a certain minimum density of population before it can develop. More correctly, it seems to require that there be a surplus of workers left over from the extractive and food-producing industries. Such a surplus may be created in various ways: by the prolongation of life, by a liberal immigration policy, by increased productivity of the land resulting from improvements in crops and in agricultural techniques, by the mechanization or automation of routine work procedures, by the encouragement of large families, and by admitting women and children to the labor force — to name only a few of the ways the labor force has been enlarged during the past 150 years. Whether there is a limit to the population which can be supported in this industrial stage is a moot question. If there is a limit, there is as yet no hint of what it is.

Resources and their uses: a reciprocal relationship

In whatever stage an economy may find itself, its roots are firmly fixed in the resources available. The study of resources — their distribution, their uses, and their abuses — is therefore a very important facet of economic geography. Among the specialized forms of resource studies are mineral geography, the geography of soils, hydrogeography, plant geography, and conservation.

So far as resources are concerned, both the type and the intensity of their uses tend to reflect the degree of complexity in the economy. For the sake of discussion, we may divide economies into two very broad classes: primitive economies wherein production is based upon local resources almost entirely for immediate consumption, with little or no trading outside the group; and exchange economies wherein commodities are produced or articles manufactured to be traded for other goods and services. There is no necessary theoretical relationship between the type of local economy and the level of material prosperity, but few local-resource bases can supply the amount or variety of wealth that can be accumulated by trade.

The exploitation of resources in a primitive economy tends to be governed by what Renner calls the *Law of Primacy in Resource Use,* which states that "in all primitive economies, and in present-day local economies not yet fully invaded by modern means of transportation, those resources possessing the greatest richness of fertility tend to be exploited first"[1]. This is most obviously true of the most basic of all resources, agricultural land, as witness the early importance of such prime agricultural sites as the Nile Valley, the Tigris and Euphrates Valley, the Ganges Valley, and the valley of the Hwang Ho. But it is equally true of mineral resources; the easily-accessible tin of Cornwall, for instance, was exploited so early in man's history that by now it is practically all gone.

Primitive man has, as a matter of fact, little choice in the matter of what resources he will use. Equipped with only the simplest of tools, he can use only those resources which will yield to these tools. Commonly, therefore, the wearing out of easily-exploitable resources or the growth of population beyond the carrying capacity of the resources leaves him no alternative but to emigrate.

"Under an exchange economy," on the other hand, "lower-grade resources, if readily accessible to a large market, can be utilized profitably, while richer grades of resources, less accessible, remain unexploited"[2]. There are any number of examples of the truth of this *Law of Accessibility* in the economic geography of our own country. We had an especially good example in Chapter 11 when we examined phosphate production in the United States. The logic behind this law is, of course, derived from the nature of an exchange economy. Movement itself involves cost, and the less accessible a resource is, the greater will be the cost of moving it. It may, therefore, be more profitable to mine an ore which runs 20 per cent iron but which can be mined by the open pit method and shipped by barge to a nearby steel center than to mine an ore which runs 50 per cent iron but which has to be dug out from narrow and discontinuous seams far beneath the surface and then shipped a long distance by rail. Similarly, man has found it profitable to invest heavily in the improvement of land suitable for truck crops near large cities while large areas of better land lie unused in more remote parts of our country. In an exchange economy, the final decision on re-

---

[1] *Ibid.*, p. 16. Reprinted by permission.
[2] *Ibid.*, p. 17. Reprinted by permission.

source use comes down, in the final analysis, to a matter of relative costs — except in times of national emergency when the only issue is survival.

Since profits represent the margin between costs and selling prices, it will be obvious that anything which tends to raise prices will have approximately the same effect as reducing costs. So far as the geonomics of a particular industry or activity are concerned, this means that its area of occurrence will normally be enlarged when prices rise, and diminished when prices fall. Certain mineral industries in the United States have provided good examples of this contraction-expansion pattern. A particularly good example is the mining of lead in the old lead-mining districts of southwest Wisconsin. On several occasions in the past, the mines have been closed, only to be reopened when, because of national emergency or for some other reason, rising lead prices made mining profitable. For the student of economic geography this means that he must be cautious about assuming that because at some given time he finds a certain crop being raised or a certain industry carried on at an apparent profit in a given place, the crop or industry must be satisfactorily adapted to that particular environment. There were years when it was profitable, in the short run, to raise wheat in that part of the southern plains which later became the Dust Bowl. Indeed, it is one of the great truisms of geography that increasing demand for a commodity, reflected in higher prices, causes its production to expand into marginal situations where it is ordinarily not produced and where, perhaps, it would be better if it had not been produced.

Why not sell refrigerators to Eskimos? All that we have said up to this point derives from, or is related to, the idea of limits as stated in the Law of Limits. We have seen that these limits may be physical, e.g., matters of climate or soil or relief; or they may be cultural, e.g., matters of technology or population density or economics. Once the reality of such limits is granted, it follows logically that there must be some kind of progression from situations where a crop could just barely survive or an industry could just manage to make a profit, to a situation where the crop would be at its very best and the industry would be most "at home." Huntington maintains that this is actually the case and has framed his conclusion in what he calls the *Law of Optima:* "For every plant, animal, or activity there is a certain combination of conditions which is most favorable" (1). ("Optima," from which the word "optimist" is derived, is simply the plural form of the Latin word meaning "the best.")

The idea of Optima has been much misunderstood and, therefore, widely misinterpreted. It does not mean that there is somehow built into the scheme of things an ideal and unchangeable place for each form of life or for each kind of human activity. This would, indeed, be the wildest form of determinism. It does not even hold out to man the hope that he might be able to devise some sort of checklist on the basis of which he could unerringly pick out the one best place on earth for any given plant, animal, or activity — although it does suggest that at any given time there may be such an ideal place.

Perhaps the best way to illustrate the meaning of the Law of Optima is by example. Everyone is acquainted with the cliché about selling refrigerators to Eskimos. As a matter of fact, a fair number of Eskimos do have refrigerators, but we would probably all agree that the salesman who is working the Eskimo territory is well within the operational area of the Law of Limits; in this case limits set not only by need but by dietary habits, space, and purchasing power. Where, then, would the optimum territory for a refrigerator salesman be? If need were the only consideration, undoubtedly a tropical land such as India would be the answer. But few Indians could afford a refrigerator, however much they might need it. But purchasing power is not the whole answer either. One could conceive of tribes of wealthy nomads who would not be interested in buying anything as difficult to transport as a refrigerator. The most we can say is that it would be by taking these and many other factors into account, and by balancing them against each other, that our salesman would finally hit upon some territory which, if not *the* optimum, would at least approach the optimum.

This is not the end of the story, however, for today's optimum may become tomorrow's problem area. There was a time when the best place to sell marine insurance was, no doubt, Venice. This would certainly not be true today. There was a time when, apparently, the type of climate most conducive to human well-being and progress was the Mediterranean *(Cs)* type; most people today who talk in terms of climatic optima would consider the *Cfb* type of climate closer to the optimum for man. Any change that takes place within the environmental complex may call for a complete re-evaluation of optimal location.

And there is yet another matter that needs to be taken into account in this consideration of optima. It is very possible that a particular place or region may be so well endowed in so many ways that it offers something approaching optimal conditions for a considerable range of crops or a considerable number of activities. When this is the case, the *Law of Comparative Advantage* normally resolves the question of which use or activity will be given preference. This law states that "wherever there are several alternative uses for land or other natural resources, that use which is most advantageous or productive will be selected"[1]. To see the practical working of this law one need look no farther than the fringe of any reasonably large city in our country, where land equally well suited to agriculture or to subdivision development has been given to the economically more advantageous use: subdivision development.

Another way of stating the Law of Comparative Advantage is to say that where there are several alternative uses of a resource, the use which is most restricted in space will be given preference. The state of Wisconsin, for instance, was the major center of wheat production in the United States at the time of the Civil War. Wheat still grows well in Wisconsin, better perhaps than it does along the dry-humid margin where most of our country's wheat is grown today. But Wisconsin is not a major wheat-producing state today; its forte is dairying. And why? Because there are vast areas in which wheat can be grown at a reasonable profit, while there are few regions where physical and cultural conditions conjoin in just the right way to make dairy farming profitable. What is involved here is the concept of the value created by scarcity or uniqueness, the same concept that is involved when one is confronted with a choice of careers. Normally, if one is interested in financial rewards, one chooses from among the various occupations which he *could* pursue with some hope of success, the one for which there is the greatest unsatisfied demand.

One reason why Americans have been so little aware of the significance of geographical factors is simply this: they have the good fortune to live in a country, the greater part of which is so richly and so variously endowed that even a foolish or thoughtless choice of resource use rarely has fatal consequences. Occasionally, of course, nature has risen up and struck back, as in the denuded hill lands of the southern Appalachians or the now-sterile wastes of the Dust Bowl. But by and large whatever we have done has yielded a profit — whether the highest theoretically possible profit or not we do not know.

Geonomic laws

Something should be said, perhaps, about the psychological factors that are involved in the explanation of world geonomic patterns. Most students have known the frustration of getting low grades in a course in which they have worked hard, but for which they have no apparent aptitude. Nations and regions can become frustrated, too. Nothing succeeds like success and, by the same token, poverty breeds poverty. Huntington has put it more formally: "A geographical environment which fosters success is essential if people are to make continued efforts to improve their methods" (1). For reasons which are obscure to us, it has pleased the Creator to distribute the resources of the earth so unevenly that some countries have to work just as hard to keep their people on a bare subsistence level of survival as other countries work to maintain a level of affluence. Perhaps the idea of Kismet — fate — in the resource-poor Moslem countries of North Africa and the Near East is only a way of shrugging off what could otherwise be an intolerable burden upon the mind and heart: the recognition that man's best efforts could not do a great deal to create wealth where the raw materials of wealth are so

[1] Renner, *op. cit.*, p. 19. Reprinted by permission.

One of the major landmarks in man's cultural history was the replacement of nomadic herding by the pasturing of animals on cultivated grasses. For one thing, man himself became free to settle down in one place and develop stable communities. For another thing, the animals themselves had an easier time of it and, as a result, took on more weight and produced more milk. On this Peruvian experimental farm, Brown Swiss, Holstein, and Shorthorn cattle graze on a mixture of Italian rye, orchard grass, alfalfa, and red clover. How does this forage compare with the typical forage of nomadic herds? (Courtesy U. S. Department of Agriculture, Office of Foreign Agricultural Relations)

largely lacking. And perhaps the new oil-based prosperity of some of these lands will dispel, in some measure, this attitude of fatalism.

Traumatic experiences can have somewhat the same consequences as actual lack of endowments in a region. An example that comes immediately to mind is that of the American South during and immediately after the Reconstruction period. Devastated by war, demoralized by defeat and occupation, and despoiled by "carpetbagger" administrations, the Southern states understandably adopted a defeatist attitude and found themselves tempted to live on the recollection of past glories. Fortunately leadership of the type exemplified by Henry W. Grady in Georgia roused the South from self-pity and pointed it toward a still-promising future. There are those who believe that Spain's loss of her former glory may help to explain the failure of that country to keep pace with the social and economic progress of the rest of western Europe.

Finally, there are two laws which, while not originally formulated by geographers, are nevertheless of primary importance in geonomics — the *Malthusian Law,* and the *Law of Diminishing Returns.*

In 1798 a young clergyman named Thomas Robert Malthus propounded the thesis that population tends to increase geometrically while food supplies increase only arithmetically, and that population growth is limited only by such natural checks as war, famine, diseases resulting from malnutrition, and abstinence from marriage. For a long time during the latter half of the nineteenth century and the first half of the twentieth Malthus' thesis was looked upon as an unnecessarily pessimistic one, but more recently it has been revived by the "neo-Malthusian" school which sees in present population trends the prospect of economic disasters. The neo-Malthusians differ from Malthus himself chiefly in seeing these trends not as chains of events which are bound to happen but as tendencies of which man must be aware so that he can intelligently plan (e.g., by increasing production or lowering the birth rate) to keep population and food supplies in balance.

The economic geographer can hardly refuse to recognize the basic soundness of Malthus' contention that population tends to increase at a much faster rate than do food supplies and other resources. This recognition does not, however, in itself provide him with directives for recommending social or even personal actions; such recommendations come, if at all, out of his moral, ethical, and religious convictions. There are geographers who see in the phenomenon which they call overpopulation a stultifying force which sets in motion a vortex of inaction, despair, and deepening poverty. There are others who see in the constant demand for more food a goal or incentive to greater economic development, without which a nation might be content to follow the path of least resistance. The present writer is intrigued by the possible implications of the Law of Optima both for population itself and for population increase. Is it possible that for any given country or region, at any given time, there is some "best" population level and some "best" rate of increase?

Students may be familiar with the Law of Diminishing Returns from their study of economics or from their experience in "cramming" for examinations. In essence, this law states that at a certain point the additional yield from any given type of production becomes proportionately smaller than the amount of extra time, energy, and resources needed to accomplish it. Students will recognize the point of diminishing returns as the point at which they begin to wonder whether the extra sleep wouldn't do them more good than the little extra information they might memorize by staying awake for another hour. Business recognizes this point as the point at which costs rise more rapidly than profits. Nations or regions may recognize this point as the point at which a comparatively large extra expenditure of wealth or energy would be required to achieve a proportionately smaller increase in gross national product or physical standard of living. In our own country, for instance, we could, at enormous cost, vastly increase the amount of agricultural land in our dry and semidry states. We do not do so because, at present levels of demand for foodstuffs, we would actually lose money by developing these additional resources. There may be a time in the future when it will be profitable for us to do so.

What is sometimes overlooked by the student of economic geography, particularly if he happens to be an American, is that the compulsion to be doing things merely for the sake of being busy is by no means a universal compulsion. In many societies and among many peoples, work and production are clearly understood to be means, rather than ends. The end, in such cases, is likely to be something as "immoral" to the Western mind as a great three-day feast or an additional wife or simply the freedom to live without having to work. In such cultures it is obvious that the Law of Diminishing Returns may imply that at some point the improvement of economic conditions begins to cost more than the culture is willing to pay in terms of the loss of other values. Our own preoccupation with material things makes us prone to condemn those who do not give first priority to material values. We call them lazy or backward or primitive when it may very well be that they are advanced enough or civilized enough to know what they really want out of life.

How these laws work out in reality. Having

looked at some of the basic laws which underlie the study of economic geography, let us now look at the very broad geonomic patterns which characterize the modern world. We shall base our discussion on the map, Figure XII-1.

This map shows, first of all, how little of our earth man is presently using in the process of making his living. He has hardly touched the sea, although it is teeming with plant and animal life, rich in minerals, and underlain by materials we have yet to discover. Here, perhaps, is the next great frontier, the El Dorado for which men have looked in vain on all of earth's continents and islands. But whatever economic promise the sea may hold, those land regions which are presently of little or no economic use are probably destined to remain useless —unless they should prove to contain some radioactive or fuel mineral. Notice where these regions are—the icecap *(EF)* lands of Antarctica, Iceland, and Greenland; a very large part of the tundra *(ET)* lands of the north polar region; the desolate hearts of the great deserts, especially in northern Africa, Arabia, and Australia; and the range tops of such high and rugged mountain systems as the Andes and the Himalayas.

The U. S. Navy Hydrographic Office in Washington gives the area of the earth as approximately 197 million square miles. Of this, approximately 140 million square miles are ocean and another 5 million are desert. Thus, in the paragraph above, we have in effect written off almost three-fourths of the earth's surface as economically unproductive, even at the very lowest level of productivity. This leaves some 52 million square miles to feed, clothe, and shelter the three billion of us who depend upon it for a living. That works out to a density of roughly sixty people per square mile of productive land—most of which is, at present, only marginally productive for such uses as hunting, fishing, forestry, and nomadic herding. A population density of sixty to the square mile is comparable to that of Alabama or Louisiana. The real significance of the figure derives, however, from the very *un*equal distribution of population over the face of the earth—a distribution pattern which is not closely related to the distribution of fertile soil and other resources.

Probably the least productive use of land that can still be called a use is nomadic herding. The map shows that it is associated with the vast stretches of desert and semidesert in the Old World, not because these are the best lands for grazing flocks and herds but because these are all that have been left to the nomad by the incursions of agriculture and range-type grazing. Associated with this type of grazing is oasis agriculture in those more fortunate parts of the region where water is available, either along exotic stream courses or from subsurface supplies. The more than ten million square miles lightly sprinkled with nomadic herdsmen and oasis farmers cannot, however, be said to contribute a great deal toward the world economy. We must look to the remaining 42 million or so square miles for probably something on the order of 98 per cent of man's necessities.

A very large percentage of these 42 million square miles has remained essentially untouched by man. Two great areas, particularly, have resisted every effort of man to sustain large or even moderately large populations. These are the circumpolar forest (*taiga*) lands of the Northern Hemisphere and the equatorial forests. Both of these regions are dealt with more thoroughly in other chapters. For our present purposes it is necessary only to say that, except for relatively small clearings in the equatorial forests, these lands are in a very primitive economic state. Those who might be tempted to dispute our above statement that nomadic herding is the least productive use of the land would probably assign that dubious honor to the hunting, fishing, and gathering that goes on in these lands. There is no point in quibbling about it. Except for a few forest products, neither the taiga nor the equatorial forest contributes notably to the world economy, nor does either support any large number of people.

An exception should, perhaps, be made for the equatorward margin of the taiga. Here, where the trees are larger and of better quality, is the most important commercial forestry region in the modern world. By far the greater part of the pulpwood required by the paper industry of North America comes from the Great Lakes–St. Lawrence section of the region in North America. A fairly large num-

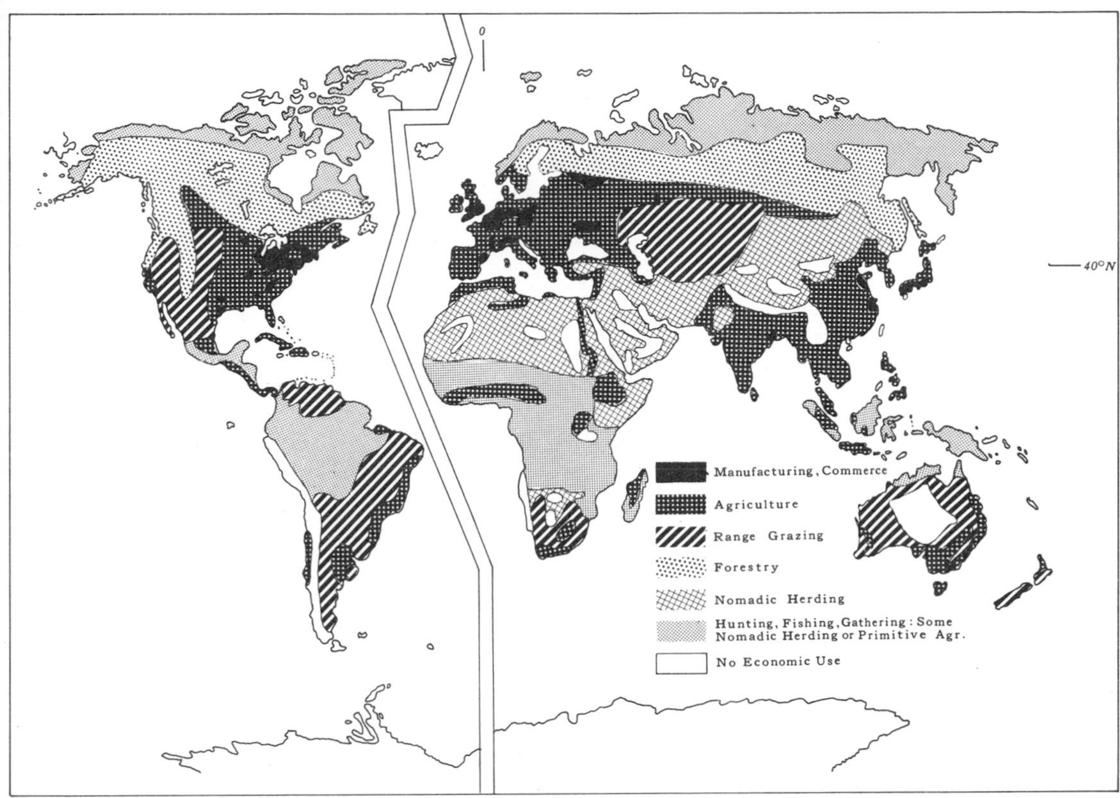

XII:1 Man's economic activities are shown on this generalized map.

ber of the paper mills are within this region. Similarly, from the Scandinavian section of the region comes most of the paper required by the printing industries of Europe. Traditionally we have thought of forestry as a "primitive" or "exploitive" industry, and in certain respects it is. But the mill towns of Canada, Norway, Sweden, and Finland are distinctly modern in their appearance and the people who live in them are indistinguishable from their compatriots farther south.

In the subhumid to semiarid lands of the Americas, South Africa, Australia, and the Soviet Union, stock raising on ranges has, during the past century and a half, developed into an important industry. Here is a good example of an industry that had to wait until just the right moment to develop. Man has always liked meat, but he has seldom been able to afford it in any quantity. Through most of history, the countries which were at all densely populated could not afford to take land out of intensive agriculture for grazing; at best there might be a limited amount of grazing on barren hill slopes. At the same time, the nomadic herdsman, because of his isolation from the centers of population, had only a limited market for animal products, especially for meat, which is highly perishable.

The opening of vast new grazing regions in the Americas and Australia, the invention of the railroad and the steamship, and the development of techniques for refrigerating meat changed the whole picture. It became possible to bring meat over long distances from producing areas to consuming centers. The result was that in a few decades per capita meat consumption stood at an all-time high. Today, the situation has altered. As J. Russell Smith states:

¶ There are no more great plains to discover, and the population is increasing much faster than the numbers of meat animals and as a result meat has risen sharply in price in practically all parts of the world since the close of the free land epoch in the United States, about 1900 A.D. For

In this experiment in scientific farming, the plants are planted in rows at one-week intervals to determine the effect of length of day on plants. The land itself, near Santiago de las Vegas, Cuba, is irrigated. The principle illustrated here is Renner's "Principle of Geonomic Relationship," which states that "every industry represents the capitalization by man of some element or combination of elements in the natural environment." Intelligent human use can make this kind of land highly productive. (Courtesy U. S. Department of Agriculture, Office of Foreign Agricultural Relations)

this there is no remedy in sight, and it may not be an entirely fanciful prediction that fifty years hence a juicy beefsteak will be the centerpiece at the banquet table.[1]

Actually, the shape of things to come may be even more doleful than Smith predicts. Machinery already exists for the manufacture of homogenized chicken — a substance consisting of a whole chicken, bones and all, ground up into a very fine paste. It is only a step from homogenized chicken to homogenized beef.

The preferred ranch animal in a ranching economy is the cow, but in very warm drylands or in regions of poor forage, cattle do not do well and sheep take their place. Australia is a special exception. The Australians developed sheep ranching early and established close ties with the British woolen industry. Thus undergirded, the industry in Australia has prospered. Long distance to market would no longer prevent the Australians from shifting to cattle, but there would be no advantage to be gained from doing so

[1] Smith, J. Russell, and Phillips, M. Ogden, *Industrial and Commercial Geography,* Holt, Rinehart and Winston, New York, 1946, p. 595. Reprinted by permission.

The modern factory is less than two hundred years old, and yet in most of the Western world it is the symbol of industry. We who live in the Western world are impressed by the extent to which the whole landscape has been transformed into an urban, industrial landscape. But for the world at large the factory is what it appears to be in this picture, a minor human intrusion into a landscape which is still predominantly natural. This factory is an iron works and foundry at Salzburg, Austria. (Courtesy Austrian Information Service)

and in all probability the shift would be highly unprofitable. (It should be noted that the introduction of cattle alongside sheep is not really feasible. By the time sheep have grazed an area there is nothing left to sustain cattle. Moreover, efficient operation requires specialization in one animal or the other.)

We come now to the two great industries which sustain the vast majority of people in the modern world, each of which is dealt with more fully in the following three chapters: agriculture, and manufacturing and commerce.

Agriculture of one kind or another is found in most places of earth between Latitude 40° in the Southern Hemisphere and the Arctic Circle in the Northern Hemisphere. In equatorial regions, much of the agriculture is of a primitive, migratory nature, as described in Chapter 23. Near the poleward limits most of the agriculture is of an experimental nature, as on the Soviet frontier and in the Canadian Northland. The great agricultural regions of the world are most typically associated with the so-called middle latitudes, except in Asia where there is a very significant extension into the tropics. Three very large and productive regions should be singled out for particular notice.

The oldest region, and still by far the greatest in terms of the number of people which it supports on an essentially agricultural base, is the Far Eastern, extending from the lowlands of Manchuria through humid

China and Southeast Asia into the Indian subcontinent, with offshoots into the Japanese islands and the islands of Indonesia. Next in order of age, and also in order of population, is the agricultural triangle of Western Europe with its base extending from the Scottish highlands to Morocco and its apex in Soviet Central Siberia. And the third is in North America, extending from the Gulf of Mexico to about Latitude 50, east of the Rocky Mountains. Each of these great regions will be discussed in more detail in Chapter 13.

In addition to these great regions, there are smaller regions which have notable local or historical importance. The Western world is, for instance, greatly indebted to the early agricultural peoples of the Nile Valley and the Tigris-Euphrates Valley in Mesopotamia, who were among the first to domesticate wild plants and cultivate them. Fringing the Atlantic coast of South America and, to a lesser extent, the Pacific coast, are relatively small agricultural districts which are important beyond their size because they constitute the economic heartlands of the South American republics. The relatively small agricultural regions of South Africa and Australia are similarly significant in the total life of those countries.

In tropical and subtropical lands, fixed or sedentary agriculture advances little by little each year at the expense of the resisting forest. In many cases, it is a question of accessibility; for that reason, many of the districts large enough to be mapped are associated with river valleys. In other cases it is a matter of temperature or relief. The Mexican and Ethiopian highlands and the mountain slopes of Central America stand out clearly as agricultural islands in a sea of more primitive economies.

This brings us to the most complex and, economically speaking, rewarding of all human occupations, manufacturing and commerce. The two are not separated in the map legend or in this discussion because they can never be separated in reality. Most of the world's commerce today is dependent, one way or another, upon manufacturing. And all of manufacturing is dependent, both for raw materials and for markets, upon commerce.

The map shows clearly two large regions of the world where the manufactural and commercial landscapes dominate. These are in east central North America and western Europe. There are, of course, many smaller areas which have developed similar landscapes, most notably the eastern coasts of the two Japanese islands of Honshu and Kyushu. But what should impress the American student is that the landscape with which most Americans are best acquainted is actually an atypical landscape and would be altogether inexplicable to probably three-fourths of the world's population.

What have we tried to accomplish by pointing out these distributional patterns which are, after all, obvious enough on the map? Essentially we have tried to do two things: first, to present the regionalization of man's activities in such a way that the student will be prepared to fit the activities which are discussed in subsequent chapters into the larger world framework. But beyond that we have attempted to show that the reality of earth patterns lends a considerable measure of credibility to the rather abstract laws and principles that were set down in the earlier part of this chapter. From his understanding of previous chapters in this book, and from such general information as he may have picked up along the way, the student should now be able to do some fairly respectable "geographizing" on his own, by organizing his information around geonomic laws and principles. If, at this point, the student cannot yet suggest two or three good reasons why the Amazon Valley has not developed into a major industrial region, it is probable that he is taking the wrong course. But by the same token, if a student at this point thinks that he knows all the reasons why there is no Amazonian Gary, he still has a great deal to learn.

APPLICATION OF GEOGRAPHIC UNDERSTANDING

I. To what extent can man be said to enjoy any real freedom of choice if the Law of Limits is valid? Do you think it is permissible to extend the idea of physical limits to the idea of limits set by the cultural environment?

II. How would you account for the fact that certain attitudes, capabilities, and skills eem to be particularly well developed mong some people and not among others?

III. Why might a country which is very eavily populated tend to avoid experimenation with new ideas, new techniques, new rops, new technologies? Why might a oung, lightly-populated country be particuarly inclined toward such experimentation?

IV. What is meant by the statement that he industrial stage is characterized by "the pecialized use of people"? What does this nean—assuming it is true—in terms of the ndividual's opportunity to develop his own alents and abilities? Can you think of any ther cultural phenomena (forms of govern-nent, philosophies of life, types of families) hat might tend to follow the same re-gional pattern as that of manufacturing and ommerce?

V. Can you think of any good argument —other than mere self-interest—for man's xploiting first those resources which possess he greatest richness or fertility? To put it nother way, what good argument might here be for *not* saving the best soils or min-ral deposits for our children?

VI. What means does man have at his dis-osal for changing the optimal producing egion for—let us say—corn?

VII. To what extent may the colonialism f the nineteenth century have been the product of a different evaluation of the purpose and utility of resources? For example, what might the nickel of New Caledonia have meant to the native of that island, and what might it have meant to the Frenchmen who came in to exploit it? How might such a differential evaluation, within the context of nineteenth-century political ideas, have eventuated in colonialism?

VIII. Which, if any, of the presently little used regions of the world would you consider a possible economic frontier in the future? What would be the handicaps that man would have to overcome in order to bring these lands under effective control? What, if any, natural advantages might he find there if he could overcome the handicaps?

IX. If, as is generally the case, labor costs are the most important single item of cost in the products of American and European industry, why should there not be much more industry in the heavily-populated countries of the Far East where the tremendous populations tend to depress wages to almost starvation level?

X. Which, if any, of the regions delimited on the map in this chapter do you expect to see expand during your lifetime? Which to contract? In each case, why?

References

1 Huntington, Ellsworth, *Principles of Economic Geography*, John Wiley and Sons, Inc., New York, 1940, pp. 18, 191, 226.

2 Renner, George T., "Some Principles and Laws of Economic Geography," *The Journal of Geography*, Vol. XLIX, No. 1, January, 1950, pp. 16, 17, 19, 20.

3 Smith, J. Russell, and Phillips, M. Ogden, *Industrial and Commercial Geography*, Henry Holt and Company, New York, 1946, p. 595.

Chapter 13

The geography of farm products

In a crude clearing in the New Guinea rainforest a wrinkled, prematurely old woman digs a shallow hole in the hard, red soil, drops a seed into it, and covers it with dirt. She is a farmer. In an intermontane valley in Japan, a whole family works from dawn to dusk in a flooded patty, meticulously picking each weed that crops up to claim the little bit of land and water that it needs to grow. They are farmers. On a hillside in Italy, men from an ancient village pluck grapes from trellised vines and lay them carefully into large barrels that rest on bullock-drawn carts. They are farmers. On a fazenda in the highlands of São Paulo, Brazil, an impeccably-dressed graduate of one of the great universities of Europe neglects his breakfast while he scans the financial pages for the latest word on coffee prices. He is a farmer. On a tractor in central Illinois, one man moves endlessly back and forth cutting deep furrows into the rich prairie and debating with himself about whether he should send his son to the state agricultural college or to an eastern school. He is a farmer.

There was a time when farmers were basically similar the world around. Crops, it is true, have always been different from one part of the world to another. But the farmer himself tended to run to type. He was up early and worked till late in the day seeding and cultivating and harvesting, always by hand or with the help of his family and perhaps a few animals. By the sweat of his brow he ate his bread, assuming that there was any bread after rain and drought, heat and frost, bugs and blight, tax collector and moneylender had all exacted their toll of his production. Some were technically free men but with neither the time nor the learning to exercise their freedom. Some were technically serfs or peasants, bound to lands which were not theirs. Many died young, worn out prematurely by the unequal struggle with nature. In the past two centuries, many more forsook the land or were driven off it by economic forces which they were powerless to withstand. A few became wealthy and prosperous and developed a deep attachment for the land, which provided the basis for a whole way of life.

The agricultural geographer today finds himself confronted by a range of farming types, activities, and landscapes which, at first, seems altogether bewildering. Could any conceivable generalization cover the old woman with the pointed stick in New Guinea, the bent-over patty worker in Japan, the Italian grape-picker, the Brazilian *fazendeiro*, and the Illinois grain farmer? Is it even accurate to say that they are all engaged in the same occupation?

Superficial differences often tend to obscure basic realities. The farmer, wherever he is and however he may go about his job, is engaged in essentially the same job, the primary production of food and other useful materials from the land. His enemies are no different from those which plagued his fathers, although in many parts of Europe and America he enjoys the assistance of powerful mechanical, scientific, social, and economic allies in the battle. And the fruits of his labor are as vital to society as they have ever been — perhaps more so as more and more people must depend upon the production of fewer and fewer farmers.

A successful farmer — whether in New Guinea, Italy, Japan, Brazil, or the United States — is essentially a practicing micro-geographer; that is, he deduces from the whole complex of natural and cultural factors and conditions that bear upon his little patch of the earth the uses of the land that will give him the best return on his investment of time, energy, and resources. From the costly trial and error discipline of his forefathers he has learned what crops "do well" on his land. He knows the food habits and preferences of the people who constitute his market. He watches market trends and anticipates such hazards as overproduction and falling prices. He watches weather reports for signs of flood or drought or frost or hail. He follows the debates in Congress or Parliament for clues to possible shifts in farm policies. The use to which he puts his land thus epitomizes his understanding of its geography.

From the consensus of individual farmers emerge broad patterns of land-use on a regional scale and their resulting landscape ensembles, all reflective of regional natural and cultural conditions. And from these regional patterns and ensembles, in turn, it is possible to deduce certain principles which seem to be generally valid. Thus it is an observable fact that where population density is low, agriculture tends to be extensive, that is, carried on by relatively few people on large areas of land, whereas population growth tends to cause an intensification of agriculture, that is, greater production from smaller areas of land. Equally observable is the fact that isolation resulting from poor transportation facilities tends to encourage diversity of crops because the local population must depend primarily upon local production for the whole range of its food requirements, while the introduction of good transportation permits specialization in those crops for which the region is best suited and the importation of foodstuffs which can be more efficiently produced elsewhere.

If it is borne in mind that there are exceptions to every rule and that every generalization is, in some respects, an overgeneralization, the following statements from Ellsworth Huntington's *Principles of Economic Geography* (1) may serve as examples of some of the principles of agricultural geography which are believed by geographers generally to have a high degree of validity. The numbers in brackets refer to the pages in the text from which the statements are taken.

¶ The cost of production tends to be low where geographical and economic conditions favor the production of an article in large quantities, high where they lead to small production. [247] (Compare the cost of production of vegetables in the Rio Grande district of Texas, for instance, with that of the U.S.S.R.'s new experimental agricultural districts in the lower Yenisei Valley.)

Economic conditions often make it less profitable to raise certain products under optimum conditions of climate, soil, and relief than under less favorable natural conditions. [241] (Yields of wheat are larger in humid lands than in drylands, but wheat cannot stand the economic competition of more valuable crops in the humid lands.)

So long as there are no artificial restrictions, a more profitable crop drives out a less profitable one. [249] (The introduction of sugar cane and pineapples almost destroyed subsistence agriculture in Hawaii.)

Intensive cultivation and fertilization produce remarkable results almost everywhere, but they pay best and are most likely to be practiced where the soil, relief, and especially climate are best for the crops. [232] (A classic example is the dairy farming of Denmark, northern Germany, and the Netherlands.)

Most crops are of the best quality, or give the greatest yield, or both, near limits set by low temperature. [233] (The tobacco of the Connecticut River valley, for instance, is premium-grade tobacco.)

One of the chief ways in which energetic and progressive people show their superiority is by specializing in products of high quality in regions where the natural resources are scanty or where isolation makes it difficult to market products that are heavy or bulky. [456] (Examples: Australian wool and New Zealand butter.)

First, the area where [an agricultural] product is raised tends to expand, for people try experiments. Then it contracts, and production becomes intensified in the most favorable areas [311]. (Our own cotton districts have shown this trend.)

As civilization rises higher, the most advanced countries tend to find substitutes for products which come from a distance, especially if the products are difficult to obtain [399]. (Silk, for instance, has been largely replaced by nylon for hosiery.)

When people from a more advanced economy come to a relatively backward economy . . . they tend to discover new uses and markets for hitherto neglected resources [400]. (The Amazonian people, for instance, used rubber chiefly for balls. Western man has discovered new uses and markets for it.)[1]

The statements cited above are meant to be suggestive rather than exhaustive of the principles which have been deduced from the study of the agricultural geography of the world. Most of them will seem self-evident to anyone who takes the trouble to examine their implications. One which may not be so self-evident requires some discussion.

The idea that crops do best toward their poleward limit is an apparent contradiction

---

[1] Huntington, *op. cit.*, Reprinted by permission.

of the general rule that warmth makes for luxuriant growth. The fact of the matter is that most of the common grains are native to "temperate" latitudes and adapt poorly, if at all, to tropical conditions. But beyond that fact there is a process of natural selection that takes place under the greater rigors of colder climates, resulting in the extinction of inferior strains and the perpetuation of the hardier strains. Climatic variability and the greater length of the day during the growing season also come into the picture. Finally, it seems that blights and harmful insects which attack crops in warmer latitudes are less numerous and less virulent in cooler regions. If we add to these natural factors the cultural factors—e.g., the generally higher level of cultivation practices among the more advanced peoples of the cooler latitudes — it is not surprising that the greatest yields and the highest quality of crops are found at or near the coldward limits of their growing area.

The student who has followed the arguments presented earlier for the idea of optima may ask at this point whether there is not a contradiction between the idea of optima and this principle that crops do best near their coldward limits. Not at all. Simple as a plant may seem to us, it is really a very complex organism affected by a complex of environmental conditions. Each of these conditions can be described in terms of limits and optima. Thus there will be climatic and other limits for germination, for growth, for flowering, and within these limits certain definable optima. Similarly, there will be limits and optimal conditions for the development of blights and insects which attack the plant. It may very well be, therefore that conditions less than optimal for, let us say, germination will be much more than offset by conditions which inhibit or prevent the development of a particular blight or which encourage rapid growth. Hybridization and selective breeding are, in very large measure, practical applications of the concepts of limits and optima.

Nor dare we underestimate the importance of economic and cultural factors in the determination of crop choice. Around the larger cities of the United States, for instance, one almost always finds some sort of truck cropping which produces highly perishable vegetables for the urban market. Obviously such areas fall within the climatic and other limits of the particular crops involved, but not necessarily anywhere close to the optimum. The governing factors in these cases are the perishability of the crop, its inability to survive long journeys, and the large market for it close at hand. So important may these factors be that truck crops may actually drive out less perishable crops which find their climatic and physical optima within the region. The same basic principle is involved in the replacement of commercial crops by subsistence crops in certain parts of the world — for example, some of the Caribbean islands — where increasing population densities have given sheer survival preference over trade.

Another factor that must be taken into account in explicating the agricultural pattern of any particular part of the world is the stage which the local population has reached in its cultural development. The general trend is one from a simple, inefficient, largely unspecialized type of agriculture among peoples of primitive culture to a very complex, largely mechanized, highly specialized type of agriculture among peoples of highly sophisticated culture. As a culture passes into old age, however, there tends to be a regression to lower forms of agriculture.

The chart (Figure XIII-1) attempts to illustrate the general pattern of agricultural development in diagrammatic form. Lines connecting one type of agriculture to another indicate a general tendency for one to develop out of another. In many instances, however, the succession from one form to another is not by evolution but by replacement. Thus, in the adolescent stage, nomadic herding may evolve into livestock ranching or it may be replaced by subsistence crop and livestock farming.

The student should not read into the chart more than it is meant to convey. We are dealing here with only the broadest types and trends in agriculture and we are dealing with characteristic relationships rather than with total landscape complexes. Thus, for example, some dairy farming and some specialized horticulture may be found in any stage from youth to old age. They are most characteristically associated, however, with the later stages of mature cultures. It should be noted also that once an agricultural type appears in the landscape of any country, vestiges of it tend to survive even after it has been

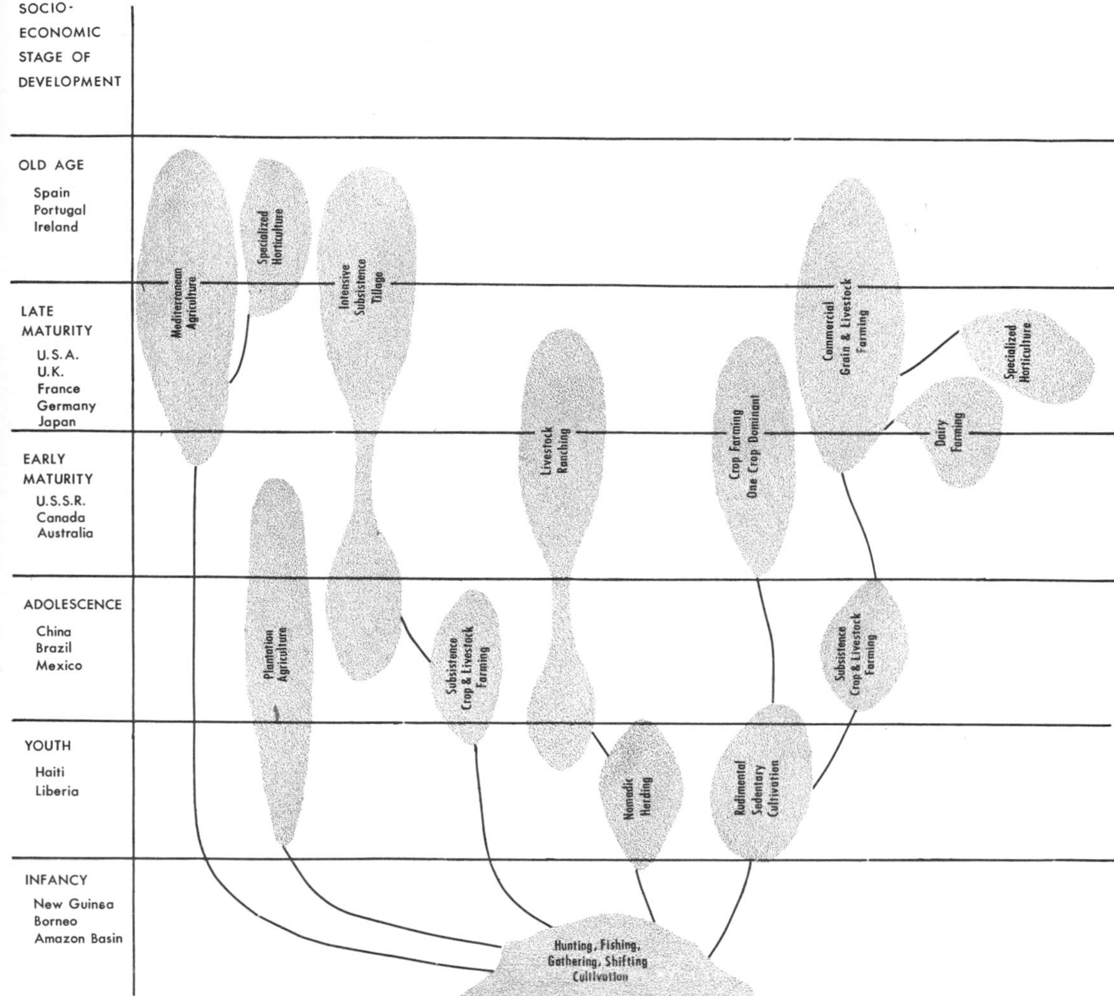

XIII:1 This diagram shows correlation between types of agriculture and socio-economic stages of development. The countries listed under the various headings are intended to serve merely as examples of countries which appear to be in these stages of socio-economic development. Not all of them would necessarily exhibit all of the agricultural types which are shown as typical of the various stages.

almost completely replaced by other types of agriculture. Even in our own country it is still possible to find individuals here and there who live by hunting, fishing, and gathering.

The types of agriculture mentioned on the chart are those defined by Derwent W. Whittlesey in his "Major Agricultural Regions of the World," one of the classics of American geography (2). Since we shall be employing this terminology through the remainder of this chapter, it would be well for us to explain briefly what is meant by each of Dr. Whittlesey's categories. The distribution of these agricultural types is shown on the map (Figure XIII-2).

Shifting cultivation is the type of agriculture referred to in Chapter 23 as *milpa, chain, chena,* or *kaingin* agriculture. It is

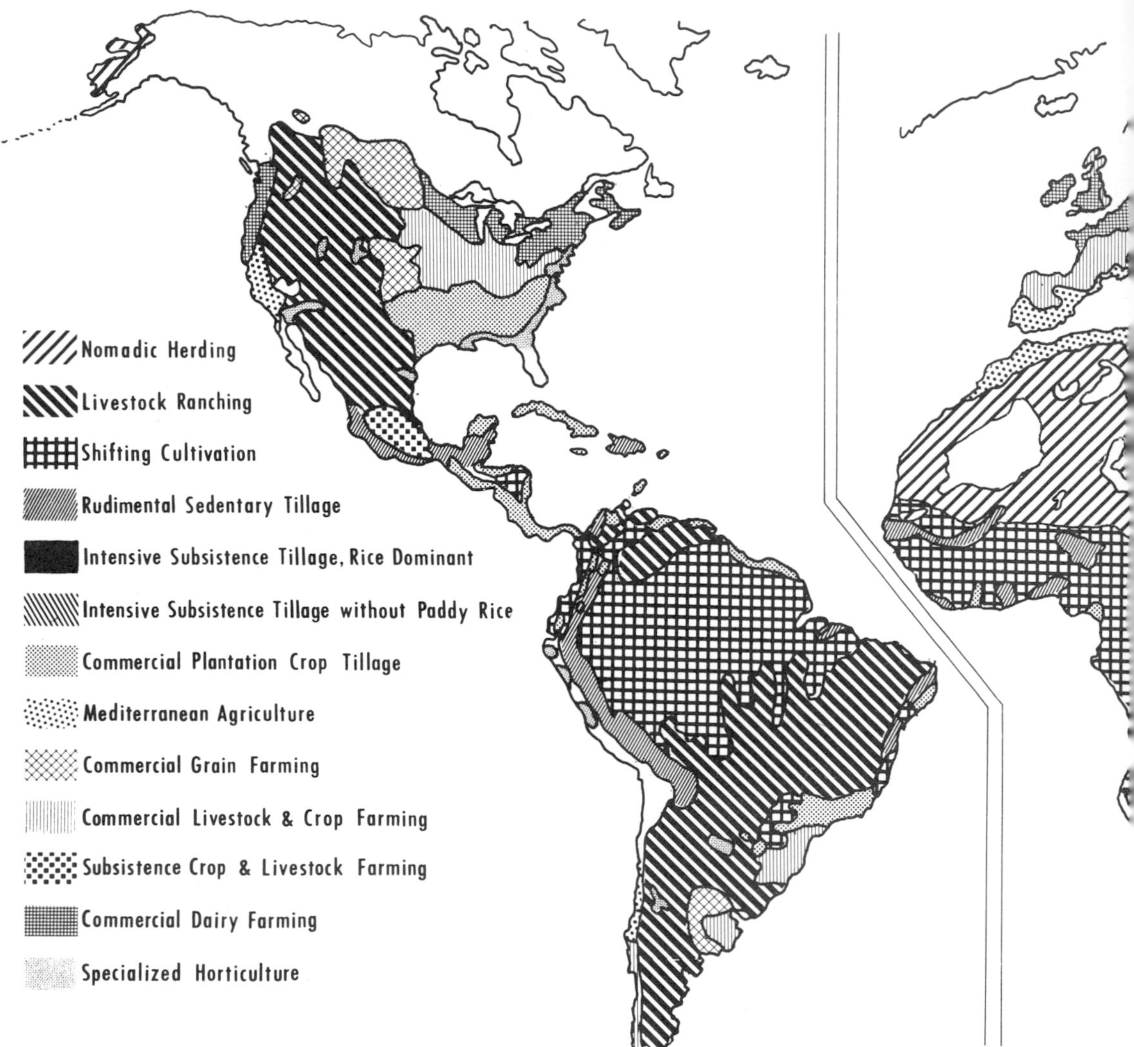

found almost exclusively in tropical rainforest lands and is carried on in crude clearings. It involves little more than sticking a pointed stick into the ground, dropping seeds into the holes thus made, covering the holes, and letting nature take its course. The clearings soon become overrun by the recrudescent rainforest and are thereupon abandoned in favor of new clearings.

Rudimental sedentary cultivation differs from shifting cultivation in that a more thorough job of clearing is done and the clearings thus established are typically maintained and worked over extended periods of time. Rudimental sedentary cultivation usually implies a more favorable physical environment, a higher type of culture, and a greater density of population than does shifting cultivation. It is most typically found in the tropics at higher (cooler) elevations and in more accessible situations (coastal plains and river valleys).

Nomadic herding and livestock ranching both involve animal husbandry, the former most typically on the Eurasian steppe lands (see Chapter 21) and the latter on the dry and semidry lands of the Americas, Africa, and Australia (see Chapter 21). Purists who question the inclusion of these activities under the heading of "agriculture" are reminded that our language has no word to embrace the idea of the total use of the land for crops and animals.

Subsistence crop and livestock farming is a type of agriculture once widespread in our own country but today largely supplanted by

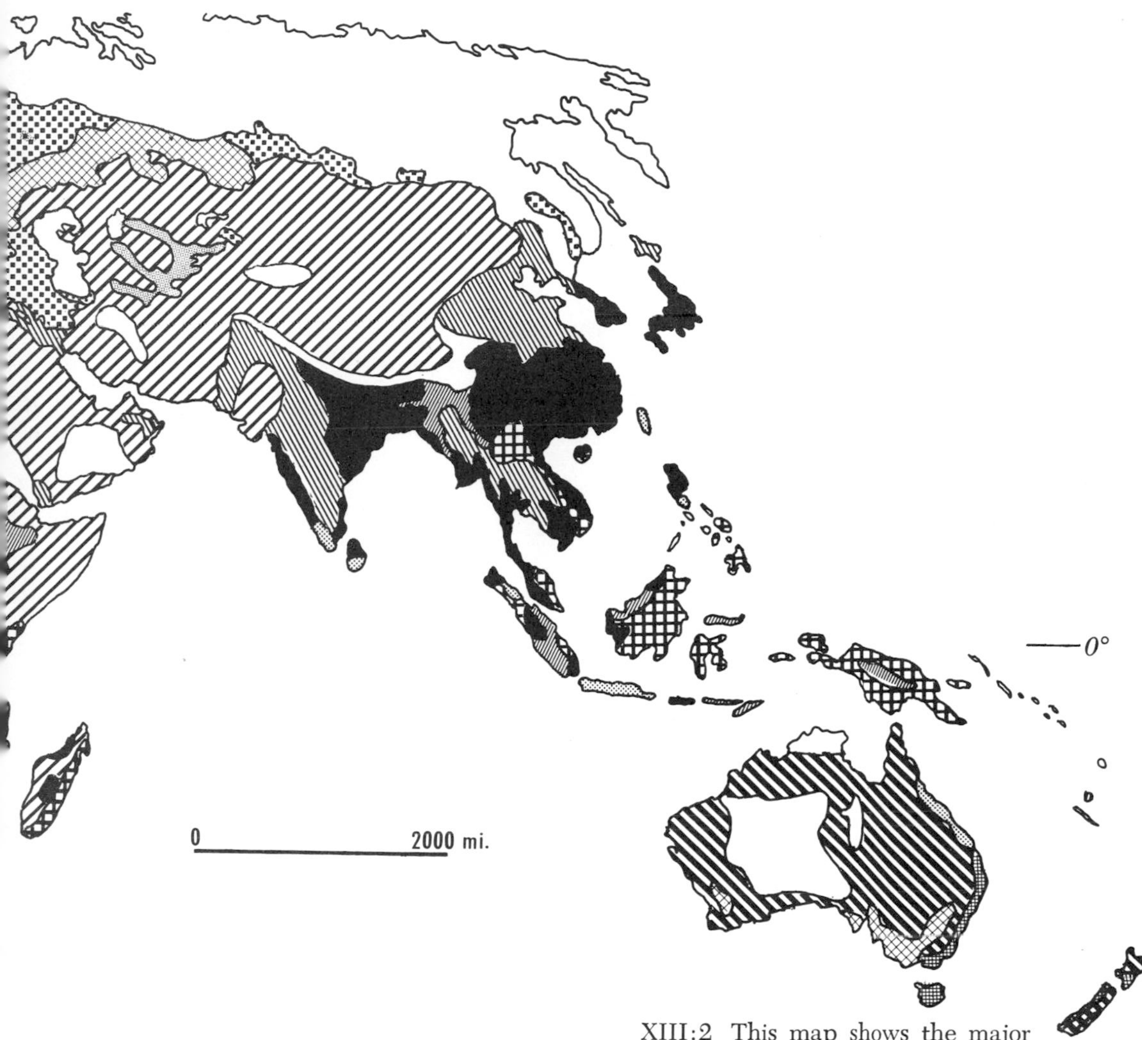

XIII:2 This map shows the major agricultural regions of the earth. (Redrawn from a map by Derwent Whittlesey in the *Annals of the Association of American Geographers,* Vol. XXVI, No. 4, December, 1936, used by permission. The base map, Goode's 201 HC, used by permission of the University of Chicago Press)

commercial agriculture. This type of farming is, in the modern world, characteristic of agricultural frontiers (e.g., the newly developed farming areas of the Soviet Union) and of underdeveloped countries (e.g., the Mexican and Anatolian plateaus). As the name implies, this type of farming combines crop agriculture, involving usually the small grains in the Old World and corn in the New, with animal husbandry—all for local consumption. Judging by the experience of other regions, the introduction of well-organized transportation systems into these subsistence areas would very likely bring about their transformation into regions of commercial agriculture.

In India and the Far East, the pressure of man upon land has forced livestock out of the agricultural picture and, at the same time, brought about an almost incredible intensification of tillage practices. On the diagram we have taken into account only the factor of intensiveness. In Whittlesey's classification, and in the discussion which will follow in this chapter, a distinction is made between the regions of intensive rice culture and those regions of intensive cultivation where some crop other than rice (typically

These white-faced Herefords are being fattened on a feed lot near Grand Junction, Colorado. Between the fence and the treeline is a field of corn which is being grown for ensilage. The water is supplied by irrigation. Why are these animals being fattened here in irrigated drylands rather than farther east in humid lands? (Bureau of Reclamation, United States Department of the Interior. Photograph by Stan Rasmussen)

wheat) is dominant. The governing consideration in either case is a very high concentration of population coupled, in most cases, with an underdeveloped system of transportation and exchange. Intensive tillage as such is not confined to the densely populated parts of Asia, but in other parts of the world intensive tillage is commonly associated with some form of specialized commercial agriculture rather than with subsistence agriculture. An example of intensive commercial agriculture is truck farming.

Mediterranean agriculture is more fully described in Chapter 24. Like the *Cs* climate with which it is intimately associated it is a highly distinctive thing. It reflects both the distinctive Mediterranean climate and the dissected topography of the Mediterranean world and combines elements both of commercial and subsistence agriculture. Crops include the small grains (with wheat given preference wherever it finds favorable conditions of growth), dates and citrus fruits, grapes and olives, in some cases flowers, and perhaps vegetables. Sheep and goats are the typical animals.

Crop farming with one crop dominant is found in two characteristic situations. The first of these is on the arid-humid margin where the great commercial wheat belts of the modern world are located—chiefly in Canada, the United States, Argentina, the Soviet Union, and Australia. The second, fragmented into areal units too small to show on the map, is the cotton landscape, once widely developed over the American South. In few places today is cotton so dominant that it can be credited with a one-crop hegemony. More commonly it is associated today with mixed-crop economies.

We come now to three agricultural regions which will be more familiar to the readers of

Where was this photograph of commercial wheat farming taken—in Manitoba? in Kansas? in the Ukraine? It could be any one of these places, for the great wheat belts of the world have a characteristic landscape of their own, a landscape compounded of flat terrain, far horizons, fenceless expanses of wheat, and, during the harvest season, several combines in a staggered row. Actually, this particular field happens to be a former desert area in the southern part of the State of Israel. (Courtesy Consulate General of Israel)

this text. Over most of the eastern half of the United States and across most of northern and central Europe extend belts of commercial livestock and crop farming. Within this belt a wide variety of crops is grown, either for sale or for the fattening of livestock. In some parts of these regions, as in the American Corn Belt, one crop may be so widely raised as to appear to enjoy a kind of dominance. But even such crops are raised in a system of rotation or a pattern of association which produces a mixed-crop landscape. Corn, which does poorly in the moderate temperatures of marine summers, is restricted to the American sector of this realm. But in both the European and American sectors important crops include wheat, rye (chiefly in Europe), oats, barley, the grasses, root crops, and (mostly in America) soybeans. Cattle and hogs are the chief livestock.

Along its northern fringe in both Europe and America the commercial livestock and crop farming region gives way to dairy farming. The boundary is primarily climatic—short, cool, damp summers—but also a matter of soils and topography. Both in America and in Europe the southern boundary of the Dairy Belt coincides rather closely with the southern limits of the most recent glaciation, which left an irregular land surface dotted with small lakes and other manifestations of imperfect drainage. North of this boundary the nutritious grasses find their optimum climatic conditions of growth, while the irregularities of the surface hamper the mechanized operations that make grain farming profitable. In addition, both in Europe and in America there is a heavy concentration of large cities and urban areas—both prime markets for dairy products—in or on the margins of the

Cattle graze in the Austrian Tyrol. The mountain meadows supply nutritious grasses. Large cities in the nearby lowlands constitute a profitable market for milk and dairy products. (Courtesy Austrian Information Service)

dairy lands. Thus physical conditions and economic considerations combine to encourage the use of the land for dairy cattle.

The most fragmented of all of Whittlesey's classifications is that of specialized horticulture—partly, perhaps, because it embraces a great variety of crops and land uses. Under this heading Whittlesey includes the wine districts of northwestern and Mediterranean Europe; the market gardening and truck farming areas surrounding the large cities of the Western world; the commercial fruit orchards of the humid mid-latitude and irrigated desert lands; and the commercial flower-raising regions of southern France, the Netherlands, and Bulgaria. Specialized horticulture tends to develop in response to unique conditions of very rich local markets unusually high land values or productior costs (as in irrigated areas), microclimates or unusual soil qualities.

Finally, in many parts of the tropics anc subtropics there are important regions oi plantation agriculture. Plantation crops are rarely produced for local consumption. Many of them travel long distances to market. We shall have more to say about plantation crops later on in this chapter.

At this point we shall try to bring some order to our discussion by attempting tc organize the various agricultural types anc regions that we have discussed under headings which may permit a broader and more intelligible regionalization. These headings are:

I. Regions of Primitive Agriculture
   A. *Nomadic Herding*
   B. *Shifting Cultivation*
   C. *Rudimental Sedentary Cultivatioi*
II. Regions of Oriental Agriculture

In a small country such as the Netherlands where agricultural land is at a premium, almost every acre must be made to produce the largest possible profit. These gardens and greenhouses near Aalsmeer show what intensive farming really means. Where in the United States might one find a somewhat similar landscape? Why? (Courtesy Netherlands Information Service)

- A. *Intensive Subsistence Tillage, Rice Dominant*
- B. *Intensive Subsistence Tillage, Rice Unimportant*

III. Regions of Occidental Agriculture
- A. *Mediterranean Agriculture*
- B. *Livestock Ranching*
- C. *Crop Farming, Grain or Cotton Dominant*
- D. *Commercial Livestock and Crop Farming*
- E. *Subsistence Crop and Livestock Farming*
- F. *Dairy Farming*
- G. *Specialized Horticulture*

IV. Regions of Plantation Agriculture

Regions of primitive agriculture

Where do primitive agricultural practices persist, and how do we explain their survival in a world which cannot afford the inefficient production of food? The answer to the second part of this question is, perhaps, implicit in the answer to the first part. One thing all regions of primitive agriculture have in common is cultural isolation. Primitive people practice primitive agriculture. The root question is, therefore, why such people have been forced or permitted to remain on a primitive cultural level.

In a sense, the answer to this root question is one aspect of the whole theme of this book. We are concerned with illuminating place-to-place differences. To a very large extent we have found and will find that cultural "backwardness" is related to enervating climates and to physical conditions which tend to isolate small groups from the mainstreams of culture. Tropical and polar climates depart so far from the optimum for man that their effects are enervating; therefore we find little agriculture, and that of a primitive sort, in these regions. Mountains, very high and rugged plateaus, broad expanses of ocean, and the dense vegetation of the rainforest tend to isolate people from the great mass of mankind; therefore we find primitive agricultural types and techniques surviving in highlands, on pelagic islands, and in the rainforest.

But if we look closely at both the polar and the tropical lands, we shall see that the problem is not one simply of cultural isolation producing primitive agriculture. Rather, both are products of certain "built in" characteristics of the environment. In the light of what is said in Chapter 19, we are not justified in supposing that, if the cultural isolations of the polar people were broken down, a higher type of agriculture would develop. This is similarly true in large parts of the tropics. One writer has said:

¶ An observant traveler is not long in the Amazon valley before learning why some of these seemingly irrational ways of growing crops and destroying timber are used. In Pará State the once heavily forested Braganca region, east of Belém and of the mouth of the Amazon River and almost under the equator, illustrates well the great difficulties in attempting to convert one of these forest regions into an intensively cultivated agricultural one. Many years ago a railroad and roads were built eastward from Belém through this Braganca region and people were encouraged to come in and settle. It was expected that this district would soon be settled and prosperous through agricultural production, for less than a thousand miles to the southeast are the sertão, the arid region of shallow soils, from which there is a continual migration of laborers seeking work, while coastwise shipping provides an easy method of transport. The sertão are the semiarid portions of northeastern Brazil from which people have to migrate more or less continuously in order to find work. Moreover, about once a decade in that region there has been a disastrous famine with many deaths by starvation. This is the source of much of the labor which has developed central and southern Brazil, and also for rubber collecting in the Amazon Valley. Thus, it was reasoned, why not develop sound agricultural colonies in the immense rainy forests just to the east of Belém, with some of this population needing farms in less droughty regions as has so often been the case elsewhere? The peasants who pioneered here soon found that while they could get a good crop the first year after cutting and burning the primeval forest and could get a following crop or two of mandioca (cassava), no further cropping was worthwhile for them, even though very little labor was needed to cut down and clear the second growth (*capoeiras*) that came in after they abandoned their 2 or 3 years' cultivation of crops in the new clearing.

The reason for the rapid decline in productivity is that practically all of the plant nutrients within reach of the roots of the forest trees have been taken up and are in the growing trees. Almost all the plant offal (dead leaves, twigs, fruit, fallen trees, etc.) which falls to the ground is quickly attacked by termites and decay organisms; as a consequence it rapidly disappears. Organic matter cannot persist long in the soil; leaf mold as it is known in the north temperate U. S. does not develop. However, the heartwood logs of certain very durable sorts of trees will last a couple of years or more. The nutrients thus released and washed into the soil by the frequent drenching rains are quickly taken up by the tree roots lying in wait just under the soil surface. All the nutrients within reach of the tree roots are in the vegetation, and are being cycled. When the forest is cut and burned the cycle is broken, the plant nutrients being released in soluble form in the ash. The soil itself is extremely acid, often being around pH4. The burning slightly reduces the acidity and supplies available nutrients for the crop plants which may be planted in the clearing. But before the annual or biennial crop plants can develop extensive root systems sufficient to absorb any considerable proportion of these liberated nutrients, most of the soluble materials will have been washed down deep into the subsoil by the almost daily rains—thus quite out of reach of the roots.[1]

This writer concludes that, since it is essential to retain a tree cover on tropical soils, the shifting cultivation which has been traditional in many parts of the tropics may be the best use of the land possible in these areas. Thus we find that, in this very diverse

[1] Pendleton, Robert L., "Agricultural and Forestry Potentialities of the Tropics," *Agronomy Journal*, Vol. XLII, No. 3, March, 1950, p. 116. Reprinted by permission.

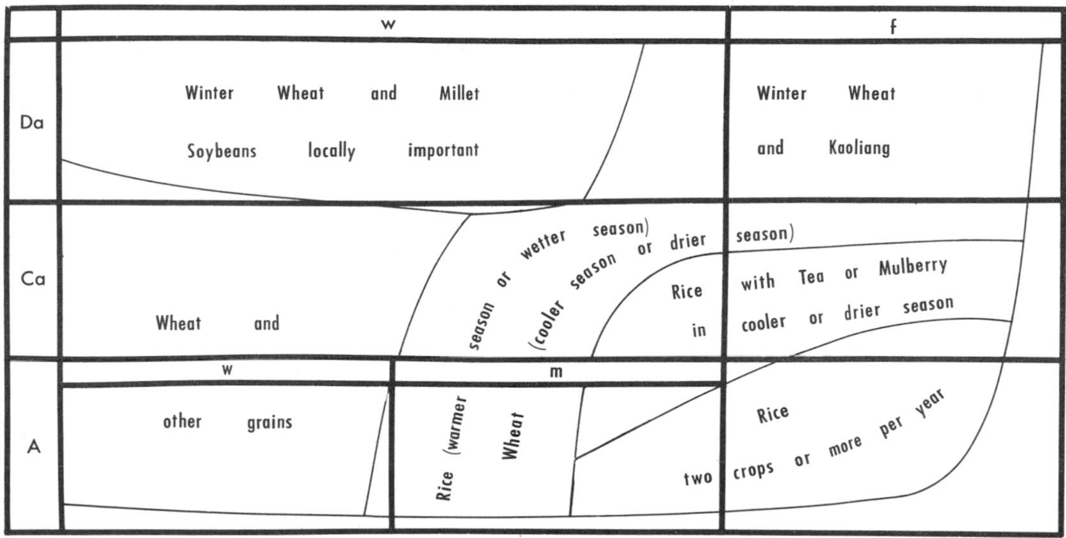

XIII:3 This diagram shows the relationship of crop regions to climatic regions in Monsoonal Asia. The boundaries of the crop regions have been generalized from maps by J. Lossing Buck, George B. Cressey, and J. B. Spencer.

world of ours, there are circumstances where a primitive use of the land may be climax.

Nomadic herding is, perhaps, a different matter. The lands of the Old World which are still devoted to nomadic herding are, in their essentials, not greatly different from the New World lands which have been taken over by livestock ranching. It seems probable that the persistence of nomadic herding may be ascribed to a combination of low population densities and immature economies associated with weak national states. It is interesting to note that wherever, as in the Soviet Union, national economies are in the process of absorbing local economies, the nomadic herdsman tends to become settled on the land.

Regions of oriental agriculture

From the Indus River eastward to Viet Nam, southward to Java, and northward to the Amur River, a combination of physical and historical factors has given rise to a type of agriculture complex within itself but strikingly different from the agriculture of any other part of the world. It is an almost unbelievably intensive type of agriculture, reflecting the necessity to provide food to feed populations which are more densely concentrated on the land here than in any other part of the world. And it is subsistence agriculture, reflecting again the density of population and also the prevalence of local economies in a part of the world where physical and historical factors have combined to inhibit the development of a transportation and communications network capable of fostering national or regional economies.

Climatically, this is the monsoon region par excellence (in the Köppen classification *A*, *C*, or *D* combined with the *w* indicating winter drought). Coastal fringes may grade into year-round humid *(f)* or semi-drought *(m)* conditions, but even these regions exhibit a decided seasonality of rainfall. Crop choices and cultivation practices thus reflect gradations both in rainfall *(f* to *m* to *w)* and in winter temperatures *(A* to *C* to *D)*. Diagrammatically, the relationships might be illustrated as in Figure XIII-3.

Diagrams can portray only crude or limited relationships. It should not be supposed, for instance, that wherever the *Af* climate dominates in Asia there will be a double cropping of rice. Other physical factors are of major significance in regionalizing this use of the land, among them topography (rice is generally restricted to land that is naturally flat or has been terraced) and soils (an impervious layer of clay beneath a clay loam provides the best patty sites, the loam allowing for good root development and the impervious layer preventing the loss of water by seepage). Cultural factors also enter into the picture. In the Philippines, for example, two crops of rice are not the usual thing despite favorable climatic conditions; because of a population density which is low by oriental standards, there is not sufficient economic pressure to require such intensive use of the land.

Rice grades out of the picture toward the drier and cooler margins of the monsoon lands, usually to be replaced by wheat where that is possible, otherwise by some more tolerant form of grain. In hilly regions, such as southern China, rice grades out of the picture altitudinally, except where there is terracing, giving way to bush or tree crops such as tea and mulberry. It is significant, though, that nowhere in monsoonal Asia does either rice or wheat give way to livestock farming. The pressure of people on the land is such that only such scavengers as hogs, goats, and chickens fit into the economy; cattle and sheep require too much care and too much land and compete with human beings for the limited amount of food that the land is capable of producing.

With so many people seeking to make their livings directly off the land, farms are necessarily small (2-3 acres in the rice lands, up to perhaps 8 acres in the wheat lands). Traditional inheritance rules tend to divide these small holdings into even more minute units. And these units are broken up into very small, almost garden-size, noncontiguous plots scattered in various directions from the farm village.

Given this kind of field pattern, it is obviously out of the question to try to farm with any kind of machinery, even if the individual farmer were wealthy enough to afford it — which he isn't. Co-operative ownership and use of machinery by all the farmers in a village might make some degree of mechanization possible, but the peasant — East or West — is very much of an individualist, disinclined toward any kind of co-operative ownership. Moreover, it is not likely that machines could wrest the high yields from the land that are accomplished by careful, painstaking hand culture. The Communist Chinese experiment will bear watching. If their socialization and mechanization of agriculture should increase production, many of our theories will have been invalidated.

We in the West marvel at the abundance which, year in and year out, the tireless hands and strong back of the Oriental farmer manage to coax from land which should long ago have become tired and sterile. We marvel all the more when we realize that nature is usually capricious, often cruel in these lands, and that populations have risen to a level which land and labor seem hardly adequate to support. One of the standard texts in economic geography summarizes oriental agriculture in these words:

¶ For thousands of years the Oriental farmer has exacted a living from the "Good Earth." By using his crops directly for food, rather than feeding them to animals, he has reached the ultimate stage of tillage, where man by the sweat of his brow produces food for sustenance. By intensive hand methods, fertilization, crop rotation, intertillage, and double cropping he has done everything possible to wring high yields from rice paddies, hillside fields, and dry-land farms. He now makes efficient use of goats, swine, poultry, and fish for providing fertilizers, foodstuffs, and certain products for sale. He allows little or nothing to go to waste. He seems to have reached the maximum subdivision of landholdings, for the average farm today barely supplies sufficient food for even a low standard of living; it does not yield much of a surplus that can be saved for the declining years of old age. He struggles to maintain soil fertility and to cope with natural tragedies that befall him. In much of the area three-fourths of the annual precipitation may come during a period of from four or five months; torrential rains often wash off fertile topsoil and erode fields, making deep gullies in them; sudden swelling of rivers and slow drainage on low, fertile plains often give rise to floods. When floods come, the farmer can only sit by and watch his crops disappear; when floodwaters retreat, he must plant new crops or starve. On dry margins erratic rainfall often brings crop failure, famine, and despair. Each disaster increases tenancy, already of alarming proportions, and lowers the standard of living still further. The better lands have long been cultivated.[1]

---

[1] Reprinted with permission of The Macmillan Company from *Economic Geography* by Jones, Clarence Fielden, and Darkenwald, Gordon Gerald, p. 235. Copyright 1954 by The Macmillan Company.

This is not a very pretty picture — particularly when one remembers that these are the circumstances under which more than half of the world's population lives. Jones and Darkenwald suggest that the situation of these people could be improved if, with government aid, new land could be brought under cultivation, seeds improved, plant and animal pests and insect diseases brought under control, dairy farming developed around the urban centers, flood control programs inaugurated, and transportation improved. Unfortunately, in so much of monsoonal Asia today governments are either too weak or too inept even to maintain civil order, let alone embark upon constructive programs for improving agriculture. And in the resultant hopelessness communism finds a fertile breeding-ground.

Regions of occidental agriculture

The occidental world, for the purposes of our present discussion, will be defined as those lands which are occupied by a predominantly Caucasian population. Thus defined, it would include Europe, temperate North and South America, South Africa, Australia, Mediterranean Africa, and all of nonmonsoonal Asia.

Within this area there is a riotous variety of crops, tillage systems, land ownership patterns, and rural landscapes. This variety is, in itself, one of the characteristics which distinguish occidental agriculture from primitive and oriental agricultural. But there are more significant differences — too obvious to be labored in comparison with primitive agriculture but worth noting in comparison with oriental agriculture. Among these differences, the following may be considered most noteworthy:

1. Farms, even the smallest ones, are typically very much larger in the Occident than in the Orient, ranging all the way up to mammoth farms and ranches that cover hundreds of square miles.

2. While hand tillage is still to be found here and there in the occidental world, the trend is toward ever greater mechanization, culminating in the totally-mechanized operaions of the dry-margin wheat farmers.

3. While there are still some areas of semisubsistence farming in the occidental world, these areas are atypical and can usually be explained in terms of cultural lag. Typically, occidental agriculture is commercial rather than subsistence, extensive rather than intensive.

4. Rice, which so largely dominates the oriental agricultural scene, is almost wholly absent from the occidental.

5. Despite the strong dominance of certain crops in certain regions (e.g., the wheat belts), occidental agriculture as a whole produces a far greater variety of crops than does oriental agriculture.

6. Livestock is a very significant element in the agricultural economy of the Occident.

Admitting the validity of these contrasts between oriental and occidental agriculture, someone may still question the propriety of subsuming so many disparate types of agriculture under the one heading of occidental agriculture. Perhaps this question can best be met by reviewing very briefly the historical development of occidental agriculture, in the course of which it should become evident that it possesses an inner unity which is not vitiated by surface dissimilarities.

The roots of occidental agriculture can be traced back to Mesopotamia, the Nile Valley, and the Mediterranean fringe — to grain farmers cultivating the fertile, well-watered lowlands and to nomadic herdsmen or shepherds grazing their flocks on the drier and more rugged uplands. From the Mediterranean world these practices spread in the wake of the advancing Roman armies up through the Rhone Valley into northwestern Europe and England, while in the East successive waves of Slavic tribesmen came pouring into the Russian grasslands, where their descendants would ultimately come into contact with similar influences reaching them from western Europe and from Greece.

Climatic, topographical, and pedological conditions in northern Europe demanded significant departures from the Mediterranean prototype. Livestock, especially cattle, played a far more important part than they had in the Mediterranean Basin. As wealth and population grew through the centuries, Europe left the raising of meat animals largely to its overseas daughters who had the advantage of cheaper land while she gave her own grassland to dairying. The grape, brought practically to its poleward limits of survival in the Rhineland and the limestone *cotes* of eastern France, made wines that the Mediterranean grape had hardly hinted at. Wheat and other grains, planted in soils newly reclaimed from forest or swamp, gave yields that amazed men accustomed to the paltry yields of the tired Mediterranean hill slopes.

There was also an important intangible in the picture. The northern European was, by temperament and disposition, a farmer. Until very recent times, he did not build great cities, and those which he has built testify to his dislike of the urban life. In France, in Germany, in England, in the Low Countries, and in all of Slavic Europe stubborn, patient men coaxed the land along, in many cases actually building it up from sand hills or peat bogs. Mediterranean man had been a farmer more by necessity than by temperament. His preference was for the urban life and his preferred solution to the problem of insufficient food was to go out and conquer some productive area that could be levied upon for food supplies. The northern European has had an almost mystic attachment to the land and a kind of blind faith in the virtues of rural living. His solution to the food problem was to give whatever land he possessed a large measure of tender, loving care. It did not always pay off; many a farmer lost everything he had and ended up as a rich man's property or a big-city beggar. Later it was from this unsuccessful class of farmers that many of the immigrants to the New World were drawn. But for surprisingly many farmers the land responded to these ministrations with abundant production. The archetype of this kind of farmer in modern Europe is the French peasant — prosperous, proud, pious, resistant to change, intensely individualistic, distrustful of townspeople and their works and ways, close to nature.

As noted above, it was not from the successful peasantry that immigrants to the New World were typically drawn. By and large, Europeans who made the venturesome trip across the ocean were idealists of one sort or another looking for a Utopia or, much more commonly, those "tired, poor huddled masses" of whom Emma Lazarus wrote. With few exceptions — notably the Pennsylvania Dutch and the French in Quebec — they had little understanding of the land, little appreciation for it, and little competence to manage it. Eventually, under the cruel discipline of necessity, they or their descendants learned to be farmers. But initially it was only the boundless wealth of virgin soil that prevented the farming practices of the pioneers from having fatal consequences.

In the New World lands, Europeans discovered that most of the crops they had known and raised in Europe found a new home where they did well. But they also came upon some plants which they had not known back in Europe, notably corn and tobacco. And since they were not, at heart, farmers but rather people who made their livings off the land, the Canadian and the American and the Australian converted farming into a business. The land was a resource to be mined until it was exhausted, then abandoned. One-crop specialization simplified operations and allowed for the cultivation of larger units of land; therefore, it received preference over general farming. Regional specializations received attention from the government and thus became secure, if not profitable, sources of income. What the Australian thought about farming is best indicated by his congregating in the state capital cities of his country. What the American thought about farming is best indicated by the unique agricultural landscape which he and his Canadian cousin have spread across a continent — the landscape not of a land-loving peasantry but of business folk who know how to make the land produce for them.

If this sounds censorious, it is not meant to. American farming has produced abundance while, particularly in recent years, maintaining the quality of the land. There is nothing intrinsically more noble in a peasant than in a businessman. Given the kind of people who came to America, and given the kind of country they found here, the pattern of our agriculture is about what one should expect. The existence of broad climatic belts over wide areas of lowland encouraged the development of agricultural regions of subcontinental proportions. The ease of movement across the continent, east and west and north and south, facilitated by the Great Lakes and by a magnificent river system, early encouraged regional specialization and exchange. The low density of population permitted large landholdings, and the invention of specialized machinery made it profitable to work vast areas as units. And the remarkable profits which Americans realized from their industry created the world's best market for agricultural products, reinforced by a European market which became more and more profitable as Europe withdrew men and land from agriculture to devote them to industry.

The types of agriculture which are included under the heading of "Occidental Agriculture" are described in more detail in certain of the regional chapters following: Mediterranean agriculture in Chapter 24; livestock ranching and grain farming in Chapter 21; commercial livestock and crop farming in Chapter 25; and dairy farming in Chapter 26.

What of the future of the kind of farming we have known in the United States? A recent collection of articles from *Fortune* magazine carries titles which may be prophetic of the directions along which American farming may advance in the immediate future: "Climate: The Heat May Be Off" (suggesting the possibility of long-range, dependable weather forecasting); "Forecast for Weather Control: Brighter" (a discussion of the possibilities of effecting precipitation and controlling storms); "A Strategy for Drought" (some clues to how "playing the percentages" in dryland farming may save the farmer from disaster); "Farming's Chemical Age" and "Farming With Hormones," both of which have to do with man's new ability to increase productivity by "playing God" with living things (5). Pity the poor Secretary of Agriculture, Republican or Democrat, who is called upon, in the midst of the most profound agricultural revolution in man's history, to make sure that no one feels its effects!

In the past half century agricultural production in the United States has doubled. Can this pace be maintained in the future? This is the answer which a knowledgeable American geographer, Dr. Chauncey Harris, suggests:

¶ Production increase in the near future does not promise to follow the pre-1920 pattern [of explosive increase]. A rapid expansion of the cultivated acreage in the next few decades appears unlikely. Many conservation and farm-management experts are of the opinion that because of high erosion hazards about 40 million acres . . . should be taken out of cultivation and put mainly into grassland. In the long run greater production from these lands may come from soil-conserving grassland farming than from utilization as plowed fields. Withdrawals from cultivation may be approximately offset by putting new land under cultivation.

. . . It is estimated . . . that 170 million acres net of land now in grassland or woodland is suited to cultivation. This is equal to half the present cultivated acreage. Under heavy population pressure, such as exists in Western Europe, or larger demand, this area could and would be put under the plow. . . .

The second possibility, the making available of additional cultivated land by the shift from animate to inanimate power, holds little promise. The transfer to tractor power has about run its course, and only 12 million acres remained in this reservoir in 1954.

The third possibility, increased crop yields per acre and increased livestock production per unit of feed, offers the greatest promise. Full and efficient application of technology already known and, under present conditions, economically feasible could increase agricultural production an estimated 86 per cent on the present acreage. But within a quarter of a century output attainable under existing conditions would be perhaps only half of this. . . .

If demand and prices for agricultural products should rise greatly, production per acre could be still further increased by larger investments of capital than are now profitable. For example, higher rates of fertilization could bring increased yields. Supplemental irrigation could augment agricultural production in the humid parts of the United States, where larger quantities of surface and ground water are available than in the arid and semiarid areas of present irrigation. A shift to direct production of human food by cultivation of intensive crops such as potatoes in place of meat would make possible the support of a much larger number of people than are fed on a given volume of agricultural production today. . . .

Still greater crop yields and livestock production may be made possible by further research. Particularly important are studies in genetics that may raise present biological ceilings on crop yields (as in the development of hybrid corn) and livestock production (as promised by the breeding of hybrid hogs), and in control of insects and diseases (as in the case of potatoes). . . .

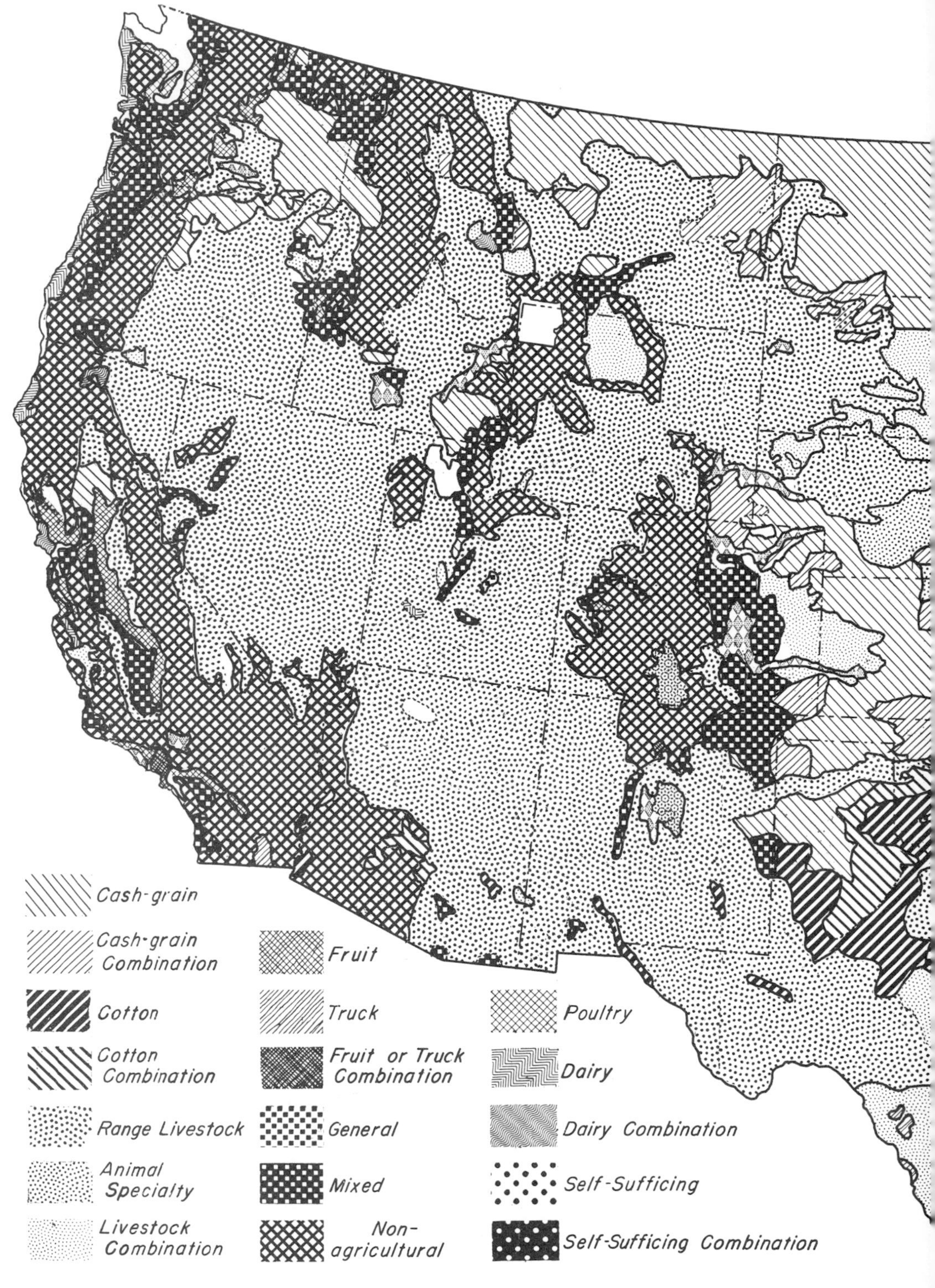
Cash-grain
Cash-grain Combination
Cotton
Cotton Combination
Range Livestock
Animal Specialty
Livestock Combination
Fruit
Truck
Fruit or Truck Combination
General
Mixed
Non-agricultural
Poultry
Dairy
Dairy Combination
Self-Sufficing
Self-Sufficing Combination

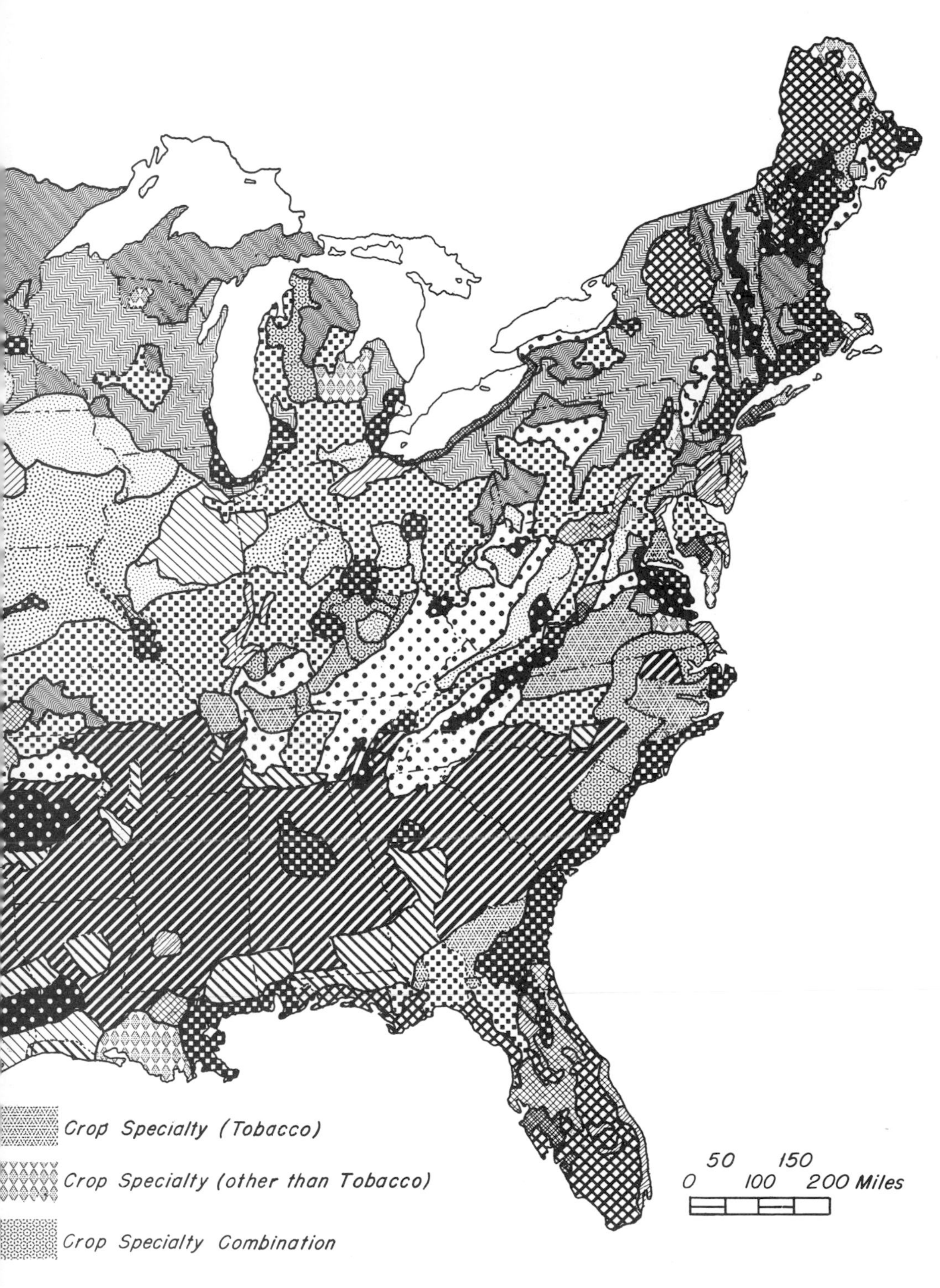

XIII:4 Agricultural regions of the United States. (Redrawn from *Agriculture Handbook No. 153,* U.S. Department of Agriculture)

Mr. James Minatani and his son, Steve, raise 65 acres of Russet potatoes under irrigation in the Columbia Basin Project near Moses Lake, Washington. This land would be wasteland without irrigation. Its high productivity under irrigation shows what can be done to enlarge the world's fund of agricultural land. What actual advantages do irrigated lands possess over lands which are watered by rainfall? (Bureau of Reclamation, United States Department of the Interior. Photograph by Stan Rasmussen)

Nearly a third of the potential value of crops, livestock, and forest products in the United States is lost—a loss equal to the potential production of 120 million acres of cropland. Losses comprise both production damage attributable to weather, insects, disease, mechanical damage, weeds, or harvesting waste and distribution losses in storage, marketing, and processing of crops, death of animals, destruction of nutrients in cooking, and waste of edible food in the kitchen. These losses could be reduced to a certain extent, though some waste-reducing practices would not pay under present conditions.

So far as markets are concerned, the outlook for the immediate future is for production to run ahead of demand: output has continued to rise since 1952 in spite of falling prices and farm income. Production capacities for wheat and cotton particularly are in excess of current markets.

Agricultural production in the United States for the next few decades, and probably for the full half century, apparently will be determined largely by the growth of population and demand. This is the reverse of conditions in certain overpopulated, underdeveloped countries, in which population growth will depend directly on increased local food production.[1]

[1] Harris, Chauncey D., "Agricultural Production in the United States: The Past Fifty Years and the Next," *Geographical Review*, Vol. XLVII, No. 2, April, 1957, pp. 189-192. Reprinted by permission.

Regions of plantation agriculture

Plantation agriculture is, by definition, commercial farming. In some ways it is the most commercial of all forms of farming. Characteristically, the plantation is called into being by peculiar local conditions of climate and soil and relief which make it possible to grow a certain crop profitably in that place, and by the absence of those conditions in areas where there is a large demand for the crop. In practice this has meant the establishment of plantations in tropical and subtropical lands to satisfy demands in the wealthy market areas of Europe and North America.

Typical plantation crops are coconuts, sugar, cacao, bananas, pineapple, cotton, sisal, and rubber. Within the *A* and *Ca* climatic regions there are many areas that are physically suitable to the production of any of these crops. One of the most distinctive characteristics of plantation crops is, therefore, their tendency to be overproduced. This tendency, in turn, accounts for two other basic characteristics of plantation agriculture:

1. An inclination on the part of plantation developers to make economic, cultural, and political factors decisive in the choice of the particular area they will develop from among all of the physically-suitable alternatives.

2. A temptation to plantation managers to abandon plantations threatened by blight or insect infestation or by any other threat to production, rather than to accept the extra cost of maintaining the plantation.

These characteristics are symptomatic of still another characteristic of plantation agriculture. With rare exceptions (Hawaii is a notable one), plantations are examples of the best and the worst in absentee ownership. On the credit side, they bring capital into areas which, usually, lacked capital for their own development. Often, along with capital, they bring in trained personnel and at least the minimal trappings of a more advanced civilization (e.g., roads, docks, perhaps schools and dispensaries). And, under humanitarian management, they may provide remunerative work for local populations. On the debit side, plantations have been known to upset indigenous cultures by importing nonassimilable laborers; to wreck local economies; to exert undue influence upon local governments or, on occasion, to bring about the overthrow of unco-operative governments; to create artificially high living standards in areas which they subsequently have abandoned.

A good example of a plantation crop is rubber. The rubber tree, *Hevea brasiliensis*, grows only in the rainy tropics, demanding as it does an annual rainfall of between 80 and 120 inches, daily temperatures between 75° and 90°, and year-around dependability of both temperature and rainfall.

If only these climatic limitations were involved, rubber might be grown anywhere in the *Af* world below 2,000 feet. Indeed, it has been introduced successfully into northern Queensland, the Fiji Islands, some of the West Indies, the Seychelles Islands, Liberia, and other areas of west Africa — not to mention the original home of the rubber tree, the Amazon Valley. But the great bulk of the world's rubber supply still comes from the Malay Peninsula and the East Indies. Why this concentration of production in one very small part of the total area available for rubber production?

One of the standard textbooks in economic geography offers this answer:

¶ While the best rubber trees can be grown nearly everywhere in the rainy tropics, there is a limiting factor—labor. The problem of getting a labor supply which will be skilled, hard-working, and above all *cheap* is the one which is causing all the would-be rubber growers over the world to despair.

The labor supply of Malaya is unique. The Straits Settlements (British) are a few settlements along the Straits of Malacca comprising a small fraction of the land area of the Peninsula. Here the British Government has kept the Malay population in order, so that the Chinese, industrious, quick to seize opportunities, have gone there for the business opportunities in a climate which they can stand better than Europeans, as census figures so glaringly attest. Within a comparatively short distance of Singapore are enormous additional labor supplies that can upon demand be furnished by the millions of China, of Java, of India. The Dutch East Indies have a teeming population of their own. Ceylon, an important rubber producer, has a dense population and, moreover, is able to draw tens of thousands of laborers across the straits from India.

It is only too apparent that rubber growing in the British and Dutch East Indies has succeeded mainly because, in addition to peace and order enforced from the outside, they have available a large supply of cheap labor to clear the forest, tend the trees, and gather the latex.[1]

This answer is somewhat dated in the light of political changes that have taken place in this region since the end of the Second World War. But the principles which it brings out are still valid: when physical factors do not set narrow limits for an activity or a crop, economic and social and political factors are called upon to define its boundaries. Actually many factors other than cheap labor favor the East Indian region over other potential rubber-producing regions, factors such as access to major trade routes, the willingness of investment capital to take its chances in this region, and, of course, the very considerable advantage of having been the first rubber plantation area to have been established.

It may have occurred to the perceptive student that, inasmuch as these are all cultural factors, they are susceptible to changes which might, in turn, bring about changes in the location of the plantation rubber industry. This is true. Naturally, there is always a tendency for a going concern to stay "put," but when the advantages which once determined its location begin to disappear, there comes a point at which the costs of relocating are offset by the disadvantages of staying. There was a time not many years ago when the very unsettled political situation in the East Indian area seemed likely to cost the area its plantation rubber industry. Fortunately for the economy of the region a semblance of peace and order was re-established in time to prevent this loss. But whether the political problems of this area have been solved or merely compromised we do not know — and therefore we do not know what prospects lie in store for the plantation rubber industry of the region.

One other characteristic of plantation agriculture should be brought to the attention of the reader who happens to be a citizen of one of the middle-latitude countries. It has already been pointed out that (a) most plantation crops tend to be overproduced, and (b) most plantation crops are produced in tropical or subtropical lands for consumption in middle-latitude countries. In practical terms this means that countries which are strongly dependent upon a plantation economy are very much at the mercy of the middle-latitude consumers, especially the greatest of all consuming nations, the United States. Few plantation crops enjoy a really free market; practically all of them are regulated, in terms of production and price, either by some sort of international agreement or by the purchasing policies of the major importers. Plantation agriculture is thus inextricably linked to the shifts and vagaries of international politics, and plantation countries chafe under the realization that, in the economic area, they are not masters of their own destinies.

APPLICATION OF GEOGRAPHIC UNDERSTANDING

I. What type or types of agriculture are practiced in the country in which you live? What are the physical bases for this type of agriculture? What are the cultural bases? Is there any relationship between types of agriculture and ethnic types? Are there any highly specialized forms of agriculture and, if so, how do you explain them?

II. Along the southeast shore of Lake Michigan in the State of Michigan there is a thriving orchard area (peaches and apples). What factors of climate, relief, soil, economics, etc., help to explain the location of this orchard district in this place?

III. Per unit of weight, rice supplies considerably more food value than any other cereal grain. In our own country there are large areas in the South which are in every physical way suitable for rice culture. Why, then, do we produce so little rice in our country?

IV. In the report of the Mid-Century Conference on Resources for the Future (*The Nation Looks at Its Resources,* Resources for the Future, Inc., 1953), the distinguished American geographer, Dr. Charles C. Colby, says: "One source of competition in the use

---

[1] Smith, J. Russell, and Phillips, M. Ogden, *Industrial and Commercial Geography,* Holt, Rinehart and Winston, 1946, pp. 677-678. Reprinted by permission.

of farm land is between the large high-production farm and the many low-production farms. . . . Some 1½ million low-production farmers struggle along spending too much labor on too little and often unproductive land, and with too little capital to provide for machinery and fertilizer." Questions: (a) What are the arguments for encouraging or forcing these low-production farmers off the land? (b) What are the arguments for helping them to stay on the land? (c) How, in either case, could the objective be accomplished?

V. One of the few successful challenges to East Indian domination in the plantation rubber industry has been the Firestone plantations in Liberia. What explanations can you suggest for the success of this Liberian enterprise?

VI. How do you think the pattern of world agriculture might be changed if there were no restrictions on the free movements of agricultural products from one country to another?

VII. Suggest ways in which food can be, or has been, used as a weapon in economic and military wars.

VIII. Why, in the light of the troublesome crop surpluses of recent years, should we in the United States be concerned about the question of how to increase farm production?

IX. Suggest examples of the truth of Huntington's statement that "when people from a more advanced economy come to a relatively backward economy. . . they tend to discover new uses and markets for hitherto neglected resources."

X. Older textbooks used to make a rather sharp distinction between arable land (capable of being farmed productively) and nonarable land (not capable of productive farming). Why should we as geographers be very cautious about making such distinctions and, particularly, about applying these classifications to particular land areas?

References

1 Huntington, Ellsworth, *Principles of Economic Geography,* 1940, John Wiley & Sons, Inc., N.Y., pp. 232, 233, 241, 247, 249, 311, 399, 400, 456.

2 *Annals of the Association of American Geographers,* Vol. XXVI, 1936, pp. 199-240.

3 Pendleton, Robert L., "Agricultural and Forestry Potentialities of the Tropics," *Agronomy Journal,* Vol. XLII, No. 3, March, 1950, p. 116.

4 Jones, Clarence Fielden, and Darkenwald, Gordon Gerald, *Economic Geography,* The Macmillan Company, New York, 1954, p. 235.

5 Ward, Richard J., and Hoffman, Lawrence A., Editors, *Readings in Economic Geography from Fortune,* Holt, Rinehart & Winston, Inc., New York, 1960.

6 Harris, Chauncey D., "Agricultural Production in the United States: The Past Fifty Years and Next," *Geographical Review,* Vol. XLVII, No. 2, April, 1957, pp. 189-192.

7 Smith, J. Russell, and Phillips, M. Ogden, *Industrial and Commercial Geography,* Henry Holt and Company, New York, 1946, pp. 677-678.

Chapter 14

The geography of factory products

Approximately one out of every three gainfully-employed Americans is employed in manufacturing. Practically every one of our major cities, and many of our smaller towns, are manufacturing centers, and the "factory district" is as much a part of our urban landscapes as is the downtown commercial district. The prosperity of whole regions may depend upon the health of a particular type of manufacturing industry, and, in smaller towns, the prosperity of the community may depend upon the success of a particular manufacturing plant. Even the leisure-time activities of many Americans are organized around the company baseball team or bowling league. An industrial dispute in one of the major factories of a town may create civil war within the community.

Since factory industry is so much a part of our way of thinking and living, it is usually something of a shock for the average American to look at a map of the world such as Figure XIV-1 and see how very small a percentage of the total area of the earth can be classified as an industrial landscape. Actually, there are only two large areas which can be classified as basically industrial in their activities and appearance. The one is in North America, extending from about the Mississippi River to the Atlantic Ocean and from the Canadian fringe of the Great Lakes to the Ohio River with projections into the Appalachian Piedmont and the St. Lawrence Lowland. The other is in northwestern Europe, extending from the Scottish lowlands to a line drawn east and west through the main range of the Swiss Alps and from about the Seine River to the Oder River. In addition to these large areas, there is a middle-sized industrial area in Japan, from Tokyo southward, and then a number of smaller ones in the U.S.S.R., in the Ganges Valley of India, around Sydney and Melbourne in Australia, in eastern Brazil and eastern Argentina, on the Mexican plateau, in the Alabama and Gulf Coast fringe of the United States, and along our Pacific coast. These smaller manufacturing areas stand out like islands in a sea of agriculture.

Nor is this association of industry with agriculture accidental, for manufacturing develops characteristically in economies which have already attained a certain degree of prosperity. In most cases, a thriving agriculture was the original basis of that prosperity. The mere desire for material things does not create a market. A market comes into being when people have both the desire for material things and the ability to pay for them. This ability to pay depends, in turn, upon the over-all profits of an economy. To put it more simply, a people which can just barely manage to satisfy its minimal needs for food, clothing, and shelter will not constitute a market for the products of manufacturing, no matter how much such people may desire those products. This is one of the most vexing problems of the modern world. Modern means of communications have made the world's less-prosperous billions aware of comforts and conveniences which they would never even have dreamt of as recently as a generation or two ago, and which they desire as avidly as do the fortunate millions who are able to afford them. Thus, at the same time that the gap between luxury and destitution becomes constantly greater, the appreciation of the enormousness of that gap becomes constantly clearer, and a kind of hopeless envy comes to dominate the attitudes of the less-prosperous peoples over against the prosperous ones. And often enough this envy is intensified by the realization that the poverty of one's own country or region is not the result of bad luck or indolence but of basic and apparently unchangeable geographical and geological limitations.

People + resources = industry

Historically, manufacturing industries have developed in countries and regions where people were able to afford more than they had, and where they either had or could get the materials needed to satisfy their desires. There is, so far as we know, no limit to human wants. The effective limit at any given time is set by the technology available to man. So long as human and animal energies were the chief sources of power available to man, the range of man's satisfiable wants was essentially the same in one part of the world as in another. But with the discovery of means to make inanimate energy do the work which had formerly been done by animal energy, certain parts of the world took a commanding lead over the rest of the world in the production of material things.

The discoveries which have put vast stores of inanimate energy at man's disposal have been the products of an imagination capable of conceiving of a better situation than the status quo and of environmental factors which gave the creative imagination something with which to work. Probably most of the people of the world are capable of creative imagination, although among some of them this ability has been stifled by a blind devotion to traditional ways of living and doing things (e.g., China before 1912, the Russian Empire before 1917). Not nearly so many people, however, have had the opportunity to do much constructive day-dreaming. The Chinese rice-farmer who is bent over his patty from dawn to nightfall is obviously little inclined to spend his limited free time and surplus energy on dreams of a better future. The Melanesian who knows nothing about electricity is obviously in no position to dream up labor-saving tools that could be powered by electricity. Like all of the other fruits of an advanced culture, manufacturing has developed in an atmosphere of constructive leisure and exchange of information. A nation which cannot afford leisure or is unwilling or unable to participate in the thought life of the world around it will either never develop manufacturing industries or will fall behind in the industrial race.

Unfortunately, vast areas of the world offer the creative imagination little with which to operate. Two of the most serious limitations upon industrial development in many parts of the world are isolation from the main currents of thought and activity and poverty of natural resources. The scattered Indian tribes of the Americas were, for the most part, highly intelligent groups, and the territories over which they ranged contained all of the resources which today support the great industries of the New World. But these tribes were cut off from the rest of mankind by two wide oceans, and from each other by vast forests and deserts. If they had remained isolated and in possession of these continents, they might never have developed a manufacturing civilization. A similar explanation might be suggested for the "backwardness" of the Negro tribes of trans-Saharan Africa, established as they were in little islands of settlement well to the south of the world's broadest and driest desert; and of the aboriginal Australians who hardly retained the memory of other peoples and cultures in their geographic "dead-end." Even Spain, isolated behind the wall of the Pyrenees and swallowed up by an alien culture for five centuries, may be considered an example of how isolation inhibits the development of manufacturing.

In the North European Plain, by contrast, a fortuitous arrangement of easily-traversable lowlands, navigable rivers, and narrow seas made isolation impossible even for those who might desire a more hermetic existence. Armies, goods, and ideas moved with relative ease from the Vistula to the Irish Sea. No new idea, no new process could long be locally confined. Every invention, every discovery that was made within the area soon became common property and often underwent considerable elaboration and refinement as it passed from one nation to another. It was the pooling of ideas and discoveries that set the stage for the Industrial Revolution of the eighteenth century in Northwestern Europe, and the early industrialization of the United States is ascribable in large part to the fact that our country was settled by immigrants who were the heirs and beneficiaries of European culture. To this initial advantage, a tremendous opportunity opened up, once our forefathers had filtered through the Appalachian wall, to live in a vast lowland even richer and more easily traversable than the North European Plain.

The lack of natural resources is an even greater handicap to industrialization than is isolation, because while man can overcome the barriers that isolate him through the development of new means of communication and transportation, he cannot undo geology. For all practical purposes, the soils, the minerals, the water supplies, and the topography which furnish man with the raw materials for his industry were all in place before man ar-

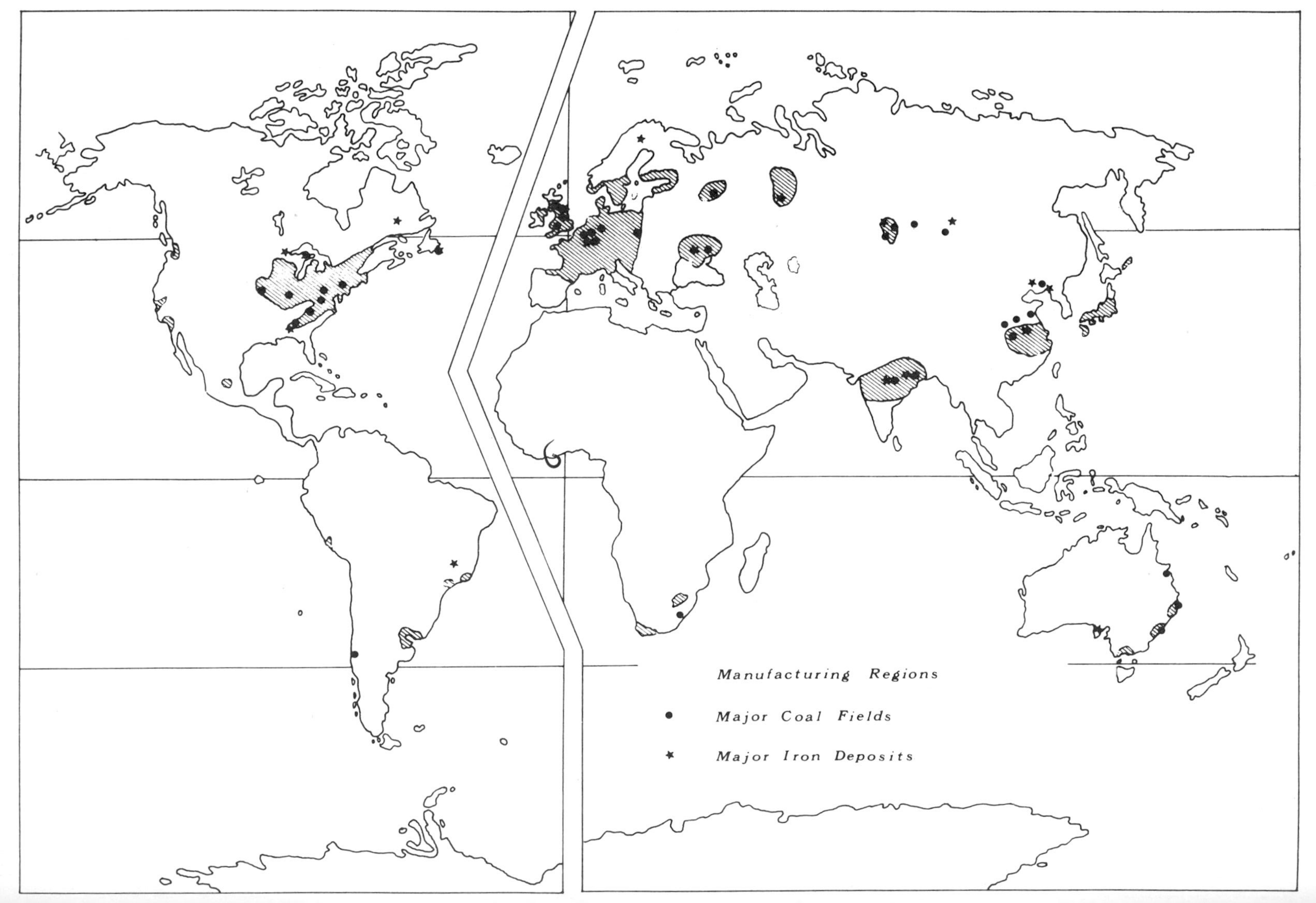
Manufacturing Regions
Major Coal Fields
Major Iron Deposits

rived upon the scene. Although man, in a limited sense, may rearrange or improve his resource base, generally speaking, he must accept it, for good or for bad, as the given quantity in his economic equation.

As pointed out above, the creative imagination is of primary importance to the development of industry. The relationship between ideas and resources is a reciprocal relationship. In large measure, man's ideas are suggested to him by nature; but man, in turn, conjures up ideas which demand, for their fulfillment, materials which nature does not directly provide but which can be made from the materials which nature does provide. Thus nature supplies iron ore and suggests certain uses for iron to man. But man developed a material more versatile in its uses than iron and assembled from the materials of nature the ingredients of a wide range of steels. And so it goes: man and nature working together make possible the countless products of factory industry.

Factory industry

The term "industry" is a very broad one and comprehends all of man's activities which produce wealth in terms of goods, utilities, and services. Manufacturing is that particular type of industry concerned with producing wealth by giving greater utility to the raw materials of the earth or the products of other industries. Manufacturing is, thus, essentially a creative process which supplies man with goods not supplied by natural or biological processes. Factory industry is a specialized type of manufacturing, carried on in relatively large establishments where the manufacture of any one item is usually not the work of one man but is accomplished by the subdivision of tasks and the large-scale use of machinery in performing them.

XIV:1 (Left) This map shows the world's major manufacturing regions. Small but potentially important regions in South America have been omitted from this map. The location of major iron and coal deposits have been included in order to emphasize the close correlation between the location of these resources and the manufacturing regions.

The greater part of the work in a factory is done along an assembly line, and individual workers are usually assigned to a particular job in the manufacturing process. Factory industries range in size from such enormous establishments as a large steel mill or chemical plant to such small establishments as apron factories. In our complex industrial structure, the line separating a factory from a shop or a laboratory is not a sharp one and similar establishments may have a variety of names.

Development of factory industries

The general principle underlying the establishment of industry in any given place has been stated by Dr. George T. Renner in the following words:

> ¶ Every industry represents the capitalization by man of some element or combination of elements in the natural environment. The choice of industry and the success with which it is prosecuted depend upon and vary with the quality and type of resources available, balanced against the level and the effectiveness of the available technology.[1]

The kinds of resources needed for the development of industry may be grouped, for the sake of convenience, under three broad headings: facilitative resources, power resources, and raw materials.

The facilitative resources. Facilitative resources embrace those elements in the natural environment which do not enter into the composition of the finished product and which do not supply power for its manufacture but which are, nevertheless, necessary for the efficient working of the manufactural process. The four most important of these facilitative resources are (1) a favorable climate, (2) level to gently rolling topography, (3) an abundant supply of fresh water, and (4) good drainage.

A comparison of Figure XIV-1 with the climates map in the Appendix will show that there is a high degree of correlation between the distribution of the world's major industrial districts and that of certain types of climate. In general, we may describe the in-

[1] Renner, George T., "Some Principles and Laws of Economic Geography," *The Journal of Geography*, Vol. XLIX, No. 1, January, 1950, pp. 16. Reprinted by permission.

These Guatemala women are weaving intricate Mayan designs into souvenirs for tourists. Their "machinery" is primitive, but a combination of skill and good taste enables these women to produce a high-value product. Why do tourists pay relatively high prices for this sort of thing? (Courtesy Delta Airlines)

dustrial climates as humid climates with a distinct seasonality of temperature and a considerable amount of day-to-day variation in temperature. It seems apparent from studies made by Huntington and others that the level of human physical and mental energy is related to climate, the highest levels being associated with the *Cfb* and *Dfb* types of climate. *Dfa* and *Cfa* are close enough to the optimum that they need not be considered at all unfavorable to industrial development. But once one gets beyond the range of these climates, obvious handicaps to industrialization become apparent. The *E, Dc,* and *Dd* types of climate are generally nonagricultural climates and industry shows little inclination to develop where there is no agricultural base for a reasonably large population. The *BW* climate and the drier phase of the *BS* are also nonagricultural climates. The *Cs* climates are almost all associated with narrow strips of coasts between mountains and sea where there is only very limited room for factory construction, and these climates are also likely to create a situation of limited or seasonal water supply. (In spite of these limitations, vigorous peoples have established significant industrial districts in such *Cs* areas as California, middle Chile, the Union of South Africa, and coastal Peru.) The *A* climates with their high temperatures and year-round monotony, coupled in the case of the *Af* and *Am* with torrential rains, have little modern factory industry. To a limited extent, the climatic limitation can be overcome by air-conditioning, but this is an expensive solution and one which is not capable of being applied to really large factory units.

For some industries, climate may be of critical importance. In the textile industry, for instance, a certain degree of humidity is essential to prevent costly loss of time occasioned by breakage of thread. In the aircraft industry, a relatively rainless climate may be advantageous for outside assembly work and for test flying. In the motion picture industry (if we may consider a studio a type of factory) dependably clear weather is of great help in maintaining shooting schedules. These are, however, unusual cases. In general, the importance of climate in industrial development derives from its effects upon the industrial worker and upon the total economy of the region.

The importance of level to gently rolling land may be deduced from comparing Figure XIV-1 with the continental relief models in Chapter 7. Modern factory manufacturing calls for the assembling of a great number of raw materials and semifinished products and the widespread distribution of finished products. Rough topography inhibits the movement of materials and goods and usually frustrates the development of an adequate transportation system. Mountain and plateau country are, therefore, unlikely to experience any considerable degree of industrialization unless they possess resources unusually valuable in terms of quantity or quality or unless they have been chosen for industrialization on the basis of factors other than the economic (e.g., military security).

An abundant supply of fresh water is almost a prerequisite for any high degree of industrialization. In a recent article, Mr. Arthur H. Carhart cites the needs of certain industries and processes to highlight the importance of water for industrial development. The steel in an auto, for instance, requires from 65,000 to 80,000 gallons of water per ton produced. Every gallon of gasoline burned in one's car involves the use of seven to ten gallons of water in its production. It takes 70,000 gallons of water to produce one ton of newsprint by the sulphate process, 200,000 gallons to produce a ton of viscose rayon, 380,000 gallons for a ton of butadine, and 600,000 gallons to ferment 1,000 bushels of industrial grain (2). Moreover, this water must be clean water, not polluted (as are most of the world's rivers) by sewage. And ideally it should be quite cold so as to be effective in industrial cooling processes. The best water supplies, accordingly, are likely to be groundwater reserves and large lakes. Rivers and small lakes are less satisfactory from the standpoint both of temperature and of purity. The vast resources of the ocean may some day become available for use if an inexpensive way can be found of freshening salt water.

Finally, it need hardly be pointed out that good drainage is essential for industrial development. Waterlogged landscapes permit neither the construction of factories nor the establishment of an agricultural base for a population. In the long run, poor drainage may prove almost as much of a handicap as is the climate to the industrialization of the humid tropics.

Civilization is essentially Promethean. In the eighth century before Christ, the Greek poet Hesiod told the story of a controversy between the gods and men at Mecone, at which Prometheus deceived Zeus, who, in revenge, withheld fire from men. But Prometheus stole fire in a hollow shaft and carried it to earth, for which he was punished by being chained to a rock where, every day, an eagle ate at his liver, which was healed again each night. To the ancient Greeks, Prometheus was the founder of civ-

In many parts of the world the artisan's shop is still the typical manufacturing establishment. This carpenter in Turkey manufactures everything from rolling pins to spinning wheels. Chances are that he inherited his craft from his father and ancestors, conceivably all the way back through twenty centuries. The industrialization of a country such as Turkey would mean the end of such shops as this one, unless its owner had the resources to build it up into a furniture factory. (Courtesy Turkish Information Office)

ilization, and as we look about us today we can readily see why they should have ascribed this honor to him. For civilization is essentially Promethean; that is, it rests upon the use of energy (most commonly some form of heat energy) to transform raw materials into useful commodities. The possession of sources of potential energy has, therefore, long been a powerful incentive to manufacturing and to the creation of the high levels of civilization which are associated with manufacturing.

Manufacturing in its broadest sense can be traced back to the dawn of civilization. Modern factory manufacturing, however, goes back only some two centuries to the time when textile mills were established along the flanks of the Pennine Range in England at sites where the kinetic energy of falling water could be used to turn the

Coke, the indispensable fuel of modern industry, falls into a quencher car from one of the 174 coke ovens of the Fairless Works near Morrisville, Pennsylvania. Sixteen tons of high-grade bituminous coal are required to produce eleven and one-half tons of coke. (Courtesy U.S. Steel Company)

mill wheels. Interestingly enough, manufacturing in our own country began at similar waterfall sites in southern New England and along the "Fall Line," the line of contact between hard rock of the Appalachian foothills and softer sedimentaries of the Atlantic coastal plain. At that time, water power was, by all odds, the most important source of inanimate energy, although wind power and charcoal were also of some importance.

It was not until comparatively late in history that man learned to use the potential energy which nature had stored up in the fossil fuels—coal, petroleum, and natural gas. But once man had learned to use these fuels, they opened the way to revolutionary new techniques of manufacturing, and those parts of the world blessed with good supplies of these fuels gained an enormous advantage, which, though perhaps not so great today as it formerly was, is still significant enough to account for the location of some of the world's great manufacturing areas. Among the more notable of these fuel-based industrial regions are the Pittsburgh-to-Lake Erie industrial district; the Birmingham (Alabama) industrial district; all of the industrial districts of Great Britain, except London; the Ruhrort and the Silesian districts of the North European Plain; the Don Basin, the Moscow-Leningrad-Gorki Triangle, and the Kuznets Basin of the U.S.S.R.; the eastern Ganges district of India; and the Sydney-Newcastle district of Australia. Most of the other great industrial concentrations of the world, if they are not actually organized around a coal field, are located at points to which coal can be brought easily and cheaply, usually by water transport. Allowing for certain exceptions, the geography of the world's industrial districts justifies the statement that "raw materials move to coal." Therefore, nations or regions which lack good supplies of metallurgical coal, if they industrialize at all, do so under considerable handicap. Good examples of such handicapped industrial nations are Japan, which has very little coal, and Italy, which has almost no coal.

In the earliest years of the industrial age, power was the most significant of all factors in localizing industrial development because it was impossible to move the power to any other site. The great advantage of coal over water power as an energy source was that coal could be used elsewhere than at the site where it occurred. The development of the steam engine and its sequel, the locomotive, made it possible to transport coal and, in the process, enlarged the area within which industry could establish itself. More recently, the various techniques which have been devised for transforming kinetic and heat energy into electrical energy have greatly expanded the potential area of industrialization. Every new technique for shipping or transmitting power cheaply over longer distances tends to reduce the significance of power resources as locative elements for manufacturing. These techniques have been largely responsible for the general decentralization of industry which has been going on since about the time of the First World War, and they have permitted industrialization to develop in areas where it had formerly seemed that manufacturing would be prohibitively expensive.

Shipping costs attract some industries to raw materials. The raw materials which industry uses may be animal, vegetable, or mineral. The distribution of animal and vegetable materials is likely to be strongly influenced by climate, while the distribution of mineral materials was long ago determined by geologic forces which operate so slowly that we cannot expect them to create any considerable supplies in the foreseeable future. The location of many industries is largely determined by the distribution of their sources of raw materials. Raw materials which are perishable or bulky (and, therefore, expensive to ship) tend to attract industries toward their areas of production.

Among industries which reflect in their location the perishability of their raw materials are butter and cheese factories, sugar refineries, canning factories, and to a certain extent flour mills and cereal manufacturing plants. Industries which use bulky materials expensive to ship include the pulp and paper industries, cement making, and the smelting industries. Smelting, particularly, is closely tied to its raw material source because most ores contain much valueless material which it would be foolish to ship any considerable distance. Most of the copper ores mined in the United States, for instance, run less than 1½ per cent copper. Even iron ores may run as low as 15-20 per cent iron. The lower the grade of the ore, the more likely it is to be processed at or near the mine.

Important as raw materials may be under certain circumstances as locative factors for industry, however, it does not follow that raw materials are a primary basis for industrialization. Much depends on the nature and the variety of the materials. One need only look at the mineral maps in Chapter 11 to note that the greatest mineral storehouses of the world are not major centers of manufacturing. Unless good fuel resources happen to be present in close proximity to mineral resources, the tendency is for these resources to be exploited for the advantage of the fuel-producing areas. This is demonstrably true, for instance, of the mineral-rich areas of the Canadian Shield, the Congo, and many parts of South America. The only major exception to this rule is the Urals of the U.S.S.R. where, chiefly for political and strategic reasons, a totalitarian government has chosen to ignore economics. But in a free economy, the Urals would undoubtedly be greatly at a disadvantage in its dependence upon coal which must be brought in from a thousand miles away.

On a small scale, movement of coal to raw materials may be found in situations where ore trains or barges carry coal back to the mining area rather than return empty. The small steel industry at the head of Lake Superior exemplifies this situation.

Geonomic factors in the localization of industry. Insofar as economic factors are spatially located and regionally distributed, they are capable of geographic description and analysis. In the study of the distribution of manufacturing, such "geonomic" factors are often of critical significance, and as technology gives man a greater measure of control over his natural environment the geonomic environment tends to become increasingly important in the localization of manufacturing. Chief among these geonomic considerations are the size and quality of the market, the nature of the available labor force, the adequacy of transportation facilities, and access to investment capital.

Factories need, and create, markets. Markets for manufactured products vary greatly both in size and in quality throughout the world. In general, the more sparsely populated a nation or a region is, the smaller is its potential market for manufactured goods. But it would not be accurate to say that the converse applies, for most of the very densely populated regions of the world (e.g., the Nile Valley, the Ganges Valley, the river valleys of China) also represent very limited markets because of the general low per-capita purchasing power of the people. Low per-capita purchasing power, in turn, tends to reflect either resource poverty or too great dependence of a local population upon local resources. Where dense populations are found in conjunction with low per-capita purchasing power, manufacturing tends to be highly decentralized and to be carried on mostly by small units: homes and shops.

Factory manufacturing, particularly in recent years, has shown a growing tendency to locate in or near its major market areas. There are many reasons for this, one of the most important being that industries more and more find themselves dependent upon other industries as the sources of semifinished raw materials. In other words, within an industrial region, a great many industries find that they are each other's best customers. To this consideration should be added the fact that the well-paid skilled workers whom manufacturing brings into a region are also likely to furnish a valuable market for the products that the factories produce. Thus manufacturing industries simultaneously tend to gravitate toward already-existent markets and, at the same time, tend to create or enlarge markets in those regions where they establish themselves.

Certain industries are particularly susceptible to the market pull. Most strongly affected are those industries which (1) produce a perishable finished product, (2) manufacture goods to the individual specifications of a customer, (3) produce a product which is bulkier than the raw materials which went into its manufacture, or (4) are strongly affected by style or technical improvement. To the first class would belong the whole class of small manufacturing industries, such as bakeries, which prepare foodstuffs for more or less immediate consumption. To the second class would belong large commercial printing establishments, certain types of machine tool industries, and custom tailor shops. The third class would include furniture factories, most machine tool industries, and automobile assembly plants. Examples of the fourth class would be the garment industries and many household goods industries.

Industries differ in their labor requirements. Several years ago, the craftsmen in a Cincinnati subsidiary of a Swiss watch-manufacturing firm thought that they had hit upon a way to show their Swiss associates that the American worker could do anything that the Swiss workers could do, and perhaps do it a little better. They made a very fine spring, as fine as a very fine human hair, put it in an envelope, and sent it without comment to the company headquarters in Switzerland. In a few weeks, the spring came back, also without comment. The absence of any comment was at first taken as a case of sour grapes, but finally someone thought to examine the spring under a microscope. The microscope revealed a comment more eloquent than words: a hole drilled neatly through the spring.

Skill of this kind is perhaps the world's most valuable industrial commodity. A people fortunate enough to possess it can afford to import fuels and raw materials and to ignore most geographic handicaps because these have little effect upon the value of the products which they manufacture. Many of the most-coveted luxury items of international trade can, therefore, be manufactured almost anywhere on earth, so long as a skilled labor force is available at the point of manufacture. Conversely, the less important the element of skill is in the manufacture of a product, the more likely is an industry to be dependent upon numbers of workers. Mass-production industries, in general, tend to require large, rather than highly-skilled, labor forces.

Where numbers of workers are important, manufacturing naturally tends to be drawn to areas of large population, particularly to areas where the population is disproportionately high in relation to opportunities for employment. Under such circumstances, wages tend to be low and the working force tends to be docile because the intractable worker is easily replaced by one more tractable. Through most of the nineteenth century and well into the twentieth century, manufacturing industries enjoyed an enormous advantage from the working out of the Malthusian principle that populations tend to increase geometrically while resources increase arithmetically. Driven off the land by sheer population increase accompanied by more efficient methods of farming, the European farm boy either migrated to the city where he became a part of the huge, low-cost labor supply, or he migrated to the New World where, in many cases, he also ended up in the cheap labor force of the cities. More recently, in our own country, growing populations and changes in the economy of our agriculture have accounted for large-scale migrations of Negroes, white sharecroppers, and Puerto Ricans into our northern industrial cities, where they play much the same economic role that immigrant labor played earlier in the century. It should be noted, however, that such cheap, submarginal labor forces do not confer any permanent advantage upon a region. Especially in the United States, the children of such labor will already have been exposed to educational processes which will remove them from the submarginal classification, and industrial unions will not long permit wage rates to remain out of line with prevailing rates in the region.

A particular kind of cheap labor which is likely to be associated with urban areas is "parasitical labor." The term has no invidious connotations but is used to refer to workers, most of them women, who are not the family breadwinners but who will take jobs to supplement the family income. Wives and unmarried daughters of industrial workers may come under this classification. Often they may possess a high degree of skill but they are not inclined to press claims for higher wages. The garment industries of New York use a great deal of such parasitical labor.

In the past, the term "labor" has been largely restricted to the production worker or the "blue-collar worker." It should be noted that a type of labor skill which is becoming more important all the time is administrative or management skill, the labor of the "white-collar worker." The growing importance of automation in industry has already greatly reduced, and in the future will undoubtedly further reduce, industry's dependence upon the unskilled worker, and has increased, and will continue to increase, its dependence upon skilled workers and highly-trained managers. This trend will make it even more difficult than in the past for so-called "backward" nations and regions to establish manufacturing industries. Other factors being equal, we may, therefore, anticipate an even greater concentration of industry than in the past in regions which are already industrial, although there may be considerable decentralization within those regions.

Transportation often follows industrialization. The modern factory is a large gathering point and distribution center. Most of what it works with must be brought in, often from considerable distances, and most of what it produces is designed for sale through a large market area, often a world market. It would seem, therefore, that good, economical transportation would be a prime necessity for the development of factory industries and, to a certain extent, this is true. Those parts of the world where transportation facilities are expensive to build and difficult to maintain suffer a major handicap to industrialization.

But where other conditions favor industrialization, transportation facilities are as likely to follow industrialization as to precede it. In all of northwestern Europe and in the northeastern quarter of our own country, the location and direction of railroads and roads were largely determined by the locations of industrial towns or potential industrial sites.

One aspect of the transportation picture which has had an influence upon industrial development in our country has been freight rate policies. For years the southern states have claimed, with what appears to be reasonable justification, that the rate structure has been "rigged" in such a way as to favor the Northeast at the expense of the South. A similar handicap, but one unrelated to rate policies, has limited the industrial development of our western states. Sparsely settled and separated by a wide expanse of lightly-populated country from the industrial concentrations of the East, these states have become accustomed, but not reconciled, to the advertiser's notation that "prices are slightly higher west of the Rockies." At the same time, much of the industrial development on the Pacific Coast can be ascribed to the insulation of this region from eastern competition.

"It takes money to make money." Anyone who has had the opportunity to visit a large steel mill or chemical plant will realize without being told that such an establishment represents an enormous capital investment. Capital is, therefore, an essential factor in the development of industry. But essential as it is, it is also perhaps the easiest ingredient to acquire when other factors are favorable for industrial development, for capital tends to flow toward any opportunity for profit and will even flow freely across international boundary lines unless it is artificially restrained. It is possible, however, for nations or regions which need capital to block its flow by threatening profits. Among the conditions which may block the flow of investment capital are governments that are hostile to private investment or too weak to maintain public order, an unsettled or unfriendly labor situation, excessive taxes on profits, too rigid supervision of corporate activities, certain kinds of currency and credit manipulations, and an unfavorable tariff structure. Industrialization in much of Latin America has been retarded by a shortage of domestic capital coupled with unstable social and political conditions which made foreign companies reluctant to risk investment.

In contrast, some foreign countries and certain of our states have actively fostered the development of factory industry by holding out special inducements to investors. One of the most notable examples of this "induced industrialization" has been Puerto Rico's "Operation Bootstrap," a program of active government assistance designed to attract industry to Puerto Rico. The New England states have also been very active in soliciting new industries to close the gap left by the southward migration of a large part of their cotton-textile industry.

Some principles of industrial geography

We might summarize our discussion up to this point by saying that the development of manufacturing industries within any given region is encouraged by an industrious and inventive population, a good supply of the fuel minerals or other sources of power, a variety of high-grade raw materials, a large and profitable market, a labor force suited to the needs of the kind of industry that is contemplated, a good transportation system, and access to investment capital. But if we examine any one of the major industrial regions of the world, we shall find that it is deficient along the line of some one or more of these factors. Northwestern Europe, for example, falls far short of the ideal in variety of raw materials, and its market is artificially restricted by international boundary lines. Japan is painfully short of coal and of raw materials. The most notable deficiency of our own industrial Northeast is in variety of raw materials.

Dr. George T. Renner has set down the general rule which governs industrial location in a statement which he calls "The Principle of Optimum Location." This principle states that "any industry tends to locate upon a site which provides optimum access to its ingredient elements. If all of these elements occur close together, the location of the industry is pre-determined. If, however, they occur widely separated, the industry will be so placed as to be most accessible to that element which would be most expensive or most difficult to transport, and which becomes, therefore, the locative factor for the industry in question."[1]

From this general principle, Dr. Renner deduces what he calls "laws" that govern the locations of the four major classes of industry—extractive, reproductive, facilitative, and manufactural. Our concern in this chapter is with the manufactural industries, which Dr. Renner believes to be located by the principles stated in the following "law":

¶ Any manufactural industry tends to locate at a point which provides optimum access to its ingredient elements. It will, therefore, seek a site near:

(a) raw materials, if it uses perishable or highly condensable raw substances;

(b) market, where the processing adds fragility, perishability, weight, or bulk to the raw materials, or where its products are subject to rapid changes in style, design or technological character;

(c) power, where mechanical energy costs of processing are the chief item in the total cost of fabrication;

(d) labor, where the wages paid to skilled artisans are a large item in the total cost of fabrication.[2]

Dr. Renner notes that capital and management skill are locative only during the industrial youth of a region (because industry tends to create both capital and a need for managers by its very existence), and that transportation facilities are locative only when a region has reached economic old age.

The dynamic nature of manufactural geography

The geography of a region, a nation, or the world itself is never static; it is always in process of change. Moreover, this rate of change is not uniform. Great discoveries and inventions so profoundly alter the relationships of things in space that we can properly describe the eras of rapid change which they introduce as revolutions. The location of industry in the world is, therefore, constantly changing also—least noticeably near the cores of the major industrial districts, much more noticeably along the margins of these districts and in the smaller industrial districts. The extent of these changes is determined by the relative strength of centrifugal and centripetal forces acting upon an industry or a region.

Among the strongest of the centripetal forces which act upon industries and industrial regions are (1) the fixed location of power and raw material resources, (2) the attraction of other industries within the region, (3) the large capital investment tied up in existing facilities and the correspondingly high cost of relocating, and (4) the inertia which ordinarily characterizes any going concern. Centrifugal forces are set in motion by economic, cultural, and political changes which increase costs of production at the existing site or promise notably greater profits at another site. A good example of how these changes operate is provided by the cotton textile industry of our own eastern states.

The first center of the cotton textile industry of the United States was New England. Around the turn of the century, the southern Appalachians began to develop a cotton textile industry which has since grown to rival that of New England. The shift of the center of this industry from New England to the southern Appalachians can be ascribed to:

¶ . . . evolution in the type and use of power, changes in organization and regulation of labor, advances in wages and living costs, mounting taxes of various kinds, conservatism and inertia resulting in the failure to keep machinery and plants completely modernized, declining profits and even losses in many mills, lack of available capital for improvements, and increased specialization for a more limited market.[3]

All of these factors operated to the disadvan-

[1] Renner, *op. cit.*, p. 17. Reprinted by permission.

[2] *Ibid.*, p. 18. Reprinted by permission.

[3] Jones, Clarence Fielden, and Darkenwald, Gordon Gerald, *Economic Geography*, The Macmillan Company, New York, 1954, p. 510. Reprinted by permission.

tage of New England and to the advantage of the southern Appalachians.

The trend away from direct water power and steam power to electric power generated by coal or water operated to the distinct advantage of the southern Appalachian area, which is 400 miles closer to the coal fields than is New England and which, therefore, pays less for coal. In the early development of the southern Appalachian district, the fact that the South was still our major source of raw cotton was an important consideration; with the movement of cotton-growing westward, some of this advantage was lost, but freight rates still favor the movement of Texas cotton to the southern Appalachians rather than New England. Capital has been no problem, being supplied both by textile corporations in the North which established branch plants in the South, and also by the large profits which the southern mills were able to make in their early years of operation. Some southern cities and towns, in an effort to attract industry, offered exemption from taxes for a certain period of years, and the more productive agricultural land of the South allows industry to carry a smaller proportion of the tax burden than in agriculturally-poor New England.

Labor has been competent and relatively less expensive in the South than in New England. The more moderate climate of the South makes food less expensive than in New England, and the laborer needs to spend less for clothing and fuel. The limited success of attempts to unionize Southern labor has also operated to keep labor costs relatively low. Mechanization of the mills, taken together with the specialization of the South in the lower grades of textiles, has allowed the southern mills to capitalize on the relatively large supply of semiskilled labor which was present in the rural South, where the handweaving of textiles had been a traditional art and where the progressive wearing-out of agricultural land under row-crop cultivation had made it necessary for a considerable proportion of the population to look elsewhere than to agriculture for a living. By contrast, the skilled, unionized New England worker, requiring a higher wage to cover the higher living costs dictated by his environment, adds notably to the cost of production in New England.

The southern Appalachians are well served by roads and railroad lines, although southern industries have long complained that they are the victims of a discriminatory freight tariff system. Greater industrialization, resulting in higher tax revenues, is enabling the South to improve its road system, further reducing the cost of hauling cotton by wagon or truck from local gins to the mills.

It should be pointed out that, while New England has been declining in relative importance as a cotton textile-manufacturing district, it is still an important one. It still enjoys the advantages of skilled labor and of experienced management, and it is still the center of the textile-machinery manufacturing industry. In the face of rising southern competition, New England has specialized in high-value textiles and specialties, for which its skilled labor force gives a competitive advantage which the South does not yet possess. In the process of specialization New England has, however, accepted the limitation of a restricted market, since the bulk of the cotton-textile market is for medium- and low-grade fabrics suitable for work clothes.

In recent years, a similar but less pronounced trend has been observable in the localization of the steel industry. Unlike the textile mills, the steel industry has so far shown no tendency to abandon its earlier sites along the Great Lakes, but the depletion of the Lake Superior iron ores, coupled with the probable necessity of eventually having to turn to new and more distant sources of raw materials for the industry, from scrap and from overseas mining areas, has resulted in the establishment of such major new facilities as those that have been built in recent years along the eastern seaboard. Here, in the heart of the nation's largest market, the supply of scrap is greatest, and here also are port sites to which ores can be brought from overseas. The Sparrows Point works near Baltimore and the Fairless works near Philadelphia are examples of large new mills thus situated. The discovery of large new ore supplies in eastern Canada and the completion of the St. Lawrence Seaway may be expected to arrest this movement to the coast and to rejuvenate the steel industry in the Great Lakes region.

A kind of centrifugal force which has only in recent years become important in the localization of industry is government intervention. The effects of government intervention are most evident in the changes that have taken place in the regionalization of industry in the Soviet Union. Both for economic and strategic reasons, the Soviet government has encouraged the decentralization of industry by placing limitations upon the growth of the older industrial areas and by fostering the development of new industrial areas. In our own country, the federal government has helped to create new industrial districts by sponsoring multipurpose power projects (e.g., the Tennessee Valley Authority) and by establishing defense plants or atomic energy plants in regions where there had formerly been little or no industry (e.g., Los Alamos, New Mexico). As new weapons broaden the area of probable destruction from enemy attack, decentralization of industry seems to be essential to national security and nations such as Great Britain or Japan which lack the space necessary for dispersal stand in very real danger of having their industry annihilated.

Location of factory industries

The location of a particular plant or factory within a region is considerably more difficult to explain geographically than is the development of an industrial region. The great industrial regions of the world reflect the unique concentration of a large number of locative factors for industry within a particular area. The location of a particular plant within that area may reflect nothing more than the whim of a proprietor or the availability of a particular piece of land at a reasonable price at some time in the past.

Certain principles of plant location within a region would, however, seem to be valid, among them the following:

1. Plants which are heavily dependent upon rail or water transportation are much more restricted in their choice of sites than is a plant which receives and ships materials largely by truck. Heavy industry therefore tends to concentrate along rail lines and harbor sites whereas light industry is much more free to choose its site on the basis of factors other than transportation.

2. The larger the plant and the more complex its ownership structure, the more likely is its location to be explainable in geographic terms rather than in terms of individual whims and preferences.

3. Except for "company towns," plant sizes tend to correlate with the sizes of the communities in which they are located. It is to be understood, of course, that the term community as used here includes not only the political unit (town or city) but the whole urbanized area.

4. The more important skilled labor is in the operation of a plant, the less restricted is its location. Corollary: the less important skilled labor is in the operation of a plant, the more closely the plant is limited to a site which is conveniently available to a large pool of cheap labor.

5. Industry begets industry. Plants will therefore tend to be sited in proximity to competitors, suppliers, and industrial customers.

6. Branch plants or assembly plants tend to be located in regional commercial centers (which usually are also transportation centers or termini).

7. In plant location, preference is given to flat, well-drained sites.

8. The greater the style or design factor is in the success of an industry, the more likely are plants of that industry to locate in proximity to each other.

9. The larger the percentage of women in the labor force of a plant, the more likely is the plant to be located near the center of an urban area or elsewhere within an urban area where public transportation is well-developed.

10. The larger the capital investment in a plant, the less likely is the plant to be relocated.

11. As a general rule, plants which give off objectionable odors or gases are likely to be found on the edge of an urban district opposite to the direction of the prevailing winds. This location may sometimes be concealed by later building around the plant.

12. Especially since the Second World War, local zoning laws have been probably the most important single influence upon the location of new plants.

Assuming, now, that a company has chosen the region in which it will open a new plant in accordance with "The Principle of Optimum Location," and that several equally desirable sites conform to the applicable principles listed above, what considerations may finally determine the precise site upon which the plant will be erected? In a panel discussion on plant location at the 1956 meeting of the Michigan Economic Development Commission, Mr. R. H. Powell, manager of the property management department of the Ford Motor Company, had this to say:

¶ Before finally selecting a site, we will attempt to make sure that the community has:

1. A genuine desire to have us as a neighbor.
2. Enough qualified people to man the operation and a friendly labor atmosphere.
3. Liberal zoning laws.
4. Adequate public services, such as sewers, water, and roads (or will construct them).
5. Fair present taxes and a reasonable attitude toward future levies.
6. An over-all air of cleanliness and progressiveness (4).

In the case of the Ford Motor Company, Mr. Powell observes:

¶ Our operating people feel that the ideally sized plant . . . is one containing approximately 1,250,000 feet, employing about 4,000 people, and built on a 200-acre site. Such a site would be about 3,500 feet long and 2,500 feet deep, with a major railroad bordering along one side, at least a four-lane highway on the other side, and perhaps a smaller highway at one end. We've found from bitter experience that such a plant should not be placed in a community of much less than 50,000 people. Nearly as many jobs are created outside the plant as within it, so the plant will probably mean at least 6,000 job openings. Small communities do not have the know-how, the people, or the utilities to handle such a development and absorb the shock it causes.

The criteria set forth by Mr. Powell would not, obviously, be applicable to all, or perhaps even most, industries. But they do serve to highlight the fact that modern industrial management knows with a high degree of precision what kind of a site it is looking for when it determines to build a new plant, and that the criteria it sets for the site which it seeks are basically geographical in character.

Special mention must be made of the importance of zoning in modern-day plant location. Mr. Fred G. Tykle, executive in charge of real estate for General Motors, cites the example of a community which had enacted a zoning ordinance and building code which provided, among other things, that no construction would be permitted which caused any dust whatsoever (4). This community, obviously, was soon eliminated from the list of possible sites for a new General Motors plant.

A more common mistake in planning and zoning ordinances is to leave for industrial development those parts of a community which, because of rough topography or poor drainage or difficult access or irregular lot size, are not considered desirable for residential building. Industry cannot use such "left-over" sites and, even if it could, it would be disinclined to locate in a community which gave such evidence of considering industry a kind of necessary evil to be tucked away in odd corners of the community.

Future manufactural patterns

Neither a prophet nor the son of a prophet would be so foolhardy as to attempt to outline the directions which manufacturing may be expected to take in the future, in either its nature or its location, for the whole history of manufactural development has been the story of practical applications given to the ideas and the inventions of men of genius. But it is possible to suggest in a tentative way some of the geographical realities to which industry will be forced to adjust in the years to come.

1. *Water supply.* As has already been indicated, the problem of failing water supplies is one which has come to plague all of the densely populated areas of the world. Industry, as a heavy user of water, may tend to concentrate more and more in areas where abundant supplies of good water are available. One might, for instance, predict a growing concentration of industry in the Great Lakes region.

2. *Atomic power.* If atomic power can be made cheaply available over large areas, many areas which are not presently suitable for industrial development might be made so. Smaller nations, and the so-called "backward" nations, would stand to benefit especially from such a development.

Fifty years ago, this might have been mistaken for an iron works in western Pennsylvania. The industrial landscape of those days was overlain by a thick pall of smoke which begrimed the town and countryside for miles around. The modern steel mill is capable of almost smokeless operation. To a country such as Yugoslavia, where this picture was taken, the rising smoke has much the same symbolic value that it had to Americans of fifty years ago; it means jobs for workers and products which will help to raise the standard of living. (Courtesy Yugoslav Information Center)

3. *National defense.* While it is possibly suicidal to permit industry to continue to concentrate in regions where it is already concentrated, it seems probable that decentralization will take the form chiefly of dispersal within already existent industrial regions rather than into presently nonindustrial areas. "The rich get richer and the poor get poorer" is an aphorism which seems especially applicable to manufactural regions, for such regions came into being because they possessed unique advantages which other areas did not possess and, so far as we can see, are not likely to acquire.

4. *Government intervention.* Offsetting what has just been said may be the factor of greater government intervention, for reasons either of economics or of national security, in the location of industries, especially the strategic war industries. If this should happen on a large scale, the study of industrial location will cease to be the field of the geographer and the economist and will become the preserve of the political scientist and the sociologist. In the U.S.S.R., this is already partially true.

5. *Less accessible raw materials.* One writer has called our world a "plundered planet." Certainly man, particularly Western man, has made heavy demands upon the resources of the earth, and the richest and most accessible resources have been the first to be used up. In the future we may, therefore, expect to see the present industrial districts

becoming more dependent upon low-grade or remote sources of raw materials with an accompanying increase in costs of production. Alternatively, we may see a declining dependence upon minerals and a greater dependence upon vegetational and animal raw materials. Any shift in the raw material base could be expected to involve some change in the localization of industry.

6. *An interdependent world.* If, as some prophesy, the world will move toward greater political and economic unity, the localization of manufacturing might be radically altered as industrial regions find themselves forced to produce in greater conformity to the law of comparative advantages. This would seem to indicate that those regions which are already the major industrial centers of the world will become even more so, although the nature of their products might change as each comes to specialize in the production of goods which it is especially adept at producing at low cost.

APPLICATION OF GEOGRAPHIC UNDERSTANDING

I. What geographical attractions does your own home town offer to industry? Are these attractions properly recognized in your local zoning ordinance or does the ordinance discourage industrial development? Do the people of your community want industry?

II. How does your state rank in industrialization among the states of the Union? What presently physical or locational resources could it develop to encourage further industrialization? What kinds of industry would be consistent with the geography of your state?

III. How would you explain the high degree of concentration of the automobile industry in southeastern Michigan? the large-scale development of the iron and steel industry at the southern end of Lake Michigan, where there is neither coal nor iron? the almost complete absence of manufacturing in Washington, D.C., despite its easy access to coal and its location on a tidal river?

IV. China is believed to have some of the world's largest reserves of coal and is known to have a considerable variety and abundance of industrial minerals. Why, then, does China have so little manufacturing?

V. Canada has only about 17 million people, most of them living within a few hundred miles of the United States border. What advantage, therefore, do American industries derive from building branch plants in Canada when these plants are often located within convenient shipping distance from the main plants in the United States?

VI. West Germany, the Benelux countries, France, and Italy are proposing to remove all tariff walls between them and to create a common tariff wall around them. What effects might the implementation of such a proposal have upon present patterns of manfactural geography within this Customs Union? What effects might it have upon manufacturing in other European countries which are not a part of the Union? What advantages or disadvantages might Great Britain expect from participation in such a union?

VII. You are director of development for the Amerlec Corporation, manufacturers of refrigerators and other electrical home appliances. The main plant of your corporation is in Cleveland, Ohio, and branch plants are located in Jersey City, New Jersey, and Oakland, California. Your assignment: to recommend to management the region into which the company should move next, to set up criteria for the selection of a plant site within the region, and on the basis of these criteria to select three specific communities for consideration by the board of directors.

References

1 Renner, George T., "Some Principles and Laws of Economic Geography," *The Journal of Geography,* Vol. XLIX, No. 1, January, 1950, pp. 16, 17, 18.

2 Carhart, Arthur H., "Our Nation's Water Wealth," *The Land,* Winter, 1951-1952, pp. 441-445.

3 Jones, Clarence Fielden, and Darkenwald, Gordon Gerald, *Economic Geography,* The Macmillan Company, New York, 1954, p. 510.

4 *Panel Talks on Plant Location at Meeting of Michigan Economic Development Commission,* April 20, 1956.

Chapter 15

The geography of trade and transportation

It may indeed be love that makes the world go round, but it is trade that keeps the world economy rolling. It may not be altogether accurate to say that no people on earth is self-sufficient—after all, a tribe which is content to live on nuts and berries and to sleep in caves may be technically self-sufficient—but it is certainly true that no nation possesses, within its own borders, a wide enough range of resources to bring its standard of living much above the subsistence level. Those resources which a nation needs, and does not have within its own boundaries, it must either take by force or stealth, acquire by trade, or do without.

Americans, who are rightly impressed by the variety and quality of their resources, tend to think that their country is an exception to this general rule. Throughout our history a great many of our people have been bemused by the idea that we could save ourselves a lot of trouble if we simply withdrew from world affairs and concentrated on making a good life for ourselves within our own borders. It is questionable whether such a course of action would be moral, even if it were feasible. But the point is that it is not feasible. The more complex an economy becomes, the wider becomes the range of resources that it requires. The nations that are most likely to be able to close their frontiers and "let the rest of the world go by" are those "backward" nations which are accustomed and content to get by on a comparatively low standard of living—Yemen, perhaps, or Bhutan. Great industrial nations such as the United States, the United Kingdom, Germany, France, Japan, and the Soviet Union must literally scour the earth for the fuels, the minerals, the forest products, and the foodstuffs which they need to maintain their people at an accustomed level of living.

But not only does a highly-industrialized country require a wide range of raw materials; it requires also markets for the surplus industrial and agricultural production of its farms, forests, and factories. In the case of the United States, it would be accurate to say that our export trade represents the margin of profit on the productivity of our economy. In the case of a country such as the United Kingdom the export trade is even more important; without it, Britain could literally not survive. The search for markets is, therefore, as keen and as competitive as is the search for raw-material sources.

Geographers are interested in trade as it reflects place-to-place differences and as it sets up patterns of movement upon the face of the earth. The first of these concerns results in attempts to isolate and define those place-to-place differences which constitute the geographical bases of trade, the second in identifying and mapping transportation routes.

What major place-to-place differences make an interchange of goods essential between regions and nations?

Trade arises, as we have said, out of place-to-place differences, some of them so obvious as to need little explication, others so subtle that their significance may be easily overlooked. The most obvious and, in most cases, the most significant of these differences lie in four areas: (1) the physical environment, particularly the climatic and the geological; (2) the socio-economic environment; (3) the differential distribution of population, both in numbers and in density, over the face of the earth; and (4) the degree of accessibility permitted by natural features and transportation routes. These factors must always be taken into account in any attempt to explain a given trade pattern. Other important differences may, however, be of critical importance in explaining a particular trade pattern or in accounting for the absence of trade between countries or regions where it might be expected. Some of these so-called "secondary" factors will be noted and discussed after we have explored the implications of the fundamental bases of commerce.

How physical differences foster commerce

Diversity of tradeable products reflects, in every case, some degree of difference in physical environments. Such differences may not, in every case, be determinative—although, in many cases, they are—but they are always present and always significant. This is most obviously true of such resources as minerals. They are where geological processes have placed them, and he who would use them must either go to them or bring them to himself. Since no one place or region on earth possesses the full range of minerals that a modern industrial economy requires, a great deal of bringing has to be done—often at great expense and inconvenience. The general trend of this trade is toward those countries and regions which possess good supplies of fuel minerals, since it is these minerals which turn the wheels of modern industry and thus play a major role in locating it. This trend is, however, much modified by socio-economic factors, so that some "advanced" countries which have no mineral fuel resources are important mineral importers while other "backward" countries which have abundant fuel resources (e.g., Venezuela and Saudi Arabia) export almost their entire production.

Differences in vegetable production are also often reflective of geological differences, particularly as these are determinants of the varying natures and capabilities of soils, but primarily they reflect climatic differences. Rubber, sugar, coffee, spices, mahogany, bananas, hemp—these are all commodities which historically have tended to move from tropical producing areas poleward (latitudinally) to the great consuming areas of the middle latitudes. But within the middle latitudes themselves there has long been a significant interchange of products between drylands and humid lands. At the present time, one of the most important commodities of international commerce, wheat, moves chiefly east and west (longitudinally) from the semidry lands into the temperate, humid lands. The importance of both of these lines of movement can be read in the nature of the great empires which were built, chiefly by European powers, during the past 400 years. Trade, it was believed, followed the flag, from which it followed that security of access to the needed products of other lands could be best guaranteed by bringing them under political control. There is probably an equally good argument for the contention that the flag followed trade. At any rate, American "Manifest Destiny" drew us westward into drylands with two or three tentative thrusts into the tropics. West European imperialism reached out equatorward into tropical Africa, Asia, America, and Oceania, with several tentative thrusts into the dry lands of the Mediterranean Basin. Russian imperialism thrust eastward into the dry lands and cold forests of central and northern Asia. Japan, coming late upon the scene, attempted to organize a "co-prosperity sphere" in tropical southeast Asia and Indonesia where British, French, and Dutch interests were already securely lodged. The tide of political imperialism has, except in the case of the Russians, been rolled back since the Second World War, but economic and commercial imperialism still survives, in greater or lesser measure, in many of the former colonial areas—necessarily, it would seem, because few of these countries have the variety or quality of resources to enable them to establish autonomous economies.

How the socio-economic environment affects commerce

When we say that trade presupposes a favorable socio-economic environment we mean that a people must have reached a stage in their cultural and economic development at which they have come to need and want goods which they cannot themselves produce; they must have discovered, invented, or produced materials or goods which other people want; they must have achieved a level of social and political stability which ensures reasonable security of person and property; they must have established the "machinery" of commerce (means of exchange, bookkeeping systems, credit facilities, etc.); and they must have developed the physical facilities of commerce (roads, railroads, airlines, docks, warehouses, telephone and telegraph systems, canals, etc.).

Basic to all of these are an attitude and a resource. The attitude is one of positive "unsatisfaction," by which we mean that there must be an unwillingness to merely "get by" on what nature provides locally, and a willingness to do those things which are necessary to participate in commercial activity. The American or the European or the Japanese or the Chinese, inveterate traders that they are, may too easily suppose that this attitude is a basic human trait like love or fear or anger. But this is not necessarily the

Mexican boys ride on their burro. In many parts of the world the pack animal is still the most expeditious carrier of commerce. In Mexico it happens to be the burro. In the Andean highlands it is the llama; in many of the Old World deserts it is the camel; in Tibet it is the yak. This is, by today's standards, a very inefficient way of getting from place to place, but the domestication of animals as burden-bearers was one of the great forward leaps of civilization, and for centuries they carried the bulk of the world's commerce. Even today animals can penetrate into remote places which it is not economically feasible to try to reach by more advanced forms of transportation. (Courtesy Delta Air Lines)

case. It may indeed be that the desire for a larger quantity and a greater variety of goods than any local environment provides is characteristic of every man and every culture, but there are cultures in which the commercial activity which is necessary to satisfy this desire is looked down upon as an undignified, if not positively shady, occupation. There is, for instance, a strong anticommercial tradition in Hispanic culture, and this tradition may account in part for the relatively low level of economic development in Spain and in some of the Latin-American countries. By contrast, the English have long gloried in the nickname which was originally fastened upon them as an epithet, "the nation of shopkeepers," and have made themselves the world's greatest trading nation.

The basic resource which a nation needs for trade is capital and, more particularly, venture capital. Trade is always accompanied by a certain element of risk, and the poor can seldom afford to risk the little that they have. But how does a nation go about accumulating this excess of wealth beyond its immediate needs which we call venture capital? Historically in one or both of two ways: either (1) by appropriating the wealth of others through conquest or plunder, or (2) by maximizing the value of its own human, land, and mineral resources. History is replete with examples of both of these methods, and the great nations of the world have employed both at one time or another. Indeed, it is difficult, if not impossible, to separate some of the great names of the past into neat categories of pirates and traders. But with the outlawing of piracy and the growing unprofitability of war, the trend has been toward capital accumulation by the maximization of resources: through popular education, through a more scientific kind of farming, through more intensive exploration and development of mineral resources, and, of course, through the conferral of greater utility upon raw materials by processing and manufacturing. The classic example from the modern world of a nation which has accumulated a large capital reserve from a very limited natural resource base is Switzerland. Lacking any other significant resources, the Swiss have maximized their human resources through education and intensive technological training and, by applying their knowledge and skill to relatively low-cost imported materials, have made handsome profits on very small material investments.

It is perhaps enough that the geographer point out that the degree of "unsatisfaction" and the size of capital reserves vary strikingly from place to place in our world—without attempting to explain why these differences should be. Certainly it would not be altogether amiss, though, to note that this attitude of positive unsatisfaction seems to be most characteristic of those lands which are elsewhere in this book described as lands of high climatic energy, and it must be obvious that in most cases those lands which are well-off in terms of venture capital are the same lands that nature has endowed with an abundance of such basic resources as good soils, useful minerals, forests, and water power.

How the distribution of people affects commerce

Trade involves people. But the mere presence of people does not necessarily ensure a large amount of commercial activity. Large populations living in a land of limited or undeveloped resources will produce little to trade and will, therefore, be in a very poor position to buy. This is the situation in India and in much of southeast Asia. In such cases, where the problem is one of developing resources rather than one of an actual lack of resources, such lands represent commercial frontiers which may someday develop into important commercial regions. Smaller populations occupying lands which are rich in resources may be engaged in a surprisingly brisk trade. Canada is a prime example of such a situation. In such a case, the full commercial potential of a country may not be realized until it has built up a population large enough to exploit the resources. Small populations living in regions of few or undeveloped resources are usually commercially unimportant. Most of the small "backward" countries of the world come under this category. Some of them, perhaps, can hope to play a larger part in the world commercial picture if they can get outside help to develop such resources as they have. Others must reconcile themselves to the harsh fact that, short of some sort of miracle, they will never be commercially important. Large populations combined with a wealth and variety of resources produce ideal conditions of trade, assuming that it is not inhibited by other factors.

The foregoing are generalizations to which individual exceptions may be noted. Their validity is, however, substantiated by the realities of the world trade patterns. The combination of large populations and an abundance of useful resources around the margins of the North Atlantic Basin coincides with a pattern of commercial activity unmatched in volume or variety anywhere else on earth, and the domestic trade within individual countries of the North Atlantic Basin is so brisk that the whole economic landscape of these countries may be best described as a commercial landscape. The relatively minor commercial importance of the North Pacific Basin, on the other hand, is surely ascribable, at least in large part, to a combination of relatively small population on the American side of that basin with impoverished populations (with the exception of Japan) on the Asiatic side. The Southern Hemisphere, with its very small proportion of land and its generally sparse distribution of population, is a much less important factor in world commerce, despite the fact that such lands as there are, are relatively well off in terms of resources.

How accessibility affects commerce

The last of the major factors which influence the volume and the direction of trade is accessibility, or the lack of it. Accessibility is, in turn, the product of an interplay of physical and cultural factors so complex that it can only be hinted at in the most general terms in this chapter.

1. Topography. High plateaus, especially if they are fringed by steep escarpments, are difficult of access and, if they exhibit deeply-incised drainage channels such as canyons, are equally difficult to traverse. Rugged mountains are often impassable barriers except at particular points where natural passes such as water gaps or glacial troughs provide through routes. Extensive areas of marsh or swamp effectively prohibit passage through them and settlement within them. Topographical handicaps can, of course, be overcome; six major tunnels pierce the Alpine barrier to allow north-south traffic between northern and Mediterranean Europe, for instance, and one of the most expensive railroads in the world (in terms of dollars per mile) ascends the steep escarpment which had long isolated the Brazilian coffee metropolis of São Paulo from the coastal plains where the great coffee port of Santos stands today. But major topographical obstacles are always expensive to overcome, and the expense of overcoming them must be justified by the profits that may be reasonably anticipated from doing so. Moreover, the cost of building transportation facilities in such ter-

By such marvelous, but expensive, engineering feats as this man leaps the barriers of nature. The Glen Canyon bridge obviously links more than the two sides of this canyon, more even than the immediate areas on either side of the canyon. Why might a geographer say that this is a bridge between Salt Lake City and Los Angeles? (Bureau of Reclamation, United States Department of the Interior. Photo by J. L. Bigby)

rain presupposes access to the large amounts of capital needed to underwrite them.

2. Location. Even on a spheroidal surface such as that of our earth, given the unequal distribution of land and water that is characteristic of our world, some places are closer to the center of population and activity and other places are "off the beaten track." Northwestern Europe, for example, is practically at the center of the "land hemisphere," that half of the earth's surface which contains almost all of its land. Australia and New Zealand, by contrast, have been nicknamed the "lands down under," lands which are remote from other land masses. A country or region which is on or at the intersection of main lines of movements enjoys advantages analogous to those of a filling station which is located along a busy highway or at a traffic interchange. Countries or regions which are off the main lines of movement might be compared to filling stations located on little-traveled country roads.

3. Shoreline configurations. Given a productive hinterland, good natural harbor sites are major stimulants to international and intercoastal commerce. The much-indented shorelines of northwestern Europe, southeastern coastal Japan, and our own northeastern states provide excellent natural harbors. By contrast, there are very few natural harbors in South America, Africa, India, or Australia. It is possible, of course, to create artificial harbors (e.g., Los Angeles) where the volume of commerce warrants it, but such harbors are expensive to build, often difficult to maintain, and usually very limited in size.

Some of the best of all harbors are the widened-out mouths of tidal rivers (estuaries) since the estuary itself provides the harbor and the river from which it is formed gives access to the interior. Among the many great world ports which occupy estuary sites are London, New York, Antwerp, Hamburg, and Liverpool.

*4. **Surface cover.*** Until very recently, thick forests were formidable barriers to overland travel—one reason why rivers and canals have historically played such a very important role in European travel and commerce. In some parts of the world, notably the tropics, vegetation is still an almost insuperable obstacle to passage, particularly since tropical vegetation, once it has been cleared at great trouble and expense, restores itself so rapidly that routes can be kept open only by constantly holding back the encroaching forest.

*5. **Special problems of cold lands.*** A reading of Chapter 19 will point up the almost insuperable difficulties of movement in and through the polar lands (*E*) and their *Dc* and *Dd* margins. Air transportation has to some degree alleviated the problem but not to the extent necessary to make these lands of any foreseeable commercial importance. Moreover, in the present state of international affairs, there seems to be little desire for closer commercial relations between the nations that lie on either side of what geographers a decade ago had hopefully labeled "the Arctic Mediterranean."

*6. **Political factors.*** Nowhere on our earth has nature built barriers so nearly impassable as those which governments have built. The "Iron Curtain" tops even the Himalayas as an obstacle to peaceful commerce and the prospects seem to be for more, rather than fewer, such barriers. New national states, self-consciously determined to work out their own destinies without outside interference, have blocked up long-established channels of trade. Many of these governments are so weak that they have not been able to maintain European-built facilities and installations which had formerly offset natural handicaps to access. Thus at the same time that technology has been busy eliminating space and surface obstacles, politics and ideologies have been even harder at work creating new barriers to trade.

Some relatively less important factors that affect trade

Before we proceed to examine some of the relatively less significant bases of trade, a word of caution is in order. It is not possible to draw up a checklist of factors which will automatically convert a nation or a region into a center of trade and commerce. Most of the great commercial nations possess all of the advantages which we have enumerated and will enumerate in a remarkably high degree, and these factors all interact with each other. Trade is something like good health, the consequence of the interplay of many factors and conditions, some of which are probably still unknown to us, or at best only dimly perceived. There is perhaps no better proof of this statement than the periodic recurrence of those periods of commercial illness which we call depressions, for which even the most widely acknowledged experts can offer no agreed-upon explanation. The list of factors which follows is meant to be suggestive, therefore, rather than exhaustive.

*1. **International relations.*** Other things being equal, people prefer to trade with their friends, or at least with people whom they like. The same is true of nations. And among nations as among individuals, friendships are based largely upon similarities of background, of likes and dislikes, of interests and objectives. Certainly one reason for the large amount of trade that goes on among the nations of the North Atlantic Basin is the binding factor of a common culture, expressed in a common history and in a basic similarity of language. At the present time, this essential unity is reinforced by unity against a common danger from the communist countries.

Another example of such a community of culture and interest is the Commonwealth of Nations — a loosely-knit association of sovereign states whose political constitution would be difficult to define with any great degree of precision but whose awareness of itself as a community is reflected, in a very obvious and practical way, in the preference which each member of the community shows toward others in its foreign commerce. The United States, although not a member of the Commonwealth, shares with it a common language, which perhaps helps to explain why so large a part of our foreign commerce is with members of the Commonwealth of Nations.

On the other hand, friendship itself is not a strong enough factor to compensate for the absence of the basic prerequisites of trade.

Despite the generally cordial relations which exist among the nations of the Western Hemisphere their economies tend to be competitive rather than supplementary and, for that reason, many of them have much closer commercial relations with European countries than with their sister republics in the Hemisphere.

One of the remarkable developments in Europe in the years since the end of the Second World War has been the trend toward economic alliances designed to lower trade barriers among their member nations. In 1948 seventeen European countries founded an Organization for European Economic Cooperation in association with the Marshall Aid Program. On March 25, 1957, six of the nations which were members of this organization signed the Treaty of Rome, which provided for the gradual elimination of tariffs among the signatory powers and the establishment of a common tariff boundary around them. Thus these six countries — Belgium, France, Germany, Italy, the Netherlands, and Luxemburg — are in the process of becoming, for all practical purposes, one economic entity while retaining their political identities. Collectively they are known as the European Economic Community (EEC). On November 20, 1959, seven other members of the OEEC initialled a convention establishing the European Free Trade Association (EFTA). Like the members of the EEC, the countries adhering to the EFTA—Austria, Denmark, Great Britain, Norway, Portugal, Sweden, and Switzerland—propose a systematic reduction in tariffs among them over a period of years but, unlike the EEC, do not propose to establish a common customs wall around themselves (1). Confusing as the initials may seem, the reality behind them is a truly remarkable thing. In effect, it means that by 1970 all of Free Europe except Greece, Ireland, Iceland, and Turkey will have been organized into two economic units, and negotiations are already under way to merge these two into one—thus eliminating the old hodgepodge of customs and tariffs and currency restrictions which for so long kept the continent fragmented into mutually competitive national economies. Such an arrangement could have dramatic consequences in the world trade picture.

2. ***Government manipulation of purchasing power.*** In modern times, an increasingly important factor in influencing the nature and direction of trade has been deliberate governmental manipulation of purchasing power. At the end of the Second World War, for example, the British government embarked upon an "austerity program" which was designed to conserve the dangerously low gold and dollar reserves which were still left after the heavy drain of the war and to reduce the huge accumulations of sterling balances. By various forms of rationing, export controls, and currency manipulation the British government managed, in the first place, to redirect a large part of the normal commerce of the United Kingdom out of the domestic market and into the overseas market, and, in the second place, to channel this overseas trade away from the countries of the sterling area toward the United States and other countries of the Dollar Bloc. The intricacies of the policies by which these ends were achieved need not detain us here. The significant fact that should be emphasized is that modern governments, particularly in times of crisis, play decisive roles in determining the nature and direction of trade.

3. ***Tariffs and embargoes.*** Characteristic as government involvement in trade is of our times, it is not a new thing. Governments have long concerned themselves with the regulation of trade. One of the factors which contributed to the outbreak of the American Revolution was the attempt on the part of the British government to make the trade of the American colonies a British monopoly. And in our own national history "the tariff question" was for many decades a major issue in presidential campaigns. In general, the industrial interests favored a high tariff which would protect them from low-cost foreign competition while the agricultural interests favored a low tariff which would stimulate our country's trade with other countries and thus enlarge the markets for their products. The question is no longer a burning one because there are now available to us more sophisticated (and more effective) devices than tariffs for controlling the amount and the direction of trade, but even today it makes headlines from time to time as one or another special interest group demands, and sometimes gets, "protection" from foreign competition.

Tariffs have the effect of drastically reducing trade with another country or region without actually prohibiting it. The embargo is a device for completely cutting off trade from a particular country or in a particular commodity. When used by one nation against another it is considered a hostile act and may be the prelude to war. It may, however, be applied without any such implications to traffic in a commodity, such as heroin, which a nation does not want imported into its territory.

A measure intermediate between the tariff and the embargo is the quarantine, properly speaking a means of preventing the importation of commodities which would be injurious to the health of a nation's people. For years the United States government prohibited the importation of Argentine beef products on the grounds that the prevalence of hoof and mouth disease in the Argentine posed a threat to the health of our people and cattle. Argentinians disputed this contention on the grounds that Europeans consumed vast quantities of their beef without noticeable ill effects and charged that the American quarantine was, in effect, a pseudo-embargo. Whether this charge had any validity is not a question which we are competent to answer, but it does point up how easily a quarantine could be used to accomplish the purposes of an embargo.

4. Foreign investments. With the disappearance of political colonialism in all but the communist portions of the world, foreign investments have become one of the most important means by which access is ensured to raw materials and to markets. How these investments affect the nature and direction of foreign trade is explained in a report of The Twentieth Century Fund:

¶ Long-term loans constitute the most important type of international investment. They usually appear in the form of stocks or bonds offered to the public in the lending nation by local banks acting on behalf of the government or private concern, but investors may also purchase domestic securities of a foreign nation. Thus, for example, British investments in United States railroads in the nineteenth century consisted of bonds floated in New York through local banks and payable in U. S. dollars. Similarly, United States investments in Canada consisted largely of Canadian bonds payable in Canadian dollars. . . .

Insofar as a loan transfers purchasing power of the lending country to the borrowing country, its immediate financial effect is the same as if the borrowing country had sold merchandise or services to the lending country. Accordingly, a foreign loan appears in the balance of payments of the borrowing country on the credit side of the ledger, on the same side as exports. In the balance of payments of the lending nation, it is listed as a debit, on the same side as imports.

The further financial impact of the receipt of a foreign loan is likewise similar to that of an export operation. The borrowing country may use the loan to purchase produce of the lending country—for example, a railway loan may be used to purchase rails, rolling stock, and other equipment in the lending country. Ordinarily the borrowing country may also use the funds for purchases in other markets. In this event, the country which sells its produce to the borrowing country is paid with the money of the lending country and ultimately will use this money for purchases in that country. The operation thus is completed in the course of triangular or multi-lateral trade. . . .

Another form of international investment occurs when a bank or business concern acquires a controlling share of all stock of a foreign concern, or establishes a branch abroad, purchases land, develops plantations or mines, builds railroads, and so on.[1]

The Cold War years of the past decade and a half have seen a dramatic increase in the number of direct loans from one government to another, indirectly influential upon the direction of trade but more immediately intended to create or cement a political alliance. The theory behind such loans seems to be that where a small neutralist nation's treasure comes from, there will its heart be also. But it hasn't always worked out that way, and some countries have displayed remarkable skill in pitting one great power against another, accepting economic aid from both while pursuing their own independent course of action.

5. National traits. The Englishman likes

[1] Woytinsky, W. S., and Woytinsky, E. S., *World Commerce and Governments*, The Twentieth Century Fund, New York, 1955, p. 188. Reprinted by permission.

his afternoon cup of tea, the American sandwiches his work in between coffee breaks, people all over the world have taken a liking to cola drinks — and these pleasant ways of relaxing have important consequences in such serious matters as the economy of the Republic of Costa Rica, the daily lives of millions of Oriental tea farmers, the balance sheets of American beverage companies, and the routes of ship lines which carry vast quantities of these mild beverages from one part of the world to another. But the Moslem does not touch pork, and so the Midwest farmer finds no market for his corn-on-the-hoof anywhere in North Africa or the Near East. The American, on the other hand, has developed little taste for mutton, and so the Australian station-owner must look elsewhere for his markets.

There is no accounting for taste. Most of our tastes are probably matters of habit and tradition, difficult if not impossible to justify on rational grounds. But they are significant factors in world trade and probably have something to do with the fact that there is a strong tendency for nations to trade with other nations which share their general cultural background.

Almost as hard to define as taste is the evocative quality of connotations which surrounds certain commodities of international commerce or the produce of certain countries. No doubt some of these connotations derive from well-earned reputations for excellence maintained over a long period of time; one thinks, for example, of Harris tweed, of Irish linen, of Swiss watches, of Scotch whisky, of Danish silver, of German scientific instruments, of Bruges lace. Whether any or all of these products are, as a matter of fact, the absolute best in their field may be impossible to determine objectively. That they are in special demand on the world market is a matter of fact, substantiated by trade statistics.

6. Advertising. Individuals and nations buy what they want. Beyond immediate necessities, wants are largely the creation of enterprising persons or corporations that have something they hope to sell. Advertising is, therefore, an essential element in the modern commercial structure and plays a very significant role in creating and developing new markets.

One of the classic examples of how advertising can open up a large new market is the case of a quinine water which was introduced into the United States in the late 1940's. Prior to that time, few Americans had even tasted quinine water and there were those who doubted that it could be made attractive to the American palate. The advertising campaign that was launched was built around the figure of a very British gentleman, allegedly a retired commander in the Royal Navy, whose great good fortune it was to possess a remarkably luxuriant beard. It might be said, without attempting to imply any kind of criticism, that the advertisements in which the bewhiskered commander appeared were designed to appeal to a certain anglophilia which has long been widespread in American culture, at the same time suggesting, ever so subtly, that entree into the commander's social circle was by way of drinking his brand of quinine water. The campaign was, probably needless to say, an unqualified success, and a new commodity was added to the list of British exports to the United States. So great was its success, as a matter of fact, that the British manufacturing company subsequently found it profitable to establish its own bottling plant on Long Island.

7. Differences in technology. The invention of the assembly line and the capacity which it has given man to mass produce vast quantities of standardized products have given the relatively few highly-industrialized nations of the world a tremendous advantage over other countries in the world market. First, machine labor is cheaper than even the cheapest human labor; machine-made products can therefore normally be sold at lower cost. Second, product standardization allows the widespread dissemination of replacement parts so that purchasers in many countries may buy in the assurance that they will not have to put up with long and irritating breakdowns. And, third, the capital structure required for such an operation tends to keep smaller competitors from entering the market or to drive them out if they do enter. With all of these advantages in their favor, the great industrial nations could hardly help dominating world trade.

There is still a place, though, for the country whose products are still hand-made or

The SS Tamar docks at the port of Haifa. A tug cuts the water in the foreground. Why are certain small countries such as Greece and Israel interested in developing large merchant marines? Why do they usually not attempt to compete with the great powers for ocean passenger business? (Courtesy Israel Office of Information)

produced in small shops in custom lots — if these products are of very high quality. The Rolls-Royce finds one of its best markets in the United States, despite the fact that we are the world's greatest automobile manufacturing country. French and German wines still enter our country in large quantities, despite the fact that we produce some very good wines in California and upstate New York. Premium quality goods, in other words, have a competitive advantage over other products in their own field everywhere in the world where there are people who want and can afford the best.

8. War and peace. One other factor, so obvious that it needs no belaboring, has an important effect upon the quantity and direction of world trade. War — whether hot or cold — rearranges the whole pattern of world commerce. Actual military hostilities bring blockades, or attempts at blockade, of ports and commercial routes. Countries or regions which are normally minor producers of certain commodities, particularly minerals, may become major sources of supply if major producing areas are occupied or blockaded. The normal flow of goods across international boundaries may be halted if the nations involved are on opposing sides or if one of them attempts to follow a neutral course.

Cold war produces the same kind of dislocations, but in a less acute form. In place of the blockade there are likely to be various forms of fiscal and commercial restrictions which, for all practical purposes, shut off trade between the opposing parties. At the same time, both parties attempt to divert the

This is a view of Tokyo station. The railroad no longer dominates the overland transportation picture as it did fifty years ago, but it is still vitally important. The scene pictured here could be of almost any large city in the world. The coaches shown will be made up into commuter trains. Why might commuter train traffic be more significant a part of total railroad service in a country such as Japan than in the United States? (Courtesy Consulate General of Japan)

flow of trade by various forms of economic and political pressure or preference. Actually, a cold war is an economic war in which the objective of each side is to weaken or destroy the other's economic and industrial capability to embark upon a military enterprise.

The paths of trade

The type of conveyance by which trade moves from one place to another is, under normal conditions, determined (1) by the nature of the intervening space and (2) by the relative costs of the alternative forms of conveyance available. For transoceanic trade, only aircraft and surface shipping are practical alternatives for conveyance, and the great cost differential gives an overwhelming competitive advantage to surface shipping for all types of goods except those which are very valuable per unit of weight or which are highly perishable. For overland trade, the alternative forms of conveyance are more numerous and more nearly competitive in terms of cost so that it is much more difficult to associate particular types of shipments with particular means of transportation.

A recent study of transportation costs gives the following estimate of costs to move one ton of goods one mile by various means of transport:

Great Lakes freighter . . . . $.0008
Ocean-going freighter 001

River barge .... .004
Railroad transport .... .02
Truck transport .... .05
Air transport .... .15
Horse and Wagon .... .25
Human porter .... .25 - $1.00[1]

The main lines of commerce are very largely determined by these cost differentials, preference being given to the form of transportation which is least expensive in view of the nature of the intervening space.

1. ***The Great Lakes–St. Lawrence Waterway.*** Nowhere else in the world has nature so thoughtfully anticipated the need of a great commercial water route as in the North American Great Lakes and the St. Lawrence River. True, it has needed considerable improvement by man to realize its full potential, but these improvements were minor and easily made by comparison with what nature itself had done. For long before there were any canals at the Sault, even longer before the St. Lawrence Seaway had been completed, this route had provided access from the sea to the heart of the North American continent.

As of this writing, it is still much too early to predict the full impact that the completion of the St. Lawrence Seaway (1959) will have on the Great Lakes trade. But in 1955 the Lakes were already carrying a tonnage greater than that of the Atlantic, Pacific, and Gulf ports of the United States, and until that year the tonnage carried through the Sault Ste. Marie canals exceeded the tonnage of both the Panama and Suez Canals (4).

The principal items of commerce on the Great Lakes have been iron ore, moving eastward from the iron ranges of northern Minnesota; coal, moving westward from the bituminous fields of Pennsylvania; stone (principally limestone), moving from the Lake Huron area both eastward and westward to the steel mills, where it is used as a flux; petroleum, brought by the Interprovincial Pipeline from Edmonton, Alberta, to Superior, Wisconsin, and from thence moving eastward to its major markets in eastern North America; and wheat, shipped through the Canadian ports of Fort William and Port Arthur and the American ports of Duluth and Superior to ocean ports for transshipment overseas (5). More recently there has been a notable increase in the amount of finished and semifinished goods moving through the Lakes, much of it coming directly from Europe to lake ports. While reliable statistics are not yet available, Chicago and Gary steelmen have complained that substantial amounts of German iron and steel have been coming into the Great Lakes region since the opening of the Seaway.

2. ***Ocean routes.*** From the foothills of the Rocky Mountains in North America to the highlands of Soviet Asia extends a vast plain, easily traversable, richly endowed with minerals and fertile soils, and populated by vigorous peoples of an advanced culture. The American and Eurasian sections of this plain are set off from each other by the relatively narrow North Atlantic Ocean, and the coastal fringes of each of these sections are broken by many excellent harbors, most of which lie at or near the mouths of great rivers which give access to the interior of the continents. This happy combination of circumstances accounts for the fact that the North Atlantic Ocean is not so much a barrier to movement between North America and Europe as it is a great, free, open highway between the two continents — the greatest by far of all the world's ocean trade routes. One of its western termini, New York, is the world's greatest port. One of its eastern termini, Rotterdam, is the world's second greatest port; and along both its margins lie other great port cities — Montreal, Boston, Philadelphia, and Baltimore on the west, and London, Hamburg, Antwerp, and Le Havre on the east. Ships moving eastward along this route carry such commodities as wheat, corn, animal products, pulp and paper, industrial raw materials, and certain types of manufactured goods. Ships moving westward carry principally manufactured goods. There is also a brisk passenger traffic both ways and the North Atlantic is the ranging area of the great, prestigious luxury liners.

From the ports of western Europe another important ocean highway runs by way of the Mediterranean Sea and the Suez Canal into the Indian Ocean where it bifurcates, one road continuing on by way of India and Singapore to Hong Kong and the ports of

[1] Bengtson, Nels A., and Van Royen, William, *Fundamentals of Economic Geography,* Prentice-Hall, Inc., Englewood Cliffs, N. J., 1956, pp. 562-563. Reprinted by permission.

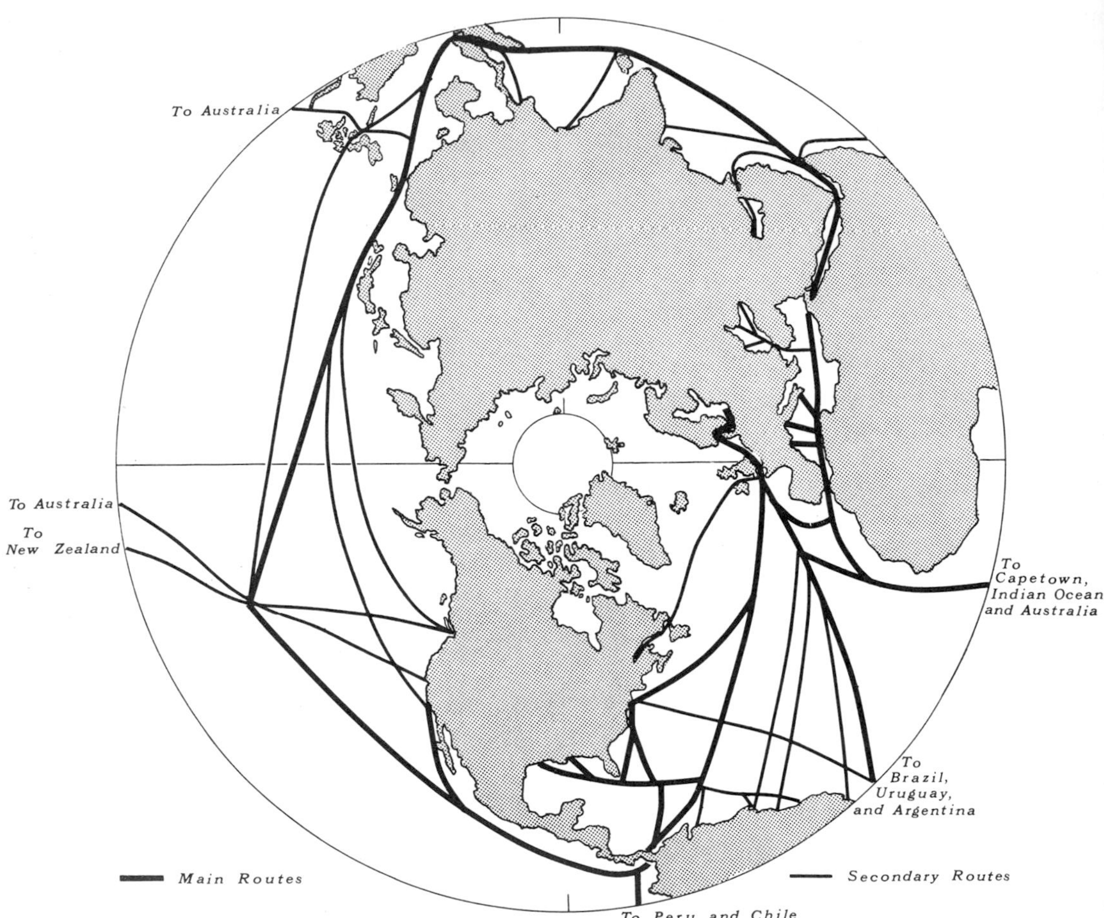

XV:1 This map of the great commercial sea lanes has been centered on the North Pole in order to show how the major ocean routes encircle Eurasia and North America. The absence of major ocean routes in the Southern Hemisphere reflects primarily the comparatively small amount of land in that hemisphere.

Japan, the other terminating in Australia and New Zealand. In the days when Britannia ruled the waves, this route was known as "the lifeline of Empire," for it connected Great Britain with her far-flung political and commercial empires in the Indian Ocean Area and in the Far East. Today its importance is different but no less crucial, for it links petroleum-thirsty western Europe with the great oil fields of Arabia and the Persian Gulf region.

An alternative route between western Europe, especially the British Isles, and Australasia is the route around the Cape of Good Hope. Two very recent developments—the seizure of the Suez Canal by Egypt and the re-awakening of Africa — have combined to give this route an importance which it had not had before. Most of its commerce is still, however, restricted to that portion of the route which lies between London and Cape Town.

Other important ocean trade routes are those between western Europe and the east coast of South America, particularly the coffee districts of southern Brazil and the meat and grain hinterland of the Plata estuary; between the east coast of North America and the east coast of South America, especially the Lake Maracaibo oil fields, the Guiana bauxite deposits, the Venezuelan iron mines, and the Brazilian coffee regions; between the east coast of North America and the west coast of South America, via the Panama Canal; between the west coast of North America and eastern Asia and Japan;

and between the west coast of North America and Australasia.

As the map indicates, the Pacific Ocean trade routes are relatively unimportant in world commerce, partly, no doubt, because of the sheer width of the Pacific Ocean but also because of cultural differences between the populations on either side of it and because of the relative poverty of the peoples inhabiting its Asiatic margins. At the present time political differences also exercise a strong inhibitory effect upon trade, the historic China trade of the United States having been reduced to a mere trickle since the establishment of the Chinese People's Republic.

*3. **Rivers and canals.*** From the earliest days of civilization in Mesopotamia and the Nile Valley, rivers have been major highways of commerce. They still are today in many parts of the world, notably western Europe and the U.S.S.R., eastern North America, much of South America, and China. The potential for a great deal of use exists in Soviet Asia and in much of trans-Saharan Africa.

Most rivers are less than satisfactory as carriers of commerce in their natural state. Meandering channels greatly increase the straight-line distance between points along the river's course, seasonal variations in volume resulting from seasonal differences in precipitation restrict the navigable season, and deposition within the channel presents obstacles to navigation. All of these are correctable deficiences, however, if the potential volume of traffic justifies the expense of improving the river. Northward flowing rivers such as those of Soviet Asia are, however, much less susceptible of improvement because the problem here is one of early freezing and late thawing at the mouth, a condition which can be ameliorated by the use of icebreakers for a few weeks but which cannot be fully offset. An equally baffling problem affects rivers flowing from humid lands into drylands; the loss of volume as they flow farther into the desert finally sets a limit to their navigability.

Rivers which have been improved by such devices as channel straightening, dam construction, and dredging are known as canalized rivers. Examples in North America include the upper Mississippi, the Illinois, and

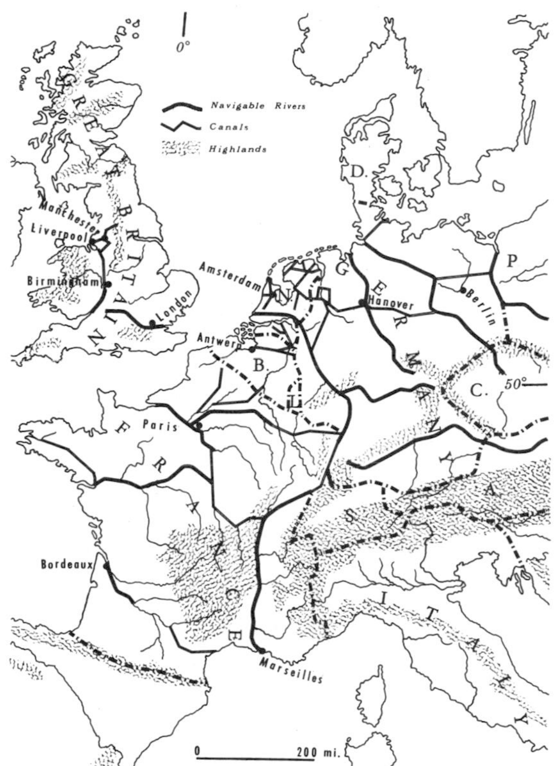

XV:2 The major river systems of Europe and some of the more important interconnecting canals are shown here. If this map showed all of the canals of northwestern Europe, large areas would be a solid mass of black.

the Ohio. Europe has, in the Rhine, the best example of all; so much has been done to improve its navigability that, in its present form, it might be more properly described as a cultural feature of the landscape than a natural feature.

Western Europe is the region par excellence of river commerce. Not only does it have a large number of rivers flowing outward from its Alpine heart; these rivers have a fairly constant volume of water because of the generally even distribution of precipitation throughout the year. Moreover, many of them, particularly in Germany, flow "against the grain" of a series of abandoned stream valleys which were formed during the glacial epoch when the northward flowing streams encountered the front of the ice sheet in its various stages and, flowing along its front, carved these valleys, thus producing ready-

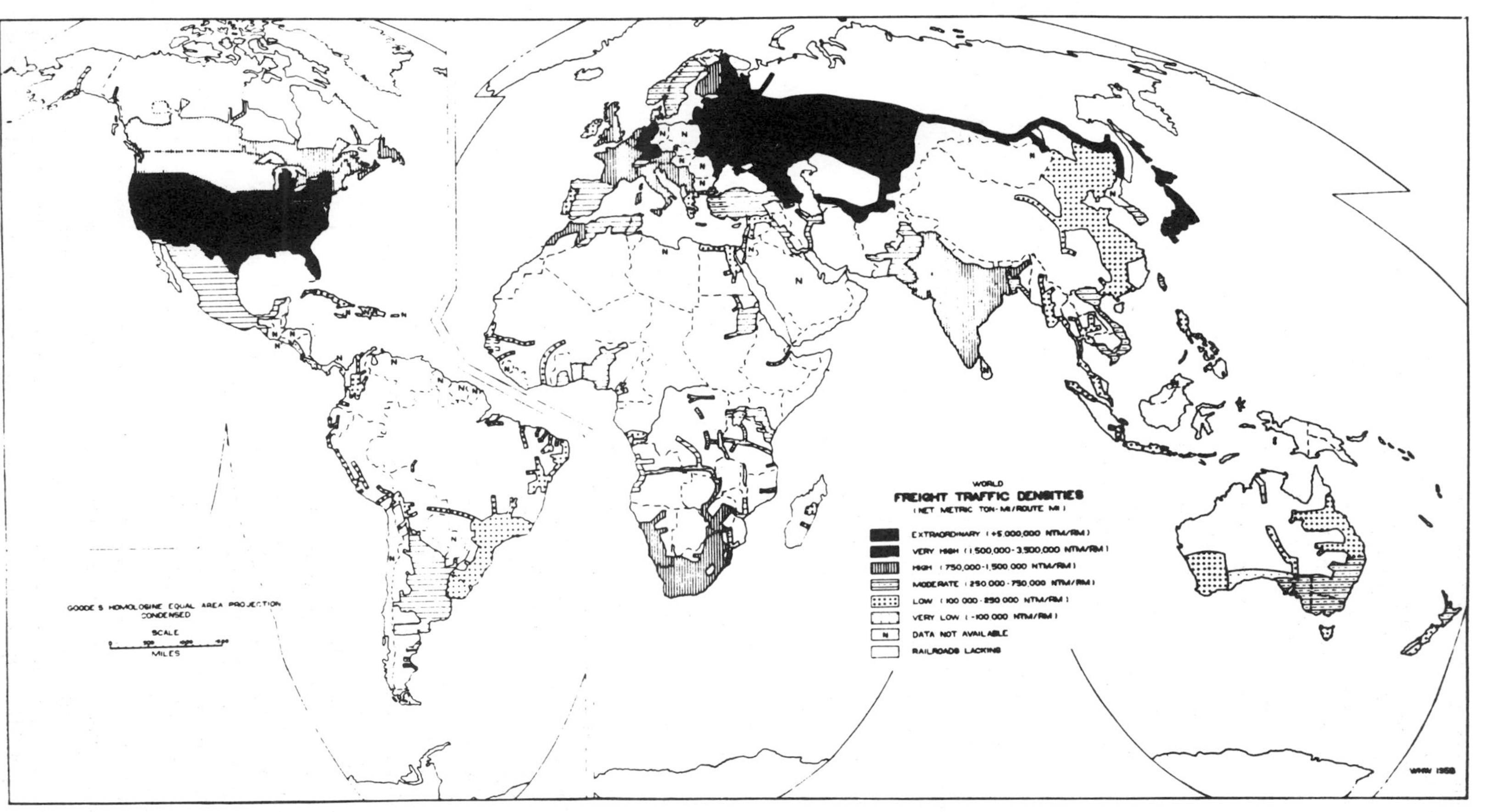
WORLD
FREIGHT TRAFFIC DENSITIES
(NET METRIC TON-MI/ROUTE MI)
EXTRAORDINARY (+5,000,000 NTM/RM)
VERY HIGH (1,500,000-3,500,000 NTM/RM)
HIGH (750,000-1,500,000 NTM/RM)
MODERATE (250,000-750,000 NTM/RM)
LOW (100,000-250,000 NTM/RM)
VERY LOW (-100,000 NTM/RM)
DATA NOT AVAILABLE
RAILROADS LACKING
GOODE'S HOMOLOGINE EQUAL AREA PROJECTION
CONDENSED
SCALE
MILES
WHW 1958

made channels for the canals which were later dug from one major river valley to the other.

Rivers and canals carry principally bulk cargoes which have no time value — such things as coal, industrial ores, petroleum, and the cereal grains.

*4. **Railroads.*** The least expensive of all overland forms of transportation, apart from pipelines, is the railroad. Even so, it is five times as expensive per ton-mile as is the most expensive form of water transportation, the river barge.

The regional density of freight traffic on the world's railways is shown on the map (Figure XV-3). It will be noted that "extraordinary" densities are indicated for the Soviet Union and the Pocahontas Coal Region of the United States. Very high densities are indicated for the greater part of the United States, West Germany, and Japan; high densities for most of the rest of western Europe, India, the Union of South Africa, and the northern part of the United States and southern Canada.

It is obvious from this map that the level of freight traffic density, i.e., the intensity of activity on the various rail systems of the world, correlates closely with the general pattern and level of activity in the regions which the railroads serve. Wallace recognizes the following as causal factors affecting railway freight traffic densities:

1. The presence or absence of significant extraction activity, particularly coal and iron mining. (He notes that the American railroads with the heaviest traffic are almost all major carriers of coal or iron ore, or both.)
2. The presence or absence of significant large-scale, heavy industrial activity, particularly the manufacture of iron and steel.
3. The presence or absence of large population concentrations with their vast production and consumption of a great variety of goods.
4. The general level of technology in a country or region, and the standards of living; hence the rate of consumption by the population.
5. The types of agricultural activity within the zone served by the railways — the intensity of farming, the presence or absence of surplus production for shipment to distant markets, and the nature of the products.
6. The pattern of the railnet in a country:
   a) The presence of a large number of light-traffic branch lines (as in the United States) will lower the average traffic density of a system and will tend to obscure even very high-density main-line traffic. (The U.S.S.R. has few such light-traffic branch lines.)
   b) The presence of alternative, competing rail routes between points will also tend to lower the average traffic density on all lines. (Again, note the contrast between competing routes in the United States and single routes in the U.S.S.R.)
7. The degree of intercarrier competition in a country: e.g., railroads vs. trucks; railroads vs. barges; railroads vs. pipelines (6).

More than thirty years ago, Dr. Mark Jefferson published in *Economic Geography* an article which has since achieved the status of a classic in the field. He called it "The Civilizing Rails." Much of the data of the article is now out-of-date but the principle is still valid: civilization has produced the railway, and the railway, in turn, has brought civilization. In South America, in Canada, in Africa, in Asia, and in Australia, civilization ends at the railhead, and in all of these lands the first thrust of civilization into hitherto new frontier areas is the building of a railroad.

*5. **Motor roads.*** The student who is tempted to write his own textbook should be warned that the most difficult job which he will face is finding a precise definition for words which he uses every day in the full confidence that he knows what he is talking about. What, for instance, is a road? Webster defines it as "a place where one may ride; a highway." Under so broad a definition, we could say that every part of the world, with the possible exceptions of the rainforests and the icecaps, is adequately served by roads. Most of these roads we would not, however, be inclined to describe as highways.

XV:3 (Left) On this map are shown the world railroad freight traffic densities. (From "Railroad Traffic Densities and Patterns" by William H. Wallace, *Annals of the Association of American Geographers*, December, 1958, used by permission)

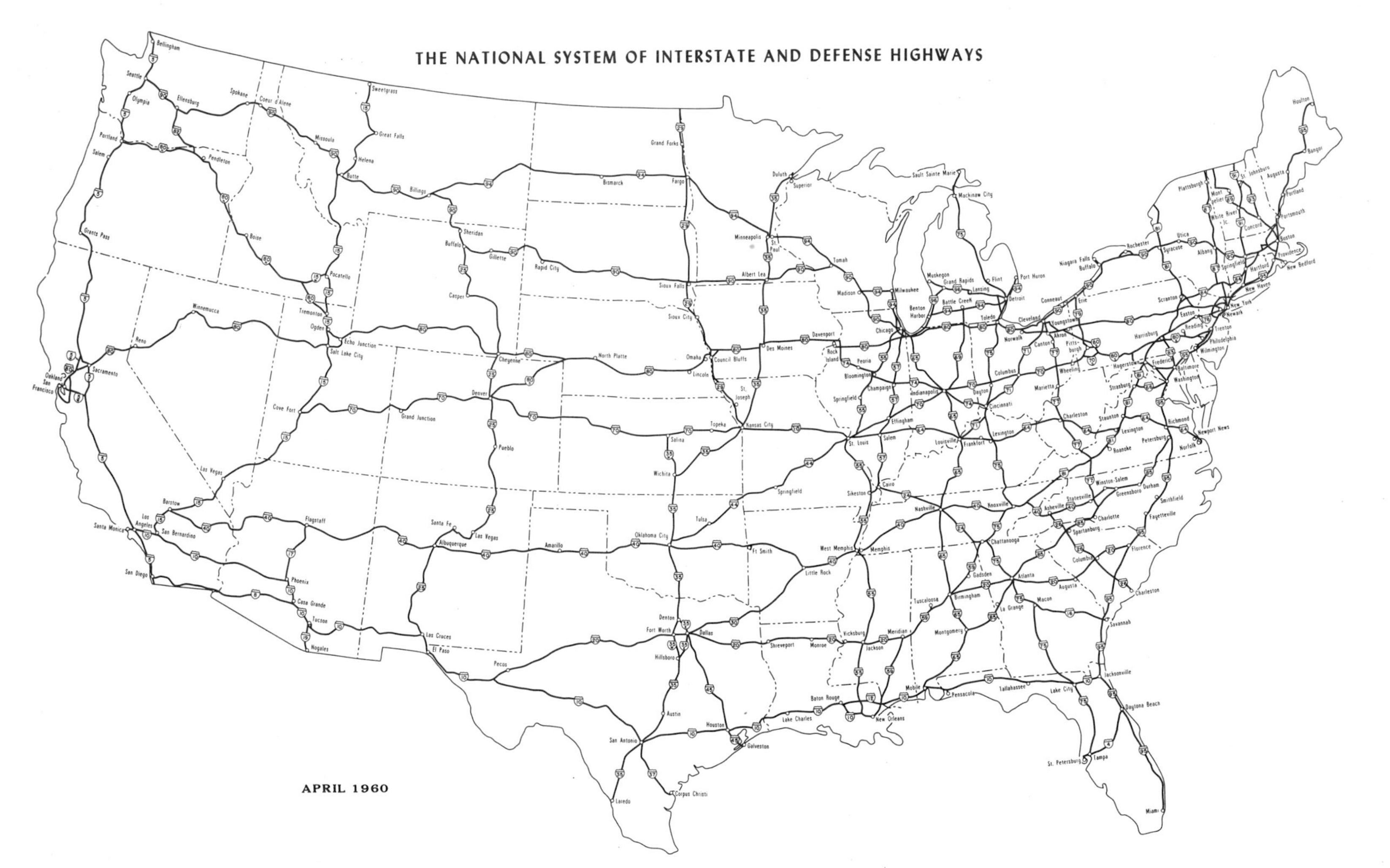

THE NATIONAL SYSTEM OF INTERSTATE AND DEFENSE HIGHWAYS

APRIL 1960

Table 15.1 Selected air and rail statistics for the United States, 1949 and 1955 (in thousands) (7)

Travel item	*1949*	*1955*	*Percentage change*
Air passengers	14,699	37,408	+154
Air passenger-miles	6,705,000	19,741,000	+293
Rail Pullman passenger-miles	9,349,000	6,440,000	−31
Rail coach passenger-miles	20,310,000	17,329,000	−15

SOURCE: Taaffe, Edward J., "Trends in Airline Passenger Traffic: A Geographic Case Study," *Annals of the Association of American Geographers,* Vol. XLIX, No. 4, December, 1959, p. 393.

For purposes of this chapter, with its particular emphasis upon channels of trade, we shall define a road as a land route, other than a railroad, upon which it is possible for wheeled vehicles to move from one place to another. Even thus defined, the term is still broad enough to include the narrow wheelbarrow paths of China at the one extreme and the autobahns of Germany and the expressways of the United States at the other. But that is all right. It is upon this wide range of roads that much of the world's commerce moves.

The origin of roads is lost in the mists of man's earliest history. In parts of western Europe, though, traffic still moves along roads built by the greatest of all of the road builders of antiquity, the Romans. And in our own country some of our major highways follow ancient Indian trails and the routes of the pioneers. Nor should this be surprising; as rivers follow the path of least resistance across a landscape, so do man's first roads in any new area tend to take advantage of mountain passes and water gaps through mountains and hilly divides through poorly-drained terrain and portage routes between major river basins. Only later does he find it possible and profitable to drive his roads through natural obstacles on the principle of the shortest distance between two points.

XV:4 (Left) America's superhighway system of the not-too-distant future will probably look like this. Already under construction, this network of interstate and defense highways will provide safer and faster links between the major cities of the United States. Thanks to modern earth-moving techniques and equipment, these highways can follow essentially straight-line routes except in the most difficult terrain. (Courtesy of the United States Bureau of Roads)

The quality of roads and their motorability are direct reflections of socio-economic factors. The best roads are found in the most advanced industrial countries and the poorest in primitive or undeveloped countries. The relationship is not, however, altogether one-sided. The building of a road is often the first step toward opening up a "new" area. Examples are the Alaskan Highway, built during the Second World War between Fort St. John, British Columbia, and Fairbanks, Alaska; the famous Burma Road from India through Burma into China; and the Pan-American Highway, gradually nearing completion, which will ultimately provide an overland link from Alaska to Buenos Aires.

The highway system of the United States has for many years been one of the marvels of the world, but the enormous growth in the number of passenger automobiles and in the importance of truck transportation during the late forties and the fifties threatened to create hopeless bottlenecks even in that system. Various states, recognizing that danger, embarked upon the construction of freeways and tollways, some of them ill-advised. Finally the federal government entered the picture and there is now under way a program of highway building which, it is hoped, will prove adequate to anticipated needs. The system of proposed new interstate highways is shown in Figure XV-4.

*6. **Airlines.*** Alone among the commercial forms of transportation, airlines are still primarily haulers of people rather than goods. The reason is not hard to find: the airplane has limited space and can carry only a limited weight of goods and is a very expen-

UNITED STATES AIR TRANSPORTATION SYSTEM
ROUTES CERTIFICATED TO LOCAL SERVICE CARRIERS
JUNE 30, 1960

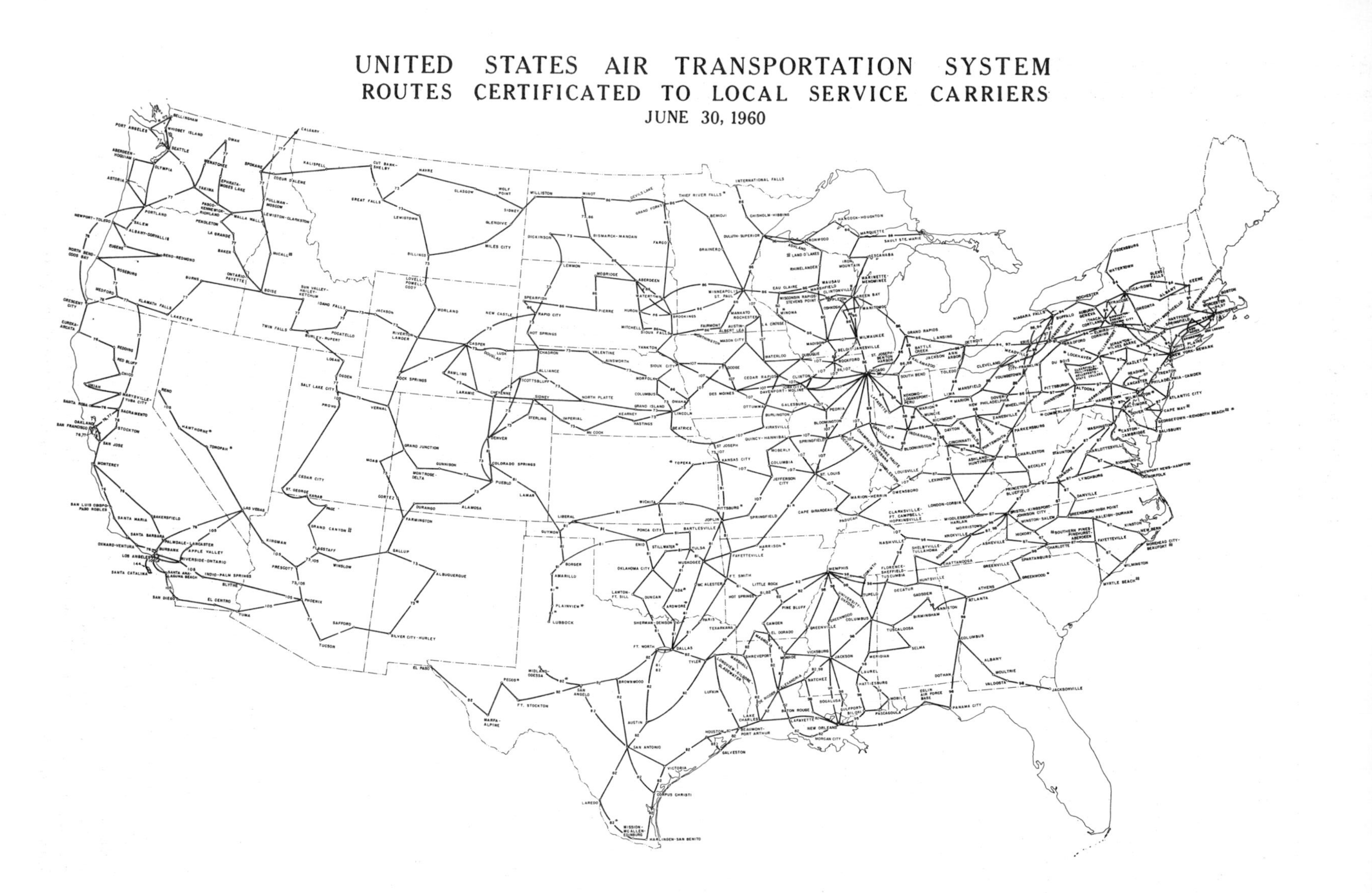

sive machine to build in terms of cost per cubic foot of usable space.

The one great competitive advantage which the airplane enjoys over all other forms of transportation is speed. For passenger traffic, this is an incalculably important advantage, one which accounts for the rapid increase in passenger traffic during the past decade. The degree to which the airplane has supplanted the railroad as a passenger carrier is illustrated by comparative figures furnished by the Air Transport Association and cited in an *Annals* article by Dr. Edward J. Taaffe (Table 15.1).

The combination of relatively high cost with a strong orientation toward passenger travel does much to determine the nature and direction of air freight. In general, we may say that it involves goods which (1) have a relatively high value per unit of weight, and can thus absorb high transportation costs without having to raise selling prices disproportionately; (2) have a very high time value, such as serums, replacement parts, jewels and gems needed for specific occasions, and so forth; and (3) move generally along the paths of passenger travel. Such items of commerce as raw materials and large machines rarely go by air freight, except perhaps under wartime conditions or in some other emergency situation when other means of transportation are not available.

Maps of airline routes show none of the characteristic twistings and turnings of road or railroad maps; rather they are a pattern of straight lines connecting one center of population with another. A more detailed map would show, in addition to the major airlines, subpatterns of feeder lines radiating outward for relatively short distances from the metropolitan centers toward smaller cities. Noticeable also on the world map is the absence of regularly scheduled air service north of the Arctic circle in the Northern Hemisphere and south of Latitude 40 in the Southern Hemisphere. Not so clearly evident from the map is the tendency for intercontinental airlines to follow a "great circle" route from one continent to another. This tendency accounts for the importance of Reykjavik, Iceland, as a way station on the trans-Atlantic route and for the key position of Alaska on the trans-Pacific route. The absence of airlines crossing what geographers at the end of the Second World War had hopefully referred to as the Arctic Mediterranean is not a reflection of physical handicaps to aeronavigation but rather of the hostility of the nations which lie at either end of the transpolar route. If this hostility were to be abated, there would doubtless be considerable traffic back and forth across the North Pole.

XV:5 (Left) This map shows major airline routes in the United States. If it seems a maze of lines, that is because the United States actually is criss-crossed by an intricate network of air routes, only the most important of which are shown here. (Courtesy of the Civil Aeronautics Board)

7. Other forms of transport. The forms of transportation which have been discussed in this chapter do not begin to exhaust the means by which men and goods are moved from one place to another. In the United States, for instance, more and more oil and gas moves from the producing fields in the Southwest to the consuming centers in the East and Great Lakes regions by pipeline. In China, the wheelbarrow is still an important vehicle of commerce. In many other parts of the world, pack animals — llamas, camels, horses, donkeys, and cattle — have not yet been displaced by motorized transport. But these are all relatively unimportant in the over-all pattern of world commerce and seem likely to become less important as time goes by.

Other forms of transportation are still in the experimental or merely theoretical stage. The monorail, for instance, which has operated so well and so efficiently in the Ruhr industrial complex for more than a quarter of a century, has not found acceptance elsewhere. Peaceful adaptations of military missiles intrigue the imagination but do not yet come within the area of economic probability. Still farther off — so far off as to be hardly within the bounds of the credible — is the ultimate form of transportation: the device which would permit goods to be beamed as a flow of electrons to some point where they would be reconstructed in their original form.

ROUTES TO UNITED STATES AUTHORIZED TO FOREIGN AIR CARRIERS UNDER PERMIT JUNE 30, 1960

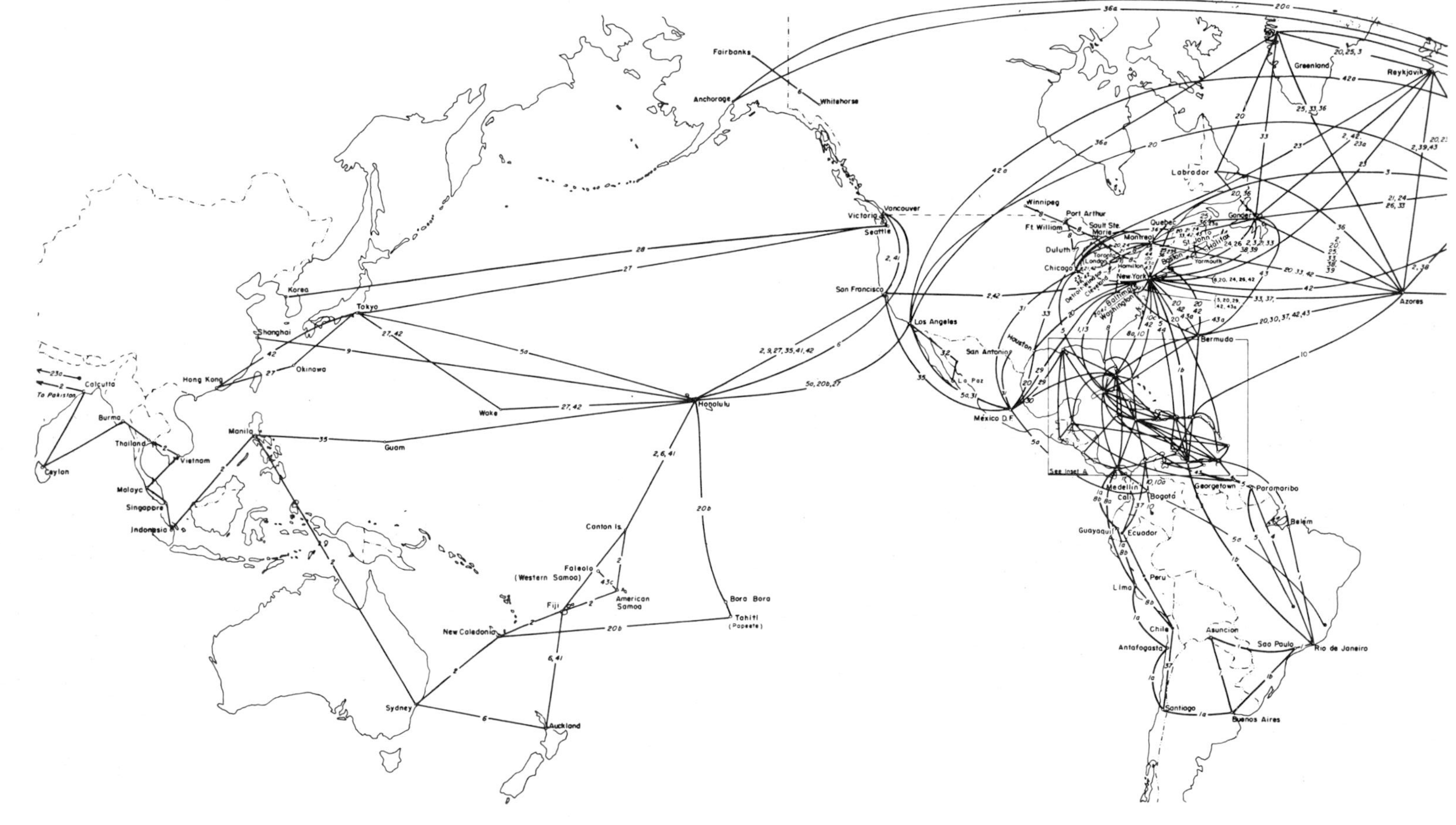

An F-27 flies over Mount Olympus in the Olympic Mountain Range. These mountains are one of the last great natural wildernesses left in the United States. But the airspace above them is no more difficult for a plane to traverse than is the air above the Great Plains. In a limited but important way, the airplane has abolished physiography and converted the whole world into one vast coast line fronting upon a sea of air. This picture, however, highlights one very important limitation upon the usefulness of airplanes. (Courtesy West Coast Airlines, Inc.)

APPLICATION OF GEOGRAPHIC UNDERSTANDING

I. Who is more likely to have logged more miles of air travel — a prosperous Corn Belt farmer or the manager of a coconut plantation in New Guinea? Why?

II. If one of the chief reasons for trading is to get what one does not already have, how do you account for the great amount of trade between North America and western Europe—both of which produce very similar agricultural and industrial products?

III. What reasons other than the competitive nature of the agricultural products which we and the Argentine Republic produce might account for that country's strong attraction to Europe as a market and a source of supply?

IV. What reasons rooted in history are there for supposing that European economic

XV:6 (Left) America's air corridors to the world are shown on this map. Note that this is not a map of world airlines, but only of the routes which have been authorized to foreign airlines for entry into the United States. (Courtesy of the Civil Aeronautics Board)

union, if it should prove successful, might lead ultimately to some form of political union?

V. Why have the railroads of Europe been much more successful in holding their passenger business than have those of the United States? Take into consideration the geography of the two areas and the nature of the competition for passenger business.

VI. In small print at the bottom of advertisements in many national magazines is the notation: "Prices slightly higher west of the Rockies." What are the geographical reasons for such a notation and what changes in the geography of the United States might someday make this notation a thing of the past?

VII. How do you account for the importance, in the world commercial picture, of such small countries as Belgium, the Netherlands, and Norway?

VIII. Figures from the Maritime Administration of the United States Department of Commerce show that the leading commercial nations of the world, in terms of registered merchant shipping, were the following on December 31, 1954:

The United States	25,483,000 tons
The United Kingdom	17,422,000 tons
Norway	6,559,000 tons
Panama	3,935,000 tons
Italy	3,634,000 tons
France	3,540,000 tons
Liberia	3,487,000 tons
Japan	3,242,000 tons
The Netherlands	3,083,000 tons

How do you account for (a) the absence of the U.S.S.R. and the Chinese People's Republic from this list? (b) the absence of Germany? (c) the presence of Panama and Liberia? (d) the importance of Norway?

IX. Mexico has almost twice as many people as Canada, and the climates of Mexico permit her to produce a wide range of foods and industrial raw materials which we do not produce, at least in large quantities. Why, then, is there so much more trade between the United States and Canada than there is between the United States and Mexico?

X. Historically, the center of world trade has moved westward and northward from the eastern Mediterranean to Rome to the North Sea area and the North Atlantic region. What is the geographical logic behind this movement?

References

1 *British Affairs,* Vol. II, No. 3, September, 1958, pp. 129-130; Vol. III, No. 4, December, 1959, pp. 164-165. British Information Services, New York.

2 Woytinsky, W. S., and Woytinsky, E. S., *World Commerce and Governments,* The Twentieth Century Fund, New York, 1955, p. 188.

3 Bengtson, Nels A., and Van Royen, William, *Fundamentals of Economic Geography,* Prentice-Hall, Inc., Englewood Cliffs, N. J., 1956, pp. 562-563.

4 Petterson, Donald R., "Great Lakes Traffic: An Aspect of Commercial Geography," *The Journal of Geography,* Vol. LVI, No. 5, May, 1957, pp. 212-213.

5 Ballert, Albert G., "Commerce of the Sault Canals," *Economic Geography,* Vol. XXXIII, No. 2, April, 1957, pp. 139-146, *passim.*

6 Wallace, William H., "Railroad Traffic Densities and Patterns," *Annals of the Association of American Geographers,* Vol. XLVIII, No. 4, December, 1958, pp. 356-357.

Chapter **16**

The geography of resource use

Until Einstein discovered his famous formula $E = mc^2$ the earth seemed to be a closed system; that is, it seemed that the "stuff" of which the lands and waters and atmosphere were made, while it could be transformed from one substance into another, could not be added to or subtracted from. Einstein's formula suggests that the energy which the earth is constantly receiving from the sun could be converted into matter, and that in this sense the earth may be still a-building. But so far as man's use (or abuse) of earth resources is concerned, the formula has little more than theoretical significance. Man, especially modern man, is quite capable of using up the resources of the earth far faster than they can, in any practical way, be replaced. The awareness of this capacity, and the evidence that it has resulted in serious damage to resources which are essential to man's continued occupance of the earth, brought about, in the first decade of the twentieth century, a new emphasis upon man's responsibility for conserving the resources which sustain his life, particularly the soils, forests, waters, minerals, and wildlife of what a later writer was to call "our plundered planet."

The conservation movement has made its influence felt on many levels of our national life: in our communities, through such organizations as the Scouts, the Izaak Walton League, soil conservation districts, and local conservation clubs; in government, through state departments of conservation and through such federal agencies as the National Park Service, the Fish and Wildlife Service, the Bureau of Reclamation, the Forest Service, and the Soil Conservation Service; in education, through the scholarly work of such pioneers as Charles R. Van Hise, H. H. Bennett, Louis Wolfanger, A. E. Parkins, Harlan Barrows, and J. R. Whitaker and through the classroom instruction of thousands of teachers. In addition, many service and social groups have made conservation a matter for consideration in their programs.

The meaning of conservation

This concern for conservation of resources is a very recent thing, historically speaking, and the question naturally arises: why so much interest in this particular problem at this particular time? The answer is simply that, in the past 200 years or so, the resources of the earth have been used up at a rate unparalleled in previous human history. For example, more minerals have been taken out of the ground since the beginning of the present century than in all the millennia prior to that time. We are, in other words, approaching a "peril point" in the depletion of the resources which sustain our lives, and for the first time in history man is forced to ask himself whether there will be enough minerals, water, trees, and soil to support his children and grandchildren.

This question, in turn, raises another one: How did we get into this situation? The best answer to that question has been supplied by Joe Russell Whitaker, one of the first American geographers to bring the problems of conservation under the discipline of scholarship:

¶ Most fundamental, it appears, is the fact that human requirements from nature's storehouse have mounted at a tremendous rate because of the increase in the number of people on earth. The population of the entire earth was roughly 660,000,000 in 1750, according to careful estimates; at present [1946] it is more than 2,000,000,000. [It is now, in 1961, approaching 3,000,000,000.] With this growth in the human population to be fed and housed and clothed, the direct appropriation of earth resources has necessarily increased, also the numerous indirect and unintentional damages which man inflicts on his natural surroundings.

The human impact on nature has increased not only because the number of people has trebled in the last 200 years, but also because the wants of most of these people have multiplied. A comparison of the relatively simple life of the American colonists with that of our own day yields numerous examples of this change, and the contrast is even more striking if the comparison be made with earlier times. In 1600, for example, only about twenty substances other than precious stones were taken from the underground realm. The principal ones were clay, whetstone, millstone, iron, copper, tin, gold, lead, silver, mica, coal, salt, and mercury. Such minerals as petroleum, potash, nickel, aluminum, chromium, vanadium, manganese, and tungsten were unknown.

In satisfying the expanding wants of increasing numbers of people, the nineteenth and twentieth centuries have had means not hitherto available for exploiting the earth. Man's hands have been multiplied many times by his machines, his power increased over and over through his use of waterfalls, natural gas, petroleum, and coal, and the application of these techniques has been stimulated by the accumulation of capital.[1]

In other words, Whitaker is saying that the past two centuries or so have been particularly destructive of resources because of the three great revolutions that have occurred during that time: the population explosion, the technological revolution, and the rise of materialism as a satisfying and satisfiable philosophy of life for the great majority of the world's people, particularly in the Western world. Later in this same chapter Whitaker refines the picture by pointing out other characteristics of recent times which have helped to create the conservation problem, among them the following:

1. The nonrenewable nature of many resources, particularly the minerals.
2. The development of the world of commerce with its emphasis upon producing something for sale.
3. The resultant opportunity for personal gain by transforming natural resources into commodities.
4. The fact that recent centuries have been an age of pioneering ("The pioneer was destructive, not only because great natural wealth was present and his needs were urgent, but also because his activities were not adjusted to the new environment").
5. The abundance of "free goods," i.e., "resources of value but either belonging to no one, or to a careless government, one which places no obstacles in the way of resource exploitation."
6. The increasing destructiveness of war, particularly in the twentieth century.[2]

You may object that we still have not answered the question: Why should we promote conservation? The geographer, operating strictly within the area of his own competence, can only point to the facts of the matter: unless we use the resources of the earth wisely and carefully, the time will come when they will be largely used up or rendered unusable. He can show by statistics and maps that a resource problem exists and that it is most acute in a particular place or region. But the question of why this or any other generation should accept responsibility for the needs of future generations is one which must be answered by ethics or religion. The study of conservation has, therefore, differed from the general pattern of academic disciplines in that it has proved practically impossible to divorce the factual content of conservation from motivational factors—from "preachments"—which supply the ethical framework within which the problem must necessarily be set.

The best short answer which the authors of this text have seen to the question: Why conservation? was supplied several years ago by the late Senator Richard L. Neuberger of Oregon:

¶ What principles and policies should guide us in our plans for conservation? I would propose these: (1) Adherence in the use of all resources to the Theodore Roosevelt concept of "the greatest good for the greatest number in the long run." (2) A realization that mountains and forests and seashores and valleys must be protected from exploitation in order to keep faith with future generations. (3) Awareness that outdoor recreation is often as important a use of resources as the production of goods and merchandise. (4) An understanding that animals and birds and fish are God's creatures too, and are not to be wiped out at the wanton whim of man. (5) Recognition of the fact that we are merely the temporary stewards of these resources and not their permanent owners.

[1] Whitaker, Joe Russell, *The Life and Death of the Land*, Peabody College Press, Nashville, 1946, pp. 17-18. Reprinted by permission.

[2] *Ibid.*, pp. 19-22, *passim*. Reprinted by permission.

They are a legacy which we must pass on in as good condition as they came down to us.[1]

Senator Neuberger concludes this article by quoting one of the early giants of the conservation movement, Gifford Pinchot:

¶ "The rightful use and purpose of our natural resources is to make all the people strong and well, able and wise, well taught, well fed, well clothed, well housed, full of knowledge and initiative, with equal opportunity for all and special privilege for none. 'Whatsoever ye would that men should do to you, do ye even so to them.' "

In summary, for the religious person, conservation is a way of behaving responsibly in God's creation; for the nonreligious humanist, it is a way of dealing honorably with his fellowman, including those still to be born; for the person who recognizes no particular responsibility either to God or to man, it is still, in the long run, the most profitable way to use resources.

What conservation is and is not

We may clear up some misconceptions that have grown up around the word "conservation" if we draw an analogy between a nation's attitude toward its resources and an individual's attitude toward his wealth. There is a kind of person—once known as a spendthrift, now more commonly as a playboy—whose attitude toward wealth is best expressed by one of his own favorite phrases: "Live it up!" And there is, at the opposite extreme, the miser who would rather do without the necessities of life than spend a dime. The playboy, all will agree, is not conservation-minded. What needs to be emphasized is that the miser is not conservation-minded, either. Indeed, in his own way, he may be even more wasteful than the playboy, for in his anxiety to preserve a relatively minor resource (his money) he may be destroying the most valuable of all of his resources (his health).

Between the playboy and the miser stands the mature, responsible citizen who handles all forms of his wealth prudently. He knows that there are times when it is advantageous to draw against future earnings, as when he builds a house. But in general he lives within his means and demands full value for any expenditure of money. This is the true conservational attitude, for a person or for a nation. To *conserve* is not, therefore, the same thing as merely to *preserve*. Conservation always implies wise, careful, and planned use of resources.

The place of the geographer in conservation

Conservation is not, in itself, a division of geography; rather, it is a separate discipline to which the geographer has essential techniques and understandings to contribute. As one writer has pointed out,

¶ Resources may be inanimate or animate, minerals, waterpower, soils, vegetation and animals, as well as location, scenery, sunshine, or beaches. All these are elements of man's environment, the study of which is an important objective of geography. Therefore any resource-use planning necessarily has to include knowledge and understanding of a geographic nature (3).

In other words, it is in the planning of resource use that the geographer's regional concept finds one of its most important practical applications.

But the geographer can make even more practical and down-to-earth contributions than this to resource education and planning. Calef notes, for example, that there is by no means universal agreement that conservation of resources is necessary and suggests that

¶ Geographers, since they concern themselves with all natural resources and with the entire surface of the earth, are especially able to furnish abundant evidence of the reality of resource destruction and misuse and its effects. Moreover, geographers study specific places and, consequently, can furnish concrete examples drawn from various places throughout the world (4).

This same writer lists three additional contributions which the geographer can make to conservation:

¶ (1) an understanding that resource impairment is a matter of universal concern since the

[1] Excerpt from "God's Resources—and Ours," by Richard L. Neuberger from March 13, 1957, issue, p. 325, *The Christian Century*. Copyright 1957 Christian Century Foundation. Reprinted by permission from *The Christian Century*.

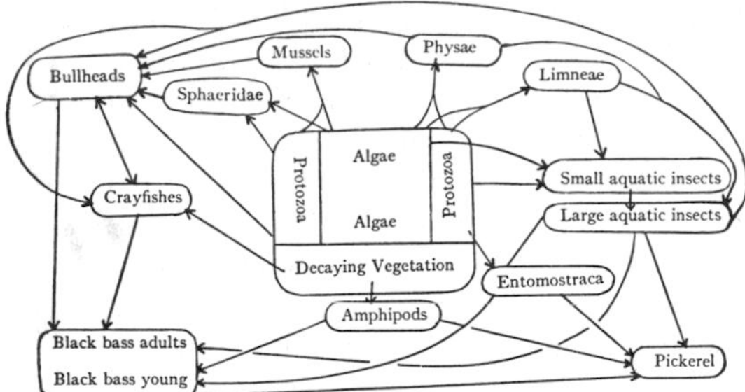

XVI:1 This diagram shows the food relations of aquatic animals. Arrows point from the eaten to the eater. (From *Animal Communities in Temperate America* by Victor E. Shelford, The Geographic Society of Chicago Bulletin No. 5. Copyright 1937 by the University of Chicago. Used by permission)

destruction of a resource anywhere affects all people; (2) an understanding of the natural characteristics of resources, particularly of their relation to, and dependence upon, the total environment; and (3) an understanding of the relations that exist between the resource and the society exploiting it (the physical-cultural relationship).

One further contribution of the geographer should be noted. Much of our misuse of resources reflects plain ignorance of basic geographical information. We do not know what the angle of slope is in this place or that and, accordingly, do not know how great a danger there may be locally of serious soil erosion. We do not know the total environmental requirements of a particular type of wildlife, and therefore cannot know how seriously its survival may be threatened. We do not know in any precise way what pollutants are entering surface waters, and therefore may not realize how much damage is being done until it is too late to do much about it. There is, in other words, a tremendous "inventorying" job to be done before we can make any sound, factually-based plans for resource use and development—and this job of inventory-taking is one for which the geographer is uniquely well trained.

The principle of environmental interrelationship

We are not concerned in this chapter to range over the whole field of conservation. Rather, we shall try to illustrate those basic *geographic* concepts, understandings, and principles which must undergird any sound conservation thinking or planning. The first of these—one which man can ignore only at his own peril—is the principle of environmental interrelationship, i.e., the principle that all things, animate and inanimate, are pieces in a vast mosaic from which no piece can be withdrawn without affecting the whole pattern of the mosaic. An example taken from a very limited and simple situation may serve to illustrate this point:

¶ Each animal prefers certain food. The food relations of pond animals are shown in [Figure XVI-1]. For purposes of illustration let us suppose the existence of a community composed of the species named *only*.

Any marked fluctuation of conditions is sufficient to disturb the balance of an animal community. Let us assume that because of some unfavorable condition in a pond during the breeding period the black bass decrease markedly. The pickerel, which devours young bass, must feed more exclusively upon insects. The decreased number of black bass would relieve the drain upon the crayfishes, which are eaten by bass, crayfishes would accordingly increase and prey more heavily upon the aquatic insects. This combined attack of pickerel and crayfishes would cause insects to decrease and the number of pickerel would fall away because of the decreased food supply. Meanwhile the bullheads, which are general feeders and which devour aquatic insects, might feed more extensively upon mollusks because of the decrease of the former, but would probably decrease also because of the falling-off of their main article of diet. We may thus reasonably assume that the black bass would recover its numbers because of the decrease of pickerel and bullheads, the enemies of its young.[1]

What is true of a living community such as the life of a pond is similarly, though less obviously, true of the inanimate landscape. What happens to the environmental mosaic when, let us say, a forested hillside is cleared and planted with corn? It is evident that

---

[1] Shelford, Victor E., *Animal Communities in Temperate America*, The Geographical Society of Chicago Bulletin No. 5, The University of Chicago Press, pp. 70-71. Copyright 1937 by The University of Chicago.

there must be immediate and profound consequences for wildlife. Most of us know also that there is likely to be rapid erosion of the cleared land and increased siltation of streams flowing from the area. In the not-too-long run there are also likely to be serious social consequences, especially for the farmers who were unwise enough to try to farm such land and also for the towns which look to those farmers for their markets and sources of supply. The impoverishment of the people will, in turn, be reflected in a dropping-off of tax revenues for such community services as schools, roads, hospitals, and public welfare programs. And in the most understandable human terms, this may mean that bright young boys and girls who, in a more prosperous environment, would have had the opportunity to develop their talents and make a real contribution to society will instead be forced to expend all their energies on mere survival.

The distinction between renewable and nonrenewable resources

Any sound conservation program must give proper recognition to the fact that certain resources are, by their very nature, nonrenewable once man has appropriated them to his use. Petroleum, once taken from the ground, is consumed in the process of being used. Iron, once it has been used, can be reclaimed to a limited extent in the form of scrap, but the ores do not replenish themselves. Even soil, once it has deteriorated to a certain point, takes a very long time to renew its strength.

A forest, on the other hand, if it is properly cared for, can continue to produce indefinitely. Surface waters, if they are protected from overuse and pollution, will constantly renew themselves. Soil, properly cared for, need not deteriorate with use; indeed, it can be significantly improved. A conservation-minded people, practicing nothing more than ordinary common sense, would never need to fear the exhaustion of these resources.

The problem lies, therefore, with the nonrenewable resources. Granted on simple moral grounds that we have no right to waste them, to what extent should any one generation deny itself their use so that there may be something left for future generations? In the New Testament parable of the talents, the steward who buried his talent in the ground for fear of losing it was roundly condemned: it seems consistent with the spirit of this parable to say that the nation which leaves its resources buried in the ground for fear of exhausting them is also practicing a false morality. It is possible that a mineral, for instance, which is highly useful to our generation may, because of scientific or technological advances, be of little or no value to our grandchildren. Our nonuse of it will not, therefore, help them, and meanwhile we have denied ourselves the benefits to be derived from its use.

This attitude toward the use of nonrenewable resources has been well expressed by a recent writer who says:

¶ I suppose there will be always a tendency to accept a concept of conservation that is based on exhaustion and that proposes restriction in the use of resources, simply because it is so easy to project the present. But I cannot concur that such a concept can ever prevail, since it ignores the fact that continual change, rather than permanent stability, is characteristic not only of the earth but of its inhabitants. I believe that the prospect of impending shortages or unsuitable supplies will continue to inspire the research and technical advances that will make it possible to resolve such problems well in advance of the doom we often are prone to foresee.

We probably need to fear, not the exhaustion of physical resources, but the dangers of inadequate or belated utilization of our intellectual resources. I hope we are currently rediscovering the need to practice this kind of conservation.

Wider recognition of the part that science and technology have played in the conversion of conservation from a movement based on fear to one calling for wise use of presently used resources and the preservation of social and esthetic values may well stimulate research by the social scientists and humanists to seek comparable progress towards the new objectives.[1]

In support of his position, this writer notes how "the great strides that have been made through the use of geology, geophysics, and

---

[1] Nolan, Thomas B., "Use and Renewal of Natural Resources," *Science*, Vol. CXXVIII, No. 3325, 19 September, 1958, p. 636. Reprinted from *Science* by permission.

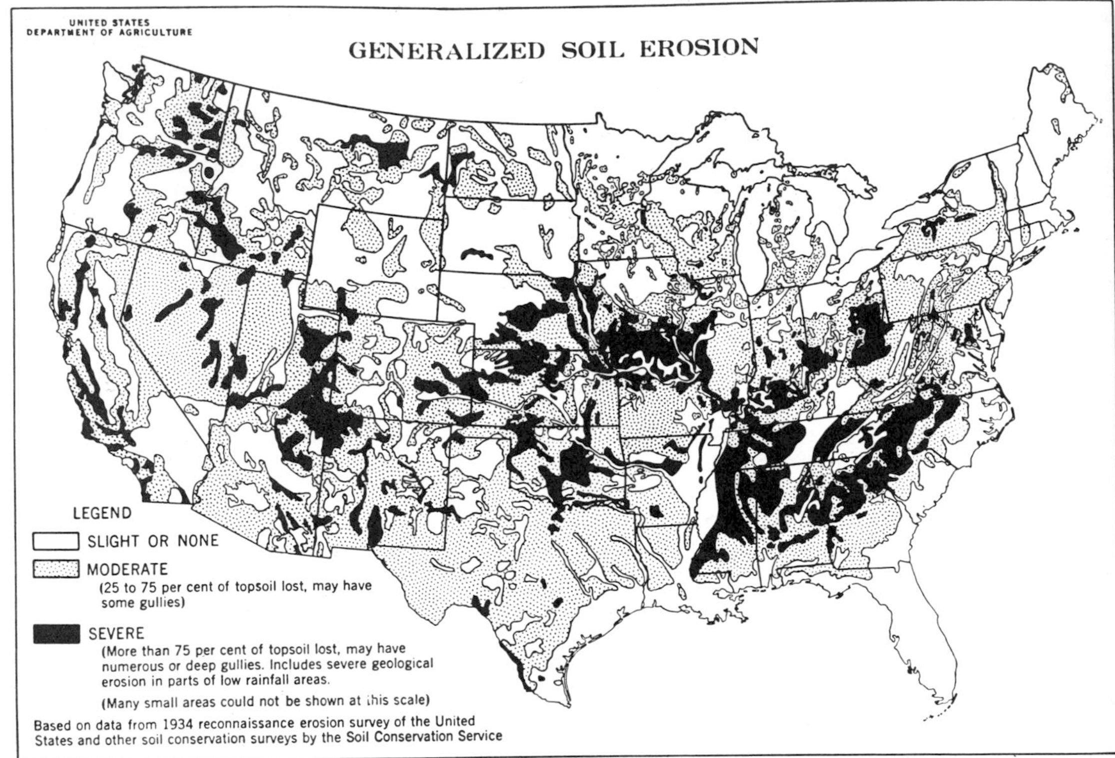

XVI:2 Generalized soil erosion in the United States is shown on this map. (Courtesy of the Soil Conservation Service of the United States Department of Agriculture)

engineering in finding and extracting petroleum from the ground" have invalidated older reserve estimates; and he further contends that, granting the fact that our oil fields must eventually be exhausted, we can still "view the possibility of exhaustion of even those reserves with some equanimity in the light of our research-driven capacity to produce synthetic liquid fuels from the tremendously large reserves of oil shales, tar sands, and in the still more distant future, low-grade coals."[1]

Is this too optimistic a view? Many students of resources, including Whitaker, think that it is. Much depends, probably, upon how one assesses man's long-run ability to rise above his traditional dependence upon materials such as iron and the fossil fuels. At present it is difficult for him to imagine any wholly satisfactory substitutes. The geographer has no prophetic insight into future technological developments, but he does have eyes to see what is presently happening. And reporting only what he sees, he must assert that there are acute shortages and decidedly unsuitable supplies of certain resources in certain regions and countries.

The soil—essential and irreplaceable

The perils of soil destruction have been dealt with in Chapter 8. The extent of the problem in the United States is indicated by the map (Figure XVI-2).

It may be belaboring the obvious to point up some of the relationships which become apparent from even the most cursory examination of this map, but our whole conservation problem derives from our apparent inability, as a people, to see the obvious. We shall attempt, therefore, to explain the pattern of soil erosion as this map illustrates it, and to state the principles which can be deduced from this pattern.

You will note that most of the severely eroded land of the United States lies east of

---

1 *Ibid.*, p. 633. Reprinted from *Science* by permission.

This picture illustrates the right way and the wrong way to manage slope land. To the left of the stream valley fields have been consolidated and the land contoured to provide for efficient management and the minimization of runoff. To the right of the valley the land remains in traditional, unplanned use, and the results are evident in gullying. This area is near Quetzaltenango, Guatemala. (United States Department of Agriculture, Office of Foreign Agricultural Relations)

the 100th meridian, the traditional dividing line between the dry and humid sections of the United States. Water is, as we know, the chief agent of erosion, and since it is also essential to agriculture we get here the combined action of two destructive forces: running water and a type of land cultivation which does not sufficiently take into account the destructive potential of running water.

The most severely eroded section of our country is the Southeast—a relatively warm, humid land, much of which is in slope. Note how the areas of most severe erosion fringe the southern Appalachians. Here the erosive powers of running water have been reinforced by slopes, by the absence of a winter season of rest, and by a type of cultivation (row-cropping of corn and tobacco) which opens up the land to maximum erosion. Soil depletion enters the picture here, also, for the traditional one-cropping practices of this part of the country have seriously damaged the tilth of the soil and thus made it more susceptible to erosion. Bennett cites the example of Stewart County, in the coastal plain section of Georgia, where a gully is said to have started about 1870 with the drip from a barn roof. By 1913 this gully was more than a hundred feet deep, had engulfed a schoolhouse and two farm buildings, and had enough farm land toppled into it for 1,400 forty-acre farms (7).

But while erosion has been most severe in the Southeast, it is by no means restricted to that region. Note elsewhere in humid United States the close relationship between areas of severe erosion and major river valleys, particularly the Missouri Valley in Missouri, the lower Illinois Valley, and the Ohio Valley, particularly in its headwaters reaches. Locally within any one of these areas can be found eroded districts as desolate as anything to be found in the Southeast.

West of the 100th meridian the districts of severe erosion continue to be closely related to stream valleys, but another factor enters the picture here. This is wind deflation, the removal of the topsoil by wind in regions of drought and scanty vegetational cover. A good example of this can be found in the dry wheat lands of eastern Washington state. In much of the rest of the West, severe erosion has been related to the overgrazing of natural grasslands.

Well—so what? We have more land than we need, anyway, and there are supposed to be fabulous food resources in the sea if the land gives out, so why worry? Two answers, at least, suggest themselves: (1) No one who possesses even a moderately sensitive palate can look forward with equanimity to subsisting on a diet consisting largely of kelp and other sea products. (2) Even the most conservative forecasts of future population indicate that our present agricultural surpluses are temporary problems; the real problem of providing sufficient palatable food for anticipated populations still lies before us. And this is how we stand on cropland resources in the United States:

Land ruined for cultivation or severely damaged . . .	282,000,000 acres
Land moderately damaged —erosion beginning or hazardous under improper use	775,000,000 acres
Land not yet damaged but in forest or brush, grassland, swamp, marsh, or other unproductive use . .	702,000,000 acres
Land whose damage has not yet been determined (desert, badlands, western mountain areas, alkali—much natural erosion) . .	145,000,000 acres
Total land eroded or idle or in non-agricultural use . .	1,904,000,000 acres
Estimated cropland resources:	
Cultivated and temporarily idle in farms	398,000,000 acres
Uncultivated plowable pasture, meadows, woodland, scrub in farms . .	164,000,000 acres
Uncultivated plowable land not in farms	90,000,000 acres
Total plowable land	652,000,000 acres[1]

Taking the figure of two and a half acres of farmland as the minimum required for the adequate nourishment of one person, we have presently enough land for approximately 260 million people, a figure which population experts expect us to reach in our country before the end of this century.

¶ Soil conservation consists of safeguarding all kinds of useful land—and most land favorably situated, climatically and topographically, is useful for some purpose–against impoverishment or depletion brought about by:

1. Excessive soil removal—erosion.
2. Deposition of the products of erosion—overwash.
3. Exhaustion of plant nutrients through leaching, overcropping, and overgrazing
4. Accumulation of toxic salts—alkali condition.
5. Burning—actual destruction in the case of organic soil (peat) and burning off dry vegetation.
6. Development of harmful waterlogging and failure to provide adequate drainage for cultivated and pasture land.
7. Improper cultivation—as plowing up- and downslope.
8. Improper land use leading to the impairment of the soil—as the cultivation of steep land that should be kept permanently in grass or trees.

[1] Bennett, Hugh Hammond, *Elements of Soil Conservation*, McGraw-Hill Book Company, Inc., New York, 1955, p. 28. Reprinted by permission.

9. Unnecessary waste of rainfall by controllable runoff.
10. Lack of crop rotation.

Soil conservation is accomplished by:

1. Using adaptable conservation practices and engineering structures to prevent or control soil erosion and the harmful deposition of the products of erosion.
2. Using improved tillage, mulching, and cropping practices to conserve needed rainfall.
3. Controlling runoff to meet the needs of the land.
4. Using water, organic matter, manure, fertilizers, lime, and so forth, with maximum efficiency and in accordance with the needs of the land.
5. Combining drainage and flooding to prevent the accumulation of toxic salts and to improve alkali land.
6. Draining to prevent waterlogging or to improve wet fields and pastures.
7. Flooding by diking and pumping to prevent the burning of peat lands.
8. Holding the water table at proper level by diking and pumping and by water-level management with ditches and gates.
9. Changing from the unwise cultivation of steep, shallow, highly erodible, or otherwise unfavorable land to the planting of grass, trees, or other protective cover to achieve better use and better protection of the land; adjusting the intensity of grazing range and pasture lands to retain sufficient vegetative cover to conserve rainfall, maintain a favorable forage stand, and prevent soil erosion.
10. Draining, irrigating, clearing off brush or rock, or otherwise improving previously unproductive land to fit it for practical, productive use, such as would encourage a shift to safer, less intensive uses of nearby or distant highly erodible or other unfavored land (as by substituting rich bottom land for poor, highly erodible hillsides.) These operations should take into account the needs of wildlife.
11. Irrigating and increasing the production of supplemental feed on adaptable areas (if available) of ranching enterprises where the dry land grazing areas are incapable of producing sufficient year-round feed to encourage safer and more profitable ranching enterprises.
12. Utilizing for wildlife the odd corners, borders, and areas of land not usable for ordinary cropping, pasture, or forestry purposes.
13. Using adaptable farm machinery efficiently.
14. Maintaining all conservation structures and practices.[1]

Water: too little and too much

Of all the earth's resources, water is probably the nearest to inexhaustible. There is an abundance of it in the oceans, the rivers, the lakes, and the atmosphere. Nevertheless, some of man's most stubborn and persistent problems have been with water, and in many places the problem is growing more acute year by year. Essentially, the water problem has been threefold: (1) finding a way to bring it where it is not; (2) finding a way to get rid of it where there is too much of it; and (3) making and keeping it suitable for use.

Historically, it was the first of these problems that first engaged man's attention. The sites of Western man's earliest civilizations were drylands, but irrigable drylands. That is, water was available from such rivers as the Nile, the Tigris, and the Euphrates, and from subterranean supplies. In these lands, then, we find the precursors of the great irrigation projects which have enriched so many once-sterile sections of our western states.

There is, though, a certain built-in fragility in irrigation works. One or two careless generations, a relatively short interval of civil disorder, and the dams crumble away, the distributary channels become silted up, and the landscape reverts to a desolation greater than that from which it had been recreated by the wit and ingenuity of man. Irrigation is not, therefore, in most cases a permanent solution to the problem of drought—nor would it be even if man's persistent tendency to destroy the works of his own hands could be held in check, for nature in its own inexorable way goes about recovering what man has wrested from it. Sooner or later, silt accumulates behind the dams and in the channels of the distributaries, the flow of life-giving water is cut off, and the people move away.

---

[1] *Ibid.*, pp. 116-117. Reprinted by permission.

Whether any given proposal for an irrigation project is feasible therefore depends upon several considerations, among them the following:

1. The cost of the project, both in absolute terms and by comparison with other possible ways of bringing new land under cultivation (e.g., by reclaiming wet lands).
2. The anticipated useful life of the project, calculated primarily on the basis of the probable siltation rate.
3. The versatility of the project, i.e., the possibility of accomplishing other objectives —e.g., flood control, water power development, recreational use—in addition to irrigation.
4. The national or regional benefits that can be reasonably expected to accrue from such a project by comparison with benefits that might result from an equal investment of money in some other project.

Feasibility is not, however, in every case the prime consideration when the decision —ultimately political—has to be made on a particular proposal. Under our federal system, every state, including the western states, is entitled to two Senators, irrespective of its population. Under the traditions of the Senate, influence and power increase with seniority. There is always, therefore, in Congress, and especially in the Senate, a bloc of very influential western Senators of both parties who are prepared to support any proposal for irrigation in that part of the country. They usually get it through Congress, too, if they want it badly enough. (This is not said, incidentally, by way of censure; one of the purposes of a federal system is to ensure that the various regions of a country as large as ours will be represented and heard when decisions are made on the development of the nation's resources.)

Irrigation is the bringing of water to land where it is needed. Reclamation, as the term is most commonly used, is the removal of surplus water from the land. The symbols of irrigation are the dam and the distributary channel. The symbols of reclamation are the windmill, the pump, drainage tile, and drainage ditches.

The classic examples of reclaimed lands are the polder districts of the Netherlands and the fen lands of eastern England. But throughout northwestern Europe and the glaciated portions of the United States, vast areas have been reclaimed from the swampy, marshy, or boggy condition in which they were left by the retreating glaciers. It has been said that the bedrock of Indiana is drainage tile. This may not be quite literally the case, but it is certainly true that very little of northern Indiana, or of like areas elsewhere in the Great Lakes region, would be agriculturally useful if it were not for drainage tile.

A form of reclamation so specialized that it is always dealt with as a separate category is flood control. Next to soil conservation, this has probably been the major concern of conservationists in our own country, for we have experienced many disastrous floods in our great river systems. Flood "control" is perhaps too presumptuous a term for what we are actually trying to do. Rivers as great as those which drain the heart of North America cannot be controlled; they can only be limited in their destructive potential. Three broad headings suffice to summarize the various means by which this limitation can be accomplished: (1) controlling the amount of water which enters the stream system by such various devices as safeguarding the absorbent soils and the retarding forests in the drainage basin, and especially in the headwaters reaches; storing runoff in catchment basins and artificial lakes; or carrying the water away by ditches or drains to some less troublesome place; (2) regulating the flow of water in the main stream and its tributaries by means of dams, regulating pools, and, in flood time, predesignated overflow areas; and (3) avoidance of those sites along the stream courses which are most susceptible to flooding. Essentially, in the case of great rivers such as the Mississippi or the Ohio, man can do very little to prevent natural flooding, but he can take measures to prevent the aggravation of this natural flooding and to escape its worst consequences. The most effective measures along this line involve intelligent planning and careful use of the headwaters areas.

The third of the three major water problems is that of making and keeping water suitable for use. What we mean by suitable is, of course, determined by the use we have in mind. Thus we expect more of drinking water than mere safety. We want water that is free from sediments and from offensive tastes or odors, that is cool and chemically neutral. For

This view is of the Grand Coulee Dam spillway. One of the best examples of a multipurpose project, the Grand Coulee is designed to control flooding, to store up water for dry periods, to provide water for irrigation, and to supply power. The contrast between the abundance of water foaming from the dam and the dry mesa in the background points up the importance of such projects to drylands. (United States Department of the Interior, Bureau of Reclamation)

other household purposes, such as bathing and washing, it is important again that the water be clear, and also that it be free from certain minerals such as lime, magnesium, iron, and manganese which are wasteful of soap, likely to form scaly deposits, and (as in the case of iron) capable of staining. For industrial purposes there may be very rigid water requirements; textile and paper industries, for instance, cannot tolerate the risk of staining from water with a high iron content, and industries which use water for cooling need ample supplies of cold water. Since, in many cases, nature does not provide the kinds of water we want, we have to make the water suitable for our uses by such means as filtration, precipitating out undesirable minerals, and the chemical removal of undesirable tastes or odors.

Whenever man enters the picture a further problem arises, the problem of pollution. Pollution is the introduction into the waters, by man, of qualities which render it undesirable or unsafe for use. Examples that come immediately to mind are the dumping of industrial wastes or of raw sewage into surface waters, or the seepage of these materials into subsurface waters. There is really no excuse for this kind of contamination, but it goes on all over the world, and even in the most advanced countries constant vigilance is required to ensure safe and palatable water supplies. Most urban water supplies in the

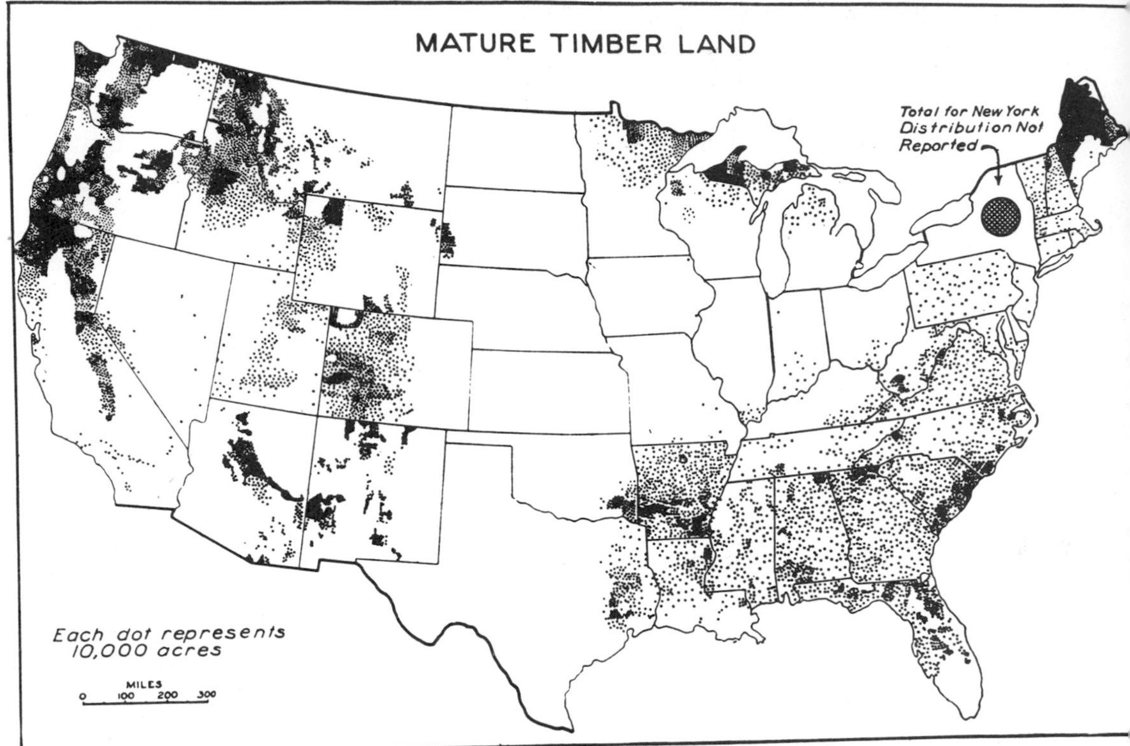

XVI:3 Forested land of the United States is shown on this map. Areas of second-growth cut, which is used for such relatively low-value purposes as firewood, mine supports, fence posts, or railroad ties, are not shown. (Courtesy United States Forest Service)

Western world are, by now, as safe as rigid supervision can make them. But outside the Western world, even urban water supplies are still often of the sewer-laundry-drinking water type, and throughout the world, nonurban waters are more likely than not to be polluted. In our own country, the spread of residential building beyond the limits of urban water mains poses a real threat to health. For, while a good septic tank is an efficient purifier of sewage, many septic tanks are poorly constructed or poorly located or poorly cared for, and as a result, fail to purify sewage before releasing it into the ground.

The forests: a potentially indestructible resource

One of the major achievements of the conservation movement, both in this country and in Europe, has been its creation of a new attitude toward the value and importance of forests. For centuries in northern Europe, and through most of our national history, the forest was The Enemy, the great obstacle to movement and to cultivation, "the Wilderness" which had to be pushed back by fire and axe before civilization could move in. The consequences of such unconsidered clearing of forests have been tragic:

¶ Not only does man, the pioneer, rob the soil of its source of humus, the fallen leaves, but he exposes a soil quite unused to the direct rays of the sun and the direct fall of the rain to the immediate influence of both. For example, much of the upland and west coast of Scotland was once forested with the beautiful Scots fir (*Pinus sylvestris*). The heavy rain, falling on the close pine woods, trickled gradually to the ground and soaked into the soil. Much was evaporated from the leaves, and the floor of the forest, covered with pine needles, remained comparatively dry, supporting a sparse cover or undergrowth of various shade-loving plants or low shrubs such as bilberry and heather. When the forests were cut down, the heavy rain fell straight onto the surface soil more rapidly than it could drain away. Especially where there was no steep slope the water was held up, and moisture-loving plants began to flourish, particularly sphagnum, or bog moss. Once the sphagnum was established it acted as a sponge. True, it prevented soil erosion, but it grew and grew until great thicknesses of moss blanketed the whole countryside. Thus huge stretches of bog land, known to the botanists as "blanket bog," extending over wide areas of Scotland and Ireland, are directly due to man's action.

A different, perhaps more familiar, example is seen in many of the hilly parts of the Southern states. The originally forested slopes were cleared by the pioneers for timber or for the creation of farmlands. The bare soil was left unprotected; heavy downpours of rain rapidly washed it away and one gets the familiar feature of gully erosion and of hillsides literally swept bare of any vestige of soil. But of course this example could be multiplied elsewhere in the United States and all over the world. No more heart-breaking story of man's improvidence is told than in the barren, eroded hills of China, land of famine.[1]

There are few places outside the tropics today where the forest is looked upon as The Enemy, to be leveled before the advance of civilization. A timber-hungry world has learned to regard its forests as valuable resources, the more valuable because, with proper care, they are practically inexhaustible. But forests are still being destroyed, not so much by design as by carelessness. The great enemy of the forest today is not the pioneer or the woodsman's axe but the tourist's campfire and cigarette. "Behold how great a matter a little fire kindleth." Fire is an ever-present danger, particularly during the dry summers in our western forests. Some of the fires, it is true, are set by lightning, but many more are started by the carelessness of man.

The price we pay for forest denudation is a high one—ruined land, muddy and flood-prone rivers, the extinction of forest wildlife, the loss of the intangible recreational values of the forest, our forced dependence upon inferior types of timber for furniture and building construction, and probably some undesirable effects upon climate. The realization of these losses long ago brought about, in Europe and particularly in Germany, an emphasis upon scientific use of the forests, the ideal of "sustained-yield" forestry. In simple terms, this means replanting as one cuts or, in agricultural terms, sowing as one harvests. Trees are treated as crops, to be planted and cared for and, at maturity, to be harvested. Under this kind of care, a forest can last indefinitely.

Wise forest management involves protecting the forest against destructive agents and practices. The greatest destructive agent is, as we have seen, fire. Against this hazard the best defense is unremitting vigilance. The fire tower and the observation plane are two very effective means by which this vigilance may be exercised. But too often the observers who man them can only report what is, by the time they see it, a disastrous situation. The vigilance that really counts is that of the ordinary citizen who, when he happens into the forest, stops to realize that he has it in his power to destroy all the beauty that surrounds him.

Overgrazing is one of the two destructive practices that threaten forest survival. Grazing animals damage young trees, destroy the water-absorbing litter of the forest floor, and often disturb the soil. In our western states there has been a conflict of long standing between the conservationists and the cattlemen over the use of public domain land for grazing. The cattlemen, understandably, would like to make greater use of the forest for grazing. The conservationists would like to limit or even forbid grazing in the national forests.

The other destructive practice which threatens forest survival is, of course, irresponsible cutting. This may take the form either of wanton destruction of the forest by simply stripping it or of failing to adjust cutting practices to the life cycles of the trees. The general rule is that trees should be cut when they are "ripe," that is, when they have reached the peak of their maturity and are just beginning to pass into senescence.

The geography of forest conservation has become, in our time, largely a study of hill, mountain, low latitude, and high latitude geography. The middle-latitude lowlands are, for all practical purposes, lost to the agriculturist, the stockman, and the city dweller. In

---

[1] Stamp, L. Dudley, *Land for Tomorrow: The Underdeveloped World*, Indiana University Press, Bloomington, 1952, pp. 181-182. Reprinted by permission.

a practical way this means, unfortunately, that the vast majority of people are rather far removed from the problem areas and, therefore, inclined to be little concerned about what happens in them. But it would be a tragic mistake to suppose that our forests, or indeed any other resource, are purely local or regional concerns—an attitude which seems to underlie the notion that the Interior Department somehow belongs to the West and should at least be headed by a Westerner.[1] Our resources are national resources and should be managed for the benefit of all of our people. This is particularly true of our timber resources, now largely restricted to the West and the reforested lands of the deep South.

Minerals—the new bread of life

Modern man, at least modern Western man, is an industrial man. He must, of course, eat, and to this extent he is still as dependent as were his forefathers upon the direct production of the soils and waters of the earth. But if he had only the soils and the waters to sustain him he would be forced down to a level of survival scarcely higher than that of the Chinese or Indian peasant. The difference between that level of living, and the remarkably high level which characterizes most of the Western world, is the product of ingenuity operating upon mineral resources to produce useful goods.

This being the case, it is not too much to say that minerals constitute a new bread of life for modern industrial man. And it is, therefore, all the more sobering to realize that, when we deal with minerals, we are dealing with resources which, unlike those we have discussed up to this point, can neither merely be preserved nor effectively be restored. Perhaps it is not altogether accurate to say that they cannot be preserved; they can, of course, but an unusable resource ceases to be a resource and, in the long run, no society will deny itself the use of any resource for which it has a use. So preservation is, for all practical purposes, impossible in the long run. And restoration is a job for geological processes, not for man.

Another distinctive characteristic of mineral resources is their uneven distribution over the face of the earth. It bears no close relationship to the distribution of population except, perhaps, in the case of the fuel minerals such as coal and, to a lesser extent, petroleum. Indeed, many minerals are found in situations which, to a greater or lesser degree, discourage large-scale settlement. Thus many of the metallic minerals are associated with the stumps of once-great mountains, now eroded to low mountains or hill country. Some of the major oil fields, notably those of Southwest Asia, underlie barren deserts. Even much good coal is found in country which is otherwise unlikely to attract heavy population; fortunately, there is also a great deal of good coal in more hospitable places.

These minerals are not only very unevenly distributed but also highly concentrated in certain places. Two examples will serve to illustrate this point:

¶ Iron is one of the most widely distributed minerals on earth. Yellow, buff, red, and brown colors of soil and rock are nearly always evidence of its presence. One or two per cent of iron are sufficient to produce rusty stains on rock that has been exposed to moisture and air. However, the mining industry in the Mesabi region began with ores containing from 75 to 85 per cent iron and is still working with ore containing 35 per cent iron. The industry has been experimenting with another ore containing 18 per cent iron but only one company seems to have considered this ore sufficiently valuable to warrant the investments necessary to begin operations. At present the greater part of the world's steel requirements are met from a few areas containing one or more very large and rich deposits.

Aluminum is a component of clay but in such small quantities that commercial recovery is impossible. Arkansas contains the only sizeable deposits of commercially recoverable aluminum in the United States and these are of such low grade that our country meets most of its aluminum needs from deposits located in Dutch and British Guiana.[2]

---

[1] Of the sixteen Secretaries of the Interior who have served in this century, ten have come from west of the Mississippi, including all who have served since 1946. Significantly, the most vigorous of recent secretaries, Harold L. Ickes, came not from the West but from Illinois.

[2] Buls, E. J., "Foundations of National Power," *The Cresset,* Vol. XIX, No. 9, September, 1956, p. 8. Reprinted by permission.

These reforested strip mine banks in southwestern Indiana illustrate what Whitaker means by "man's impact on nature." Man's desire for coal meant the transformation of this area into something reminiscent of a lunar landscape. Happily, man is capable of repairing much of the damage he does, as this picture also illustrates. To what worthwhile uses can an area such as this be put? (Courtesy National Coal Association)

Finally, the exploitation of minerals almost always involves the destruction of other resources. Since minerals almost always occur in rock or soil, the surface of the earth must be damaged either by removal, as in strip mining operations, or by undermining, as in subsurface operations. Still more damage is likely to be done by the piling up of the stripped-away materials in the form of spoils banks.

A sound mineral conservation policy must take into account these basic realities. Ideally there should be some world-wide authority which would supervise mineral exploitation, particularly in those "backward" parts of the world where local governments encourage or tolerate the kind of rapacious exploitation which is no longer permitted in most advanced countries. Such an authority is, however, a very unlikely prospect in the foreseeable future. That means that the next most effective level of control, the nation, must attempt to do within its own territory what a world authority would attempt to do on a worldwide level, that is, carefully inventory mineral deposits, determine the conditions and limits of their use, and insist upon a pattern of use which will postpone, as long as possible, the inevitable day when they will no longer be usable.

Such a national mineral policy should

include, at a minimum, the following considerations:

1. The most efficient mining practices possible within the limits imposed by our technological skill. In the past, wasteful mining methods have been, in some cases, economically profitable in the short run. The result has been a "grab and run" type of exploitation which enriched the few at the expense of the many. Money is replaceable; minerals are not. If private capital cannot operate at a profit using the best tools and techniques known to technology it would be, in the long run, more profitable to subsidize it than to ruin, for the sake of short-term profits, the very resources upon which our long-term prosperity is based.

2. The most efficient use of minerals once they have been taken out of the ground. Western man has been profligate in the use of irreplaceable minerals, in altogether too many cases using them in the manufacture of goods which have little or no utility. In other cases he has used irreplaceable materials, such as minerals, when replaceable materials, such as vegetable products, would have served as well or better.

3. A vigorous program of research to discover more abundant substitutes for scarce materials. Much has been done along this line in recent years, particularly in the development of synthetic substitutes, such as plastics, for the metallic minerals. Much more needs to be done.

4. Recovery and re-use of minerals wherever possible. Some minerals, such as the precious metals, can be used over and over again with little loss of volume or quality. Others, such as iron, have much more limited possibilities for re-use. Still others, such as the mineral fuels, can not be re-used at all. A conservation-minded nation would not consider the old maxim, "Waste not, want not," an amusing and slightly old-fashioned piece of moralism, but a sound principle of resource use.

5. Beneficiation of low-quality resources. This, too, is an expensive policy since it is so much easier and, in the short run, so much more profitable to "skim off the cream" and move on when the best grades of minerals have been mined out. But, again, the social gain would more than justify subsidizing, if need be, the producer who is willing to avail himself of the technological means already available for using lower-grade resources.

6. Limitation on production of scarce minerals in peacetime so as to ensure an adequate supply in case of war or other national emergency. There are many minerals which we can easily afford to import in times of peace. In the case of some of these, we even have to subsidize domestic producers in order to make it profitable for them to compete with foreign suppliers. Surely it would be better to set aside these small or low-grade domestic reserves as emergency sources of supply in times of national emergency than to subsidize their exhaustion in peacetime and then go to enormous expense to bring in foreign supplies in times of emergency.

Scenic and wildlife resources

The resources which we have discussed up to this point are bread-and-butter matters. Without them, man either does not live or lives very poorly. But man lives also in a community of life which extends beyond his own species to every part of the plant and animal kingdoms, and when these are despoiled he himself suffers damage. He lives with something in his nature that needs and responds to beauty, and when beauty is destroyed man himself suffers a measure of destruction.

This need—and the attitude of mind which must be the starting-point of any genuine concern for conservation—has been eloquently stated by Professor Paul B. Sears in a short monograph which will serve as a fitting conclusion to this section and this chapter:

¶ The state of Ohio, containing about 40,000 square miles, was once a magnificent hardwood forest. The forest types, thanks to the records of early surveyors, have been largely mapped. Yet it is almost impossible to form an adequate picture, from any surviving records, of the appearance of that forest. The state has its full share of memorials—statues, libraries, institutions; some useful, some not; some beautiful, many ugly. But somehow it never occurred to anyone to set aside a square mile, much less a township six miles square, of primeval vegetation for future generations to see and enjoy. Yet this could have been done for less than the cost of a single pile of stone of dubious artistic and cultural merit. . . .

There exists, I suppose, such a thing as fundamental decency and gratitude and there are ways to acknowledge it. The Mormons have their

An undeveloped area. Or is it? There are those who see a great future for a spot such as this—meaning, of course, that this would be a good place for a couple of hotels, a casino, a trailer park, some cottages, and a neon-lit hamburger drive-in. The cabin cruiser may already be prophetic of the day when this reservoir will throb to the sound of outboard motors. But many an ulcerous, tension-ridden urbanite would like to see a few places kept pretty much this way as retreats for those brief vacation periods he needs to rediscover nature and himself. (United States Department of the Interior, Bureau of Reclamation)

monument to the gulls which saved them from the locusts. The Lord Chancellor sits upon a woolsack, memento of the source of England's early economic power. Many of us have seen the block expressing gratitude to the boll weevil which first obliged the South to begin diversifying its crops—a curious but impressive tribute.

We are, and rightly, generous in our regard for the group of most unusual men who made possible our Nation and planned its greatness. But we ought to remember, too, that in large measure our power and leadership are based upon the lavishness of Nature, building undisturbed through millenniums. The ancients thought it not unworthy to worship the gods who gave them grain—rice, wheat, maize. Is it unworthy in our enlightened day to commemorate, by generous preservation, the natural wealth which has been the lifeblood of our economy? I, for one, do not think so. To me it seems a matter of ethics and national self-respect.

An American commander in eastern Europe told me that he gave permission to the cold and hungry people of a city to help themselves to the trees in their ancient forest-park. This they refused to do, and the hard-headed general was deeply moved by their decision. It will not do to write off sentiment.

There is also, in the need for generous natural

areas, the question of important scientific knowledge. The undisturbed community of plants and animals is a beautifully organized dynamic system, employing energy from the sun for the use and re-use of water, air and minerals in sustaining abundant life, while keeping its own organization going. Technically this presents an exceedingly important phenomenon, the approximation of a steady state. Our knowledge of this phenomenon can do with considerable improvement, and again we need generous examples for its study. When men are beginning to talk rather seriously of raising some billions for the exploration of space, we ought not to neglect a more immediate, and definitely hopeful, source of knowledge. Knowledge for its own sake, like sentiment, is not lightly to be written off by a civilized nation. . . .

Yet neither knowledge nor sentiment alone can afford the most powerful justification of ample wilderness or natural areas set aside in perpetuity. Rather it is the mixture of practical, theoretical and ethical symbolized by the question: "What kind of a Nation do we want?" Do we wish to build a future completely and ruthlessly mechanized, standardized and artificial? Do we really mean to crowd back Nature to the utmost minimum, depending upon ingenious artifice at every turn for physical and spiritual sustenance, until we have to eat standing up and the healing which comes of solitude survives only in dreams?

The hour is late, but we still have a measure of freedom to choose.[1]

This, to a geographer at least, is the heart of the matter. For what is all of our measuring and mapping and describing if it does not, in some way or another, contribute to the solution of man's problems and the satisfying of his needs? Possessed of the ultimate human freedom—the freedom to choose—the geographer sees in conservation the opportunity to put his knowledge to practical use in the service of mankind. His contribution begins in showing men what the resource problems are and where they manifest themselves on the face of the earth. It culminates in suggesting ways and means of overcoming them or postponing their effects.

[1] Sears, Paul B., "What Worth Wilderness?" *Bulletin of the Schools* of the University of the State of New York, March, 1953, reprinted by Nature Conservancy, Washington, 1953. Reprinted by permission.

APPLICATION OF GEOGRAPHIC UNDERSTANDING

I. When we talk about resources for the future, the first thought that strikes us is that we do not know for sure what our descendants may find useful from among materials which today seem useless to us. What implications does this fact have for our present thinking?

II. In what sense may it be true that "the most careful preservation can be the worst enemy of conservation"?

III. What is the significance of the statement that "the glory that was Greece and the grandeur that was Rome were washed away by the winter rains"?

IV. In what various ways does the removal of a vegetational cover from the land tend to accelerate the rate of erosion?

V. What is meant by "plowing on the contour"? How does such a practice help to retard erosion?

VI. What is the highest and most valuable type of use for any given piece of land?

VII. What direction does the geographer's concept of the "region" give for the problem of flood control? In what concrete ways may the Tennessee Valley Authority be described as "the regional concept in action"?

VIII. How may a nation avoid or postpone the depletion of its most essential mineral deposits? Is it possible to reconcile any deliberate controls upon the mining and use of minerals with a free-enterprise economic system?

IX. In what various ways are the scenic resources of the United States being damaged? What measures could or should be taken to preserve them?

References

1 Whitaker, Joe Russell, *The Life and Death of the Land*, Peabody College Press, Nashville, 1946, pp. 17-18, 19-22, *passim*.

2 Neuberger, Richard L., "God's Resources—and Ours," *The Christian Century*, March 13, 1957, p. 325.

3 Diettrich, Sigismond deR., "To Provide Vocational Guidance," *Nineteenth Yearbook of the Social Sciences*, 1948, p. 85.

4 Calef, Wesley, "To Understand the Nature of Conservation," *Nineteenth Yearbook of the Social Sciences*, 1948, p. 78.

5 Shelford, Victor E., *Animal Communities in Temperate America,* The Geographical Society of Chicago Bulletin No. 5, The University of Chicago Press, 1937, pp. 70-71.

6 Nolan, Thomas B., "Use and Renewal of Natural Resources," *Science,* Vol. CXXVIII, No. 3325, 19 September, 1958, pp. 633, 636.

7 Bennett, Hugh Hammond, *Elements of Soil Conservation,* McGraw-Hill Book Company, Inc., New York, pp. 28, 31-32, 116-117.

8 Stamp, L. Dudley, *Land for Tomorrow: The Underdeveloped World,* Indiana University Press, 1952, pp. 181-182.

9 Buls, E. J., "Foundations of National Power," *The Cresset,* Vol. XIX, No. 9, September, 1956, p. 8.

10 Sears, Paul B., "What Worth Wilderness," *Bulletin of the Schools* of the University of the State of New York, March, 1953, reprinted by Nature Conservancy, Washington, 1953.

Chapter 17

The geography of hunger and disease

At the very moment that North Korean troops were marching into South Korea in 1950, three boys were born in widely-separated parts of the world: one in the United States, one in Japan, and one in India. The little American boy was almost certain to reach his first birthday, and the statistical probabilities were that he would live to be almost 67 years old. The Japanese boy had a good chance of reaching his first birthday and could probably count on a life span of about 56 years. The Indian boy had only two chances in three of surviving to his first birthday, and it was not likely that he would live to be thirty years old.

The expectation of life which these three boys had at birth had little or nothing to do with the fact that a war had broken out and that their countries would or would not be involved in that war. Wars, especially modern wars, do, of course, claim millions of lives, but they are minor factors in determining the prospects of longevity among the peoples of the world. Historically—and this is still true today—the most significant causes of death have been hunger and disease. Even in wartime, people are less likely to die from enemy action than from famines and epidemics which are the by-products of war. And the end of a war brings no armistice in man's age-long struggle with these enemies.

Everybody is hungry, but some more so than others

Hunger is the lack of sufficient food to maintain optimum physical and mental health. Hunger may be apparent (starvation) or hidden (malnutrition). The Hindu dying of starvation on the streets of Calcutta is a victim of apparent hunger. He does not get enough food to maintain minimum life processes and, therefore, dies. But the Chicago "Gold Coast" matron who is troubled with a thyroid condition may also be the victim of hunger, in this case a hidden hunger resulting from a deficiency of iodine in her diet. It is possible that most, if not all, of us are the victims of some hidden hunger, some dietary deficiency of which we may be altogether unaware but which prevents us from enjoying the highest possible degree of physical and mental health.

Malnutrition: a form of human erosion

When we say that a person is in good health, we mean essentially two things: that his body operates efficiently in repairing or replacing tissue, and that he enjoys a high level of energy. Malnutrition, accordingly, implies some diminution of either or both of these qualities. Malnutrition results from deficiencies in food intake, either in terms of quantity or quality. Quantitative deficiencies are, properly speaking, a form of starvation and will be discussed later. Qualitative deficiencies result in impairment of the body's capacity to replace or repair tissue, in increasing the body's susceptibility to disease, and in lowering the energy level.

One of the most common forms of malnutrition is protein deficiency. Proteins are the sources of the amino acids, at least ten kinds of which have been shown to be essential to human nutrition. The only fully satisfactory sources of these amino acids are meats, dairy products, and eggs. Vegetable products are almost always deficient in one or more of the amino acids. But animal products are relatively expensive. Protein deficiency is thus one of the banes of the poor. The greater incidence of communicable diseases among poor people and in the impoverished lands of the world must be ascribed in large measure to protein deficiency, because that deficiency lowers resistance to infection. Another manifestation of protein deficiency is hunger edema, a condition characterized by distended bellies and bloated faces, common in many parts of the tropics and often encountered in middle-latitude countries after a war or a period of famine. (It was almost pandemic in Greece after the Second World War.) A long-range effect of protein deficiency has been suggested by Dr. Josue de Castro, who notes that:

¶ In the lands of the world which lie between the two tropics, practically all the inhabitants are of less than average height; this is true of Latin Americans, Pygmies and other Negro groups of equatorial Africa, of Indians, Filipinos, Indonesians, Chinese and others. Now all these people live on a predominantly vegetable diet—cereals, tubers and legumes—because tropical soil and climate are inappropriate to cattle raising, and therefore to the production of animal products. The only exceptions, the only tall peoples living in equatorial regions, are the pastoral groups that consume large quantities of animal products: the Berber tribes of the Sahara, the Sudanese Negroes, cattle raisers of the African savannas, herdsmen of the upper Nile, the Masai already referred to and the inhabitants of the Punjab in India. These are the only peoples of the tropical-equatorial region who escape chronic hunger for proteins of high biological value.[1]

It might be noted that, even in Europe, average height increases as one goes northward from the poorer Mediterranean lands toward beef-eating Britain and the dairy lands of the North Sea area.

A second common form of malnutrition is mineral deficiency. The body requires a considerable number of minerals, the most important of which are calcium, phosphorus, iron, iodine, and sodium. Usually the sources of these minerals are the soil and the water. Any deterioration of the soil, therefore, will aggravate the problem of malnutrition resulting from mineral deficiency.

Calcium is, perhaps, the most essential of the body minerals since it is the principal constituent of the bones and the teeth. Calcium is normally relatively abundant in dryland soils and in the soils of the temperate lands. It is generally lacking in the leached soils of the tropics. Sunlight, however, is an important factor in "fixing" calcium in the body. Therefore calcium deficiency is less common in the tropics than in the higher latitudes. To quote de Castro again:

¶ So it is seen that even though larger quantities of calcium may be taken into the body in temperate climates, the specific hunger for this element is, nevertheless, more intense and its consequences more apparent in these very regions. What happens in the tropical zones, where available calcium is scarce, is that the skeleton does not develop so fully; the average stature is lower, but the bony tissue is solidly built. In temperate areas, on the other hand, the skeletons are more elongated but more fragile, more subject to abnormalities and deformations. This tendency toward skeletal weakness in the more advanced countries, far from lessening, is apparently increasing with the development of civilization. The anthropologist Hooton, speaking of the United States, says that the skeletons of grandchildren, as compared to their grandparents, are longer but slighter.[2]

Specific diseases which are largely the result of calcium deficiency are rickets and probably dental caries.

Phosphorous, while it is the most common mineral in the human body and is present in the nucleus of every cell, seems to be present throughout the world in quantities sufficient for man's biological needs. In the tropics, however, phosphorous deficiency associated with leached soils seems to be largely responsible for the poor quality of the domesticated animals that are raised in these lands and the low quality of these animals, in turn, reduces the nutritional resource base of these lands.

The chief function of iron in the body is to form hemoglobin molecules. Iron deficiency, therefore, exhibits itself in a low red corpuscle count in the blood (anemia). Since the body's only source of iron is meat products, iron deficiency also is associated with poverty, as in the large cities of the middle latitudes, or with areas which cannot support a prosperous animal industry either because of natural limitations or because of the need for a very intensive agriculture.

A deficiency of iodine exhibits itself in a high incidence of goiter and cretinism. One of the best-known regions of iodine deficiency is the Great Lakes region of the United States which, because of this deficiency, has been called "The Goiter Belt." The Great Lakes area is a continental-interior location where, until quite recently, seafood (perhaps the best natural source of iodine) rarely appeared in the diets of even the wealthier classes. Coastal peoples, on the other hand, show a very low incidence of goiter. Indeed, in coastal China and in

[1] De Castro, Josue, *The Geography of Hunger,* Little, Brown, and Company, Boston, 1952, pp. 38-39. Copyright, 1952, by Josue de Castro. Reprinted by permission.

[2] *Ibid.,* p. 43. Reprinted by permission.

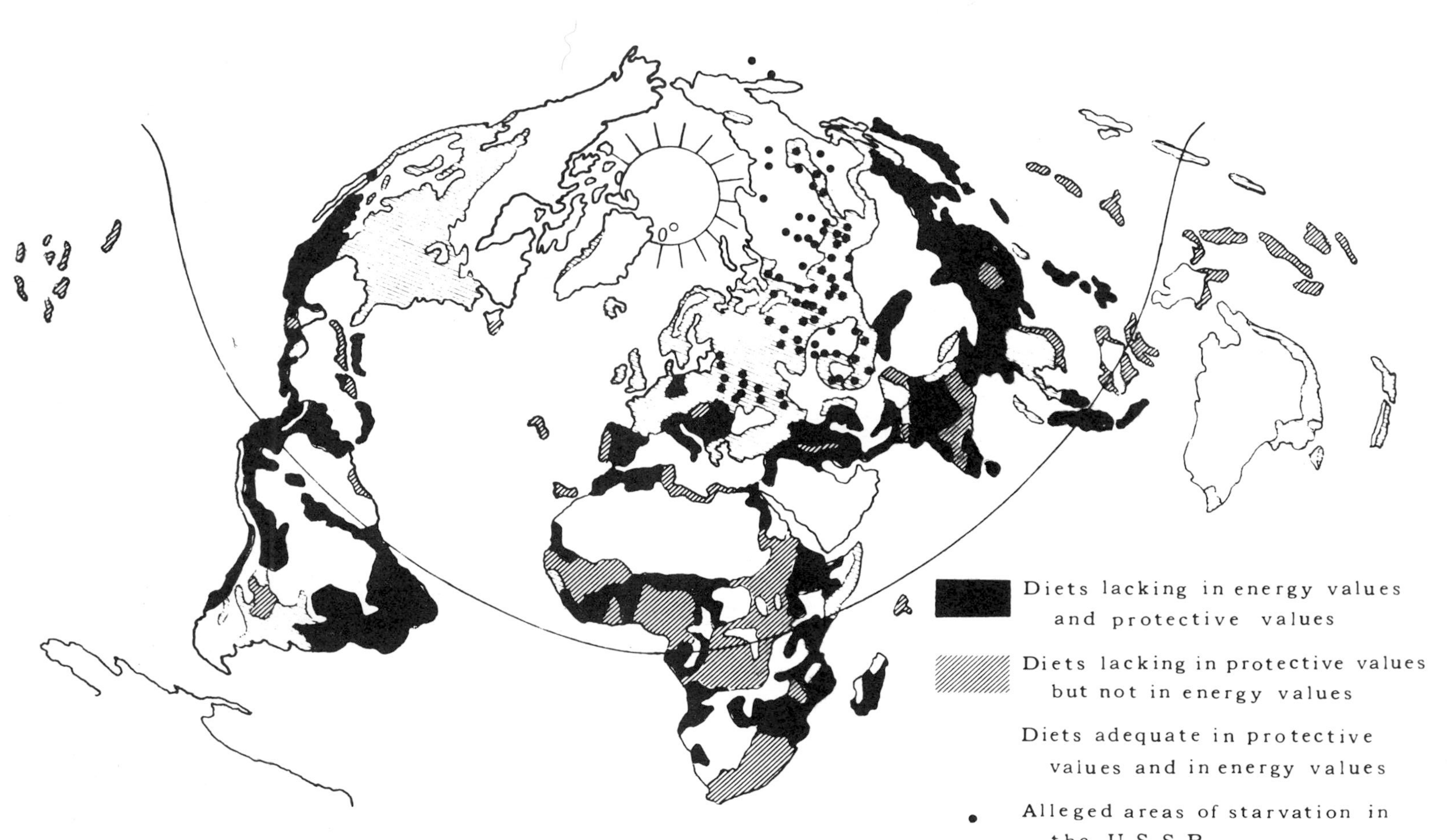

Diets lacking in energy values and protective values
Diets lacking in protective values but not in energy values
Diets adequate in protective values and in energy values
Alleged areas of starvation in the U.S.S.R.

Table 17.1

Vitamin	*Function*	*Chief sources*	*Deficiency diseases*
A	Maintenance of normal cellular structure and the functioning of the body's external and internal surface membranes.	Butter, whole milk, eggs, liver, certain fatty fish and fish oils, leafy green and yellow vegetables.	Nightblindness.
B_1 Thiamine	Promotes burning of carbohydrates and other foodstuffs	Meat, poultry, fish, eggs, lightly milled grain.	Beriberi, depression, irritability, quarrelsomeness, fearfulness.
B_2 Riboflavin	Promotes growth and normal nutrition at all ages.	Milk, meat, fish, poultry, eggs.	Digestive disturbances, nervous disorders, eyestrain, low general resistance.
Niacin	Promotes general health at all ages.	Meat, poultry, fish, lightly milled grains, potatoes, peanuts.	Pellagra.
C Ascorbic Acid	Promotes health of gums and teeth, maintains conditions for normal growth and calcification of bone, regulates muscle tone.	Fruits, leafy green and yellow vegetables, citrus fruits, tomatoes, potatoes (if taken in large quantities).	Premature aging, brittle bones, dental caries, pyorrhea, hemorrhaging, scurvy.
D	Promotes utilization of calcium.	Fish-liver oils and ultra-violet rays.	Rickets.

SOURCE: Dewhurst, Frederic, and Associates, *America's Needs and Resources,* The Twentieth Century Fund, 1947, pp. 108-109. Reprinted by permission.

Japan, goiter is almost unknown. Fortunately, the use of iodized salt will compensate for this deficiency. However, in many parts of the world iodized salt is not available. It is possible that the high incidence of feeble-mindedness among groups of people who have lived in isolation in small areas (as in certain of our own mountain districts) may be as much the result of an iodine deficiency as of interbreeding.

The symptoms of sodium deficiency are extreme nervous depression and muscular fatigue. Sodium deficiency is likely to be occasioned by any condition or activity which results in profuse sweating. This being the case, there is probably more to be said for the morality of the tropical native who respected the laws of his Creator by keeping his clothing at a minimum than we can say for the morality of the missionary who insisted that the mores of New England with respect to clothing constituted some sort of universal moral law. Among middle-latitude peoples, sodium deficiency is normally a temporary condition associated with summertime work or play and is easily corrected by taking supplementary salt.

XVII:1 (Left) This map shows the areas of various dietary deficiencies in various parts of the world. (Simplified from a map by Vincent Kotschar in *Focus,* May, 1954, published by the American Geographical Society, used by permission)

Vitamin deficiency has only in comparatively recent times come to be recognized as a cause of disease and poor health. Long before man had come to recognize the existence of vitamins, however, he had stumbled upon the fact that certain foods provided specific protection against certain diseases. The nickname "Limey" for Englishmen memorializes the routine issue of lime or lemon juice to crews of the Royal Navy as a protection against scurvy, a disease which we now know to be symptomatic of a deficiency of Vitamin C, one of the best sources of which is citrus fruits.

The six vitamins which are of greatest im-

To the uninformed, this baby's "bay window" may look "cute." Actually, it is one of the first and most obvious signs of malnutrition. (Courtesy Puerto Rico Office of Information. Photo by Rosskam)

portance for human health are Vitamin A, thiamine, riboflavin, niacin, Vitamin C (ascorbic acid), and Vitamin D. Their functions and sources are shown in Table 17.1, along with certain conditions which result from specific vitamin deficiencies.

Vitamin deficiencies are found, in greater or lesser measure, throughout the world, but are most common among the poor. Riboflavin deficiency, for example, is reported to be the most prevalent nutritional deficiency of southern United States. Long-winter climates are likely to be associated with a Vitamin D deficiency. China and India, where the pressure of people on the land and low per-capita purchasing power make meat and dairy products prohibitively expensive for all but the wealthiest, and where (especially in the case of India) the killing of animals is forbidden by religious taboos, are lands of chronic vitamin deficiency. Interestingly enough, as de Castro points out, tropical peoples, so long as they remain in their native setting, usually get a well-balanced diet. When they go to work in the white man's cities or on his plantations, the variety of their diets rapidly drops and they quickly develop the symptoms of malnutrition. This may account, at least partially, for the rapid decline in native populations in lands which were opened up to white settlement or control after the Age of Discoveries.

Malnutrition is an exceedingly difficult problem to correct because one of its most immediate consequences is to lower the level of physical and mental energy so that its victim is disinclined to make the exertions which would be necessary to solve his problem. The lassitude and inertia of tropical peoples, which has often been ascribed to the monotonous, debilitating climate, may be, in large measure, the products of malnutrition. Certainly in our own country, the stereotype of the ambitionless southern hillbilly cannot be related directly to climatic factors but would appear to correlate rather closely with diets that are manifestly insufficient in terms both of quantity and quality. In Australia, which was settled chiefly by poor people from the crowded cities of the British Isles, the children of the immigrants were so much taller than their parents that the first Australian-born generation was called the "Cornstalk Generation" and it is generally assumed that their greater height was the result of better nutrition. Similar responses to better diet are apparent among the children of southern Negroes and white sharecroppers who have improved their economic condition by migrating to regions of greater opportunity in our own country.

A second consequence of chronic malnutrition may be greater fertility. De Castro observes that:

¶ The psychological effect of chronic hunger is to make sex important enough to compensate emotionally for the shrunken nutritional appetite. . . . The exaggerated sensuality of some societies or social classes who live in a state of chronic undernourishment is explained by this mechanism of compensation. Their high fertility index, however, is also due to an important physiological aspect of hunger.[1]

[1] De Castro, *op. cit.*, pp. 69-70. Reprinted by permission.

Dr. de Castro then offers interesting suggestive evidence that malnutrition, especially protein deficiency, operates to increase fertility and notes the following correlations between birth rates and protein consumption:

Table 17.2

Countries	Birth Rate	Daily Consumption of Animal Proteins, in Grams
Formosa	45.6	4.7
Malay States	39.7	7.5
India	33.0	8.7
Japan	27.0	9.7
Yugoslavia	25.9	11.2
Greece	23.5	15.2
Italy	23.4	15.2
Bulgaria	22.2	16.8
Germany	20.0	37.3
Ireland	19.1	46.7
Denmark	18.3	59.1
Australia	18.0	59.9
United States	17.9	61.4
Sweden	15.0	62.6[1]

This would seem to indicate that the traditional idea that malnutrition is a result of overpopulation may have to be modified to allow for the reciprocal relationship between malnutrition and high fertility. Such an understanding, in turn, would suggest that raising a country's level of nutrition would go a long way toward solving any alleged problem of overpopulation.

Starvation: a living death

Starvation is the extreme form of malnutrition and takes place when the body does not receive enough nutritive material to maintain life. Dr. Jacques May includes serious malnutrition under the heading of starvation and, on the basis of that definition, asserts that two-thirds of the world is starving (6). Most of these people live within the tropics and the subtropics, although both in Africa and in eastern Asia the starvation belt extends well into the middle latitudes.

[1] *Ibid.*, p. 72. Reprinted by permission.

Starvation in its narrowest sense, i.e., more or less immediate death resulting from an absolute lack of food, is usually the consequence of war or natural catastrophe. China is the prime example of a land which periodically experiences this kind of starvation. Here, in a regime of periodic but unpredictable floods and droughts, closely related to the vagaries of the monsoonal climate, true starvation is an ever-present threat. Alexandre Hosie has compiled statistics which show that during the thousand-year period between 620 and 1629, 610 were drought years in one province of China or another and 203 of these were years of serious famine. Add to this the tendency of the great rivers of North China to overflow their aggraded beds after any period of heavy rain and it will be evident that life for the Chinese is an exceedingly precarious thing.

Starvation in the broader sense, however, is such a common thing in our world that it attracts little notice. The Mexican Indian sitting under a tree and staring apathetically out toward the treeless mountains, the Egyptian fellah reaching out his withered hand for "an alms for the love of Allah," the Papuan emaciated and toothless in his early thirties — these people are starving, but by inches. If, when they finally die, anybody takes the trouble to report the cause of death, it may be listed as tuberculosis or pneumonia or beriberi or malaria, but the root cause will have been starvation. Indeed, of most of these people it could be said that they had never really lived at all.

Why this widespread starvation in a world where, according to conservative estimates, less than one out of eight potentially cultivable acres is actually being used for the production of food?

Dr. May divides the starvation lands of the world into two classes which he calls the "have-nots" and the "use-nots." "In the have-not countries," Dr. May says:

¶ the carrying-capacity law (i.e., the amount of human, animal, and vegetable life that land and the waters connected with it can support) has been broken. The soil is milked of more than it can produce. Some of the reasons for this disruption stem from the environment. Such disruptions may be occasional or permanent; but in some regions the occasional environmental catastrophes occur so often that they are almost a feature of the region.[1]

He cites here the flood-and-drought regime of China.

"The carrying capacity of the land," Dr. May continues,

¶ can be lowered by permanent disruptions, such as natural erosion. [The Hwang Ho, for example, carries some 25,000,000 tons of soil into the sea every year.] Locusts and other pests limit in a regular fashion the productivity of the land, as they do in China and the Middle East, for instance.

Other disruptions of the carrying capacity of the land stem from the human element. Foremost of these is overpopulation, the most glaring examples of which are China, India, Pakistan, Puerto Rico, northern Viet Nam, Egypt, and Japan. [It will be recalled that Dr. de Castro considers overpopulation as much the effect as the cause of starvation.]

The social structure of a society, again chiefly exemplified by India and China, is a serious cause of food shortage. In some places the customs governing inheritance divide and subdivide the land to such a point that it is not soundly workable. Yet people refuse to migrate because they have heard frightening tales about foreign lands, or because there are no better places within reach, or because they can not afford transportation, or are bound by religious beliefs to stay near their buried ancestors.[2]

(Dr. May might have added that the immigration policies of practically all of the "advanced" nations effectively deny admission to natives of the overcrowded lands.)

¶ In many regions poor technology has broken the law of the carrying capacity of the land or is on the verge of breaking it in the near future. In India, Mexico, certain parts of Africa, and the Caribbean islands there is competition between men and animals for the food produced, and so both starve. In the Lake Chad region, in many other parts of Africa, and in the Caribbean, cattle are currency, a sign of wealth, a local means of exchange. Eating a cow would be like eating one's capital. Also as a result of this concept little is done to increase milk supply, and this source of food is not explored.

In other places—and they are many—poor farming methods do not get out of the land as much food as might be produced. Poor technology is also the cause of man-made erosion, which is sending to the bottom of the ocean topsoil that should feed future generations. Some people in the United States have been guilty of this when they applied machines to lands that required a more motherly care.[3]

So much for the "have-not" countries. What of the "use-not" countries, such countries as the Congo, Brazil, Colombia, Cuba, East Germany, Indonesia, and Venezuela?

Dr. May ascribes the failure of these countries to utilize efficiently the land and the food resources available to them to five major causes: inadequate transportation, poverty, religious taboos, absentee ownership of large estates, and bad government.

The Old Testament has several accounts of famine and abundance occurring side-by-side in small areas, and the situation is no different, in many lands, today. Indeed, in a large country such as Brazil, it is not unusual for one region to be suffering from low prices brought on by overproduction while another region is in the throes of famine. A good network of roads and railroads would go far toward equalizing food supplies and would, in addition, permit a greater variety in diets than is normally permitted by purely local conditions.

Poverty operates both to prevent farmers from using land to produce foodstuffs and to prevent those who need food from buying it. In many countries usurious interest rates keep the farmer constantly in debt, forcing him to raise cash crops for sale, often in overseas markets, when he and his neighbors lack sufficient food for themselves. In other countries, per capita income is so low that the landless captives of the urban slums must subsist chiefly on waste materials. A typical day's garbage from the average American home would be a banquet for a family living in the slums of Seoul or Calcutta or Cairo.

Both the Hindu and the Buddhist religions forbid the taking of life. Throughout India, therefore, scrawny cows and scrawny people

[1] May, Jacques, "Human Starvation," *Focus*, Vol. IV, No. 9, May, 1954, p. 2. Reprinted by permission.

[2] *Ibid.*, p. 2. Reprinted by permission.

[3] *Ibid.*, pp. 2-3. Reprinted by permission.

Poverty, often rooted in infertile land, underlies much of the world's hunger and disease. The Haitians who live in these rude shacks can hardly hope to be well fed or to practice the minimal rules of good health and sanitation. (Delta Air Lines Information Services)

stare vacantly at each other and compete for the limited food that is available. A good Moslem would literally starve before he would defile his lips with the meat of the hog, despite the fact that the hog is a scavenger which will somehow find its own food, even in the most unlikely places. One reason — probably a minor one — for the relatively high level of nutrition in Christian countries may be the fact that Christianity imposes no taboos on food short of cannibalism.

Absentee ownership of large estates is or has been an important cause of hunger in such countries as Italy, Egypt, and the plantation areas of the tropics. Typically, these estates or plantations are given over to the production of commercial crops despite the fact that local laborers do not have enough food to feed themselves and their families.

Finally, bad government — bad either because it is unjust or incompetent — is almost always associated with famine conditions. Sometimes it is just a matter of the government's being unable to maintain sufficient order to permit farmers to go about their work without harassment and to keep transportation moving. Sometimes governments play the role of absentee owners, demanding the production of commercial crops where there is an insufficiency of food production, or confiscating crops that have been raised. The communist governments of eastern Europe have been guilty of both of these practices. Sometimes governments create artificial food shortages by inequitable pricing regulations or currency manipulations. Internationally, governments have created artificial shortages by such devices as blockades, embargoes, shortsighted economic and tariff policies, and the deliberate destruction of surplus food supplies.

Must men go hungry?

There is little or no disagreement over the dimensions of the problem of human hunger and starvation. Those who have taken the trouble to inform themselves on the problem are in essential agreement on the geographic extent of the problem, both in terms of area and in terms of the number of people involved. Disagreements arise over the causes of the problem, over the nature of the solutions that should be brought to bear upon it, and upon the likelihood of our solving it.

Dr. May is openly pessimistic. He writes:

¶ The conclusion is unfortunately a rather gloomy one. Sizing up the problems involved in feeding the world makes one realize that there is no one solution. . . .

. . . it can be hoped that in limited areas such programs as technical assistance and Point Four will help improve farming methods, develop local resources, increase yields, and improve transportation. If this is done some relief to world starvation may be expected in these areas; but even such limited projects will require careful planning and sustained cooperation on the part of the more fortunate countries.[1]

Dr. George B. Cressey is somewhat more optimistic. He concludes a survey of the world food situation with some observations that point up the role that the geographer might play in helping to solve the problem:

¶ On the basis of geographic evidence, it seems probable to the author that our food potential is adequate for all the population likely to inhabit the earth during the present century. Unfortunately, the areas where production can be increased do not correspond with the areas of excess people. Unlimited migration and a free movement of food are essential if the expected population is to be fed. It is doubtful whether we shall soon cultivate the Amazon and Congo basins or northern Canada and Siberia; but if we do, the crowded areas of China, India, and Europe will demand access to this food.

What does all this mean to the geographer? Variations in land capability are obvious. Unfortunately, we do not yet know what all the earth is like. We have no world inventory of land or its potentials. Soil surveys are incomplete, so are data on agricultural climatology. We do not even know how much of the earth is level. In fact, large areas are without basic maps. Geographers are concerned with inventory, with how much of what is where. This is the beginning of all wise planning. Before anyone can predict the potential extent of arable land, or of food supply, or of world population, we must greatly extend our fundamental knowledge of land itself.[2]

Dr. Theodore W. Schultz suggests that the best solution to the food supply problem lies in the over-all economic development of the hunger lands. "The food supply," Dr. Schultz says, "may be represented as a function of a set of economic conditions." Then he goes on to say:

¶ The supply of food is slowly becoming more elastic as a consequence of economic development. This important structural change has gone virtually unnoticed, mainly because of the overemphasis of agricultural land in gauging food-producing possibilities. As agriculture declines in relative importance, a new factor of safety emerges with regard to food because more resources than formerly can be transferred into agriculture from other lines of endeavor on fairly short notice; and, at the more advanced stages of economic development, enough resources can be transferred to increase substantially the amount of food produced, assuming, of course, normal weather and for the moment leaving aside the additional favorable effects of new production techniques and growth in total factor supplies . . . (4).

Taking India as an example of an economically underdeveloped country suffering from a food shortage, Dr. Schultz finds that:

¶ With normal weather and with growth in factor supplies and with advances in production techniques that are within reach and that probably will be realized, the supply schedule of food

[1] *Ibid.*, pp. 5-6. Reprinted by permission.

[2] Cressey, George B., "Land for 2.4 Billion Neighbors," *Economic Geography*, Vol. 29, 1953, p. 9. Reprinted by permission.

n India can not be moved forward during the next decade as much as 20 per cent. The evilence, fragmentary as it is, indicates a forward hift of about 10 per cent under the conditions specified (4).

Dr. Schultz thus concludes that "there is room enough for both optimists and pessimists" on the question of future food supplies and asserts that "the answer depends on what can be done in achieving economic development" (4).

The most unequivocally optimistic of the experts is Dr. de Castro. It is his contention that "human societies are ordinarily brought to the starvation point by cultural rather than natural forces, that hunger results from grave errors and defects in social organization. . . . Hunger due to the inclemency of nature," he maintains, "is an extraordinary catastrophe, while hunger as a man-made blight is a 'normal' condition in the most varied parts of the world."[1] Dr. de Castro finds his guidelines toward the solution of the world's food problem in "treating domestic plants and animals as food-producing machines whose output can be increased in quantity and quality"; in expanding agriculture "by farming new lands and new kinds of soil, and by introducing new plants and animals for food purposes"; by "exploiting virtually untapped food reserves like the great wealth of the seas" and possibly by "raising living things in ocean waters to provide additional human subsistence"; by utilizing foods more intelligently in accordance with the findings of the science of nutrition; and by changing social, political, and economic patterns which underlie the present inequitable distribution of the means of human subsistence.[2] He cites with apparent approval the findings of a special committee of experts set up by the Food and Agricultural Organization of the United Nations in 1949:

¶ There are five major fields in which an attack must be made. All are intricately connected and all are of vital importance. They do, however, have an appropriate time sequence and we list them in that order. The necessary measures are:

1) The maintenance of a high level of production and employment, particularly in the United States. In this case, as in others, the issue is not that the United States economy is less stable than that of other countries but rather that this economy is so critically important in that of the world.

2) The reduction of trade restrictions, including tariffs and quantitative and monetary restriction. In particular, the present dollar disequilibrium calls for measures to facilitate access to the United States market.

3) An increase in the standards of productive efficiency, particularly in countries of Western Europe.

4) The provision, by private enterprise and by national and international action, of large and continuing capital investments by the developed in the less developed areas of the world. This is necessary to finance the export surpluses of the former and the import surpluses of the latter.

5) The restoration of convertible currencies and multilateral transactions as the basis of world trade.

It would appear from the quotations that have been cited that the experts are essentially agreed that the earth has the physical capacity to feed its present population and to take care of reasonably anticipatable increases in population. They are optimistic or pessimistic about the future, depending upon their estimate of man's willingness to come to grips with the problem and his capacity for unselfish action.

It is not likely that the more prosperous nations of the world will show any great capacity for unselfish action so long as they are left with the comfortable rationalization of "overpopulation" as an explanation of the hunger in the lands of greatest food deficiency. "Overpopulation," like "underweight," is a word of some limited usefulness when we bear in mind that it describes a condition and do not attempt to use it as a diagnostic term. A man may be underweight because of poor diet, because of some physiological imbalance, because of cancer, or for any of a number of other reasons. To suggest that a hungry country solve its problem by reducing its population is analogous to suggesting that a cancer patient solve his weight problem by gorging himself on carbohydrates.

Hunger, as we have pointed out, is a regional problem, the solution to which must

[1] De Castro, *op. cit.*, p. 24. Reprinted by permission.
[2] *Ibid.*, pp. 26-27. Reprinted by permission.

be sought in the interregional exchange of knowledge, techniques, tools, and foodstuffs. The impassable political and economic boundary lines which we have drawn around hunger regions are of human devising and can be removed or rendered less tragic in their effects by applying, in our relations to all people, the moral imperatives which we accept as binding in our relations to "our own people." If human concern and compassion take precedence over economics in our treatment of our fellow-townsmen and fellow-countrymen, they should also govern our response to the needs of the hungry in more remote parts of the world. If we accept, as a matter of cold reality, the fact that hunger and destitution in one part of our own country set up shock waves which may have unfortunate and even dangerous consequences to our whole national economy, we should realize that hunger and destitution in any part of our interdependent world have similar consequences.

In the long run, it will not be possible for the world to remain one-fourth well-fed and three-fourths hungry. Self-interest, if not morality, dictates that the more prosperous nations of the world exert themselves to alleviate the world's hunger problem while it is still susceptible of intelligent and peaceful solution. The alternative is violence, born of despair and governed by passion rather than by reason. As the most prosperous of all of the nations of the world, the United States can expect to be the chief object of that violence.

This brings us to one final comment on the matter of "overpopulation." There are diseases, in themselves incurable, which man can learn to live with so long as he can keep their painful symptoms under control. So also with overpopulation. Where the root causes of the imbalance between people and resources cannot, at the present time or in the foreseeable future, be cured, the symptom of these causes ("overpopulation") can be relieved. There is thus an obligation on the part of the hunger lands to accept their share of the responsibility for the human suffering which is found in these lands. The reckless multiplication of people without regard to present food resources can no more be justified than can the unconcern which has so generally characterized the attitude of the more prosperous nations. And if, as a result of greater concern on the part of the more prosperous nations, subsidies of food or other resources were to encourage an accelerated rate of population growth in these hunger lands, the situation would be even worse than it already is.

The ills that flesh is heir to

No one has yet calculated the total number of diseases which afflict the human race. Their number is, however, sufficient to provide a sound basis for the remark of the laconic Vermonter to the effect that the mortality rate in his state is one per person. Some diseases, such as cancer and diseases of the heart and arteriosclerosis, are the results of structural changes or damage in the body and their incidence is almost universal. Other diseases are the result of infection and the incidence of many of these infectious diseases is highly localized. Still other diseases are the results of malnutrition and the incidence of such diseases is governed by considerations which we have dealt with in our discussion of hunger.

Medical geography is primarily concerned with the infectious and nutritional diseases because these are brought on by environmental conditions which, once identified, are susceptible of improvement. Unfortunately, the number of qualified medical geographers is still so small that we have only the most fragmentary knowledge of the relationships between specific diseases and environmental conditions.

Some idea of the complexity of the problems involved in the study of medical geography is suggested by the authors of a study of health conditions in Africa:

¶ The health problems encountered among these heterogeneous population groups are contingent not only upon the climatic and etiologic factors which influence the spread of specific infections but also upon the social, educational and economic progress of the people themselves. The increasing industrialization and development of communication facilities within the last half century have wrought changes in the life and the ambitions of the people, the full significance of which is still uncertain. Foremost among the problems of the different territories, regardless of their political affiliations, are those of public health—as related not only to medical care but also to basic sanitation, nutrition, improved standards of living and education. In many respects, environmental factors appear to have a more direct bearing upon the health of the inhabitants than in more highly developed countries. The inadequacy of water supplies over considerable areas; soil erosion and the loss of soil fertility under primitive methods of cultivation; and the congestion of limited areas, such as the Nile Valley, the Lake Victoria region, Ruanda-Urundi and sections of the Guinea coast, as opposed to the relative sparsity of population over most of the continent, are problems which can not be separated from those of health and social or economic welfare. . . . Moreover, the thoughtful observer must be impressed not only by the interrelationship of vital issues in these under-developed regions but also by the inter-dependence of one territory upon another. The expansion of communications has enlarged the boundaries for the control of epidemic diseases. The health and standards of living of the inhabitants of West Africa, for example, are no longer of purely local concern but affect directly or indirectly the lives and the economic well-being of other peoples, not only in adjacent portions of the continent but throughout the world[1].

Few geographers are competent to isolate or describe *pathogens,* disease-causing organisms or viruses. The study of pathogens is properly the field of the medical doctor, the biologist, and other students of the life sciences. The geographer does, however, have an important contribution to make to the study of *geogens,* environmental factors known or believed to be correlated with a disease or its pathogens (6). A definitive recent study of the scope of modern American geography lists some of these geogens, noting that since their number is legion, such a listing can give only an idea of their nature:

1) PHYSICAL
    CLIMATE
        Latitude
        Rainfall and humidity
        Temperature
        Barometric pressure
        Sunshine and cloudiness
        Wind direction and velocity
        Radiation
        Static electricity
        Ionization
    RELIEF
    SOILS
    HYDROGRAPHY
    TERRESTRIAL MAGNETISM

2) HUMAN OR SOCIETAL
    POPULATION DISTRIBUTION AND DENSITY
    STANDARD OF LIVING
        Housing
        Diet
        Clothing
        Sanitation
        Income
    TRANSPORTATION AND COMMUNICATIONS
    RELIGIOUS CUSTOMS AND SUPERSTITIONS
    DRUG ADDICTIONS

3) BIOLOGICAL
    VEGETABLE LIFE
    ANIMAL LIFE, ON EARTH AND IN WATER
    PARASITISM, HUMAN AND ANIMAL
    PREVALENT DISEASES
    DOMINANT BLOOD GROUPS
    (6, 7, 8)

Since it would manifestly be impossible to deal in detail with the whole range of human disease, much less to identify all the environmental factors that correlate with these diseases, let us examine three case studies: the first illustrating the geogenic elements associated with a particular disease, the second outlining the spread of a recent epidemic, and the third showing how control of a particular set of geogens eliminated a disease that had formerly plagued a large area.

The medical geography of tsutsugamushi (serum typhus) in Japan

In 1950 there were 116 cases of *tsutsugamushi* disease in Japan, most of them in the Japan Sea area of northern Honshu. Since 1950 new morbidity districts have been discovered in the Kanna River district and in

[1] Simmons, James Stevens; Whayne, Tom F.; Anderson, Gaylord W.; and Horack, Harold M., *Global Epidemiology: A Geography of Disease and Sanitation,* Vol. II, J. B. Lippincott Co., Philadelphia, 1951, pp. xi-xii. Reprinted by permission.

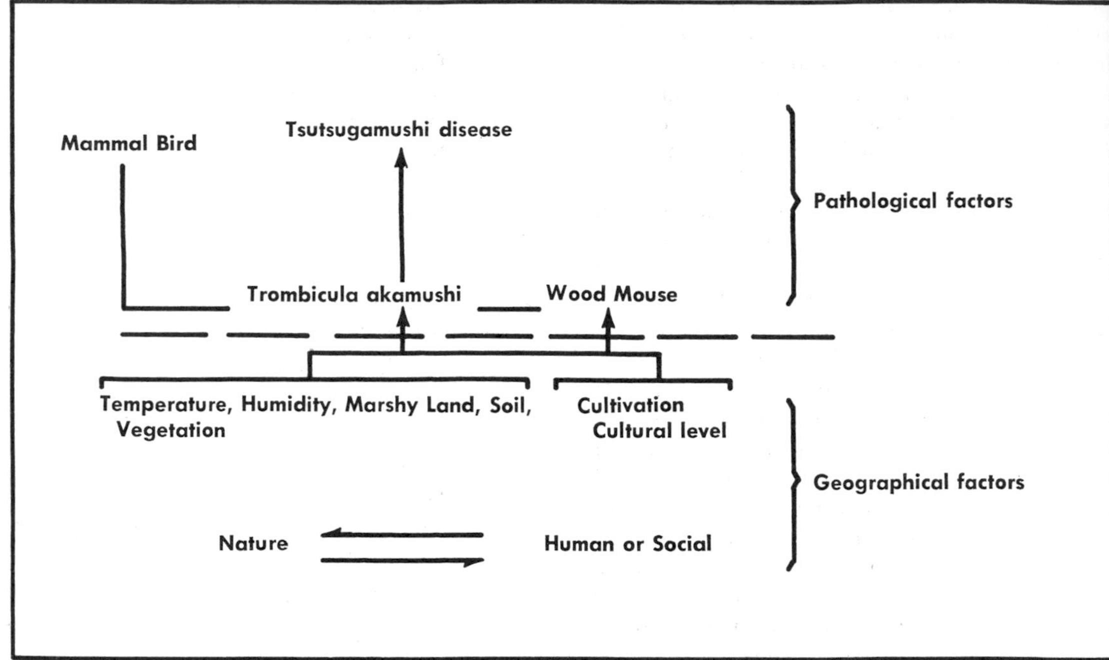

XVII:2 This diagram shows the pathogenic complex of tsutsugamushi disease. (From "The Medical Geography of Tsutsugamushi (Scrub Typhus) in Japan," by Tomoichi Horibuchi, *Proceedings of the Eighth General Assembly and Seventeenth International Congress of the International Geographical Union,* used by permission)

the Gotemba district at the foot of Mount Fuji. The disease is also found on Hachijo Island in the Pacific Ocean.

The causative agent, *Rickettsia orientalis,* bores through the skin of man and other mammals bitten by the larval form of the vector, *Trombicula akamushi,* and then propagates in the liver, spleen, lymphatic glands, and so on causing the symptoms of *tsutsugamushi* disease such as ulcer of the bitten skin of the mouth which becomes red and then blisters. Then follows swelling of the affected part, pain in the lymphatic glands, and fever.

Trombicula akamushi lives in marshy places, river deltas being particularly favored sites. It can crawl out on the land in summer during periods of high temperature and, by biting the skin of human and other mammals, can infect them with the disease germ, *Rickettsia orientalis.*

The two most important geogens of *tsutsugamushi* disease are temperature and humidity. The pathogenic complex is controlled by pathological factors which are, in turn, controlled by temperature.

The following relationships to temperature and hence to seasons can be cited:

1) *Rickettsia orientalis* dies in 10 minutes at 131° F. but can exist at 29°. The range of its activities is therefore very wide. It will be remembered that *Rickettsia* live in the bodies of the *Trombicula* which live in animals.

2) *Trombicula akamushi* has least resistance to environment; it is especially weak at low temperature but is quite animate above 36°. As a result, *tsutsugamushi* disease is rampant from June through September.

3) Other types of *Trombicula* also show a highly seasonal occurrence, one appearing in spring, another in summer, and a third type in autumn.

Humidity is essential for the existence of *tsutsugamushi,* directly and as a factor in affecting the habitat of the host. *Tsutsugamushi* are abundant on marshy deltas. However, the thick-growing reed in these delta areas is also of great importance, for it shelters the wood mice which are the most important hosts for *tsutsugamushi,* and the vegetation mould has been related to the ecology of the *tsutsugamushi.*

Geographic features and soil rank next to temperature and humidity in their effect on morbidity from *tsutsugamushi* disease. For example, along the bluff-bordered portion of one of Japan's rivers, no *tsutsugamushi* are found although in the floodplain and in scrub areas along the same river the land is infested with *tsutsugamushi.*

Along with the causative agents and intermediate host, man plays a role, though a passive one, as part of the pathogenic complex of *tsutsugamushi* disease. The occupation and cultural level of the people is significant. The delta lands, so fertile that little or no manure is needed, are cultivated in spite of the difficulty of working the scrub areas. Because they go in and out of the infected land, almost all the farmers suffer from *tsutsugamushi* disease. People in other occupations are seldom afflicted. Although the natives are afraid of the disease, they continue to go in and out of the infected areas because they lack information (9).

Around the world in eighty days: The story of the spread of Asian flu

Early in May, 1957, an illness which had broken out among refugees from the Chinese mainland in Hong Kong was diagnosed as a new strain of influenza. By the time the diagnosis had been confirmed, the disease had spread to Taiwan, to Japan, and to Singapore.

From Singapore the disease spread rapidly. Ship passengers from Singapore carried it to Australia, where it rapidly assumed epidemic proportions, and to India, which became another center from which it was dispersed throughout the Near and Middle East. The Philippines also were infected and suffered an unusually high mortality rate.

By June, Asian flu had appeared in such widely-separated countries as Korea, Iran, Czechoslovakia, and Dutch New Guinea. Cases of the disease were found among ship passengers in British port cities and in San Francisco and among the crew of an American naval vessel that had docked at Newport, Rhode Island. By the end of July the disease had traveled all the way to South Africa and within the next month had reached all of the major metropolitan areas of Central and South America.

Fortunately Asian flu, while causing a great deal of discomfort to its victims, was a relatively mild disease. But the speed with which it traveled around the world provides a sober warning that health problems are not local or even national, but universal. Nor was it perhaps altogether accidental that the disease first appeared on the Chinese mainland. Crowded populations subsisting on a low level of health and nourishment provide ideal incubators for communicable diseases. The spread of such diseases from their incubation areas is not a new phenomenon in world history. It has been happening for centuries. But the speed with which such a disease can girdle the globe has been greatly stepped up by faster means of transportation and by the far greater mobility of people which is characteristic of modern times. In most cases, Asian flu entered a country by way of its seaports or its airports, and from these centers spread out into the hinterlands.

The United States is particularly susceptible to invasion by communicable diseases because of its world-wide interests and commitments. Civilian and military personnel, stationed in practically every country of the world and frequently brought home for duty or consultation, can be brought back to the United States so fast that diseases which they contracted overseas may not reach the symptomatic stage until several days after such personnel have re-entered the country and had a chance to infect others. The geography of epidemics in the modern world is, for all practical purposes, one aspect of the geography of transportation. Irrespective of one's judgment of the value of such an international agency as the United Nations, one could hardly question not merely the value but the fundamental necessity of such a supranational watchdog for the world's health as the World Health Organization (WHO).

How Indiana was taken away from the mosquito

There is hardly a schoolboy in Indiana

who has not heard of the Battle of Tippecanoe when General William Henry Harrison defeated the great and noble Tecumseh and secured not only Indiana but most of the rest of the Middle West for the United States. But, while no dependable statistics can be cited, it may be confidently asserted that the wiliest and most implacable enemy that faced the early settlers of Indiana was not the Indian but the mosquito. Hardly an issue of the small-town weeklies that were published prior to the Civil War fails to report at least one death due to "the fever," and settlement in some of the richest river-bottom lands of the southern half of the state was for long inhibited by the high incidence of malaria in such lands.

In northern Indiana, it was not the river bottoms so much as the swampy, marshy intermorainal basins that encouraged the growth of mosquitoes. Morainic ridges were, therefore, preferred for settlement and only gradually did people drift down into the lowlands.

The lowlands were reclaimed, little by little, by ditch construction and by the laying of drainage tile. So effective was tiling in the reclamation process that within the space of less than a century Indiana has been transformed from a highly malarious area into an area where malaria is almost unknown.

It is interesting to note that in the southern part of the state the original malarious nature of the river lowlands had some interesting consequences in settlement patterns. The earliest settlers, entering the state generally from the south or the east, avoided the lowlands and laid out their farms on the higher ground. Around the middle of the nineteenth century, German immigrants, largely from the flat reclaimed lands of northern Germany, especially Hanover, came into the area and found much bottom land available at very low cost. They bought up these swampy tracts and, by applying methods and techniques which their forefathers had applied to similar lands in northern Germany, rapidly converted them into some of the best agricultural lands in the state. Their descendants, in many cases, still farm these lands and are among the most prosperous farmers in the state.

Climate and health

The great pioneer investigator of the effects of climate upon health was Ellsworth Huntington, for many years professor of geography at Yale University. Huntington was an indefatigable worker, an original thinker, and a brilliant and persuasive writer. Convinced that "the geographical distribution of health and energy depends on climate and weather more than on any other single factor," Huntington assembled an impressive mass of evidence in support of his thesis. In later years, however, he significantly revised some of his views, and in his last book, *Mainsprings of Civilization,* he assigned first place to diet.

Meanwhile, other investigators assembled a great deal of evidence which, while not altogether discrediting the idea of the paramount influence of climate upon health and energy, tended to suggest that the idea of a direct relationship between climate and energy was an oversimplification. Unfortunately, these later investigators lacked both Huntington's capacity for brilliant generalization and his mastery of words, and their findings, as a result, are not well-known outside the geographical profession.

Among the lines of investigation which have been pursued by more recent students of climate and health have been studies of the role which climate plays as a stimulus to basal metabolism, studies of "effective temperature" and its effects upon biological processes, studies of heat-exchange between the body and its environment (together with the part that clothing plays in affecting this exchange), and studies of human reaction to climatic stress. The armed forces have been particularly interested in some of these studies because of the possible significance of their results for the planning of military operations in areas of climatic extremes.

Health and race

Another line of investigation which has intrigued a number of scholars is the relationship, if any, between over-all health, and particularly the incidence of specific diseases, and racial or ethnic groups. This is an exceedingly difficult area of investigation because it is almost impossible to isolate race, as a factor, from such other factors as climate, diet, and culture. Conclusions so far are few and highly tentative. As an example, however, of the kind of tentative conclusions that have been suggested, the following table may be of some interest.

COMPARATIVE PATHOLOGY OF NEGROES AND WHITES IN THE UNITED STATES[1]

Difference Definite and Marked, Almost Certainly Racial

Lower Incidence for Negroes

Diphtheria
Yellow Fever
Hemophilia (non-clotting)
Peptic Ulcer
Psoriasis
Lupus
Trachoma
Surgical Suppuration

Higher Incidence for Negroes

Sickle-Cell Anemia
Whooping Cough
Uterine Fibroids
Keloid Tumors
Nephritis

Difference Perceptible, Some Probability of Being Racial

Lower Incidence for Negroes

Scarlet Fever
Measles
Infantile Paralysis
Angina Pectoris
Arteriosclerosis
Coronary Occlusion
Gallstones
Urinary Stones
Most Cancers

Higher Incidence for Negroes

Lobar Pneumonia
Hypertension
Cerebral Hemorrhage
Syphilitic Heart Disease
Carcinoma of Female Genitalia

Fact or Cause of Difference in Dispute

Lower Incidence for Negroes

Pernicious Anemia
Diabetes

Higher Incidence for Negroes

Tuberculosis
Syphilis
Typhoid Fever
Malaria

[1] Adapted from *Anthropology* by A. L. Kroeber, copyright, 1923, 1948, by Harcourt, Brace and World, Inc., and used with their permission.

The unfinished task

It is safe to say that the study of the geography of both hunger and disease is still in its infancy. Already we have reason to believe that the systematic study of the distribution of these two age-long enemies of the human race will greatly increase our knowledge of the *whys* of hunger and disease.

An example of the kind of basic research which is our most urgent need for the study of medical geography is the series of maps which have been published from time to time by the American Geographical Society under the direction of Dr. Jacques May. With the permission of the Society, the maps dealing with the distribution of cholera, 1816-1950, have been reproduced for this chapter. When maps of comparable quality and dependability have been drawn for all of the major diseases of man, we shall have taken a very long step toward the elimination of many diseases and the control of many others.

APPLICATION OF GEOGRAPHIC UNDERSTANDING

I. What factors other than malnutrition might produce a condition of "overpopulation" in a nation or a culture? To what extent are these factors susceptible of change or correction? To what extent is it possible that they may themselves be products of malnutrition?

II. What inventions, discoveries, or cultural changes can you think of that may account for dietary changes in the United States during the past half-century? To what extent does it seem possible to you that some of these same factors might be at work in the present hunger lands of the world in the latter half of this century?

III. If de Castro is correct in concluding that malnutrition is a factor in high fertility rates, how would you project the population curve of India if, during the next decade, the level of nutrition in India were to rise to the level of Mediterranean Europe and remain at that level for the rest of this century?

IV. How do you account for the docility of the people and the general good order in societies where hunger might be expected to create a great deal of personal and social discontent? Do you think that these cultures would be more or less orderly if there were a notable increase in the level of nutrition? What do you think would happen in our own country if we were to be faced with the probability of a notable decline in our level of nutrition?

V. In what respects, and to what extent, is the world problem of hunger a moral problem? What moral principles, if any, should govern our thinking about this problem?

VI. Why would a geographer expect to find that kinds of diseases and other health problems differ from place to place on the earth?

VII. What religious customs and superstitions can you think of that might be considered disease-causing or disease-spreading factors?

VIII. On the basis of the discussion of malaria in Indiana, attempt to draw up a pathogenic complex of malaria modeled after Horiguchi's diagram on page 356.

IX. What geogens in your own community are capable of being corrected or modified in such a way as to improve general health conditions?

X. What factors other than race do you think may help to explain the differences in the incidence of the diseases listed in the table on page 359?

References

1 De Castro, Josue, *The Geography of Hunger,* Little, Brown, and Company, Boston, 1952, pp. 24, 26-27, 38-39, 43, 69-70, 72.

2 May, Jacques, "Human Starvation," *Focus,* Vol. IV, No. 9, May, 1954, pp. 2-3, 5-6.

3 Cressey, George B., "Land for 2.4 Billion Neighbors," *Economic Geography,* Vol. XXIX, 1953, p. 9.

4 Schultz, Theodore W., "The Supply of Food in Relation to Economic Development," *Proceedings of the Eighth General Assembly and Seventeenth International Congress of the International Geographical Union,* 1952, pp. 107-110, *passim.*

5 Simmons, James Stevens; Whayne, Tom F.; Anderson, Gaylord W.; and Horack, Harold M., *Global Epidemiology: A Geography of Disease and Sanitation,* Vol. II, J. B. Lippincott Co., Philadelphia, 1951, pp. xi-xii.

6 May, Jacques M., "Medical Geography: Its Methods and Objectives," *Geographical Review,* Vol. XL, 1950, p. 5.

7 James, Preston, and Jones, Clarence F., *American Geography: Inventory and Prospect,* Association of American Geographers, Syracuse University Press, 1954, p. 455.

8 Bonne, C.; van Veen, A. G.; and Tjokronegro, S., *"Over het experimenteele botergeel carcinoom van de level," Geneeskundig Tijdschrift van Ned. Indie,* Vol. LXXXI, 1941, p. 2448.

9 Horiguchi, Tomoichi, "The Medical Geography of *Tsutsugamushi* (Serum Typhus) in Japan," *Proceedings of the Eighth General Assembly and Seventeenth International Congress of the International Geographical Union,* 1952, pp. 192-195.

10 Kroeber, A. L., *Anthropology,* Harcourt, Brace, & Co., New York, 1948, p. 188.

Chapter 18

The geography of religions

Among the many and often contradictory definitions of man that have been suggested, none is more concise or more accurate than the description of man as "a worshiping animal." History knows of no human group which has failed to acknowledge the existence of Something outside and beyond the world of observation, a Something which plays its own part—great or small, good or evil—in the human drama. To this Something men have given names: Yahweh, Allah, Brahman, Zeus, the Great Spirit. The best men in every age have tried to live their lives in conformity to what they believed to be the will of their god. Human societies have sought to realize in their laws and systems of government the perfection of a higher law which they conceived to be of supernatural origin. And in every community of man there stands as tangible evidence of his preoccupation with a world unseen but nevertheless very real to him some sort of place of worship: a mosque, a temple, a church, or perhaps only a sacred tree or mound. On these places of worship men have lavished the energies and often the wealth of generations. Around them they have built their homes. Too often unhappily and tragically they have gone from the shrine of their god to persecute and destroy the votaries of other shrines and other gods. Thus at his best and at his worst man has testified to the faith within him.

Man's religions are so numerous and so diverse that any attempt to classify them must run the risk of oversimplification and, perhaps, offense to the convictions of those who adhere to them. Nevertheless, as one examines the wide range of faiths, a kind of threefold division suggests itself and this division seems satisfactory for purposes of discussion.

To the first class of religions belong those which originated in the dry and semidry lands of southwest Asia and which are represented today by Judaism, Christianity, and Islam. These religions are fervently monotheistic, essentially equalitarian in their social implications, strongly ethical in their teachings, and generally optimistic in their view of the nature and purpose of the universe. The sacred writings of these religions require some understanding of the nature of the physical and cultural environment of the drylands to be fully explicable. In many places they depict the Deity in anthropomorphic symbols reflective of a pastoral or nomadic culture. In all of these religions there is a strong emphasis upon the absolute sovereignity of the Deity, an emphasis which sometimes tends toward a kind of fatalism. Two of these religions, Judaism and Christianity, have supplied the spiritual basis for Western culture and through their sacred writings have played a major role in shaping the patterns of Western philosophy and literature. The third, Islam, has created a culture world of its own, close enough to the West to be generally intelligible to Western man but different enough to allow the development of many vexing misunderstandings.

The second class of religions includes those which originated in the hot, wet, Indian subcontinent and which today are represented by Hinduism, Jainism, Buddhism, and Sikhism. These religions tend to a much greater degree than those of southwestern Asia to survive on two levels: the one a very high level of philosophy and mysticism, the other a very low and debased level of ritualism and magic. In terms of adherents, the lower level is more significant to the geographer because it largely sets the tone of the culture and gives personality to the landscape. These religions, in their popular form, are polytheistic, divisive along class or caste lines in their social implications, only slightly ethical in their teachings, and generally pessimistic in their view of the nature and purpose of the universe. Their sacred writings are often of a very high literary quality but little known to most of their adherents. They therefore offer little comfort or encouragement to their adherents, most of whom find such hope as they can in the prospect of ultimate extinction.

The third class of religions includes those which originated in the Far East and which, in the proper sense of the term, should per-

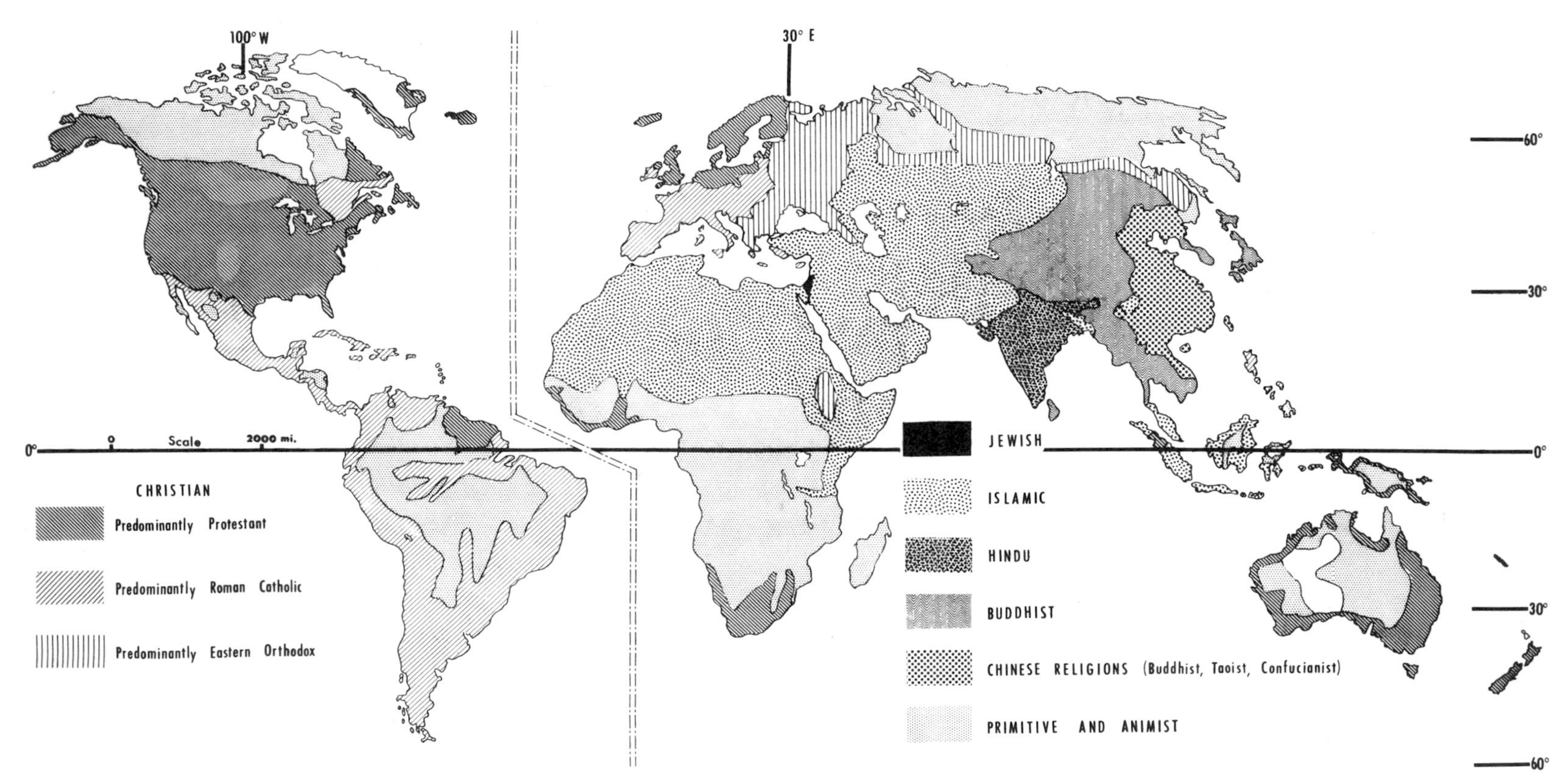
100° W
30° E
60°
30°
0°
30°
60°
0°
0
Scale
2000 mi.
CHRISTIAN
Predominantly Protestant
Predominantly Roman Catholic
Predominantly Eastern Orthodox
JEWISH
ISLAMIC
HINDU
BUDDHIST
CHINESE RELIGIONS (Buddhist, Taoist, Confucianist)
PRIMITIVE AND ANIMIST

haps not be defined as religions at all, for in their pure form they are little or not at all concerned with the supernatural and are concerned, rather, with the good life as it can and should be lived on this earth. To this class belong Taoism, Confucianism, and Shinto. The justification for including these "way of life" philosophies in a discussion of religions lies in the fact that they developed within the context of very ancient religious beliefs and practices which, in process of time, have tended to absorb them and, in many cases, to obscure their high moral and ethical teachings. In their popular and debased forms these religions also tend to be polytheistic, strongly nationalistic, and generally optimistic in their view of the nature and purpose of the universe. Among the more educated adherents to these religions there is little preoccupation with the supernatural. Among the masses there exists a strong belief in divinities and demons whose favors must be sought and whose displeasure must be appeased by sacrifices and rituals. These religions characteristically offer the prospect of survival after death, although the form of that survival is not generally clearly indicated.

In addition to these three great classes of religions there exist many local or tribal religions in various parts of the world. Generally speaking, these "primitive" religions have little or no philosophical or ethical content. Instead they concern themselves with practical questions of survival in a world which is conceived to be a kind of battleground between good and evil spirits or influences. The key figure in such religions is the man (or sometimes the woman) who is believed to have some degree of control over these spirits or influences. The responsibility of this person is to manipulate supernatural powers toward the attainment of group or personal ends. Examples of primitive religion may be found among the Negroes of central Africa, the tribes of Melanesia, and the Amerindians. Vestiges of earlier primitive religions survive also in the popular religions of people who profess adherence to the "higher" religions.

It is the purpose of this chapter to examine, in very broad outline, the distribution, the landscape manifestations, and the social consequences of several of the religions of the world. In order to do so, it will be necessary to furnish some background on the origins and basic teachings of these religions.[1]

XVIII:1 (Left) Distribution of the world's major religions is shown on this map. (Simplified from *Karte der Religionem und Evangelischen Missionem der Erde,* published by Prof. D. Martin Schlunk and Dr. Horst Quiring in cooperation with the International Mission Council [London] and Missionary Research Library [New York]. Evangelischer Missions-Verlag, Stuttgart. Geographischer Verlag Kummerly und Frey, Bern, 1955, used by permission)

Religions of the drylands

1. Judaism. From its original homeland in the impoverished hills of Palestine the worship of the God of Israel has been carried by a people often conquered and often dispersed into every part of the world. And if Christianity and Islam are considered as offspring of Judaism, the area dominated by the worship of the God of Abraham and Isaac and Jacob is vastly enlarged.

Wherever Judaism has gone, it has taken with it a demanding ethic, a fierce devotion to learning, and an uncompromising insistence upon the dignity of the individual person as a creature of the One God. Hardened by centuries of antagonism, often culminating in bloody pogroms, the Jewish people have developed an unusually tenacious hold upon their doctrines and traditions and have, accordingly, tended to be a people apart, even in those lands where their persons and beliefs have not suffered actual persecution.

Driven out of their ancient homeland and, too often, denied the right to own land in the Christian world to which most of them fled, the Jew has for centuries been forced to settle in cities, often in certain prescribed sections of cities (ghettos). Restricted in his choice of occupation, he has been compelled to seek his livelihood in occupations which for a long time were prohibited to his Christian neighbors (e.g., money-lending) or

[1] Information on the teachings of the world's major religions has been taken, for the most part, from Frost, S. E., Jr., *The Sacred Writings of the World's Great Religions,* The New Home Library, Garden City Publishing Co., 1943.

which carried some degree of social stigma (e.g., surgery). Ordinarily, his best hope of escape from the constricted life of the ghetto lay in excelling in endeavors necessary to his society but so demanding of time or energy that his gentile neighbors were little inclined to pursue them. The great Jewish scholar, the great Jewish artist, the successful Jewish merchant or banker represents essentially the same response to the limitations imposed upon him by his gentile neighbors: a single-minded devotion to the job at hand as a means of gaining acceptance, if not as a person then at least as a socially-necessary member of the community.

For centuries, the center of the Jewry of the Dispersion lay in eastern Europe: eastern Poland and the western part of the Russian empire. In this area, apparently, Judaism won many converts among the early Slavic immigrants, thus introducing a very considerable non-Semitic strain into Jewry. But despite the accession of non-Jewish blood, the teachings of Judaism as they are contained in the Torah ("Law") and the Talmud ("Tradition") have displayed an amazing capacity for survival.

In much of North Sea Europe (Germany, France, Britain, the Low Countries, and Scandinavia) the Jew during the past four centuries or so had achieved a status of nearly complete social and political equality with his gentile neighbors. It must be reckoned one of the great tragedies of our century that the virus of hatred for the Jewish people which was introduced into the formerly tolerant body of German culture by the National Socialists has spread outward from Germany, though in less virulent form, to other countries of the North Sea area.

One product of this new upsurge in anti-Jewish terror was the intensification of the ancient Jewish hope for a return to what many of them had always considered their true homeland, Palestine—a hope which was realized when, in 1954, the state of Israel was proclaimed and began its long struggle to carve out a place for itself in the midst of hostile Arab neighbors. But as of 1955 less than 14 per cent of the world's Jews were citizens of Israel. Almost half of the world's Jewish population lives in the United States, chiefly in the large cities of the northeastern states. New York City alone had half again as many Jewish people in 1955 as did the State of Israel.

Other large Jewish communities remain in the Soviet Union (2 million), Great Britain (450,000), France (300,000), Romania (225,-000), and Hungary (155,000). South America has large Jewish populations in Argentina (360,000) and Brazil (120,000). In North Africa, Morocco (264,000), Algeria (140,-000), and Tunisia (105,000) still provide homes for large Jewish populations despite the dominance of Islam in all of these lands. Indeed, there is no country on earth where the ancient confession of the faithful Jew—"Hear, O Israel, the Lord our God, the Lord is One"—is not daily spoken by some child of Israel.

*2. **Christianity.*** Traditional Christianity claims to be the culmination and fulfillment of pre-Christian Jewish hope and prophecy. Accepting as it does the Yahweh of the Old Testament as the one true God, Christianity claims that Jesus of Nazareth was the Son of God and the Messiah foretold by the Jewish prophets. Believing that this Jesus, having ascended into heaven, would soon reappear to destroy this earth and to judge the living and the dead, the earliest Christians ranged far and wide from their first centers in Jerusalem and Syrian Antioch to warn men of impending catastrophe and to offer them salvation through faith in their Master.

Although Christianity spread outward from the eastern Mediterranean in all directions, even reaching as far eastward as central Asia, its chief line of advance was westward along the Mediterranean Basin, then northward through the Rhone and Seine valleys into North Sea Europe. When the New Testament writer says that Jesus was born in "the fullness of time," he displays a clear understanding of the historico-geographic realities of his day, for never before and never since has the Western world been so ideally structured for the rapid spread of a belief deeply held by its adherents. From the Tigris to the Irish Sea, from the Danube to the Sahara men under the protection of Roman law and the Roman legions could move about with a freedom surprising even to us today. Throughout most of this world men could communicate with each other in the debased Greek *(koine)* which was the language of commerce and which became

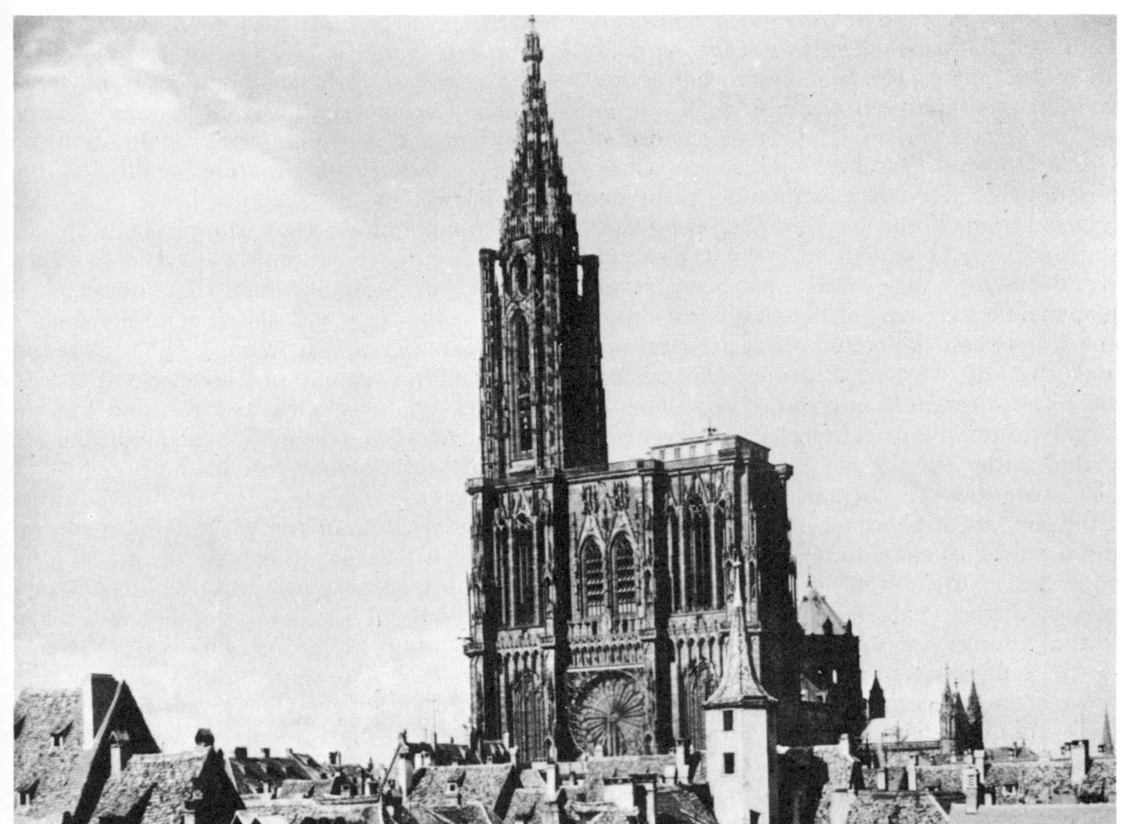

In many towns and cities of Europe, as in Strasbourg, shown here, the local cathedral towers above the roof tops like a shepherd standing guard over his sheep. The symbolism is not strained. For at least a millennium the church dominated the cultural and political life of the continent as fully as its cathedrals dominated the urban skyline. (Courtesy French Government Tourist Office)

the language of the New Testament. In every part of the Empire Rome had built roads along which men could move swiftly and with relative safety. And finally, there were Jewish communities in practically all of the large cities of the Empire—still Jewish in their religion but largely Hellenized in their culture and thus capable of serving as excellent "bridges" to the gentile world.

Thanks to all of these factors, and to the energies of the early missionaries, Christianity spread rapidly. Beginning in Palestine and what is now northern Syria, Paul and other itinerant preachers carried the Christian Gospel into Asia Minor, the coastal districts of the Aegean Sea, the coast of Illyricum (modern Albania), and the west coast of Italy from Rome to present-day Naples. Within the following century Christian congregations had been planted throughout most of Asia Minor, in the Nile Valley, in present-day Tunisia, in key spots in Spain and France, and along the Rhine frontier of the Empire. Another century and a half saw Christianity spread throughout the Empire except for the Celtic highlands of northwestern France, western England, and Wales. In the Near East it had even spilled across the boundary of the Empire into Armenia and northern Mesopotamia.

In the process of expansion Christianity wrought profound changes in its environment and was, in turn, changed by its environment. From Greece it borrowed a great deal of its intellectual equipment. From Rome it borrowed much in the way of organizational structure. By the time Christianity achieved the status of a state religion (during and after the reign of Constantine, *ca.* A.D.

325) it had become, like its great missionary Paul, a Greek-speaking Jew, ready to enjoy all of the advantages and opportunities that went with Roman citizenship.

The first great split in the structure of Christianity resulted in the division of Christendom into two great communions, the one focused upon Rome and the other upon Constantinople. This division, which has persisted down to our own day, has been largely responsible for many of the significant differences between the culture of eastern Europe and that of western Europe. The eastern churches ultimately established a pattern of largely autonomous patriarchates loosely federated under the presidency of the Patriarch of Constantinople. In time, and particularly after the fall of Constantinople to the Turks, these churches came to be, in effect, national churches. Since most of their lands were occupied for centuries by the Turks, the formal training of their clergy suffered and much of the content of the Faith was passed down from generation to generation through the symbolism of a richly elaborate liturgy. At the same time, the clergy of these churches in country after country were forced by circumstances to function not only as the religious leaders of the people but also as the organizers of such opposition as there was to Turkish rule. Thus the churches of the East tended, first of all, to become intimately identified with particular national groups and, later, to pass under the control of the secular rulers of the emergent national states. At the same time, Eastern Orthodoxy gave to the Slavic tribes whom it had brought into its fellowship the Cyrillic alphabet and, with it, the cultural heritage of Greece and of Byzantium. So highly prized was this heritage that when the rulers of newly-independent Muscovy sought to dignify their position they claimed succession from the Byzantine Caesars and took the title of Tsar.

In the West, the Church developed along radically different lines. Patterning its organization after that of the Latin Empire, it developed a highly centralized structure under the sovereignty of the Bishop of Rome. Stricken in its early years with the loss of a strong supporting secular power, the church itself was forced to provide whatever element of unity could be injected into the confused pattern of minuscule sovereignties and petty principalities that resulted from the breakup of the Empire. By common consent, the papal court took on many of the functions of an international referee and, in the process, gathered into its hands much of the power and much of the wealth of the continent.

Throughout western Europe, even in our own day, the landscape still bears evidence of the key position which the church occupied in the lives and activities of her people for more than a millennium. The homes and shops of the people still cluster within the shadows of her great cathedrals and the villages still center around the parish church. In the courts of law and in the precincts of her ancient universities the ceremonial dress is an adaptation of the garb of the medieval clergy. In Roman Catholic countries the roads are dotted with wayside shrines and the stillness of the late afternoon is broken by the sound of the Angelus bell. National banners bear the sign of the cross and the great festivals of the church year are observed even in the most secularized countries as public holidays. The face of Europe remains Christian, whatever may be said for her heart.

In the early sixteenth century, the unity of Western Christendom was shattered by a series of religious revolutions, climaxed by Luther's in Germany, which constituted the Protestant Reformation. In the course of these events most of North Sea Europe became quite firmly Protestant. Mediterranean Europe, however, remained just as firmly Roman Catholic. These two stronghold areas are separated from each other by a belt of religious interdigitation which extends through central Europe from the English Channel to the Netherlands, through central Germany and northeastward to the mouth of the Vistula. It is possibly significant that through most of this belt the physiographic pattern is a rather complex mosaic of hill masses and river valleys, conducive to the development of tiny political units which, under absolutistic rulers, tended to become also religious units. This tendency was greatly reinforced by the principle adopted for the religious settlements at the end of the Thirty Years' War: *"cuius regio, eius religio"*—political units took the religious affiliation of their rulers.

The religious divisions of Europe were carried into the new areas of European settlement during and after the Age of Discoveries. Roman Catholicism was planted in Quebec by the French, in Brazil by the Portuguese, and in the rest of the Americas south of the Rio Grande by the Spanish. Protestantism came with the English into their North American colonies and into Australia and New Zealand, and with the Dutch into South Africa. Later migrations brought large numbers of Roman Catholics into these originally Protestant lands but by the time significant numbers of Roman Catholics had arrived in them the essentially Protestant tone had already been well established. In these lands the chief centers of Roman Catholicism have usually been the large cities where the bulk of the Irish, Polish, and Mediterranean Catholics have settled.

Throughout its history, Christianity has been distinguished by its intensely missionary spirit. Only Islam among the other great religions has displayed a comparable interest in making converts. With the end of colonial rule in most parts of the non-Christian world, Christian missionary activity has been suspended in some countries and faces the danger of suspension in others. Nevertheless missionary activity is still being carried on vigorously by almost all of the major Christian bodies, and in some parts of the non-Christian world it has been successful enough that indigenous churches have grown strong enough to carry on without outside assistance.

3. Islam. In A.D. 622 an Arabian trader and camel-driver named Mohammed fled from his home town of Mecca to the town of Medina where he established himself as a ruler and the inspired spokesman of the One God whose name in Arabic is Allah. This flight from Mecca, the *Hegira,* marks the birthdate of Islam (Submission), an intensely monotheistic, profoundly ethical, and austerely fatalistic religion which in the space of a few centuries swept over the drylands of North Africa and southwestern Asia and sent outrunners into the Indian subcontinent and the wet tropical East Indies. Today, more than 300 million of the world's people accept Islam's holy book, the Koran, as the revelation of the divine mind, and Mecca as the holiest of the cities of the earth.

Islam is the youngest of the three great religions which originated in southwestern Asia and it incorporates elements of both Judaism and Christianity, underlain by earlier animistic religions. Culturally it reflects strongly the dryland environment and the tribal social structure within which it developed. Far more militant than any of the other major religions, it has confronted nonbelievers with a choice from among "Islam, tribute, and the sword." To the loyal followers of Mohammed who die while waging Holy War against unbelievers, Islam promises immediate entrance into a paradise which offers a variety of material and sensory pleasures.

The faithful Moslem is required to believe in the absolute one-ness of Allah and in the complete sovereignty of his will; in the prophets as messengers of Allah and Mohammed as the last and greatest of the prophets; in the Koran as the inspired revelation of Allah; in angels and devils; and in the judgment of the soul at death. Beyond these basic beliefs Islam has accumulated additional beliefs and practices from local cultures into which it has moved so that beneath its appearance of uniformity it is characterized by a great deal of diversity. Basic obligations which are laid upon all Moslems are five in number: the recitation of the creed, "There is no God but Allah and Mohammed is his prophet"; prayer five times a day spoken in the direction of Mecca; the giving of alms "for the love of Allah"; fasting from sunrise to sunset each day during the holy month of Ramadan; and the pilgrimage, at least once in a lifetime, to the shrines and holy places in Mecca.

At the present time there are more than seventy sects of Islam grouped under two major headings. The Sunni, or orthodox, Moslems accept tradition (*Sunna*) and the Koran as of equal authority and acknowledge the authority of the first three caliphs, or successors to the prophet. Shiah accepts only the authority of the Koran, does not acknowledge the authority of the first three caliphs, and contains many elements of pre-Moslem Persian religion. Sunnites dominate by far the greater part of the Moslem world. Shiites are dominant only in Iran and in some adjacent areas that have been influenced by Iranian culture. These sectarian differences, plus a history of long-standing dynastic feuds

Youngest of the world's great religions, Islam came upon the scene as the inheritor and conqueror of highly developed cultures. The minarets from which the muezzins summon the faithful to prayer, such as are seen on the Al-Kadhimain Mosque, shown here, are as characteristic in the landscape of the Islamic world as are church steeples in Christian lands. (Courtesy Embassy of Iraq, Washington)

among the rulers of the Moslem nations, make it very unlikely that the Islamic world could ever be organized into one bloc to act in concert in the world power situation.

At its height, Moslem power overran the Iberian peninsula in the West and reached the gates of Vienna in the East. In the process it uprooted Christianity in some of the earliest Christian centers, particularly in Asia Minor. Of its European holdings little remains today, although there are still Moslem groups scattered through the Balkan countries and the small country of Albania remains predominantly Moslem. But while Moslem power has long since receded from Europe, reminders of its former greatness still persist, particularly in the Iberian Peninsula, in place names (e.g., Guadalquivir, Alcazar) and in magnificent relics of Moorish architecture. And it is to Moslem physicians, chemists, and mathematicians that European culture owes its gratitude for the preservation of the great products of the classical Greek mind which were neglected or banned in the Christian West during the "Dark Ages."

Today, the great bulk of the world's Moslem population lives in a band approximately twenty degrees wide along the Tropic of Cancer from the Atlantic to the head of the Ganges valley and in an arc running from Bengal through Malaya into Indonesia and the southern Philippines. Thus we find Islamic dominance associated with two very different types of landscape: the dry and semidry trade-wind deserts of North Africa and southwestern Asia and the tropical rainforests of southeastern Asia. In this respect Islam, like Christianity, has displayed a universality of appeal which has permitted it to override the physical and cultural bounds of its early homeland.

Of the many imprints which Islam has set upon its environment, at least four would seem to be essential for an understanding of Islamic cultures. The first of these is the almost universal presence of poverty and its acceptance by both rich and poor, to both of whom the ways of Allah are beyond comprehension and therefore to be accepted in a submissive spirit. The second is the ancient tradition of political unrest, with assassination as an instrument of political action and condoned, if not approved, by the mores of the community. The third is the absence of pictorial art and the unique development of nonrepresentational art resulting, we may well suppose, from the Moslem's horror of any art object which might possibly be construed as an idol. And the fourth is the high degree of development—in recent generations, unfortunately, arrested—of the physical sciences and mathematics. To these might be added such minor imprints as polygamy (which predates Islam but has been permitted by it), architectural forms derived from Arabic and North African sources and sometimes curiously incongruous in other environments, and the absence of industries such as hog-raising and distilling, both of which produce products forbidden by Islamic dietary laws.

As both Turkey and Pakistan have demonstrated, the Moslem religion as such cannot be charged with responsibility for the apparent backwardness of so many parts of the Moslem world. The lands which today constitute the Moslem world were basically poor long before Mohammed appeared upon the scene, and this basic poverty of the land is primarily responsible for many of the other problems of the Moslem world. Meanwhile Islam has provided the people of these lands with a rationale for their existence which they find satisfying, and it has provided them with the spiritual motive to assert their dignity and their worth in a world which for centuries prior to the Hegira had either ignored them or oppressed them.

In recent years, Islam seems to have experienced a resurgence of the missionary spirit but this time its advance is along spiritual rather than military lines. Its most notable successes have been in trans-Saharan Africa among Negro tribes whose animistic religions have proved inadequate to their new and rapidly-changing cultural situation, and to whom Christianity does not appeal because of its association with European colonialism and American and South African racialism. In Islam they find a religion which for all of its traditional hostility to the infidel has refused to discriminate on racial or ethnic grounds among its own followers. Even a small number of American Negroes have been attracted to Islam by its "color blindness."

Indian religions

*1. **Hinduism.*** Nothing in the landscape of India is more all-pervading than the presence of Hinduism. Despite recent legislation to the contrary, a man's status is still primarily determined by his caste. Despite human poverty and starvation, cattle still roam the streets, competing with human beings for the very limited food supplies. Despite their education in the best American and European universities, the leaders of republican India are careful to perform the ancient rites and ceremonies of Hinduism, and in its neutralist foreign policy, the government of independent India gives an intensely practical application to the traditional Hindu emphasis upon nonviolence and passive resistance.

And yet none of the major religions is harder to define or describe than is Hinduism. The name itself offers no useful clue, for it stems from an Indo-European root meaning simply "river," in this case the Indus. Tribesmen streaming into the Indus Valley called their new homeland Hindustan, that is, the land of the river; and the name of their religion, Hinduism, means really nothing more than the religion of the people of the river.

As a description of what Hinduism actually is, such a definition is perhaps as good as any that could be suggested. For present-day Hinduism represents an accumulation, over more than four thousand years, of beliefs and doctrines and practices which originated in many different sources. In a sense, therefore, Hinduism is not *a* religion but rather a family of religions, the members of which are related to each other but are individually capable of standing on their own. What Hinduism means to a highly-educated Indian scholar is, therefore, something quite different from what it means to a peasant on the

Trimurthi, Hindu trinity of Brahma, Vishnu, and Shiva, at the Elephanta Caves. (Courtesy Information Service of India)

land or an artisan in one of the thousands of small villages.

Basic to all of Hinduism are (1) the institution of caste, (2) a profound respect for life, and (3) a belief that history, like a wheel, moves neither forward nor backward but always in an endless circle. One's caste is determined by one's birth, and one's duties and limitations derive from the caste into which one is born. It is the duty of the Brahman to meditate and to perform priestly functions; of the Kshatriya to bear arms and to rule; of the Vaisya to engage in handicraft trades and in agriculture; and of the Sudras to act as servants to the higher castes. Outside the caste structure altogether are the millions of untouchables whose very shadow defiles the Brahman and whose lives differ little from the lives of animals.

The harshness of the caste structure is, however, greatly softened by a belief that the soul, at death, enters another body, either animal or human, so that the Sudra or the untouchable may hope that in his next incarnation he will be born into a higher caste. The eventual hope of every good Hindu is to escape the cycle of birth, suffering, and death and to achieve union in the impersonal, passionless divine soul (Brahman). Meanwhile, in every living thing he sees souls which perhaps once inhabited human flesh or perhaps in the future will be clothed in a human body. It is this view of the unity of life which prompted Gandhi to assert that "he who does not believe in cow protection cannot possibly be a Hindu." And it is this longing to escape the cycle of life and death that prompts the Hindu prayer: "Oh, that I could be delivered from the power of my karma over me."

The main streams of religious expression which have been incorporated into present-day Hinduism are six in number, each preserved in its own sacred literature and each characterized by its own distinctive features.

The earliest and most primitive of these streams, having its sources in ancient nature worship and persisting to the present as the popular religion of the masses, is preserved in the Vedas, which date from 2000 to 1000 B.C., or before the migration of the Hindus into India. In the 200 years following the entry of the Hindus into India, there developed a vast system of laws and sacred formulas which were interpreted by a priestly class, the Brahmans. These are incorporated into the prose writings known as the Brahmanas. After 600 B.C. a strong philosophical strain found its way into Hinduism by way of a group of speculative writings known as the Upanishads. This movement, in turn, was followed by a strong legalistic movement (*ca.* 250 B.C.) which produced a code of law, the Laws of Manu, which aimed at perpetuating the mores of that time. At the beginning of the Christian Era, Hinduism experienced a kind of Golden Age characterized by a strongly devotional approach to religion and preserved in the Bhagavad Gita, one of the world's truly great religious masterpieces. And this period, in turn, was followed by a period of popularization which found its highest expression in two great epics, the Mahabharata and the Ramayana.

In the modern world, Hinduism has tended to lose adherents among the better-educated classes but such losses are more than offset by the natural increase (about one million annually) in the population of India. Converts from Hinduism to Christianity have come chiefly from the lowest castes and from the untouchables. Apostasy in the higher castes has ordinarily led to agnosticism and Western humanism. If present trends continue, it is possible to foresee serious conflict between government policies established by humanistically-oriented political leaders and certain doctrines and practices of the popular religion. The outlawing of untouchability may be only the first engagement in this conflict.

2. *Buddhism.* Of the many movements in Hinduism which have diverged so far from its main stream as to have achieved the status of separate religions, the most important by far is Buddhism, the religion of almost 500 million people concentrated in eastern Asia from Malaya northward to the Amur River and from the Pacific westward to the high plateau of Tibet.

Buddhism is based upon the teachings of Siddhartha Gautama, the son of a Nepalese chieftain of the warrior caste. Brought up in a wealthy home, as a young man Gautama was impressed and depressed by the misery and poverty which he saw all about him, and he sought an answer to the riddle of existence first in Hinduism and later in Jainism. Finally, at the age of 35, after a period of solitary meditation, he found the answers he had been seeking and thereafter was known as the Buddha, or the Enlightened One. Within a few years he had gathered quite a following, chiefly among Hindus to whom his teachings represented no great departure from Hinduism.

From Hinduism Gautama drew most of his basic assumptions, among which four are especially important: (1) the cyclical nature of birth, suffering, death, and reincarnation; (2) the doctrine of karma which teaches that the nature of one's future incarnation is determined by one's conduct in this life; (3) the belief that the world is essentially evil and that man's highest destiny is release from the cycle of living; and (4) the idea of the renunciation of desire as the key to the blessed life.

In its earliest and purest form, Buddhism was not so much a religion as a system of morality and philosophy. Gautama never claimed to be divine, although the claim was later made for him by his followers. For himself, he claimed only to have discovered certain truths and certain techniques for applying these truths to life situations. The "Four Noble Truths" which he taught are (1) that suffering is universal and (2) that it is the product of desire; that, accordingly, (3) the cure for suffering is the elimination of desire which (4) can be accomplished by following the Middle Way which is outlined in the Noble Eightfold Path. This Path consists of (1) right knowledge; (2) right intention; (3) right speech; (4) right conduct; (5) right means of livelihood; (6) right effort; (7) right mindfulness; and (8) right concentration. Points three and four of this Path are spelled out more precisely in the Five Precepts: (1) to abstain from killing; (2) to abstain from stealing; (3) to abstain from illicit sexual pleasures; (4) to abstain from lying; and (5) to abstain from intoxicants.

In process of time, and particularly as Buddhism expanded into eastern and southeastern Asia, the simplicity of its moral and philosophical teaching became much clouded by accretions picked up from the cultures into which it moved. Thus in China the worship of Buddha became intertwined with the worship of an earlier goddess of compassion, Kuan Yin. In Tibet it absorbed many elements of earlier indigenous religions and took on the special form which is called Lamaism. In Japan there developed an austere and highly philosophical form of Buddhism called Zen, which in recent years has attracted considerable interest among Europeans and Americans.

The broadest division of Buddhism is into two subreligions: Mahayana, or the Greater Vehicle, which developed and became dominant in China, spreading from there to Korea and Japan; and Hinayana, or the Lesser Vehicle, which is the form of the religion in Ceylon and Southeast Asia. Mahayana is more emotional, more "this worldly," more influenced by other religious traditions than is Hinayana.

One of the many striking similiarities between Buddhism and Christianity is that both in time came to find acceptance chiefly among peoples other than those among whom they had first appeared. Thus Buddhism is almost nonexistent today in India where it originated but it has become the state religion of Burma, Siam, and some of the smaller countries of Southeast Asia, and it is the dominant religion in China and Japan. The disappearance of Buddhism in India probably resulted from the highly absorptive nature of Hinduism and the many similarities between Buddhism and the higher forms of Hindu religion, and from later Islamic incursions. Its acceptance into other cultures would seem to be due chiefly to the fact that, in its pure form, it is not a religion but a system of ethical and philosophical concepts which could be readily absorbed into already existent theologies and cosmologies.

These basic ethical and philosophical ideas have made a strong impress upon Buddhist lands. In Southeastern Asia, particularly, the still essentially other-worldly nature of Buddhism has undoubtedly contributed to the apparent lack of concern with material progress and national development. Americans and Europeans find it difficult to understand a society in which the best and ablest minds are likely to be preoccupied not with the amelioration of evident social injustices or with the improvement of economic and political conditions but with the quest for extinction. Prime ministers who lay aside their offices to become monks and spend their time in contemplation are quite obviously operating with a world view that is radically different from that of their counterparts in the West. Nevertheless Buddhism has shown a strong capacity for survival even in the most Westernized parts of eastern Asia. In recent years, faced by the dual threat of Christian missions and communist expansion, Buddhism has begun to move more and more into the areas of education and social service. By so doing it has managed to retain the loyalties of its people despite the great changes that have taken place in this part of the world in the past half century.

*3. **Jainism.*** Although it began, as did Buddhism, as a reform movement within Hinduism, Jainism never spread beyond the boundaries of India nor has it won any great number of converts. But the million and a half Jains in India are much more influential than their numbers would suggest because most of them are merchants and quite wealthy, and also because they possess a remarkably rich architectural heritage.

The founder of Jainism, Mahavira, was a contemporary of Gautama and, like the founder of Buddhism, came from a wealthy high-caste family. Early in life Mahavira resolved to attain complete mastery over his body and in order to do so renounced his privileged life and wandered about naked, imposing all sorts of self-torture upon himself. When at last he was convinced that he had attained the mastery which he sought, he went back to live among his people and became a teacher and a holy man. Like Gautama, Mahavira himself made no claims to divinity. But his followers before long began to ascribe miracles to him and to worship him as divine.

Jains stand aloof from the other religions of India. Since the sacred writings (Agamas) of Jainism are written in a language that few Jains are able to understand, the profounder insights of Mahavira have little influence on the popular religion and Jains are very much divided on such questions as the number of Agamas which are to be accepted as canonical and the amount of clothing which ought to be worn. In the cool north Jains ordinarily wear clothing. In the south they go about naked, except where Islamic invaders have forced them to wear loin cloths.

*4. **Sikhism.*** A third and very recent offshoot of Hinduism is Sikhism which originated in the Punjab around the beginning of the sixteenth century. Its founder, Nanak, was born in Lahore and in his youth had occasion to become well acquainted with both Hinduism and Islam since the Punjab lay between Hindu and Islamic India. Sikhism represents an attempt to synthesize all of the great religious strains of India, a fact readily apparent from an examination of its sacred writings. These are written in Panjabi, Multani, Persian, Prakrit, Hindi, and Marathi, and several minor dialects. As a result very few Sikhs have read, or are able to read, all of their scriptures.

The most sacred document of Sikhism is the Jabji, ascribed by tradition to Nanak himself. The preamble of this document states in succinct form the essential teaching of Sikhism that "there is but one God whose name is true, the Creator, devoid of fear and enmity, immortal, inborn, self-existent." This god is held to be the God of Hindu and Moslem alike, and to be worthy of obedience and praise. A very strong devotional strain runs through the Sikh scriptures, many sections of which are reminiscent of the Koran.

There are some four million Sikhs living in India today, mostly as farmers in the Punjab. Sikhs have become famous, however, as formidable warriors and have been widely employed throughout the Far East as policemen and as bodyguards of colonial governors in British territories.

Far Eastern religions

1. Taoism. Long before the Western world had achieved any considerable degree of internal order and coherence, China had established a strong, well-run central government with a civil service staffed by philosophers and scholars whose great concern was with the principles of just, orderly, and beneficent government. For a long time religion was little more than a kind of nature worship, refined in time to a worship of spirits, good and bad, who could be manipulated by sacrifices and rituals. The more thoughtful people in China tended to support religion as a useful device for social order although they themselves took little stock in it. Nor were they surrounded, as were their more thoughtful counterparts in India, with the kind of poverty and suffering which would cause them to question the desirability of living. Instead, surrounded as they were by a life and a society which were already reasonably good and pleasant, they turned their minds to the question of how the good life might find its highest expression on this earth. And the systems which they put forward might more properly be called codes of ethics or good manners than religions. Two of these codes—those of Taoism and Confucianism—have been so widely accepted among the Chinese (and in the process debased by many believers to the level of magic and superstition) that they deserve special attention.

Tradition points to an official of the imperial government, Lao-Tze, as the founder of Taoism. Lao-Tze lived between 604 and 517 B.C., during that great period which produced also Mahavira and Gautama in India and Zoroaster, Jeremiah, and Ezekiel in southwestern Asia. Lao-Tze taught that the good life was the life lived in conformity to the divine way, or Tao, of the universe. And this Tao is not a person but rather a basic principle, existing in itself and not by the will of any supreme being. Virtue, therefore, in its highest form, "is no more than the result of compliance with the Tao." To the virtuous man "the great, the small, the many, the few are all equal in his sight." "He recompenses injury with kindness." "He ever uses his goodness in saving the inanimate creation." The three most priceless virtues are compassion, frugality, and modesty. These virtues produce the three great attributes of the sage: fearlessness, liberality, and the ability to govern men. "The Tao of Heaven has no favorites; its practice is simply to reward the virtuous."

Taoism today claims approximately forty million adherents, practically all of them in China and hardly any of them Taoist in the original meaning of the term. For Taoism has incorporated so many elements of earlier religions that the great teachings of Lao-Tze have become largely transformed into polytheistic ritualism and magic.

2. Confucianism. The national religion of China is Confucianism which sends its roots deep into the earliest history of the Chinese people but was reformed and systematized by Kung Fu-tze (Confucius), a contemporary of Lao-Tze. Like so many of the other founders of great religions, Confucius made no claims to divinity and would, no doubt, have been surprised and shocked if he could have observed the processes of adulation which led eventually to his deification.

Unlike most of the other great religious figures of history, Confucius did not even claim to have discovered any great new insights or truths. Rather he sought to bring together the traditional religious and ethical beliefs of his people in the hope that his efforts would reform the degenerate morality of his day and recall his people to the ways of their ancestors. As a result, he himself wrote little. His chief function was that of a compiler of ancient religious classics.

Of the many books which make up the sacred literature of Confucianism, the best known and most influential is the Lun Yü, the Analects of Confucius, which consists of remarks on moral issues, often stated in the form of aphorisms, ascribed to Confucius although they were not gathered together and written down until possibly half a century after Confucius' death.

The good man, and the good society, as Confucius understood them, are characterized by a reverence for learning, respect for parents and ancestors, and humility to others. The Confucian ideal is the grave scholar whose wisdom is employed in wise and benevolent government of his family, his province, and the Empire. The basic element in this man's character is a thoroughgoing integrity which admits of no untruthfulness, no meanness, no frivolity, whether in thought, speech, or action.

Although both Taoism and Buddhism claim many adherents in China, Confucianism set the tone of Chinese culture for centuries. The extreme conservatism of prerepublican China was an inevitable product of the good Confucianist's profound respect for his ancestors. The whole structure of Chinese society reflected a Confucianist respect for parents and the aged. The higher government officials were almost always old men, often in their seventies and eighties. The ceremonial nature of Chinese manners reflected the Confucianist emphasis upon gravity of speech and bearing and personal self-effacement. And while it is true that the political revolutions of 1912 and 1947 sent shock waves into the mores and etiquette of China, they seem to have laid little more than a thin layer of cruelty and crudity over the gentle politeness of Chinese society. Perhaps, like the Manchus and other "barbarians" before them, the present rulers of China, too, will simply be absorbed into this ancient, almost organic body of Chinese culture.

Like Taoism, Confucianism in its popular form has been very much debased. The very virtues which Confucius emphasized in his teachings have become, by a process of distortion, the roots of some of China's most vexing problems. Respect for ancestors has engendered an aggravated form of conservatism which has stood in the way of material and social progress. A proper concern for one's parents and family has given social sanction to the worst forms of nepotism. Attachment to home and place has played its part in overcrowding the land. And the great stress upon ceremonial conduct has produced, as a reaction, various libertarian ideas and movements which tend to be anarchistic in their effects upon the social and political structures.

Since the Second World War, Confucianism has had to contend with the most formidable enemy that has challenged it in all of its long history. This is Chinese Communism. The wholesale slaughter of millions of Chinese under the Communist regime is possibly the most eloquent testimony to the strong hold which Confucianism has had on the Chinese people, for among the chief victims of these purges have been those elements of Chinese society which were best instructed in the higher ethical and philosophical forms of Confucianism. Whether even such drastic measures can uproot so firmly embedded a faith is a question which we may not be able to answer in this century.

Meanwhile, the outward marks of popular Confucianism have left an ineradicable imprint upon the Chinese landscape. The twisted streets of the towns have been made so purposely because of the belief of the people that spirits can move only in a straight line. For the same reason, homes are built so that a solid wall stands opposite every opening. Mounds of earth stand in the villages as shrines to the fertility spirits. The best land is devoted to graveyards. Festivals and ceremonies in honor of some spirit of earth, or river, or mountain seem to be always in progress.

Together, Confucianism and Taoism have molded the Chinese temperament. Each has made important contributions—Confucianism along the line of rationality, order, matter-of-factness, and humanism; Taoism along the line of romanticism, intuition, mysticism, and a kind of pleasant imprecision. Confucianism is a philosophy for times of peace and prosperity, Taoism for times of trouble and disorder. Perhaps Dr. Lin Yutang has summed it up best: "All Chinese are Confucianists when they are successful and Taoists when they are failures."

*3. **Shinto.*** Shinto (Japanese: *Kami-no Michi,* "The Way of the Gods") is in some respects a very ancient religion and in other respects one of the youngest. Its basic documents date only from the eighth century of the Christian Era. But these documents embody myths and legends and doctrines and precepts which go back to the very beginnings of Japanese history.

Shinto in modern Japan takes two forms: State Shinto and Sectarian Shinto. State Shinto is essentially a cult of patriotism, similar to the emperor-worship of the late Roman Empire, and consists principally of certain prescribed rituals and observances through which the patriotic Japanese expresses his loyalty to his country and to his emperor. Supporters of state Shinto have claimed that any loyal Japanese, whatever his religious loyalties, could practice State Shinto without offense to his conscience. Christians and some Buddhists disagree with this contention.

Sectarian Shinto, on the other hand, is unquestionably a religion, postulating as it does many gods, chief among them the Sun Goddess, the special and miraculous creation of the Japanese home islands, and the descent of the reigning emperor through a "lineal succession unbroken for ages eternal" from the Sun Goddess. These teachings are quite obviously based upon very ancient beliefs.

Shinto as such has almost no ethical content beyond the obligation of the good citizen to defend his country against its enemies and to extend the bounds of the empire. The ethical principles upon which social and personal conduct is based in Japan derive chiefly from Buddhism or Confucianism or Taoism, all of which have coexisted with Shinto for centuries.

Both State and Sectarian Shinto share with Judaism a strong "chosen people" emphasis. But whereas the Jews thought of themselves as a people set apart to testify to the oneness and sovereignty of Yahweh, the Japanese have thought of themselves as a people divinely commissioned to rule over other and, therefore, inferior peoples. The sacrifice of one's life in the effectuation of this mission carries, therefore, a profound religious significance; and the failure to further this mission, whether resulting from intent or mischance, means disgrace that could be expiated only by self-destruction. It is still too early to say whether any essential modification of these convictions has resulted from Japan's military defeat in the Second World War.

This great Shinto god stands at Takasaki City, Japan. The essential "otherworldliness" of much of Far Eastern religion finds symbolic expression in the contemplative attitude and closed eyes of this enormous statue. (Courtesy Canadian Pacific Railway)

Religion and the environment

It has been necessary, in this chapter, to outline the historical development and some of the characteristic tenets of the world's major religions because few elements in man's cultural environment are so little understood as is religion, particularly in the West. Insofar as these tenets are a part of the cultural environment, they are in themselves aspects of the human geography of the world. And insofar as the various religions tend to find most of their adherents in particular parts of the world we may claim to have done the specifically geographical job of outlining their distribution.

As one surveys this distributional pattern, and the pattern of various movements within religions, certain geographical relationships emerge. For instance all of the great religions of the world originated along the margins of Asia among peoples who inhabited strongly differentiated natural regions but who have nevertheless been in contact with each other since earliest times. It would be interesting to speculate on the possibility that certain basic elements in all of the major religions trace back to some common source.

If there had been time in the course of our discussion to deal with reform movements which have arisen within the great religions, another interesting and probably significant conclusion would have emerged. That is, that the most intense preoccupation with "orthodoxy," interpreted as a concern for the authority of the basic religious documents, is usually found on the margins of religious regions, rather than at their centers. In Christianity itself, to take the most familiar example, the Protestant Reformation with its insistence upon the sovereignty of the scriptures and its rejection of tradition took place on what were then the remote marches of Christendom. In Buddhism one can note the same sort of tendency.

A third fact which emerges from the study of the distribution of religions is that every religion has been much affected by the environments into which it has moved from its original source. Just as water takes on the shape of the vessel that contains it, and may incorporate impurities if the vessel is not clean, so religions have tended to take on the "shape" of the cultures into which they have moved and often, in the process, to pick up "impurities" from those cultures. One might ask, for instance, what direction Christian theology would have taken if its teachings had developed within the thought systems of India rather than, as they did, within the framework of Greek logic; or to what extent it would today manifest such an intense concern for human and social betterment if it had moved southward toward the tropics rather than northward into the high-energy lands of western Europe.

This is not to suggest that religious teachings are merely products of particular environments. But the cultural expressions of religious belief most certainly are the products of specific environments. The Christian who recites the Twenty-Third Psalm in a basilica is, probably quite unconsciously, acknowledging his indebtedness to two geographical settings which are alien to his own experience, for the imagery of the Psalm derives from the pastoral culture of the Judean hill country and the basilica is the architectural descendant of the ancient Roman courthouse. The Jew who still observes the ancient dietary laws of his people is still following a system of taboos which made a great deal of sense in the warm climate of Palestine where certain animal products, particularly pork, were subject to rapid spoilage.

Religion and world affairs

Many years ago, Jonathan Swift dourly observed that "we have just enough religion to make us hate but not enough to make us love one another." How true this statement is we can discover by reading almost any daily newspaper. Not long ago, *The New York Times* ran an article under the heading, "Asia's Religions Important in Politics." In that article the writer, Tillman Durdin, referred to the then-recent crisis in Tibet and in it he made the point that the Tibetan revolt against the Chinese Communists involved, among other considerations, "opposition by an ecclesiastical hierarchy to the prospective loss of its special position in society and of monastery lands as a result of the introduction of communism to Tibet." After describing the basic tenets of the major Asian religions, he then went on to conclude that,

> ¶ For Asians, the tenets of these great religions and the way of life that they have shaped have profound political significance. India's whole neutralist nonviolent role in world affairs stems as much from Hinduism as from a reaction to centuries under Western colonialist rule. In the Philippines and Vietnam, Christianity is a solid barrier to communism and a strong element in the practices of statecraft. Islam in Pakistan, Indonesia, and Malaya predetermines the basic attitudes in public affairs and acts of the Government.
>
> Buddhism in Ceylon, Burma, Thailand, Cambodia, and Laos is a potent factor in the evolving economic and political systems. In Communist China, Confucian attitudes, still a tough problem for the Communists, have influenced even the Communists themselves in some directions. In

Japan, Buddhist-Shintoist with a leavening of Confucianism, many attitudes of political groups derive from religious sources.[1]

But we need not look to Asia for examples of the role of religion in "secular" affairs. A recent textbook in political geography notes that of the 83 independent or semidependent countries of the earth in 1957, 50 were countries where 90 per cent or more of the population belonged to the same religion, and goes on to say that "This gives us a first approximation of the extent to which maps of religious affiliations and maps of political units coincide. . . .There is hardly a country containing a significant religious minority," this text goes on to point out,

¶ . . . where this factor has no political significance. In some cases such religious minority status has hindered the assimilation of national groups: Armenians, Jews, French Canadians, Irish Catholics and many other groups have preserved their separate existence primarily because of religious differences. These differences are often an obstacle to intermarriage. Religious minorities sometimes form separate political parties, or as a group back the party friendliest to themselves. Poles in Germany were among the most reliable followers of the Catholic Center Party, the Lutherans in Austria of the German National Party. The Alsatians could not easily be assimilated into the main body of the French, not so much because of their German dialect but because of their strong Catholic allegiance in a religiously indifferent France.[2]

In our own country, the memory of the "religious issue" in the presidential campaign of 1960 is still a fresh one. In a study of the returns from that election which *The New York Times* described as "unusual among partisan documents for its scope and candor," the Republican National Committee stated:

¶ When the 1960 returns are compared with either 1956 or 1952 it is apparent that the most pronounced switch found among any identifiable group of voters occurred among Catholics. Gallup states that 62 per cent of the Catholics who voted Republican for President in 1956 switched to Democratic in 1960.[3]

This is no mere partisan rationalization after the fact. The same conclusion has been reached and publicly stated by a number of competent analysts of election trends. Nor does it reflect unfavorably upon adherents of the Roman Catholic faith; the preference which Roman Catholic citizens showed for a coreligionist candidate for President in 1960 is not significantly different from the preference which Lutherans have shown for Lutherans in Minnesota and the Dakotas or which Mormons have shown for Mormons in Utah and certain other western states. Religious groups which occupy, or feel they occupy, a minority status are inclined to seek status by voting for candidates from their own group. Once the group feels that it has been accepted—as, for instance, the Presbyterians, the Methodists, the Baptists, and the Episcopalians—religion seems to lose its former importance as a determinant of voting patterns.

To what extent the religious issue was determinative in the 1960 election is, of course, another question. The Republican National Committee itself ascribed its defeat primarily to the failure of the party to win its usually impressive majorities in the suburbs of the large cities. Students of politics recognize, however, a long-standing attachment of urban Roman Catholic, Negro, and Jewish groups to the Democratic party, and Republican leaders announced, in the wake of the 1960 defeat, their intention to attempt to make inroads upon these groups which, they believe, hold the balance of power in those states which have the largest number of electoral votes.

APPLICATION OF GEOGRAPHIC UNDERSTANDING

1. How do you account for the fact that there are so many more religious denominations in the United States than in any other country of the world?

II. Notice on the world map of religions

---

[1] *The New York Times*, Sunday, April 12, 1959, p. 4 E. Reprinted by permission.

[2] Weigert, Hans W., *et al.*, *Principles of Political Geography*, Copyright © 1957, Appleton-Century-Crofts, Inc., New York, p. 408. Reprinted by permission.

[3] *The New York Times*, Sunday, April 9, 1961, p. 47. Reprinted by permission.

that, particularly in Asia, the boundaries of the major religions tend to coincide with the margins of mountain ranges. Can you suggest why this should be so?

III. Religiously pluralistic as the United States is, certain religious groups have tended to concentrate regionally. An example is the Lutheran group north of the Ohio River and east of the Rocky Mountains, with strong concentrations in the Great Lakes area and the northern plains. Can you suggest any reasons for this concentration?

IV. What reasons other than geographical proximity might account for the inroads which Islam has made upon Christian missionary frontiers in central Africa?

V. What reasons, rooted in historical geography, might account for the concentration of Jewish people in the cities and towns of our country and their relative absence in rural areas?

VI. Explain the following boundary lines as symbols of religious differences: (1) the boundary between the Republic of Eire and Northern Ireland; (2) the boundary between Syria and Lebanon; (3) the boundary between India and Pakistan.

VII. In the light of the world religions map, what practical reasons can you suggest for retaining Latin as the official language of the Roman Catholic Church and of its mass?

VIII. What geographical reasons can you suggest for the fact that Poland, while it is a Slavic country, is also a Roman Catholic country?

IX. The State of Israel is one of many states which are predominantly of one religion. In most such states, the religious unity is associated with a high degree of cultural unity. In Israel, however, there is a great deal of cultural heterogeneity. Why?

X. What elements in all of the religions that are discussed in this chapter tend to make them obstacles to the spread of Communism?

References

1 *The New York Times,* Sunday, April 12, 1959, p. 4 E.

2 Weigert, Hans W., *et al., Principles of Political Geography,* Appleton-Century-Crofts, Inc., New York, 1957, p. 403.

3 *The New York Times,* Sunday, Apr. 9, 1961, p. 47.

The life of man as viewed in its areal setting

In Part II and Part III the student was introduced to the development of geographic concepts and principles by what we call the *systematic* approach, the former giving initial emphasis to the *works of nature*; the latter, to the *works of man*. Each element—physical, biological, or human—was given functional treatment in a *topical* globe-embracing setting, with only secondary regard for analyzing these elements in terms of total areality, region by region.

Here, in Part IV, we turn to another technique, the *regional* approach—the exploration and assessment of the interplay of natural and human forces in an areal framework demarcated by selected criteria that differentiate *life realm-regional patterns*. Selection of such criteria, because of its inherent arbitrary and hence *artificial* character, as noted in Part I, is at best an expedient to handle the complex mosaic of the world landscapes in areal dimensions capable of comprehension. However varied such criteria may be, regional differentiation must have some unitary base—essential homogeneity or functional nodality, as defined in Part I.

Climatic *realms* based on Köppen temperature and rainfall criteria, as noted in the climatic symbols in the figure at the lower right, form the basis of unitary organization, where space generalizations must be suited to the global scale. These realms are broken down into sectional or *regional* subunits, identified with the different cultures of several continents or countries which otherwise share some of the broader realm characteristics, such as climate and vegetation.

Realm chapter material follows the clockwise progression indicated in the figure, which recognizes three conceptual categories. 1. The climatic realms which up to now have, as a group, proved the most challenging: The Polar Frigid (*EF*), the year-round "Wueste" or Desert (*BW*), the semiarid Steppe (*BS*), the winter-dry tropical Savannah (*Aw*), and the highly humid tropical Rainforest (*Af, Am*). With but few singular regional exceptions (e.g., Nile Valley, Southeast Asia, West Indies), populations are very low to nonexistent. 2. In contrast, the hospitable humid, mild winter realms of the *C* world rate among the most populous and prosperous lands of the globe. 3. The likewise humid but more severe winter (*D*) realms have a sufficiently long summer season in two of them (*a-b*) to favor almost every midlatitude form of agricultural, manufactural, and commercial development.

Realm discussion, likewise, in each of the three separate categories, generally proceeds from the more nature-challenging to the more nature–co-operating environments. Thus the frustrating frigid *EF* of the first group, the summer-dry *Cs* of the second, and the severely restricted growing season of *c-d* in the third group.

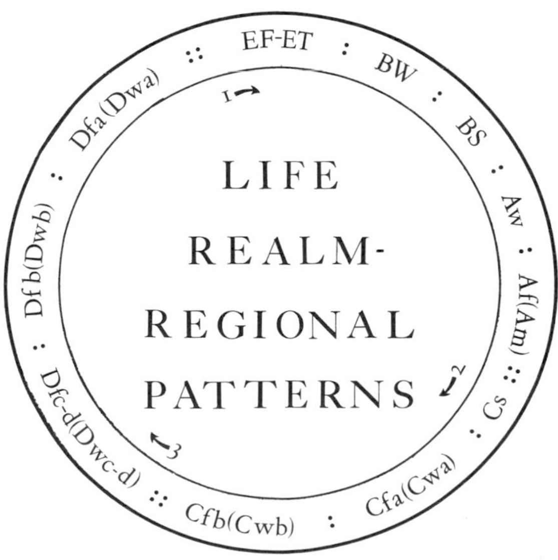

Chapter 19

The polar lands (frigid, *EF;* tundra, *ET*)–lands of political and military strategy

The people of Iceland, by their recent vote in a parliamentary election, put Communists in a position where they hold the balance of power. They may succeed in dislodging American Forces from a vital base of the North Atlantic Treaty Organization.

"Russians Already Moving in on a U. S. Base," a copyrighted article in *U. S. News and World Report* of July 6, 1956, p. 28. Reprinted by permission.

Chorogram[1]: Iceland and NATO

Strategic position is Iceland's major contribution to NATO, since the island with its small population and meager resources contributes little or nothing in the way of manpower or funds to the alliance. A glance at the accompanying map (Figure XIX-1) shows why the United States views this island, lying between Great Britain and Greenland, as one of the world's most strategic places. Although being comparatively small in size, actually about the same as the state of Virginia, the locational significance of Iceland can nevertheless hardly be overemphasized. It is truly the "eyes and ears of the North Atlantic." Iceland commands the shortest air route and sea lane linking forces in Europe with eastern United States. The island is the eastern anchor of a 3,000-mile chain of radar sights and interceptor bases guarding against Soviet attack from across the polar region. Iceland lies approximately at the mid-point of the 4,800-mile distance between Moscow and Washington, D. C.

If the United States loses Keflavik Air Base, our air and naval dominance of the North Atlantic will be reduced, radar protection of the United States will be greatly weakened, and a potential bomber base, 3.5 hours from Moscow, will be lost.[2] A service station for aircraft and naval craft would no longer be available. Large quantities of aviation fuel are stored in Iceland for the refueling of large civilian trans-Atlantic aircraft as well as for the refueling of large bombers and military transport planes. On the other hand, if Russia did gain Iceland as a base, Great Britain would be outflanked by air and sea, bombers would be brought within easy range of the United States and Canada, submarines and aircraft could turn the North Atlantic into a Soviet lake, and U.S. supply lines to forces in Europe would be in grave danger.

Weather and climate in this part of the world make flying very hazardous. The winter wind is so strong that snow often seems to be blowing sideways, instead of falling from the sky. The seas around Iceland are what airmen call "three-minute water," that is, if one's plane goes down at sea, one has three minutes before freezing to death. Because of the rough surface of the land, one's chances for survival are not much better if one bails out, because the Keflavik Peninsula is studded with the jagged joints of volcanic lava. Sharp lava also makes field maneuvers rough for the army men. The general life of an American serviceman on Keflavik Base is no picnic either because the climate and the volcanic terrain make outdoor athletics difficult, and indoor activities are limited by lack of facilities.

Economic geography also plays a vital role in the present political situation of the island. Iceland's chief income is from fishing. The average yearly catch amounts to over 7,000 pounds per inhabitant. Russia made an inroad into the economic life of Iceland four years ago when Britain, formerly her chief buyer, stopped buying Iceland's fish because

1 The term "chorogram" as used in this connection denotes a brief geographic analysis and appraisal of current history as recorded in news dispatches and reported upon in a class in geography of world affairs. Originally composed and cartographically illustrated by students, the chorograms, used in this section to introduce the several chapters, have been edited or reconstructed to adapt them to the present textual context.

2 In 1956 the government of Iceland actually requested the United States to withdraw its forces from the island. Fortunately this request was withdrawn when the government felt its "neutralism" might not after all be the best policy in view of the subsequent ruthless military invasion of Hungary by the Soviets.

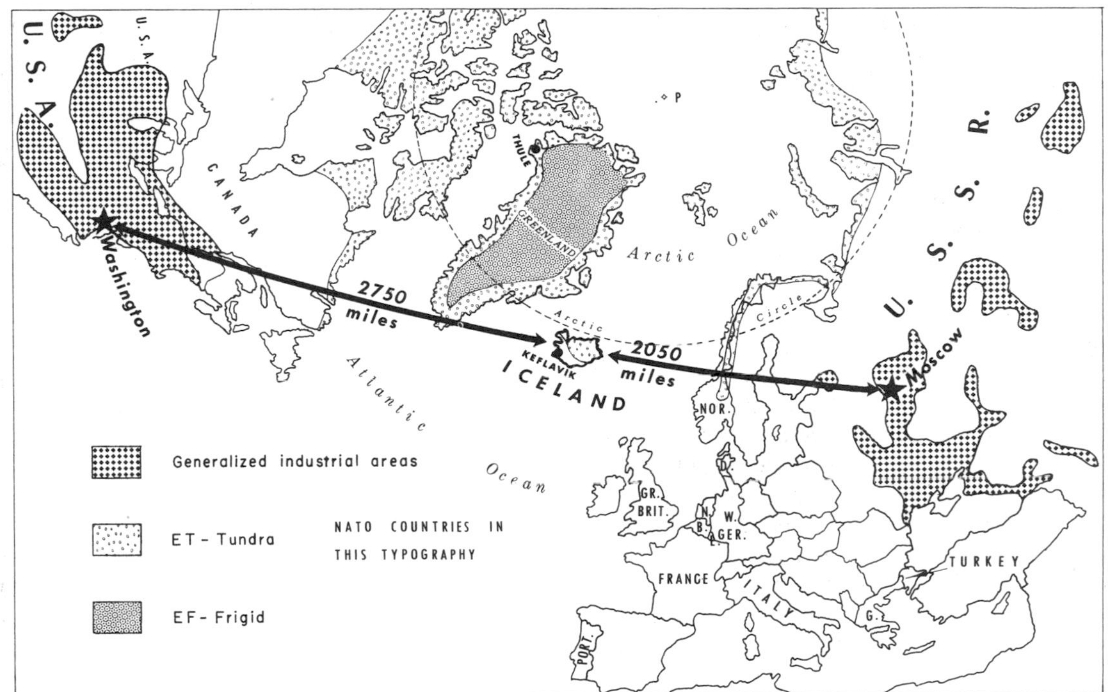

XIX:1 Iceland is known as the "Eyes and Ears of the North Atlantic" for NATO. Arctic and sub-Arctic lands, as here shown, lie on strategic pathways connecting the industrial hearts of the world's two leading cold-war "combatants." It is not difficult to imagine what courses intercontinental ballistic missiles would take in an actual air attack. Thus the Arctic region and polar projections take on an increasing geographic significance in world affairs in the middle of the twentieth century.

of a dispute over territorial waters. Russia stepped in as an eager buyer, and now the Soviet bloc is Iceland's biggest buyer. The United States also contributes considerably to the economic life of Iceland. A large part of the 150 million dollars appropriated for construction and maintenance of Keflavik Air Base goes directly into Iceland's economy in wages and salaries.

The future outlook appears to be for the Communists to exert more and more pressure to force the United States out of this key link in the eastern defense line. Whatever the outcome, a large share of Western security hinges on who controls little Iceland.

Greenland, another major North American outpost

Another subpolar security outpost for the United States by reason of its strategic position is that of Greenland. As early as the beginning of the twentieth century, the United States recognized its importance in this respect. However, in the negotiations with Denmark for the purchase of the Virgin Islands in 1916-1917, the United States ceded its earlier exploratory rights in Greenland despite the protests of Rear Admiral Robert E. Peary. As discoverer of the North Pole, Admiral Peary recognized the increasing importance of Greenland's position on the great circle route in terms of water and air attacks by a potential Eurasian enemy, stating, "Greenland in our hands might be a valuable piece of our defensive armour."

As a result of the invasion of Denmark by Germany in the Second World War, Greenland temporarily became a protectorate of the United States. Under an agreement reached with Denmark on April 9, 1941, four American air bases were constructed on the southern and western coasts of Greenland for use as refueling and repair stations for bombers. Lying in the North Atlantic, where the high and low pressure areas form, Greenland air bases possess additional geographic utility in planning air operation over Europe and Asia. In fact, this was the very reason why Germany, immediately after its occupation of Denmark, established a number of weather stations on Greenland. When it was subsequently conquered by the Americans, a score of stations were established and operated by Danes and Eskimos. The services of these stations integrated with those of the World Meteorological Organization.

The value of Great Circle positions such as Iceland and Greenland to the establishment of national defense outposts cannot be questioned. Only if we fully recognize this geographic factor, however, can we understand the justification for some of the huge expenditures required in establishing air bases such as the bomber base in Thule, Greenland. Thule, within the Arctic Circle on the northwest coast of Greenland, is situated on the shortest route to Moscow, a distance of less than 2,800 miles, and so within only a few hours of possible attack (even by conventional weapons) on Russia's Arctic seacoast shipping installations and industrial establishments of west central Russia.

Polar Great Circle navigation and global meteorological relationships

Construction of air bases, important as they are in the Arctic and sub-Arctic regions, can prove very costly. One of the frustrating elements of the environment is the so-called "permafrost." This is a form of ground ice which never thaws except for a few inches on the surface. As the terrain begins to thaw, the foundations of buildings or runways collapse. Deep excavations and piling are necessary to ensure a stable foundation. Despite costly air-base construction and inclement weather, however, airplane flights at high latitudes, commercial and military, have become commonplace. War-developed aircraft equipment eliminates or greatly reduces the earlier experienced meteorological hazards. The loran is a system of long-range navigation in which pulsed signals, sent out by two pairs of radio stations, are utilized by a navigator to determine the geographical position of an aircraft. This system, as well as loran accurate altimeters, determine plane position at all times; radar also affords constant communication. And so, speedy and dependable flights can negotiate in a few hours the abbreviated Great Circle trans-Arctic routes which form the "crossroads" connecting the industrial and commercial heartlands of Eurasia and North America and the "orbits" to the military arsenals of the two leading world powers, the United States and the Soviet Union.

Now let us turn to the opposite "end of the earth." Instead of an ice floe, Antarctica is an ice-covered continent, larger than the United States and Mexico combined. Unlike the land-surrounded Arctic region, the Antarctic is encircled by oceans. The nearest point of the continental mainland of Antarctica to the nearest continent—South America—is over 1,000 miles; to Australia, 1,900 miles; and to Africa, nearly 2,500 miles. Moreover, since none of these include world-power countries, Antarctica cannot possibly have the strategic military function identified with the Arctic region. The water-hemisphere position, as well as the low population potential of the Southern Hemisphere countries, will likewise preclude the possibility of developing Great Circle transportation across the Antarctic. The position in latitude and longitude of the Southern Hemisphere countries is such that Great Circle routes, as a matter of fact, would nowhere touch the Antarctic continent.

While Antarctica has not possessed significant intercontinental great-circle navigation such as the Arctic areas, it received areal distinction for the greatest concerted scientific investigations in history, including the most intensive survey of the physical environment ever made by man. Antarctica, moreover, was the largest single area identified with the International Geophysical Year. While the International Geophysical Year was a scientific adventure of global proportions, Antarctica received particular attention especially to extend knowledge on the basic circulation of atmosphere at both lower and higher levels with the objective of improving long-range forecasting. The stations of the nations which made such weather observations are shown in Figure XIX-2. These extraordinary efforts by explorers and scientific research expeditions, both in the Antarctic as well as the Arctic, are

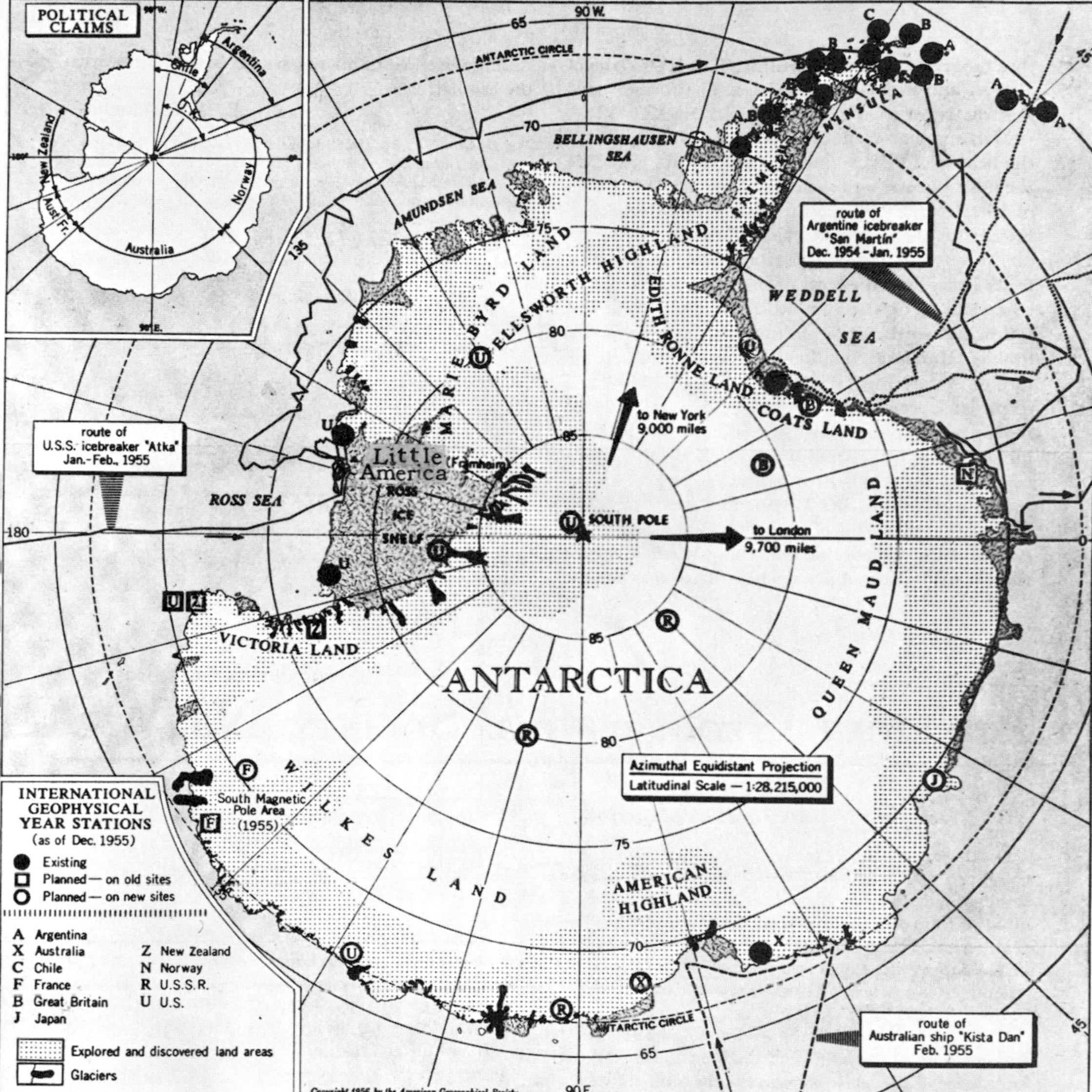

Maps drawn by Vincent Kotschar

XIX:2 Antarctica is known as "The Foot of the World." Actually, of course, the earth has neither "top" nor "bottom," but the Antarctic Continent conventionally takes an "inferior" position on a globe or world map. This is understandable in view of its water-hemisphere isolated position and consequent late discovery and difficulty of penetration as a result of its ice-capped surface. It was not until the International Geophysical Year (1957-58) that the Antarctic was brought into real geographic perspective. Note the numerous expedition headquarters as posted by the initial letters representing the various countries. (From *Focus* by permission of American Geographical Society, Vol. VI, No. 5, January, 1956, p. 3)

of global importance. The polar fronts give rise to many of the Lows and Highs, which in their drift eastward by the prevailing Westerlies, effect the variable cyclonic and anticyclonic weather characteristics of mid-latitude lands. (For these space relationships, see Chapter 6 on "Climates and Culture.")

Climate is impressed everywhere on the polar landscape

Current news references on the Arctic and the Antarctic, such as the above, should dis-

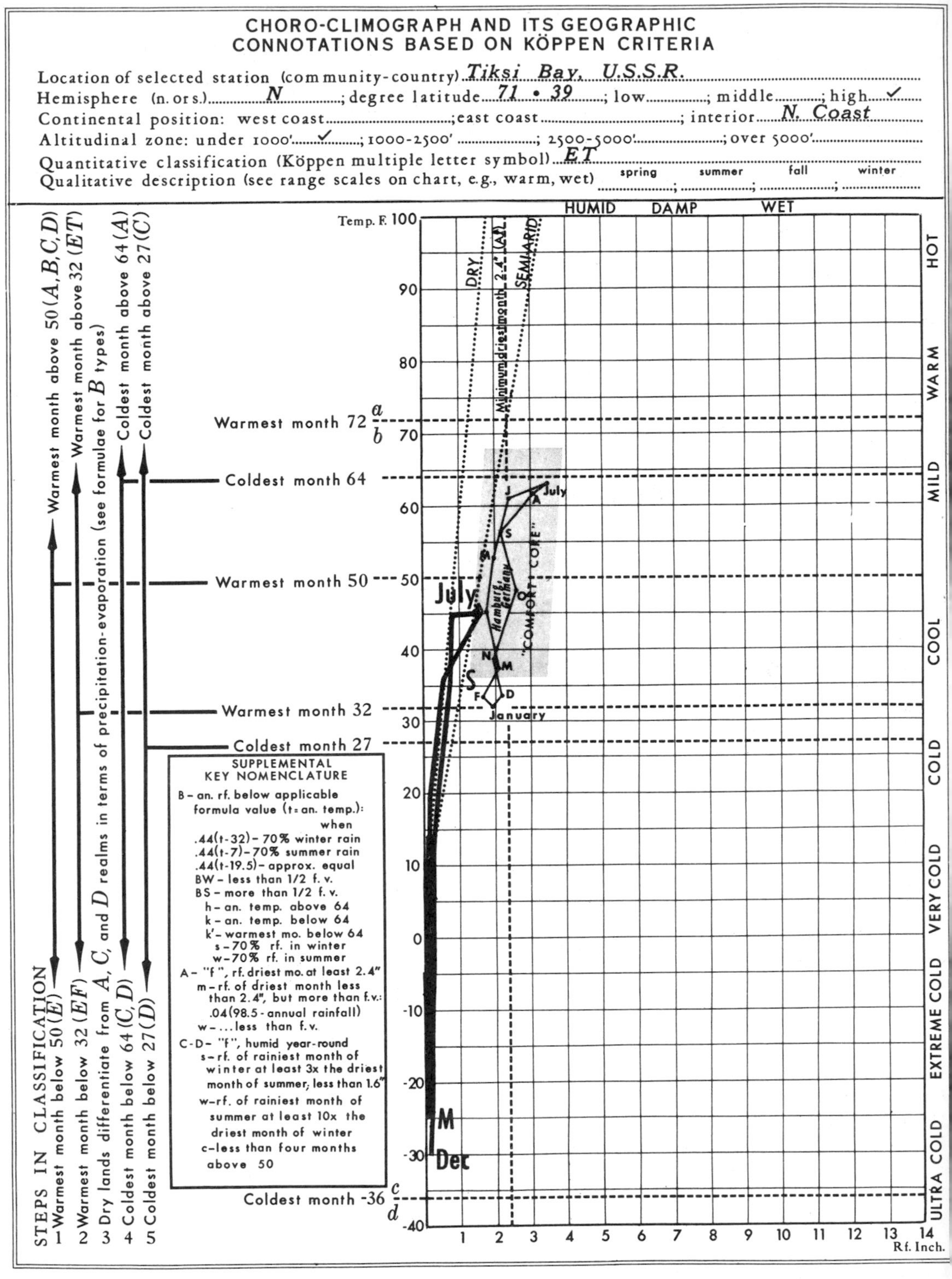
CHORO-CLIMOGRAPH AND ITS GEOGRAPHIC CONNOTATIONS BASED ON KÖPPEN CRITERIA
Location of selected station (community-country) Tiksi Bay, U.S.S.R.
Hemisphere (n. or s.) N; degree latitude 71 • 39; low; middle; high ✓
Continental position: west coast; east coast; interior N. Coast
Altitudinal zone: under 1000' ✓; 1000-2500'; 2500-5000'; over 5000'
Quantitative classification (Köppen multiple letter symbol) ET
Qualitative description (see range scales on chart, e.g., warm, wet) spring; summer; fall; winter
STEPS IN CLASSIFICATION
1 Warmest month below 50 (E) — Warmest month above 50 (A, B, C, D)
2 Warmest month below 32 (EF) — Warmest month above 32 (ET)
3 Dry lands differentiate from A, C, and D realms in terms of precipitation-evaporation (see formulae for B types)
4 Coldest month below 64 (C, D) — Coldest month above 64 (A)
5 Coldest month below 27 (D) — Coldest month above 27 (C)
Warmest month 72 a b
Coldest month 64
Warmest month 50
Warmest month 32
Coldest month 27
Coldest month -36 c d
Temp. F.
HUMID DAMP WET
DRY
Minimum driest month 2.4" (A,F)
SEMIARID
HOT WARM MILD COOL COLD VERY COLD EXTREME COLD ULTRA COLD
"COMFORT CORE"
Hamburg, Germany
July
S
M
Dec
January
Rf. Inch.
SUPPLEMENTAL KEY NOMENCLATURE
B – an. rf. below applicable formula value (t = an. temp.): when
.44(t-32) – 70% winter rain
.44(t-7) – 70% summer rain
.44(t-19.5) – approx. equal
BW – less than 1/2 f. v.
BS – more than 1/2 f. v.
h – an. temp. above 64
k – an. temp. below 64
k' – warmest mo. below 64
s – 70% rf. in winter
w – 70% rf. in summer
A – "f", rf. driest mo. at least 2.4"
m – rf. of driest month less than 2.4", but more than f.v.: .04(98.5 - annual rainfall)
w – ...less than f.v.
C-D – "f", humid year-round
s – rf. of rainiest month of winter at least 3x the driest month of summer; less than 1.6"
w – rf. of rainiest month of summer at least 10x the driest month of winter
c – less than four months above 50

pel many misconceptions concerning the polar regions. Factors inherent in the region, besides the one of global position, must be understood properly to be appraised. Not all polar lands are permanently frigid; even the *EF* section (warmest month below 32°F.) is not covered with ice and snow throughout the year. Precipitation in some areas is very low.[1] Barren landscapes are not the only criterion by which their economic value is assayed; rich mineral emplacements may occur. When students are asked, "Why is the population of Arctic lands extremely low?" the answer usually given is, "It is too cold." The answer should rather be: "There is too short a growing season in the tundra, and none at all in the *EF*." Snow houses are uncommon; in fact, Eskimos usually do not occupy snow igloos, but live in crude houses.

A second major factor of inhospitableness occurs because of the low temperatures which may turn a man "into an icicle" by freezing his body perspiration and breath moisture, unless every precaution is taken to keep such moisture congelation under control.

To get a true picture of regional variations, we must recognize that there are two distinct subregions in the polar world—the tundra (*ET*) and the ice cap (*EF*), Figure XIX-4. Whereas the temperature of the warmest month in the ice cap region remains below the freezing point, the temperature of the tundra for the same month may rise to 50° in the equatorward areas. Thus there is no growing season whatsoever in the icecap region, but the growing season of the tundra is a sufficiently warm interval to support lichens and mosses. Moreover, subregional variations in temperature and precipitation occur with diverse exposures to sea and air mass conditions. Thus greater extremes of temperature occur over land as compared to those over water or ice. Another regional variable stems from differences in elevation. Moreover, the lapse rate of the temperature varies considerably over the different areas of land, sea, and ice. Since polar lands are spread through a considerable latitude (Figure XIX-5), it is obvious that the seasonal contrast as well as the diurnal differences of daylight and darkness result in considerable differences in plant and animal ecological relationships. Although the lowest average annual temperature is found in the polar region, the coldest part of the Northern Hemisphere, as far as is known, is in Northeast Siberia, in the vicinity of Oimyekon (63° north latitude).

During the short summer months, not a day passes without frost accumulating, while during the six-month winter, the sun is below the horizon. Moderate temperatures are rare, since the high velocity wind sweeping across the icecap areas lowers the temperature about one degree Fahrenheit for each mile per hour of wind.

Although there is considerable variation in depth of snow in various types of the polar areas, in most of the Arctic region the amount of precipitation in the form of either snow or rain would amount to approximately ten inches of water. In lower latitude regions, such low precipitation would cause aridity, or at least semiaridity, but at this higher latitude, evaporation is much reduced. Low evaporation, moist ground surface, and poor underground drainage owing to permafrost, cause numerous bogs and lakes, especially during the summer season. Consequently, the surface of the ground is usually moist. Precipitation is light because of the low absolute humidity and high atmospheric pressure. It is the long winter night that accentuates the congelation of moisture in polar areas, plus, of course, the low angle of the sun's rays during the summer season.

Polar climates are becoming less severe, and progressive deglaciation is in prospect, but the observation has been made that at the present rate it would take several millennia to melt all of Antarctica's ice, in places 7,000 feet thick. It has been calculated that if all the ice were melted from Antarctica, the sea

---

[1] For definition and comparative classification of climatic symbolism used in this chapter and other chapters in this book, see Köppen Key in the Appendix.

XIX:3 (Left) This choro-climograph represents a tundra *(ET)* station. Supply, in the space provided, a seasonal t-rf characterization as per illustration, Figure VI–8. Is there a growing season? If so, how long? Would you expect heavy snowfall in this area? To which, do you think, is the paucity of population primarily related—cold winters or short summers?

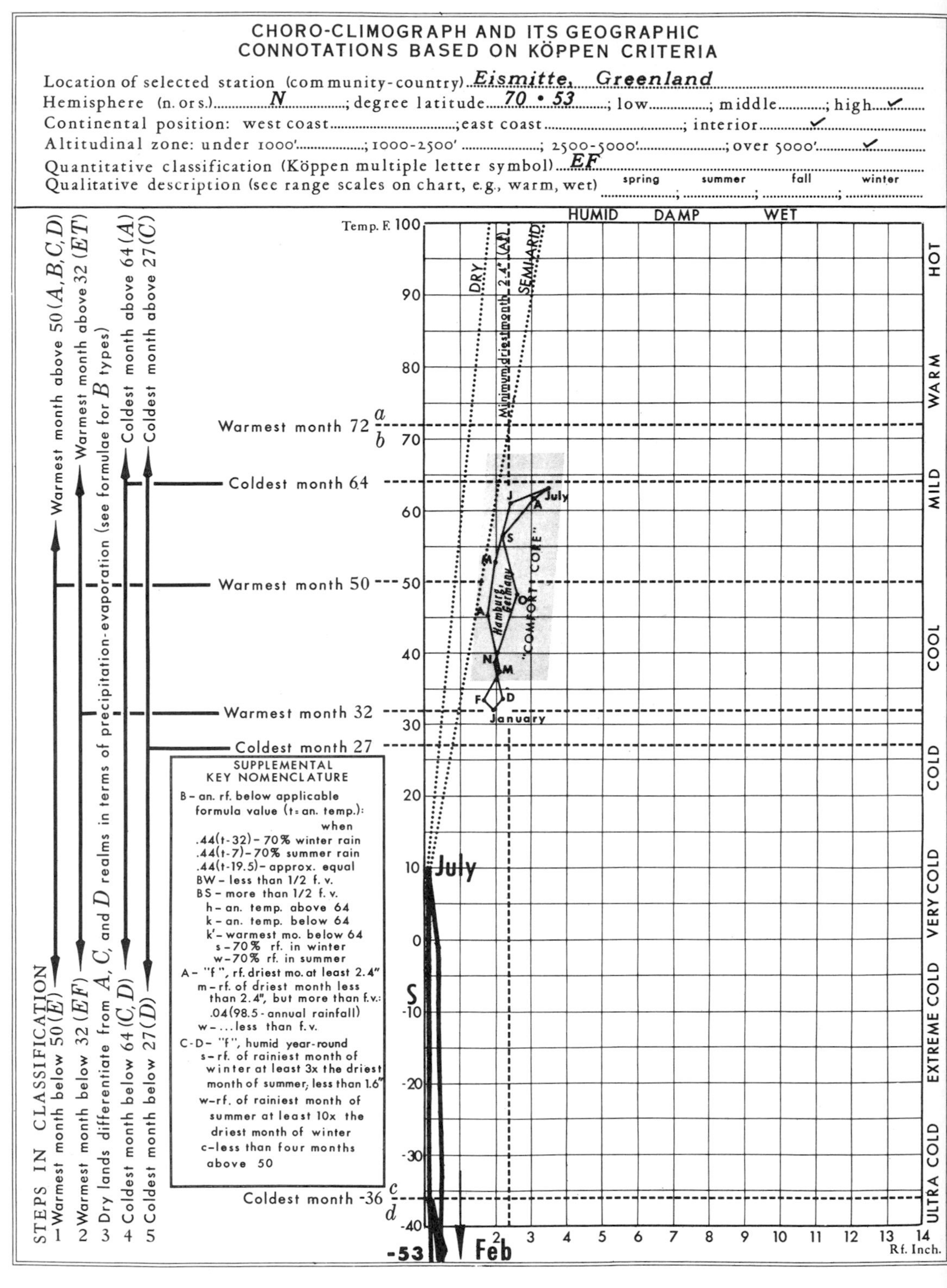
CHORO-CLIMOGRAPH AND ITS GEOGRAPHIC CONNOTATIONS BASED ON KÖPPEN CRITERIA
Location of selected station (community-country) Eismitte, Greenland
Hemisphere (n. or s.) N; degree latitude 70 • 53; low; middle; high ✓
Continental position: west coast; east coast; interior ✓
Altitudinal zone: under 1000'; 1000-2500'; 2500-5000'; over 5000' ✓
Quantitative classification (Köppen multiple letter symbol) EF
Qualitative description (see range scales on chart, e.g., warm, wet) spring; summer; fall; winter
HUMID
DAMP
WET
Temp. F.
DRY
Minimum driest month 2.4" (Af)
SEMIARID
"COMFORT CORE"
Hamburg, Germany
July
January
HOT
WARM
MILD
COOL
COLD
VERY COLD
EXTREME COLD
ULTRA COLD
Warmest month 72
Coldest month 64
Warmest month 50
Warmest month 32
Coldest month 27
Coldest month -36
July
S
-53
Feb
Rf. Inch.
STEPS IN CLASSIFICATION
1 Warmest month below 50 (E) — Warmest month above 50 (A, B, C, D)
2 Warmest month below 32 (EF) — Warmest month above 32 (ET)
3 Dry lands differentiate from A, C, and D realms in terms of precipitation-evaporation (see formulae for B types)
4 Coldest month below 64 (C, D) — Coldest month above 64 (A)
5 Coldest month below 27 (D) — Coldest month above 27 (C)
SUPPLEMENTAL KEY NOMENCLATURE
B – an. rf. below applicable formula value (t = an. temp.): when
.44(t-32) – 70% winter rain
.44(t-7) – 70% summer rain
.44(t-19.5) – approx. equal
BW – less than 1/2 f. v.
BS – more than 1/2 f. v.
h – an. temp. above 64
k – an. temp. below 64
k' – warmest mo. below 64
s – 70% rf. in winter
w – 70% rf. in summer
A – "f", rf. driest mo. at least 2.4"
m – rf. of driest month less than 2.4", but more than f.v.: .04(98.5 - annual rainfall)
w – ...less than f.v.
C-D – "f", humid year-round
s – rf. of rainiest month of winter at least 3x the driest month of summer, less than 1.6"
w – rf. of rainiest month of summer at least 10x the driest month of winter
c – less than four months above 50

level of all the oceans would rise 150 feet, enough to flood the world's seaports (2). It is estimated that 85 per cent of the world's ice is in the Antarctic.

The known rock types and structures in polar areas do not differ basically from those of other major areas of the world. Likewise, major relief features may vary from low plains along the coast to high plateaus and glaciated mountains in the interior. Rocky peaks or ridges, called *nunataks,* may rise like islands above the sea of ice. Distinguishing surface features result from extensive glaciation as well as disintegration of rock caused by extreme temperature changes. Ice sculpturing often produces hanging valleys and deep fjords along coastal mountains, as in Labrador and Greenland. The ice itself is often wind-eroded into scalloped ridges called *zastrugi.* The physical disintegration, as contrasted with the chemical decomposition in the low latitudes, results in large fragments of rock which often form rock fields. Due to the seasonal thawing and freezing, much of the tundra soil takes on a geometrical design known as *patterned ground.* The process of alternate contraction and expansion of the soil is known as multigelation. The transformation is similar to that of a drying lake bed. Not only do these actions result in differential soil zones but they also cause zonation adjustments of vegetal life as well.

Due to the generally low temperatures obtaining in the polar regions, soil forming processes are slow. The predominantly physical disintegration, resulting from extreme temperature changes, produces coarse-textured surface materials. With low temperatures, chemical and biological changes slowly take place. Organic matter is concentrated on or near the surface, and, owing to the permafrost condition, the soil profile, such as we find in the pedalfers and the pedocals, is poorly developed. Such profile as does exist is distinguished from that of steppe or desert soils in that it is developed under poorly-drained conditions. And so, tundra soils are similar in texture and structure to those found in marshes or bogs of the podsol zone of the middle latitudes and higher middle latitudes. In general, tundra soils consist of brown peaty layers, underlain by a grayish substratum, which usually remains frozen. Suited primarily to pasturage based on tundra vegetation, these poorly drained acid soils hold little promise for future agricultural tillage.

XIX:4 (Left) This choro-climograph represents a frigid (*EF*) station. Characterize the seasons. Compare this station with the preceding one. Account for the climatic difference in terms of latitude, land–water relations, elevation.

Vegetation reflects "physiologic drought"

Plant life in the polar regions is chiefly herbaceous and must be adapted to an extremely short growing season. This is compensated in part, however, by the longer days of the summer months. Moreover, it must be adapted to low moisture requirements, perhaps best expressed by the term "physiologic drought." Though precipitation generally is low, comparable with that of the drylands, the chief problem is not necessarily inadequate precipitation, but rather lack of available moisture due to frozen ground conditions, and rapid evaporation and transpiration of moisture due to high winds. Consequently, the vegetation for the most part takes on a xerophytic aspect. (Compare with *BW* forms.) Trees are stunted with compacted annual rings; bushes grow lopsidedly, generally revealing prevailing wind direction, and dry up on the windward side. Stems of plants are rather short and tussocky, bearing leaves with leathery texture and often covered with down-like growth to help retard transpiration. Plants for the most part are shallow-rooted in the thin soil, which thaws out for only a few months in the summer on top of the permanently frozen ground. Another group of plants—the *hydrophytes*—occurs in bogs and marshes, known as *muskegs* in North America. Annuals must be fast growing. Germination, sprouting, and the development of the plant to full maturity, including the seed formation, must take place within a growing season of one, two, or at most three months.

The ice-capped regions of Greenland and Antarctica represent, of course, botanical deserts. Lichens, marking the poleward limit of land vegetation, grow on rock exposures with minimum requirements of mois-

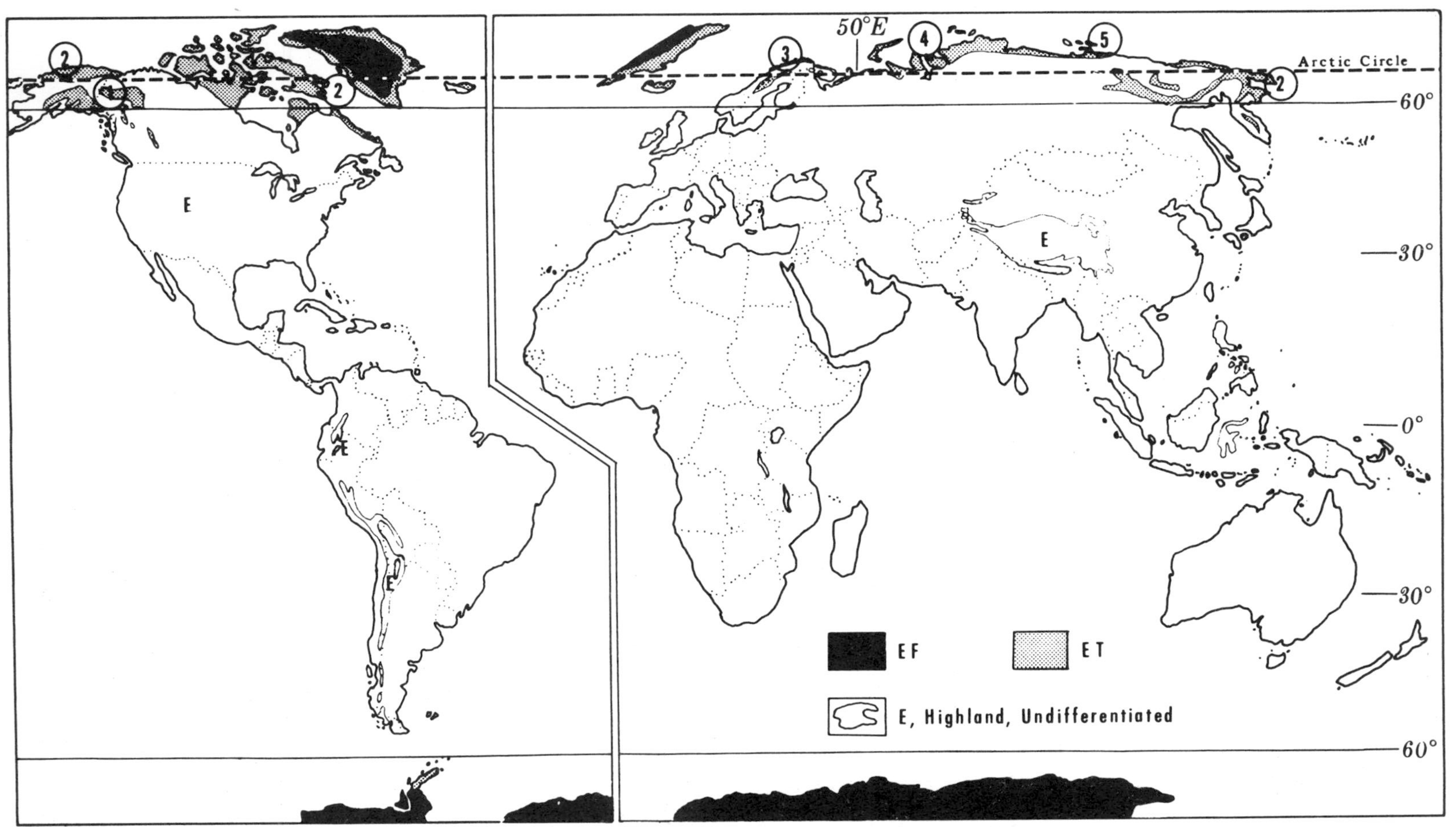

50°E
Arctic Circle
60°
30°
0°
30°
60°
E
E
E
E
2
2
2
3
4
5
EF
ET
E, Highland, Undifferentiated

ture, nutrients, and sunlight. The other low order of plant life includes algae and mosses. In addition to these, only two flowering plants, a grass and a pink, have been found growing in Antarctica. On the other hand, "the land fringe of the Arctic supports more than 400 species of flowering plants, and the tree line extends north of 70° on the Lena River" (3).

At least three zones must be recognized to understand Arctic flora conditions—the bush tundra, just to the north of the taiga; the grass and heather zone, northward of the bush tundra; and the barren or desert tundra of the frigid (*EF*) zone.

The bush tundra characteristically consists of dwarf alder, birch, and willow; and such berry plants as crowberry and bilberry. The second zone consists of heather type of vegetation, including mosses, lichens, sedges, and some stunted bushes. Finally, the northernmost zone is mostly bare of vegetation, except for a few mosses, lichens, and a few other Arctic plants of the general cushion type. The lichen is actually a dual organism—an alga and a fungus, existing in symbiotic relationship to each other. The alga requires the organic nutrients supplied by the fungus, whereas the fungus provides the mineral plant food material to the alga by producing acids which disintegrate the rock into a shallow soil base. Varied combinations of color of both the rock and the lichen often produce a most colorful carpeting in what is otherwise a very bleak and drab landscape.[1]

XIX:5 (Left) Place can have no meaning apart from position, i.e., apart from other places. Thus a climatic realm map, such as this, is a standard feature of each chapter in Part IV. Geographically significant questions related to such a map may refer to: (1) the position of the realm in relation to those global and regional factors genetically responsible for the climatic type; (2) the position of this realm in relation to its neighboring realms; (3) its comparative size to other realms and to the land areas of the world as a whole; (4) the pattern of world distribution and the varying shapes in the several regions. But, above all, upon such space representation is to be focused the life–land relationships characteristically identified with the realm mapped: vegetal, animal, and human. Sparse, yet diverse, populations occur in the widely longitudinal spread of the *ET:* (1) Indian, (2) Eskimo, (3) Lapp, (4) Samoyed, (5) Yukagir, as shown on the map. Compare the functions of the anthropologist and the geographer in exploring the bases for both these characteristics. (This and the succeeding climatic realm maps adapted from the basic Köppen-Geiger map, "Climates of the Earth," by Clarence E. Koeppe and George C. DeLong, McGraw-Hill Book Co., Inc., 1958)

Animal ecology and economy focus on marine life

Though rather limited in number of species, animal life is considerably more plentiful in subpolar regions than commonly believed. Such unexpectedly large numbers may be explained on the basis of three factors: (1) the prolific marine life on which land and water forms feed, (2) the migration of several land animals from the taiga into the subpolar areas, and (3) the seasonal flights of birds. The cold seas teem with plankton (primarily diatoms and algae), which support a rich crustacean life, which in turn supplies food for fish, upon which in turn the seals feed. The seal is eaten by the polar bear, which in turn is preyed upon by the Arctic wolf. The microscopic plant life itself utilizes fertilizing elements.

¶ This richness of life is traceable to the abundance of nitrates and phosphates brought to the surface by the continuously upwelling waters. Diatoms and other floating microscopic plants utilize these nutrients directly in the presence of sunlight and in turn provide food for the microscopic animals, or zooplankton, which themselves are food for the larger animals that feed on them and one another. The chain of life culminating in the blue and fin whales is so clear that the local distribution of these whales can be predicted from the distribution of phosphates in the water.[2]

Corpses and excreta of the animals sink to the ocean floor, where bacterial action makes

[1] For one of the best published colorful illustrations of such see "Ice-bound Barrens of the Arctic Tundra," Lincoln Barnett, "The World We Live In: Part X," *Life,* June 7, 1954.
[2] Gould, Lawrence M., "Antarctic Prospect," *The Geographical Review,* Vol. XLVII, No. 1, January, 1957, p. 23. Reprinted by permission.

the nutrients again available; upwelling currents return them to the sun-lit zone, and another cycle begins.

To a limited extent, a similar chain of animal life relationships may be recognized in the forms on the land. As already indicated above, tundra vegetation is rich in lichen and other flora upon which herbivorous animals feed. These are primarily the reindeer and musk ox of Eurasia and the caribou of North America. Also included in this group are the lemming and the Arctic hare. Carnivores in turn, like the Arctic wolf and fox, prey upon the reindeer and other herbivorous animals.

Again contrary to popular notion, almost held universally, the tundra marshes and bogs constitute some of the most favorable habitats for insect propagation. Mosquitoes particularly are a pest, and make life miserable for both beast and man. It is this rich insect life in part which attracts large flocks of migratory birds into the subpolar regions, and gives rise to numerous rookeries. Illustrations in *Life* magazine mentioned above include: willow, ptarmigan, the rock ptarmigan, the snowy owl, the long-tailed jaeger, semipalmated plover, golden plover, northern phalarope, snow bunting, sand-hill crane, herring gulls, old-squaw ducks, red-breasted merganser, lesser Canada geese. Even the Antarctic region is not without bird life. Here we find the Adelie penguin, the Emperor penguin, and the skua gull, which feeds upon the young of the penguin. "Additional species of birds nest on the islands or coasts of Antarctica or spend much of their time there. Among them are the beautiful snowy petrel, Wilson's petrel, the Cape pigeon, the giant fulmar, and the silver-gray fulmar (4).

The coastal waters of polar lands rate as the richest fishing grounds of the world. These include the world famous fishing banks off the coast of northern Scandinavia and Labrador, noted for halibut, cod, and other species of high commercial value. Whaling has become an industry of world importance in both Arctic and Antarctic waters. It is significant to note that it was this very activity, along with sealing, that led to the discovery and exploration of the Antarctic Continent.

Another animal of limited economic utility is the walrus, valued for its ivory tusks, oil, and skin. On land, we do not have a parallel economic situation. Only the reindeer and the caribou hold some promise of herding beyond subsistence for the native. Herding on a commercial scale is a difficult task. Herds of animals must be moved continuously to supply enough tundra food or forage, especially during the winter season. Large herds also become the prey of the Arctic wolf and fox. Moreover, in practically all the tundra regions there is a lack of transportation facility to market meat products.

To yield an accurate geographical evaluation of a region for any purpose—economic, commercial, military, political—it can be compared with another in the same general category for the criteria which distinguish them. A U.S. Air Force manual lists the criteria shown at the top of the next page.

Contrasted Eurasian and North American subpolar cultures

With the above background, what kind of land–man relationships would you anticipate in polar regions? Since Antarctica is not permanently inhabited by white man, our discussion will be restricted to the North American and Eurasian settlement areas. Unique in such settlement conditions is, first of all, the close adaptation of man to his environment. Although human life patterns vary in tundra lands just as there are varied zones of vegetation, time or space will not permit a detailed discussion of all settlement types. We shall concern ourselves here with the life of the North American Eskimo, the Eurasian Lapp, and the Samoyed. It seems to be a good pedagogical principle at this point to introduce the student to an article by Powers entitled "Polar Eskimos of Greenland and their Environment." Powers' article is particularly instructive in that it reviews an earlier article on the Polar Eskimo by W. Elmer Ekblaw (1927) and tells how in time the settlement conditions changed "as a result of European contacts, introduction of outside goods and a trading economy, and the disturbing impact of military activities." Since both Ekblaw's and Powers' articles are readily available to the reader, we shall abstract only the part concerned with the changes that have taken place.

Arctic	*Antarctic*
Ocean surrounded by continents.	Continent surrounded by oceans.
Winds, currents broken by arrangement of land masses.	Winds, currents circumpolar and unbroken by land masses.
Glacier icebergs.	Tabular and glacier icebergs.
Glaciers in limited area.	Glaciers everywhere, shelf ice.
Beaches, shallow water.	Beaches rare, vertical ice cliffs, deep water offshore.
Much paleocrystic sea ice.	Little paleocrystic sea ice.
Puddled sea ice common, hard.	Puddled sea ice less common and frequently rotten.
Variety of soils.	Mantle rock rare, no soils.
Tundra.	No tundra, some mosses and lichens, grasses and flowers very rare, no sphagnum.
Center: Ice-covered ocean with marine life present.	Center: Ice-covered plateau, no food supply, no life.
Land mammals: Musk ox, reindeer, caribou, fox, hare, etc.	No land mammals.
Amphibious mammals: Seals, walrus, polar bears.	Amphibious mammals: Seals.
Great auk (extinct).	Penguin (extant).
Flying insects, other insects plentiful.	No flying insects, other insects rare.
Primitive man.	No primitive man.
One million population north of 60° N.	No population south of 60° S., except whalers and explorers.[1]

[1] *Military Aspects of World Political Geography,* Air University, Air Force Reserve Officers' Training Corps, Montgomery, Alabama, Vol. III, Book 2, September, 1954, p. 907. Reprinted by permission.

Material possessions of the Eskimo.

¶ Previous to their discovery in 1818, the Polar Eskimos appear to have pursued their primitive mode of life for many centuries. Their only wood was drift wood, mainly fragments. Ivory and bone were used for harpoon shafts, tent poles, knife handles, kayaks, frames and sleds. Sled runners were made of fragments of bone or driftwood carved to fit together and lashed with rawhide thongs. Stone points were used generally for weapons. Snow knives were made of slate. However, small bits of meteoric iron secured from Cape York were hammered into suitable form to tip harpoons or, inserted in narrow grooves, to form the cutting edges of ivory knives. . . .

Heating of the igloo was by an oil lamp of soapstone, carved into a flat shallow dish. Blubber in the dish was melted and fed a wick of peat or moss placed along one side. When properly trimmed this wick gave a clear yellow flame without smoke. The stone and wood igloo used as the permanent winter habitation and the snow iglooyak used on the march, were nearly air-tight above and were entered from the side or below by a tunnel. A single lamp often kept the air temperature near the ceiling at 80° or 90° F., even though the temperature at floor level was zero or below. In summer the stone igloo was thrown open and abandoned in favor of a skin tent or tupic which was airy and clean.

Dress consisted wholly of skin prepared, cut and sewn by the mother. The necessity for securing different types of skins for special purposes—bear skins for pants, caribou skins for winter coats and sleeping bags, bird skins for undershirts, hair seal skins for boot soles, et cetera—was partly responsible for the continual shifting of habitation from place to place, for certain animals frequented certain known localities. Clothing was cut with considerable skill, according to established patterns of long standing, and sewn with sinew from the back muscles of narwhal or caribou. Such seams were watertight and strong.

Impact of civilization on the eskimo's mode of life.

. . . Within the decade following Peary's successful attainment of the Pole in 1909, the Danish government allowed the establishment of a trading post at Thule (formerly Umanak) on North Star Bay. By the second decade after Peary, other trading posts were established at Savigsivik and Siorak-pa-doo. . . .

The availability of trade goods has had considerable effect on the Polar Eskimo's pattern of life. Better weapons have enabled him to slaughter more game than formerly, and some animals—particularly the caribou—have become scarce. Luxuries have taken earnings that could better be spent for food and clothing, and health has probably suffered from this cause as well as the introduction of the white man's diseases. Teeth, in particular, have deteriorated badly. Having discovered the reluctance of the white man to let them starve, the Eskimos have been drawn toward the villages, particularly Thule, and have in considerable part adopted permanent huts in which they reside the year around. It is to the Danes' credit that they have strived to enable the Eskimo to earn his living. . . . The basic changes have been from a pure primitive hunting economy to a semi-commercial economy, and to a more fixed rather than a nomadic mode of life.

The effects of the Second World War.

The establishment of an air base and weather station at Thule during the Second World War, and contacts with occasional naval and military groups, have been unsettling influences. Large amounts of supplies have been given away or wasted by these outsiders, and both the Eskimo's economic pattern and his ideas of economy and frugality have been badly shaken. A readjustment to the former sparing standard of living is going to be very difficult.

The future of these children of the North is difficult to predict. They have increased since Peary's time from 250 to nearly 350. If a closed and stable trading policy, with exclusion of outsiders, can be maintained here by the Danes as in South Greenland since 1780, the present semi-commercial economy will probably allow a considerable increase in numbers. If, however, Polar Greenland is thrown open to outsiders and the Eskimos are placed in competition with newcomers from Europe, they are likely to succumb or to be submerged as a racial group.[1]

1. The Lapp and the Samoyed. The Eurasian tundra forms of occupance are different from those of the Eskimo. Though similar in culture—Mongoloid stock, language, and certain ways of living—the Scandinavian Lapp and the Siberian Samoyed differ considerably from the Eskimo in their economy. Whereas the Eskimo, as we have seen above, subsists largely on water animals, his Eurasian counterparts depend primarily on reindeer for food, clothing, and shelter. Since reindeer have to be moved seasonally for foraging, the native of these parts practices a form of transhumance. He moves southward into the taiga during the long winter months and northward to the coast in the summer, where his diet of reindeer meat and milk is supplemented by fish or other sea foods. While the Eskimo, as we have seen, is nomadic in the sense that he must often extend his travels many miles by dog sledges to pursue game on the ice or fish along the various coastal areas, the Lapp is a seasonal migrant.

As in the case of Powers' article on the Eskimo above, excerpts from the article on the Lapp by Hickman have been selected likewise for their value as "sample study."[2]

1 Powers, William E., "Polar Eskimos of Greenland and their Environment," *The Journal of Geography*, Vol. XLIX, May, 1950, pp. 191-193, *passim*. Reprinted by permission.

2 This article is of particular value to prospective teachers of geography in view of the stress it places on making unfamiliar homelands of other people familiar to the American student. "Our problem," says Hickman, "has not only been the choice of material from an impossibly wide (a world-wide) field, but also to make our teaching of those areas of the 'home-land' that are unknown to our pupils, realistic, interesting and profitable."

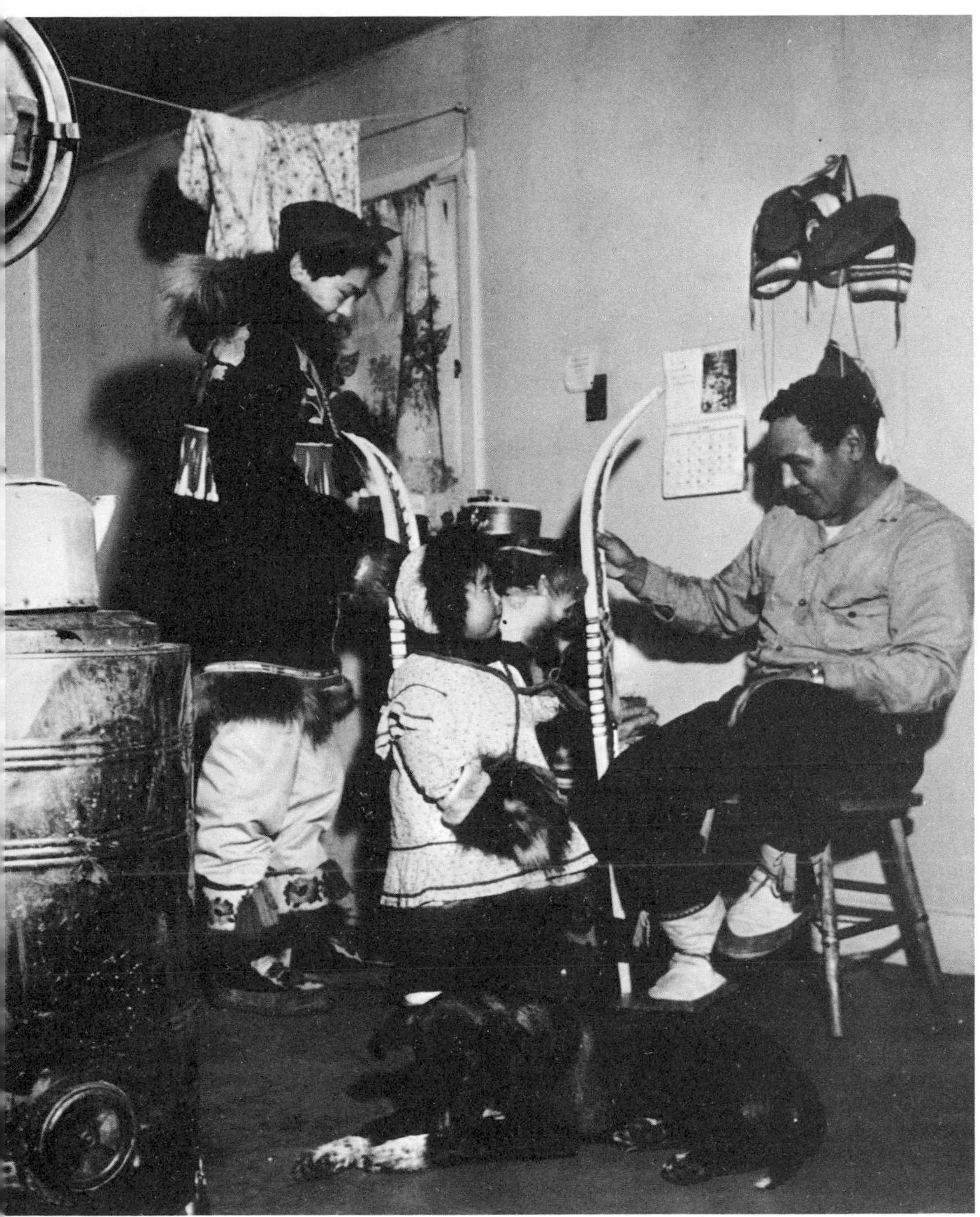

At Inuvik, Northwest Territories, Canada, an Eskimo father presents his daughter with her first pair of handmade snowshoes. What features does the photo suggest as to the type of natural environment of the Eskimo? What elements of the cultural environment are here revealed? (Courtesy National Film Board Photo of Canada)

2. The Lapp communities of the Scandinavian sub-Arctic.

¶ Part of Northern Scandinavia is inhabited by groups of Lapps who formerly gained a living

This herd of reindeer lives in Lapland, northern Scandinavia. Four of the best-acclimatized mammals of *ET* lands are the reindeer, the musk-ox, the lemming, and the hare. Of these the reindeer *(Rangifer tarrandus)* is of pre-eminent economic importance. Readily domesticated and himself a migrant, browsing alternately on the tundra lichens and mosses in summer and foraging in the neighboring forests in winter, the reindeer is excellently adapted to the migratory life of the Lapp, for whom he supplies clothing, meat, and dairy products. Why do we read comparatively little about his North American counterpart, the woodland caribou, or about the smaller tundra reindeer? (Courtesy Swedish Travel Information Bureau)

mainly from herding reindeer and from fishing. The need to provide enough pasture in this area of meagre vegetation has resulted in transhumance, the seasonal movement into the Norwegian mountain pastures in summer as the snow clears, and a return to the lowland settlement as the ground takes on the snow-cover of winter, in rhythm with the seasonal changes throughout the year. Hence the summer tent of poles, formerly covered with skin and now with coarse cloth (like sacking) is easily moved, while the "permanent" or winter home (Katan) is made from turf and stone—a sod hut. This formerly had an earthen floor covered with brushwood, a window, stove and various items of furniture, and the softest reindeer pelts as bedding. Food, clothing, and fuel for most of the year would be produced by the locality, from the reindeer herds themselves, from rivers and lakes, and from the stunted birch vegetation. Problems were the winter dark or twilight period and that of feeding the reindeer unless the snow cover is so thin that they can nose out the moss for themselves.[1]

The author then tells how modern technology has affected these settlements, especially those in the vicinity of Kiruna. Despite the somewhat isolated character of such communities, electricity by wind-driven dynamo, telephone connections to the nearest village, and weekly shopping from the store eight hours away, are some of the modern conveniences introduced. Some settlements even shared a school (elementary) after

[1] Hickman, Gladys M., "A Method and Its Limitations," *The Journal of Geography*, Vol. XLIX, April, 1950, p. 152. Reprinted by permission.

which children might attend the "state boarding school in Kiruna," where the Lapps learn Swedish as well as their own language.

Frigidity imposes severe limitations on land resource developments

Thus far we have been concerned with only the subsistence economy of the polar regions, which may be said to be the most distinguishable feature of human occupance and is more markedly developed here than in any other region in the world. However, after the first explorer appeared, there was a steady influx of opportunists to exploit the fur and fin products. Increasing demands for seal furs and whale oil threaten to exterminate these animals unless stringent conservation methods on an international scale are adopted. Commercial fishing for herring, halibut, cod, and other marine forms have already been described. Such encroachment on extraterritorial waters has often resulted in international incidents calling for treaty negotiations.

Land biological resources for exploitation are not as promising. There has been considerable speculation about the usefulness of developing large reindeer herds on the tundra pastures. This has been tried in Canada and Alaska, but proved to be unsuccessful. On the other hand, it is reported that the Soviet Union has established reindeer ranches from which carcasses are marketed on a limited scale to supplement the Soviet meat supply. Similarly, the southern fringes of the tundra offer some promise in sheep raising. Although it has been reported from the Soviet Union that certain vegetables, root crops, and grain have been produced in favorably exposed areas of the tundra, it is not to be expected, in view of the two-month or less growing season that crops for export will ever prove significant.

In contrast to the biological resources, the mineral wealth of both the Arctic and Antarctic regions may yet prove to be of great importance. Although much of Greenland and Antarctica remain unexplored due to the enormous depth of ice coverage, geologic formations and structures indicate potential resources of many base metals. The student should keep in mind that, unlike plants and animals, mineral emplacements, with few significant exceptions, are genetically unrelated to climate. The genesis of ore concentrations instead has a relationship to rock classifications and structure and ore-forming processes for the most part indifferent to present-day pattern of climates.

Duncan Stewart in his studies on the petrology of Antarctica, as part of the researches of the International Geophysical Year, enumerates 174 minerals. However, they do not at present assure commercial concentrations. In the Northern Hemisphere ores of proven concentration do occur and actual exploitation in Arctic, or fringe Arctic areas, includes cryolite at Ivigtut; uranium near Great Bear Lake; nickel in the Petsamo district of the former northern Finnish coast, now in the hands of the U.S.S.R.; coal at Svalbard and at the mouth of the Lena Delta; and natural gas in northern Alaska, with prospects also for petroleum.

In addition to the inherent difficulties of mining in such regions, accessibility and transportation present almost insurmountable problems. Consequently, minerals either have to be very precious or must occur in high concentrations to make exploitation worthwhile. Uranium minerals presently would indeed attract the attention of every nation. But it is doubtful whether recovery of such a mineral in Antarctica beneath a mile or two of ice would ever be attempted. Uranium is now being mined near Great Bear Lake in Canada on the southern fringe of the Arctic and is the chief outside source of supply for the United States.

The problems of crop production in regions of "perpetual frost," which extend even southward beyond the Tundra line, are cited by Koral:

> ¶ Eternal frost covers up to twenty five per cent of the total surface of the land of our planet. . . . [It] comprises or covers almost half of the entire territory of the U.S.S.R. . . . [and] explains the intensive interest of the Soviet in this zone. . . . [It] is a natural phenomenon that leaves certain layers of the earth's crust in a state of permanent congelation. . . . Experimental stations [are established] throughout the entire European and Asiatic North of the U.S.S.R. with the aim of transforming the zone of perpetual frost into an agricultural area. . . . It would not be a mistake to maintain that agriculture in the zone of per-

petual frost would probably never assume any industrial importance. In some exceptional cases, such as in the southernmost reaches, it may secure for the family grain and vegetables on a small scale, provided that the density of population does not increase very much. . . . With rare exceptions, all reclaimed land for agriculture requires soil amelioration, which consists of draining it. . . . However, in spite of all measures toward improving the water, air, and temperature conditions of the soils, the microbiological activity here remains most suppressed, and the sources of mineral nourishment for the plants are severely limited. . . . Only by application of large amounts of organic, mostly manure, and mineral fertilizer can one maintain the subsequent crops on a more or less medium output level. . . . The peaty and peat gley soils are more difficult to reclaim for agriculture because of the proximity of the ever-frozen layer (30-40 centimeters). . . . Therefore these areas must be dried and the moss and peat must be burned. . . . The best agricultural plants are of the precocious sorts, with the shortest growing period.[1]

Formidable barriers to transpolar travel now being conquered by modern transportation technology

It is obvious that the economic development of any region is dependent upon effective and facile transportation. In view of the climatic and terrain conditions indicated above, the provision of such transporation facilities is difficult. You will recall from your history that it was not until recent times that the Northwest and Northeast Passages were negotiated, finally made possible by the invention of modern icebreakers. Because of its high latitude position and far-flung Arctic coast line, the U.S.S.R. has probably made the furthest advance in this direction. Though carrying only a few vessels each year, the Northern Sea Route has established regular traffic across the Arctic waters. In summer, lumber and grain freighters likewise ply the North American coastal waters into Hudson Bay. During winter, as in other Arctic waters, icebreakers are used on occasion to keep lanes open.

Highways and railways are virtually nonexistent in the Arctic region owing primarily to the difficulty and costliness of construction of such roadbeds and right-of-ways due to the alternate seasonal thawing and freezing and the difficulty of establishing a permanent surface upon the permafrost zone. Such surface zones become saturated with water during the thawing season and account for the characteristically poor drainage in the area. Over glacier ice surfaces, crevasses often create hazardous "roadblocks." Sledges are used, both in winter and in summer, rather than wheeled vehicles, with dogs and reindeer as the chief draft animals in Arctic North America and in Arctic Eurasia, respectively. Experiments are now being carried on with wheeled vehicles and special types of tractors suited to the changing seasonal terrain conditions. Overcoming surface handicaps to land and ice transportation, they have brought universal connection with any part of the Arctic and Antarctic realms.

Such difficulties as the polar environments present to air navigation are not so much of flight as of the take-off and landing. These operations involve difficulties in constructing and maintaining air fields adversely affected by snow and frost-heaving of the terrain. Specially constructed appliances now adapt many of the planes to landing on water, ice, or snow. The invention of new navigation devices, such as the Pfund compass and the loran, as well as radar, helps solve navigation problems due to deflection of the compass needle by the proximity of the magnetic poles.

Polar proprietary patterns differentiate Arctic and Antarctic regions

Interest of the outside world in polar lands seems to have followed four stages—discovery, exploration, exploitation, and national appropriation. The last stage of development is a definite outcome of the Air Age with Great Circle projected flights of commercial and military importance. Instrumental to its development has been the role of the U.S. and U.S.S.R., both occupying a trans-Arctic position.

¶ The peripheral lands of the Arctic are owned and administered by proprietary nations, specifically the six countries whose coasts encircle the polar sea. Of these barren dominions, 37 per cent belongs to Canada, 28 per cent to the Soviet

[1] Koral, Nestor, "Agriculture in the Zone of Perpetual Frost," *Science*, Vol. CXXII, No. 3172, October 14, 1955, pp. 680-682, *passim*. Reprinted from *Science* by permission.

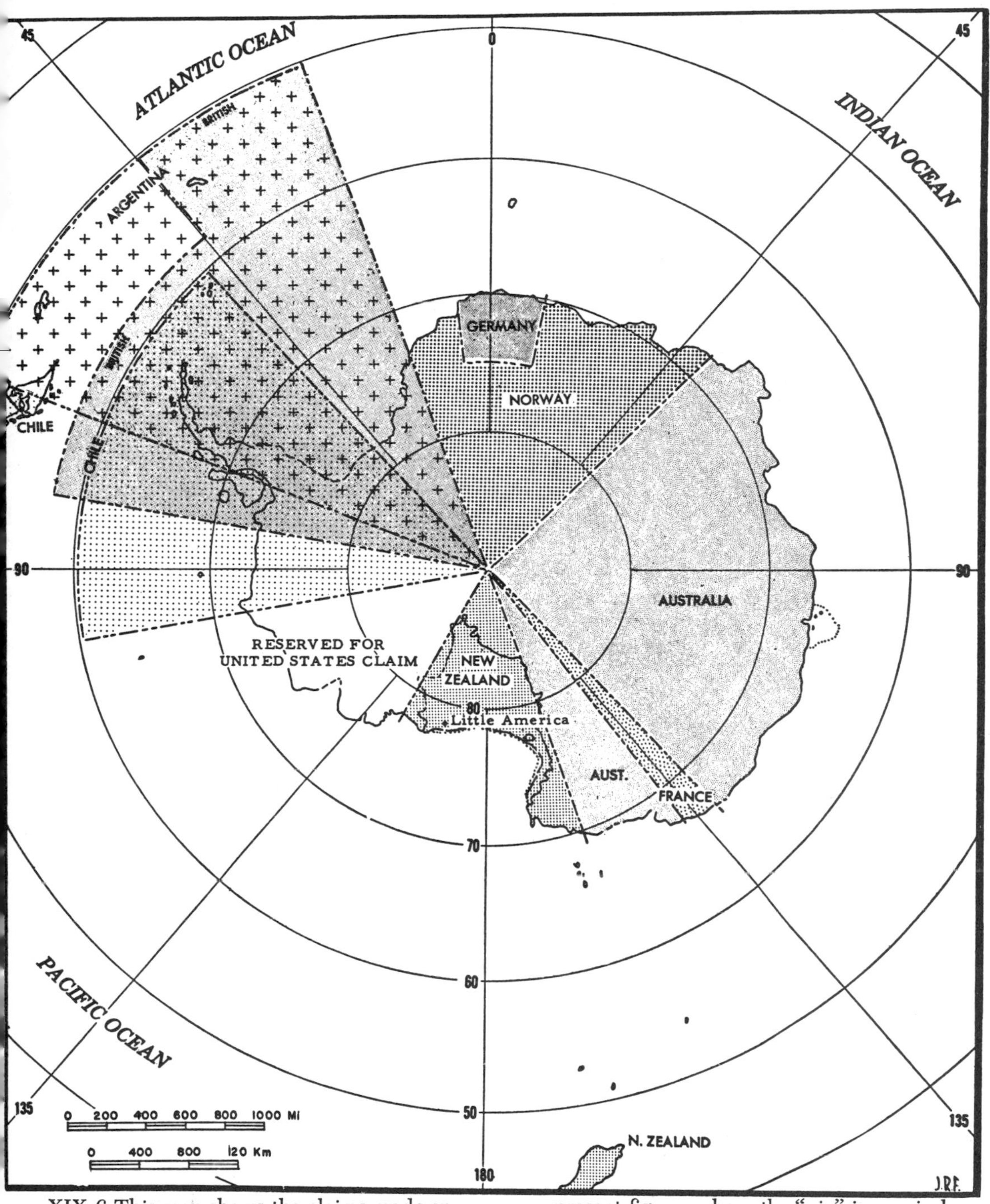

XIX:6 This map shows the claims made on Antarctica. Meridians and longitude (unlike parallels of latitude) normally play an insignificant role in genetic or generic principles of geography. But meridians are sometimes appropriated for convenience in establishing political boundaries, especially in relatively poorly settled and developed regions (e.g., our western frontier and Australia). This is particularly well exemplified, you will note, in the present figure, where the "pie" is precisely, if unequally, sectioned along meridional lines. Even peripheral seas and small islands get into the picture of this artificial survey, in which parallels in part have also played their role. (From "The Nature and Functions of Boundaries," *Principles of Political Geography*, by Hans W. Weigert *et al.*, Appleton-Century-Crofts, Inc., New York, 1957, p. 84, used by permission)

Union, 28 per cent to Denmark, 6 per cent to United States and 1 per cent to Norway and Iceland (8).

Claims to Arctic islands have resulted from exploration, colonization, and bases of proximity, such as Svalbard off the coast of Norway and the near-by islands of Northern Canada. Former President Truman's declaration of 1945, announcing United States claims to continental shelf areas, is a doctrine that the U.S.S.R. might readily support in view of its own claims to continental shelf islands. But the State Department has generally held that any just claims to new territory are based on colonization. Here then we seem to have a definite conflict of geographic perspective which probably can be settled only by the court of the United Nations.

Antarctica presents quite a different prolem, based on claims of ownership to the continent itself. Here for the most part the pie-sector principle of proprietorship, as shown in Figure XIX-6, has been applied. Although the size of claims and the bases for claims vary, boundaries, you will observe, arbitrarily for the most part, follow meridians to the Pole. Several sectors correspond to the meridional position of the Southern Hemisphere countries claiming them, e.g., New Zealand, Australia, Argentina, Chile, Falkland Islands (British). It was a Norwegian who first set foot on the mainland of Antarctica, and also a Norwegian who discovered the South Pole; hence this outside claim by Norway. It is interesting particularly to note in the diagram three overlapping conflicting claims—the British against Argentina and Chile, as well as an overlapping claim between Chile and Argentina. It will also be noted that one sector is unclaimed, done purposely so that the United States might claim it and thus at the same time recognize the ownership of the other sections. The Soviet Union has already indicated its intention to establish a claim to Antarctica on the basis of its own exploration. The new interest in Antarctica in connection with the International Geophysical Year has already been referred to.

APPLICATION OF GEOGRAPHIC UNDERSTANDING

I. Review the list of comparative characteristics given in the USAF article, and evaluate each for their economic, commercial, military and political implications.

II. This list is not intended to be complete. Which other basic data do you believe are significant? Consider environmental factors and geographic forces under the following headings:

A. Continental–Intercontinental space relations.
B. Regional physiographic and resource differences.
C. Effect of present and future potential forms of human occupance on our military strategy program.

III. Why, do you think, has the United States, the most extensive explorer of the Antarctic, failed thus far to claim any of its territory? Or refused to recognize national claims to sections of Antarctica on the basis of discovery and exploration? Do you believe this issue can be most appropriately handled by the United Nations? Do "pie-section" boundaries seem geographically valid?

IV. In which way does the innovation of intercontinental missiles and orbital satellites affect the recognized strategic space values of the Arctic? One way of approaching this question is to reread the opening chorographic remarks on Iceland and Greenland and ask yourself whether these observations are likely to hold in the new "Sputnik Age" into which the world has been catapulted.

V. Many people, not geographically trained, think of geography only as a statistical and static "location" and "production" subject. Show how, in light particularly of this chapter, that geographic discipline is inherently *dynamic* and deals with space in terms of national "survival" as well as native "subsistence."

References

1 "Russians Already Moving in on A U. S. Base," *U. S. News and World Report*, July 6, 1956, p. 28.

2 *Focus*, Vol. VI, No. 5, January, 1956, pp. 2-3.

3 Gould, Lawrence M., "Antarctic Prospect," *The Geographical Review*, Vol. XLVII, No. 1, January, 1957, pp. 23, 24.

4 *Military Aspects of World Political Geography,* Air University, Air Force Reserve Officers' Training Corps, Montgomery, Alabama, Vol. III, Book 2, Part IV, September, 1954, p. 907.

5 Powers, William E., "Polar Eskimos of Greenland and their Environment," *The Journal of Geography,* Vol. XLIX, May, 1950, pp. 191-193, *passim.*

6 Hickman, Gladys M., "A Method and Its Limitation," *The Journal of Geography,* Vol. XLIX, April, 1950, p. 152.

7 Koral, Nestor, "Agriculture in the Zone of Perpetual Frost," *Science,* Vol. CXXII, No. 3172, October 14, 1955, pp. 680-682, *passim.*

8 "Ice-bound Barrens of the Arctic Tundra," by Lincoln Barnett, *Life,* "The World We Live In: Part X," June 7, 1954, p. 111.

Chapter 20

Drylands—the desert xerophytic shrublands (*BW*)—lands of desolation and drama

Nations which get their independence by exercising a boundless nationalism often appear incapable of keeping their nationalism within boundaries. A case in point: the inchoate Republic of Indonesia, which cannot govern itself but claims half of New Guinea. Another: Egypt, which had hardly said goodbye to the British before it was reaching out for the Sudan. But these claims hardly match those of the new Serifian Empire of Morocco, which until a year ago was a part-French, part-Spanish protectorate. Fanatical Moroccan nationalists have staked out a claim to a slice of northwestern Africa roughly equal in area to Western Europe.

"North Africa," *Time*, March 18, 1957, p. 28. Courtesy *Time*. Copyright, Time, Inc., 1957.

Chorogram: "Empire of sand"

Moroccan nationalists, fighting for a slice of the desert, base their claim on the fact that 900 years ago the famed Almoravide Dynasty, from which they are descended, ruled all of Northwest Africa from the Strait of Gibraltar south to about the point of Dakar and as far west as the present western border of Morocco (Figure XX-1).

The new kingdom of Morocco occupies about a fifth of this old Almoravide empire. The remainder of the area is divided between Spain's Rio de Oro, a corner of Algeria, the French West African province of Mauritania, and part of the French Sudan.

Most of the area is a true desert with the classification of *BWh*. The coastal area is only little better off, it being in the steppe lands *(BSh)*. From this one can see there is little land value involved.

Morocco and the province of Mauritania[1] have the richest stores of mineral wealth along the west coast of Africa. Iron ore is the most important mineral, but copper is also found in abundance. In 1934 the French finally subdued the nomadic tribes of the province of Mauritania. Since that time they have done little to develop the mineral resources; in fact, the area is not even adequately mapped (2).

The Moslem religion, a common bond throughout the area, is being used to arouse the Moroccan people to a sense of imperial glory awaiting them at their back door. The leader of this expansive move is Si Allal el Fassi, a leader of the fiercely nationalistic Istiqlal Party. His rallying cry is, "Our culture is the culture of the Sahara. Our religion is the religion of the Sahara. I proclaim that we will be traitors if we lose one single grain of Saraha sand" (1).

Commandos of El Fassi's liberation army no longer need to fight the French in Morocco. Joined by nomadic camel riders who make a living by fighting, they have moved through the Rio de Oro and launched attacks on isolated French outposts in the sparsely settled Mauritania.

According to General Rene Cogny, the French are not worried about military defenses, but it is a serious political problem. In order to get their iron and copper out of Mauritania and western Algeria, the French would like to establish a link through Morocco. To create such a route, they must have good relations with the new kingdom over which they now have no political control. The Moroccan government has officially asked France to negotiate on the future of the Saharan frontier. The outcome remains unsettled.

The above chorogram features geographic principles of not only regional but worldwide importance—social, economic, political, and military. The spirit of anticolonialism and nationalism has emerged in the twentieth century throughout southwestern Asia and northern Africa. Among such dryland peoples who have won their independence in recent years are those of Iran, Iraq, Syria, Jordan, Arabia, Egypt, Libya, Sudan, and Morocco.

The policy of most proprietary nations has been to grant independence to colonies where there is sufficient assurance of their political and economic stability. The re-

[1] Now a republic.

source-minded geographer is therefore particularly interested in determining how far dryland peoples can be self-sustaining. When such countries try to become economically independent on an agricultural basis, large-scale irrigation projects must be established, largely by capital from foreign sources. Consider, for example, the newly created Republic of Sudan which has concentrated much effort on developing the Geriaz area for the production of cotton, including cotton seed, which comprises about 70 per cent of the country's exports. The aim of Sudan is to become economically independent "without strings," that is to say, without any dependence on the outside world.

Drier countries, like Jordan, likewise aspire to complete economic independence, but are as yet unable to support their native population. When such countries have to rely on outside subsidies, as Jordan relies on Great Britain, new political problems arise. Defection from Britain by Jordan came about as a result of the British invasion of Egypt. Following the Suez crisis, Jordan rejected further British subsidies in lieu of financial aid promised by Egypt, Syria, and Saudi-Arabia; but Syria and Arabia subsequently renounced such aid. King Hussein of Jordan applied for aid from the United States, but again without "strings attached."

Some dryland political regimes have become immensely wealthy and powerful in international relations owing to a number of geographic conditions. We refer here to such countries as Iran, Iraq, and Arabia, which, in the Upper Persian Gulf area, share the greatest oil reserves in the world. To these we may add the Bahrein Islands, also in the Persian Gulf. The geographical location of these countries and their petroleum deposits are of strategic concern not only to Western Europe but also to the United States. On the north, Iran borders the U.S.S.R., while the commercial life-line of the Mediterranean–Red Sea–Gulf of Aden waterway, has critical importance not only to Western Europe, but also to the commerce and shipping of all other countries of the world. If we add the Suez Canal to these routes, we can realize how critical a combination of vital resources and strategic commmercial waterways is in the world of affairs, despite desert wastes, migrant nomads, and a few oasis dwellers.

Geographic location alone, irrespective of any economic resources, can make an otherwise poor country significant in world affairs. Libya, 85 per cent of which is true desert, was an Italian colony until the conclusion of the Second World War and has been subsequently administered by the French and British. In 1951 it became an independent constitutional monarchy, and in 1954 a twenty-year treaty was negotiated with the United States providing air bases for the United States in return for an annual stipend to Libya for its economic development. But the Soviet Union has moved to make a competitive offer. Thus a desert area once again is in a position to pit the East against the West for allegiance. The fiasco of the British-French invasion of Egypt, primarily to protect their canal interests, may be said in part to have grown out of an economic situation—construction of dams on the Nile for purposes of both irrigation and hydroelectric power development. Here likewise were competitive East-West interests and promises by both the United States and the Soviet Union to aid in this project.

Irrigation projects dramatize transformation of desert landscapes

Reclamation of desert lands by some kind of irrigation has been carried on since time immemorial in the valley of the Indus, the Tigris-Euphrates, and the Nile—among the most ancient centers of civilization. Added emphasis on the creation of new, or extension of old, irrigation systems results from increasing population, technological advances in dam construction and deep well drilling, and the increasing capital available under circumstances indicated above. Not only is this true for the desert areas mentioned above but also for almost all other dry regions of the earth including the Kalahari Desert of Southwest Africa where it has been proposed to dam the Kunene and Linyanti rivers. In recent years similar large-scale irrigation developments have taken place in Russian Turkestan and in the interior heart of the Australian desert. In the case of our own country, one of the most ambitious programs contemplates the construction of three new dams and eleven new irrigation projects in the upper Colorado River Basin;

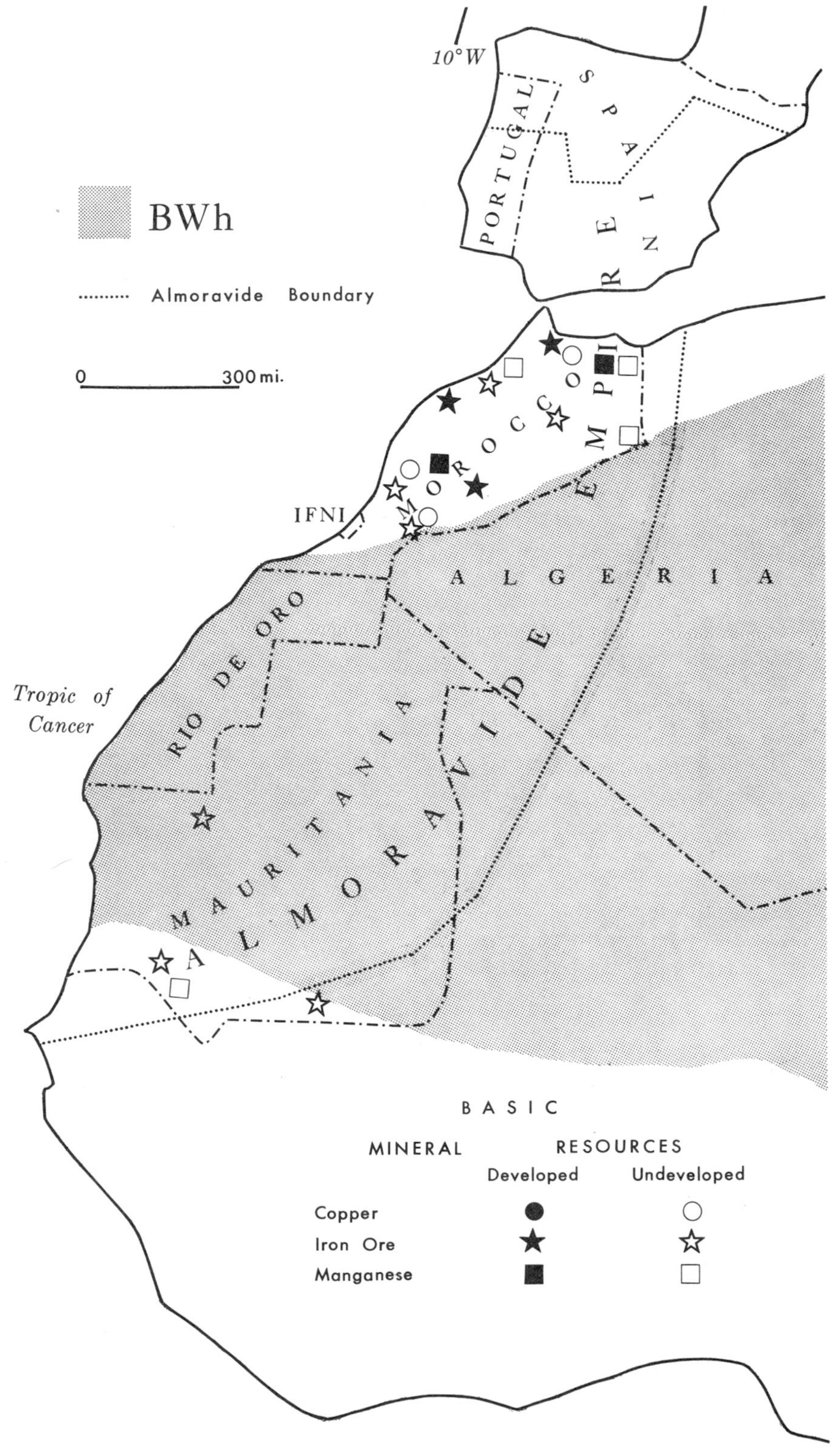
10° W
PORTUGAL
SPAIN
EMPIRE
BWh
Almoravide Boundary
0
300 mi.
MOROCCO
IFNI
ALGERIA
RIO DE ORO
MAURITANIA
ALMORAVIDE
Tropic of Cancer
BASIC
MINERAL RESOURCES
Developed
Undeveloped
Copper
Iron Ore
Manganese

Oil is where you find it, that is, in "rock traps," quite irrespective of climate, here concealed by desert dunes. Winding its way through the Rub' al-Khali, the "Empty Quarter" in southern Arabia, this seismograph party of the Arabian Oil Company is headed for its next exploratory site. (Courtesy Arabian American Oil Company)

already four dams, including the famous Hoover Dam, involve some of the world's largest hydroelectric projects (Figure XX-2). Some observers look upon these reclamation programs as America's last frontier of agricultural settlement. Proponents of this major regional project point out that the additional water supply impounded by the dams will be sufficient to add a half million acres of agricultural production in northeastern Colorado alone. It has been estimated that almost a million additional kilowatts of power will be available upon its completion. This should in turn attract major industries, particularly those developing local resources of the region centered upon the primary mineral deposits of the area, such as uranium, oil, coal, and other militarily and economically important minerals, and perhaps some food-processing establishments.

XX:1 (Left) In the desert empire of northwest Africa, desolate wastes are conventionally considered of little historic and geographic moment. Yet, deserts seem to have their own way of commanding a share of historic research and publicity in today's press. Once it was Genghis Khan's far-flung empire of the dry heart of inner Asia; in the middle of the twentieth century, Sahara and Arabia hold the desert spotlight.

While the natural desert may be transformed by man "to blossom as the rose," the

Located at Ras Tanura on the Persian Gulf Coast of Saudi Arabia is one of the richest oil areas of the world, here marked by the refinery and tank farm of the Arabian American Oil Company. Examining jointly the landscape scenes of the seismograph party of the companion photo and of this refinery, compare the relative advantages and disadvantages of exploring and exploiting petroleum products in the desert world with those of the humid lands. (Courtesy Arabian American Oil Company)

geography student should consider both sides of the question. He will raise questions, perhaps, such as these: How many people live in the area who can benefit from such irrigation and hydroelectric power development? Are transportation facilities available to export the perishable products which may be raised through irrigation? Does the United States need the extra grain and crops which may be grown in this region, since we already have large surpluses now in storage? Incidentally, is the high altitude of this particular plateau area conducive to grain crops? What will happen to certain features of this river basin that are of special scientific or scenic interest? For example, the Dinosaur National Monument? As has been pointed out by opponents of these projects, this monument is being destroyed by the damming of tributaries of the upper Colorado. Western legislators have pointed out that a major benefit of such development will be in national defense. It is admitted that dispersion of defense industries into the open spaces of the Midwest is an added national feature of security. Whatever the merits of the development of such a region may be, it is recognized as a very expensive project, not only regional but also national in scope. It illustrates once more the geographic principle that a country as large as the United States is interregionally

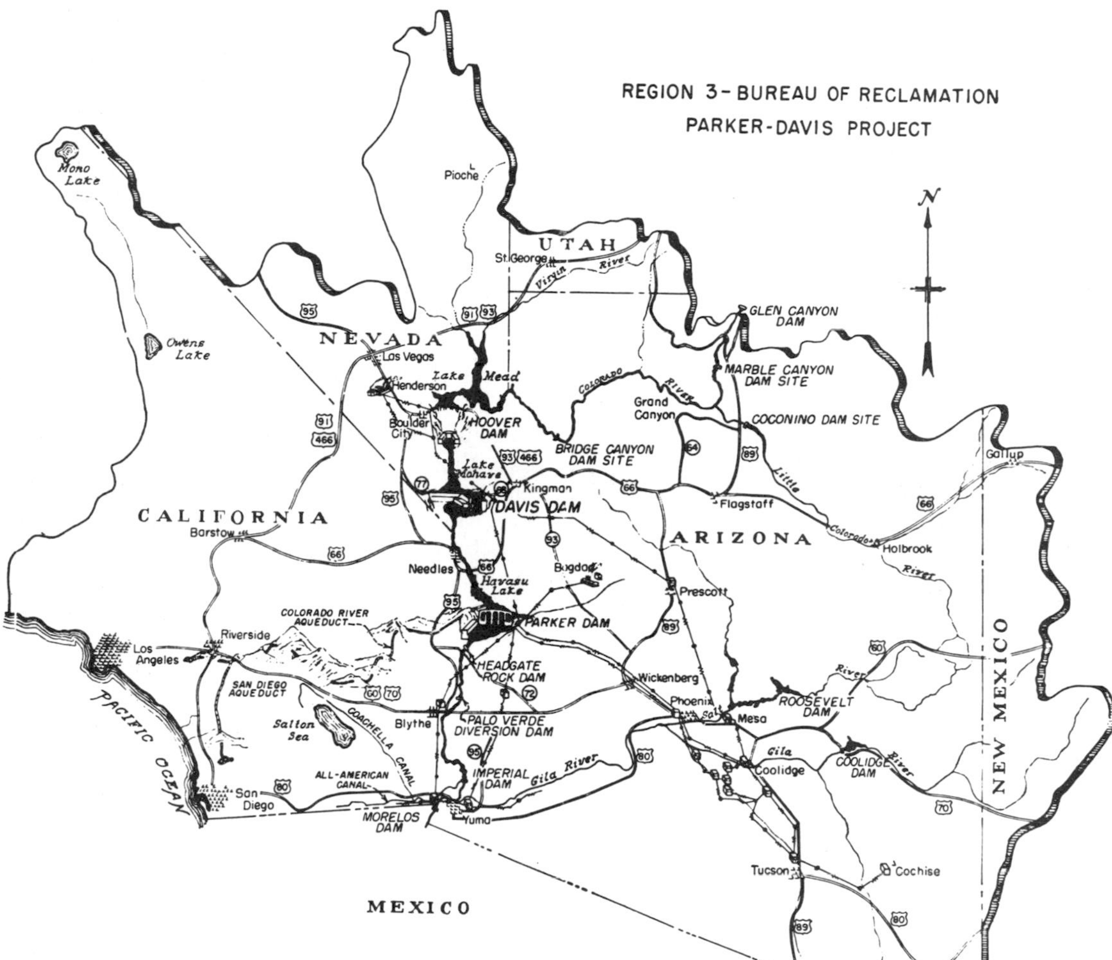

XX:2 This shows the reclamation on the lower Colorado River. One way by which certain desert regions might be radically transformed is through hydroelectric power developments. Note the lines of power from various dam sites and the numerous communities served thereby. Along with the transformation of the industrial landscape go the agricultural innovations incident to irrigation. The many competitive demands of the impounded waters have created new problems and controversies—and litigations. Examine the growing needs of water supply for Los Angeles and the court suits and decisions relating to the city's effort to tap onto the Colorado River. (Bureau of Reclamation, U. S. Department of Interior.)

dependent, one area upon the other. Incidentally, another activity, the tourist industry, would be greatly benefited by such development. Population increase would follow. Already, as for example in Arizona and New Mexico, desert areas share in the largest percentages of increasing population of any area in the union. This is partly the result of the establishment of large atomic plants and air bases in areas where once only cactuses and jackrabbits flourished. The other major attraction is the sunny weather. Though temperatures are high in summer, humidity is low, and thus high temperatures are not unbearable. On the other hand, winters are very mild, and outdoor conditions most favorable. The area has thus become an attractive region for both tourists and permanent residents. The key to the ultimate development of the region lies in the amount of water available to supply not only the needs for the large tracts of land under irrigation, but also for the increasing number of industrial concerns which will draw heavily on the water supply.

The above human affairs touch upon almost every aspect of geography—social, economic, political, and military. They also point out many geographic principles. No longer do the major deserts of the world suggest only a wasteland area occupied by a few roaming nomads or dwellers of isolated oases. Some of them become strategic areas for defense; they contain the world's largest petroleum reserves, and they include leading areas of critical mineral production, as of uranium in the Utah-Wyoming-Colorado fields in western United States. No longer do desert areas present road blocks to transportation, since the building of modern highways, railways, and airfields has altered the former isolated pattern of deserts. The increasing importance of such areas challenges us to know more about the Dry World: in what respect the major deserts are similar; in which ways they differ; and how each is to be evaluated in terms of its own regional, national, as well as international, significance.

On the quantitative side, Dickson has made a strong case in showing the areal importance of arid lands, where rainfall averages less than ten inches.

¶ It is difficult to get precise figures. But it is generally believed that the total land surface of the earth is of the order of 25,000 million acres; of this at present, about 2,500 million, or 10 per cent, are under some form of cultivation. But it is also estimated that about 6,400 million acres are arid—in other words, about ¼ of the total land surface of the earth. That is, the arid area is just over 2.5 times as large as the presently cultivated area.[1]

Subregional differentiation of deserts needed for proper resource appraisal and appropriation

Thus we see in both the qualitative and quantitative areal measurements that drylands seemingly are much more significant in the world than most people think, and if we are to appraise such land properly we must dispel, as in the case of the Arctic regions, some illusions which are popularly held concerning such lands. Such impressions or misconceptions rather commonly originate from motion pictures which have a tendency to stress the "exotic" elements of landscape rather than the typifying pattern characteristics. Thus, the familiar picture is of the camel caravan moving in a limitless sand dune region without any vegetative cover, and devoid of any animal life other than is indicated in the conventional picture of the camel and the Bedouin, implying a region where no rain ever falls and temperatures at all times and in all places are unbearably hot. At any one time or place such conditions as pictured above actually do obtain, but desert lands vary notably from place to place. Deserts are generally distinguished by low and erratic rainfall, scanty vegetation, animal life highly specialized to adapt itself to the moisture available, and such forms of human occupance as the oasis dweller and the nomadic herdsman. But varied regional conditions of rainfall, *(s, w)*, and temperature, *(h, k, k')*, do exist; these with varied topography, and other conditions, result in regionally diverse patterns of ecological adjustments by plants, animals, and man.

It becomes necessary to determine the climatological criteria which, in the first place, differentiate the dry regions from the humid; and secondly, the arid from the subarid and then the various subtypes. Originally the twenty-inch and the ten-inch rainfall lines were used to demarcate the boundaries between the humid and semiarid and between the semiarid and arid lands, respectively, since in many parts of the world it was observed that at least twenty inches of rainfall were required for most forest cover, and from ten to twenty inches to produce a continuous sod of the steppe type. Such criteria may still be found in elementary textbooks of geography, and, while they conveniently provide for ready differentiation of dry, semiarid, and humid lands, they do not reflect a true relationship between climatic types and the kind of vegetable cover supposed to correlate with them. Moisture availability to the plant, rather than the amount of precipitation, is the correlative factor. Much of the rain that falls in a given

---

[1] Dickson, B. T., "Challenge of Arid Lands," *Scientific Monthly*, Vol. LXXPII, No. 2, February, 1956, p. 67. Reprinted from *The Scientific Monthly* by permission.

area may be lost to the plant in the form of runoff as on a steep slope; a large percentage likewise may flyoff (evaporate); only the cutoff, or groundwater, becomes available to the plant. This is the rainfall effectivity. Another factor, which introduces even more complication in determining ecological relationships, is the amount of moisture that the plant transpires. These varied moisture losses, as related to moisture deficiency or effectivity when classifying drylands, have been studied in extensive researches by Thornthwaite and other geographers. A classification of subtypes of climate on the basis of transvaporization formulae is too involved to be used here for purposes of merely gaining a general concept of world climates and their relation to nature and man. Despite some recognized shortcomings of the Köppen system of climates in providing a precise base for climate and vegetation, the Köppen dryland formulae serve our elemental purpose. The original metric formulae have been transposed to the American system of notation (inches of rainfall and Fahrenheit degrees), so as to facilitate ready understanding of climatic evaluation and differentiation by the student. The classification and identification of stations under this system are simple enough, once the student recognizes the bases on which such formulae were evolved. These principles are: (1) rainfall effectivity is a function of temperature as well as rainfall, and (2) rainfall effectivity is also a function of seasonal precipitation. If temperatures are high, evaporation will be great and correspondingly reduce rainfall effectivity. Likewise, as a corollary, if most of the rains come in summer when temperatures are high, there will be greater loss of moisture by evaporation than when most of the rains come in winter, or are more or less evenly spread throughout the year. Consequently, a different temperature–precipitation relationship formula has to be used for each type of rainfall–temperature situation. Thus, if the rainfall of a given station is less than the formula value, it is classified as a dry *(B)* station. If it is less than half of such formula value, it is classed as a desert *(BW)* station; if more than half, a steppe *(BS)* station. Since we would expect both the natural environment and human adjustment forms to vary in part as a result of differences in seasonal rainfall, we should, therefore, recognize three subtypes: *BWs,* indicative of summer dryness; *BWw,* to indicate winter dryness, or simply a *BW* to indicate an approximate even distribution of rainfall throughout the year.

Not all deserts have a hot climate. Since deserts may occur from the Equator to 50 degree latitude, we may expect, on the basis of latitudinal differences alone, a great range of temperature differences. Thus the Köppen system recognizes three temperature dryland types—the hot desert *(BWh)* (Figures XX-3 and XX-4) with an average annual temperature above 64.4°F.; the cool desert (*BWk*) (Figure XX-5) which averages below this figure; the cold desert *(BWk′)* (Figure XX-6), whose warmest month average is below this figure. (As indicated, these temperature subtypes are denoted by adding the small letter *h, k, k′*, respectively.)

As a result of the variable factors of temperature and seasonal rainfall, nine types of deserts may be recognized in this system: *BWh, BWhs, BWhw, BWk, BWks, BWkw; BWk′, BWk′s, BWk′w.* Though space limitations will not permit analytical description of all these types, or the discussion of man–land relationships to them, the geography student should keep these differentiations in mind when reading about the various deserts of the world.

Global and regional determinants of dryland design

At this point, the student will want to know, in a general way at least, the climatological basis for the different types of world deserts. An approach to this may be made by the student himself, by noting recurring space relationships of the desert and other major earth phenomena represented by planetary patterns, such as the wind belt system, the oceanic currents, the trends of mountain ranges, and the like.

Probably the most conspicuous factor is that several deserts occur in the latitudes of approximately 18-30 degrees (Figure XX-7). The Thar, Arabian, Sahara, and Colorado-Sonora deserts are crossed by the Tropic of Cancer; while the Kalahari of South Africa, the Atacama of South America, and the Victoria Desert in Australia, are crossed by

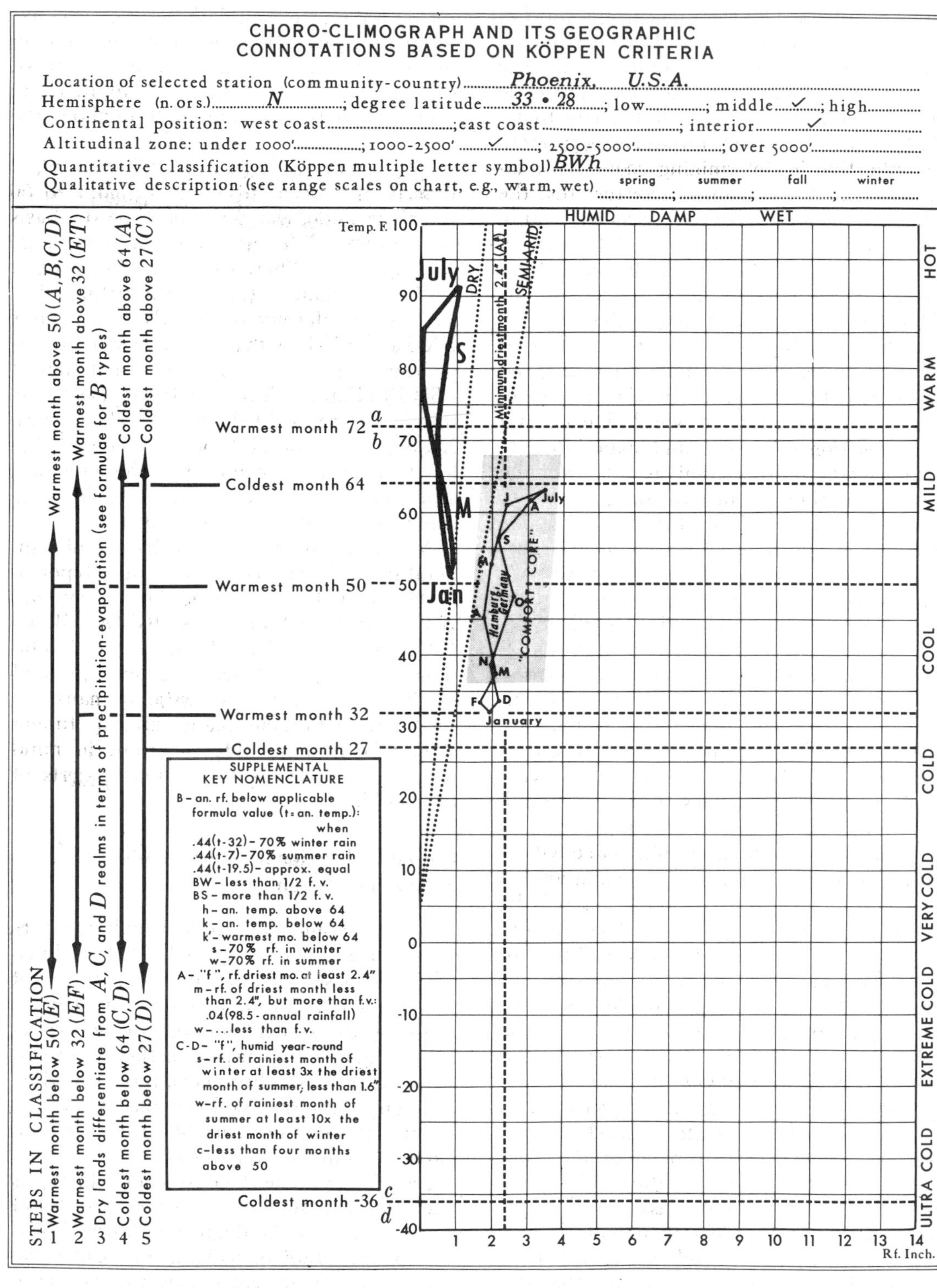

CHORO-CLIMOGRAPH AND ITS GEOGRAPHIC CONNOTATIONS BASED ON KÖPPEN CRITERIA
Location of selected station (community-country) Phoenix, U.S.A.
Hemisphere (n. or s.) N; degree latitude 33 • 28; low; middle ✓; high
Continental position: west coast; east coast; interior ✓
Altitudinal zone: under 1000'; 1000-2500' ✓; 2500-5000'; over 5000'
Quantitative classification (Köppen multiple letter symbol) BWh
Qualitative description (see range scales on chart, e.g., warm, wet) spring; summer; fall; winter
STEPS IN CLASSIFICATION
1 Warmest month above 50 (A, B, C, D) / Warmest month below 50 (E)
2 Warmest month above 32 (ET) / Warmest month below 32 (EF)
3 Dry lands differentiate from A, C, and D realms in terms of precipitation-evaporation (see formulae for B types)
4 Coldest month above 64 (A) / Coldest month below 64 (C, D)
5 Coldest month above 27 (C) / Coldest month below 27 (D)
Temp. F.
Warmest month 72 a b
Coldest month 64
Warmest month 50
Warmest month 32
Coldest month 27
Coldest month -36 c d
HUMID
DAMP
WET
DRY
SEMIARID
Minimum driest month 2.4" (Af)
"COMFORT CORE"
Hamburg, Germany
July
S
M
Jan
J
A
O
N
D
F
January
HOT
WARM
MILD
COOL
COLD
VERY COLD
EXTREME COLD
ULTRA COLD
Rf. Inch.
SUPPLEMENTAL KEY NOMENCLATURE
B - an. rf. below applicable formula value (t = an. temp.): when
.44(t-32) - 70% winter rain
.44(t-7) - 70% summer rain
.44(t-19.5) - approx. equal
BW - less than 1/2 f. v.
BS - more than 1/2 f. v.
h - an. temp. above 64
k - an. temp. below 64
k' - warmest mo. below 64
s - 70% rf. in winter
w - 70% rf. in summer
A - "f", rf. driest mo. at least 2.4"
m - rf. of driest month less than 2.4", but more than f.v.: .04(98.5 - annual rainfall)
w - ...less than f.v.
C-D - "f", humid year-round
s - rf. of rainiest month of winter at least 3x the driest month of summer; less than 1.6"
w - rf. of rainiest month of summer at least 10x the driest month of winter
c - less than four months above 50

the Tropic of Capricorn. These latitudes have a high pressure belt with a descending airmass which becomes warmer as it approaches the earth's surface and evaporates rather than precipitates moisture. But we must always be careful in circumstances of this type not to oversimplify explanations. Other causes may be involved.

In these instances, all the deserts have a west-coast position (consider in this connection the Thar, Arabian, and Sahara deserts as a unit). In each of the five west-coast positions (two in the Northern Hemisphere; three in the Southern Hemisphere), the atmosphere is affected by a cold ocean current moving out of the westerlies at about the 40-50 degree latitude toward the Equator. Such movement of cold currents to warm latitudes increases the capacity of the air to hold moisture, and thus reduces the percentage of relative humidity; the cold ocean waters and currents also frequently produce excessive fogs.

Other deserts such as the interior dry heart of Asia, including the desert of Gobi and other deserts as well, like the Great American Desert extending northward into Utah and Oregon, lie largely outside the high pressure belt. These deserts suggest other causal relationships. The Great American Desert lies to the east, or the lee side, of our coastal and near-coastal mountain ranges. Winds upon rising on the windward side become adiabatically cooled, possibly precipitating moisture, and then proceed as descending warm air currents down the east (leeward) slope of the mountains with an increasing capacity to take on more moisture, and hence evaporate moisture instead of precipitating it. A similar situation obtains in interior Asia when the monsoons, bringing in their moisture from the Indian and Pacific Oceans during the high sun season, shed their moisture on the south side of the Himalaya Mountains, thus producing rainshadow conditions to the north. Another major contributing factor is, of course, the distance from the source of moisture. The farther winds have to carry moisture vapor, the less will be the chances for precipitation, in view of mountains or other intercepting phenomena.

It should be obvious to the student by this time that usually not one but several climatic controls operate in conjunction with one another. In fact, all three forces combine in one way or another to produce the Sonoran-American desert—the descending dry heavy air of the high pressure belt, the cold California Current moving down on the west coast, and the rainshadow produced by the Sierra Nevadas. Also, it should be noted that high pressure influence alone may not produce a desert or even semiarid conditions; for example on the east coast of the several continents, where warm coast-wise currents, with their water vapors move to higher latitudes and hence become cooled, precipitation is promoted. Strongly developed horizontal air movements, such as the summer monsoons of southeast Asia, likewise counteract the descending high pressure air currents. Similarly, in the cyclonic belt of North America, air moving in from the south over the Gulf of Mexico brings in water vapor which becomes chilled in the course of rising toward the center of low pressure airmasses moving eastward across the country.

Weather, like climate, distinguishes the desert world in a number of ways. For the latitude in which it occurs, a desert is likely to have extremes of temperature, both diurnally and seasonally. A temperature change of as much as 100 degrees has been noted within the same 24-hour period (126° in a late afternoon hour; down to 26° in early morning). While *BWh* deserts represent the high temperature areas of the world (136°F. at Azizia; 134°F. Death Valley), the humidity is rarely over 40 per cent. Often it is very much lower, and therefore, the moderate temperature affects man less adversely than the combined high temperature and high humidity found in the rainforest climate.

XX:3 (Left) Supply seasonal entries, as per previous instructions. Many people are "crazy" about a climate such as that of Phoenix. Test your graph-reading ability in terms not only of what the climate seasonally is like, but also your interpretations of life's potentials in such environs, as far as climate itself is concerned. How would you explain the fact that despite being classified a desert area Phoenix has become one of the fastest growing and most enterprising communities in the "Great American Desert"?

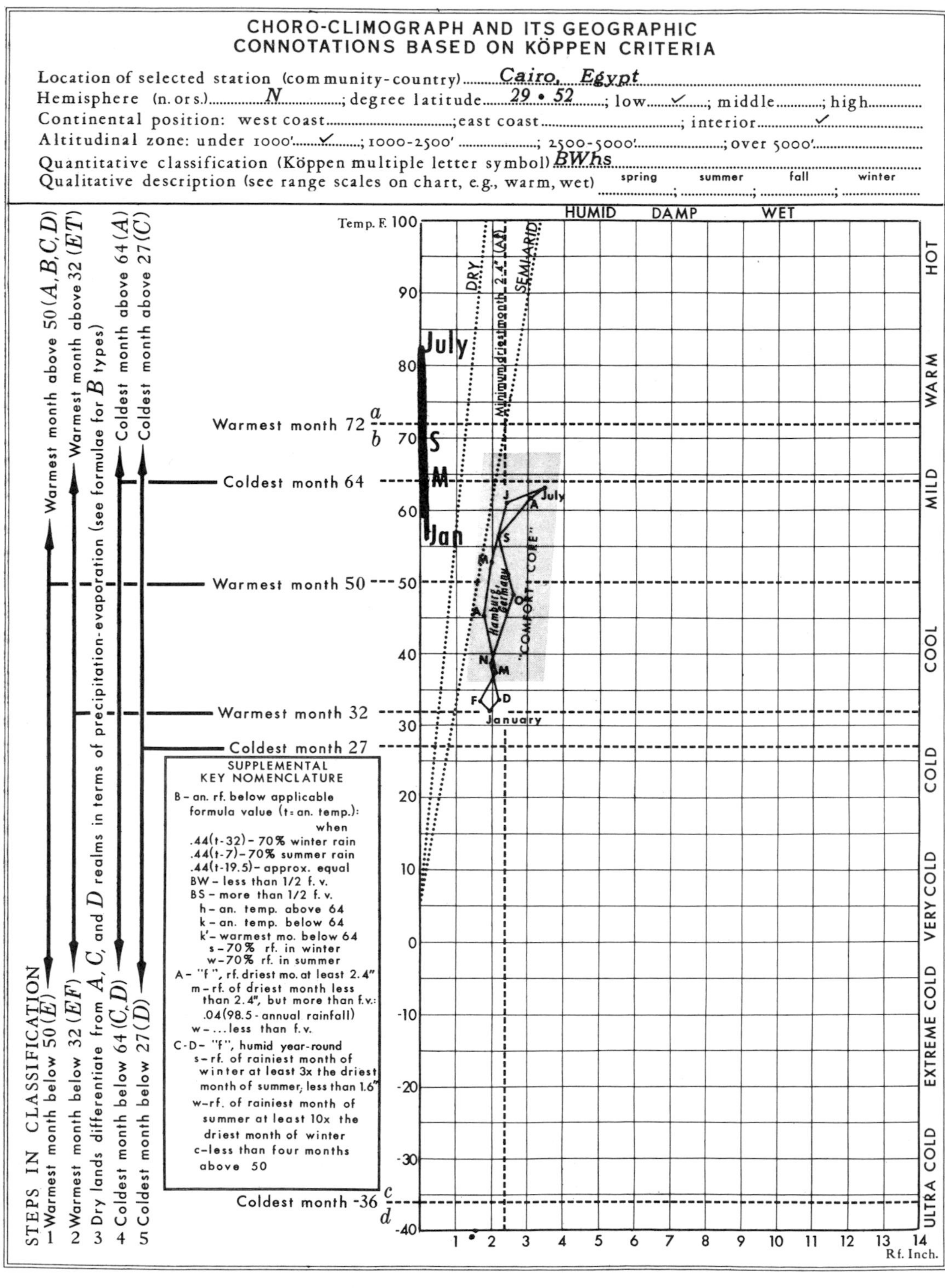

CHORO-CLIMOGRAPH AND ITS GEOGRAPHIC
CONNOTATIONS BASED ON KÖPPEN CRITERIA
Location of selected station (community-country) Cairo, Egypt
Hemisphere (n. or s.) N ; degree latitude 29 • 52 ; low ✓ ; middle ; high
Continental position: west coast ; east coast ; interior ✓
Altitudinal zone: under 1000' ✓ ; 1000-2500' ; 2500-5000' ; over 5000'
Quantitative classification (Köppen multiple letter symbol) BWhs
Qualitative description (see range scales on chart, e.g., warm, wet) spring ; summer ; fall ; winter
HUMID
DAMP
WET
Temp. F.
DRY
Minimum driest month 2.4" (A,f)
SEMIARID
HOT
WARM
MILD
COOL
COLD
VERY COLD
EXTREME COLD
ULTRA COLD
July
S
M
Jan
Warmest month 72 a b
Coldest month 64
Warmest month 50
Warmest month 32
Coldest month 27
Coldest month -36 c d
"COMFORT" CORE
Hamburg, Germany
January
July
Rf. Inch.
SUPPLEMENTAL
KEY NOMENCLATURE
B - an. rf. below applicable formula value (t = an. temp.): when
.44(t-32) - 70% winter rain
.44(t-7) - 70% summer rain
.44(t-19.5) - approx. equal
BW - less than 1/2 f. v.
BS - more than 1/2 f. v.
h - an. temp. above 64
k - an. temp. below 64
k' - warmest mo. below 64
s - 70% rf. in winter
w - 70% rf. in summer
A - "f", rf. driest mo. at least 2.4"
m - rf. of driest month less than 2.4", but more than f.v.: .04(98.5 - annual rainfall)
w - ... less than f.v.
C-D - "f", humid year-round
s - rf. of rainiest month of winter at least 3x the driest month of summer; less than 1.6"
w - rf. of rainiest month of summer at least 10x the driest month of winter
c - less than four months above 50
STEPS IN CLASSIFICATION
1 Warmest month below 50 (E) — Warmest month above 50 (A, B, C, D)
2 Warmest month below 32 (EF) — Warmest month above 32 (ET)
3 Dry lands differentiate from A, C, and D realms in terms of precipitation-evaporation (see formulae for B types)
4 Coldest month below 64 (C, D) — Coldest month above 64 (A)
5 Coldest month below 27 (D) — Coldest month above 27 (C)

Erratic and undependable to the extreme, rains do occur sometime in all deserts. They often come in the form of cloudbursts ("when it rains, it pours"). Thus paradoxically enough, washout of highways is quite common as well as the complete demolition of bridges and trestle work of railways built over "arroyo" river channels. Rains are mostly of the local convection type which result in such spotty distribution of moisture that average annual rainfall figures of dryland stations may be very deceptive in their regional application. Thus while many stations in the Sahara Desert may record rainfall of as much as five inches or more, many areas may receive no rain at all for an entire decade. Even if raindrops do form in the clouds, they may evaporate before reaching the ground. On the other hand, a convection may develop into a downpour and cause a washout.

Desolate landscapes accentuate skyline profiles

Among the first impressions of the view of a desert are its natural emptiness and desolation, with its human concomitants of isolation, loneliness, and austerity. The characterization is probably best summed-up in the German word for wilderness, *Wueste*; hence its designation in the Köppen system as the *BW* type. Land surface configuration, both major and minor, near and far, stand out in revealing profiles. Sharp angular contours mark the more elevated structures whose bedrock has resisted in part the elements of erosion by water and wind. Billowy configuration of sand dunes, or otherwise featureless flats, characterizes the basin or intermontane valley areas.

The boldness of the horizon profile, of course, results from the general bleakness as contrasted to the usual vegetative cover of humid lands. Since the process of weathering is one of physical disintegration rather than chemical decomposition, the resultant regolith is characterized by coarse, rather than fine, rock materials; thus, the heavy *talus* at the foot of rocky elevations as well as the rock-covered plains (*reg*). Erosion by rushing torrents and sand blasting by winds result in finer rock particles, known progressively as sand, silt, and clay. Such are generally found farther out from the rocky highland areas.

XX:4 (Left) Compare this graph with the preceding one. Both are desert, but note that Phoenix is humid, compared with Cairo; and Cairo is cool in July, compared with Phoenix.

The desert world includes plains, plateaus, and mountains, as do the humid lands. Likewise, practically every class of rock, constituting the structure of these major land forms, may be found in the dry world, as are found in the humid. The distinction between the forms in the two cases is one, then, primarily of the accentuated configuration in the former, whereas in the latter the profiles are much subdued by chemical as well as physical weathering and the protective vegetative cover. Several major landscape types have been recognized. One of them, the so-called *mountain and bolson* type of topography, typifies a large section of the Basin and Range Province of Western United States. "Bolson" (Spanish for "pocket") denotes a depressed basin terminating or separating linear sections of mountain ranges. Air currents rising against mountains may become adiabatically cooled to the saturation point and thus produce rain, often in the form of cloudbursts. Such torrential rains flush the *arroyos*, which transport gravel, sand, and silt to the foot of the mountains, forming individual *fans*, or *piedmont alluvial plains*. The silt, carried farthest out by the distributaries, often forms extensive sites occupied by settlements and field culture. Such gently sloping fans are among the most coveted spots for natural irrigation. Drainage may extend at times even beyond alluvial fans into low shallow spots, forming temporary lakes known as *playas*—or *salars*, when flats become encrusted with salts, resulting from evaporation of the standing water. An example of such a phenomenon on a large scale is Great Salt Lake, bordered as it is by broad alkali flats.

The American Desert continues southeastward onto the Colorado Plateau, which typifies another kind of terrain, distinguished by *mesa* (table) and *canyon* (deeply cut stream) topography. (See Grand Canyon

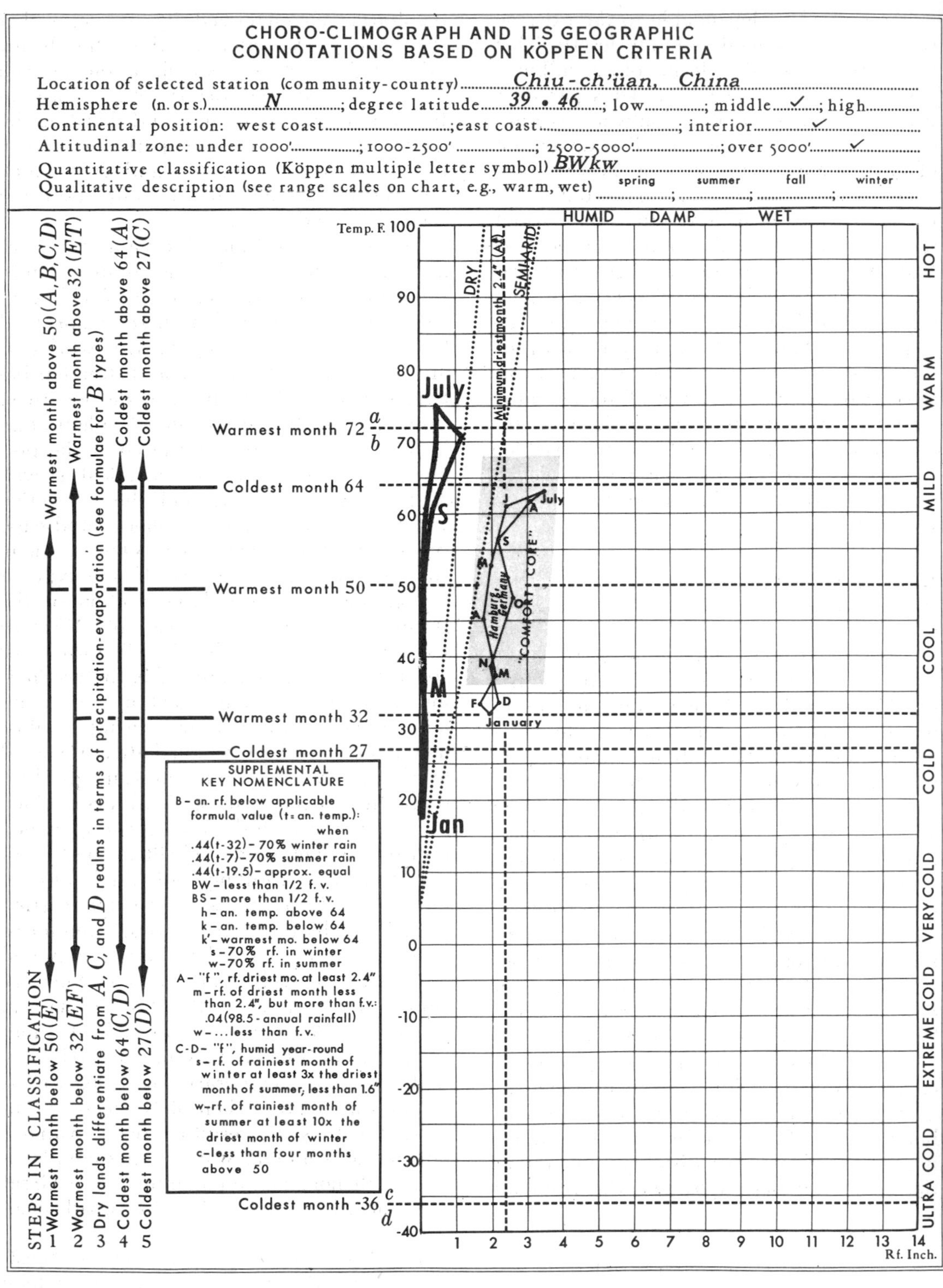
CHORO-CLIMOGRAPH AND ITS GEOGRAPHIC CONNOTATIONS BASED ON KÖPPEN CRITERIA
Location of selected station (community-country) Chiu-ch'üan, China
Hemisphere (n. or s.) N; degree latitude 39 • 46; low; middle ✓; high
Continental position: west coast; east coast; interior ✓
Altitudinal zone: under 1000'; 1000-2500'; 2500-5000'; over 5000' ✓
Quantitative classification (Köppen multiple letter symbol) BWkw
Qualitative description (see range scales on chart, e.g., warm, wet) spring; summer; fall; winter
STEPS IN CLASSIFICATION
1 Warmest month below 50 (E) Warmest month above 50 (A, B, C, D)
2 Warmest month below 32 (EF) Warmest month above 32 (ET)
3 Dry lands differentiate from A, C, and D realms in terms of precipitation-evaporation (see formulae for B types)
4 Coldest month below 64 (C, D) Coldest month above 64 (A)
5 Coldest month below 27 (D) Coldest month above 27 (C)
Warmest month 72 a b
Coldest month 64
Warmest month 50
Warmest month 32
Coldest month 27
Coldest month -36 c d
Temp. F.
HUMID DAMP WET
DRY
Minimum driest month 2.4" (Af)
SEMIARID
July
S
M
Jan
"COMFORT CORE"
Hamburg, Germany
January
HOT WARM MILD COOL COLD VERY COLD EXTREME COLD ULTRA COLD
Rf. Inch.
SUPPLEMENTAL KEY NOMENCLATURE
B - an. rf. below applicable formula value (t = an. temp.): when
.44(t-32) - 70% winter rain
.44(t-7) - 70% summer rain
.44(t-19.5) - approx. equal
BW - less than 1/2 f. v.
BS - more than 1/2 f. v.
h - an. temp. above 64
k - an. temp. below 64
k' - warmest mo. below 64
s - 70% rf. in winter
w - 70% rf. in summer
A - "f", rf. driest mo. at least 2.4"
m - rf. of driest month less than 2.4", but more than f.v.: .04(98.5 - annual rainfall)
w - ...less than f.v.
C-D - "f", humid year-round
s - rf. of rainiest month of winter at least 3x the driest month of summer; less than 1.6"
w - rf. of rainiest month of summer at least 10x the driest month of winter
c - less than four months above 50

photo.) Here the jagged crags of the canyon reveal nature's classic "cliff and platform" profile, resulting from the differential weathering and erosion of alternating hard and soft horizontal beds of sedimentary rock, producing one of the world's wonders in landscape sculpture of unmatched scenic and scientific attraction. The variegated colors of the sedimentaries of the upper and outer gorge and of the igneous and metamorphics of the inner gorge, produced largely by oxidation and hydration of iron and other minerals, here stand out more revealingly than they do in humid regions where surfaces are covered by moss or other vegetation.

Another type of landform topography is known as the *hammada and erg.* This is featured particularly in the northeastern part of the Sahara Desert and throughout the Arabian Desert. The *hammadas* usually do not reach mountainous elevations and their configuration is more of the plateau type, upon which occasionally mountains may rise known in German by the term "Inselberge." Mesa and cuesta-like rocky crags feature such landscapes. On the interplateau basins we generally find the type of moving sand dunes commonly pictured in popular magazines and in desert movie scenes. Such landscape is known by the Arabian term, *erg.* Hammadas (plateaus) may be sufficiently elevated to intercept moisture-bearing winds. As a result, *wadies* carry water down their steep slopes in a manner similar to the *arroyos* in our American desert. However, due to considerably less precipitation, lakes or playas seldom form, the water being mostly cut off at the foot of the *hammadas,* and thus immediately becoming ground water. The core of the *erg* region is among the driest areas on earth; such, for example, is the "Tanezrouft" in Algeria.

Since desert soils have developed primarily from physical rather than chemical weathering, with evaporation in excess of precipitation, and with very sparse vegetation, such soils do not exhibit the distinct soil profiles found in humid regions. They are generally grey in color, coarse in texture, and contain very little, if any, humus. Since rainfall is low, there is little leaching. This, together with high evaporation, produces in many cases a calcified zone at or near the surface, characterized by calcium carbonates and aluminum oxides; hence the term *pedocal.* Alluvial soils are particularly rich in mineral nutrients because of an admixture of soil particles from varied parent rock material, and, unless they are too coarse (too sandy or gravelly), or too saline, they classify among the richest soils on earth. This is especially true where humus has been added by natural cover, or by growing and turning under a green-manure crop, such as a legume.

XX:5 (Left) "All deserts are hot" is a common fallacy dispelled by this graph. What do you record for winter and spring?

Probably the most distinctive major drainage features of desert lands are those found in mountain-rimmed basins, producing what is called *interior drainage.* The mountain-girt feature itself may be the primary cause of aridity. *Orographic* precipitation against the higher mountains accounts for such streams as do exist. But their termini are usually a lake or a playa somewhere within the basin. Such, for example, are the Tarim River of Takla Makan Desert of inner Asia, the Cooper and other rivers emptying into Lake Eyre in inner Australia, and our own Humboldt River of Nevada, whose waters seep into the desert sand. Prominent streams, such as the Indus, the Nile, and the Colorado River, noted for their irrigation development, are inherently not desert streams. They should be thought of as *exotic,* receiving their moisture from outside, humid regions, commonly highland regions. Despite the loss of much water along their courses due to high evaporation, such streams are able to maintain a flow all the way to the sea.

There is no better portrayal of arid land geomorphology than that by William Morris Davis:

¶ The essential features of the arid climate, as it is here considered, are: so small a rainfall that plant growth is scanty, that no basins of initial deformation are filled to overflowing, that no large trunk rivers are formed, and hence that the drainage does not reach the sea.

The agencies of sculpture and their opportunities for work in arid regions are peculiar in several respects. The small rainfall and the dry

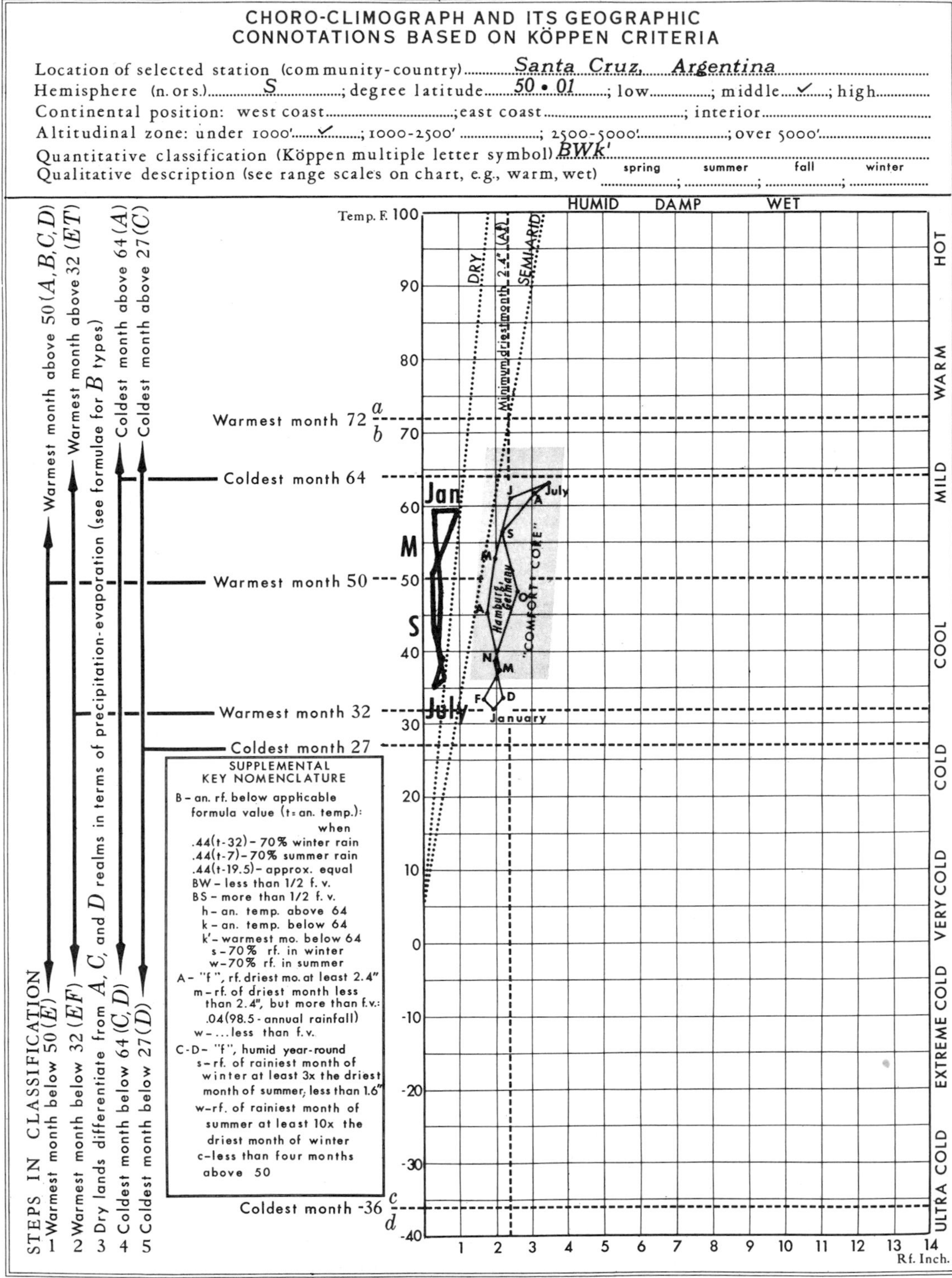
CHORO-CLIMOGRAPH AND ITS GEOGRAPHIC
CONNOTATIONS BASED ON KÖPPEN CRITERIA
Location of selected station (community-country) Santa Cruz, Argentina
Hemisphere (n. or s.) S; degree latitude 50 • 01; low; middle ✓; high
Continental position: west coast; east coast; interior
Altitudinal zone: under 1000' ✓; 1000-2500'; 2500-5000'; over 5000'
Quantitative classification (Köppen multiple letter symbol) BWk'
Qualitative description (see range scales on chart, e.g., warm, wet) spring; summer; fall; winter
HUMID
DAMP
WET
Temp. F.
DRY
Minimum driest month 2.4" (Af)
SEMIARID
"COMFORT" CORE
Hamburg, Germany
Jan
M
S
July
January
HOT
WARM
MILD
COOL
COLD
VERY COLD
EXTREME COLD
ULTRA COLD
Warmest month 72
Coldest month 64
Warmest month 50
Warmest month 32
Coldest month 27
Coldest month -36
Rf. Inch.
STEPS IN CLASSIFICATION
1 Warmest month above 50 (A, B, C, D) — Warmest month below 50 (E)
2 Warmest month above 32 (ET) — Warmest month below 32 (EF)
3 Dry lands differentiate from A, C, and D realms in terms of precipitation-evaporation (see formulae for B types)
4 Coldest month above 64 (A) — Coldest month below 64 (C, D)
5 Coldest month above 27 (C) — Coldest month below 27 (D)
SUPPLEMENTAL
KEY NOMENCLATURE
B - an. rf. below applicable formula value (t = an. temp.): when
.44(t-32) - 70% winter rain
.44(t-7) - 70% summer rain
.44(t-19.5) - approx. equal
BW - less than 1/2 f. v.
BS - more than 1/2 f. v.
h - an. temp. above 64
k - an. temp. below 64
k' - warmest mo. below 64
s - 70% rf. in winter
w - 70% rf. in summer
A - "f", rf. driest mo. at least 2.4"
m - rf. of driest month less than 2.4", but more than f.v.: .04(98.5 - annual rainfall)
w - ... less than f. v.
C-D - "f", humid year-round
s - rf. of rainiest month of winter at least 3x the driest month of summer; less than 1.6"
w - rf. of rainiest month of summer at least 10x the driest month of winter
c - less than four months above 50

air reduce the ground water to a minimum. In its actions, weathering is almost limited to the surface, and is more largely physical than chemical. The streams are usually shorter than the slopes, and act as discontinuously at their lower as at their upper ends. The scarcity of plant growth leaves the surface relatively free to the attack of the winds and of the intermittent waters. Hence, in the production of fine waste, the splitting, flaking, and splintering of local weathering are supplemented rather by the rasping and trituration that go with transportation than by the chemical disintegration that characterizes a plant-bound soil.[1]

Xerophytes and halophytes dominate the dry wastelands

Vegetation is of the *xerophytic* type, adapted to paucity of water. Sand deserts have droughty soils and thus add *edaphic* dryness to meterological drought. Desert plants by their manner of growth reflect adversity of environment in much the same way as the tundra plants. Plants are generally dwarfed in stature and occur commonly in isolated clumps with considerable bare spaces in between. Compared with humid land plants, desert plants have extraordinarily well-developed root systems. These may laterally spread over large areas, as in the case of the creosote bush. On the other hand, the *mesquite* may send its roots down several score feet to reach lenses of sand in which stored water may have traveled many miles from the foothills of mountains on which the precipitation fell. Stems are woody and, if they bear foliage, the leaves are generally small, thick and leathery, generally bearing fine down-like covering that retards transpiration of moisture. Succulent plants, like the cactus, have the capacity to store large quantities of water; a thick epidermis retards transpiration as do its leaves in the form of conical spines, which, in addition, serve to protect the plant against excessive animal browsing. Other special survival features may include a waxy or resinous coating, malodorous and unpalatable to animals, thus protecting the plant against being overgrazed.

A patch of annual flowering plants in the desert almost always reveals recent rains, for such plants must mature quickly; in fact, one shower of rain must often suffice to germinate the seed and to develop a full grown plant, including the formation of seed which then may lie dormant in the sands until another rainfall. Such plants may be found in the true desert, which is otherwise entirely without vegetation, as in many of the *BWh* deserts. Other *BWh* types may be comprised of desert shrubs, such as sagebrush, greasewood, and cacti, where there are saline flats or the soil is otherwise highly alkalized. Salt desert shrub or halophytic grasses may well constitute an important source of fodder for cattle.

Among the few cultivated plants, the date palm stands as the symbol of sustenance of the oasis dweller (see photo, page 419).

Animal life primarily nocturnal

Desert animals, like desert plants, reflect the scarcity of water. Many get along without water altogether by merely subsisting on herb vegetation, as in the case of many of the rodents. Some of the carnivores absorb water from the animals they eat. The antelope and the camel, particularly the latter, are so anatomically constructed that they can store a copious supply of water which may last them a week or more. While plants normally find desert soils well supplied with mineral plant food, animals must be adapted to range far and wide for their sustenance. There is a continuous war of survival raging among the carnivores, the rodents, the reptiles, the birds, and the insects, so well pictured in the several day-night panoramas in *Life's* article "The Land of the Sun" (5). It is well worth the student's time to consult these portraits which portray in one view as many as twenty-six

[1] From "The Geographical Cycle in an Arid Climate," by William Morris Davis, *Geographical Essays*, Edited by D. W. Johnson, Dover Publications, Inc., 180 Varick Street, New York 14, New York, pp. 296-297. Reprinted by permission.

XX:6 (Left) "At least all summers of desert regions are hot." Note that this desert station is cooler in July than Hamburg, Germany, and this *Cfb* station is considered delightfully cool. How would you go about determining the cause of the *k′* condition? Are there any data on the chart which offer clues?

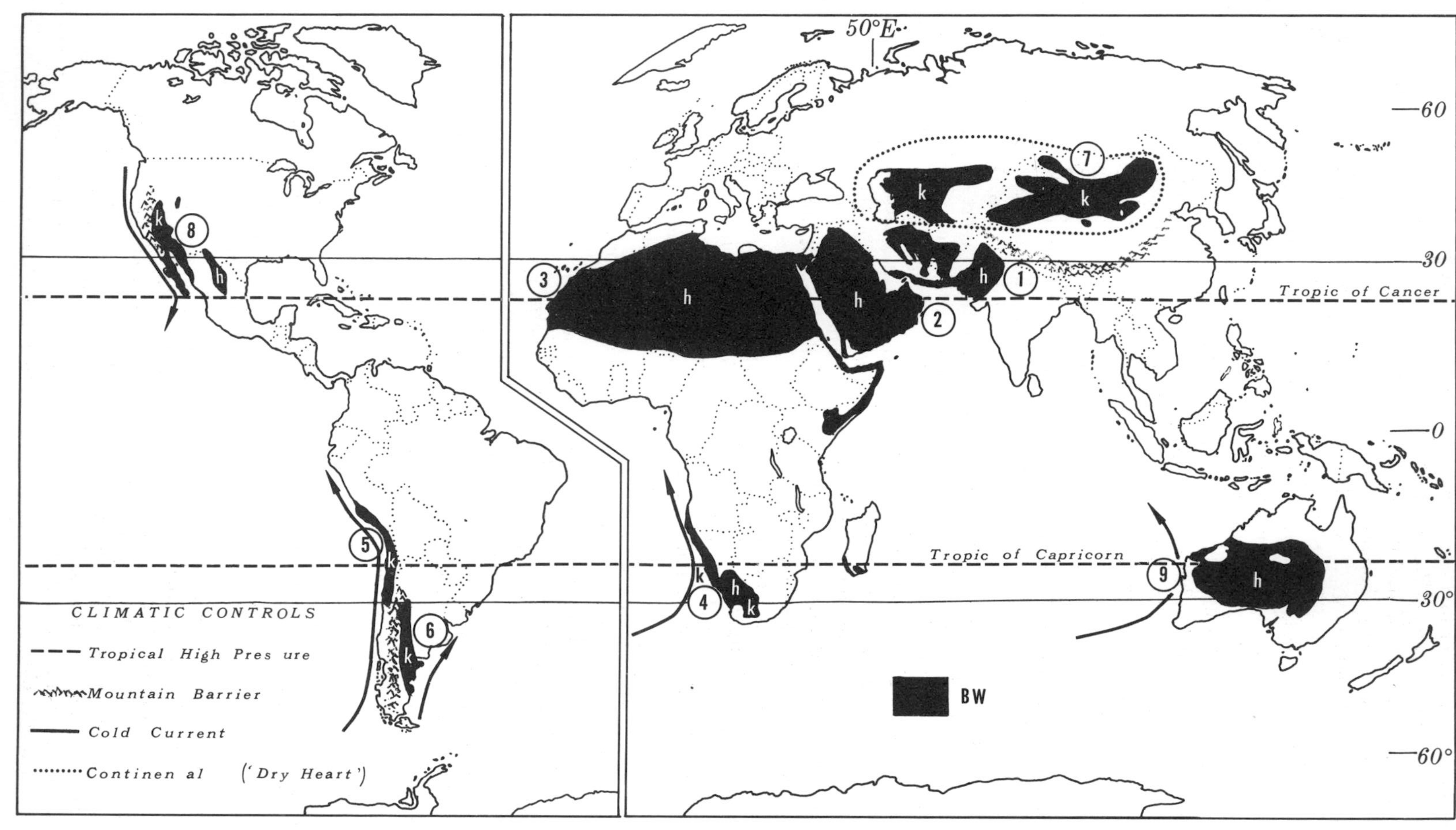

50°E
60
30
Tropic of Cancer
0
Tropic of Capricorn
30°
60°
BW
CLIMATIC CONTROLS
Tropical High Pres ure
Mountain Barrier
Cold Current
Continen al ('Dry Heart')

These sand hills are twenty-seven miles west of Yuma in Imperial County, California. Does this portray wind deposition or wind erosion? (U. S. Department of Agriculture)

types of animals in their normal habitat, both on the surface and underground. The day and night settings, contrasted as they are, reveal that desert animal activities are primarily nocturnal. This may explain the common assumption that desert life is practically nonexistent. The desert world indeed presents a challenging ecological study of the meticulous natural adaptation of animal to animal, of animal to plant, and of plant to soil, landforms, and waterforms of the greatest complexity of ecological patterns.

XX:7 (Left) Here are shown the major deserts of the world: (1) Thar Desert, (2) Arabian Desert, (3) Sahara Desert, (4) Kalahari Desert, (5) Atacama Desert, (6) Patagonia Desert, (7) Desert of Gobi, (8) Great American Desert, (9) Great Victoria Desert. Actually, most of the "realm" deserts are regionally differentiated as are humid lands, and thus have their own regional or local toponymy. Of the various general climatic controls here indicated, which seems to be the most influential?

Desert dust and drama as portrayed in the world's largest arid region

Having considered above some of the systematic relationships of natural phenomena in the desert world, it would now seem appropriate to study man in relationship to such environmental factors as are particularly well portrayed in an article on the Sahara, the world's largest desert, by Peveril Meigs, a leading authority in this field.[1]

[1] Dr. Meigs studied drylands for a period of 30 years and for some time served as chairman of the Arid Zone Commission of the International Geographical Union.

Here is a unique study in combined land surface and cloud design. What are the physical and biological evidences of aridity? How is bedrock geology related to the varying slope profiles of the canyon? What is the nature of precipitation? (Note the cumulo-nimbus cloud formation penetrating a thin layer of alto-cumulus and the dark column of rain making contact with the earth on the horizon to the left.) You should have no trouble identifying this national park spectacle, seen by thousands of tourists annually. (Photo by Madison Gilbert of the U. S. Weather Bureau)

The following is an abstract from the extended article, entitled "Outlook for Arid North Africa: The Sahara" (Figure XX-8).

¶ The Sahara, tawny from dust, dusty from dryness, is the vastest desert in the world, stretching across the widest part of Africa from the Atlantic to the Red Sea. The continental United States could be spread out in the Sahara and still leave enough desert around the edges to make an Alaska.

Most of the Sahara gets an average yearly rainfall of less than one inch, which means anywhere from none to 5 inches in a given year. The core of extreme dryness grades off into less dry lands to the north and south, which in turn merge into the still moister steppes of the Mediterranean and Sudan borders. . . .

Most of the Sahara is a patchwork of dry plains and plateaus, dotted with a few mountains (notably the Ahaggar and Tibesti) and numer-

The date palm (*Phoenix dactylifera*), one of the most drought-resistant of all fruit trees, finds its optimal environment in the abundant sunshine and dry air of the tropical desert oasis. Note the shiny pinnate foliage and how the farmer's attire reflects this type of environs. The date harvest scene is in the al-Kharj region of Saudi Arabia. Dates, next to oil, are the chief source of Arabian wealth. (Courtesy Arabian American Oil Company)

ous long, low cuestas. Most feared of all the plains is the Tanezrouft, "land of thirst," over which a camel can walk day after day in the glaring heat without finding a drop of water or a vestige of pasture. Since there are no natural landmarks, and previous tracks are quickly obliterated by wind and sand, travelers must depend upon stars, sun, and compass for guidance. Careless navigation may bring disaster.

The flat, wind-worked sand and gravel surface (called *reg* by the Arabs) characteristic of the Tanezrouft is widespread in the Sahara. There is usually plenty of sand between the stones, and movement is easy for animal or automobile. Travel is much more arduous in the *hammada*, where bedrock is exposed, swept clear of loose mantle, and in the *erg*, where wind has piled the sand into steep-sided dunes over vast areas.

Bare, rocky, impervious slopes are highly important to desert man, for they serve to concentrate the meager rainfall. Instead of evaporating in place, the water soaks the ground at the base of the slope enough to support considerable vegetation. Such vegetation is the only forage available for livestock in some parts of the desert. Runoff also converts the beds of dry streams (wadies or oueds) into roaring rivers for brief periods, so that crops can be raised in the mud after the water recedes. In some places the runoff creates ephemeral salt lakes (*sebkhas*). . . .

The people of the Sahara are as unevenly distributed as the water; about 23 million live in the 13,000-square-mile Nile Oasis, from Khartoum to Alexandria. In the Djerid Oases there are 2,500 people per square mile; in the desert west of Egypt, only about one per square mile. Hundreds of thousands of square miles are entirely uninhabited. . . .

Two distinct ways of life characterize the Sahara: pastoral nomadism, and oases agriculture. The nomads outnumber the oasis dwellers in the Sahara margins and in the mountains, where rainfall and forage are best; the oases dwellers predominate out in the desert, where life is dependent on ground water.

The Berber and Arab nomads are raisers of sheep, goats, and camels, and eaters of milk and cheese, with grain and dates when obtainable. In the moister margins, where seasonal forage can be counted upon every year, they migrate periodically with their sheep and goats over established routes. Farther out in the desert the fickle rains bring sporadic growth of short-lived grasses and weeds (*acheb*); long rapid treks between pastures are necessary. Mobility is the rule, and the symbol of the nomad is the camel and the black goat-hair tent (goat hide among the *Tuaregs*), which is low wind- and sun-resistant and roomy. . . .

The range of grazing is limited by the availability of drinking water as well as of pastures. With juicy acheb, camels can go indefinitely without drinking in winter, but sheep need water at least every fourth day. In summer, sheep must drink every other day, camels every three or four days. . . .

Camel traffic remains vitally important for nomad and oases trading, and places such as Goulimine, Ghardaïa, . . . are busy distributing centers for the caravans of the desert margin. However, modern means of transportation are now competing for the long haul. Trans-Saharan passengers use airplanes or automobiles. An excellent network of air routes and limited automobile routes serve the Sahara. Regular though infrequent buses cross the desert on two roads, and trucks on four roads, all of which consist chiefly of the natural desert floor. . . .

The Nile, the most ancient Trans-Saharan tract, is still navigated, paralleled by a railroad. . . .

The Oasis is a different world from that of the grazing, trading nomad. In the north, the compact *ksar* villages consist of adobe houses, often several stories high, with flat roofs for sleeping, and narrow-covered streets for shade. Southern houses are conical and thatched. Basically the livelihood of the ksar is derived from date palms introduced in Roman times. . . .

Varied and ingenious are the methods of obtaining water in the oases. Aside from the Nile and its barrages, and a storage dam in the mountains back of Biskra, permanent irrigation depends upon ground water, which may percolate great distances through porous sands or rocks. The most fortunate oasis dwellers have natural springs, some of them very large, where ground water issues unaided.

Next best are the man-made ones: *foggaras* and artesian wells. Foggaras are tunnels one to six miles long and big enough for a man to walk through, dug not quite horizontally to tap underground water and conduct it to the oasis by gravity. Water flow from foggaras is modest but dependable and automatic.

Few artesian wells were dug until the development of modern machine boring. They had been exploited spectacularly in the Oued Righ, an ancient, half-buried wadi southwest of Shott Melrhir. . . . By 1924, there were 1,033 wells and springs, supplying 69,000 gallons per minute and supporting 1,610,000 palms. The boon lasted until the inevitable overdraft of water reduced flow and lowered the water table. . . .

Ordinary dug wells, from which the water has to be raised by means of a bucket at the end of a rope, are the commonest source of irrigation water in the Sahara. . . .

Where ground water lies near the surface, pits, up to 45 feet deep, may be dug to permit the roots of plants to reach the moist ground without irrigation. . . .

Share cropping is the prevailing system of land tenure. The standard share of the cropper is one fifth of the harvest—he is called *khammès*, meaning fifth—though in some oases he receives a somewhat larger proportion. The land owner, whether nomad, merchant, Marabout, or corporation, provides tools, seed, water supply, and fertilizer. . . .

Highly pertinent to the outlook for the Sahara is the question of rainfall: is it decreasing, as some believe? Probably there have been no significant changes in the Northern Sahara since Roman times. Apparent desiccation can be traced to human rather than climatic causes, particularly over-use of the native vegetation, overdraft of ground water, and past razzias. . . .

Though agriculture and grazing still predominate by a wide margin, mineral exploitation in

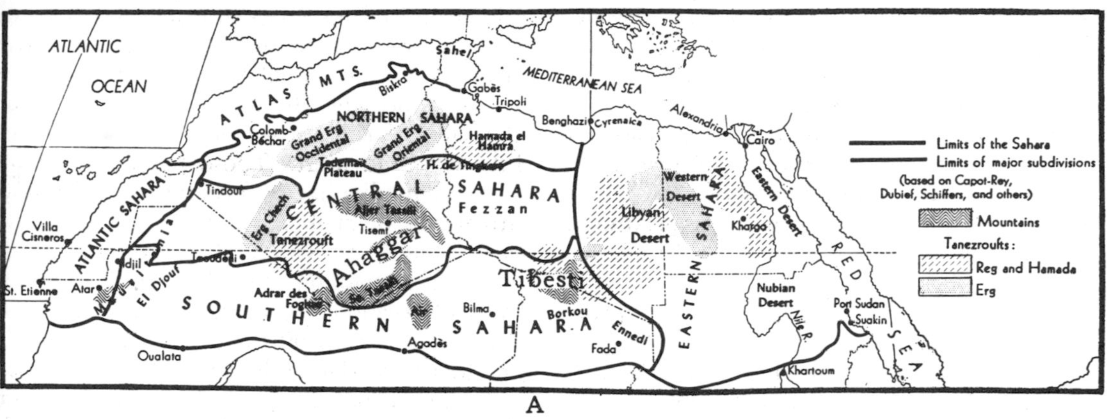

A

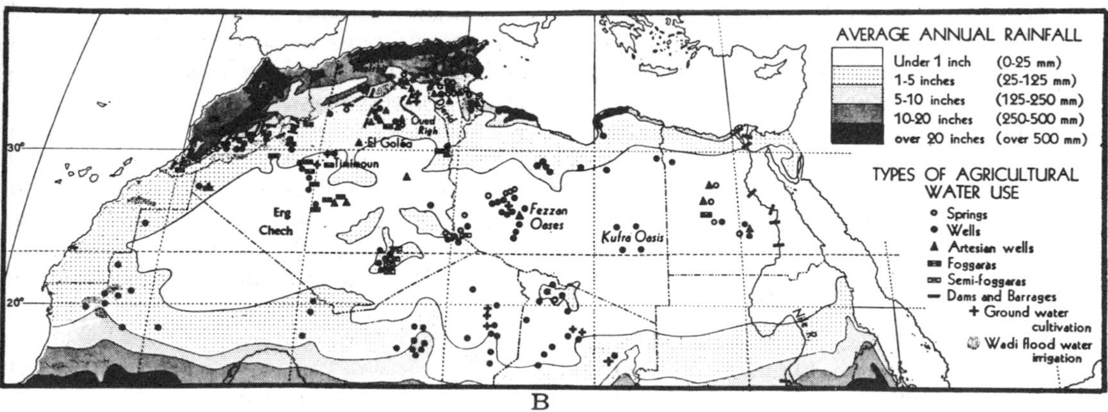

B

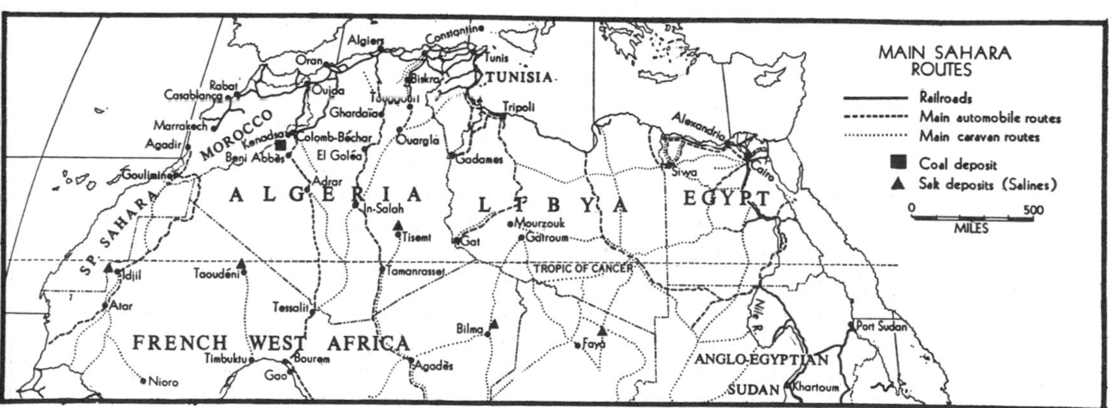

C

XX:8 In Arabian the Sahara means "wilderness," an apt characterization, just as in German, a desert is called a *Wueste* (*BW*, in Köppen symbolism). Water, of course, is the chief conditioner of settlement. Correlate the annual rainfall and various types of agricultural water use (B), with the land forms of the Sahara (A). (Three maps excerpted from *Focus*, American Geographical Society, New York, used by permission)

the Sahara is increasing. A great variety of minerals has been located, and some of the more accessible ones are being mined, especially in Eastern Egypt (oil, iron, phosphate). Since 1949, a little tin has been mined near Agadès in the Southern Sahara. The major mineral in the west is coal, mined near Colomb-Béchar. . . .

With its coal, railroad, and near-by exploitable deposits of manganese, copper, and lead, Colomb-Béchar seems destined to become the industrial center of the Sahara. . . .

Fishing along the extensive Saharan coast has distinct possibilities for further development. . . .

Tourism is still another possibility. The Northern Sahara, with a January mean temperature a bracing 50° F., dry sunny days, skies clearer than those of southern Europe, and exotic natural and cultural attractions, is only a plane jump from the Riviera.

For the immediate future, problems of nomadism and agriculture are likely to remain paramount. The tendency for nomads to settle down, and of oasis dwellers to migrate out of the Sahara, is still only a slow drift. . . . The oases may be made more attractive by improvement of water supply, health, tenure, and transportation. But the Sahara will probably long remain what it has long been: a fiery barrier between Black Africa and the Mediterranean, a Moslem world of dust, dromedaries, and dates.[1]

Environmental considerations of historic dryland cultures

In view of austerity of living conditions, as pointed out above, it may seem a historic paradox that most of the earliest cradles of civilization occupied desert or near desert regions. Such were, for example, the Babylonian, the Syrian, the Assyrian, the Persian, the Egyptian, and the Indus Valley civilizations. Of course, we must always remember that these were nearly altogether river or other oasis habitats where exotic flow of water made extensive irrigation possible. Despite this fact, it is remarkable to what extent advanced cultural traits were developed in such areas at this early date. Geographers like Huntington of America and Brunhes of France held strongly to the "influence of environment" theory as accounting in many ways for the mode of life and thought of people, particularly as it reflects itself in lands of difficult life. And so, as Brunhes observes, the very adversity of life's circumstances may very well bring out near perfection of occupance and cultural forms. Regardless of the part that the theories of "determinism" or "possibilism" may play in the picture, certain cultural traits do show strong accordant relationships with the dry world. Both the Berbers and the Arabs of the Old World are phenomenally resourceful, wiry and alert. These people show no signs of mediocrity in striving for maximum utilization of such meager resources as the environment provides. Courageous, loyal, and self-respecting, the Arab is a distinct lover of freedom; he recognizes no class distinction of race or office. He is strictly obedient to the leader of his tribe but the tribal chieftain is looked upon as a servant rather than master. A cosmopolitan in his outlook on human relations, he conducts himself with dignity and poise in dealing with fellow men of his own group as well as with outsiders. His hospitality extends to generosity in sharing his meager resources with all those who are in dire need. On the other hand, in the tradition of desert peoples, he does not consider it unethical to dispossess another desert dweller of his goods in order to survive.

The Moslem religion, especially in its earliest development, is almost coterminous with the dry world (see Chapter 18 on Religion), the environmental influence of which is clearly revealed in a precept of the Koran: "No one can refuse surplus water without sinning against Allah and against Man." Huntington expressed himself on this point as follows:

¶ The Islamic idea of one supreme God brings up the much discussed statement that the animistic and Hindu belief in many gods and innumerable minor spirits is the natural result of life in the tropical jungle, whereas the monotheism of Judaism, Christianity, and Islam is an equally natural product of deserts. . . . Out in the deserts, where dwell the nomad, the things that man chiefly fears are big—winds, sun, cold, heat, drought. They have little of the local, intimate quality of the jungle man's mudholes, snakes, sticks, and malevolent mosquitoes. The desert man is as free as the jungle man to believe in spirits that inhabit stones, bushes, lizards, and beasts of prey, but there is less incentive to do so. Even if he does believe in them, they are unimportant compared with big things like sun, wind, and drought. Hence it is natural for the primitive desert man to pin his faith to a few powerful gods who rule large areas. This does

[1] Meigs, Perveril, "Outlook for Arid North Africa: The Sahara," *Focus*, Vol. V, No. 4, December, 1954, pp. 1-6, *passim*. Reprinted by permission.

not compel him to believe in a single god, but it makes the transition to that belief easy and natural. It would be false to say that belief in one universal god necessarily evolved in a desert, but it is true that the evolution of such a belief is more probable there than in the jungle.[1]

Modern mining and its exotic ethnographic effects

Aside from certain strategic minerals to be noted later, the dry world normally does not supply resources of any major economic concern to the outside world. We have already noted how the desert dweller is dependent almost entirely on subsistence economy, except in the larger oases, such as the Nile Valley, where cotton, dates, wheat, and barley may be grown in surplus quantities for export. The same is true for industrial products, largely home-made. Household activities, as in the case of weaving, may locally be a fairly important industry. The chief *BW* industry monetary-wise is mining. Genesis of ore bodies is largely unrelated to climatic conditions, except in near-surface secondary enrichments or superficial concentrations of a limited number of minerals; hence so many metalliferous as well as nonmetalliferous products may yet be discovered. Among the metalliferous products, those of Coolgardie of Australia stand out as probably most significant, though here again, the exploitation of the minerals required the importation of water from several hundred miles distant. Certain nonmetallic deposits, like chlorides and nitrates, are definitely indigenously related to dry climate, and in local regions have become noteworthily exploited. Such, for example, are the great salt deposits around Great Salt Lake, Utah, the world-famous Atacama mineral nitrates, and the guano excrements off the shore of Peru.

The guano deposit furnishes another interesting example of ecological animal-human chain relationships. The cold Humboldt Current is rich in micro-organisms, which supply food for fish; the fish in turn are fed upon by the birds, which produce the guano; the aridity of the area conserves the guano; the guano in turn is immediately available for the fertilization of the Peruvian oases, which support sizable populations.

The most important mining industry of all is the recovery of petroleum (see page 404). As already previously pointed out, the Middle East fields alone are reported to comprise at least one-half of the present world reserve. The exploitation of such fields has completely changed not only the commercial but also the political relations intraregionally as well as with the humid lands. The refining of petroleum has in many ways Westernized the living habits of the natives and boosted the standard of living. The petroleum pipeline and the sea tanker may be said to symbolize a new era in trade and transportation between the dry and the humid world.

Geo-strategy and geonomics of the vast desert domains

As noted in the beginning of this chapter, one of the most noteworthy governmental phenomena of modern times is the agitation of dryland dependencies for independence from proprietary powers. More recently the intense nationalism of a number of such states has been supplanted regionally by a spirit of Pan-Arabism. Pan-Arabism is a political concept developed on the basis of geographic regionalism, whose homogeneous criteria combine the elements of Mohammedanism (or Islamism) with a certain set of ethnographic and economic interests, influenced by its World-Island position. This reminds one of the aggresive militarism of *Pan-Islamism* in its spread over Southern Europe as far as France, upon the death of Mohammed in the seventh century. There is probably little prospect for effective union of Arab states, however, in view of the rivalry for power and prestige among the various states, and because of the complex rela-

[1] Reprinted with permission from Ellsworth Huntington, *Mainsprings of Civilization,* copyright 1945, John Wiley & Sons, Inc., New York, pp. 292-293, *passim.* (The late Ellsworth Huntington, along with Ellen Churchill Semple, has often been considered the classical exponent of the "theory of determinism." Many sections of the work of both these authors (and other geographers), especially when quoted out of context, may suggest man's inordinate commitment to his physical environment. But here, at least, is evidence that Huntington, along with many of his contemporaries, did not hold that man is "compelled" by his environment to be or to do a certain something, but rather at times (especially in the primitive world) is impelled or repelled by favorable or unfavorable environmental factors (Part I). In any case, the student will recognize here, merely a "philosophical" observation which may or may not have greater validity than another anthropo-geographic concept concerning this co-ordinate space relationship.)

tionships between each individual state and the world powers. Thus at the moment several states are jockeying for the most favored position of world influence, making independent agreements with the East or the West as best fits their immediate financial gain, political prestige, and their own national security. Because the French own the greatest dryland territory, they are chiefly concerned with pacifying agitators in North Africa for political independence. A classic example is the rebellion in Algeria, a political-economic crisis in French colonialism.

Unquestionably water will always remain a critical factor in the development of the dry world. In view of the climatological controls which predicate low rainfall, there is little prospect man will ever be able to change the basic pattern of irrigationless aridity. Rain making attempts to change all this by seeding clouds carry little promise of introducing more moisture into a desert area. After all, precipitation, whether "artificial" or natural, presupposes clouds, indicating presence of moisture, before there can be successful seeding. And clouds are one of the most uncommon features in the desert world; many places rate as low as 10 per cent of cloudiness. Furthermore, the high temperatures and resulting evaporation dissipate most of the rain droplets falling through the air. But this is not to say that more water cannot be made available by better recovery through storage and utilization methods, as is demonstrated by many improved systems of irrigation—better impounding of flood waters, using closed ducts for directing irrigation waters to prevent loss by evaporation, and tapping deeper aquifers through which water is naturally transferred and stored many miles away from sources from which the water is received. But at best, the total supply, even if entirely recovered, is limited, and losses by evaporation and transportation are very difficult to control. Thus, such transformation as we may expect in the dry world will likely result from other factors. Modern technological and transportational developments have now made themselves felt in some of our major desert areas—the Sahara, the Australian, and American deserts—resulting in radically changed forms of human occupance. The traditional economic dependence of such desert areas, as Johnson points out, is undergoing shifts:

¶ (1) toward plant economies with numerous artificially developed oases in addition to the original and actual one; (2) toward a manufacturing and mineral economy with great enlargements of desert extractive industries; (3) toward some phases of an economy of commerce with the building of many transdesert transport facilities i.e., highways, power lines, aqueducts, and air bases.[1]

Johnson further points to an article by a University of Oklahoma chemist who indicates that in Mexico cacti have been cultivated which produce as much as nine tons of fruit per acre with a sugar content as high as 14 per cent; that the mesquite fruit pod has a higher sugar content than sugar beet or sugar cane; that the gum mesquite may be made into a pharmaceutical product to replace gum arabic; that yucca has fiber as well as soap-making potentialities; and that *jojoba* has properties resembling those of whale oil.

Driving through the great southwestern American desert and noting the proliferation of sagebrush, one is disposed to speculate on the possibilities of the development of some synthetic products from such a common plant, without irrigation. But even if such useful products could be processed, the question remains whether wholesale removal of desert vegetation could perpetuate the industry because of the threatened extermination of the species.

A more immediate and revolutionary type of transformation would be to develop those desert areas which have rich mineral endowments, or otherwise occupy a world-power strategic position, such as is enjoyed by the countries of the Middle East. Revenues from petroleum export have not only stabilized the internal economy of the Arab countries, situated at or near the land bridge of the Triad—Europe, Asia, Africa—but have given these countries political and military significance out of all proportion to those qualities commonly associated with the connotation of "desert." Revenues derived from oil royalties are applied, as in the case of Arabia by King Saud, to the establishment of an entirely new occupance pattern. The migrating nomad may soon be a thing of the past, as

[1] Johnson, Charles W., "Shifting Desert Economies," *The Journal of Geography*, May, 1946, p. 201. Reprinted by permission.

he is being settled on newly established irrigation oases. Modern improvements in highway transportation, the building of hospitals and schools, and the introduction of sanitation on a large scale will contribute to higher education, better health, and higher living standards. But the geography student sees trouble ahead as the oil fields are exhausted. This will eventually occur regardless of how large the reserves may be. Mining communities are traditionally known as "ghost" communities. After the exploitation of this liquid gold, will these desert countries "revert back to type?" Or will they become "relief" nations or nations subject to rehabilitation by some such program as "Point Four" (developed at end of Chapter 22, under Savannah Grasslands)?

We have thus primarily considered the true desert lands (*BW*) when in reality the countries referred to actually incorporate, in most cases, sections of the *BS* as well. Such sections naturally present a less inhospitable picture, with the classification of "semiaridity" instead of "aridity," to be considered in the next chapter.

APPLICATION OF GEOGRAPHIC UNDERSTANDING

The following poem by Helen Trafford Moore might be said to dramatize the need of placing an historic event in the geographic framework of which it is inseparably a part.

Grim is my face and restless my heart
  As I gaze on my vast domain.
Mine is a kingdom of grassy land,
  Mountain and desert and plain.
Far and forever the distance lures,
  Beckoning, beckoning on—
On where the desert mirages flame—
  Calling to me Genghis Khan.
Cruel, am I? But what of you—
  You in your houses of ease?
I was cradled in weary lands
  With hunger and fear and disease.
Mine was the life of the nomad tribe
  Near to the desert's heart,
There where the cold winds swept the plain,
  There where the grasses parched;
A land of thirst and death and fear,
  A land of roaming bands,
Where dwelt the ruthless robber hordes
  That stole my home and lands.
No rest for me of idle ease;
  For ever did my eye
Scan out some distant pasture land
  Where my loved flocks might lie.
Forever moving, roving on—
  On my swift horse I pass.
Up, Horsemen, on, another day
  Is calling us at last.
Far out the distant desert waits,
  The unscaled mountain calls,
The luring plain in verdure breaks
  Where tinkling water falls.
My spirit fears not God nor man,
  But restless seeks a rest
Beyond the sunsets of my land—
  I go at its behest![1]

I. How does the above poetical version of dryland description fit the more prosaic one supplied in this chapter?

II. To what particular type of desert dweller is the poem "dedicated"?

III. Does the author seem to be aware of the regional diversity of desert landscapes; if so, how indicated?

IV. With what "desert heart" and other regions do you associate the exploits of Genghis Khan and the Mongol Empire which he built in the early thirteenth century?

V. Indicate in each case specifically what intelligence of this leading historic event would be gained by mapping such space phenomena as:

A. Karakorum, the most celebrated cultural, commercial and political center of the Khan domain.

B. The routes of trade and raids emanating therefrom.

C. The Asiatic and European cultures and countries "beyond the sunsets."

VI. Which type of "base" outline map would you find most useful on which to plot your data? (a) "political," (b) landform, (c) vegetation, (d) climate, (e) hydrography. Evaluate.

VII. Outline on a map the limits of the Mongol Empire. How does the area compare in size and distribution pattern with those of other empires of the world—past and present? Regional and global significance?

VIII. How do you account for this un-

---

[1] Moore, Helen Trafford, "Genghis Khan," *St. Nicholas*, Vol. LVII, July 1930, p. 687.

paralleled territorial conquest by a "nomadic tribe near the desert's heart?"

IX. How does the geographic position of this "heartland" compare with that upon which Sir Halford Mackinder in 1917 based his theory of "World Island" conquest?

References

1 "North Africa," *Time,* March 18, 1957, p. 28.
2 Atwood, W. W., and Thomas, H. G., *The Growth of Nations,* Ginn & Company, Boston, 1943, p. 262.
3 Dickson, B. T., "Challenge of Arid Lands," *Scientific Monthly,* Vol. LXXXII, No. 2, Feb., 1956, p. 67.
4 Davis, William Morris, "The Geographical Cycle in an Arid Climate," *Geographical Essays,* Edited by D. W. Johnson, Dover Publications, New York, 1954, pp. 296-297.
5 "The Land of the Sun," *Life:* The World We Live In, Part IX, pp. 176-196.
6 Meigs, Peveril, "Outlook for Arid North Africa: The Sahara," *Focus,* Vol. V, No. 4, December, 1954, pp. 1-6, *passim.*
7 Huntington, Ellsworth, *Mainsprings of Civilization,* John Wiley & Sons, New York, 1945, pp. 292-293, *passim.*
8 Johnson, Charles W., "Shifting Desert Economies," *The Journal of Geography,* May, 1946, p. 201.
9 Moore, Helen Trafford, "Genghis Khan," *St. Nicholas,* Vol. LVII, July 1930, p. 687.

Chapter 21

Drylands—the semiarid steppe grasslands (*BS*)—lands of marginal utility

One of the chief objectives in studying geography is to recognize the problems of human adjustments in local, regional, and national economy. Probably the best regional example in our own country of such a study is the Great Plains. In fact, this province represents the primary problem area of the United States. The desert realm, just considered, may seem to the student to present the greater problems because of the greater aridity, but it should be apparent at once that when regions are as deficient and undependable in rainfall as the true desert areas, very few people would be attracted by them, and settlements would be almost altogether of the oasis type. The steppe lands, on the other hand, having approximately at least twice as much moisture as the desert regions, are at least hospitable enough to invite the grazier who finds here a continuous sod of grass instead of the scanty bunch grass and herbs of the desert. Moreover, though rainfall may not be sufficient or dependable to grow agricultural crops indiscriminately, there is adequate moisture, particularly in the eastern section next to the humid lands, to grow on an extensive scale grain crops of a type adapted to semiarid or dryland farming. Hence, specialized grain agriculture has often proved very profitable in the more humid years. Accordingly, in the wet cycle, settlers have been attracted to the Great Plains in ever-increasing numbers. But then follow the dry-cycle years when not only grain but stock grazing as well may prove a complete failure, especially now since excess acreages of sod have been turned under by the plow and dust storms despoil the vegetation and deflate the area of its topsoil.

Several press news items will illustrate this historic problem and some of the geographic principles underlying it.

The Great Plains

¶ Plowboys on iron horses are riding the range again under the stimulus of $2.00 wheat and plenty of rain, buffalo grass is being turned over at a clip reminiscent of World War I. If it quits raining, the Dust Bowl will be as dusty as ever and the West again will have justified its reputation as a country of boom and bust. This is the considered opinion of ranchers, county bankers, county agricultural agents and grain elevator men along our route through Western Nebraska, Kansas and Eastern Colorado. . . . Just look over the barb wire fences on both sides of the highway. You will see mile after mile of freshly turned sodland that never felt the point of a plow before, not even during the plowup of 1918 to 1921. Everywhere you hear the same story. Land is going out of sod and row crops into wheat. They are turning over good grass land, much of it too rough to be safely farmed. The West again is a speculator's paradise. Who cares what happens when one crop of wheat will pay for the land, planting and harvest and leave something besides? . . . "80% of these new wheat farmers plowin' the range coming from the East and Texas. They're payin' $15 to $25 an acre. If they hit with one good crop the land won't owe 'em anything."[1]

Concerning another area of speculation in Colorado which was seeded for the first time with wheat, the article continues:

¶ This land normally is priced at $2.00 to $10.00 an acre for grazing. Speculators are paying $15.00 to $30.00 for it; hoping to clean up before the price of wheat collapses and the area reverts to its normal rainfall . . . much of the Great Plains is a land of transients. Workers driving with their tractors, plows and drills to put in a wheat crop. They live in a hotel or rooming house until their work is done. Then they leave, not to return until harvest. "Suitcase farming" the natives call it. There's nobody around to plant and care for tree shelterbelts or check wind erosion once it begins . . . when the next drought strikes and the wind starts picking up loose dirt, watch for news from the Dust Bowl. Days will become as black as night, cattle will die from dust in their lungs and mud

[1] *Chicago Daily News,* July 1, 1947. Reprinted by permission of the United Press International.

A dust storm advances onto a town in Potter County, Texas. What residential and transportational problems does such a storm pose for the urban dweller? (Photo by U. S. Department of Agriculture)

in their stomachs. The exodus of the '30's will be on all over again.[1]

The prophecy was well founded, for a decade later we read another news item — from Denver, "Dust Bowl Days Back in the Dry Southwest."

¶ The current drought is the worst on record in many parts of the Southwest and Rocky Mountain regions, worse even than the "dirty thirties" of dust bowl fame. Pastures are barren of grass and crops have withered. Livestock in Oklahoma, Texas, Kansas, New Mexico, Wyoming and Colorado face a winter of nothing but supplemental feed such as hay and concentrates, and that at a premium price. Thousands of acres of cropland in most of those states have been abandoned. Some ranchers have been forced to sell their basic breeding herds. . . . In some instances, drought-dismayed farmers and ranchers, and even their city neighbors, have asked divine help. Governor Raymond Gary proclaimed last Sunday as a day of prayer in Oklahoma and the state's residents asked God "to send rain on our parched land.". . . In Oklahoma, hay brought $50 a ton . . . farmers have had to leave the farm and seek jobs elsewhere. . . . Streams throughout the region are either dry, or only moist. Eleven of the fourteen major streams in Kansas are reported no longer flowing consistently. A group of motorcyclists at Wichita, Kan., drove their vehicles 100 miles up the Arkansas River bed before being halted by water. . . . In Dallas bottled water was selling for more than gasoline. Crop abandonment has been high. In Texas, for example, from July 1 to Oct. 1 a total of 925,000 acres of cotton alone were [*sic*] abandoned. . . . The extreme dryness in the mountain states has caused a record number of forest fires this year which destroyed thousands of acres of choice timberland. In Colorado and New Mexico deer, bear and other wild animals have been chased from their high-elevation summer homes to lower ground in search of food, and at lower elevations they run into civilization.[2]

Chorogram: "Dust Bowl" (Figure XXI-1)

The settlement and use of such a region as the above raises many questions in social, economic and political geography. For example, at a time when most regions of the United States are gaining in population, why are large parts of the Great Plains (North Dakota and South Dakota) losing in population? How are the various forms of man's economic adjustments to and of the environment related to the earlier ecological patterns? Is it possible to determine to what extent we have overextended plow culture which has been blamed as the source of the Dust Bowl problem? What kind of conservation measures have been recommended to check soil erosion under the varying environmental conditions found in the various regions of the Great Plains?

The '54-'57 drought was so critical as to engage the attention of Congress and the President's cabinet. President Eisenhower, Secretary of Agriculture Benson, and other government officials toured the southern section of the Great Plains to determine the magnitude of the drought and the needs for

[1] *Ibid.* Reprinted by permission.

[2] *Chicago Daily News,* October 20, 1956. Reprinted by permission of the United Press International.

Wind-drifted sand advances onto a vacated house in Colorado. Note the partial dune-fixation by ground cover. Does this appear to be a natural or cultivated form of vegetation? What type of farm management would have to be undertaken to rehabilitate a farmstead with such a wind-erosion-deposition problem as this? (Photo by U. S. Department of Agriculture)

relief and rehabilitation by the government. This raises additional questions. Should the federal government exercise a certain measure of control in planning the general economy of a problem region, such as the Great Plains, so as to mitigate the effects of catastrophic droughts and floods? Under such circumstances, is regional planning of some form, such as the Tennessee Valley Authority for the humid regions, with its own problems, the answer? Should there be a Missouri Valley Authority established to control the headwaters of the Missouri River so as to provide irrigation water in dry seasons and prevent flood waters in the wet from destroying property? Should we follow the philosophy of those residents of the area who want no deal in planning or other measures of government control, but wish to remain free to speculate on land values and crop incomes for major gains; then become dependent on the government in a drought crisis? Actually, as you see, this poses an issue of governmental policy clearly resulting from a geographic maladjustment.

It is our purpose in this chapter to seek further understanding or clarification of such problems as those presented by the Great Plains and to indicate such measures as have been taken by the farmer himself as well as by local, regional, state, and federal agencies in resolving this recurring regional problem. As we shall see, ecologic, economic, conservational, and political principles of geography are involved. But geographic principles are meaningless without a knowledge

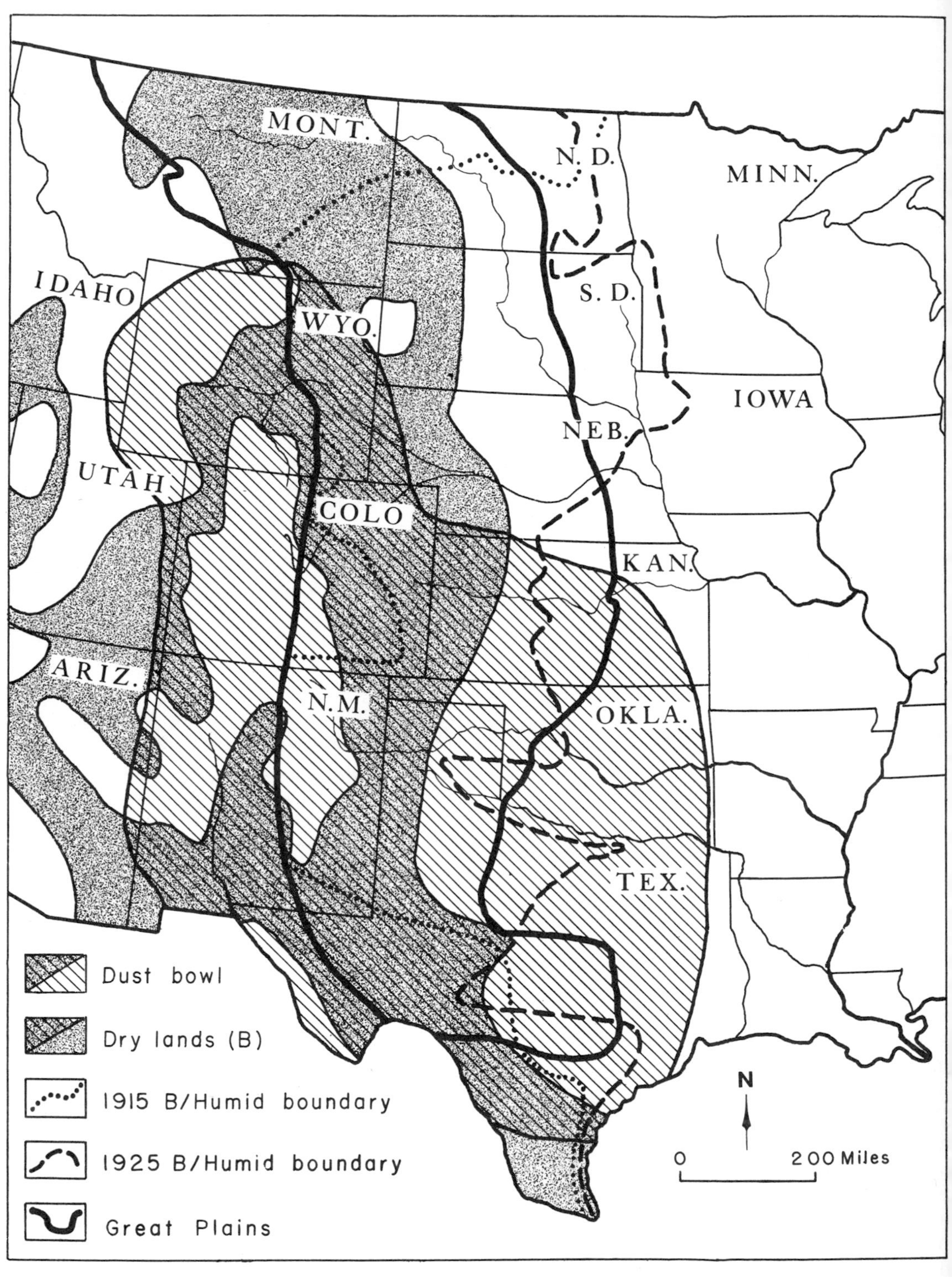
MONT.
N. D.
MINN.
IDAHO
S. D.
WYO.
IOWA
NEB.
UTAH
COLO
KAN.
ARIZ.
N.M.
OKLA.
TEX.
Dust bowl
Dry lands (B)
1915 B/Humid boundary
1925 B/Humid boundary
Great Plains
N
0
200 Miles

of the inexorable space patterns of natural phenomena upon which they are based.

The unpredictable rainfall regimen

It will be noted on the Köppen map (see Appendix) that the *BS* lands are peripheral to the *BW* and intermediate in position between *BW* and humid lands. The steppe region (Figure XXI-2) is, therefore, transitory in its climatological, pedological, and ecological characteristics. The boundary between *BS* and humid lands, as pointed out in the previous chapter, is not a function specifically of total amount of rainfall (conventionally put at 20 inches) but rainfall effectivity, as determined by the dryland formula used in the Köppen system. Such types of dryland classification presume that potential evaporation exceeds precipitation. Therefore, if the annual rainfall of a station is less than the rainfall effectivity value determined by formula in terms of inches of rainfall and average annual temperature, then such a station is considered a dryland station; if more, then a humid station. Since the rainfall effectivity value will vary according to the seasonality of the rain, three formulae, instead of one, have to be considered to determine rainfall effectivity data in accordance with summer rainfall or excess winter rainfall or rainfall more or less equally distributed in terms of plant growth relationships. Also, with high temperature there will be greater evaporation; consequently even a 25-inch rainfall may have a steppe grass rather than a prairie grass or forest cover; on the other hand, annual rainfall as low as 15 or even 12 inches may support tree vegetation, where under *BSk* or *BSk'* conditions. Thus it is important also to recognize subtypes of the steppe climate with three variable temperature conditions—a *BSh* (Figure XXI-3) where the annual average temperature is above 64.4; a *BSK* where the average annual temperature is below 64.4 (Figure XXI-4); and a *BSk'* where the warmest month temperature is below 64.4. Similarly on an ecological basis it is important to differentiate steppe climates based on a summer "max" rainfall (*BShw*) (Figure XXI-5), a winter "max" (*BSks*) (Figure XXI-6), and "even" distribution. These subtypes parallel those we have already considered in connection with *BW* lands. The student will thus recognize that several dryland types must be considered in any evaluation of biotic or human occupance relationships.

XXI:1 (Left) This map of America's drought-dust bowl has been composed to embrace several overlapping concepts of significance in understanding America's leading regional problem—the Great Plains (W. W. Atwood): land form fit for extensive agriculture; the drylands, *BS* and *BW* (Köppen and Geiger); the rhythmic shifting of the dry-humid boundary (Henry F. Kendall); and the Dust Bowl of 1956 (*Chicago Daily News*). Why is not the real desert region to the southwest included in the Dust Bowl?

Land–life studies in the dry world become infinitely more complicated in view of the fact that the rains of the *BS* world are diurnally, seasonally, and annually highly unpredictable. Frequently the 20-inch rainfall line, coinciding approximately with the 100th meridian, has been used to demarcate the western drier and the eastern humid section of the United States, but unscientifically so. Now, while the substitution of the dryland formulae mentioned above gives us a more nearly realistic picture of the situation, the additional fact must be recognized that fluctuations of this line, even formulae-determined, have varied in position as far eastward as Minnesota and as far westward as central Montana (Figure XXI-1). Though rainfall fluctuations of this character are a common and regular phenomenon, the swing of the line eastward or westward is unpredictable, and follows no particular pattern from year to year. Particularly the dry years in any one area may succeed themselves at two, three, four, five, or six-year intervals.

It is during such dry cycles that dust bowl or near dust bowl conditions develop such as occurred on a major regional scale in the Great Plains as noted in the introductory press dispatches.

High winds on the open steppes are also a contributing factor to desiccation, accentuating high evaporation and transpiration. A special type of desiccating wind is known as *chinook* or *foehn*. It results from a descending air mass, such as moves down the eastern slopes of the Rocky Mountains. Since such air currents become warmer under compres-

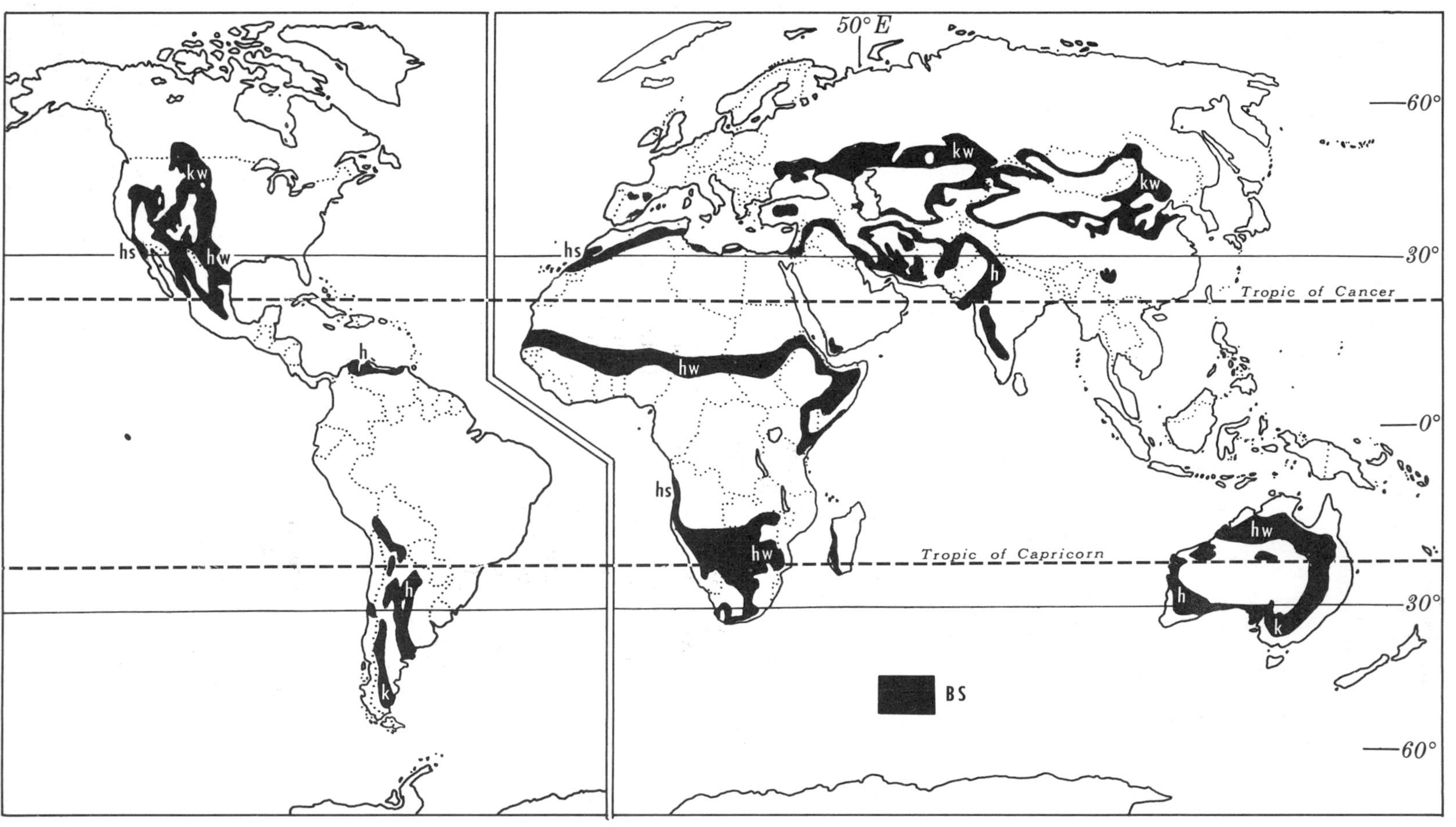
50° E
60°
30°
0°
30°
60°
Tropic of Cancer
Tropic of Capricorn
kw
hw
hs
h
k
BS

sion, their relative humidity is reduced and thus they become evaporating rather than precipitating. Temperature rises as great as 50 degrees have been noted in a few hours, resulting in accelerated evaporation of heavy snow cover in winter and rapid drying up of streams in the summer. The influence of the Rockies on the Great Plains steppe climate is even more pronounced. The mountain ranges in the West act as barriers to transfer of Pacific moisture vapor eastward by the westerly winds, and effect a *rainshadow.* Thus, the Great Plains area, as well as central and eastern humid United States, must depend primarily on the Gulf of Mexico or the Atlantic Ocean for its source of moisture directed into the low pressure centers, but normally such Lows are not sufficiently developed to counteract the *Coriolis Force,* which deflects the vapor-laden winds from the Gulf of Mexico eastward; as described by Stevens:

¶ One of the reasons for failure of rains in the Great Plains is the deflective force (Coriolis Force) caused by the rotation of the earth. This force deflects every wind in the Northern Hemisphere to the right. Since the Gulf of Mexico is the origin of the moisture which falls in the Great Plains, moist air may start moving from the Gulf towards the Plains and be deflected eastward so that it flows up the Mississippi Valley and on to Eastern Canada. If moist air from the Gulf is to reach the Great Plains, it must start moving northwestward across the West Gulf States gradually curving to the right. (For the moist air to reach Nebraska usually requires a low pressure center over Colorado later moving slowly eastward across Kansas.) Furthermore, this flow must occur at frequent intervals of time, and there must be frequent outbreaks of cold, or cool, air from Canada reaching the Plains and forcing the moist air to rise and release part of the moisture.[1]

[1] Stevens, W. R., "Some Causes of Droughts in the Great Plains," *Journal of Geography,* September, 1955, Vol. LIV, p. 305. Reprinted by permission.

XXI:2 (Left) Compare the distribution patterns of the *BS* with those of the *BW.* To which climatic controls are the *BS* areas chiefly related? What percentage of the United States is classified as dry, *BS-BW?* Which continent is least fortunate in having adequate rainfall?

Contrasted landforms and their influences on settlement and occupancy

Major landform features of the *BS* realm are similar to those of the *BW.* Here also we may find the land surface taking the form of plains, plateaus, and mountains. Advancing westward from the great prairies of the Interior Plains onto the Great Plains, we enter the more elevated steppe without noting any marked change in topography, vegetation, or other forms of the natural environment. As we approach the foothills of the Rockies, we encounter the higher plateau country characterized by mesas and canyons with a cliff and platform profile. Finally, upon entering the foothills we encounter spurs or ranges from the Rocky Mountains.

Highlands favor increased precipitation. Thus, peninsular-like extensions from the peripheral *BS* region or smaller islands of *BS* in the interior of the *BW,* as in the case of Inner Australia and the Sahara of North Africa, almost always connote mountain ranges or high plateaus. The reason for this, as we recall, is that air is cooled in being forced up the highland areas, which thus increases relative humidity, conducive to orographic rains. Porous rock outcrops, if any, may thus store a large water supply, and, if favorable rock structure exists, as when formations are folded or tilted to form cuesta outcrops, a great amount of the cutoff water may thus be transmitted by the rock aquifers for hundreds of miles as in the Great Sahara, and become the source of considerable artesian water in many sections otherwise devoid of any other water supply. The same thing is true of parts of the western Great Plains where cuestas outcrop in the adjacent mountains.

Surface streams originating at the top of moisture-precipitating highlands are normally not permanent since here also, as in the *BW* world, evaporation exceeds precipitation. Hence, the term *intermittent stream.* The loss of water by seepage and evaporation frequently results in aggradation of the stream channel, producing what is known as a *braided stream,* typified by the Platte River in Nebraska. Another aggradation feature, common in *BS* mountain foothills, is the *alluvial fan,* sometimes compounded in adjacent stream areas into a *piedmont alluvial*

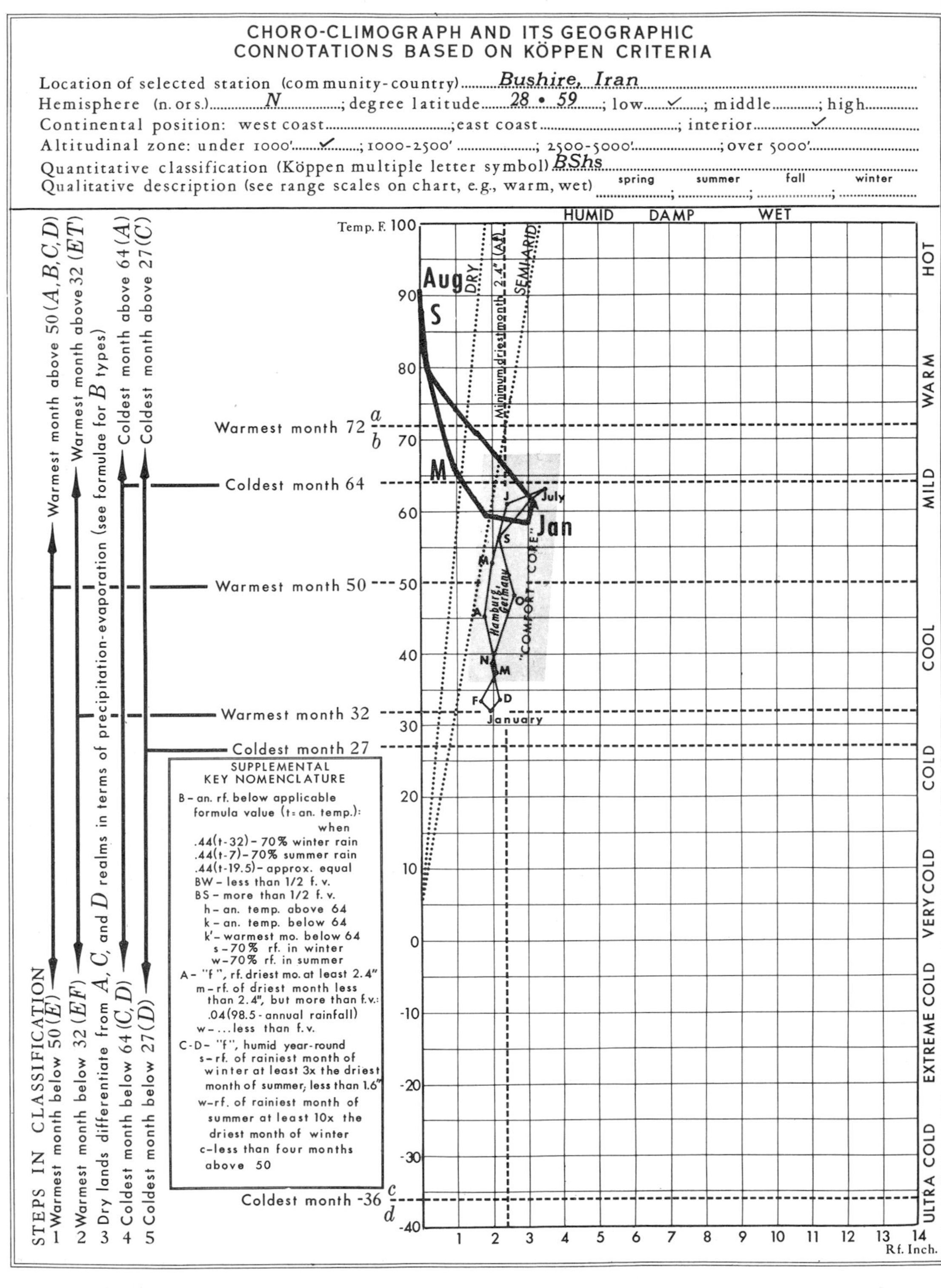
CHORO-CLIMOGRAPH AND ITS GEOGRAPHIC
CONNOTATIONS BASED ON KÖPPEN CRITERIA
Location of selected station (community-country) Bushire, Iran
Hemisphere (n. or s.) N; degree latitude 28 • 59; low ✓; middle; high
Continental position: west coast; east coast; interior ✓
Altitudinal zone: under 1000′ ✓; 1000-2500′; 2500-5000′; over 5000′
Quantitative classification (Köppen multiple letter symbol) BShs
Qualitative description (see range scales on chart, e.g., warm, wet) spring; summer; fall; winter
STEPS IN CLASSIFICATION
1 Warmest month below 50 (E) Warmest month above 50 (A, B, C, D)
2 Warmest month below 32 (EF) Warmest month above 32 (ET)
3 Dry lands differentiate from A, C, and D realms in terms of precipitation-evaporation (see formulae for B types)
4 Coldest month below 64 (C, D) Coldest month above 64 (A)
5 Coldest month below 27 (D) Coldest month above 27 (C)
Temp. F.
Warmest month 72
Coldest month 64
Warmest month 50
Warmest month 32
Coldest month 27
Coldest month -36
HUMID
DAMP
WET
DRY
SEMIARID
Minimum driest month 2.4″ (Af)
"COMFORT CORE"
Hamburg, Germany
January
Aug
S
M
Jan
July
HOT
WARM
MILD
COOL
COLD
VERY COLD
EXTREME COLD
ULTRA COLD
Rf. Inch.
SUPPLEMENTAL
KEY NOMENCLATURE
B – an. rf. below applicable formula value (t = an. temp.): when
.44(t-32) – 70% winter rain
.44(t-7) – 70% summer rain
.44(t-19.5) – approx. equal
BW – less than 1/2 f. v.
BS – more than 1/2 f. v.
h – an. temp. above 64
k – an. temp. below 64
k′ – warmest mo. below 64
s – 70% rf. in winter
w – 70% rf. in summer
A – "f", rf. driest mo. at least 2.4″
m – rf. of driest month less than 2.4″, but more than f.v.: .04(98.5 - annual rainfall)
w – ...less than f.v.
C-D – "f", humid year-round
s – rf. of rainiest month of winter at least 3x the driest month of summer; less than 1.6″
w – rf. of rainiest month of summer at least 10x the driest month of winter
c – less than four months above 50

plain. Such a form results from a partial check in the rate of stream flow. As the velocity of a stream is reduced, in passing from a steep to a more gentle gradient, its sediment carrying capacity is likewise reduced. Progressively, such streams deposit the gravelly material first, then sand farther out, and finally, the finer silt or clays farthest from the alluvial flats. These alluvial sites are favored spots for settlement and agriculture. The water-transported soils are rich in nutrient material, ever renewed by freshly decomposed rocks from which the minerals are derived. Moreover, this may be, and usually is, the only dependable source of adequate water for general crop culture. Here also very little energy may be required to adapt the water to irrigation uses, since frequently the stream distributaries at the base of the mountain automatically distribute water fairly evenly over the alluvial fan. Alluvial fans compare favorably to flood plains in productivity, and are among the most highly prized agricultural lands in the world.

So far we have pointed to some of the similarities existing between the landforms of the *BS* and *BW* worlds. Since the rainfall of the steppe averages roughly twice that of desert, and in many cases considerably more, there occur also differences in surface features. As a result of the grass sod cover typically found in the *BS* regions, landscape profiles are not as angular as those in the *BW*. Also, because of the greater rainfall, there is more chemical decomposition, even though physical disintegration will still likely be the dominant weathering phenomenon. Rock fields (*regs*) and sand dune wastes (*ergs*) are not as common in the *BS* as in the *BW* regions, for similar reasons. Indigenous streams, though still intermittent in flow, are more numerous and extended in the *BS* realms, as we would expect.

Soils and their adaptive relations to vegetation and agriculture

Steppe soils belong to a group classified by Marbut as *pedocals* (4). "Cal" refers to calcium, suggestive of high concentration of calcium carbonate and other alkaline minerals. Such soils are formed in climates of low rainfall, where there is little solution and therefore leaching of surface mineral materials. Iron and aluminum minerals are therefore left almost unchanged in the surface zone of eluviation, whereas sufficient moisture penetrates or percolates through the ground to dissolve the calcium minerals which are subsequently deposited in the so-called zone of illuviation. Three such steppe soils are recognized—the *chernozems* occurring on the subhumid margin of the Great Plains steppe of eastern North Dakota, South Dakota, Kansas, Oklahoma, and north-central Texas; the chestnut-brown soils covering nearly all the rest of the Great Plains area; and a limited amount of *sierozem* in the driest south-westernmost section of Texas. Associated respectively with these three types and contributing largely to their major differences are the tall grass cover of the easternmost belt, the short grass steppe of the rest of the major steppe area, and the arid scrubland of the extreme southwest steppe region. The sierozem classifies primarily as a desert soil.

Agricultural productivity likewise parallels these classifications from the most productive soil in the peripheral humid belt on the east to the driest type on the west. The chernozems accordingly are favored by the best soil-forming conditions of climate and vegetation on the side of semiaridity. There is little leaching of mineral nutrients; on the other hand, since these soils are on the transition zone between semiarid and humid regions, their moisture is adequate to support practically a complete cover of sod-grass, short towards the west, long towards the east. Such grass cover contributes to humus formation, the other necessary ingredient for a perfect soil. Accordingly the chernozem or black earth belt, as it is known from its humus content, which is found on the north shore of the Black Sea and extending eastward in the U.S.S.R. at approximately the 50° latitude, is one of the leading productive areas in the world, particularly for wheat growing. The same is true of large sections of our chernozem belt between the 95th and 100th meridian where specialized crop agriculture, centered particularly on

XXI:3 (Left) What is the length of the growing season at Bushire, temperature-wise and rainfall-wise? Do you think that normal groundwater storage during the rainfall period is adequate for certain types of crops during the rainless hot summer?

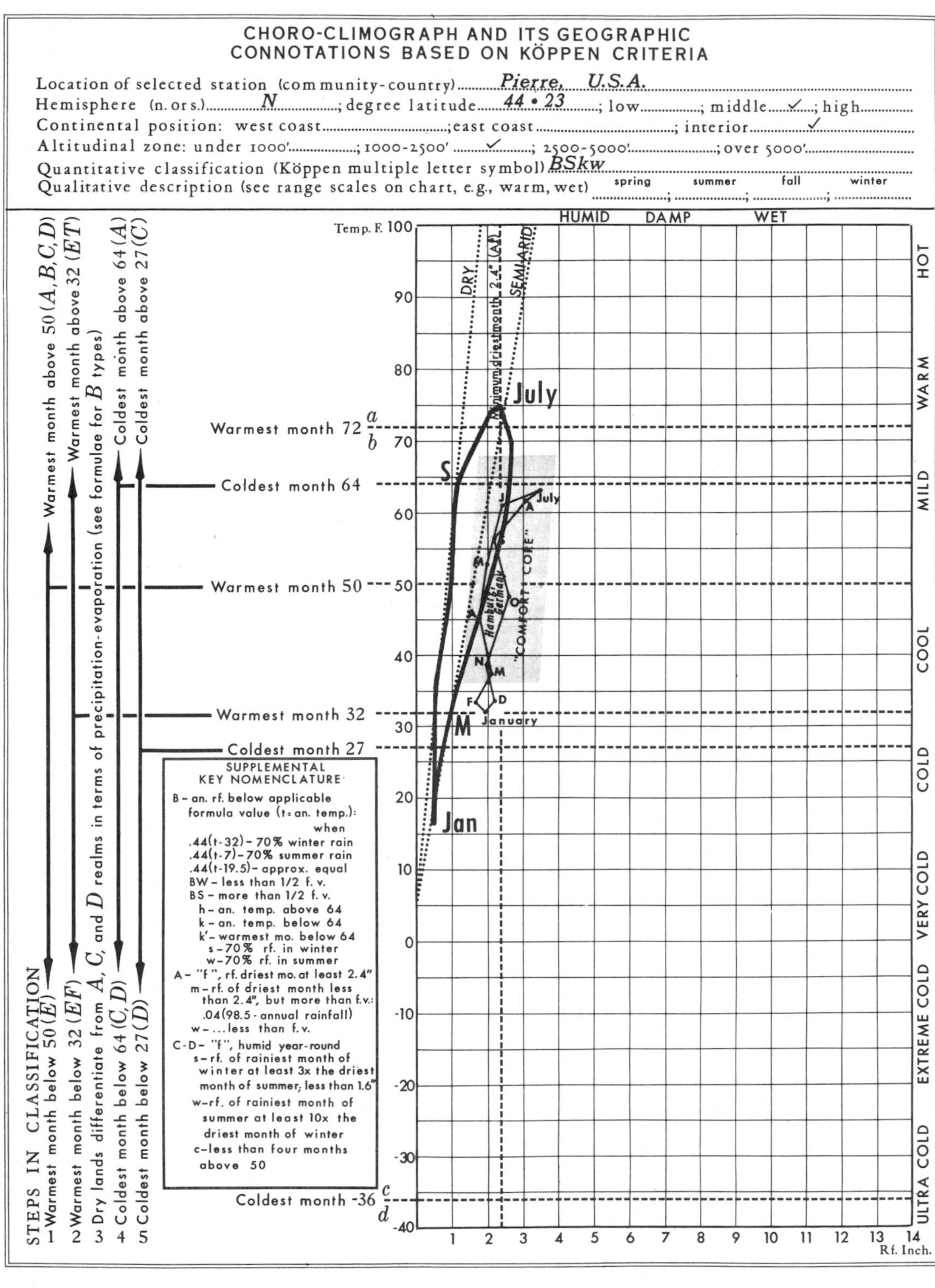
CHORO-CLIMOGRAPH AND ITS GEOGRAPHIC CONNOTATIONS BASED ON KÖPPEN CRITERIA
Location of selected station (community-country) Pierre, U.S.A.
Hemisphere (n. or s.) N ; degree latitude 44 • 23 ; low ; middle ✓ ; high
Continental position: west coast ; east coast ; interior ✓
Altitudinal zone: under 1000′ ; 1000-2500′ ✓ ; 2500-5000′ ; over 5000′
Quantitative classification (Köppen multiple letter symbol) BSkw
Qualitative description (see range scales on chart, e.g., warm, wet) spring ; summer ; fall ; winter
STEPS IN CLASSIFICATION
1 Warmest month below 50 (E) — Warmest month above 50 (A, B, C, D)
2 Warmest month below 32 (EF) — Warmest month above 32 (ET)
3 Dry lands differentiate from A, C, and D realms in terms of precipitation-evaporation (see formulae for B types)
4 Coldest month below 64 (C, D) — Coldest month above 64 (A)
5 Coldest month below 27 (D) — Coldest month above 27 (C)
Warmest month 72 a b
Coldest month 64
Warmest month 50
Warmest month 32
Coldest month 27
Coldest month -36 c d
SUPPLEMENTAL KEY NOMENCLATURE
B - an. rf. below applicable formula value (t = an. temp.): when
.44(t-32) - 70% winter rain
.44(t-7) - 70% summer rain
.44(t-19.5) - approx. equal
BW - less than 1/2 f. v.
BS - more than 1/2 f. v.
h - an. temp. above 64
k - an. temp. below 64
k′ - warmest mo. below 64
s - 70% rf. in winter
w - 70% rf. in summer
A - "f", rf. driest mo. at least 2.4"
m - rf. of driest month less than 2.4", but more than f.v.: .04(98.5 - annual rainfall)
w - ... less than f. v.
C-D - "f", humid year-round
s - rf. of rainiest month of winter at least 3x the driest month of summer, less than 1.6"
w - rf. of rainiest month of summer at least 10x the driest month of winter
c - less than four months above 50
Temp. F.
HUMID DAMP WET
DRY SEMIARID
Minimum driest month 2.4" (Af)
July
S
Jan
M
"COMFORT CORE"
Hamburg, Germany
July
January
HOT WARM MILD COOL COLD VERY COLD EXTREME COLD ULTRA COLD
Rf. Inch.

wheat, is found. Thus wheat and other grain culture has been well extended across the chestnut-brown soils. Because of lesser rainfall and less humus, due to shorter and sparser grasses, the effects of crop failures are more frequent and devastating, giving rise in places to the Dust Bowl conditions referred to above.

We have seen that the grass cover of the Great Plains steppe varies from the taller continuous sod on the humid eastern limits to the shorter grass occurring more sparsely on the western, drier, leeward foothills of the Rockies. We should likewise expect differentiated ecological conditions of plant life on the basis of temperature differences latitudinally expressed by the *BSh* or hot steppe in the south and the *BSk* (or even *Bsk'*) in the northern part of the Great Plains. And so in Texas we find primarily what has been called the thorn-bush steppe or the *mesquite* with a mixed stand of woody shrub and spotty growth of grass. Northward, short steppe grass becomes increasingly predominant, ultimately forming continuous sod. Thus the *BSk* pasture conditions are more favorable for livestock grazing as far as summer foraging is concerned. However, because of the severe winters in this latitude as well as the shorter summer growing season, cattle cannot be grazed over as long a period as in the south where the less desirable forage may be found.

Animal ecology

The native animals of the steppe region are similar to those of the desert areas. However, because of more favorable grazing conditions, life is more prolific, both in number of species and actual number of animals. This is especially true in *BSh* regions bordering *Aw* lands in the subtropics. These regions have the greatest variety and number of combined herbivores and carnivores in the world. These constitute the famous hunting areas of Africa. Many of the ungulates migrate seasonally from *Aw* into *BSh* areas, and vice versa. These animals include various species of antelopes, gazelles, zebras, and a score or more of other ungulates or herbivorous types. Such animals, of course, become prey for the carnivores, for example, the leopard and lion. Animal life in Australia is more restricted in number and types. Here are found several representatives of the marsupial family, including the well-known kangaroo. Equally distinctive of our own Great Plains regions was the bison, now practically extinct except as it is protected in animal refuge areas and in national parks. The antelope, wild horse, and a few other ungulates also may still be found in the more or less unsettled areas of the Great Plains. Following in their wake are the coyote, the wolf, and the fox. As feeders on both grass and roots of plants, rodents occupy practically all the *BS* lands. They can become a real pest as in the case of the rabbit introduced in Australia, where thousands of acres of croplands have been devastated, requiring joint efforts of the farmers and the government to eradicate them. In the Great Plains the jack rabbit, gopher, prairie dog, and other burrowing animals have created hazards for livestock, since cows may break their legs by stepping through the sod into the burrows of the rodents.

XXI:4 (Left) What can you infer from the graph as to the grazing and cropland conditions of the Pierre community? Note that almost half of the climograph lies within the zone classified as humid.

Man–land relationships in diverse regions

Despite the relative uniformity of steppe landscapes with their sod cover and high grazing potentialities, occupance forms of the various steppe lands of the world present decided contrasts. Thus in the interior dry heart of Asia, as in sections of the desert of Gobi, one will still find nomadism based on herding of cattle with little change from the earliest knowledge of the area. On the other hand, the Western Range of North America, with its original Amerindian hunter, has long since passed the pioneer fringe stage. Most of the land in the eastern section has now been fenced in and developed into mixed grain and stock farming, many farmsteads appearing little different from those of the humid prairies immediately to the east. Colonization of the steppe lands in South America by the Spanish, as in Patagonia, and of the large South African region by the early Boers and subsequently the English, and of

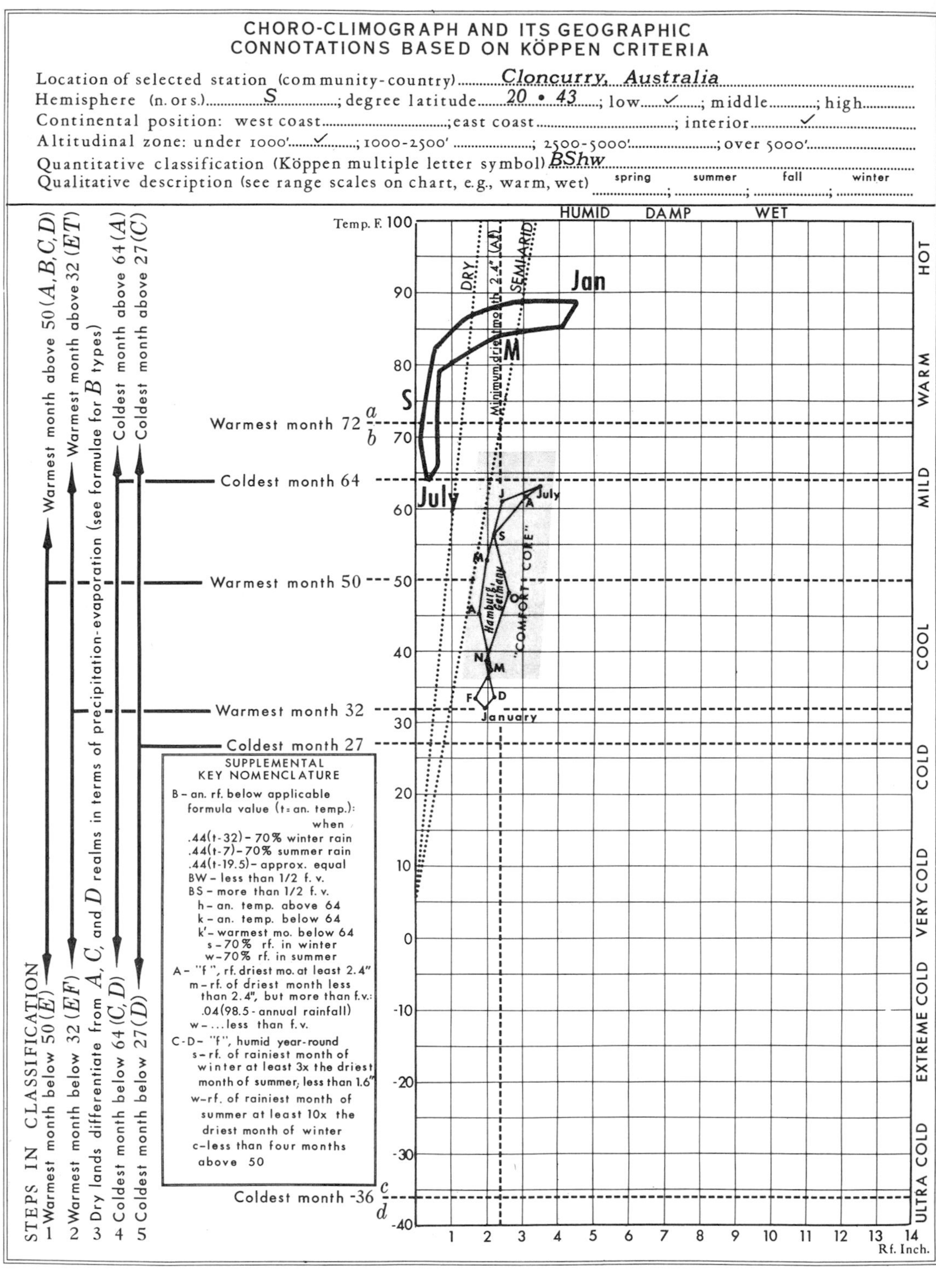

CHORO-CLIMOGRAPH AND ITS GEOGRAPHIC CONNOTATIONS BASED ON KÖPPEN CRITERIA
Location of selected station (community-country) Cloncurry, Australia
Hemisphere (n. or s.) S; degree latitude 20 • 43; low ✓; middle; high
Continental position: west coast; east coast; interior ✓
Altitudinal zone: under 1000' ✓; 1000-2500'; 2500-5000'; over 5000'
Quantitative classification (Köppen multiple letter symbol) BShw
Qualitative description (see range scales on chart, e.g., warm, wet) spring; summer; fall; winter
HUMID
DAMP
WET
DRY
SEMIARID
Minimum driest month 2.4" (Af)
Jan
July
S
M
"COMFORT CORE"
Hamburg, Germany
January
Temp. F.
Rf. Inch.
HOT
WARM
MILD
COOL
COLD
VERY COLD
EXTREME COLD
ULTRA COLD
Warmest month 72
Coldest month 64
Warmest month 50
Warmest month 32
Coldest month 27
Coldest month -36
STEPS IN CLASSIFICATION
1 Warmest month below 50 (E) — Warmest month above 50 (A, B, C, D)
2 Warmest month below 32 (EF) — Warmest month above 32 (ET)
3 Dry lands differentiate from A, C, and D realms in terms of precipitation-evaporation (see formulae for B types)
4 Coldest month below 64 (C, D) — Coldest month above 64 (A)
5 Coldest month below 27 (D) — Coldest month above 27 (C)
SUPPLEMENTAL KEY NOMENCLATURE
B – an. rf. below applicable formula value (t = an. temp.): when
.44(t-32) – 70% winter rain
.44(t-7) – 70% summer rain
.44(t-19.5) – approx. equal
BW – less than 1/2 f. v.
BS – more than 1/2 f. v.
h – an. temp. above 64
k – an. temp. below 64
k' – warmest mo. below 64
s – 70% rf. in winter
w – 70% rf. in summer
A – "f", rf. driest mo. at least 2.4"
m – rf. of driest month less than 2.4", but more than f.v.: .04(98.5 - annual rainfall)
w – ...less than f.v.
C-D – "f", humid year-round
s – rf. of rainiest month of winter at least 3x the driest month of summer; less than 1.6"
w – rf. of rainiest month of summer at least 10x the driest month of winter
c – less than four months above 50

the large rim of steppe land in Australia by the English has transformed the early wild animal ranges into modern stock ranges, chiefly sheep rearing. The population of such steppe sections then will depend in large measure upon the stage of economic development. Their occupance normally follows the sequence of nomadic herding, nomadic grazing, sheep herding, cow punching, and finally some special form of agriculture. None of these pursuits contributes heavily to population despite the fact that the environmental habitat otherwise is reasonably suited for it. Sizable urban communities are to be found only where focal points of attraction are involved, as in the case of the exploitation of critically important minerals. Examples of this type occur at the northern end of the Persian Gulf, on the northwest shore of the Caspian Sea; in southern Russia (Donetz Basin), which is favored by its combined industrial and commercial setting; in our Great Plains area, where Denver, located at the foothills of the mountains and in proximity to a pass beyond them, occupies a strategic trade and transportation position between the Great Plains and the Rocky Mountain province.

Settlement and land utilization patterns of the Great Plains

Marked latitudinal difference of climatic conditions between the northern and southern Great Plains and a diversity in the longitudinal belts of soils from the eastern *chernozems* through the brown earths to western and southwestern *sierozem soils,* result in differentiated coherent relationships in the several subregions. Several subtypes within each of the main belts are recognized by the U.S. Department of Agriculture.

*1. **Major land-use regions.*** Largest areal extent of a single type land-use is that of the arid high plains, flanking the Rockies, and classified as grazing-woodland-irrigated cropland. This constitutes a continuous strip all the way from Montana to the Rio Grande of Texas. The second largest use area is cropland grazing. This includes the Dakota Plains, the Central High Plains of Colorado and Kansas; the Oklahoma-Kansas Plains, and the Llano Estacado of the panhandle of Texas. The third category of land-use is the grazing cropland of the Northern High Plains, extending from Montana southeastward into Kansas; and in the south, the redbeds and gypsum plains of north central Texas and west central Oklahoma. In the Middle Great Plains at the easternmost boundary, primarily centered in Nebraska, is the cropland-pasture-forest, designated in this case as the Central Farm Belt, which is an extension of the general Corn Belt area from the east.

In terms of specialized grain culture, the Dakota Plains feature spring wheat, whereas the hard winter wheat section is centered on the Kansas-Oklahoma Plains. A wedge of the Corn Belt, previously mentioned, extends on the Central Farm Belt to the southwest corner of Nebraska.

*2. **Population per square mile by counties (1950).*** Numerous contiguous counties in the northern half of the Great Plains show less than 2 people per square mile. By far the larger number of remaining counties rate less than 5 per square mile. A majority of counties in the plains to the south range from 6 to 18 per square mile, with some major or sizable units under 5, and a few under 2. The percentage of farm population in comparison to the total is considerably higher in the north where numerous counties rate from 60 to 80 per cent.

The proportion of the area in public lands is also considerably higher in the Northern Plains. In value of land and buildings per acre the Northern Plains in most cases is under $25 per acre, whereas in the southwesternmost section of Nebraska and extending across Kansas, Oklahoma, and northwestern Texas, the acreage of land is about evenly divided between $25-$50 and $50-$75 per acre. The average size of commercial farms on the Great Plains increases in a general way from east to west. Only a very small percentage of farms, as found on the eastern extremity of the Central Plains, runs between 200 and 500 acres. In the central meridional belt, they average from 1,000 to 2,500 acres. In large contiguous areas of the foothill

XXI:5 (Left) How do you account for the fact that though the July temperature is approximately the same for both Cloncurry and Hamburg, the January readings are about 60° apart?

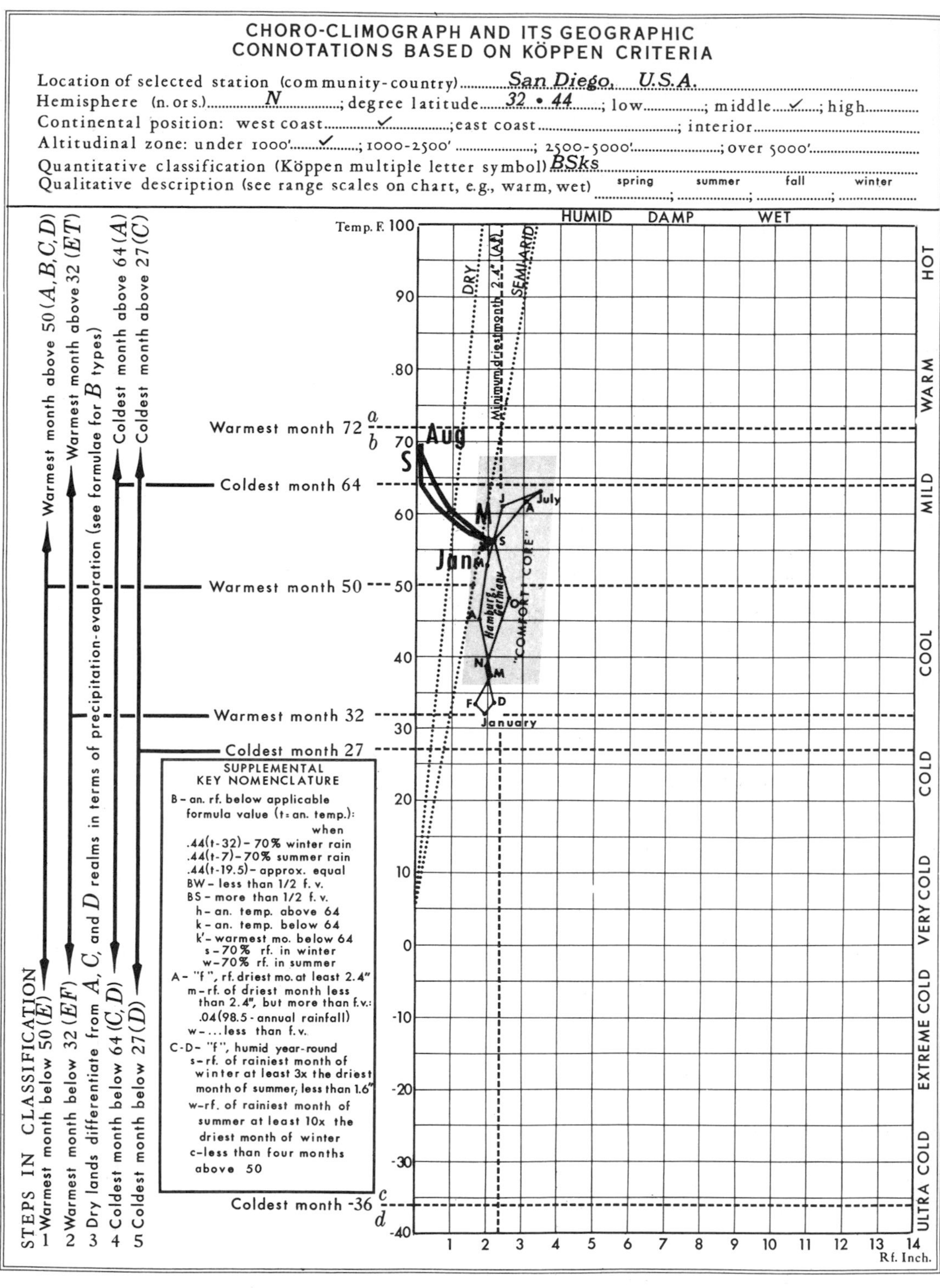
CHORO-CLIMOGRAPH AND ITS GEOGRAPHIC
CONNOTATIONS BASED ON KÖPPEN CRITERIA
Location of selected station (community-country) San Diego, U.S.A.
Hemisphere (n. or s.) N; degree latitude 32 • 44; low; middle ✓; high
Continental position: west coast ✓; east coast; interior
Altitudinal zone: under 1000' ✓; 1000-2500'; 2500-5000'; over 5000'
Quantitative classification (Köppen multiple letter symbol) BSks
Qualitative description (see range scales on chart, e.g., warm, wet) spring; summer; fall; winter
HUMID
DAMP
WET
Temp. F. 100
90
80
70
60
50
40
30
20
10
0
-10
-20
-30
-40
1 2 3 4 5 6 7 8 9 10 11 12 13 14
Rf. Inch.
DRY
SEMIARID
Minimum driest month 2.4" (Af)
HOT
WARM
MILD
COOL
COLD
VERY COLD
EXTREME COLD
ULTRA COLD
Warmest month 72 a b
Coldest month 64
Warmest month 50
Warmest month 32
Coldest month 27
Coldest month -36 c d
Aug
S
M
Jan.
July
J
A
S
O
N
M
F
D
January
Hamburg, Germany
"COMFORT CORE"
Warmest month above 50 (A, B, C, D)
Warmest month above 32 (ET)
Coldest month above 64 (A)
Coldest month above 27 (C)
STEPS IN CLASSIFICATION
1 Warmest month below 50 (E)
2 Warmest month below 32 (EF)
3 Dry lands differentiate from A, C, and D realms in terms of precipitation-evaporation (see formulae for B types)
4 Coldest month below 64 (C, D)
5 Coldest month below 27 (D)
SUPPLEMENTAL
KEY NOMENCLATURE
B - an. rf. below applicable formula value (t = an. temp.): when
.44(t-32) - 70% winter rain
.44(t-7) - 70% summer rain
.44(t-19.5) - approx. equal
BW - less than 1/2 f. v.
BS - more than 1/2 f. v.
h - an. temp. above 64
k - an. temp. below 64
k' - warmest mo. below 64
s - 70% rf. in winter
w - 70% rf. in summer
A - "f", rf. driest mo. at least 2.4"
m - rf. of driest month less than 2.4", but more than f.v.: .04(98.5 - annual rainfall)
w - ... less than f.v.
C-D - "f", humid year-round
s - rf. of rainiest month of winter at least 3x the driest month of summer, less than 1.6"
w - rf. of rainiest month of summer at least 10x the driest month of winter
c - less than four months above 50

Rockies, as in Montana, Wyoming, New Mexico, and Texas, farms average 2,500 acres and over. This latter feature reflects the increasing importance of the grazing range type of agriculture, with increasing aridity as we approach the Rockies. Irrigation land likewise increases in percentage. The pattern of irrigation projects is for the most part linear, revealing stream courses whose headwaters rise in the Rockies. The highest percentages of county cropland values (40-60-80 per cent) is found in the Central Plains and in areas extending southward into Panhandle Texas. North Dakota also ranks high. But the western portion of South Dakota, due to the Badlands topography, is rated well under 20 per cent.

3. Cropland harvested: increase and decrease in acreage, 1899-1949. While most states in the humid east declined in harvested cropland, practically all the sections in the United States west of the 100th meridian gained in this farmland category. Particularly conspicuous are major increases noted in the tiers of Great Plains states all the way from North Dakota south to Texas, especially in the central and western parts of those states as well as sections in Colorado and Wyoming. This reflects not only increasing settlement of such regions but intensification of cropland agriculture based on specialized crops (wheat and other grains in the north; cotton and sorghums in the extreme south). Part of such increases is attributable to increased dryland farming and irrigation projects.

4. Hay acreage as percentage of cropland harvested, 1949. Except for fragmentary Rocky Mountain foothill acreages of this type, there is very little of such land in the Southern Plains. The Northern Plains, on the other hand, includes contiguous counties where the percentage generally runs from 25 to 50, and in single counties from 60 to 80. This excess acreage in forage crops coheres with the longer winter season of the *BWk* region and its requirements of an ample supply of forage (5).

Farming in the *BS* world consists of various types. It may center, in the more humid regions, upon one particular crop, as in the Dakota spring-wheat belt. This type of farming on a featureless plain lends itself to large-scale agriculture. Farms are large, fields are large, and practically all the farm operations are mechanized. Tractor-drawn plows, seeding drills, combines, or other harvesting machinery, make possible tillage of one or more 640-acre sections. Abroad, this type finds its most extensive development in the trans-Caspian region of the Soviet Union where, on the so-called giant state farms *(Sovkhoz),* areas comparable to multiple counties in the United States are devoted to a single crop tillage.

Though yields may be only half of those in humid lands, the extensiveness of the acreage normally results in high total production. More than average rainfall may actually result in bumper crops, but subnormal rains may result in partial or total failure. And as pointed out above, a succession of especially dry years, when *BS* areas are transformed to *BW* lands, may very well lead to bankruptcy or famine. Single crop agriculture, moreover, results in soil impoverishment of both its inorganic and organic plant food material.

5. Dry farming. In areas where precipitation is annually too low to ensure a reasonable crop yield, land may be left lying fallow for two or three years. Meanwhile, the soil is stirred frequently to maintain a porous surface ready to absorb such rains as do fall. Moreover, such frequent tillage conserves moisture by preventing high evaporation through the capillary attraction of moisture to the surface as well as by eliminating weed growth, which also extracts moisture from the soil storage of underground water supply. Such practices may thus make possible the seeding of fields every second or third year. Even so, yields of wheat, or other grain even more dry tolerant than wheat, such as barley and rye, may amount to only one half of yields of more humid areas. It is interesting here to note that historically dry farming on an extensive scale and in a rather scientific manner was first introduced into Utah in the vicinity of Great Salt Lake by the Mormons. The practice was subsequently extended to the Western Great Plains and other drier sections of the West. But dry farming meth-

XXI:6 (Left) The San Diego–Los Angeles region rates well among America's leading "amenities" communities. What role does climate play?

ods probably are more responsible for the Dust Bowl developments than is any other factor. The ground stripped of its sod cover and lying bare for several seasons is particularly subject to a form of wind erosion and soil removal known as deflation. Because of the usually very low yields, farming units of this type are likely to be even larger than those of the specialized grain-farming unit just mentioned. Dry-farming is based on groundwater storage and water-conservation practices, which include: (1) summer fallowing (planting but one crop in the course of several years); (2) frequent cultivation of the soil to eradicate moisture-extracting weeds and otherwise to arrest loss of moisture caused by capillarization; (3) planting of such crops as millet, sorghum, barley, or wheat, which have low moisture requirements compared with other crops.

6. Irrigated croplands. Except for moisture deficiency as previously noted, dryland soils can prove very productive. In fact, because of their nonleached condition, due to low precipitation, they are generally more fertile than many of the soils of humid regions. Moreover, the high percentage of sunshine likewise favors the growth of crops, and low humidity usually prevents blights and other plant diseases. All that is needed, then, is water, supplied to the roots of a plant in adequate quantities, regulated according to the needs of the growing season, and controlled drainage, which will prevent the soils from becoming over-alkalized. Practically all crops will greatly benefit in quantity and quality from application of irrigation waters. But the limited supply of such water constitutes a real problem. Most of such water is exotic, that is, imported from humid sources outside the area by streams, or conducted by aquifers from some adjacent, usually more highly-elevated, region. Due to the limited supply, such drought-tolerant crops as wheat, millet, and barley are normally not irrigated except where waters are unduly plentiful. In the *h* steppes we may expect to find sugar cane, cotton, tobacco, fruit, and vegetables; in cooler climes (*k-k′*), sugar beets, forage crops, fruits, and vegetables. But irrigation also presents problems. Aside from the cost of developing such projects, the lower slopes may become water-logged and also increasingly saline, as a result of high evaporation, which leaves the salt behind. Tile drainage may be needed to eliminate the excess alkalinity to restore productivity, since only a few cultivated plants are tolerant of alkaline conditions.

The role of drylands in history

Though commonly distinguished from other lands by their isolation and desolation, the major arid lands of Eurasia, of Africa, and of North America particularly have exerted a profound influence throughout ancient, medieval, and modern history. We need only to recall the ancient centers of civilizations and culture of the Indus Valley of India, Northern Babylonia, East Palestine, Assyria, Egypt, Arabia — all of which classify as *BW*, or *BW-BS* lands. Under conditions of year-round rainfall deficiency and summer-desiccation, we note Babylon pioneering astronomy; Egypt, from which originated our mathematics (geometry and algebra), and Alexandria, founded by Alexander the Great in 332 B.C., where the University of Egypt was established as well as the largest library in the world at that time, said to contain over a half million volumes.

We recall the journeys of the Arab Moslem who in the early part of medieval times advanced through northern Africa westward, crossed the Strait of Gibraltar into Iberia (Spain) and established at Toledo the greatest library and center of learning during the Middle Ages in Europe. Relict occupance forms of Moslem Spain are still recognizable in the cultural landscape, as in the architecture of certain buildings and in the structure of early irrigation works. Such cultural influences from without, as well as the similarity of physical features of southern Spain compared with those of northwest Africa across the strait, have suggested to some geographers that Spain actually belongs to Africa rather than to Europe. In that case, the Pyrenees Mountains, instead of the Strait of Gibraltar, would be the regional boundary.

Now turning our attention to the other half of the Arabian Mongolian axis, the desert of Gobi in Central Asia, we note that in the thirteenth century under the leadership of Genghis Khan, the ruthless hordes of nomads surged out in successive waves into all the peripheral lands of Asia and Europe, impelled apparently by dry cycle conditions.

The historic thesis is based on the idea that when the dry interior, as a result of progressive desiccation through several years, had almost completely lost its vegetation, and even the oases were on the verge of extinction, the Mongol horseman would move out of the dry heart into the more humid peripheral steppe lands. But when prolonged drought reduced the steppe lands likewise to desert conditions, the nomad would extend his forays into the pasture areas of the more humid lands, southward into China, eastward into Manchuria, northward into Siberia, southwestward into India, and westward into Russia and Turkey. All these migrations, of course, did not happen during one season, but occurred in a series of waves in accordance with the extent and severity of the drought in interior Asia. Subsequent hordes would successively press upon the heels of the preceding migrants in chain fashion pushing them farther and farther into peripheral Asia and Europe. Evidence exists that the Mongolian nomad extended himself as far westward into Europe as France and Italy. The areal expansion through successive conquests and exploitation of neighboring peoples by the Asiatic Mongolian "empire" might be geographically considered as an expression of the *lebensraum* type of economics and political philosophy of the late medieval period. The empire finally crumbled due to internal strife among various nomadic chieftains as well as among the newly established countries on the border until finally, during the eighteenth century, the core area came under control of the Chinese Manchus. Today, this area is known as Outer Mongolia and constitutes the Mongolian Peoples Republic.

The historical geography of drylands in North America is quite different from the oriental picture just drawn. Instead of the Amerindian of the dry West moving into more humid lands, we have the European immigrants and the American colonists advancing westward on to the Great Plains steppe and then occupying the drier regions of the West. In other words, the Great Plains and other western sections of the U.S. and Canada posed as frontier country, beginning about the middle of the nineteenth century. Settlement experiences here, as we shall presently note, afford an interesting study in human geography—an example of how the culture of a people developed in humid land, and under forest cover, became radically modified to conform to the landscape conditions of an entirely different world. This example classically illustrates how a region under certain circumstances challenges tradition and heritage as man seeks to make suitable working connections with a new type of environment. One of the best expositions on the subject is that of Walter Prescott Webb in *The Great Frontier*. The following is a highly excerpted or abstracted observation of Webb under the title, "The Frontier as a Modifier of Institutions":

¶ The Great Plains afford some excellent examples of the breaking or bending of institutions by an environment . . . the last region of the United States to be taken by the American pioneers. . . . It was left to the last because the Anglo-American people had not in all their history had any experience with such a country . . . they could not use boats, for there were no streams to bear them; they could not build log cabins or rail fences because there were no trees for logs or rails. Their weapons were ineffective against the horsemen of the prairies. Their methods of agriculture were those of the humid country and brought only disaster to those who followed them in the arid land; their plows would not turn the grass-matted sod. Their whole culture recoiled on the border of this strange frontier and before they could take it they had to devise a whole new set of practices from their way of fighting to their way of farming.

The frontier weapon of the Eastern American woodland was the long rifle commonly known as the Kentucky or Tennessee rifle . . . it served the purpose of the hunters and fighters until they emerged from the forest onto the open plains where the Indians met them on horseback in a new type of warfare. The Plains Indians occupying the Great Plains from Mexico to Canada were all bedouins, became superb horsemen, who lived, hunted and fought on their horses. When the Americans entered the plains they had to go on horseback, too. They quickly found that their long rifle was no longer a suitable weapon, for with it they were unable to meet on equal terms the mounted Indian armed with bow and arrow. To fight, they had to dismount leaving the initiative in the hands of the enemy who could come and go at will. What the American needed when he left the forest was a multiple-shot weapon that could be used on horseback, and such an arm he did not have. The answer to this need was the revolver invented by Samuel Colt of Connecticut about 1830-31, at the time when fingers of immigration were being tentatively extended into the open country.[1]

Here follows an interesting account of the colonization of the Province of Texas in Mexico by Stephen Austin and others and of local raids upon the settlements by Comanches and Apaches on horseback; of the defection of the Texans against Mexico in setting up of the new independent republic of Texas in 1836, for the defense of which the Texas Rangers were organized or rather legalized to defend the republic. It appears that revolvers were first used in the Indian battle of the Pedernales, where it was demonstrated that at last the Rangers could successfully pursue the Indians on horseback. Then subsequently came their use in the Mexican War.

¶ Here the revolvers were on the proving ground before the whole United States Army, and the demand for them was immediate and insatiable. . . . The Texas Rangers was the first American institution created in response to the plains environment and the revolver was the first mechanical adaptation to the needs of the country . . . the rise of the ranch cattle industry on the Great Plains illustrates the effect of an environment on an economic institution, how a frontier modifies an economic system . . . the Cattle Kingdom had its birth at the spot where men began to handle cattle on horseback on an open range instead of on foot in small pastures and cow lots. This beginning took place in the Nueces Valley at the southern tip of Texas where wild cattle, wild horses, and almost equally wild men were thrown by the exigencies of history into close juxtaposition. Both the cattle and the horses were of Spanish extraction—tough, wiry, and hard to handle. They had been brought in by the Spaniards and left there by the Mexicans when they retired south of the Rio Grande before the American advance. There the young Americans, mainly Texans, began to handle cattle on horseback and so became the first cowboys. What these first cowboys did was to borrow from the Mexicans their methods, their gear for horses and much of their terminology, and all these they adapted to their own uses in creating within the Great Plains an institution entirely new to the people of the United States. . . .

The common fence in the eastern half of the United States was made of rails split from the tree trunks of the cleared fields . . . for want of fencing the agricultural frontier was almost brought to a dead halt on the edge of the plains, and it was unable to move forward until a practical fence was invented, every device imaginable was tried such as thorny hedges of bois d'arc, cactus, running roses; even mud fences were built to go along with the sod houses. None of the substitutes were satisfactory and all were expensive. The fence problem may be said to have been acute from 1850 to 1875, leaving the Great Plains in the hands of the cattle kings of the open range . . . the solution, the invention of barbed wire was the work of a group of farmers living in the open prairies of Illinois near the little town of DeKalb . . . what they discovered was that a cheap and practical fence, one easy to construct and to maintain could be made by twisting two wires with barbs spaced at regular intervals, and that three strands of this infernal contrivance stretched tight on posts would keep cattle and crops separated . . . barbed wire was shipped into the plains by the trainload, and within twenty-five years nearly all the open range had become privately owned and was under fence. Ranching was converted from the open range into the big pasture type . . . but the ability to fence did not give them the ability to farm, as they were to find out in that greatest of all experiment stations, trial and error. . . . Their accustomed methods of farming, so well integrated with forty inches of annual precipitation, were to prove disastrous in a land where rainfall averaged twenty inches, and in years of drought close to ten or twelve. The suffering that resulted from efforts to farm in the traditional manner, in the only manner that they knew, is a tragic story of broken fortunes, broken men, and broken women . . . the solution was irrigation farming in lands where water was available and dry land farming in the much greater area where all must depend on the scanty rains . . . accompanying the discovery of the principles of dry farming went the search for new plants adapted to an arid climate, and the development of new varieties of old plants by breeding. The very names of the imported plants which have proved successful indicate

[1] Webb, Walter Prescott, *The Great Frontier*, Houghton Mifflin Company, Boston, 1952, pp. 239-256, *passim*. Reprinted by permission.

their origin in the dry country—Sudan grass, feterida, hegira, Rhodes grass, and so on. From Russia came the red fife wheat, brought in tiny bundles to the plains by the Mennonite immigrants. . . . The final example used to illustrate the modification of an institution by the Great Plains environment is in the field of law. It is generally conceded that the law is devoted to tradition and is exceedingly slow to change its basic principles. In spite of this the Great Plains afford the striking example, not only of modification but also of a complete abrogation of the English common law of water from England to the humid portion of the United States where it underwent slight modification, thence into the margins of the Great Plains where it was radically altered and then into the heart of the Great Plains where it has been abrogated and a new law devised. . . . Now the law, as it had developed in England and as it was adopted by most of the forty-eight states, is known as the law of riparian rights. . . . The important provision with which we are concerned is that under the law of riparian rights only the owner of the bank of the stream had certain water rights, hence *ripa*. The nonriparian owner was excluded. The riparian rights were divided into two classes, natural and artificial. Under natural rights came the use of water for livestock and ordinary domestic purposes, and there was no limit on the amount, necessarily small, that was used in these ways. Artificial rights were those under which the riparian owner could use water, usually but not always by diverting it, for the purpose of turning a mill wheel or for other work. If the owner diverted water, he was required to return it to the channel within the limits of his own land; he could not permit it to damage a neighbor.

The basic principle of the riparian law was the correlative or equal rights of all riparian owners. By this principle each riparian owner had a right to the full and undiminished flow of the stream. Obviously this precluded any possibility of irrigation because water for irrigation is absorbed, leaves the stream less than full-flow, and diminishes it by the amount of water drawn off. In a humid country where irrigation was unnecessary and unknown the law worked well enough. . . . The law moved west as the states were admitted, and by the middle of the nineteenth century it was entering the eastern margins of the Great Plains. . . . Immediately, from the drier portions of these states demands began to be made for a *modification* of the riparian law so as to permit irrigation. This modification was brought about, not by making a new law but by further modifying the old one. This task was performed through the courts by reinterpretation, the argument being that in an arid land irrigation was an absolute necessity, something of a natural right and not an artificial one at all. The courts resolved the problem by substituting the words *reasonable* and *unreasonable* for natural and artificial. If, the courts ruled, A's use of water was reasonable and did not deprive the riparian owners B and C downstream of any benefit, then A could use it for irrigation. This modification, adopted by all the states bordering the Great Plains, is known as the Western American Doctrine of Riparian Rights. In the central portion of the Great Plains there are eight states, all arid, and here the radically modified riparian law was not radical enough. These eight states have abandoned completely the English common law and evolved an indigenous law on an entirely different principle, the Arid Region Doctrine of Prior Appropriation. In essence this law grants the first water to the first comer, whether he be a riparian or nonriparian owner. Once a given amount of water is granted to him, he may continue to have that amount *as long as he uses it*. Not to use it is to forfeit it. . . . "He who is first in time is first in right," is the classic statement of the principle. The Arid Region Doctrine of Prior Appropriation prevails in New Mexico, Arizona, Colorado, Utah, Nevada, Wyoming, Idaho, and Montana.[1] (For a classification of water rights see Figure XXI–7.)

Despite this new dryland water regulation or legislation, increasing litigations for water rights have arisen in the Southwest, as a result of increasing population and correspondingly decreasing water supply. One of the fastest growing metropolitan and suburban areas in the United States is that of Los Angeles. For many years it has had to depend on Lake Owen and other natural and artificial reservoirs in the southern Sierras hundreds of miles away (Figure XX-2). Increasing industrial activity and popularity of the area in satisfying the amenities of life have now convinced municipal authorities that the population saturation point will soon be reached unless new sources of water are found. Experiments are under way to distill

[1] *Ibid.* Reprinted by permission.

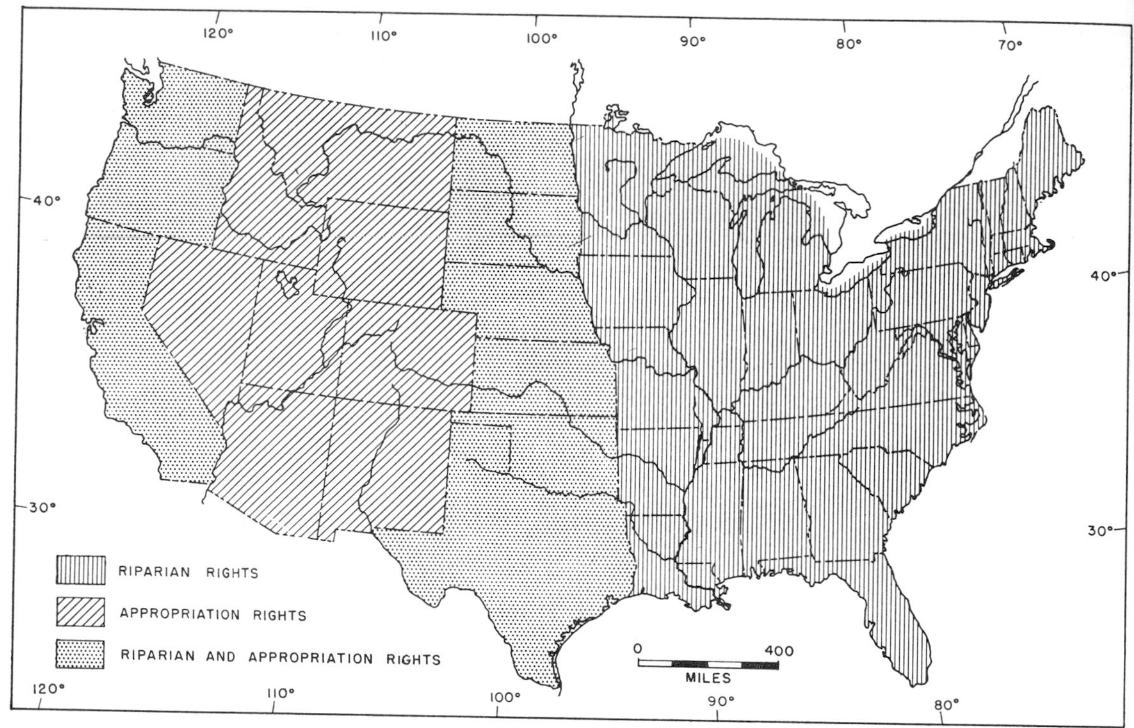

XXI:7 Water rights in the United States are shown on this map. A water legislation map, such as this, clearly suggests the close relation of the study of law and the understanding of geography as they apply to the regional diversities in water distribution and water appropriation principles. Note the four regional distribution patterns of the two doctrines —riparian rights and appropriation rights, as explained in the text. On what geographic grounds and historic antecedents are these based? (From "Water Legislation," by Dr. Edward Hamming, in *Economic Geography*, Vol. XXXIV, No. 1, January, 1958, used by permission)

fresh water from the sea — at present much too costly. Accordingly, the community is now seeking to tap the Colorado River. This has brought the state of California into legal conflict with Arizona, and may ultimately raise additional legal problems if water rights of the other states tributary to the Colorado River become involved. It may even renew an earlier water-rights conflict with Mexico, which also is guaranteed its share of water at the mouth of the Colorado.

Still other legal aspects of dryland water have now arisen as a result of rain-making experiments, based on seeding of clouds by sodium iodide, dry ice, or some other similar materials. Despite the controversial aspect as to the efficacy of such a process, suits have already been brought against "rain makers." It is obvious that conflict would arise since extraction of moisture from clouds in one area would result in a decreased vapor supply in another. And since clouds, unlike rivers, are not confined to restricted courses, a new set of legal principles has to be evolved adapted to atmospheric, as distinct from earth surface, waterforms.

On the meteorological side of the question, it appears from the best of authorities that rain-making experiments of this type are only locally effective, and even then are dependent upon existing clouds well saturated with moisture. Such conditions rarely obtain in the dry world, particularly in *BW* lands, where the skies may be partially clouded only about 10 per cent of the time. The dry world, indeed, is the "land of the sun."

The rainfall-deficiency lands in future world resource perspective

More promising than rain making in finding a solution for the problems of the dry world are the public and private research experiments conducted along the lines of better conservation or utilization of water. These involve, first, an adequate survey or inventory of surface and subsurface water available, and second, a study of all edaphic, biologic, and human factors conducive to greatest conservation of moisture and maximum utilization by man. Third, overpopulation, overindustrialization and overextension of plow agriculture must be guarded against in order to guarantee a stabilized economy in the area. Moreover, since water is a mobile resource, a planned economy of water resources cannot be effectively developed on a single state or country basis. It is encouraging, therefore, to note that the problems of the world's wastelands and marginal lands are now being attacked on many fronts by research agencies sponsored by world-wide organizations, such as the United Nations Educational, Scientific and Cultural Organization (UNESCO), the Food and Agricultural Organization (FAO), the World Health Organization (WHO), the International Labor Organization (ILO), as well as the World Meteorological Organization (WMO) (7).

UNESCO is reported concerned with projects such as the following: (1) Seeking the extension of cultivation of such plants as can utilize moisture in the form of dew, or fog, and store it in the ground for subsequent use. (2) Further developing the culture of halophytic plants which not only survive but thrive in salty soil. (Experiments already conducted in Morocco by the agronomic research service indicate that certain plants such as cabbage, asparagus, spinach, and date palms can and do grow in salty soil.) (3) Exploiting the inexhaustible, if somewhat intermittent, wind resources of the drylands as well as the almost universal and continuous daytime sunshine of the dry world. The task now is effectively and economically to convert such sources of energy into electrical energy, available when wind and sunshine are nonfunctional. Windmills have long been used for the purpose of power. And mirrors, for focusing the sun's rays, have been experimented with on a limited scale in all types of heating, including water distillation.

The World Meteorological Organization is currently engaged in experiments developing wind energy. It is also concerned with artificial rain making.

The Food and Agricultural Organization is primarily, of course, interested directly in increasing food productivity of the dry world. One of its projects is the investigation of various types of irrigation used in ancient times, as far back as 2,000 years ago, when cisterns were used for storing rain water on a large scale by the Nabataeans. Also investigated are their dew mounds which supplied moisture to the vine or olive tree planted within them. Besides developing interest in conventional forms of irrigation, the FAO is further exploring projects of sand dune fixation and reforestation. Recognizing that substandard food consumption is a major problem of the underdeveloped countries, the FAO believes that in the long run this problem can be solved only by helping the native increase his own food production.

Another related rehabilitation program is sponsored by the World Health Organization, which is presently focusing its attention on combating diseases endemic to the arid zones.

Immeasurable, no doubt also, are the benefits of the publications of UNESCO, which disseminate the results of the various research projects. Included is a directory, listing ninety institutions which participate in arid zone research, distributed among twenty-three countries and territories. Twice a year, conferences are held and reports received from experts of many foreign countries, indicating progress in dealing with problems of the arid lands. Member states of UNESCO have shown increasing interest in the results of such research, requesting special technical assistance related to the rehabilitation of their own areas. Says the Director: "More and more of the underdeveloped countries are coming to realize their obligation to improve the living conditions in their desert and near desert areas, and also that the key to the solution of these problems is research and the training of local personnel in scientific techniques and development."

In concluding this two-chapter treatment of the drylands, several basic geographic concepts suggest themselves: Next to the low-temperature lands, the low-moisture lands are the most distinctively nature-dominated realms of the world. Destined to be dry by reasons of continentality, predominance of high pressure, cold water currents, and orographic rainshadows, dryland sections of the world must be accepted as problem areas, not only by the inhabitants living within the region but also by the people of the humid lands. Of the two subtypes, the steppes, rather than the desert, present the greater problem to society and government because of their erratic annual and seasonal rainfall, encouraging a flourishing occupance during humid cycle years which dry-cycle years cannot support. Viewed from another point, the difference lies, one might say, in the "nature-made" dust bowls of the former and the "man-made" dust bowls in the latter. The sand-dune *ergs* are so forbidding that, except for the isolated oasis dweller, the migratory nomad, the transient trader, or the transitory miner, few settlers are adventurous enough to seek their life's fortunes here; on the other hand, dust bowls of the steppe indicate past exploitation and future possible rehabilitation by speculative man for gains worth the gamble. But here geographic adaptation must be practiced with a long-term vengeance if self-sufficient security is a serious objective.

Another major dryland concept deals with the dynamic aspect of such landscapes. The barbarian hordes, once finding refuge in these lands, are practically extinct in all the dryland realms in the world. Even the nomad of Central Asia, North Africa, and Arabia may soon become a mere tradition. One of the political-economic policies of King Saud of Saudi Arabia is to establish the nomad in dense habitations. The French in northern Africa are following a similar pattern to bring the Arab and the Berber nomads under control. On a more extensive scale, the U.S.S.R. has extended its totalitarian control, with some local autonomy, to her dryland border provinces. This, likewise, presages the passing of the lawless and unrestrained nomad. With the types of economic and social rehabilitation mentioned above, distinctly new types of culture may in time completely displace those indigenous to the Arab World. Because of the influences of the United Nations, such cultures in time may be expected to become almost completely Westernized.

Technological advances in the next few decades may effect a complete transformation of settlement and occupance forms of the dry world as a result of harnessing nature's gratuitous, diurnal, and perennial solar energy characterizing the dry world. Such abundant and economic power could then in turn be used to reclaim fresh water from the inexhaustible sea and thus solve the age-old water problem of drylands, where now all water sources have to be carefully husbanded and rationed.

In many instances, the airplane has already made conventional references in textbooks to deserts as areas of isolation and insulation obsolete, and the bedouin's camel may in many areas conceivably go the way of his fossil counterpart in North America. With the recent advent of the atomic age, now highlighted geographically by man-made satellites and interregional and intercontinental ballistic missiles of the newly erupted space age, the affairs of all problem lands of the world are tied in more intimately than ever with the affairs of the world as a whole.

APPLICATION OF GEOGRAPHIC UNDERSTANDING

I. With the geographic principles developed in this and related chapters, and with the aid of such other sources as you can find (e.g., *A Water Policy for the American People,* Report of the President's Water Resources Policy Commission, Government Printing Office, 1950), explore and evaluate the problems and potentialities of either (1) the Columbia River Basin, or (2) the Missouri River Basin. Some guideline suggestions or questions:

A. Systematic Geography

1. What physical and cultural elements and coherent relationships characterize the area?

2. Specifically point out in each case which geographic factors should be considered in relation to: (a) drought, (b) floods, (c) erosion, (d) sedimentation, (e) irrigation and other forms of agricultural land-use, (f) domestic and industrial water supply, (g) stream pollution, (h) navigation, (i) hydro-electric power, (j) plant and wildlife conservation, (k) recreation.

B. Regional Geography

1. What are the significant space-relationships of the basin with respect to:

(a) percentage of dryland involved, (b) states included, (c) neighboring physiographic regions, (d) the U.S. as a whole?

2. Which, do you think, is the better unifying base for regional study — a river system or a climatic unit? Relative values?

3. In which respects would resource development of dryland sections of river basins differ from those in humid regions (Tennessee Valley Authority)?

C. Planning Geography

Geographic planning starts with regional and systematic inventory. But not all field data are equally germane to land-use study. In this connection, which particular elements would you select for special evaluation?

II. Some people do not believe in any kind of regional planning; others strongly support it (see Chapter 36, on Planning). Give reasons, pro and con.

III. Differences of opinion exist also as to planning jurisdiction. In a basin type of region, such as this, which governmental level would seem to operate best in providing maximum results in resource development — local, regional, state, interstate, or federal government? Clearly indicate the geographic adjustments you believe should be realized and how best obtained.

References

1 *Chicago Daily News,* July 1, 1947.

2 *Chicago Daily News,* October 20, 1956.

3 Stevens, W. R., (United States Weather Bureau, Lincoln, Nebraska), "Some Causes of Droughts in the Great Plains," *Journal of Geography,* September, 1955, Vol. LIV, p. 305.

4 Marbut, F., "A Scheme for Soil Classification," *Proceedings and Papers of the First International Congress of Soil Science,* Commission 5, 1927, p. 20.

5 "Land Utilization, a Graphic Summary (1950)," U. S. Dept. of Commerce and U. S. Dept. of Agriculture, Washington, D. C., Vol. V, Part 4, December, 1952.

6 Webb, Walter Prescott, *The Great Frontier,* Houghton Mifflin Company, Boston, 1952, pp. 239-256, *passim.*

7 "Experiments in Reviving the World's Wastelands," *United Nations Review,* Vol. I, No. 2, August, 1954, pp. 44-48.

Chapter 22

The tropical savannah monsoon grasslands (*Aw*) —lands of seasonal frustration and regional famines

Good Neighbor in Action. Last November [1946] Nelson Rockefeller went to Rio De Janeiro on business of hemispheric importance: to translate Good-Neighborliness from words to deeds. Through his American International Association for Economic and Social Development (Time, Nov. 25), he proposed to increase Brazil's production (especially of food), thereby increasing Brazil's capacity to buy sorely needed U.S. goods, which the U.S. sorely needs to sell.

Last week, at the invitation of Venezuela's New Dealish Government, he set out to do the same for Venezuela. As in Brazil, corporations with mixed U.S. and Venezuelan capital (plus Venezuelan government aid) will invest in specific projects to improve the country's backward agriculture. (At present, Venezuela imports fresh vegetables from the U.S.)

In time the Rockefeller plan is to: (1) increase the food supply; (2) raise living standards; (3) diversify an economy now top-heavy with oil; (4) stop the stampede from farms to oil camps and cities. First projects will be truck farms and dairies, with flour mills and model cattle ranches to follow.

"Venezuela" *Time,* February 10, 1947, p. 38. Courtesy *Time.* Copyright Time, Inc., 1947.

Chorogram: Aid to Venezuela

Venezuelan project suggests need of preliminary regional inventory and geographic planning

The average reader, upon a cursory examination of the above article, perhaps thinks that the Rockefeller plan is an excellent idea and should by all means be carried out. The geographer, however, upon reading the above article, immediately evaluates the physical and cultural factors of the Venezuelan environments to determine (1) the general soundness of the proposal and (2) the kind of geographic survey and evaluation that needs to be made to realize fully this type of program beneficiation. A few observations follow.

Venezuela (Figure XXII-1), situated on the northern coast of South America, has an area slightly larger than the combined states of Texas and Oklahoma. Yet it has a population equal only to that of the city of Chicago. Thus, immediately, Venezuelan industry is handicapped by a lack of manpower. A population density map reveals that most of it is concentrated in the northern highlands and in the vicinity of the Lake Maracaibo oil producing area.

The interior grasslands, the *llanos,* have been assumed to occupy a central and significant relation to agricultural development (Figure XXII-2). As far as soil and relief are concerned, the llanos could be well utilized for food crops. However, climate imposes many problems on industry. There are two seasons—the winter, in which the vegetation dries up, due to extreme aridity; and the summer, in which the precipitation is so heavy that floods occur. Temperatures are high the year round, the monthly average never falling below 65°F. The extreme wet season impedes transportation; so travel in the llanos is mostly restricted to the dry season. The meat quality of the cattle is low, due in part to the poor quality of the grasses in the dry season.

The economy of Venezuela is built around its most important resource, petroleum. Oil comprises 90 per cent of Venezuela's exports (2). In return Venezuela receives foodstuffs and manufactured goods.

What does the future hold for Venezuela? With the development of dry-season irrigation and wet-season flood control projects and the establishment of modern transportation facilities, Venezuela could assume an important role in world economics. To accomplish this, however, she will need outside help. This is the opportunity for the United States to be a "good neighbor."

The selection of this chorogram on Venezuela is based on several considerations: (1) Venezuela, perhaps more than any other country, is coextensive with the *Aw* (Figure

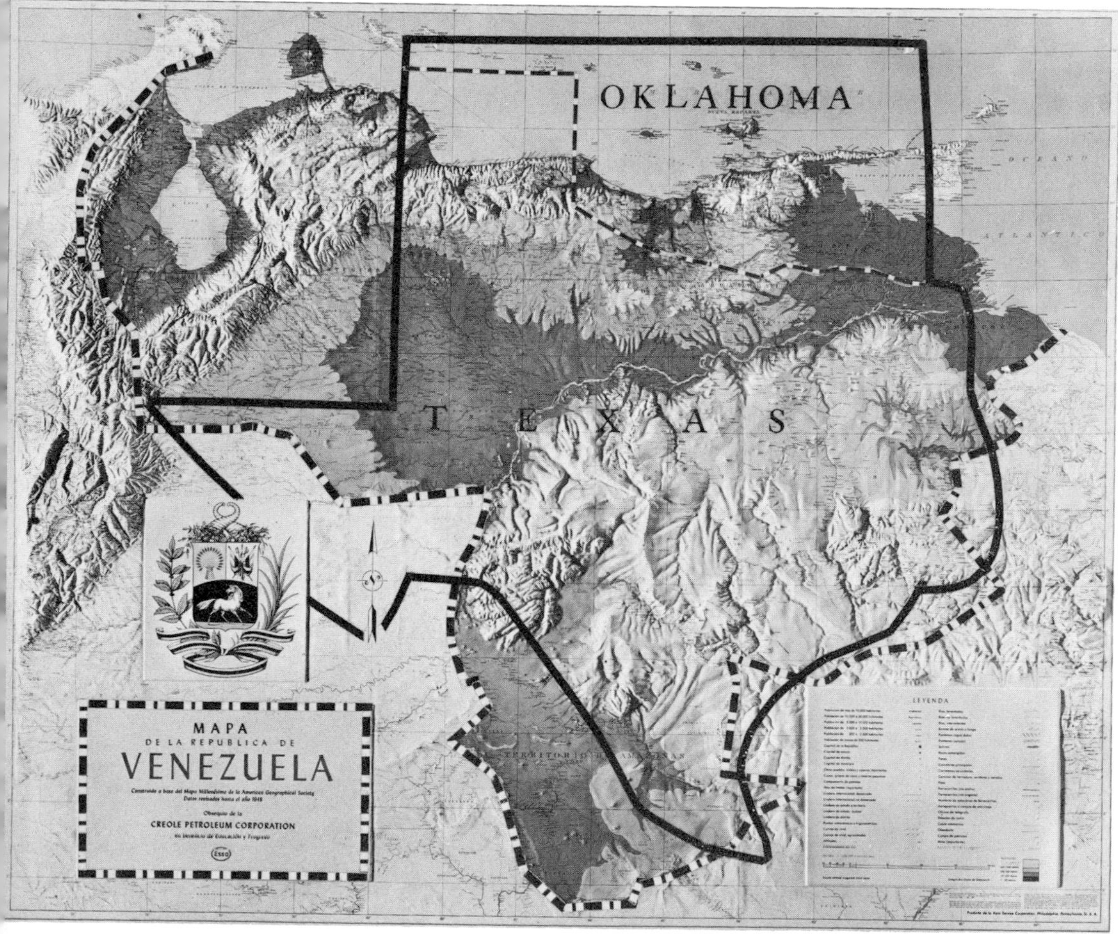

XXII:1 Venezuela is shown here in areal and relief perspective. Superimposing other political entities of comparable size, as done here, aids our comprehension of the area of countries with which we may be less familiar. But the size of a country may be its least important characteristic. Compare the landforms of Venezuela, here pictured in Aero relief, with those of Texas–Oklahoma (consult any good atlas). Note also differences in latitude and climate. How would you evaluate the relative potential of the two regions as grazing areas? Consult also Figure XXII:2. (Relief map copyright Aero Service Corporation, used by permission)

XXII-3). Only on its periphery do we find other climatic types included within its boundaries (small areas of *Af* and *Am* on the south and east, and minor coastal sections of *BW* and *BS* on the north). (2) The country is of sufficient size to introduce the various relief features commonly associated with *Aw* lands. Plateaus dominate the south and southeast, and plains in the north are featured by the *llanos* (Spanish for plains) along the Orinoco, chief river of the area, and by the Lake Maracaibo plain to the northwest, separated from the llanos by the Andes. (3) These major relief features in turn suggest the kind of regional study which has to be made of any savannah land in order to understand the major regional differences typical of such lands, with respect to both cultural and economic conditions. (4) Typical of such *Aw* lands are some of the problems noted: the year-round high temperatures, leading to concentration of population on highlands, particularly by the whites; the contrast of the dry and wet seasons, suggesting the need for irrigation and flood control projects; the practice of transhumance, resulting from the alternating dry and wet seasons as well as

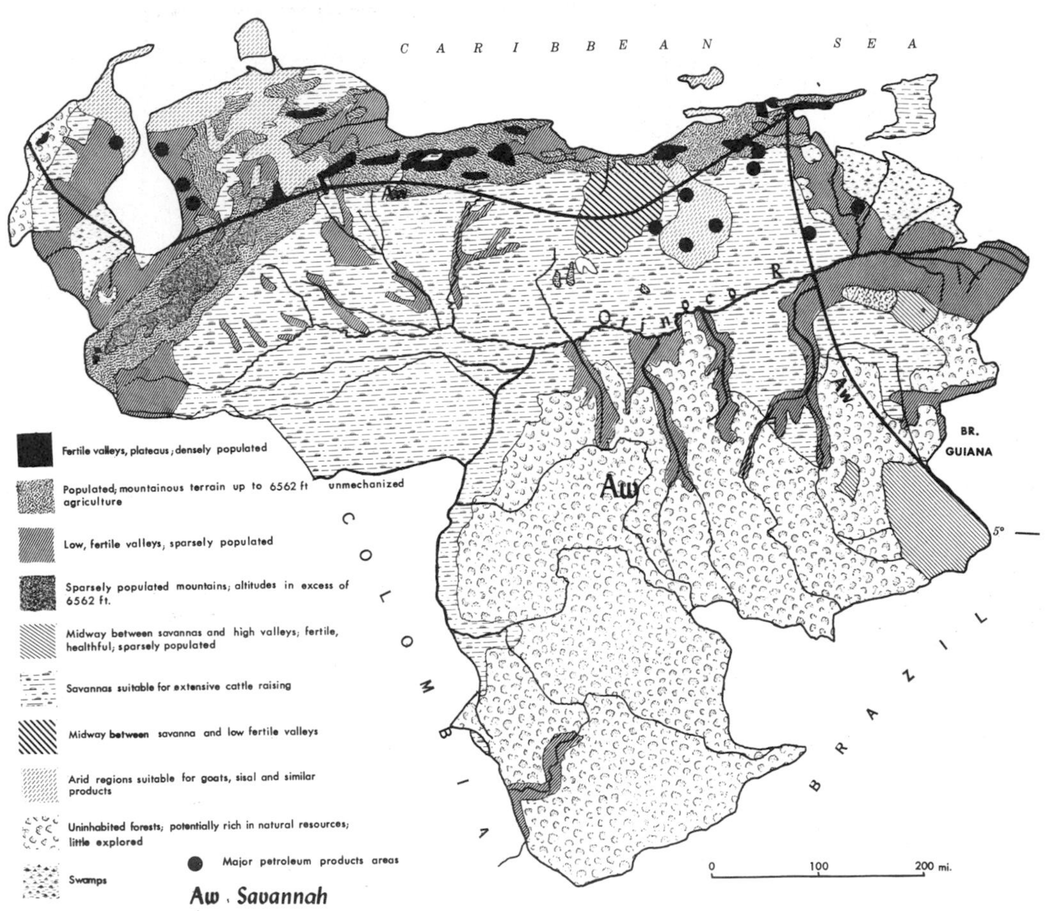

XXII:2 Venezuela is shown here in demographic and economic perspective. Evaluate regionally the relation of natural environmental factors to the population pattern. What major correlations do you observe? The basic data on this map are from a government investor's manual. What things does this map reveal which are useful? What other data would you want to examine before launching into some industrial enterprise? (Adapted from map, "Venezuela Surface Configuration," in *Investment in Venezuela*, Office of International Trade, U. S. Department of Commerce)

the seasonal limitations of transportation. The article moreover suggests the predominance of the grazing economy, but dispels the illusion that natural savannahs afford the best grazing conditions in the world. (5)

As also pointed out, Venezuela typifies a one-sided specialized economy in the development of mineral resources, as is quite characteristic of *Aw* lands. The genesis of ore bodies has for the most part little classifiable connection with environmental conditions, and so, here as elsewhere in the *Aw* world, minerals of an extraordinary variety and economic importance may be found. In this instance, the export of petroleum is the mainstay of Venezuela's economy. But, as the above chronicle indicates, this is not a healthy situation. Though the oil industry today accounts for about three-fourths of the country's revenue and has been responsible for a tremendous rise in the standard of living in the oil field area, one is reminded of the ephemerality of all mining adventures.

And so, as is recognized in this project, one of the major economic considerations needed in any country is a diversification of resource development to stabilize both its present and future economy. (6) One further concept suggested here is the need for a country to establish foreign relations, both in the way of trade and good-neighborliness.

As we hope to show subsequently, investigations of geographic character of the problems of *Aw* lands, dominating both Venezuela and Brazil, are needed to properly direct investments for the improvement of land utilization and industrial development programs in such countries. Except for such carefully prepared geographic inventory and appraisals of natural and human resource potentials, investments of this type may prove quite ineffective, as was the case of the Fordlandia rubber plantation experiment in the Amazon region of Brazil.

The disconcerting flood–drought regimen

The most geographically significant and distinguishing environmental factor of the *Aw* realm is the combination of extreme ranges between high-sun and low-sun rainfall, and the extraordinary minimum range in seasonal temperatures which it shares with the *Af*. Climatic stations of the *Aw* characteristically show 75 per cent or more of the annual rainfall coming during the high-sun period (Figures XXII-4, XXII-5). As a matter of fact, in many cases the low-sun months may have no measurable rainfall whatsoever, whereas during the mid high-sun period, rains may produce catastrophic floods. Famines are a common occurrence. A uniformly high temperature during the year, combined with high humidity during the rainy season, makes this one of the most enervating regions of the world. However, since the total relative humidity is normally lower than that of the *Af* and there is a dry season when temperatures are lower, the climatic conditions of *Aw* are less enervating on the whole than they are in the *Af*.

The humid classification of this climate with its dry low-sun period is largely due to the position of these lands relative to the trade-wind belt and the continental monsoons. Note on the Köppen map (Figure XXII-3) that in the Americas the *Aw* areas extend from a few degrees of the Equator poleward, in both the Northern and Southern Hemispheres, to about the boundaries of the tropics (Tropic of Cancer and Tropic of Capricorn, respectively). A similar pattern roughly exists in the Old World, considering Asia, Africa, and Australia as a unit.

These areas for the most part lie in the trade-wind belt, the winds of which blow equatorward, hence becoming warmer with a declining relative humidity. This in itself would account for the lower annual rainfall, compared with the *Af-Am* regions. But the contrast of the wet and dry seasons must be sought in another factor. In the rainforest lands, the high annual rainfall is related to the doldrums, with almost daily convectional showers. The dryness of *BW* and *BS* lands is related to the high pressure belt of the Horse Latitudes, where the descending air produces an evaporating rather than a precipitating condition. Thus the intermediate position of the *Aw* areas between the equatorward *Af* and the poleward *BS-BW* belts suggests that the rainy season of the *Aw* occurs during the high-sun period when the convection belt has shifted poleward, whereas the dry season results from the shifting equatorward of the high pressure belt. We might say the *Aw* shares seasonally the characteristics and the conditions of both the *Af* and *B* realms.

Still another meteorological factor is involved in the explanation of the distribution of the *Aw* climate. This time let us trace the succession of differentiated climatic realms on the east coast of Asia, starting with the *Aw* in Thailand. As we advance poleward, there follow successively *Cwa, Dwa, Dwb, Dwc* and *Dwd*. These wide latitudinal expressions of climates, all characterized by wet summers and dry winters, obviously reflect another factor, namely, continentality. Due to an interior low pressure developed during the hot summer months, winds from the Indian Ocean and the Pacific bring summer rain to these areas, whereas during the winter months, winds blowing from the high pressure interior seaward carry little or no vapor. Thus, in this instance, *Aw* partakes of the monsoon influences, which have given the name Monsoonia to this part of the world. *Monsoon* is of Arab origin, meaning season. While it has its chief application in connection with the continent of Asia, its

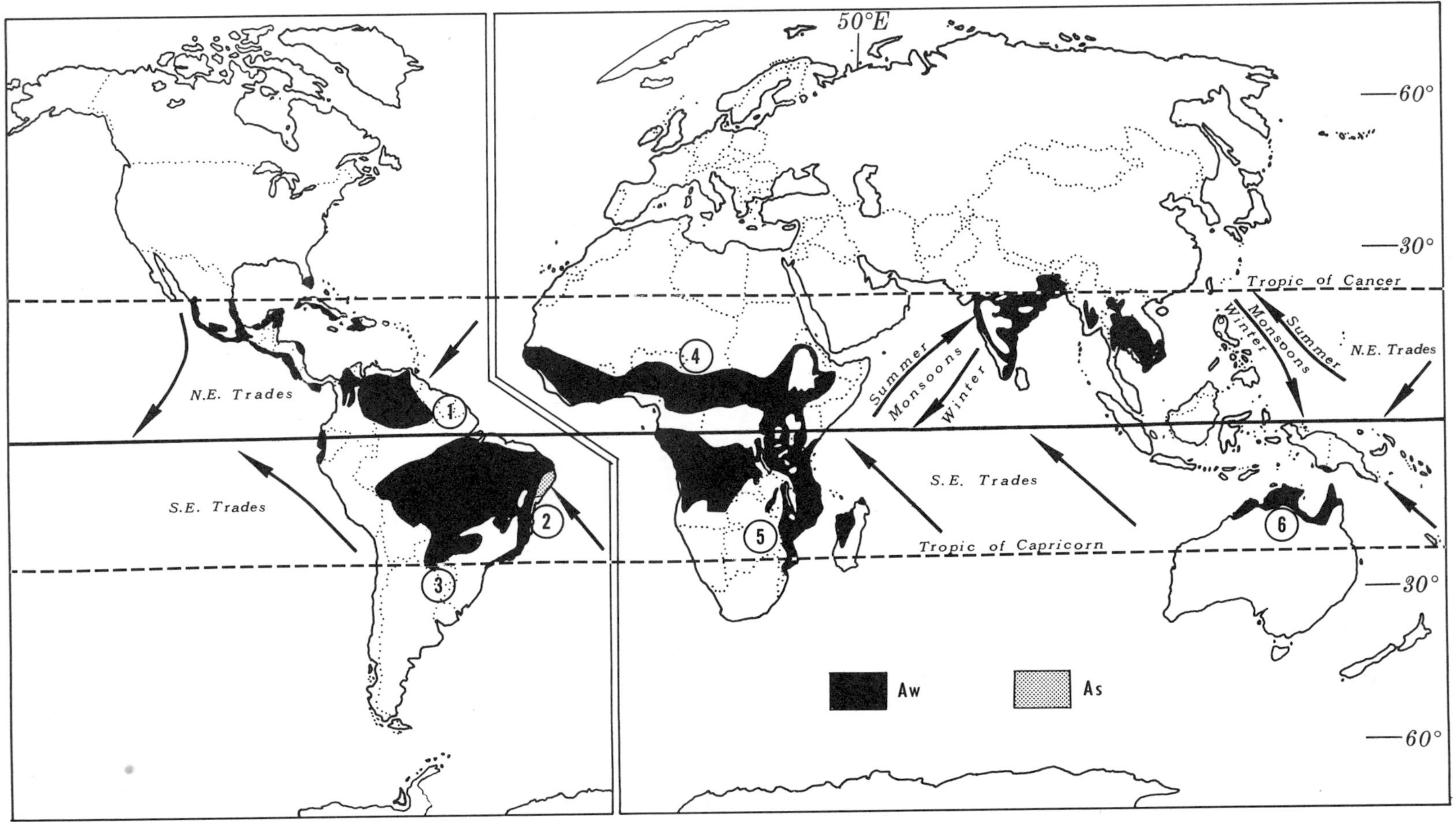
50°E
60°
30°
Tropic of Cancer
N.E. Trades
Summer
Monsoons
Winter
S.E. Trades
Tropic of Capricorn
30°
60°
1
2
3
4
5
6
Aw
As

seasonal connotation applies also in a degree to *Aw* and *Cw* Africa as well as parts of winter-dry South America.

A distinguishing feature between the *Am* and *Aw* is the difference of dryness in the dry season, the former receiving sufficient moisture to support year-round growth of tropical rainforest whereas such forests as exist in the *Aw* along the grasslands (*BS*) constitute a scrub growth of deciduous types of trees. The distinction between the *Aw* and *Am* is based upon rainfall of the driest month as determined by formula — .04(98.5-r)', below which the station classifies as *Aw*.[1]

The green landscape of summer—the brown earth of winter

Natural vegetation, or cover, more than anything else, distinguishes landscapes. Moreover, vegetation forms reflect more precisely than other factors the various climatic types, as already noted — the xerophytes of the desert, the short grasses and low shrubs of the steppe. In *Aw* lands, grass, ranging in height from three to twelve feet is the most characteristic cover. But trees, mostly of a scrub type, also occur, commonly dispersed, and rising only a few feet above the tall grass. Though savannah grass, then, is the dominant form of vegetation in all the *Aw* lands of the world, a cross-section profile from the equator-steppeward lands reveals varied belts of the following types: monsoon forest, including some evergreens and semideciduous trees as well as deciduous trees (mahogany, teak); admixture of scrub vegetation of the thorn forest or acacia type, occurring in small clusters or park-like stands in a sea of tall savannah grass; then, approaching the border zone of the *BS*, the longer savannah grass giving way to shorter grasses and fewer and smaller acacia trees and other scrub vegetation. On the profile transect, this sequence, from a phalanx of tall trees to low grass, may be variegated by clumps or strips of evergreen tropical forest which have struggled for a foothold in depressions close to the groundwater table, and otherwise formed so-called *galeria* along indigenous or exotic streams.

Varied as are the mixed associations of tree and grass savannahs in different parts of the *Aw* world, one must also recognize marked contrasts between the low-sun and high-sun landscapes, a contrast quite as marked as would be the summer and winter landscapes of the high-middle latitudes. But in this instance, it represents a rainfall instead of a temperature seasonal regimen.

James' description of the Shari Plain of north-central Africa artistically portrays the point.

¶ Grass! Grass which rises to heights of twelve feet overhead and shuts in the narrow trails; monotonous stretches of grass where nothing can be seen of the country beyond the rank vegetation, with here and there a few low trees all but hidden from view. The prevailing color is brown, a parched dead brown; for this is January, the middle of the dry season, and the vegetable world is at rest. The trees have dropped their leaves. In the scorching heat, tempered by only scattered clouds, everything is withered. Even the rivers have become mere trickles of water. The flood plains stand out as broad sandy flats, glistening white in the sun, marked here and there by stagnant pools covered with green scum, or by reed-filled swamps. Along the river banks are scattered the native villages: small clusters of huts shaped like beehives, and built of grass which blends at this season of the year with the prevailing brown color of the landscape. In late January or February the natives burn the savannas. The air is filled with the smoke of grass fires. The timid, grazing animals, concentrated near the water holes, run for their lives before the fires, for this short period substituting this new fear for the fear of their natural

[1] See Köppen Key in the Appendix.

XXII:3 (Left) Note the almost 100 per cent coterminous position of the Savannah Realm with the tropics. Note also the two basic wind controls. The distribution pattern of the *Aw* varies in details on authors' maps, in terms of climatic data and vegetation, from that of the original. Parts of southern Florida and portions of the West Indies appear to be *Am* (or possibly even *Af*) rather than *Aw*, according to various authorities. Savannahs vary, as do other regions. Here shown are those most commonly recognized: (1) Llanos, (2) Campos, (3) Gran Chaco, (4) Sudan, (5) Veldt, (6) Downs of Northern Australia.

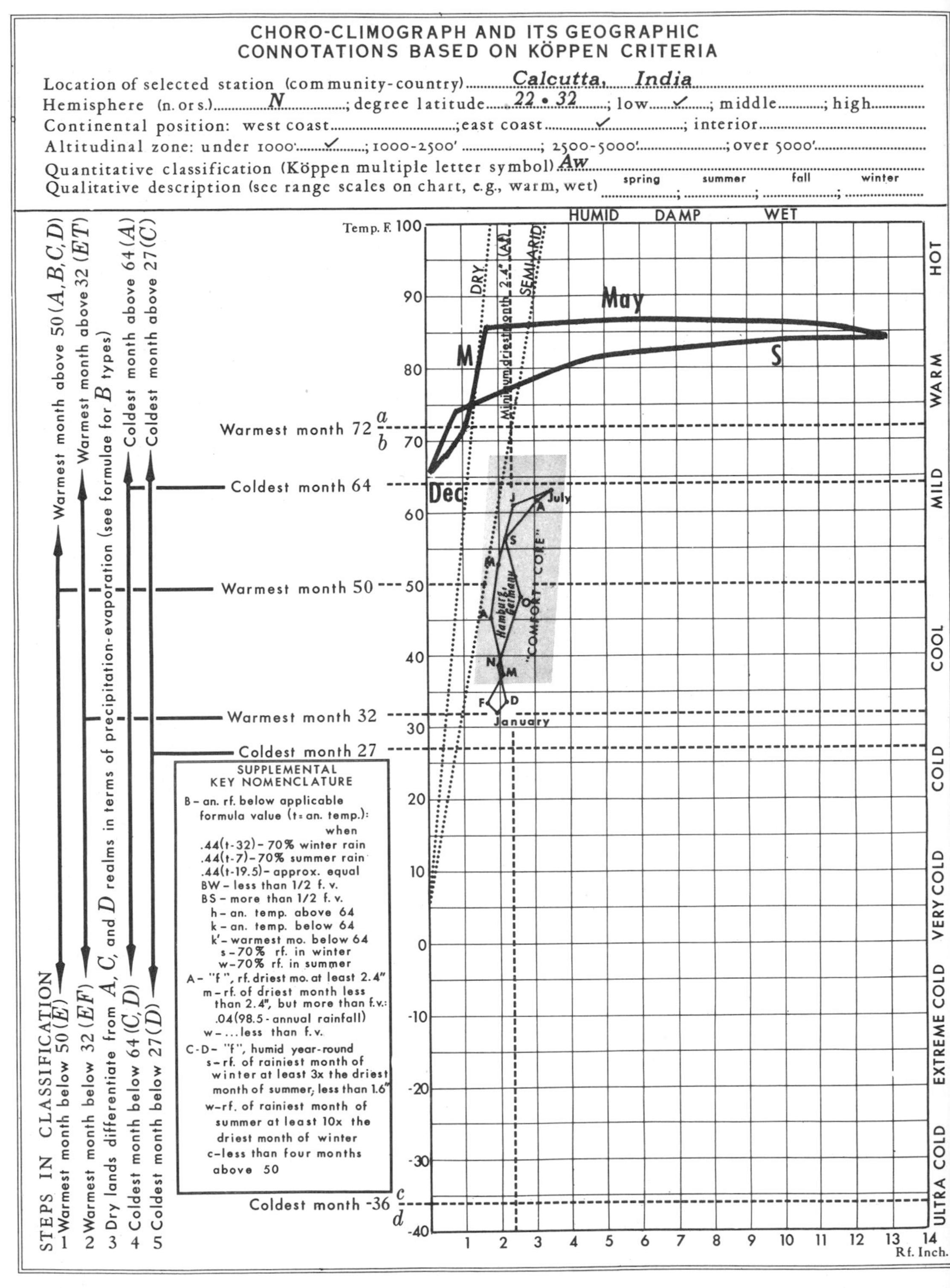

CHORO-CLIMOGRAPH AND ITS GEOGRAPHIC
CONNOTATIONS BASED ON KÖPPEN CRITERIA
Location of selected station (community-country) Calcutta, India
Hemisphere (n. or s.) N ; degree latitude 22 • 32 ; low ✓ ; middle ; high
Continental position: west coast ; east coast ✓ ; interior
Altitudinal zone: under 1000' ✓ ; 1000-2500' ; 2500-5000' ; over 5000'
Quantitative classification (Köppen multiple letter symbol) Aw
Qualitative description (see range scales on chart, e.g., warm, wet) spring ; summer ; fall ; winter
STEPS IN CLASSIFICATION
1 Warmest month below 50 (E) Warmest month above 50 (A, B, C, D)
2 Warmest month below 32 (EF) Warmest month above 32 (ET)
3 Dry lands differentiate from A, C, and D realms in terms of precipitation-evaporation (see formulae for B types)
4 Coldest month below 64 (C, D) Coldest month above 64 (A)
5 Coldest month below 27 (D) Coldest month above 27 (C)
Warmest month 72 a b
Coldest month 64
Warmest month 50
Warmest month 32
Coldest month 27
Coldest month -36 c d
SUPPLEMENTAL
KEY NOMENCLATURE
B - an. rf. below applicable formula value (t = an. temp.): when
.44(t-32) - 70% winter rain
.44(t-7) - 70% summer rain
.44(t-19.5) - approx. equal
BW - less than 1/2 f. v.
BS - more than 1/2 f. v.
h - an. temp. above 64
k - an. temp. below 64
k' - warmest mo. below 64
s - 70% rf. in winter
w - 70% rf. in summer
A - "f", rf. driest mo. at least 2.4"
m - rf. of driest month less than 2.4", but more than f.v.: .04(98.5 - annual rainfall)
w - ... less than f.v.
C-D - "f", humid year-round
s - rf. of rainiest month of winter at least 3x the driest month of summer; less than 1.6"
w - rf. of rainiest month of summer at least 10x the driest month of winter
c - less than four months above 50
Temp. F.
100
90
80
70
60
50
40
30
20
10
0
-10
-20
-30
-40
HUMID DAMP WET
DRY
Minimum driest month 2.4" (Af)
SEMIARID
May
M
S
Dec
July
J
A
S
O
N
D
M
F
January
Hamburg, Germany
"COMFORT CORE"
HOT
WARM
MILD
COOL
COLD
VERY COLD
EXTREME COLD
ULTRA COLD
1 2 3 4 5 6 7 8 9 10 11 12 13 14
Rf. Inch.

enemies, the lions and other carnivora. The surface which is revealed by the fires is monotonously level, dotted with scattered low trees, or with trees grouped together to form small thickets. The vegetation gives the landscape an aspect not unlike that of a park or orchard. Then come the rains—perhaps in March or April. The transformation is remarkable. Tender shoots of succulent green grass appear; the trees are quickly covered with leaves; insects in great numbers come forth; the rivers are filled with torrents of water; from a death-like sleep the landscape throbs with luxuriant growth, a forced growth hastened by high temperature and humidity.[1]

As we shall subsequently see, *Aw* savannah lands constitute important foraging grounds, not only for the world's richest wildlife but also for nomadic as well as commercial grazing. Among the regionally prominent savannahs are the Llanos of the Orinoco Valley in Venezuela, the Campos of the highlands of the Gran Chaco ("great hunting-ground") in Argentina, Paraguay, and Bolivia, inner Brazil, the Sudan and Veldt of central and southeast Africa, respectively, and the Downs of northern Australia.

Savannah faunal hierarchy and its regional supremacy

The seasonally wet-and-dry tropical savannahs harbor the richest fauna in the world, in numbers as well as in variety of species. Practically every class of the animal kingdom is represented here. Particularly significant is the widespread representation of large mammals, the largest in the world, including the African elephant and the giraffe. The savannahs of Africa particularly have thus become the richest hunting ground in the world, for the native hunter as well as for the visiting sportsman. In some sections of the *Aw* world, as in the Deccan of India and in parts of Nigeria where population reaches densities of 125 to 250 per square mile, several forms of wild animal life still constitute a threat to human safety and call for constant vigilance on the part of the inhabitants.

*1. **Diverse habitats—rich fauna.*** The abundance and variety of animal life are accounted for by a variety of habitats. Predominating, of course, are the large savannah grasslands. The tall grass, even when it becomes tough and fibrous during the dry season, and thus generally unfit for domestic cattle, is still well suited to wild herbivorous animals. The scrub tree vegetation, clustered or sprinkled throughout most of the savannah grasslands, affords a varied diet for some of the herbivores. These include such fleet-footed and sleek-bodied animals as the gazelle, the hartebeest, the kudu, the topi, the zebra, and the giraffe. The giraffe is the tallest animal in the world, frequently attaining heights of 15 to 18 feet. It has an advantage with its long neck of being able to browse on tree herbage as well as to graze on savannah grasses. The most dangerous of the herbivores is the buffalo; while those of the largest bulk are the rhinoceros and the African elephant.

The abundance of herbivorous life allows a large carnivorous fauna to exist. And so we have a large number of the cat family represented here, including the tiger, the leopard, the jaguar, and the lion, which lie hidden in the tall grass ready to stalk their prey. Dead and decaying carcasses of both the carnivores and herbivores become carrion food for the scavenging hyenas and jackals. Forest forms include the American peccary, the African warthog and other wild hogs, which feed on nuts and fruits of the tree savannahs. The tall tree savannahs, bounding the *Af* neighboring lands and forming the *galerias* along the streams, are the homes of countless arboreal animals—birds, monkeys, and baboons. Streams which do not dry up altogether have their share of aquatic life, including tropical fish and turtles; the hippopotamus, the crocodile, and the Florida alligator inhabit the perennial rivers and marshes. Though not very numerous, marshes and swamps in places are very extensive following the flood season and constitute ideal breeding grounds for innumerable insects, among the most significant of

---

[1] James, Preston E., "The Shari Plain," *The Journal of Geography*, Vol. XXIX, No. 8, November, 1930, pp. 319-320. Reprinted by permission.

XXII:4 (Left) Which is normally the hottest month in Calcutta? Account for this. What characteristic seasonal problems are reflected in this graph?

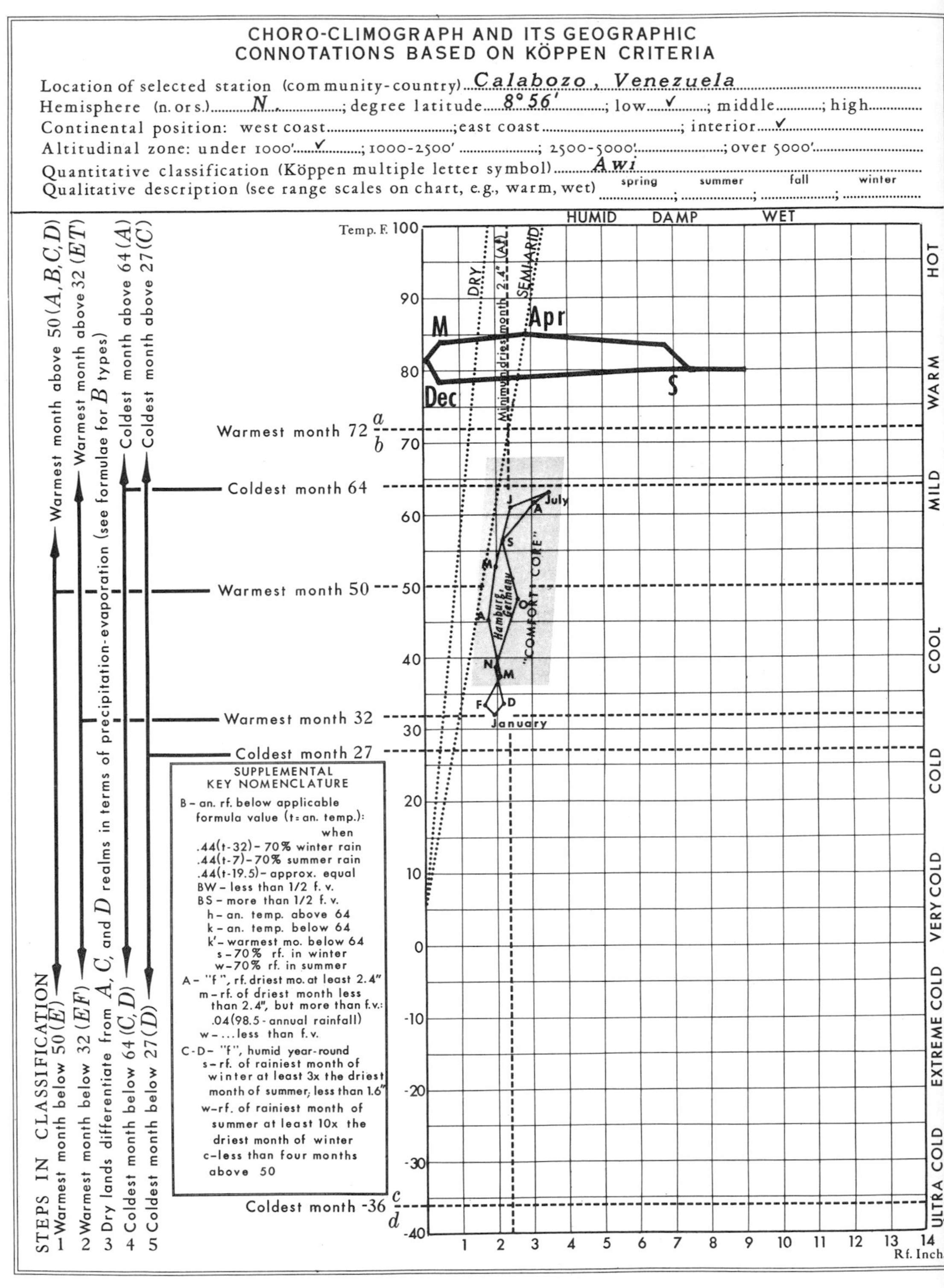
CHORO-CLIMOGRAPH AND ITS GEOGRAPHIC CONNOTATIONS BASED ON KÖPPEN CRITERIA
Location of selected station (community-country) Calabozo, Venezuela
Hemisphere (n. or s.) N.; degree latitude 8° 56'; low ✓; middle; high
Continental position: west coast; east coast; interior ✓
Altitudinal zone: under 1000' ✓; 1000-2500'; 2500-5000'; over 5000'
Quantitative classification (Köppen multiple letter symbol) Awi
Qualitative description (see range scales on chart, e.g., warm, wet) spring; summer; fall; winter
STEPS IN CLASSIFICATION
1 Warmest month below 50 (E) — Warmest month above 50 (A, B, C, D)
2 Warmest month below 32 (EF) — Warmest month above 32 (ET)
3 Dry lands differentiate from A, C, and D realms in terms of precipitation-evaporation (see formulae for B types)
4 Coldest month below 64 (C, D) — Coldest month above 64 (A)
5 Coldest month below 27 (D) — Coldest month above 27 (C)
Warmest month 72 a b
Coldest month 64
Warmest month 50
Warmest month 32
Coldest month 27
Coldest month -36 c d
SUPPLEMENTAL KEY NOMENCLATURE
B - an. rf. below applicable formula value (t = an. temp.): when
.44(t-32) - 70% winter rain
.44(t-7) - 70% summer rain
.44(t-19.5) - approx. equal
BW - less than 1/2 f. v.
BS - more than 1/2 f. v.
h - an. temp. above 64
k - an. temp. below 64
k' - warmest mo. below 64
s - 70% rf. in winter
w - 70% rf. in summer
A - "f", rf. driest mo. at least 2.4"
m - rf. of driest month less than 2.4", but more than f.v.: .04(98.5 - annual rainfall)
w - ... less than f.v.
C-D - "f", humid year-round
s - rf. of rainiest month of winter at least 3x the driest month of summer; less than 1.6"
w - rf. of rainiest month of summer at least 10x the driest month of winter
c - less than four months above 50
Temp. F.
100
90
80
70
60
50
40
30
20
10
0
-10
-20
-30
-40
HUMID
DAMP
WET
DRY
SEMIARID
Minimum driest month 2.4" (Af)
M
Apr
Dec
S
J
July
A
S
M
Hamburg, Germany
"COMFORT CORE"
O
A
N
M
F
D
January
1
2
3
4
5
6
7
8
9
10
11
12
13
14
Rf. Inch.
HOT
WARM
MILD
COOL
COLD
VERY COLD
EXTREME COLD
ULTRA COLD

which are the mosquito and the tsetse fly, pest of both beast and man. The largest birds in the world, the ostrich of Africa and the rhea of South America, also find their haven here.

2. *Effect of landforms on wildlife.* A wide diversity of land surface conditions, particularly in Africa where there are extensive areas with elevations ranging from a few hundred feet to a mile or more, accounts for a richly diversified fauna. Depending on the latitude, variation in temperature from fifteen to twenty degrees Fahrenheit occurs between the lower and higher elevations. Such higher elevations are also likely to experience a less severe drought in the dry season. Thus there is considerable zonation of both flora and fauna. It should be noted on the Köppen map (Appendix) that equatorward extensions of the *Cw* penetrate into *Aw* territory. This is particularly noteworthy in South America, Africa, and India, at corresponding latitudes of the *Aw*. This obviously reflects high land elevation with temperatures lowered to a point during the coldest month to below 64.4°F., delimiting the *A* type of climate. Many of such areas possess both indigenous and migratory fauna found identified with the *Aw* and thus further serve to enrich wildlife in quantity and type of species.

3. *Wild animal and civilized man are incompatibly related.* Perhaps in no other region of the world is the relation of man to wild animal life as significant as it is in the *Aw*. To understand such relationships we should perhaps first turn to a world population map (Appendix). You will observe at once that, with very limited exceptions, the savannah animal lands are among the least heavily populated areas in the world. Virtually all of northern Australia, interior South America, and even large sections of savannah Africa have less than two people per square mile. The largest areas of savannah lands having a population greater than this, but still for the most part under 15 and 20 per square mile, occur in Africa where the largest stock of wildlife is to be found. Thus we may conclude by regional correlation that one reason for the high density of wild animal life is the low density of human population. This general principle is not out of line with what is to be observed elsewhere in the world, for it is almost a universal law that with increasing settlement and civilization, including field culture, there is less and less opportunity for wildlife to find a haven. However, as with other generalizations in geography, we must also look for exceptions to this rule. India monsoon savannahs support a population of from 50 to 250 persons per square mile, as do sizable sections of Thailand, Tanganyika, and Nigeria. But even in these regions animal population declined as man's occupation of the land increased. One of the basic reasons for the coexistence of man and wild animal life in India is the Hindu religion which forbids the killing of wild animals. However, even here such a taboo is being relaxed as human beings are attacked by such animals.

XXII:5 (Left) Calabozo is an "i" station. What does this mean, and what is the basis for such limited range between summer and winter temperatures? Which climate would you prefer, that of Calabozo or Calcutta?

4. *Some environmental limitations to wild animal life.* The alternating seasonal wet-and-dry conditions are not altogether favorable to animal life. Indeed, the dry seasons are often so severe as well as prolonged that entire herds perish for lack of water or suitable forage. This is particularly true of such animals as must sooner or later find water to survive. But migrating to the water courses in itself often proves fatal to the herbivore. Seeking a drink along a stream may be his own undoing. Here, of course, is the best chance for predators to pounce upon their prey. Members of the fleet-footed antelope family probably have the best chance to survive by migrating with the high-sun and thus remaining, as it were, in the continuous convection rain belt. One of the greatest hazards to all animals is a devastating fire. It is frequently set by natives during the dry season to burn out the weedy and rank growth to provide better growing conditions for the newly sprouting herbage at the beginning of the rainy season. It is at this time that thousands upon thousands of animals, particularly of the less fleet-footed type, are destroyed.

5. *The world's leading hunting grounds.* Naturally, an environment so favorably dis-

Can you identify the species of herbivores in this grass-tree savannah of southern Ethiopia? Looking sharply to the left, what seems to have attracted the animals to this spot? (Courtesy of Chicago History Museum)

posed to the propagation of wildlife provides an ideal hunting ground. Natives find better means for animal subsistence here than in the *Af* world. Sometimes organized hunting is engaged in, as in the case of sections in Sudan, to kill off animals that prey on the domestic cattle, or even on man himself. Thus, natives are often quite willing to serve as guides in hunting down wild game, guides to sportsmen who come from largely middle latitude countries for big game hunting. Such adventures may lead to progressive extermination of wild animals, as is already manifest in some of the major hunting grounds of the African savannahs. As long as these lands were mostly colonial territory, almost indiscriminate hunting occurred in the contiguous *Aw*, *Cw*, and *BS* regions. But the establishment of independent governments, as in South Africa particularly, has led to the creation of regional game preserves similar to our own national park refuges in America. It is obvious that unless hunting is thus areally or seasonally restricted, this world's largest remaining reservoir of wildlife may also eventually disappear from the world scene, with the result that such animals may become almost restricted to zoological parks.

6. Insect plagues. Extermination of tropical diseases would indeed prove a blessing to both beast and man. Endemic to the tropical and subtropical world are elephantiasis, dengue fever, and yellow fever (spread by the anopheles mosquito), and nagana as well as sleeping sickness, both transmitted by the tsetse fly. Probably the most universal scourge is malaria, transmitted by the aedes mosquito over large sections where stagnant waters constitute its ideal breeding ground. In Chapter 17 (Medical Geography), tropical diseases are featured as a study in the environmental relations of man to disease-producing animal forms. While tropical native animal life is largely immune to insect infestations, domestic cattle, especially imported types, are exceedingly vulnerable.

Some insects like locusts, cicadas, and grasshoppers may also become so numerous as to consume completely the natural vegetation and cultivated crops. This has occurred repeatedly in some of the better settled sections, as in the Gran Chaco of South America. On the other hand, an occasional insect may prove beneficial. Thus, the termites build 10-20 foot mounds, which constitute some of the most fertile spots of the savannah landscape. Such soils, freshly brought to the surface, are unleached, rich in calcium carbonate and other minerals.

A realm distinguished for its contrasting regional populations and cultural patterns

1. Demography. A broad generalization of the population density of the *Aw* world would be relatively meaningless and even misleading because of major differences among the several regions in the different continents. We have already alluded previously to large-sized areas almost completely devoid of population, and to others which are much more populated than most middle latitude lands. About the only generalization which will hold is that the total population per square mile would be somewhere intermediate between that of the drylands and that of the humid lands outside the *A* world. Much more important to the geographer are those considerations of environmental characteristics, both physical and cultural, which have contributed to low populations in certain regions but to considerable growth in population in other regions.

Among the factors conducive to low population are: (1) low annual rainfall, or annual or seasonal erratic rains, making for low and undependable yields of crops; (2) predominant hunting and fishing economies, characteristic in the *Af* realm, which normally support only a few people per square mile; (3) industries such as migratory herding, commercial grazing, mining or lumbering, which are not conducive to heavy populations; (4) heavily leached soils or eroded slopelands, resulting from the concentrated monsoon rains, which reduce crop potential; (5) weak local governments, which are ineffective in preventing intertribal raids and wars; (6) insect infestation, especially of poorly drained regions, where prolific insect breeding is responsible for a high incidence of tropical diseases and high death rates; (7) famines, resulting from severe droughts or floods; (8) poor transportation facilities, and hence difficulty in transporting food from surplus food producing areas to regions of crop failures.

While northern Australia to date has proved to be unattractive to white settlement, many Asiatics from overcrowded Southeast Asia would have welcomed the opportunity of settling these lands; but here the exclusion policy of Australia has operated to keep these lands virtually unoccupied.

2. Factors conducive to greater densities of population. Looking at the population map once more, we note that the largest areas of concentration are in India, Thailand, Kenya, Nigeria, and portions of the Caribbean area. With one or another of these regions are associated the following: ancient civilization (India); plateau habitat with its cooler temperature (India and Kenya); major streams (the Niger affording irrigation waters and facilities of navigation, likewise Kenya with its Nile); coast-wise navigation and proximate position to large markets or tropical plantation goods (Jamaica and other Caribbean islands, such as Cuba). In such regions, population density may rise to a hundred or more per square mile (e.g., Deccan, 200; Cuba, 150; Jamaica, 320; Nigeria and Kenya, 100-200 per square mile).

3. Urban population. Much of the economy of *Aw* regions is of the subsistence type, which does not lend itself to concentrated settlement. Nevertheless, just as rural settlement in the *Aw* is usually greater than in *Af*, so are also the number of cities, especially on the highlands which are more hospitable. On lowlands urban settlement commonly occupies sites of commercial advantages (Recife in Brazil, Kingston in the West Indies, Calcutta in India, and Darwin in Australia).

The widest divergence of ethnographic types is found here: the exceedingly primitive aborigines of northern Australia, Negro of Africa, and the admixture of racial stocks in tropical Latin America, where the original Indian interbred with the Negro, who had been introduced as a slave in the colonization period by the Spanish and the Portuguese.

Savannah regions are readily brought under cultivation, once modern agricultural implements become accessible. Though the summer drought is in itself an annual handicap, it does challenge the native to become more provident; to plan seasonally for security, carefully husbanding his crops grown during the rainy season and storing sufficient quantities to tide him over the dry season. Thus one may see in many of the savannah settlements not only thatched cottages but also bins where grain and other food are stored. Also, for the same reason, the dry low-sun months suggested the usefulness of irrigation. And so the native throws a mud wall across a stream to impound waters during the wet monsoon, and directs the waters in canals across his fields during the dry monsoon. Colonial governments in some cases have required farmers to contribute part of their surplus crops at the end of a productive year to a form of communal storage, to be used in the seasons of threatened famines. Also, concerted efforts are now being made between such governments and the natives to raise living and health standards by the eradication of insect pests, particularly those, like the mosquito and the tsetse fly, which are responsible for sleeping sickness, malaria, and other infectious diseases which prey on both man and beast.

4. Houses. Native houses are generally constructed of mud walls (wattle) with thatched roofs; approaching the *BS* border, one may also expect to find some adobe houses or sod houses. Some settlements are of the communal type, which include storage huts, as already mentioned, usually built on stilts to protect grain from vermin and rodents. Where accessible, high mounds—even termite hills—are selected for settlements, thus elevating them above the extensive marshes of the flood season. Chickens, pigs, and goats are common communal adjuncts.

5. Transportation. With some major exceptions, savannah lands are notorious for poor land transportation facilities. The 80-90 degree temperatures, which often obtain in the dry season, leave little unevaporated water or only salt water available to a traveler; during the wet season roads become impassable due to the heavy and sticky wet laterite clays. Circuitous routes are then used to circumvent extensive marshes which form in low spots. Owing to the wet and dry seasons, streams, like those of the large Campos in Brazil, may alternately flood and dry up, and are thus unsuited to navigation. The Orinoco in Venezuela is one of the major streams in the world of which large stretches become unnavigable, the channel often assuming a braided condition similar to our *BS* Great Plains streams. On the other hand, navigation is maintained on such streams as the Congo and the Upper Nile, which are fed by the heavier highland rains, partially stored in the great lakes area of Lake Victoria and Lake Tanganyika. But falls and rapids obstruct the Upper Nile, and the high escarpments bounding the eastern plateau in Africa form a topographic barrier to penetration from the east coast. Costly as is railroad construction, particularly in the tropics, railways are commonly built for only one purpose—to move an economically important product, usually a mineral or a highly valued agricultural product, from some point in the interior to a port on the coast.

There is one major exception in that India has a surprisingly large number of railways. This is explained in part by the density of population and the number of major cities. Major mining and some manufacturing enterprises are located here. But there is an additional reason: India suffers from chronic famine. Floods and droughts are experienced regularly in one or another of the food-growing provinces. To meet such exigencies, adequate transportation facilities need to be provided to transfer food to famine-stricken areas.

Coexistence of subsistence and commercial agriculture

1. Nature and native. The tropical savannah leaves little to be desired for primitive subsistence. We have pointed out the richness of fauna among which many forms, especially wild cattle, exist, which are suitable for human consumption. Religious taboo, as in

India, of course, arbitrarily restricts the killing of any animals. Along the major streams which do not dry up in the summer, fishing is important; the great lakes of the east interior of Africa are exceptionally fine for fishing. Seacoast fisheries may also assume considerable commercial importance, as with pearl diving off the coast of Australia. Sponge fisheries in the West Indies are a commercial enterprise. During the flood season, the inundation of large areas adjacent to streams and lakes creates exceptionally good fishing conditions as the waters recede with the coming of the dry season. In most instances, however, the native does not depend upon the hunting and fishing economy alone for subsistence, but also engages in livestock raising and migratory agriculture. The former is likely to develop more on the exclusive grasslands next to the *BS* areas which are drier and hence less suitable for growing crops.

2. Soil—crops. Crops thrive better in the tree savannah lands close to the *Af*, where the seasonal droughts are shorter and less severe. Unfortunately, the farmer cannot combine the advantages of greatest fertility of soil with the better climatic regime, because near the *Af* areas the soils are more leached. Conversely, on the poleward side, with its lower rainfall, the soil will be less leached, and with an increasing amount of grass cover, more humus is incorporated into the soil. Particularly is this true in the short grass savannahs which take on characteristic sod cover similar to that of the *BS* lands. Generally speaking, then, the *Aw* soils, like those of the *Af*, are laterites, reddish in color, but become more reddish-brown or even dark brown and progressively less lateritic poleward. The best soils are the alluvial soils along major streams. Other exceptionally fertile spots, with high concentrations of calcium carbonate and other related minerals, are, as previously pointed out, identified with termite mounds. Commonly associated with trees, such sites likewise are desirable for village settlements, since they supply both wood and shade. The rudimentary forms of cultivation of the native garden are much the same as those of the tropical rainforest. Here also the cover is fired, but naturally the clearing is easier because of the fewer and smaller trees—if any exist at all. The grass itself, of course, is readily disposed of.

Subsistence crops are likewise similar to those of the *Af*. Chain agriculture (*Chena* or *Milpa*) follows *Af* practice. Though there may be less leaching due to less year-round rain and greater amount of runoff during the rainy season, the soils cannot maintain their fertility for more than several years of crop planting. Consequently the natives here, too, must practice migratory agriculture.

3. The grazing economy. Native stock, like the Indian zebu and other allied cattle species indigenous to the tropical world, are well acclimatized. Accordingly, they serve well the purposes for which the Hindu native largely uses them, namely, as draft animals. Elsewhere such animals may also be used for milk and meat production. However, such products cannot compare with the quality of meat or the quantity of milk from cattle reared in middle latitude lands. Cattle ranchers, then, must consider the following factors:

(1) Since the optimum temperature required for cattle to give high milk yields is about 50°F., European or American dairy breeds do not thrive in such uniformly high temperature environments as are found in the *Aw* or the *Af*. (2) Though the tough, reedy and fibrous grasses during the dry season may be successfully foraged by some native cattle, imported breeds require a different type of forage. (3) Moreover, the scarcity of water becomes a critical factor in areas so dry that even the wild migratory beasts may perish for the want of it. (4) Almost everywhere some kind of tropical insect besets the beast. The destructive tsetse fly, which dominates practically the whole of the African savannahs, has so far defied all measures of control. (5) The large number of carnivores in the *Aw* takes a great toll of domestic cattle, particularly in India. (6) Except for a few local regions, there is little market for fresh milk, and the marketing process at best is difficult due to poor transportation. This has already been mentioned in connection with Africa. It is likewise true of the great Campos interior of Brazil and the Llanos of Venezuela. Consequently, cattle are driven "on hoof" long distances to slaughter-houses. Such long journeys leave cattle in very poor condition.

Whatever their original quality of beef may be, such a product cannot compare with that of the more favorably situated grazing lands, such as our Great Plains, the Pampas of South America, southeastern Australia and New Zealand. As a matter of fact, many regions of the savannah world feature hide exports rather than meat exports. Such are, for example, parts of *Aw* South America and India, the latter being a great exporter of goat hides and kid skins.

4. General agricultural potential. At this point it would be interesting to postulate the agricultural possibilities of the savannah world. It is a way for a geography student to test his observations and deductions on the basis of such regional facts as he possesses and the deductive reasoning and generalizations which appear legitimate in the light of such facts. Before doing this, however, let us briefly review those environmental characteristics which limit agricultural development: (1) the total high annual rainfall and frost-free conditions which favor heavy leaching of the soil; (2) severe drought that usually lasts from four to six months with extraordinarily high temperatures and therefore high evaporation; (3) the other extreme of rainforest type of rainfall during the wet season, causing excessive runoff and therefore a great deal of soil erosion; flooded lowlands may destroy an entire summer's crop; (4) the swamps of the tree savannahs and the marshes of the grass savannahs, ideal breeding grounds for some of the most infectious epidemic diseases known to man; (5) the unreliability of the total annual rainfall and its undependability at both the beginning and the end of the rainy season; (6) with a few regional exceptions, the extraordinary dearth of road and railroad transportation facilities, which handicaps the marketing of goods.

On the basis of the above environmental handicaps, one may readily understand how one might conclude that savannah regions are likely to have low present-day agricultural productivity as well as an unpromising agricultural potential for the future. Rationalizations are always in order, but conclusions of this kind are unreliable when based on a consideration of only the environmental limitations which nature imposes upon man. For, even as adverse as some of the *Aw* environmental limitations may seem through circumscribed opportunity of economic development of a community or region, the natural setup must also be evaluated for such favorable aspects as it may have. Moreover, in such widespread lands as the savannahs, incorporated as they are in all the continents of the world exclusive of Europe, we would expect to find major regional differences in climate, natural vegetation, soil, and landforms. What is even more significant are the contrasts in demographic and ethnographic qualities of the varied oriental and occidental cultures (Amerindian, Negro, Malayan native, as well as Caucasian immigrant, and numerous mixed types).

Perhaps, then, the student will now recognize that it would be much more judicious to analyze present and potential agricultural conditions as well as the development of other economies in relation to the contrasted landscapes—the tree savannah as distinct from the grass savannah, the highland savannahs as distinguished from the lowland savannahs; and the equatorial savannahs as differentiated from the subtropical savannahs. On the cultural side, he will reflect upon differences between the stages of development of civilization between the aborigines of northern Australia, southern and southeast Asia, north tropics and south tropics of Africa, as well as between the West Indian Caribbean, the Brazilian and other South America cultures. Also to be considered is the time element. For what length of time has the aborigine occupied the area? Even much more significant are the historic antecedents concerned with the exploration, colonization, and possible settlement of such areas by white men.

All these varied factors must necessarily be considered, since diversification of regional agricultural economy as well as other economies is about the only over-all generalization which one can make for the world savannah lands. This should help to dispel the illusions, on the one hand, that savannah lands are good for nothing except supplying limited amounts of native migratory grazing; or at the other extreme, that savannahs hold the greatest potential commercial grazing lands of the world—the answer to the growing population problem in the world.

5. Crop diversification. Though native agriculture generally still depends upon the crudest implements for cultivating, seeding, and harvesting the crops, white man's innovation of the modern steel plow and other farm machinery makes it possible to exploit the savannah lands for agricultural purposes much more readily than those of the rainforest. The wider latitudinal and altitudinal spreads of savannah lands likewise conduce to greater diversification of crops, particularly where irrigation facilities are available. Such crops include a host of indigenous varieties of vegetables—cassava, beans, peas, ground nuts (peanuts), yams, melons, pumpkins, tomatoes; grains (rice, maize, sorghum, millet, wheat); tree crops (mango, avocado, banana); fiber crops (cotton, jute, sisal) and sugar cane. Several of these—banana, sugar cane, coconuts, rice, peanuts, rubber fiber and beverage crops—are in some places plantation products grown for export, especially under conditions of irrigation. Thus almost every class of vegetable food can be and is being grown. Add to this the wildlife and domestic animal food supplies and one might readily come to the conclusion that here we have the richest food potential in the world. Yet we know at the same time the rather striking paradoxical fact that many regions of this realm are among the world's most poorly settled and developed lands, with the utmost primitive and substandard living; in fact, some of the worst famine lands in the world.

Perhaps this "geographic paradox" can in part at least be resolved by considering the varied types of agricultural practices and productivity — actual or potential — related to the tropical savannahs. Under the climatic handicaps indicated, the best workable connections result from recognizing the possibilities of three crop-growing regimens: (1) wet-season crops planted in the beginning of the rainy season and harvested at the end of the dry season, which would include the major cereals and vegetables; (2) supplemental agriculture during the dry season, based on perennials, drought-tolerant grains (millet and sorghum), or crops raised by dry-farming methods; (3) irrigated crops during the dry season, which may include almost any type, but especially plantation rice, cotton, sugar cane, coconuts, peanuts, and other crops of major subsistence or commercial value.

Plantation landscapes in many instances feature exotic cultural forms as a result of investments and operations by midlatitude corporations.

Midlatitude white man's influences on native savannah culture

While a primitive subsistence agricultural economy is still the predominant hallmark of savannah lands, white man has superimposed, or at least is disposed to superimpose, his Western culture on both the Oriental and Occidental savannah aborigine. At first, during the days of exploration, as in the sixteenth and seventeenth centuries, the native's services were exploited primarily in the discovery and mining of minerals. The next stage of exploitation took the form of plantation-crop production designed for exports to European markets. Thus, first using the Indian, and subsequently Negro slaves imported from Africa, the Portuguese in Brazil and the Spanish elsewhere in tropical America developed extensive sugar and other plantations. The Dutch and the British were likewise thus engaged in the Eastern as well as Western Hemisphere. A systematic and expanded system of commercial agriculture has been inaugurated in Southeast Asia, as well as in the savannah lands of Africa. Here both local and larger regional irrigation projects have been developed with the aid of outside capital, at first primarily by the British in their own colonies and more recently on a larger, more intensive and extensive regional scale by various private national and international agencies.

Along with the construction of dams for the creation of water reservoirs for irrigation have come also the innovations of Western technology which may aid the natives in various ways: (1) substituting, in some cases at least, machine agriculture for hoe culture; (2) advising the natives on new forms of soil management; (3) introducing crop rotation, plant and animal breeding; (4) supplying such other guidance as may be necessary for extending agricultural tillage and increasing yields.

Varied relationships of land-use may still exist in the community where side by side are

Bullocks are being brought to drafting camp in northern savannah Australia, the largest cattle run in the Kimberleys. The grass of the genus *Spinifex* is excellent forage. How would it compare with our prairie grasses? (Australian Official Photograph by W. Pedersen)

elements of the primitive hoe culture, large plantation culture almost entirely administered by the whites and completely mechanized, and a sort of intermediate combination where natives may still practice a limited amount of subsistence agriculture combined with tenant service to a grower of commercial crops. In some instances there may be even a fourth type, where progressive natives have come to own and operate their own lands for specialized crop culture and commercial production.

Unquestionably one of the greatest benefits which have accrued to the native as a result of outside capital and other technological aids is the construction of large irrigation dams and water distribution devices. These have proven particularly effective in expanding agriculture during the dry season, and providing supplemental water for rice even during the wet season as needed. It has very definitely mitigated famine disasters in such traditional famine areas as over-populated India and Thailand. India, of course, has long practiced diversion canal irrigation by damming many of the smaller streams, producing "tank" storage, and thus utilizing the seasonal flood waters. The combined irrigation sites of the *Aw* Deccan, the *Cw* Brahmaputra, and the *Bw* Indus regions are estimated to total one-half of the world's irrigated land.

One of the most noteworthy irrigation projects, established with the aid of outside British capital, is a dam constructed across the Blue Nile in the former Anglo-Egyptian Sudan condominium (now the Republic of Sudan) where over a million acres have irrigation facilities, a quarter of which is devoted to cotton culture. One of the original designs was to make Great Britain less dependent upon foreign sources, including the United States, for cotton to support its textile industries.

Regional agricultural differentiations. Many of the *Aw* lands, particularly the low population areas or areas in the early stages of white settlement, are largely without major irrigation projects. Included among such are the savannah lands of northern Australia, Arnhem Land and Cape York Peninsula. These may be said to have reached only the first stage of commercial occupance, namely, livestock ranching. Here the white grazier lives in proximity to one of the most primitive races and cultures of mankind—the aboriginal inhabitants of Australia. In contrast, the heavily populated monsoon India and Thailand have intensified agricultural practices to attain the optimum supply of grain in the form of wheat and rice. The African savannahs probably represent the most diversified and mixed combination of agricultural stages and practices, ranging from primitive hoe culture combined with hunting and fishing to the most advanced form of tropical plantation specializations. In addition to the cotton project mentioned in connection with the Sudan, the French as well as the British have promoted irrigation cotton culture along the Niger River. A few years ago, another large irrigation venture was launched by the British in Tanganyika to grow peanuts. Even with the assistance of other foreign aid, this project, however, proved abortive. For cash export crops Caribbean America has focused upon sugar cane (West Indies), sisal (Yucatan), and bananas (Central America).

How significant a role can environment play in the world economy?

(A Case Study in Coffee Culture)[1]

Commercial coffee production exemplifies many coherent environmental linkages, both physical and cultural, a unified consideration of which most effectively illustrates various geographic principles of economic geography. In common with other tropical plantations, production units are typically large, employ native and/or immigrant labor, are financed by outside capital, supervised by white management, primarily consist of a one-crop specialized agriculture, and seek to market their product primarily in middle-latitude lands of the Western world. Though the per capita consumption of coffee may be great in the regions in which it is grown, the much greater population of the United States and western Europe focuses the market on these sections. The world's commercial production is concentrated in very few areas due to a complex set of physical, social, economic, and political factors. There are two primary producing regions of commercial coffee—southern Brazil in the hinterlands of Santos, the world's greatest coffee exporting port, and northern Colombia. Brazil alone produces between one-half and two-thirds of the world's commercial crop. The United States by far is the leading consumer of coffee, importing more of it than all the rest of the countries in the world together. Arising in part from the high degree of concentration of production and consumption, price control is also a factor of geonomics, since Brazil virtually enjoys a monopolistic world market. It has introduced the practice of *valorization* which involves several expedients for controlling the supply of coffee in relation to consumption in order to maintain profitable price levels.

Now let us look at some of the physical-cultural correlates which help to explain the concentrated regionalized distribution of this product—once centered in southwest and southeast Asia but now, as indicated, primarily focused on the hinterlands of the São Paulo region.

In the first place, the coffee tree is a distinctive tropical plant which cannot tolerate frost. Though the *A* world on its poleward limits does experience occasional frost, the temperature limit of 64°F. for the coldest month represents reasonable security against severe frost hazards. As a matter of fact, the 55°F. isotherm has sometimes been used to express the poleward limits of coffee production. Extremes of high temperatures, humidity or sunshine can be distinctly unfavorable to the growth of the coffee bean, whereas high temperature and intense sunshine are naturally favorable for drying the bean. Year-round rain totaling from 50 to 70 inches is considered ideal, with maximum distribution during the growing season and with light rains during the blossoming season, since heavy rains during this time are deleterious to fertilization. Little rain during the dry season facilitates the maturing of the crop as well as the harvesting and drying of the bean.

[1] Coffee production illustrates a type of culture not confined to any one climatic realm, e.g., *Aw* northeast Brazil; *Cwb, Cwa, Aw* eastern Brazil; *Af, Aw* West Indies: *Cwb, Aw* southeastern Mexico and Central America; *Aw, Am* western Africa; *Aw, Af, Cwb* eastern Africa. In many of these areas the seasonal temperature range is less than 9° F., denoted by the added letter "i." Such symbolism together reveals a tropical-subtropical, highland, winter-low rainfall association, perhaps best typified in the forested *Awi-Cwbi* lands. It appears that some areas now shown by Köppen as *Aw* are really *Am*, or even *Af*.

The plant growth is also favored by deep friable red clays, such as result from the decomposition of basic igneous rocks. Newly decomposed volcanic soils, usually rich in potash, are highly adaptive. Also needed for best production is good soil drainage and air drainage, generally found in rolling topography. A tree plantation of this character in itself may retard excessive soil erosion, while a certain amount of such erosion proves beneficial in renewing the soil base resulting from the progressive decomposition of bed rock or the regolith. If such slope lands have at the same time considerable elevation, as for instance the 2000-foot plateau level of southern Brazil, there is the added advantage of more ideal living and working conditions, since the temperature drops one degree for approximately every 300-foot rise in elevation.

As we have seen above in connection with the general railway transportation pattern of the tropical world, the lack of adequate and efficient transportational facilities may be a deterrent factor in the economic development of any area. Particularly is this true when, as in the case of a product like coffee, it becomes necessary to build railways across steep escarpments into high interior plateaus or mountains from ports, as in the eastern highlands of Africa and eastern Brazil, or in the mountainous terrain of northern Colombia, where the most favorable conditions for coffee growing occur. And this points to another geo-commercial principle: Despite unfavorable terrain transportation conditions, which may prove very expensive to overcome, transportation facilities can and will be provided if the product has sufficiently high value for its weight to carry such costs. This, as we know, is true of the coffee bean, which has a much higher per unit weight value than many other agricultural commodities. And there is still another transportation principle: Products of high nonperishability, such as coffee, can weather long and delayed transport, as is true of most of the Colombian coffee, which, because of the mountain habitat and rough terrain, is transported over tortuous routes by pack animals to the nearest rail or road facility.

Future considerations. Authorities competent to judge such matters believe that the São Paulo region will continue indefinitely as the world's leading coffee producer. While it is true that the exploitation of its lands has pointed to declining production, there still remain thousands of acres of virgin soil which can be planted to coffee. Moreover, a complete deterioration of soils is said to take about fifty years, when no fertilizer is used. However, deterioration has been observed to set in already after a half dozen crops. The practice in the past has been to clear new areas, but in some cases limited diversification and locally multiple crop agriculture, plus grazing, are carried on to help maintain productivity.

Brazil's permanence of coffee production is predicated on the following advantages: (1) The total amount of annual rainfall over much of the area approximates 50-60 inches, with a summer maximum, and no month is completely without rain. These conditions are said to be fairly ideal for coffee. (2) Temperatures likewise are practically ideal, and in this respect coffee production seems to conform to the principle that many of our world's most important commercial crops thrive best on their "poleward limits." Turning once more to the climates map, notice that the *Aw* poleward boundary almost coincides 100 per cent with this coffee growing area. Somewhat paradoxically, however, such decidedly favorable locales involve an occasional frost hazard; this is particularly true, as in this area, not only in a relatively high latitude but also at a high altitude (2,000 feet). Thus frost occasionally, though only quite infrequently, can damage or completely destroy millions of coffee trees, as has occurred several times. (3) Another favorable regional advantage of this latitudinal position is that the coffee trees can be planted row upon row exposed to full sunlight, whereas in the more direct high-sun equatorial regions, coffee trees have to be protected by partial shade provided by other trees, as is the case in Colombia. (4) Here also are the famous Terra Roxa soils, rich in potash, resulting from decomposition of diabase parent material. Because of less rainfall, leaching which occurs is not as pronounced as in the heart of the tropics. (5) Since environmental conditions favor settlement, as already pointed out, there has been very little difficulty in supplementing native labor by the importation of immigrant labor.

(6) This, together with the extraordinarily huge plantations favored by the landscape conditions, has put this area in a most favorable competitive position in the economics of production compared with other regions.

But as is usual in the growing of practically any crop in the world, each regional culture commonly experiences some disadvantages. We have already pointed out the possible frost hazard. There is also the problem of the coffee borer, the "broca," which has on occasion threatened almost entire coffee-growing communities. At this point we may recall that insect depredations elsewhere in the world, on the older and original plantations of coffee growing, were primarily responsible for the shift in commercial coffee producing areas. And despite the fact that coffee, because of its high value, can stand relatively high transportation costs, unusual difficulties in railroad construction have to be faced in transporting coffee to the port of Santos. Negotiating the plateau's steep escarpment proved a real challenge to railroad engineers, who had to resort in part to the use of cog rails (4).

Industrial and commercial potential of tropical monsoonia

The designation "savannah grassland," like so many other abbreviated classification terms, can prove quite misleading. Actually considerable forest stands may occur in some of the more humid sections adjoining the rainforest belt, or in the form of *galerias* along rivers. Trees are characteristically scrubby or thorny, as in the case of the common acacia group. But zonal differentiations do occur, which include commercially valuable timber such as cabinet woods. These include the broadleaf deciduous type that occurs chiefly in the African and Indian savannah lands. Elsewhere, as in Australia, evergreen broadleafs are found along with semideciduous trees. Sal and teakwood in India and Thailand have a wide range of constructional uses. Quebracho of the Gran Chaco is the world's chief source of tannin extract; whereas certain varieties of acacia in Africa are the chief sources of gum arabic.

It is extremely difficult to generalize on the economic significance of minerals in the *Aw* world. Most significant perhaps is the fact that much of the realm awaits further geological exploration. Present-day mining is confined to relatively few regions. Of particular geographic significance is the fact that outside of the Maracaibo and the Tampico petroleum fields in Caribbean America, the *Aw* realm is strikingly deficient in this economically strategic mineral, as well as in coal. This has proved a great handicap in the exploitation of other industrial minerals of great regional importance. Thus we have the rich mineral treasures of the state of Minas Geraes (general minerals) of Brazil, where reportedly the greatest single rich iron ore deposit in the world occurs beside a sizable deposit of manganese, the leading ferroalloy in steel manufacturing. Other industrial minerals are bauxite, source of aluminum, industrial diamonds, and quartz. Of particular ferroalloy significance is Rhodesia with its chromium, cobalt, and vanadium ores. Here also are important deposits of tin and copper. These ore deposits figured significantly in the construction of the railroad from Northern Rhodesia to the Cape of Good Hope. Very little coal occurs in the area, but the area has a great hydroelectric potential, and utilization of such power is planned.

Monsoon India possesses iron and manganese and other minerals of industrial importance, but, like Minas Geraes, the Deccan is short in power minerals. It does possess some coal. With the eyes of the world now centered on atomic energy both for peacetime and wartime uses, uranium, one of the most important sources of fissionable materials, may very well bring hitherto obscure geographic places into the world spotlight, as in the case of Arnhem Land of the Northern Territory of Australia.

Manufacturing on any extensive scale calls for suitable combinations of raw materials, power, capital, labor, transportation, and markets. Nearly all the major savannah regions appear to lack one or more of the natural and human endowments necessary to create large manufacturing communities. Whatever the regional potential may be, few areas have reached an advanced stage of economic and technological development. An exception is the state of São Paulo in Brazil (partly *Aw*) a leader in South American industry. Even in centers of ancient culture, like India, we still find many industries of the household type. Despite generally retarded manufacturing in the realm as a whole, certain industries have taken root locally as, for example, those in the Caribbean, featuring oil- and sugar-refining and food-processing establishments; the cotton and jute textile industries of India and Burma; the mining and metallurgical establishments of India and Rhodesia; the plants for processing tropical fruits and vegetable oils in various sections of *Aw* Africa and for processing coffee in Brazil.

Trade depends upon transportation facilities as well as differentiated regional surpluses. Motorable roads are practically absent in *Aw* Australia and in the Campos of Brazil. Even navigable streams are lacking. Though the poleward sections of *Aw* Africa are connected by motorable roads, the long projected railway from the Sudan to Rhodesia has not yet materialized. Airline routes do make peripheral contacts with most savannah countries but leave much of the interior without such travel facilities. The primary form of commerce consists of the marketing of tropical food products. Naturally, insular, peninsular, and coastal positions of production have a marked favorable geographic position in world commerce. The surplus crop production, as we have seen, is largely a matter of plantation enterprise. Commercial activity in the past has been closely linked with the colony-holding nations —in the early days by Portugal and Spain in the New World, and in Africa by the various powers of western Europe (England, France, Belgium, and Italy). Actually it was a medical missionary, Dr. Livingstone, who paved the way for commercial penetration of the South African savannahs, and the celebrated Cecil Rhodes highlighted the efforts of bringing the Rhodesian and adjacent territories under British commercial and political control (5).

Tropical monsoonia in political and economic transition

As diverse as the natural features of the *Aw* realm are, so likewise is the political character of its organization. Among the two-score nations which share an *Aw* territory, varied types of government are represented. Moreover, practically every major race and religion is represented. A political feature of mid-twentieth century interest is the emergence of the spirit of independence and nationalism felt throughout most of the regions in the realm. Witness the independence of India and Burma, of Cambodia, of Anglo-Egyptian Sudan (now the Sudan Republic), the miniature Ghana Republic, reminiscent of the ancient huge Ghana Empire (remnant, Gold Coast), and others. Associated also with the *Aw* world is the geopolitical concept of regionalism, based on a continental or subcontinental framework, reflected in the U. K. Caribbean Federation and the agitation for some kind of a federation for the countries of the entire African continent, whose geographic (and political) slogan is "Africa for the Africans."

The movement from colonialism and dependency to independence and nationalism is an inexorable trend. The French are beginning to recognize this, hence their organization of the Federation of French West Africa. Following the same spirit and pattern, the British hope for the inclusion of their former colonies and mandates into the British Commonwealth of Nations. These transitions are bound to have impacts on the native in establishing a new social and economic order over the greater part of the *Aw* world, as well as in its adjacent territories.

Economically, this presages large regional changes in the native forms of occupance—from hunting, fishing, and nomadic herding, to commercial grazing, and even to sedentary agriculture, as in Sudan and the Campos. Probably the greatest changes will result from huge irrigation projects, developed especially with outside private or governmental aid, as probably best exemplified in India, which recognizes that in irrigation, more than anything else, there is hope for resolving its immediate food problem.

¶ Realizing that irrigation holds the key to any substantial increase in acreage under cultivation, the government is attempting to develop multi-purpose projects (which provide water for agriculture and hydroelectric power for industry) along lines of the TVA. Some of these . . . have already added 1,500,000 acres to the irrigated area of India. . . . Community Development Projects have been initiated by the Indian Government, with the financial assistance of the

United States government, the Colombo Plan, and the Ford and Rockefeller Foundations, and with loans from the International Monetary Fund and the World Bank.[1]

And this seems to be a good theme with which to close this chapter: Irrigation during the dry season with waters stored during the wet season unmistakably holds the key to the successful exploitation of the *Aw* lands the world over.

APPLICATION OF GEOGRAPHIC UNDERSTANDING

The introductory chorogram on Venezuela (largely *Aw*) was selected to point to (1) a type of problem area typical of *Aw* regions, which cover a major section of the world; and (2) the inherent potential resources awaiting development; and (3) how Rockefeller funds have been made available for such development. Let us now, after reading this chapter, see how in practice geographic study is related to the principles and practices of the so-called "Point Four Program" of our government. This program deals largely with government aid (capital, technical skill, etc.) through private and public agencies, to mostly the underprivileged and underdeveloped countries of the world, a great preponderance of which are found in the *A* realm.

Become reasonably familiar with those findings and provisions of the Congressional Act (7) which suggest particular relevance to the need of geographic investigation and evaluation, to properly implement this program (italics ours):

¶ (a) The peoples of the United States and other nations have a common interest in the freedom and in the *economic and social progress* of all peoples. Such progress can further the secure growth of democratic ways of life, the expansion of mutually beneficial commerce, the development of international understanding and good will, and the maintenance of world peace.

(b) The efforts of the peoples living in *economically underdeveloped areas* of the world to realize their full capabilities and to develop *the resources of the lands* in which they live can be furthered through the cooperative endeavor of all nations to exchange technical knowledge and skills and to encourage the flow of investment capital.

(c) Technical assistance and capital investment can make the *maximum contribution to economic development* only where there is understanding of the mutual advantages of such assistance and investment . . . in the case of investment this involves confidence on the part of the people of the underdeveloped area that investors will *conserve* as well as develop local resources. (Section 403.)

(a) It is declared to be the policy of the United States to aid the efforts of the peoples of *economically underdeveloped* areas *to develop their resources. . . .*

(b) Agencies of the United States Government, in reviewing requests of foreign governments for aid for such purposes, shall take into consideration (1) whether the assistance applied for is an appropriate part of a program reasonably designed to contribute to the *balanced and integrated development of the country or area concerned;* (2) whether any works or facilities which may be projected are actually needed in view of *similar facilities existing in the area* and are *otherwise economically sound. . . .* (Section 405.)

Due regard shall be given to endeavor to facilitate the development of the *colonies, possessions, dependencies, and non self-governing territories. . . .* Assistance shall be made available only where the President determines that the country being assisted *provides all necessary information concerning such program. . . .* (Section 407). . . . Joint commissions shall prepare studies and reports . . . recommendations as to any specific projects which they conclude would contribute to the *economic development* of the requesting countries (Section 410) (7).

I. Regional and Political Geography

A. Now, do you agree that *Aw* regions need and can benefit from this kind of program? Defend your answer in terms of both the physical and cultural aspects of geography.

B. Would the political unit (country) have something to do with the merit of allocation of aid? Which countries or regions dominated by *Aw* type would you recommend for high priority consideration? Basis?

C. How would you rank *Aw* regions with *B* regions for high priority aid?

---

[1] "India's Population Problem," *Focus*, Vol. V, No. 2, October, 1954, p. 5. Reprinted by permission.

II. Systematic Geography

A. What material of this and the preceding chapters has made you particularly conscious of the deficiencies of the humid tropical countries? Which of these geographic conditions do you think can be corrected by such a program as The Point Four?

B. Specifically what type of projects might be undertaken to improve (1) social, (2) economic, (3) political conditions?

C. If you were a geographer employed on one of these Point Four programs (as some geographers now are), just how would you proceed to assess the environmental need and appraise the geographic potentialities of a country or area applying for aid under this program?

References

1 "Venezuela," *Time,* February 10, 1947, p. 38.

2 *The Foreign Trade of Latin America,* Compiled by United States Tariff Commission.

3 James, Preston E., "The Shari Plain," *The Journal of Geography,* Vol. XXIX, No. 8, November, 1930, pp. 319-320.

4 Jonasson, Olof, "Natural Conditions for Coffee Culture," *Economic Geography,* Vol. IX, No. 4, October, 1933.

5 Stamp, L. Dudley, *Africa—A Study in Tropical Development,* John Wiley & Sons, Inc., N.Y., 1953.

6 Kuriyan, George, "India's Population Problem," *Focus,* Vol. V, No. 2, October, 1954, p. 5.

7 Public Law 535, Chapter 220, Title IV, 1950.

Chapter 23

The tropical rainforest and jungle (*Af* and *Am*)—lands of superabundant rainfall

Chorogram: Island in the sun

"It is the fairest land that eyes have beheld," wrote Christopher Columbus when he discovered the Caribbean island of Jamaica in 1494. Nearly every winter 100,000 sun-seeking North American tourists are discovering Jamaica and echoing Columbus. The lush British colony, only three hours by air from Miami, is the Temperate Zone dweller's vision of Eden: white sand beaches and an emerald surf, blue mountains and waterfalls in the distance, a green landscape of palms, banana trees, and sugar cane, splashed with gaudy contrasts of scarlet poinciana blooms, yellow and coral bougainvillaea vines, and fragrant orchards of mangoes, limes, and tangerines.

Unlike most other islands of the impoverished Antilles, Jamaica can boast of more than sunshine and scenery. By the low living standards of the Caribbean, Jamaica's 1,500,000 inhabitants are comparatively well off. Jamaica's soft-spoken natives (80 per cent Negro) look healthy, clean, and sleek beside the ragged poor of neighboring islands. Most of them wear shoes, and at least 70 per cent can read and write. Rarely is a beggar seen in the orderly capital of Kingston (pop. 155,000), a city of paved streets, department stores, supermarkets, and good restaurants.

Jamaica's moderate prosperity is newfound and self-made. Britain, whose absentee landlords drained profits from the place with regularity after the British routed the Spaniards in 1655, did not grant Jamaica limited self-government until 1944. At that time the island was so rundown that a visiting British commissioner called it "a dung heap of physical abomination."

Still under a British-appointed governor, but with an elected local assembly running most of the island's affairs, Jamaica has come along fast. The government is now headed by Chief Minister Norman Washington Manley the West Indies' most successful lawyer before he entered politics in 1938. Under his shrewd eye, Jamaica balances its 60 million dollar annual budget. Money that Britain used to spend to bail the island out of debt is now funneled into "extras" like land development schemes and the newly-built University College of the West Indies.

Chief Minister Manley firmly believes that Jamaica's economy can support the growing demand. He has launched an island-wide land reform program, buying land from big holders and distributing it to peasants. With irrigation projects, expert advice, and new crops, he hopes eventually to make Jamaica's 2 million tillable acres support 2 million people. His slogan: "For every man an acre and for every acre a man" (1).

Jamaica—a Garden of Eden?

Is Jamaica the virtual Garden of Eden it is claimed to be by so many?

Jamaica's climate is of the *Am-Aw* type, (Figure XXIII-1) with the northeastern part of the island receiving the most rainfall. This section of the island is an area of narrow interior plains; wider coastal plains fringe the southern coast. The rest of the island is mountainous. The main products of the island are coconuts, bananas, and sugar cane — these constitute a large portion of its export trade.

Many of Jamaica's natives can read and write, and they wear decent clothes. Kingston, the capital, can be compared with our own cities. These facts, however, do not prove that Jamaica is a Garden of Eden. What has given Jamaica this new moderate prosperity?

Jamaica, when formally controlled by British absentee landowners, was continually in debt because of her many imports. Any extra money that came in went to pay for her debts. Today, this extra money is going into land development schemes and educational institutions to educate her people.

The greatest development in Jamaican policies has been her curtailment of imports. Her banana export has again been built up

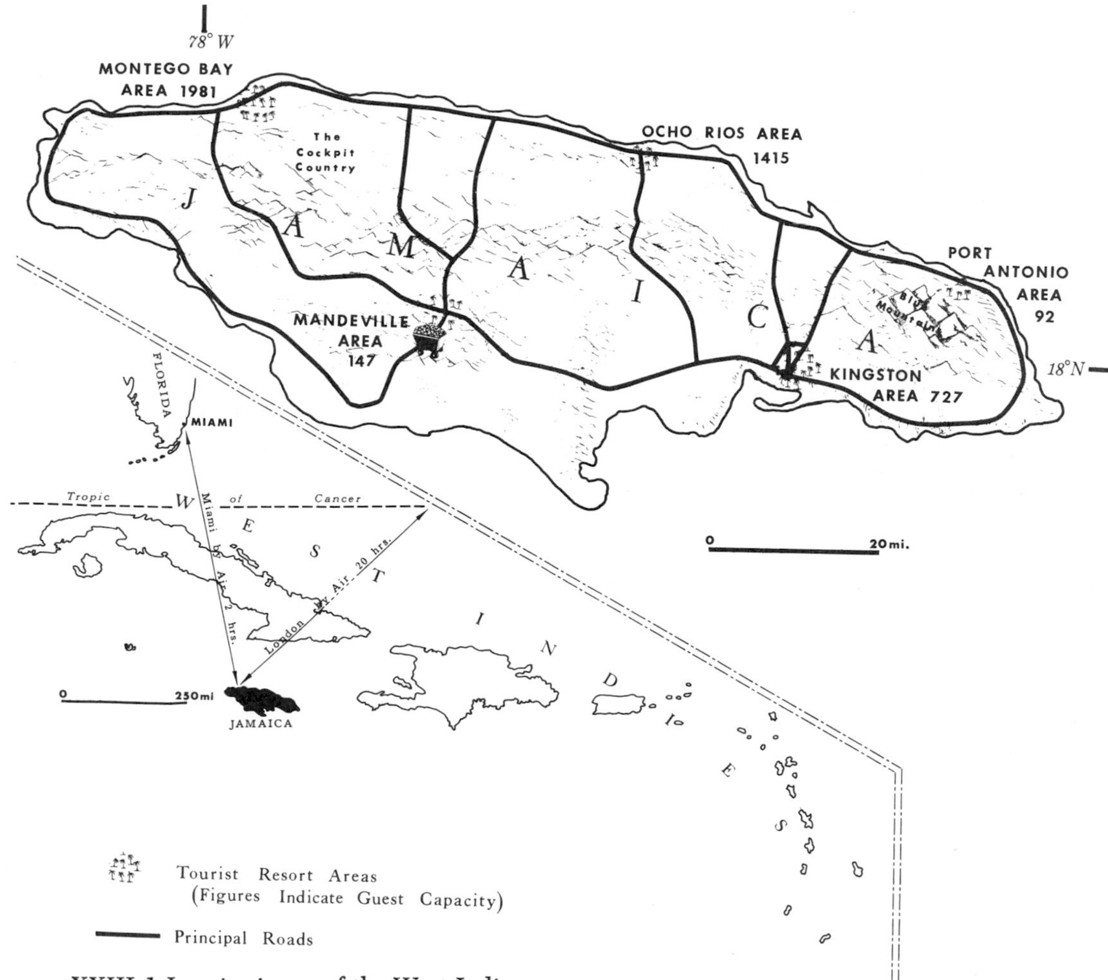

XXIII:1 Jamaica is one of the West Indies islands which, for its modest size, has attained wide distinction as a tropical resort center, combining both *Am* and *Aw* climatological characteristics. Principal centers of tourism and resorting are here indicated with sketches of surface configuration and chief roads. (Adapted after maps and data from *Jamaica, Tourist Guide Magazine*, Jamaica Tourist Board, September, 1960)

since the war. The sugar cane industry has grown into a 21 million-dollar-export. Rice, which has been a staple food for many years, used to be entirely imported; now the island has become almost totally self-sufficient in rice. The industries of Jamaica have expanded enough to satisfy most of her needs for shoes, clothing, soap, and many other necessities of life.

The prosperity of Jamaica was given a big boost by the discovery of several rich deposits of bauxite. Jamaica now exports 2 million tons of this valuable mineral to the United States and Canada every year.

Jamaica has a great tourist trade of over 100,000 "sunshine seekers" a year. Many of these are from North America since Jamaica is only four and a half flying hours from Miami. Montego Bay and Ocho Rios are the centers of this trade.

However all is not bliss in Jamaica. The population of the island is increasing rapidly. Many of the people lack steady jobs. It is believed, however, that with a land reform project going, the economy can absorb the increase in population. The program will include the irrigation of the southern coast and the introduction of new crops.

With this new program and with a continuation of present intelligent leadership Jamaica could well become a model island.

This chorogram and the article from *Time* on which it is based bring together, in a remarkably compact way, many of the basic understandings that the student should derive from a study of the *Af-Am* lands, the forest lands of the tropics. For Jamaica typifies both the natural attractions and the severe limitations of the rainy tropics. More than that, it shows how man, co-operating with his natural environment, and exploiting the advantages which it offers him, can make his life moderately comfortable even in parts of the world which do not, in their natural condition, supply him with any bounty of resources or opportunities.

Both the title of the article and the title of the chorogram reflect the somewhat romantic notion which Europeans and Americans have of the tropics. Depressed by the long-continued cold of winter and wearied by its attendant snow-shoveling, middle-latitude man thinks, or at least hopes, that the tropics are a kind of idyllic paradise peopled by Rousseauan noble savages living a pleasant carefree life in an always-warm environment with the sea lapping at the shore. He daydreams of tropical societies in which handsome, scantily-clad natives spend their time "doing what comes naturally" while nature showers down her resources upon them effortlessly and without pain. Not all middle-latitude people, of course, carry about in their minds such an idealized picture of the tropics. There are romantics at the opposite extreme who imagine the tropics as sinister lands swarming with all manner of wild animals, poisonous snakes, and horrendous insects carrying disfiguring and often fatal diseases.

As it happens, both of these romantic pictures of the tropics are based upon reality. But both are oversimplifications and distortions of reality. For the tropics are many things, many landscapes. There are the seasonally-dry tropics, the *Aw* lands which are discussed in Chapter 22, with their vast stretches of savannah. There are the *Af* tropics with heavy rainfall the year around and great areas of dark, unbroken forest, and there are the *Am* tropics with their short less-rainy season when the dropping of leaves admits light to the forest floor and causes jungle development. It is with these latter two the *Af* and the *Am* tropics, that we shall deal in this chapter.

Forecast: hot and humid

The *Af* and *Am* lands lie astride the Equator with a somewhat larger proportion of their area in the Northern Hemisphere than in the Southern (Figure XXIII-2). Their location largely accounts for their nature, for these lands lie within the equatorial band of rising air which is the product of constant heating by a sun which is always or nearly always overhead. As the air rises, it cools, causing condensation and precipitation. This convectional rainfall provides most of the precipitation of the *Af* lands.

There is another type of rainfall, however, which occurs in the *Af* lands and especially in the *Am* lands. This is orographic rainfall. Orographic rainfall occurs when winds blowing off a water body rise over highlands. The rapid chilling that accompanies the rise causes condensation of moisture in the air and precipitation follows. In the case of the *Am* lands, the winds involved are generally Trade Winds. Thus a map of climates shows long thin belts of *Am* climate following the coast lines of the exposed or windward sides of continents.

The distinguishing difference between the *Af* and the *Am* lands is in the pattern of their rainfall. In the *Af* lands, rainfall is heavy and quite evenly distributed throughout the year with at least 2.4 inches of rain in the driest month. There may be, indeed there usually is, a less rainy season but even this season is short and could not be properly described as a dry season (Figure XXIII-3, XXIII-4). The *Am* lands, by contrast, do exhibit a distinct seasonality of rainfall with at least one month which is distinctly dry (less than 2.4 inches of rain but more than the formula .04[98.5-r]) — dry enough to cause trees to lose an appreciable amount of their foliage. The chief difference between the dry season of the *Am* and the dry season of the *Aw* is that rainfall in the *Am* lands during the rainy season is so heavy, and the dry season so short, that there is no complete stoppage of growth processes in the *Am* lands, as there is in the *Aw*. The vegetational landscape of

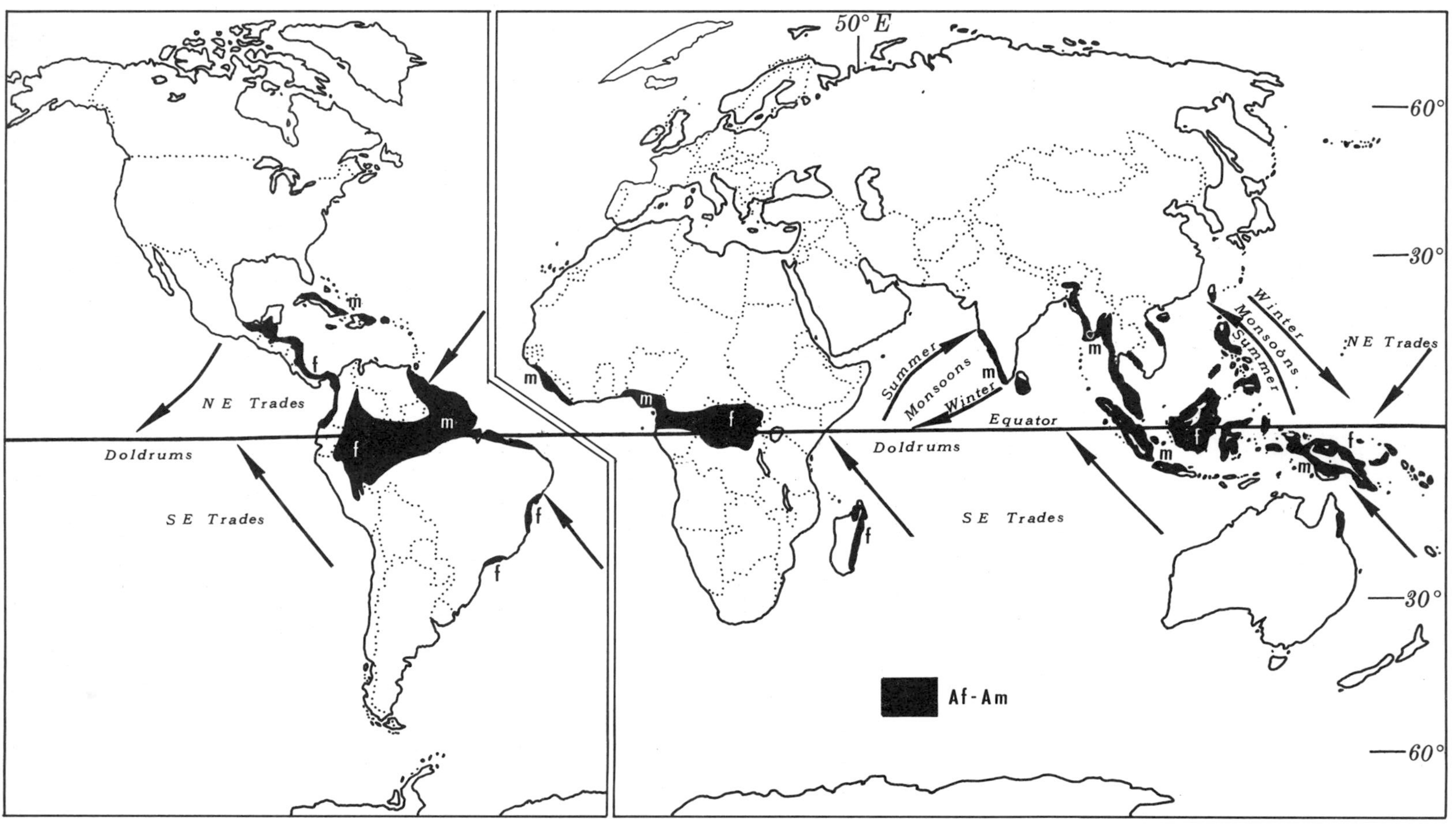
50° E
60°
30°
30°
60°
NE Trades
Doldrums
SE Trades
Summer Monsoons Winter
Winter Monsoons Summer
Equator
Af-Am

the *Am* is, therefore, much more similar to that of the *Af* than it is to that of the *Aw*.

In those parts of the rainy tropics where rainfall is mostly of convectional origin, thunderstorms are frequent and heavy, averaging between 75 and 150 a year. On the island of Java, one station reports thunderstorms on 322 days in the year.

Temperatures in both the *Af* and the *Am* lands run typically in the high 70's or the low 80's, with occasional extremes in the 90's. Temperatures of as high as 100°F. are almost unknown, and temperatures in the 60's are uncommon although they may be encountered in mountains or on plateaus. Generally speaking, these lands also exhibit a low range of temperatures, this range being least at or near the Equator and gradually becoming greater farther from the Equator. Both the annual range and the diurnal range tend to be low, the range from coldest month to warmest month often averaging no more than two or three degrees.[1] The range within the day is usually greater than the range within the year, averaging perhaps as much as fifteen degrees. For this reason it has been said that "Night is the winter of the tropics."

The figures that have been cited would seem to leave little place for the idea that the tropics are uncomfortably hot. Many places in temperate lands have recorded extreme high temperatures ten or fifteen degrees higher than even the highest temperatures recorded in the tropics. But mere figures do not tell the whole story. What makes tropical temperatures often seem oppressively high is the great amount of atmospheric humidity. This combination of high temperatures and high humidity creates high sensible temperatures. And when one adds to these a rising air motion which affords no suggestion of wind or breeze, it is possible to visualize how uncomfortable these lands can be.

The high relative humidity of the air is the chief reason for the lack of any significant temperature range from season to season. The almost saturated air, coupled with a heavy cloud cover, prevents heat from radiating from the land surface. During a dry or less rainy season, therefore, some places may record lower seasonal temperatures just because of the greater amount of heat radiation although, for the same reason, daytime temperatures may be higher than they are during the rainy season. Finally, it should be noted that significant temperature modifications result from exposure to winds blowing off the ocean. The result is that islands and coasts that lie in the path of onshore winds and breezes are much more attractive places to live than are the steaming interiors.

One of the most knowledgeable contemporary experts on the geography of the tropics has written an account of a typical day in an *Af* land which is reproduced here both for its content and for its style:

¶ On a characteristic day the sun rises in a clear sky. Fog is sometimes hanging in the low valleys, but this speedily rises in curling wisps of vapor as the land is heated by the sun's rays. Soon puffy cumulus clouds appear, before long covering a large part of the sky. A light shower may occur, often as early as eight or nine o'clock in the morning. This is followed by a period of brilliant sunshine and then by another shower. Showers and sunshine alternate in this way throughout the day, the former becoming more severe and of longer duration as the day progresses. About four in the afternoon a very heavy shower occurs—a deluge of rain accompanied by little wind. The storm, at first torrential, later settles down to a steady rain which continues into the evening. It is a characteristic remembrance of the rainy tropics: the beat of rain on an iron roof, the monotonous splash as the water runs off onto the ground, and the sticky wetness that penetrates everything and leaves one soaked with perspiration. Well into the night the rain gradually ceases and it is suc-

[1] A range of less than nine degrees between the warmest and coldest month is indicated in the Köppen symbolism by the letter "i."

XXIII:2 (Left) The Amazon type of climate (*Af-Am*) is so called because of its focal association with the prominent South American river by this name. With what other prominent river systems is this type identified? What island groups? In the southern tip of Florida, notably the Miami area, there are small patches of *Am* fringing the *Aw*. This is in the belt of equatorial convections and heavy rainfall.

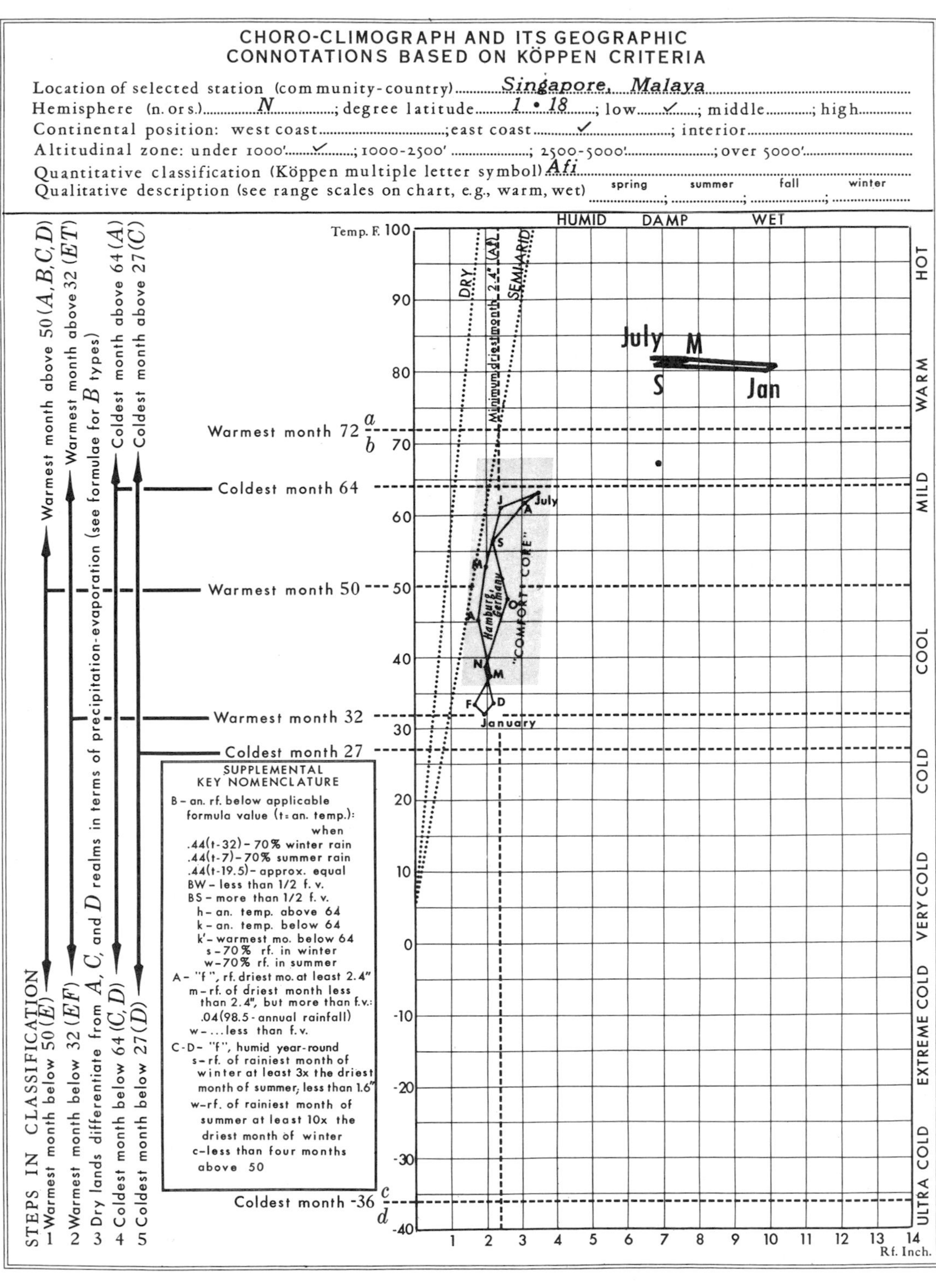

CHORO-CLIMOGRAPH AND ITS GEOGRAPHIC CONNOTATIONS BASED ON KÖPPEN CRITERIA
Location of selected station (community-country) Singapore, Malaya
Hemisphere (n. or s.) N; degree latitude 1 • 18; low ✓; middle; high
Continental position: west coast; east coast ✓; interior
Altitudinal zone: under 1000' ✓; 1000-2500'; 2500-5000'; over 5000'
Quantitative classification (Köppen multiple letter symbol) Afi
Qualitative description (see range scales on chart, e.g., warm, wet) spring; summer; fall; winter
STEPS IN CLASSIFICATION
1 Warmest month below 50 (E) — Warmest month above 50 (A, B, C, D)
2 Warmest month below 32 (EF) — Warmest month above 32 (ET)
3 Dry lands differentiate from A, C, and D realms in terms of precipitation-evaporation (see formulae for B types)
4 Coldest month below 64 (C, D) — Coldest month above 64 (A)
5 Coldest month below 27 (D) — Coldest month above 27 (C)
Temp. F.
HUMID
DAMP
WET
HOT
WARM
MILD
COOL
COLD
VERY COLD
EXTREME COLD
ULTRA COLD
DRY
SEMIARID
Minimum driest month 2.4" (Af)
Warmest month 72 a b
Coldest month 64
Warmest month 50
Warmest month 32
Coldest month 27
Coldest month -36 c d
July
M
S
Jan
"COMFORT CORE"
Hamburg, Germany
January
SUPPLEMENTAL KEY NOMENCLATURE
B - an. rf. below applicable formula value (t = an. temp.): when
.44(t-32) - 70% winter rain
.44(t-7) - 70% summer rain
.44(t-19.5) - approx. equal
BW - less than 1/2 f. v.
BS - more than 1/2 f. v.
h - an. temp. above 64
k - an. temp. below 64
k' - warmest mo. below 64
s - 70% rf. in winter
w - 70% rf. in summer
A - "f", rf. driest mo. at least 2.4"
m - rf. of driest month less than 2.4", but more than f.v.: .04(98.5 - annual rainfall)
w - ...less than f.v.
C-D - "f", humid year-round
s - rf. of rainiest month of winter at least 3x the driest month of summer; less than 1.6"
w - rf. of rainiest month of summer at least 10x the driest month of winter
c - less than four months above 50
Rf. Inch.

ceeded by a deep silence, relieved only by the dripping of water from the soaking foliage and by the hum of the dreaded mosquito.[1]

Tropical diseases

For centuries the tropics have been described as "the white man's graveyard." The survival of apparently healthy white stock in certain of these *Af* and *Am* lands over a period of several generations, and the remarkably low mortality rate from disease among troops who served in the tropics during the Second World War, would seem to indicate that white man can survive in the tropics if he is aware of the special threats which these lands pose to health and if he will exercise reasonable precaution.

Malaria, which is carried by the female anopheles mosquito, is universally present in the tropics except in those rare places where local governments maintain a continuing program of prevention. The key to malaria prevention is the draining or coating of stagnant water where the mosquitoes breed. Other fever diseases, carried by mosquitoes or other insects, are also prevalent and require special precautions.

Pollution of surface waters and traditional methods of fertilization of the soil, often involving the use of human excreta, encourage the spread of gastrointestinal ailments ranging from the uncomfortable but seldom fatal diarrhea to the much more serious dysentery. Native populations, among whom the more susceptible have died off, appear to have inherited a certain immunity to these diseases. Outsiders, who enjoy no such inborn immunity, must exercise great care in food and drink.

Since the intensity of sunlight over the tropics is much greater than it is over Latitude 40, ultraviolet radiation is greater than in middle-latitude lands and may cause heat stroke. "Mad dogs and Englishmen go out in the noon-day sun." Occasional combinations of very high temperatures and high humidity will also cause heat stroke.

Recent medical studies suggest that newcomers from cooler lands, particularly women, may develop anemia in the tropics. For this reason and others it is advisable for those not born to the climate to take frequent vacations in cooler latitudes or cooler altitudes. In tropical countries where there are any considerable number of Europeans, one will often find "hill stations" to which at least the women and children resort during the warmest season of the year.

There is no point to extending the list of tropical diseases indefinitely[2], for every part of the world has enough ailments to debilitate and kill its population. For the traveler who may be planning to spend time in a tropical country the emphasis should be not so much upon the nature of the diseases which he may encounter as upon the reasonable precautions that he should take against them. In general, the precautions which one needs to take in the tropics are those which one ought to practice as a matter of daily routine in any part of the world: sufficient exercise, scrupulous cleanliness, care in the selection of food and drinking water, and regularity of habits and bodily functions.

More difficult to cope with — and no doubt responsible for a considerable proportion of the physical ailments from which white man suffers in the tropics — is the psychological climate in which the white man finds himself. He is in a land where nature itself is different from anything he has been accustomed to, where the culture is strange (and therefore somewhat frightening) to him, where he lacks relatives or friends to encourage or censure him, where complexion and language set him apart as an outsider, and where physical and mental labor alike easily overtax resources which have already been drained by the hot, humid, monotonous climate. The alcoholic derelict and the ragged beachcomber are not figments of the novelist's imagination, but living examples of the price a person pays for attempting to live in

[1] James, Preston E., with the collaboration of Hibbert V. B. Kline, Jr., *A Geography of Man*, Ginn and Company, Boston, 1959, p. 95. Reprinted by permission.

[2] For a more extended discussion of tropical diseases see Chapter 17.

XXIII:3 (Left) Climatic charts are not weather charts. However, could you infer the day-to-day weather conditions from this graph? Does Singapore need a weather forecaster?

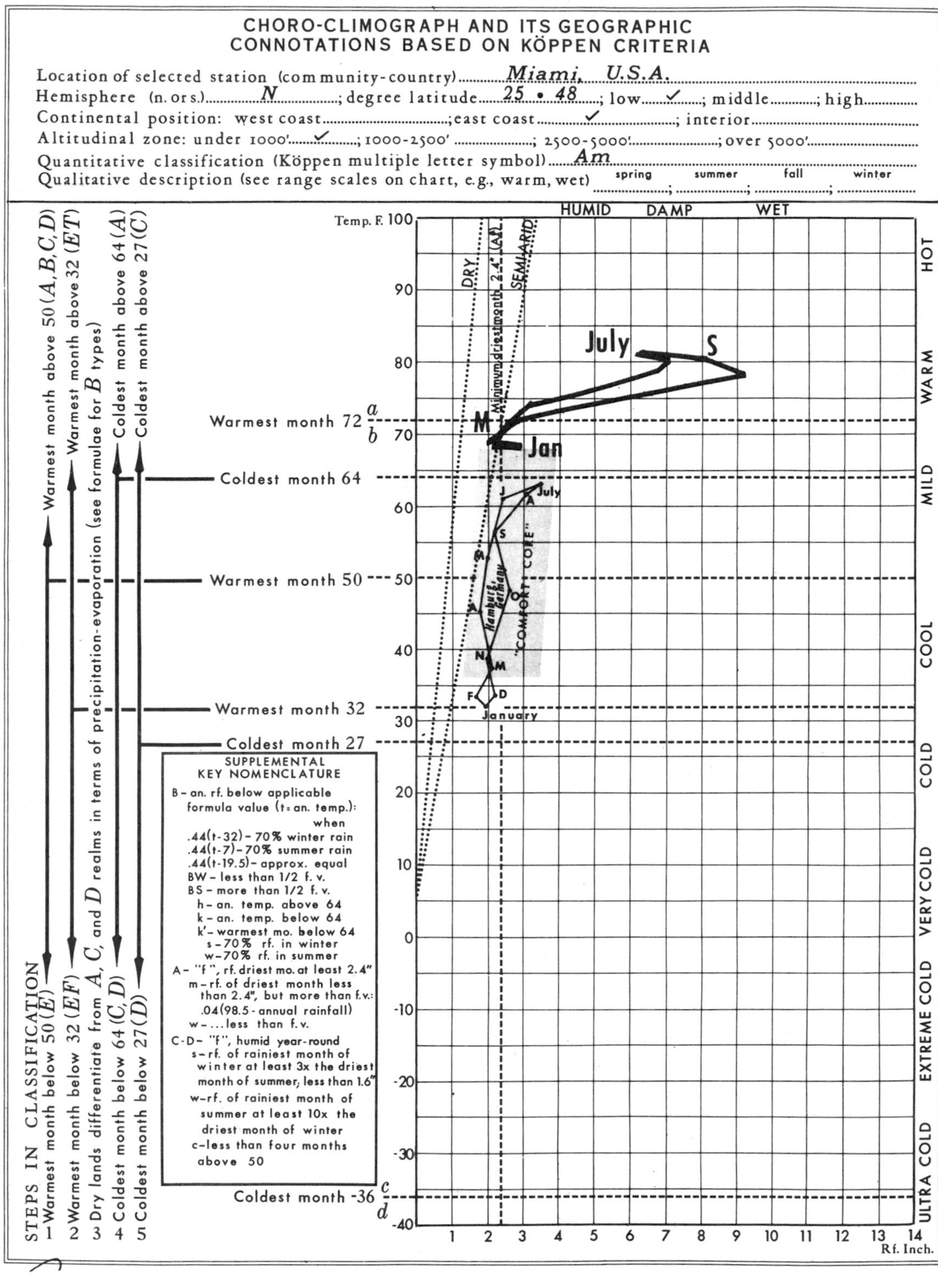
CHORO-CLIMOGRAPH AND ITS GEOGRAPHIC CONNOTATIONS BASED ON KÖPPEN CRITERIA
Location of selected station (community-country) Miami, U.S.A.
Hemisphere (n. or s.) N ; degree latitude 25 • 48 ; low ✓ ; middle ; high
Continental position: west coast ; east coast ✓ ; interior
Altitudinal zone: under 1000' ✓ ; 1000-2500' ; 2500-5000' ; over 5000'
Quantitative classification (Köppen multiple letter symbol) Am
Qualitative description (see range scales on chart, e.g., warm, wet) spring ; summer ; fall ; winter
STEPS IN CLASSIFICATION
1 Warmest month below 50 (E) — Warmest month above 50 (A,B,C,D)
2 Warmest month below 32 (ET) — Warmest month above 32 (ET)
3 Dry lands differentiate from A, C, and D realms in terms of precipitation-evaporation (see formulae for B types)
4 Coldest month below 64 (C,D) — Coldest month above 64 (A)
5 Coldest month below 27 (D) — Coldest month above 27 (C)
Warmest month 72 a b
Coldest month 64
Warmest month 50
Warmest month 32
Coldest month 27
Coldest month -36 c d
Temp. F.
HUMID
DAMP
WET
DRY
SEMIARID
Minimum driest month 2.4" (Af)
July
S
M
Jan
"COMFORT CORE"
Hamburg, Germany
January
HOT
WARM
MILD
COOL
COLD
VERY COLD
EXTREME COLD
ULTRA COLD
Rf. Inch.
SUPPLEMENTAL KEY NOMENCLATURE
B - an. rf. below applicable formula value (t = an. temp.): when
.44(t-32) - 70% winter rain
.44(t-7) - 70% summer rain
.44(t-19.5) - approx. equal
BW - less than 1/2 f. v.
BS - more than 1/2 f. v.
h - an. temp. above 64
k - an. temp. below 64
k' - warmest mo. below 64
s - 70% rf. in winter
w - 70% rf. in summer
A - "f", rf. driest mo. at least 2.4"
m - rf. of driest month less than 2.4", but more than f.v.: .04(98.5 - annual rainfall)
w - ... less than f.v.
C-D - "f", humid year-round
s - rf. of rainiest month of winter at least 3x the driest month of summer; less than 1.6"
w - rf. of rainiest month of summer at least 10x the driest month of winter
c - less than four months above 50

an environment which he cannot cope with because he lacks the knowledge and the inner resources.

Selva, not jungle, the dominant tropical vegetation

The forests that cover the *Af* and *Am* lands represent, next to the taiga, the greatest expanse of forest left on the earth. Their enormous extent and the variety and quality of their trees would seem to suggest that they might constitute a major merchantable resource for the peoples of the tropics. That this is not, in fact, the case should become evident from a closer examination of these forests.

Most outsiders, and indeed most native people who have occasion to travel through the forest, follow rivers or streams or coast lines. Seen from such passageways the forest looks like a solid wall of trees rising from a tangle of undergrowth. This is jungle, and its development along such natural breaks in the forest long supported the mistaken idea that the entire tropical forest is a jungle.

Actually, the greater part of the forest, especially in the *Af* lands, is tropical rainforest or, to use its Brazilian name, *selva.* The selva is a broadleaf evergreen forest consisting of a remarkable variety of trees, chiefly hardwoods. (It has been estimated that there are as many as 2,500 species of tree in the Amazon Basin, with as many as 150 species on a single acre.) Unlike the forests of middle latitudes, the rainforest does not consist of pure stands of two or three species; rather many species are represented by individual trees scattered throughout the forest. This characteristic of the forest, in itself, makes timber exploitation difficult and generally unprofitable. Since conditions in the selva favor year-round growth without interruption, trees show no growth rings, and on any individual tree buds and mature leaves and dying leaves and fruit in all stages of development may be found simultaneously. The trees are involved in a life and death struggle for light. Their trunks, therefore, stretch upward, straight and limbless like the columns of a Gothic cathedral toward the "roof" of the forest, the billowy canopy of foliage which is formed by the interweaving crowns of the trees. Hanging from the trees and often intertwining them are long vines, *lianas,* some of them as delicate as spider webs and some of them thick and knotty like stout ropes. The tallest trees may be as much as 125 feet high and 15 to 20 feet in girth. Below them there may be a second story of trees 75 to 100 feet high. Many of the forest plants are brightly colored parasites. Still others are epiphytes or air plants, an example of which would be the orchid.

XXIII:4 (Left) Tropical Miami, as everyone knows, is in a leading resort region. What does this chart indicate as to its relative *seasonal* advantages—and disadvantages?

The selva is an awesome thing. The canopy of foliage is so thick that it allows very little light to penetrate to the forest floor, even at mid-day. The light that does filter through takes on a greenish tinge from the vegetation and diffuses through the vapor which rises from the soaked ground. Travel is difficult, not because of conditions underfoot but because there are no landmarks, no ways to determine one's direction. The great danger of travel through the selva is the danger of becoming hopelessly lost.

Selva, as has been noted, comprises the major part of the *Af* forest. Jungle develops where, for whatever reason, sunlight can get through the forest canopy to the surface. Typically such conditions might be found (1) along the edge of the selva, (2) along watercourses, (3) on steep mountain slopes, (4) in places where the selva has been cleared, or (5) in portions of the rainy tropics, such as the *Am* lands, where a pronounced dry season tends to limit the number of trees that will grow in a given area and thus prevent the development of a solid canopy.

The underbrush which develops in the jungle makes the jungle even more difficult to get through than the selva. But the wider spacing of the trees makes jungle easier to clear. On the drier edges of the jungle the greater amount of sunlight and the presence of grassy undergrowth make it possible for surface animals to survive as they cannot in the selva.

Finally, there is a third type of forest which is found in the rainy tropics, typically in low coastal swamps and lagoons. This is

the mangrove forest. Unlike the jungle and selva, it is a pure stand of trees belonging to the genus *Rhizophora*. The mangrove tree has bushy branches and stands on stilted roots which, at high tide, are covered by salt water. New trees develop from seeds which germinate in the air and attach themselves to the root system of the parent tree. Since the root systems of the mangrove intertwine, it is exceptionally hard to get through them. During the Second World War the sites of particular invasions in the Pacific theatre were largely determined by breaks in the mangrove fringe along the islands. Towns, also, are likely to be located at such breaks.

The trees of the tropical forests supply some of the most valuable and most coveted woods of commerce. Their extensive exploitation is, however, prohibited by numerous practical difficulties. It has already been noted that the trees do not occur in pure stands. To this difficulty must be added the great difficulty of access. Railroads and roads, or even trails, are difficult to establish and maintain in these lands of rust-favoring humidity and riotous growth. Many of the most valuable woods have a specific gravity greater than that of water and cannot, therefore, be floated on the rivers. And their weight makes them almost prohibitively expensive to ship any considerable distance. Most famous of the tropical woods are mahogany, teak, rosewood, and logwood. Even more valuable to local populations are the versatile palm, especially the coconut palm, and the bamboo.

Big game rare in these lands

Contrary to popular opinion, the *Af* and *Am* lands are not especially noteworthy for big game. Indeed, except for the drier margins of the jungle, large land animals would find difficulty in simply moving about in the close-grown forest, not to mention finding sufficient forage. Life in the selva and in most of the jungle is primarily arboreal or aquatic. Skittering and chattering in the forest canopy are the apes, bats, birds, lizards, and many varieties of monkey. Then, neither skittering nor chattering, hangs the tree sloth, rump down, apparently unaware of anything around him. In the rivers are the carnivorous alligator and crocodile, the herbivorous hippopotamus (found only in Africa), many varieties of snakes, and a great variety of fish, some of them poisonous. In more open parts of the jungle one may find elephants, buffaloes, rhinoceroses, anteaters of various kinds, tapirs, pigs, okapis, warthogs, and many other animals. In any particular part of the tropics the herbivorous animals which are locally present will be related to the vegetation which furnishes their food. The carnivorous forms, in turn, will be related to the species which they can prey upon. Many of the animals that have been mentioned are actually denizens of the savannah (Chapter 22) which enter the forests during the dry season in search of water and forage.

The most abundant form of life in the *Af* and *Am* lands is insect life. Dr. Marston Bates has said that no one has the slightest idea how many different kinds of insects there are in the tropics. Only a few of the more important kinds can be mentioned here. First and foremost, there are the mosquitoes, some of them carriers of diseases which enter the body through the blood stream. There are the termites, insatiable in their appetites for anything that contains cellulose. There is the Congo cockroach that eats the backs off books and the paint off picture frames. There are the driver ants that advance in infantry formation and drive all other animals, including man, before them. There are the tsetse flies, carriers of sleeping sickness. There are blood-sucking leeches that can penetrate through the sleeves of a cotton shirt to get at their victim. And there are still smaller forms which may be the carriers of the dreaded scrub typhus.

The outsider who finds it necessary to spend some time in the tropics often goes in

(Left) This road winds through the rainforest. Note how the tree in the foreground seems to be raising its limbs toward the sun. Any break in the forest, such as a road, admits sunlight to the forest floor along its edges and results in a luxuriant growth of vegetation. Although the temperate forests of our country contained different types of trees, they bore a striking resemblance to the tropical rainforest and were almost equally difficult to traverse. (Embassy of Indonesia, Washington) dread of being eaten alive by some great, hungry animal or crushed to death by a python. He would be well-advised to spend whatever energy he can spare for worry on those much smaller enemies that account for so much discomfort and death in the tropics.

The soils wear out quickly

The profuse vegetation of the tropics has led many to the erroneous conclusion that tropical soils must be among the richest in the world. Locally this may be true, particularly in areas where rich lavas have weathered down into excellent soils or where fine alluvial material has been deposited and drained. However, most soils of the tropics, because of the climatic conditions, are subject to unremitting attacks upon their structure and fertility, attacks which, in the long run, must prove highly damaging to any soil, however great its original fertility.

There is, in the tropics, no season when the soils enjoy that relative immunity from attack which the soils of cooler latitudes enjoy during the long, frozen winter. Day after day the rains come, often in torrents, and day after day the water runs off the surface or penetrates into it. Surface runoff washes the soil away, especially the valuable topsoil. Percolating water seeps down through the soil, carrying with it the soluble minerals that eventually accumulate in a hardpan layer deep beneath the surface, leaving the upper layers devoid of soluble minerals. Among the insoluble minerals left as a result of this leaching process are the compounds of aluminum and iron. These give a red or orange or yellow color to the soil.

Along with the process of leaching goes the process of eluviation. In eluviation, the percolating water carries the finer soil particles down with it into deeper layers of the soil, leaving a surface which constantly tends to become coarser and more cloddy.

Soils which are in an advanced stage of leaching and eluviation are called laterites. Laterites have about the same appearance and the same fertility as a soft brick.

One might think that the destruction of the soil by water action would at least partially be offset by the vast amount of humus potentially available from the abundant vegetation. But it must be remembered that organic matter, both animal and vegetable, decays very rapidly in the tropics, too rapidly to contribute much to the soil. It is perhaps not so strange a paradox that in these lands of riotous vegetation the soils are starved for humic material.

Finally, it should be noted that the very presence of a great deal of tree vegetation tends to make the soils infertile for cultivated plants. Most of the tropical trees are shallow-rooted. The trees take up all of the plant nutrients within reach of their roots and rapidly convert them into vegetation.

And yet trees are necessary to prevent soil destruction. In the October, 1949, issue of *The Journal of Geography,* the veteran economic geographer, Professor J. Russell Smith, had a brief but illuminating article entitled "Soil Destruction or Tree Crops in the Tropical Forest." This is what Professor Smith had to say:

¶ The enormous growth and density of the tropical forest in the rain belt near the Equator, stands in the minds of millions as the highest type of rank luxuriance, but it is erroneous to assume that this luxuriance signifies great fertility. The tropical forest grows with great speed, reaches great height, produces a vast quantity of vegetation, but often the forest rests upon a base of laterite,—namely soils high in aluminum or iron and very low in fertility. In some places the soil has so much of one of these metals that we shovel it up as ore. The elements of fertility are soluble and have been leached out by rain and the continuous heat, but on top of this fertility stands the forest. There is a certain resemblance here to a glass case (wardian case) the botanist puts in a window to make a little torrid zone where he can keep plants. He puts some earth and some water in the case of glass—adds a few plants, and seals the case. There are records of these forest worlds having lived for fifty years in this case. The plants drink their little supply of moisture, exhale it, drink it again, as they take up fertility, make leaves, and drop them. The leaves decay and feed the plants;—thus fertility and moisture run round and round the cycle of life and death. The process bears a resemblance to the water in the boilers of an ocean steamer, the same fresh water being used for the boilers over and over again—boiling and condensing; boiling and condensing, hundreds of times as the boat crosses the ocean.

The plants of the tropic forest produce leaves, fruits, stems, and trunk. The trees drop leaves, twigs, fruit, and finally die, rot, become plant food, and are picked up again by the plants and thus rebuild the forest once more. The circuit is complete. There stands the magnificent forest like a giant wardian case, using a small quantity of endlessly circulating fertility, with some continual reinforcement of carbon, oxygen and nitrogen from the air.

Man comes with axe and fire. Man cuts the trees of the forest, burns the wood, sets out a plantation, cultivates the soil. The hot sun destroys the humus and the rain carries fertility away. The plantation fails, the forest is gone now, it cannot replace itself. Coarse grass takes its place. In all continents the equatorial rain forest is shrinking by this means.

It is estimated that by this process the equatorial forests of Africa are perishing at the rate of half a million acres a year (see William Vogt, "Road to Survival"). The native system is to deaden the trees, plant a patch of garden among the dead trees, use it for a season or two, then move on before the possibility of forest re-growth has disappeared. Thus the forest and the Negro and other tropical denizens have lived together for ages. The white man with his system of forest destruction is the greatest destroyer that ever trod the earth. H. L. Shantz says that soils show that two-thirds of the land where tropic forest has grown is now treeless.

If much of the tropic forest is to be preserved, we must make use of tree crops. Tree crops will safeguard fertility while producing food for man. In most cases there can be an undergrowth of leguminous nurse crops of small tree and bush to catch nitrogen, hold the soil, make humus and feed the crop trees—nuts, oils, fruits, gums, fibers, even choice woods.

There is nothing revolutionary about this idea. Note the chief exports of the tropic forest areas today—rubber, cacao, palm kernels, palm oil, coconuts, cinchona, mango, Brazil nuts, ivory nuts (tagua, Ecuador), babassu nuts. There might be a host of other nuts and fruits for export or home consumption if they should receive half the effort that has been given to the apple or the orange.

In some cases like the coffee and cacao plantations of today, the nurse tree crop towers above the harvest tree crop furnishing nitrogen and partial shade. Perhaps a fruitful legume might be found for this purpose.

The need is for a realization that the choice is—*tree crops or nothing but coarse grass of almost no value*—Cognales they call such wastes of the tough cogon grass in the Philippines.[1]

The article which introduced this chapter noted that Jamaica's prosperity is new-found and self-made. In the light of Professor Smith's recommendations, what promise does there seem to be that Jamaica's prosperity will grow in the years to come?

Islands of settlement in a forest ocean

As one examines a map of population densities in the *Af* and *Am* lands, one is immediately impressed by how nearly empty most of these lands are. And the more detailed the population map, the greater is the contrast between huge areas with hardly any people at all and small islands of population where densities run up into the hundreds per square mile. It becomes easy, therefore, for the geographer who has an appreciation of the handicaps imposed upon man by the physical geography of these lands to conclude that the general low density of population is the result of the basic natural inhospitality of the *Af-Am* lands and to suspect that islands of high density reflect some local exception to the usual *Af-Am* conditions.

It may be well, therefore, to preface a consideration of man's use of these lands with a word of caution from Dr. Pierre Gourou, professor of tropical geography in the *Collége de France* and director of the Institute of Geography of the University of Brussels:

¶ No progress in the understanding of the human aspects of the landscape is possible if these aspects are simply considered to react to the physical elements of the landscape. The relations between the two are not direct; they are obliged to cross the prism of a civilization. Explanation does not progress if the human groups are considered to be compelled by the natural environment to adopt such-and-such techniques. Nor does the explanation make better progress if we consider that a human group examines the natural environment, evaluates the "possibilities," and chooses the more attractive. "Determinism" (physical determinism) and "possibilism" are

---

[1] Smith, J. Russell, "Soil Destruction or Tree Crops in the Tropical Forest,". *The Journal of Geography,* October, 1949, pp. 303-305. Reprinted by permission.

This farmstead is in the tropical rainforest. Although there are some very densely populated areas in the *Af-Am* lands, the more typical pattern is one of isolated dwellings like this one, set in the middle of the forest and provisioned by the trees of the forest. Note that this house is supported by poles and stands above ground level. In the shade under the house live pigs and chickens and perhaps a dog. The house itself is made of palm thatch. Behind the house, coffee and cacao grow under the shade of the forest trees. In the lower left-hand corner of the picture are banana trees. In the lower right-hand corner is a fenced clearing where vegetables are grown. (U. S. Department of Agriculture, Office of Foreign Agricultural Relations)

unable to give a total explanation. The "possibilities" are in man much more than in nature; they are given to man by the civilization. Civilization is not a product of the physical environment, nor is it a product of a choice oriented by a finality. If a human group selected a certain type of exploitation of some resources, the choice was undetermined. Man has made himself, without knowing where he was willing to go. He has made himself by the making of himself. There was no physical determination, finalistic predestination, or conscious decision; there was a necessity for an undetermined choice and, consequently, a departure into the future. This geographical interpretation of the position of man on earth and in history is full of hope. The future, good or bad, will be the work of man and not the result of physical constraints.[1]

The truth of Dr. Gourou's remarks is best evidenced by the broad range of civilizations that can be found within the *Af* and *Am* world. At the one extreme are the Stone Age Amerindian tribes of the Amazon Basin. At the other extreme are the high civilizations

[1] Reprinted from *Man's Role in Changing the Face of the Earth*, edited by William L. Thomas, Jr., by permission of The University of Chicago Press. © The University of Chicago 1956. Published 1956, composed and printed by The University of Chicago Press, Chicago, Illinois, U.S.A.

of the Philippines, Malaya, Java, and the West Indies. If it is possible to point to any one factor as the great roadblock to social and material progress, that factor would seem to be isolation from the mainstreams of human thought and activity. And this isolation, in turn, may result from physical barriers or from isolationistic attitudes based upon pride, fear, or suspicion.

On the physical side there are several conditions characteristic of the *Af* and *Am* lands that tend to keep people isolated. The forest itself is difficult to traverse and even the rivers which flow through it are in many places made unnavigable by rapids and waterfalls. Roads and railroads are difficult to build and, more important, to maintain in these lands of heavy rainfall and rapid vegetational growth. And when to these factors is added the factor of rough or even mountainous topography (as in the interior of many of the smaller islands), isolation may be virtually complete.

It is not surprising, therefore, that in terms of area the greater part of the *Af* and *Am* world is a world of primitive culture, a world of small, seminomadic tribes that occupy themselves in hunting and fishing and gathering the products of the forest. The more advanced of these tribes practice a kind of migratory agriculture known locally as *caingin* in the Philippines, *milpa* in the Americas, *fang* in parts of Africa, *humah* in Java, *taungya* in Burma and *tamrai* in Thailand. The variety of local names is in itself suggestive of the universality of this type of cultivation in the tropics. Whatever the name, the practice involves essentially the same kinds of procedures: the clearing of a part of the forest, commonly by fire; the planting of crops in the clearing; the abandonment of the clearing after a season or, at most, two seasons (by which time the land has deteriorated so much that it will not produce any more); and the clearing of a new patch of forest. Work is done entirely by hand with the assistance of a hoe or dibble, there are no work animals (although there may be a few scavenging pigs and dogs and chickens), and fertilization of the land is unknown.

The people who practice this type of cultivation live in small villages, commonly along streams that provide them with fish and a water supply. The villages are formless and consist of very simple huts constructed of locally-available building materials—grasses, bamboo, palm logs. In some of the wetter areas the huts stand on poles. Essentially the hut is a sleeping place. Cooking is done outside, and the social life of the tribe is communal. Furnishings, therefore, are simple and, since the tribe frequently moves, easily transportable. Clothing is simple and minimal. The diet of the people is also without exception unbalanced, leaning far too heavily upon such starchy foods as cassava (manioc), taro, yams, and arrowroot. The consequences of such diets are evident in the distended bellies of the children and in the premature aging of the adults.

But it should be noted that even among such primitive peoples the simplicity of their economy goes side by side with social structures that are often extremely complicated and with rituals that may be quite elaborate. White travelers and missionaries who have failed to appreciate the complexities of native religions or the sacredness of native taboos have gotten into many difficulties and, occasionally, have paid for their ignorance with their lives.

A refinement on shifting cultivation is a kind of cultivation called "storeyed farming." This involves, as does milpa, the clearing of the forest, but the clearing is more selective. The larger food trees, such as breadfruit and the nut trees, are left standing, as may be also bananas. Under their cover, crops of manioc, corn (maize), sugar cane, upland rice, and tobacco may be planted, interspersed with such plants as yams, beans, peas, eggplant, tomatoes, and taro. "Storeyed agriculture" produces a wide range of foodstuffs on a small unit of land, but it is very hard on the soil.

Throughout the tropics, these native ways of life and their accompanying economies are changing rapidly as a result of contacts with the outside world. In a photographic essay on tropical Africa, Dr. George H. T. Kimble notes that "fifty years ago few Africans had been outside their tribal limits. Today Gold Coast Africans work in Leopoldville banks and merchants from the Sudan sell their wares in the marts of southern Nigeria" (5). In New Guinea missionaries have built medical dispensaries in interior highlands that had not even been seen by

This is a newly cleared and burned hillside in eastern Peru. In many parts of the *Af-Am* world, the best drainable lowlands were long ago pre-empted. Since the cultures are still predominantly agricultural and since, in many cases, agricultural technology is still very imperfectly developed, there is a chronic shortage of land. Attempts to enlarge the area of cultivable land often produce scenes such as these—the removal of forest cover from steep slopes in regions of heavy rainfall and the settlement of small farmers on the land. What are the long-range prospects for such areas? (U. S. Department of Agriculture, Office of Foreign Agricultural Relations)

white men until a little more than a decade ago and are still accessible only by airplane. Cotton cloth from Manchester has replaced native clothing in many parts of the tropical world, discarded gasoline tins have replaced native baskets and jugs, and tribesmen who perhaps had not seen a European until a few years ago have thronged into the native quarters of great new cities.

Such dramatic changes in a people's way of life, taking place within the lifespan of a generation or two, obviously bring with them many tensions and dislocations. A recent study indicates that large sections of tropical Africa are losing population, not only by emigration but by an actual decline in the birth rate. This study would seem to suggest that Africa is experiencing very much the same thing that happened in the tropical islands of the southwest Pacific in the late years of the nineteenth century when they first came into intimate contact with European civilization. Speaking of the consequences of those contacts, Bronislaw Malinowski has observed,

¶ Once you make life unattractive to a man, whether savage or civilized, you cut the taproot of his vitality. The rapid dying out of native races is, I am deeply convinced, due more to wanton interference with their pleasures and normal occupations than to any other cause (6).

Ribbons of settlement along water

Where population densities are higher, migratory agriculture is, obviously, an insufficient base for the population and, accordingly, some form of sedentary agriculture will be practiced. But it must be understood that sedentary agriculture is both a cause and an effect of heavy population. Underlying both the type of agriculture and the density of population are conditions which make both possible. These include land more fertile than is common in the tropics (alluvial river valleys or coast lines, high-quality volcanic flows), accessible locations, and a reasonably sophisticated civilization.

Sedentary or permanent agriculture falls generally under two headings: native subsistence farming and plantation agriculture. The bulk of the native population is engaged in subsistence farming, and this form will, accordingly, be discussed first.

The most important areas of subsistence farming are in the Far East, in southern and southeastern Asia and in the islands of Indonesia, the Philippines, and the southwest Pacific. Another important subsistence farming area is in the West Indies. In both of these areas populations are dense and the peoples have had continuing cultural contacts with outsiders. Farm units are characteristically small, so small that they may be properly termed "gardens," and cultivation is intensive. In the Far East, rice is the staple crop, two or three crops of rice commonly being raised on the same land year after year. In some places, particularly in the *Am* lands where there is a pronounced less-rainy season, crops less dependent upon water may be raised in alternation with rice.

Rice is the most prolific of the cereal grains and will support large populations per unit of area. As a result, populations tend to outrun the resource base in rice lands, and cultivation must often be extended from the lowlands up onto the mountain sides. This may lead to the creation of artificially-made flat land by terracing.

Rice cultures tend to be conservative, because the results of unsuccessful experimentation may prove fatal in a system which, at best, just barely meets the food requirements of the people, and they tend to produce intricate social organizations because of the need to maintain internal peace and order so as not to interfere with the regular production of food. In most rice areas the small farmer just barely "gets by" and a bad year can plunge him hopelessly into debt. Crop surpluses and crop deficits alike can mean disaster, because surpluses are often difficult to market profitably and deficits mean hunger. At the root of both problems lies an inadequate distribution system, sometimes resulting from inadequate transportation, sometimes from political and economic barriers to the free movement of goods.

Domestic animals are as characteristically associated with rice culture as they are characteristically absent from the migratory farming landscape. Cattle, especially, are used to plow the fields and their manure makes a valuable fertilizer.

Elsewhere in the *Af* and *Am* lands, the crops grown under sedentary subsistence agriculture tend to be those which are indigenous to the particular area. In most tropical lands there is some production of sugar cane, especially in Java and in the islands of the West Indies. On the mainland of the Americas corn is as much the staple crop as rice is in southeast Asia and the East Indies.

Where physical and economic conditions permit, sedentary farmers may produce cash crops in addition to subsistence crops. Among the more important cash crops are bananas (chiefly in the Caribbean area), jute (mostly in India), and cotton (especially in British Africa). Sugar cane, noted above as one of the subsistence crops, may also be raised for sale, as in Cuba. In some parts of the tropics, especially in the West Indies, lands formerly devoted to cash crops have had to be returned to the production of subsistence crops because of rising demands for foodstuffs to support growing populations. Recalling again the article and chorogram on Jamaica, would a policy of "For every man an acre and for every acre a man" seem to work out best under a system of subsistence farming or under a system of commercial farming?

Javanese work in their rice field. Under such painstaking care as this, the land of the *Af-Am* world produces abundantly. This is a *sawah* or irrigated field. Where irrigation is not possible, an inferior grade of rice is grown under *ladang* or dry culture. Java, however, illustrates one of the most pressing problems of the arable tropics: despite its richly productive land and despite the care lavished on it by an intelligent and industrious people, food production cannot keep pace with the rapid growth of the population. (Embassy of Indonesia, Washington)

Tropical plantations

While migratory farming and "garden farming" support the bulk of the population of the tropics, their significance in world commerce derives principally from certain products which are much desired by middle-latitude peoples but can be grown only in the tropics. Several of these products were formerly raised by natives on their own lands and then gathered and sold to white traders. More commonly today they are raised on plantations owned and managed by Europeans and, often, worked by imported labor. The chief products of these plantations are rubber, coconuts, bananas, and sugar cane.

The rubber of present-day commerce comes mostly from the *Hevea Braziliensis,* a tree which is indigenous to the Amazon Basin of Brazil. Originally rubber was gathered by Amazonian tribesmen and Brazilian workers who sold it to European traders. Brazil jealously guarded her monopoly in rubber by prohibiting the export of seeds, but in the 1870's an Englishman, Sir Henry Wickham, managed to smuggle 70,000 seeds out of Brazil. These seeds were planted in the Royal Botanical Gardens near London and in 1876 two thousand seedlings were shipped to Ceylon. From Ceylon the rubber industry spread to Malaya and Indonesia. Within a few years the Far East displaced Brazil as the world's principal source of rubber.

The chief advantage in rubber production which the Far East enjoyed over the Amazon

Basin was its large supply of dependable labor. This had always been a problem and remains a problem even today in the plantations established in Amazonia during the 1930's. A second advantage was the location of the Malayan and Indonesian plantations on the important shipping route between the Mediterranean and the China coast. They were much more accessible than the relatively isolated interior of Amazonia. Moreover, since rubber can be stockpiled for months without deterioration, it was possible for plantation owners in Malaya and Indonesia to store their rubber at dockside, awaiting shipping which was returning to Europe light-loaded from the China coast. Perhaps the fact that these areas were controlled by European colonial administrations also aided the industry.

More recently, the Far East has lost some of its former advantages. Plantation destruction during the war, followed by guerrilla warfare, self-government, and a decline in the Far Eastern trade, has unsettled the Far Eastern rubber industry and new areas have risen to the position of important challengers. Two of these have become especially important: Amazonia and Liberia. Also, thousands of square miles are available in other parts of the tropics for rubber cultivation if it should become necessary or desirable to abandon the Far Eastern plantations.

Perhaps a side comment would be in order at this point. Not only rubber, but all of the tropical plantation crops, could be grown in vastly larger areas than are presently devoted to them. There is, therefore, a constant temptation to relocate plantations whenever, for any reason, they become unprofitable. The reason might be such a thing as infestation by crop diseases, or it might be unsettled political conditions or an unfriendly government. This tentative nature of the industry represents a constant threat to the health of local economies. And while the threat is somewhat offset by the growing cost of establishing plantations, it is a very real threat, nevertheless.

Coconuts come chiefly from Ceylon, southeast Asia, and the islands of the southwest Pacific. One of the most versatile of tropical products, coconuts enter world commerce as copra, the dried meat of the nut; coir, the fiber of the nut which is used extensively in the manufacture of soap; and, of course, fresh coconuts. Regions of production appear to be determined not so much by the needs of the coconut tree as by possible alternative uses of the land. Thus in the islands of the southwest Pacific coconuts are the chief article of export simply because local conditions are not considered favorable for the production of other tropical crops.

Bananas grow throughout the *Af* and *Am* lands, but by far the greater part of the world's commercial banana production is localized in Middle America. This is chiefly because this area is most accessible to the most important banana markets in the United States and, to a lesser extent, northwestern Europe. As bananas are highly perishable, banana ships must be equipped with both heating plants and air conditioning so as to maintain constant temperatures on the voyage from the plantation areas to middle-latitude port cities. Since the ships must be thus equipped and since there is comparatively little movement of people back and forth along their routes, banana ships often serve as the chief passenger carriers in the regions which they serve.

The location of plantations in Middle America has undergone many changes since the industry was first established there. The banana plant is extremely fragile and is not, therefore, capable of standing up to the hurricane winds that regularly attack certain of the Caribbean islands. Plantations that had been established along the main track of hurricanes did not long survive. On some of the islands and along the Caribbean coast of Middle America, the infestation of the plantations by sigatoka and Panama disease forced the abandonment of some plantations and their relocation on the Pacific coast *(Aw)*, where they are now raised under irrigation.

Sugar cane is the fourth of the important crops that tropical lands raise primarily for export to middle-latitude countries. Like those previously mentioned, it can be raised in many parts of the tropics, its actual areas of heavy production being determined largely by the market factor.

Sugar cane is strictly a tropical plant, requiring uniformly high temperatures, abundant moisture, and bright sunlight. The ideal sugar climate has an annual rainfall of 50 to 65 inches, occurring in a long wet season, followed by a comparatively dry season. The dry season is necessary for two reasons: first, to prevent spoilage of the cane during the harvest season, and, second, to maintain a high sucrose (sweetness) content in the cane. The climate should not be characterized by strong winds because a cane field is even more susceptible than is a corn field to serious wind damage. Cane soils must be rich in calcium and nitrogen; must be able to hold moisture but, at the same time, must be well-drained; and must be easy to work. Because of the organization of the sugar industry, the best sugar areas are flat, permitting the construction of roads and railroads to take the cane from the fields to the refining plants or, as they are called in Cuba, the *centrales*.

Sugar is a perennial in the tropics, but production tends to drop off noticeably after the first crop. However, since the most expensive item of cost in cane culture is the preparation of the land for planting, some sugar areas find it more profitable to take several crops from one planting than to replant after each harvest. Any crop beyond the first is called a *ratoon* crop. In Java, where the population is so heavy that the land must produce at its highest potential, ratooning is forbidden. In Hawaii, two ratoon crops are usual. In Cuba, on the other hand, where cane production is extensive and highly mechanized, three to seven ratoon crops are the common thing.

Sugar is a good example of the difficulties under which all tropical plantation economies operate. In most cases, such economies are built around one crop, the returns from which depend not so much upon the region's ability to produce as upon the market demand in other countries. Such economies are, therefore, usually susceptible to cycles of "boom and bust." Even in the best years, the periodicity of work in the plantations creates conditions of high labor demand at certain seasons (planting and harvesting) while little labor is needed at other seasons. And always, in the background, hovers the specter of calamity from wind and weather. It is very difficult for plantation areas to achieve stability, either economical or political. Demagogues find fertile soil for the propagation of economic panaceas, and "strong men" are often admired for their ability to maintain a semblance of peace and order in lands which have known more than their share of unrest.

The new tropics

For some three centuries, the standard European explanation of the relatively low level of material prosperity and progress in the *Af* and *Am* lands has been based upon the allegedly enervating nature of the climates and the lack of soil and mineral resources. The most effective remedy for these natural limitations was believed to be strong and intelligent white leadership. In the late nineteenth century it was fashionable in Great Britain and in other imperial lands to talk about "The White Man's Burden"—his obligation to act as guardian to the childlike natives of the tropical world.

Even before the Second World War, many of the more intelligent and better trained leaders of the native peoples were questioning both the right and the ability of Europeans to refashion the tropics according to their own notions. The questioning became outright denial during the war, and with the coming of peace many of the lands formerly colonial refused to revert to their former status. They had seen the white man working at menial tasks under the bayonets

(Right) This is a street scene in Djakarta, Indonesia. A picture such as this may help to correct the mistaken notion that the *Af-Am* lands are wholly blanketed by impenetrable forests inhabited by primitive tribesmen. While most of the great cities of the tropics were built by colonial administrations, they continue to thrive under their newly-independent governments. Like cities everywhere, many of the great tropical cities are severely overcrowded as a result of the world-wide shift of people from the land to the towns. Lack of a sufficient number of people trained in technical fields and in administration makes it difficult for some of the new governments to maintain the public works which they inherited from their former masters. Therefore, although they are jealous of their new-found political independence, many of the new nations welcome outside economic and technological assistance. (Embassy of Indonesia, Washington)

HONEY BRAND

of nonwhite guards, and the myth of white supremacy was pretty thoroughly exploded. Many of them also had accepted many of the white man's ideas. Whether these ideas derived from Western political philosophers or from Marxian theorists, there was one point on which they seemed to agree, and that was the idea that men had a right to order their own affairs without the interference of some self-appointed guardian. At first, leaders of native independence movements were supposed to have been Communists or Communist stooges. Gradually it became more and more evident that, while Communism had made some inroads into the former colonial lands, the major force at work there was a vigorous nationalism.

Since the Second World War, therefore, the tide has been running strongly against colonialism. Indonesia, long Dutch, is now self-governing. The formerly French territories in Indo-China have become independent, as have also Burma, the Malay states, Ghana (the Gold Coast), Ceylon, and the Philippines. Puerto Rico and the islands of the British West Indies are, for all practical purposes, independent, although they retain close economic ties with their former colonial rulers.

The interesting thing about these newly-independent areas is that, with the exception of Indonesia, Congo, and perhaps Ghana, they have made far greater progress in their few years of independence than anyone had supposed they were capable of making. Heat, humidity, rainforest, and lateritic soils did not disappear with the coming of independence, but a great deal of the lethargy did disappear as native peoples found themselves free, for the first time in centuries, to work out their own problems in their own way. How Jamaica has gone about it is indicated in the news report which introduces this chapter. An even more exciting story is that of "Operation Bootstrap" which has been going on in Puerto Rico under the wise leadership of the island's first freely elected governor Luis Munoz Marin. One of the key figures in this highly-successful campaign to revitalize the economy of the island has been Dr. Rafael Picó, a geographer who, as might be expected of a geographer, made his initial attack upon the problem by setting up a land-use survey to determine what was actually being done with the land and its resources and what could be done with the resources.

Experiences in Puerto Rico, Jamaica, and Ceylon give strong grounds for hope that the tropics, for all of their physical limitations, are capable of supporting their people on a level of physical comfort far higher than any that they have known so far. As Dr. Gourou says, "The future, good or bad, will be the work of man and not the result of physical constraints."

APPLICATION OF GEOGRAPHIC UNDERSTANDING

Apply the same principles of the "Point Four Program" outlined in the previous chapter to a consideration of the problems and potentialities of the countries incorporating major portions of the *Af* (*Am*) realm.

Which of the two tropical types—*Aw* or *Af*(*Am*)—would seem in general to have the best claim to this kind of aid program? (Consider benefits to both the beneficiary and benefactor.) On a geographic basis compare similarities and differences in needs and administration of the programs of the two types.

References

1 "British West Indies," *Time,* March 12, 1956.
2 James, Preston E., with the collaboration of Hibbert V. B. Kline, Jr., *A Geography of Man,* Ginn and Company, Boston, 1959, p. 95.
3 Smith, J. Russell, "Soil Destruction or Tree Crops in the Tropical Forest," *The Journal of Geography,* October, 1949, pp. 303-305.
4 *Man's Role in Changing the Face of the Earth,* Edited by William L. Thomas, The University of Chicago Press, 1956, p. 346.
5 Kimble, George H. T., "Tropical Africa in Transition," *Geographical Review,* Vol. XLII, No. 1, January, 1952, p. 13.
6 Malinowski, Bronislaw, *Argonauts of the Western Pacific,* E. P. Dutton and Company, Inc., New York, pp. 465-466.

Chapter 24

The subtropic summer-dry forest lands (Cs)

The Italy most Americans know is a wondrous land of luxurious cities and six-course meals, summer-night opera in the baths of Caracalla and fat Venetian pigeons in the Piazza San Marco. But there is another Italy that millions of Europeans, and a few discriminating Americans, know and love. It is a lovely and unhurried land of inexpensive little hotels, majestic mountain views and sunlit beaches. This Italy is a vacationland of relaxation and fun.

"Mediterranean Leisure Land," *Life*, July 18, 1955, p. 81. Reprinted by permission.

Chorogram: Italian Riviera—leisure land

The long coast line of year-round "sunlit beaches" of Italy accounts for much of Italy's fame as Europe's vacationland. But more than that, the high summer skies and subtropically mild winters that characterize the area symbolize this happy and holiday climatic realm the world over. The Riviera, however, skirting the northwest coast of Italy, stands out as the world's playground (Figure XXIV-1). The salubrious climate, enchanting land- and seascapes, year-round green and floral vegetation, scented gardens, innumerable bathing beaches, health resorts, recreation outlets, and historic shrines attract a cosmopolitan clientele, and together form the gayest global spectacle of leisure life. Organized land sports include soccer, golf, tennis, netball, target shooting, boxing and fencing, cycling, roller skating, and horse racing. Nautical competitive sports include surface and underwater fishing, water polo, water-skiing, yachting, motor racing, and international sailing regattas. Cinemas —indoors and open-air—abound, as well as operas. Exhibitions are designed to fit every taste—fashion parades, dog shows, marine exhibits, international postage-stamp exhibitions, etc. The arts—literature, painting, music, sculpture—and the works of science are featured in special lectures and concerts, or on display in museums or libraries. Moreover, the Riviera is a land of year-round festivals, fitted to the natural seasons, as in the case of flowers, and to the religious calendar of high church festivals. Tours are conducted to places of particular geographic and historic interest. There is no idle hour in the tourist's itinerary.

How this popular idol of show places takes its place in world reality is of special interest to the geographer. Its regional identity is firmly rooted in the traditions of the Ligurian Sea and the Province of Liguria, of which the Riviera is an integral part. The term Riviera derives from *riva,* meaning bank; here applied to the Ligurian Appennine-girted coast, the mountain wall shutting out the cold *mistral* north winter wind.[1] Extending from La Specia on the east to the French frontier on the west, the Italian Riviera is subregionalized sun-wise into the "coast of the rising sun," Riviera di Livante, and the "coast of the setting sun," Riviera di Ponente. Genoa, leading Mediterranean port, is the midway orientation point. Ponente Riviera merges westward into the French Riviera, the *Cotê d'Azur,* which extends westward to Nice.

But directional orientation is only one feature that distinguishes Oriental from Occidental Riviera, as they are known in English. In the former, the mountain spurs generally extend farther beachward, the slope talus forming the source of the beach gravel and sand. Cultural features likewise differentiate the eastern and western strands. The somewhat broader beaches and gentler valley slope approaches of Occidental Riviera, for example, feature floriculture, particularly in the section from Alassio to the French frontier (see Figure XXIV-1). Accordingly, this sector has appropriately been named *Riviera dei Fiori.* Next to tourism, the production here of flowers and perfume for the European markets, particularly Paris and London, is its most world-famed enterprise.

Despite these severally recognized rivieras,

[1] Genoa, about the northernmost point, has a January mean of 46° F.; points further south attain 50° F. and above. Even in the rainy season of winter, the sun-facing beaches beneath the cliffs average as much as eight hours of sun.

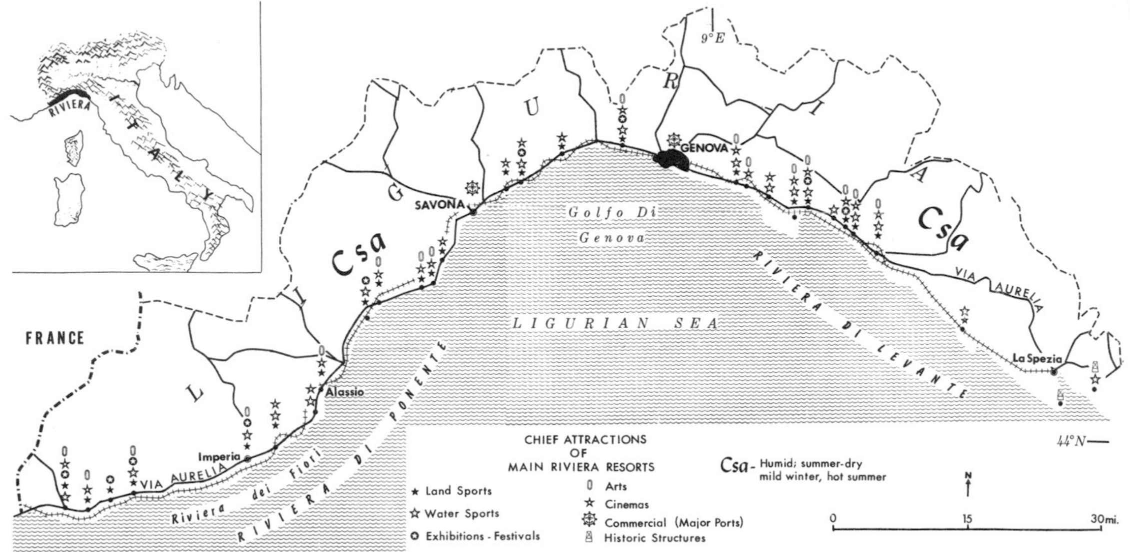

XXIV:1 This map is of the Riviera, the fabulous world resort center. It was composed by classifying detailed descriptive data on attractions of the chief resort sites along the Ligurian coast in a way that would render them regionally mappable on a reasonably small scale. At best, such cartographic representation falls far short of expressing the diversity of natural and cultural features which attracts tourists and resortists from all parts of the world. (Arranged from mapped and other data supplied by tourist literature, especially *Seaside Resorts in Italy,* Touring Club Italiano, Milan, courtesy the Italian State Tourist Office, Chicago, Illinois)

the Italian-French Riviera is tied together by the historic thoroughfare, the *Via Aurelia.* This road, itself regionally characterized as the Eastern Riviera to the east of Genoa, and Western Riviera to the west of Genoa, dates back to the original Roman flagstone roads of the second century B.C., although now its surface is tarred. Similarly, a railroad line parallels the road, and tunnels through some eighty promontories. Thus, by road or by rail, one may observe the settlement relation of each of the principal slope villages (*bourgs*) to its own little beach (*marine*), which, as Vidal de la Blache points out, complement each other.

The "pleasure garden" epitomizes world famed outdoor gracious living and Bible geography

The tone of leisurely life and gracious living, as suggested in the above chorogram, dates back to the most ancient times; in fact, to the Garden of Eden.

Man's first abode on this earth is recorded in Genesis as a garden, and in this connection, one might say, we also have the first geographic statement of the physical–biotic–human relationships of man in this world:

¶ And the Lord God planted a garden in Eden (Heb. "pleasure"), in the east; and there he put the man whom he had formed. And out of the ground the Lord God made to grow every tree that is pleasant to the sight and good for food, the tree of life also in the midst of the garden, and the tree of the knowledge of good and evil. A river flowed out of Eden to water the garden, and there it divided and became four rivers. (Genesis 2: 8-10) (2).

The Garden of Eden and its New Testament counterpart, the Garden of Gethsemane, moreover, may be said to represent the geographic symbol of the Old and New Testament Judeo–Christian tenets and traditions.

Identifying thus the created order of man's habitat, the watered garden thereafter also came to be prophetically the sustaining symbol of Providence: "And the Lord will guide you continually, and satisfy your desire with good things, and make your bones strong; and you shall be like a watered garden, like a spring of water, whose waters fail not" (Isaiah 58: 11).

That the pleasure garden was fully appreciated for both its utilitarian and aesthetic appointments in Homeric times is revealed in *The Odyssey*. For example, in the adventures of Ulysses, we read of his admiration of the premises of Alcinous, ruler of all the Phaeacians:

¶ Without the hall, near the gates, there is a large garden of four acres; around it a hedge is extended on both sides. And there tall flourishing trees grew, pears, and pomegranates, and apple-trees producing beautiful fruit, and sweet figs, and flourishing olives. Of these the fruit never perishes, nor does it fail in winter or summer, lasting throughout the whole year; but the west wind ever blowing makes some bud forth, and ripens others. Pear grows old after pear, apple after apple, grape also after grape, and fig after fig. There a fruitful vineyard was planted; one part of this ground, exposed to the sun in a wide place, is dried by the sun; and some grapes they are gathering, and others they are treading, and farther on are unripe grapes, which have thrown off the flower, and others are slightly changing color. And there are all kinds of beds laid out in order to the farthest part of the ground, flourishing throughout the whole year: near by are two fountains; one is spread through the whole garden, but the other on the other side goes under the threshold of the hall to the lofty house, from whence the citizens are wont to draw water. Such indeed were the glorious gifts of the gods in the house of Alcinous.[1]

And Strabo, the reputed leading geographer of antiquity (born *ca.* 63 B.C.), in his unmatched descriptions of the ancient world, did not overlook this element of landscape architecture. Thus in a section on ancient Greece, replete with river references, he points to the relationships of flowery temple "precincts" to river sites: "The whole country is full of temples of Artemis, Aphrodite, and the Nymphs, being situated in sacred precincts that are generally full of flowers because of the abundance of water."[2]

A comprehensive and distinctively geographic analysis of the place of the pleasure garden in the Mediterranean world is that by Ellen Semple. In her chapter entitled "Ancient Mediterranean Pleasure Gardens," Miss Semple tells of the various physical phenomena which favored the propagation of vegetation forms characteristic of the pleasure gardens, and then relates how man discreetly availed himself of every natural environmental circumstance in the development of such gardens. Such coherent relationships are reviewed regionally throughout the Mediterranean Basin and Middle East areas. Not only is this chapter instructive in illustrating effective landscape descriptions but it is noted as well for its distinctiveness of style and technique in developing a truly historical geography treatment.

Sections from Miss Semple's work will illuminate to best advantage the character of the pleasure garden and the importance it played throughout Mediterranean Basin and Middle East history:

¶ Climatic conditions go far towards explaining those lovely pleasure gardens which were so widely distributed in the ancient Mediterranean lands. They still persist in many of the old localities, retaining their traditional features of confining wall or hedge, their seclusion and shade, flower beds and ornamental fruit trees, their fountains and murmurous waters, their central pool, sunken paths, marble seats and colonnades, the gleam of statuary mid the green twilight of the shrubbery, and the vine-grown pergola for the outdoor repast.

The ancient Mediterranean garden was a place of retreat from the searching Mediterranean sun during the long summer drought, when the thirsty Etesian winds blew down from the north to drink up the moisture from air and vegetation; or when the Sirocco swept down from the

[1] *The Odyssey of Homer*, translation by Theodore A. Buckley, Charles E. Merrill Books, Inc., Columbus, Ohio, 1911, p. 37. (Book VII.) Reprinted by permission.

[2] *The Geography of Strabo*, Vol. IV, English translation by Horace L. Jones, 1927, the Loeb Classical Library, Harvard University Press, Cambridge, Mass., p. 49. Reprinted by permission.

parched plateau of Africa, wilted the trees in plantations and orchards, and sent the limestone dust flying in clouds along the highways or through the narrow streets. Only the garden kept moist and green and fresh. A high enclosing wall, screened by cypresses and box trees, and the marble portico opening from the dim recesses of the house served to shut out from this shady retreat the dust and glare and sere vegetation of the Mediterranean summer outside. The spray of fountains cooled and moistened the air within, while the slender runlets from the irrigation channel distributed reviving waters to the garden beds.

The Mediterranean climate encouraged the maintenance of pleasure parks and gardens because the mild temperatures kept a succession of trees and plants in blossom all year round, brought winter blooms to the rose and almond tree, even in northern Italy, and renewed the freshness of the evergreen foliage during the winter rains; hence it rewarded the labor of the cultivator and preserved the beauty of the garden in the cold season. But gardens were the boon of summer. The long, hot, cloudless months made the shelter of vine-grown arbor and cypress avenue a welcome refuge. Eyes tired by a relentless sun and its reflection from the limestone roads rested gratefully upon the dark foliage of laurel or oleander. When the stifling afternoon passed and the people issued from their darkened houses, the garden paths invited to leisurely strolls between fragrant flower beds along murmurous irrigation conduits. . . . [Ornamental gardening] grew out of the widespread fruit, flower, and herb culture, which in greater or less degree depended upon summer irrigation. The pleasure gardens originated in walled orchards and vineyards, in plantations of flowering pomegranates, quinces, plums, and apricots, in groves of stately date-plums, all with their irrigation pools and canals. The spaces between the rows of trees, for the more economic use of the precious soil, were often planted with flowers at once useful and beautiful. . . . In point of size the ancient gardens varied from the ample palace grounds and parks of kings . . . to the private home garden, whose size depended upon its location in town or country and upon the means of the owner. . . . It lay near or behind the house to form an outdoor extension of the residence itself; and here much of the family life was led. . . . This small scale was yet further reduced in the exquisite miniature gardens planted in the Peristyles of Greek and Roman houses in the last century before Christ, or perhaps earlier. . . . In contrast to the small private gardens, the sacred groves and temple grounds reveal a larger scale. . . . The summer drought dictated the introduction of water as an unfailing feature of the garden. The air was cooled by the shower of a fountain; flower beds and shade trees had to be irrigated. . . . Like their Persian prototypes, the Mediterranean gardens were for the most part formal and achitectural in style. They were not an idealized landscape like the English park, or a miniature landscape like the Japanese garden.[1]

After reviewing these general correlations indicating the general principles under which the ancient Mediterranean pleasure gardens were laid out, Miss Semple, in good geographic tradition, relates then by region how the Mediterranean cultures evolved various patterns of gardens to suit their own tastes and needs. Thus are differentiated the oriental gardens, Egyptian gardens, Greek gardens, Roman gardens, as well as those of the Saracens in Spain.

Rainfall seasonality the environmental key to analysis of Mediterranean nature and culture

Except for its physical and biotic characteristics, which repeat themselves again and again the world over and hence facilitate geographic generalizations, the Mediterranean does not lend itself readily to realm generalizations. Culturally, regional contrasts are probably as diverse as those found in any other realm of the world—population, dense or sparse (Italy—Australia); literacy, low or high (southern—northern Italy); agriculture, intensive or extensive (Greece—Australia); poverty or riches (Algeria—California); form of government (Communist Yugoslavia—Republic of Turkey). In addition, the realm presents a regional paradox —a romantic view of life against a background, in many cases, of abject poverty, frustration, and rebellion, as reflected in the agitations for agrarian reform laws and in the revolts against political authorities in nearly all the Mediterranean Basin countries.

---

[1] Semple, Ellen Churchill, *The Geography of the Mediterranean Region,* Henry Holt and Co., Inc., New York, 1931, pp. 474-479, *passim.* Reprinted by permission.

As in all such cases, the challenge to geographic description and evaluation is to generalize such contextual elements to which the entire realm lends itself and then to explore for the major regional differences. Climate, as you will have noted in the previous chapters, is always basic to the understanding of any realm or region, not because of its determining but rather because of its conditioning attributes to environmental analysis. Hence one of the most valuable aids in geographic learning is to examine rainfall–temperature graphs of meteorological stations identified with their respective climatic realms. The one global generalization that you would immediately recognize is the correlation of maximum rainfall with summer—the "low-pressure" high-sun period. However, as is true of most generalizations in nature, exceptions do occur. And these are almost altogether identified with regions in the 30-40 degree latitude, thus suggesting a clue in accounting for this phenomenon.

We observe that the Mediterranean lands lie in the transition zone of the subtropical high pressure areas and the westerlies (Figure XXIV-2). Thus, in the summertime when the sun's position has shifted poleward, the area comes under the influence of descending air and hence experiences the drying effects of the Horse Latitudes. The Horse Latitudes, derived from a seaman's name of obscure origin, are either of two belts or regions in the area of 30° N. and 30° S. latitude, characterized by high pressure air masses, calm and light baffling winds, especially that part of the northern belt which is over the Atlantic Ocean. With the seasonal shift of the wind belt system equatorward in the wintertime, the area is dominated by the prevailing westerlies characterized by lows and highs (Chapter 6). Thus, we might say, the intermediate position of the *Cs* partakes seasonally of the characteristics of the dry climates on the equatorward side and the humid *Cf* and *Df* on the poleward side. The relatively low latitude position also predicates mild winters and warm to hot summers (Figures XXIV-3, XXIV-4); and the rather narrow range between maximum summer and minimum winter temperatures is further conditioned by the maritime position of these lands. Being only part of the year under the influence of the westerly cyclonic storms, this realm is also distinguished by its clear blue skies.

The combination, then, of sunny skies for the major part of the year and mild winters, with the concomitant associations of fruit and flowers, has given these lands a popular reputation as health and pleasure resort areas, rich in glamorous and gracious living such as that symbolized in the so-called "pleasure garden" referred to repeatedly in Old and New Testament history as well as in other ancient literature of the Greek and Roman world. In modern times, it is singularly recognized in the celebrated Riviera of southern France and northwest Italy, in the still-existent Moorish gardens of Spain, and in our own famous gardens of California.

Paradoxically, however, the economic standards of evaluation do not always measure up to the aesthetic aspect so frequently associated with the amenities of modern living in these areas. It should be obvious to the student that when two, three, or even as many as four or five months may pass in the summer without virtually a drop of rain, we may envision only parched landscapes where irrigation is not feasible. In other words, at this season the equatorward desert is transposed to the *Cs* world. On the other hand, the rain that does fall may be concentrated in only three, four, or five months, and on occasion may come in the form of cloudbursts, producing flood conditions. Since much of the Mediterranean land is characterized by steep slopes, and unfrozen ground in the winter season, the heavy rains are all the more destructive in producing slope wash and other forms of erosion. Moreover, deforestation of such slope lands, in preparation for agricultural tillage, has still further accelerated soil erosion. Some historical geographers have, therefore, concluded that the combination of these several meteorological and landscape factors has been responsible in a great measure for the decline of the ancient Aegean, Greek, and Roman civilizations.

But the chief problem of Mediterranean lands is concerned with summer rainfall deficiency as well as the undependability of "early" and "later" rains. Old and New Testament passages repeatedly refer to these phenomena. Thus the Psalmist exclaims, ". . . my soul thirsts for thee; my flesh faints for

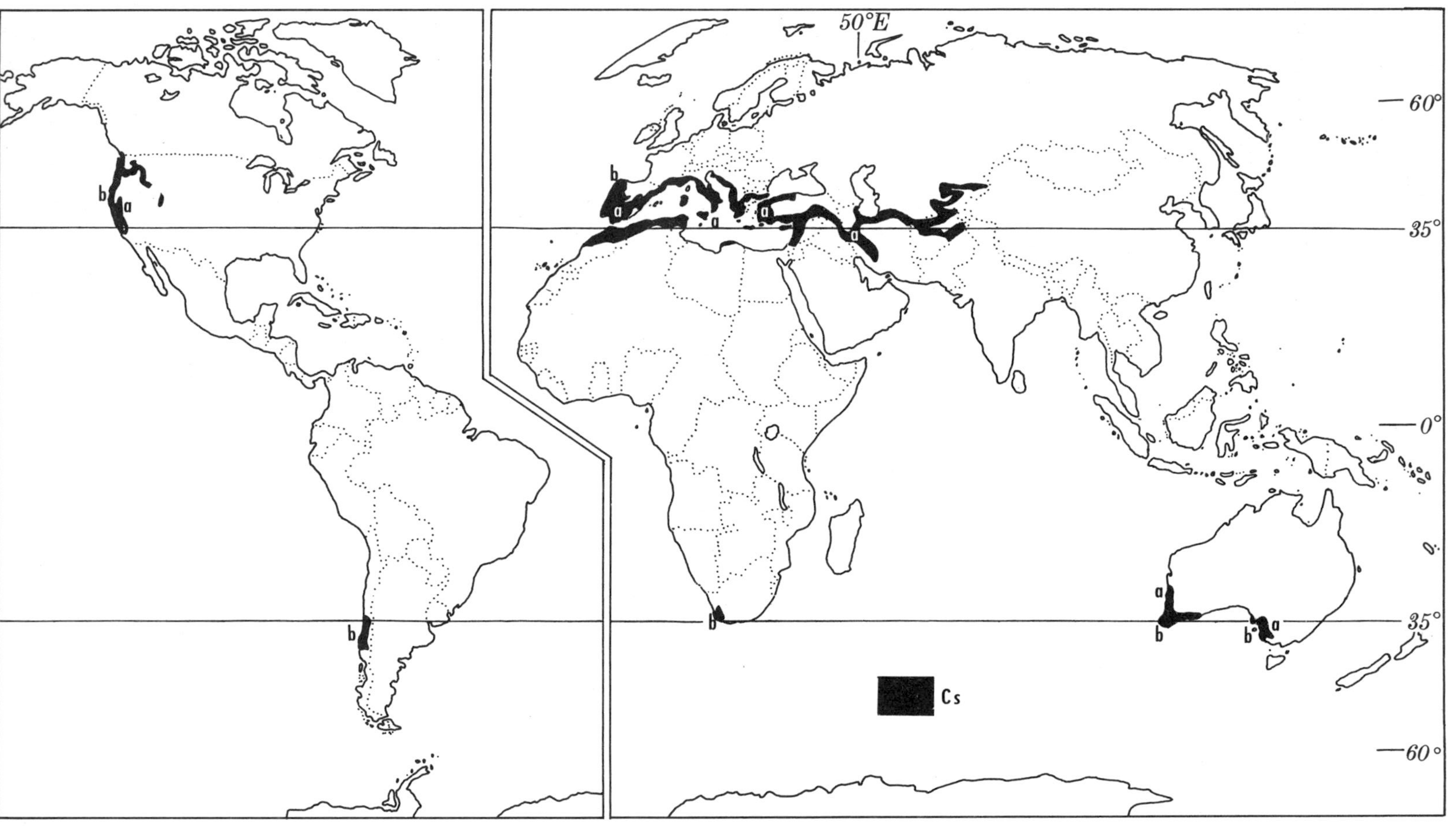
50°E
60°
35°
0°
35°
60°
Cs
a
b

thee, as in a dry and weary land where no water is" (Psalm 63: 1). And again, "I stretch out my hands to thee; my soul thirsts for thee like a parched land" (Psalm 143: 6). The general dearth of water during the dry season, moreover, placed an extra premium on springs and wells and such few streams as maintained their flow during the summertime.

So important were the wells that they were, in nearly all cases, identified (e.g., the established dwelling place of Isaac by the Well of La-hai-roi, Genesis 25: 11). One way of defeating an enemy was to destroy his wells, and thus the Philistines filled with earth the wells which had been dug by the servants of Isaac's father, Abraham. Subsequently, Isaac had the wells reopened, but the strife over the water supply continued, for we read:

¶ And Isaac dug again the wells of water which had been dug in the days of Abraham his father; for the Philistines had stopped them after the death of Abraham; and he gave them the names which his father had given them. But when Isaac's servants dug in the valley and found there a well of springing water, the herdsmen of Gerar quarreled with Isaac's herdsmen, saying, "The water is ours." So he called the name of the well Esek, because they contended with him. Then they dug another well, and they quarreled over that also; so he called its name Sitnah (Genesis 26: 18-22).[1]

The seasonal wet and dry rhythm has likewise been a recognized phenomenon of greatest importance from the earliest record of this area. Many Bible readers may have often wondered about the meaning and significance of the seasonal rains referred to in such passages as: "He will give the rain for your land in its season, the early rain and the later rain, that you may gather in your grain and your wine and your oil" (Deuteronomy 11: 14). And again: "Be glad, O sons of Zion, and rejoice in the Lord, your God; for he has given the early rain for your vindication, he has poured down for you abundant rain, the early and the latter rain, as before. The threshing floors shall be full of grain, the vats shall overflow with wine and oil" (Joel 2: 23-24).

In view of the fact that Canaan has been referred to as "the land of milk and honey," perennial hardships and austere living in the Canaanitic-Palestine world may be hard to reconcile. Especially is this true in view of the frequent references, particularly in the Old Testament, to "famine in the land." Bible readers have looked upon such accounts as Providence withholding his blessings. Be that as it may, we should keep in mind that a summer drought was an annual phenomenon, and that another general characteristic of Mediterranean rains is that for some consecutive years the total annual rainfall may be appreciably less than at another period in the cycle. Moreover, the so-called first, or former, rain, which comes in the fall, may be delayed. This could result in a crop failure due to lack of germination of the seed; thus we read, "The seed shrivels under the clods" (Joel 1: 17). But, let us say, the seasonal rains in the fall did arrive and the grain did germinate, and so a good crop of wheat or barley is in prospect as the winter rains supply the necessary moisture; yet the harvest is not assured, and, unless the so-called last, or latter, rains come in the spring, crops may fail to mature.

A repetition of the failure of such rains to arrive in due season, then, may, through a number of years, create real famine conditions. Such was the well-known example of Abram's journey into Egypt: "Now there was a famine in the land. So Abram went down to Egypt to sojourn there, for the famine was severe in the land" (Genesis 12: 10). Egypt, you will recall, depends upon the irrigation waters of the exotic Nile, and,

[1] This and other shorter Bible quotations from the Revised Standard Version, copyrighted (1946-1952) by the Division of Christian Education of the Churches of Christ in the United States of America and published by Thomas Nelson & Sons. Reprinted by permission.

XXIV:2 (Left) This map shows the Mediterranean climate, or, if you prefer, California climate. Rather severely restricted in distribution, it enjoys renown as the world's playground, with each continent (except Antarctica, of course) boasting its own "Riviera." Rather unique also are the meteorological and topographic conditions that account for its linear 35° latitude pattern. With the aid of Figure VI:7, note the relation of this latitudinal position to the planetary wind belt system.

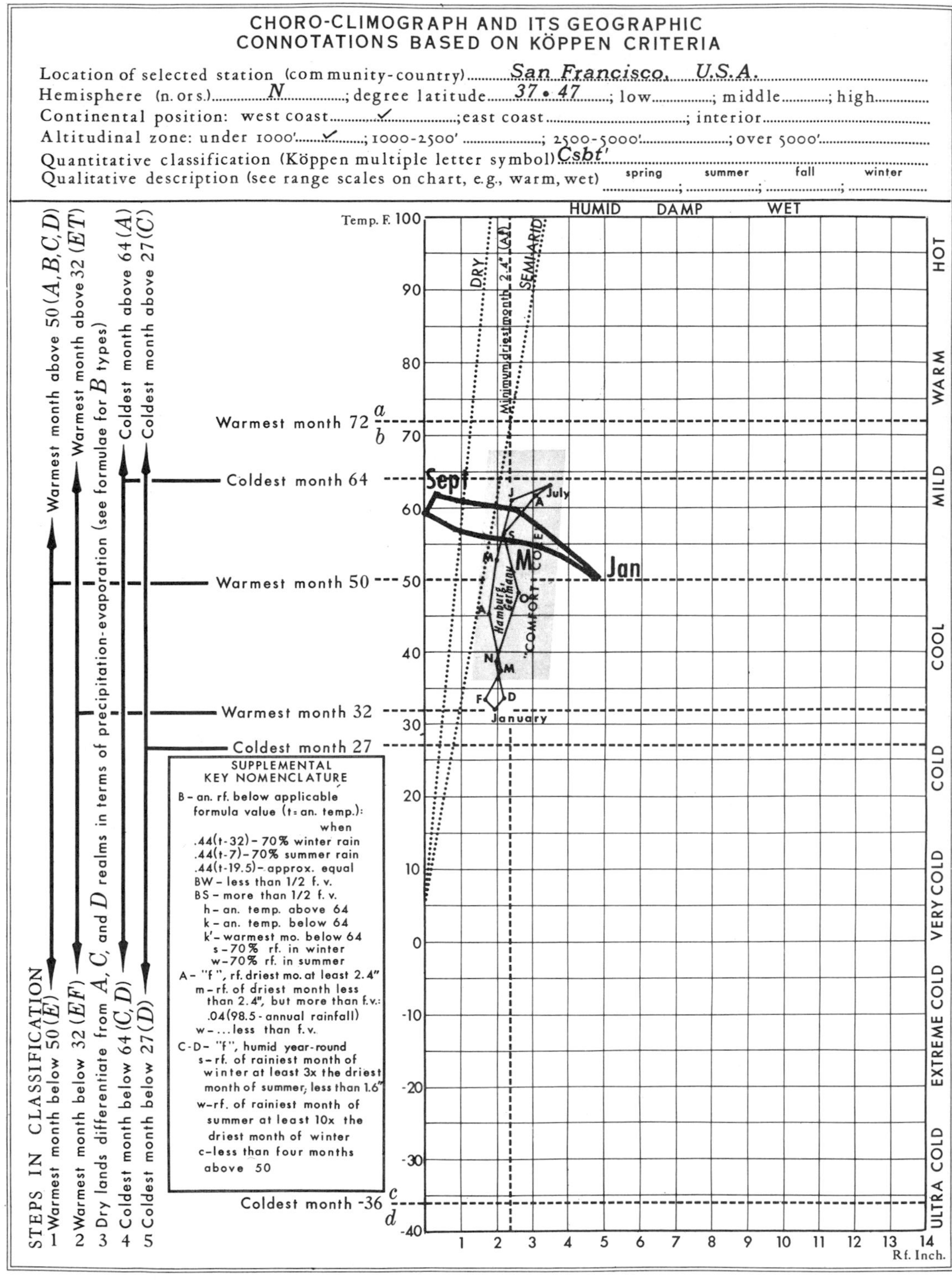

CHORO-CLIMOGRAPH AND ITS GEOGRAPHIC CONNOTATIONS BASED ON KÖPPEN CRITERIA
Location of selected station (community-country) San Francisco, U.S.A.
Hemisphere (n. or s.) N ; degree latitude 37 • 47 ; low ; middle ; high
Continental position: west coast ✓ ; east coast ; interior
Altitudinal zone: under 1000′ ✓ ; 1000-2500′ ; 2500-5000′ ; over 5000′
Quantitative classification (Köppen multiple letter symbol) Csbt′
Qualitative description (see range scales on chart, e.g., warm, wet) spring ; summer ; fall ; winter
HUMID
DAMP
WET
Temp. F.
DRY
Minimum driest month 2.4″ (A.f.)
SEMIARID
HOT
WARM
MILD
COOL
COLD
VERY COLD
EXTREME COLD
ULTRA COLD
Warmest month 72
Coldest month 64
Warmest month 50
Warmest month 32
Coldest month 27
Coldest month -36
a
b
c
d
Sept
July
Jan
January
Hamburg, Germany
"COMFORT" ZONE
Rf. Inch.
STEPS IN CLASSIFICATION
1 Warmest month above 50 (A, B, C, D) — Warmest month below 50 (E)
2 Warmest month above 32 (ET) — Warmest month below 32 (EF)
3 Dry lands differentiate from A, C, and D realms in terms of precipitation-evaporation (see formulae for B types)
4 Coldest month above 64 (A) — Coldest month below 64 (C, D)
5 Coldest month above 27 (C) — Coldest month below 27 (D)
SUPPLEMENTAL KEY NOMENCLATURE
B - an. rf. below applicable formula value (t = an. temp.): when
.44(t-32) - 70% winter rain
.44(t-7) - 70% summer rain
.44(t-19.5) - approx. equal
BW - less than 1/2 f. v.
BS - more than 1/2 f. v.
h - an. temp. above 64
k - an. temp. below 64
k′ - warmest mo. below 64
s - 70% rf. in winter
w - 70% rf. in summer
A - "f", rf. driest mo. at least 2.4″
m - rf. of driest month less than 2.4″, but more than f.v.: .04(98.5 - annual rainfall)
w - ... less than f. v.
C-D - "f", humid year-round
s - rf. of rainiest month of winter at least 3x the driest month of summer; less than 1.6″
w - rf. of rainiest month of summer at least 10x the driest month of winter
c - less than four months above 50

as a real desert, does not depend upon indigenous rainfall for its own harvest. Consequently the vicissitudes of climates and seasons, of former and latter rains, were of no concern to the Egyptian. A grain supply was always available not only for themselves but also for the neighboring Mediterranean countries which could not depend upon a perennial water supply.

The normally summer-parched pasture might disappear entirely during seasons or years of protracted drought. Thus the repeated references to feuds between herdsmen whose flocks competed for the scant and spotty forage and water supply: "We have come to sojourn in the land; for there is no pasture for your servants' flocks . . ." (Genesis 47: 4). And again we read, "The beasts of the field cry also unto thee: for the rivers of water are dried up, and the fire hath devoured the pastures of the wilderness." It is at such a time that insect pests, such as "the locust, the canker worm and the caterpillar, and the palmerworm," brought about complete desolation.

The view may be held that drought was only local and aberrant. Conceding that the Levant and other eastern Mediterranean sections may have experienced cyclic periods of greater rainfall, as is the case of other climes, the ancient Mediterranean Basin records, secular as well as sacred, reveal drought to have been a region-wide and seasonally regular recurring phenomenon. Some years or cycles, of course, were less desiccative than others; and some regions, as now, less arid than others.

Because of more favorable position in relation to the cyclonic storms of the westerlies, the Greek and Roman areas were less affected by severe drought, particularly the latter. Nevertheless, periodic protracted droughts and resulting famines are reported for these areas by Virgil, Livy, Tacitus, and others. Thus Tacitus in his *Annales* comments on a panic in Rome during Claudius' reign when "scanty crops" and "consequent famine" betokened calamity, it being "ascertained that Rome had provisions for no more than fifteen days." In such cases Athens and Rome usually imported heavy shipments of grain from Egypt or from southern Russia bordering the *Pontus Euxinus* (Black Sea).

Thus we note that the regular pattern of summer droughts, the wide variation in total annual rainfall, and the frequent undependability of former and latter rain have not substantially changed from ancient to modern times.

XXIV:3 (Left) "Summer in fall" (t') is a San Francisco feature worth checking for its meteorological basis. Describe a non-irrigable summer and winter landscape with this type of climate.

Glamorous responses of tourism and movie industries

Mediterranean lands hold a high rank in tourist trade because of their great diversity in physical, biotic, and cultural features. By virtue of its location between the Horse Latitudes to the south and the westerly wind belt to the north, the realm has seasonal variation of both these climatic changes, as noted above. Yet there are no distinctively cold and hot seasons, so that the area enjoys a year-round hospitable temperature suited to both winter as well as summer travel. Whereas other, somewhat higher, latitude countries have in their own way strong tourist attractions in summer, Mediterranean lands can and do enjoy a heavy traffic of tourists and resort business in winter (e.g., the renowned and romantic Riviera of southeastern France and northwest Italy, the Crimea of Russia, and our own *Cs* California).

Another major attraction is the relationship of the climatic pattern to the sea and to the mountains. Articulated by many large and small embayments, the Mediterranean Basin lands are unique in their peninsular and insular structure and in their far-flung sandy and sunny beaches, which take on increasing charm where alternating mountain ridges and valleys approach the coast. As we have noted earlier, mountains in nearly all cases rim the coast lands and provide diversification of landform scenery, of vegetation, and of settlement forms, so different from the more or less uniform and often monotonous tourist-catering sights of other lands.

We must not forget, moreover, that in the Mediterranean realm are rooted the most ancient cultures of the world, embracing the

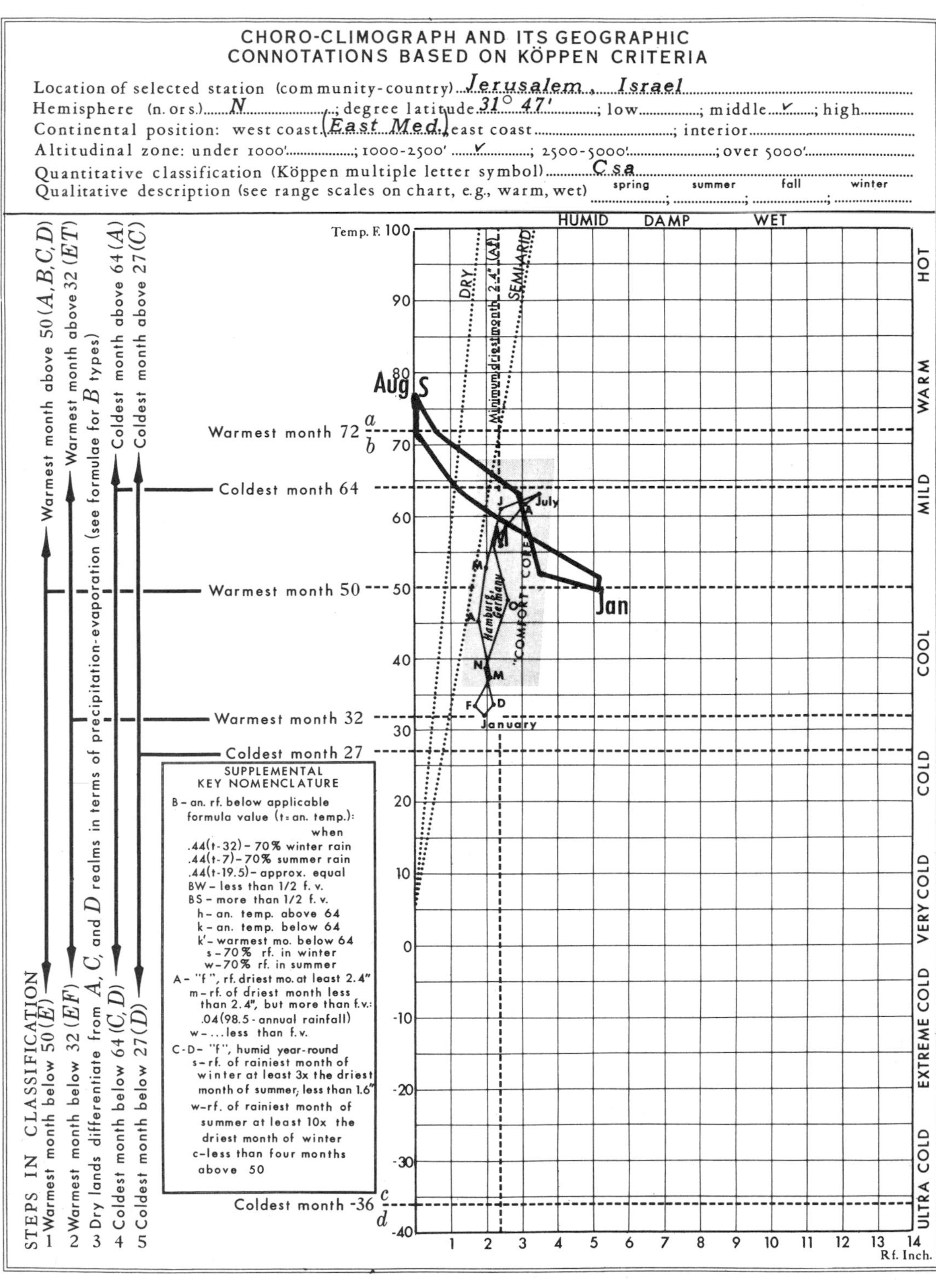

CHORO-CLIMOGRAPH AND ITS GEOGRAPHIC CONNOTATIONS BASED ON KÖPPEN CRITERIA
Location of selected station (community-country) Jerusalem, Israel
Hemisphere (n. or s.) N ; degree latitude 31° 47' ; low ; middle ✓ ; high
Continental position: west coast (East Med.) east coast ; interior
Altitudinal zone: under 1000' ; 1000-2500' ✓ ; 2500-5000' ; over 5000'
Quantitative classification (Köppen multiple letter symbol) Csa
Qualitative description (see range scales on chart, e.g., warm, wet) spring ; summer ; fall ; winter
STEPS IN CLASSIFICATION
1 Warmest month below 50 (E) — Warmest month above 50 (A, B, C, D)
2 Warmest month below 32 (EF) — Warmest month above 32 (ET)
3 Dry lands differentiate from A, C, and D realms in terms of precipitation-evaporation (see formulae for B types)
4 Coldest month below 64 (C, D) — Coldest month above 64 (A)
5 Coldest month below 27 (D) — Coldest month above 27 (C)
Warmest month 72 a b
Coldest month 64
Warmest month 50
Warmest month 32
Coldest month 27
Coldest month -36 c d
Temp. F.
HUMID
DAMP
WET
DRY
SEMIARID
Minimum driest month 2.4" (Af)
HOT
WARM
MILD
COOL
COLD
VERY COLD
EXTREME COLD
ULTRA COLD
Aug S
Jan
July
January
Hamburg, Germany
COMFORT CORE
Rf. Inch.
SUPPLEMENTAL KEY NOMENCLATURE
B - an. rf. below applicable formula value (t = an. temp.): when
.44(t-32) - 70% winter rain
.44(t-7) - 70% summer rain
.44(t-19.5) - approx. equal
BW - less than 1/2 f. v.
BS - more than 1/2 f. v.
h - an. temp. above 64
k - an. temp. below 64
k' - warmest mo. below 64
s - 70% rf. in winter
w - 70% rf. in summer
A - "f", rf. driest mo. at least 2.4"
m - rf. of driest month less than 2.4", but more than f.v.: .04(98.5 - annual rainfall)
w - ... less than f.v.
C-D - "f", humid year-round
s - rf. of rainiest month of winter at least 3x the driest month of summer; less than 1.6"
w - rf. of rainiest month of summer at least 10x the driest month of winter
c - less than four months above 50

Babylonian, Palestinian, Phoenician, Minoan, Cretan, Grecian, Roman, and Moslem cultures. And so tourist attractions include such ancient sites as Tyre and Sidon in the eastern Mediterranean; Tunis and Algiers in North Africa; Naples, Rome, and Genoa in Italy; Marseilles in France; Istanbul in Turkey; and Athens in Greece. Truly this region has been aptly called the "Cradle of Civilization," and the many ruins and restorations of classical antiquity which the tourist has read about and is anxious to see attest to their history.

A rather novel regional development in tourism is developing in Turkey. This country, once noted for its veiled women and its traditional isolationism in foreign affairs, is now rapidly becoming Westernized, not the least evidence of which is its bid also for tourist trade. Here, the tourist's itinerary suggestively includes the seven sites of the early Christian missions in Asia Minor, including the city of Ephesus, the Roman commercial entrepôt of Biblical times. As a matter of fact, the entire Mediterranean Basin is dotted with Christian landmarks, whose geographic distributional pattern is worth scrutinizing in advance of a tour of the area, or in Bible study, for that matter.

Palestine, the "Holy Land" of Judeo-Christianity, with its historic sites as noted in Old and New Testament geography, has always been a major tourist attraction, the one geographic "point," as Baly expresses it, "at which God himself entered the arena and acted directly on history" (6).

Thus the Mediterranean Basin lands not only offer relaxation and recreation in ways normally found in other lands, but in a unique form or degree provide cultural and spiritual edification as well.

Significantly also, many of the factors of this realm which cater to tourism foster the movie industry as well. Blue, sunny skies are ideal for photographic "takes" and rapid filming. Temperatures the year round allow for outdoor shots, and only in winter need there be occasional concern for interference from rain. In no other single realm in the wide world can one find such a kaleidoscopic panorama of natural and cultural subjects of such intriguing photographic interest—the sea and its variegated coast lines of embayed beaches and cliffed headlands; the skirting plains with their backdrop of hill country or mountains, some of the latter rising high enough to be snow-capped; dune sand, suggestive of the desert, and rock formations accentuating contrasted slope profiles; grassland, bush, and forest types of flora and diverse fauna to suit the needs of the most diverse scenarios; the flowery pleasure gardens, the charming vineyards and orchards, the sweeping grain fields and far-flung ranches; and the unique contrast of Old and New World settlement forms. And if we are impelled to look for still other regional backdrops for our shots, the rainfall lands poleward and the drier lands equatorward require only a few hours journey.

XXIV:4 (Left) Valuable as the climograph generally may be in portraying co-ordinated temperature-rainfall distribution of stations, technical graphical space limitations sometimes occur. Here it may appear, for example, that Jerusalem has only two summer months with practically no rainfall, when there are actually five with one-tenth of an inch or less. Determine what these months are by consulting the Appendix, and indicate these in the appropriate places. What differences would you expect to find in the summer-winter landscapes between Jerusalem and San Francisco, omitting any consideration of irrigation?

Sclerophyllous vegetation exhibits a fascinating spectacle in plant moisture husbandry

The trees of Mediterranean lands are predominantly evergreen broadleaf and conifers. Though generally scrubby and sparse, some of the world's tallest trees and densest stands occur regionally in the rainier areas, such as in the Sequoia and certain eucalyptus forests of southeast California and Australia, respectively.

Unlike the evergreen forests of the tropics, there is seasonal rhythm in the sprouting of new leaves at the beginning of the rainy season in the fall and in the florescence and fruitage at the end of the rainy season in the spring. This contrasts with the tropical selva where new shoots, buds, flowers, green fruit, and ripe fruit may occur in the same forest, or even on the same tree, at any season. Though rainfall is adequate in most

Tourism has become a sizable business in Israel, where signposts—some 300 of them—mark Biblical and other historic spots, as in this case, Sodom. Describing the destruction of Sodom and Gomorrah, the sign additionally points to the significance of this place as the lowest habitation in the world and as a modern industrial potash-producing center. (Courtesy Israel Government Tourist Office)

places to support some kind of forest or scrub cover, the vegetation takes on adaptive characteristics reflective of the intermediate position of this subhumid clime between the lower latitude year-round drylands and the higher latitude year-round humid lands. Responsive to the long summer-dry season, xerophytic-like plant characteristics are common. Trees normally are not tall and commonly occur in thin stands with a shrub-like undergrowth. Plant life generally manifests many adaptations in root, trunk, branch, leaf, and even fruit structures designed to conserve moisture. Deep taproots may thus explore the low groundwater table, whereas other plants with extensive lateral branching systems exploit near-surface moisture over as large areas as possible. Thick bark, or even a heavy layer of cork, as in the case

This ancient Palestinian fishing village is called Jaffa, meaning "beautiful" in Phoenician. One of the famed east Mediterranean ports, this is the harbor to which the great ships of Tyre, some 3,000 years ago, brought the cedars of Lebanon for Solomon's Temple. The white mosque marks the site of the house of Simon the Tanner, where once the Apostle Peter lodged. Today, Jaffa is part of the municipality of modern Tel Aviv. (Courtesy Israel Government Tourist Office)

of the cork oak, helps arrest transpiration of moisture. Foliage is generally slight and characteristically aromatic—leaves relatively small, thick, and leathery; commonly waxy, resinous, shiny, or covered with fine down-like hair which retards moisture loss from circulating air.

The same effect is achieved in certain trees like the eucalypti, which orient their leaves edgewise to the sun in order to reduce transpiration. Some of the woody and fibrous plants have protective spines very similar to those found on desert plants. Mesophytic plants with such drought-resistant and protective devices have been termed *sclerophytes.*

Because most of the Mediterranean regions are in slope and a considerable amount at relatively high elevations, wide variations occur in the species and size of forest cover. It is peculiar that in this realm two extremes, the most stunted as well as the tallest trees in the world, are found. Among the latter, for example, is the eucalyptus, which includes species among the largest broadleaf trees in the world—often attaining a height of 200 feet. Even larger in diameter as well as in height are some of the tree trunks of the Sequoias and redwoods of California, the tallest trees in the world, reaching maximal heights of 300 feet. Situated high on the windward slopes of the Sierras (Where *Cs* grades into *Ds*), these forests receive an unusual amount of rainfall and enjoy a year-round growth. Mediterranean forests at the higher altitudes include fir, pine, and cedar. Among the latter are the renowned cedars of Lebanon, source of lumber in Old Testament times in the building of Solomon's palace and temple at Jerusalem.

But, as stated previously, the long summer droughts are unfavorable in most cases to a luxuriant growth of forest, either of stocking or of size. Beech, chestnut, and many varieties of oak do grow at somewhat lower elevations, below the conifer zone; also the characteristic leatherleaf vegetation represented by the myrtle, the laurel, the holly, and the olive. Much of the cover today takes on a scrubby aspect in the form of evergreen brush known as *maquis* in southern France, *bush* in South Africa, and *chaparral* in California (a term introduced from Spain, where such vegetation likewise occurs). Authorities differ as to the cause of the extensive scrublands of this type. Some hold that they are due to a combination of meteorological and edaphic dryness; others attribute the dwarf characteristics to repeated pasturing of the area. Species included here are commonly the scrub oak, myrtle, laurel, carob, rock rose, and the chestnut. Under still more adverse growing conditions of intensive aridity, steep slopes, and thin soils, we may find the so-called *garigue,* a consociation of recumbent shrubs, including such plants as the juniper and sage.

It is quite probable that originally Mediterranean plant cover was primarily of the tree or bush variety. Limited grasslands were probably restricted to the poorly-drained marsh areas along the coast, to the more rugged and rocky areas, or to the very high altitudes above the tree-line. Elsewhere, presently existing grasslands have resulted from deforestation in preparing land for tillage. Fairly extensive grass cover is found today on the Meseta in Spain and in the California ranch country, reportedly introduced in the latter area by the Spaniards via Mexico during the days of the establishment of the California Spanish missions.

The historically significant pastoral economy and its regional utility

The most frequently occurring and strongly unifying theme of land-use in Old and New Testament times is centered in pastoral economy, as is reflected in the oft expressed solicitude of God for the temporal and spiritual well-being of the Palestinian inhabitants. This is probably best symbolized in the "Shepherd Psalm" (23rd). However, as any student of Bible literature well knows, the theme of the Deity as the Shepherd of his flock occurs over and over again in scores of Psalms and other Bible passages. Similarly, much ancient secular Mediterranean literature is replete with passages on grazing.

Various stages of pasturage occur in *Cs* Australia, Union of South Africa, the central region of Chile, Italy, and California. From the reading of such literature, an impression may arise that the ideal pasture regions of the world occur here. Such a conclusion, however, as in other cases, should be checked against criteria on the growing of good pasture grasses and other forage crops. And here again regional comparisons should prove helpful for such evaluations. One may here recall, for example, the steppe lands of the *BS* which flank the *Cs* areas equatorward. Such areas, especially those with cool summers (*BSk*), have been highly rated as good range pastures. With a greater amount of annual rainfall in the *Cs* world, one would expect, therefore, more prolific growth of grass and forage crops. While this is true, there are factors unfavorable to extensive and optimal pastoral economy. It should be apparent to the student by this time that five, four, or even three months of desert-like conditions are not conducive to green summer pastures. Moreover, such climatic aridity is regionally accentuated by edaphic aridity. Much of the eastern Mediterranean area is underlain by soluble limestone, resulting in poor groundwater storage conditions. This is particularly noteworthy in the so-called *karst* topography of Yugoslavia, as well as in the Judean hills of Palestine. As noted previously, pasture lands are mostly relegated to areas unsuited to other forms of agriculture and consequently are marginal in character. Since much of the Mediterranean world is in slope, a considerable part of the region, too steep for arable agriculture, especially near the bounding or rimming mountain tops in the interior, is thus appropriated. Similarly, the low-lying and poorly-drained coastal areas unsuited to other forms of land-use may be thus utilized. But such high mountain and low-lying coastal pastures have their own seasonal grazing adaptabilities. In summer, when pastures dry out on the lowlands, the herdsman, with or without his family, moves his herds or flocks to the highlands benefited by the irrigating meltwaters of mountain glaciers. Then, in the late fall, he returns his herds or flocks to the valley floor or coastal lowlands to escape the mountain snows and to take advantage of the mild winter weather and winter rains which now here provide excellent foraging conditions for his animals. This practice is commonly known as *transhumance*.

Grazing economy in the *Cs* world features sheep and goat herding rather than the rearing of beef and dairy cattle. The smaller animals can subsist on the sparser and shorter herbage and lower water supply during the dry season. They are, moreover, much better steep-slope climbers. Of all livestock, the goat is least discriminating of foraging conditions, getting along, if necessary, on the meager weedy and woody shrub patches on rocky and precipitous terrain which characterize so much of the higher slopes of the farflung hill and mountain country. In probably no other well-populated realm does the goat assume such importance for dairy and meat products. Sheep have also played a dominant role in Mediterranean economy, being selectively reared for wool and mutton. The Merino, bred in Spain, is world famous for the superb quality of its wool. Where luscious grazing and other animal feed are in so short supply, draft animals likewise are selected which get along best on minimum forage, such as the mule and the donkey. Oak, chestnut, and other mast-producing forests are utilized for raising pigs. In the Old World, mutton rather than beef is the normal meat diet, supplemented by fish in the coastal areas. Friday fasting, then, as a religious institution conforms well to the general low meat supply in Mediterranean countries. Some geographers maintain that this environmental aspect directly contributed to the institution of Friday religious fast.

The persistence since ancient times of the type of environmentally associated pastoral pattern of the Mediterranean as outlined above is well brought out by Miss Semple:

¶ Stock-raising in the ancient Mediterranean world bore the unmistakable impress of its environment. It was conditioned primarily by the summer drought. . . . The flocks and herds fed in winter on the untilled lands, the lowland meadows, and stubble fields of the home farm; but before the advent of summer they were driven out for their half-year on the highland pastures. This is the rule also today. . . . The arable land, scant at best because of the predominant mountainous relief, was carefully apportioned to field crops, gardens, fruit orchards, olive plantations and vineyards, according to its suitability for each. Meadows for hay or forage crops could be maintained through the summer only by irrigation; but irrigable fields were scarce and valuable. . . . Palestine, because of its climate, geology, relief and the deep Jordan rift which makes the highland over-drained, has always had scant natural grazing for cattle and horses, though sheep and goats can find enough forage of a poor kind. But flocks and herds alike suffered from the frequent droughts or half-droughts which visited the land, when cow and ewe, like the hart, "panted for the water-brooks." . . . The small natural meadows of ancient Palestine seem to have been reserved for the cows and oxen which performed the farm labor of ploughing and treading out the grain, and which served also for food and religious sacrifices. . . . Swine production, which in the ancient Mediterranean world depended chiefly on mast-yielding forests, flourished in Italy, because climatic conditions permitted beech, oak and chestnut groves in nearly all parts of the peninsula. Pigs were raised on every landed estate. They were fed mainly on the mast of the home woodland or the mountain forests, and then fattened on barley and other grains to give the meat various flavors. . . . Thus the economic history of the Mediterranean lands can never ignore the factors of climate, relief, and the uniting force of the *Mare Internum*.[1]

The general Mediterranean agricultural pattern evinces a high correlative index in terrain adjustments

1. Distinguishing criteria. Mediterranean agriculture is not especially distinguished from that of all other realms by any distinctive product or products but rather by the great diversity of floriculture, horticulture, and agricultural crops in combination. Also unique is the land–crop adaptation evidenced by the precise discrimination exercised in exploiting to the utmost every avail-

1 Semple, *op. cit.*, pp. 297-335, *passim*. Reprinted by permission.

able drop of moisture, and in utilizing every parcel of land, including the steeper slopes, for the economy for which it is best suited.

The wide range of crops produced is favored by the position of the Mediterranean lands. Thus the subtropical position and marginality make possible almost a year-round growing season, temperatures seldom averaging below 45°F. during the coldest month. This is about 20 degrees above the winter temperature limit designated by the symbol *C* in the Köppen system. To be sure, the summer drought without irrigation does arrest agricultural productivity, but even when such moisture is not available numerous horticultural products constitute part of the perennial pattern of fruit and nut production. Actually, even cloudless skies can be a boon to certain forms of crop productivity. And rains can be a detriment to grain like wheat and barley during the heading season. Heavy rain in middle latitudes during the blossoming season of fruit trees also often interferes with proper pollenization. Mediterranean sunshine in summer is particularly beneficial to floriculture; flowers bloom best and are freer from plant diseases under dry atmospheric conditions, assuming, of course, that adequate irrigation waters are otherwise available. Of particular benefit also are the sunshine, high temperatures, and very low humidity in the drying of fruits, for which the Mediterranean realm is distinctive. Thus the realm is famous for its dried grapes (raisins), dried plums (prunes), dried apricots, peaches, and the like. Cloudy skies and rainy weather, such as we find poleward of the Mediterranean lands, would not only retard the drying and curing process, but even contribute to deterioration of fruit by molds and vermin.

The summer-dry, winter-wet regimen generates a distinct rhythm of agricultural activity. The first rains begin the fall growing season and continue through the winter months. Thus the first rains prepare the soil for seeding of such staple grain crops as wheat and barley; at about the time that the rains cease in spring, these grains mature and are thus harvested at the end of the dry season. On the same rhythmic basis, the seared pastures of summer are followed by green pastures during the winter months. And fruit trees, after sprouting anew in the fall, mature their fruit in late spring or early summer. These include the indigenous olive, citrus fruits (orange, lime, lemon, grapefruit), grapes and currants of many varieties, stone fruits such as peaches, apricots, nectarines, plums, and a host of other fruits. The vine is the most ubiquitous plant of the realm, being cultivated in all Mediterranean countries and grown primarily for wine production. Figs and dates are restricted equatorward. Chestnuts are widespread through the Mediterranean Basin, and in certain areas, such as large parts of Spain, constitute food for both man and beast. English walnuts are likewise grown, particularly in California.

Summer-grown vegetables and flowers normally have to be irrigated to insure successful commercial production.

Most of the Mediterranean lands are in slope, a large percentage being too steep to irrigate or to cultivate properly. Accordingly, many of the hill slopes in the more humid sections are utilized for orchard crops, such as figs and olives, as well as the vine, the last frequently on terraces. Thus, there is some continuous productivity all year round.

2. *Land surface and soils.* Distinctive as is the summer-dry climate of the Mediterranean realm, no less noteworthy is the small amount of low and level land, particularly critical in densely populated sections rather common in Mediterranean Basin countries. In nearly all cases hill land, elevated plateaus, or even mountains hem in the narrow coastal lands. Note the plateau in Asia Minor with its Taurus Mountains, and eastward the plateaus of Kurdistan and Iran in southwest Asia. West across the Aegean in coastal Europe, there are the Pindus Mountains in Greece, the Dinaric Alps in Yugoslavia, the Appenines which form the backbone of Italy, the Maritime Alps of southeast France, and the Meseta plateau of Spain flanked or transected by several ranges of mountains. Crossing the strait of Gilbraltar into north Africa, we see the Atlas Mountains hemming in and almost crowding out entirely several discontinuous patches of *Cs* lands. Distribution of *Cs* patches in the Americas follows the same pattern—the high Sierra Nevadas flanking the Great Valley of California, and the high Andes bordering the middle Chilean section. In southwest Africa

These girls are reaping the olive harvest in Israel. The olive (*Olea europaea*), apparently indigenous to Palestine, is one of the most widespread and prolific fruit trees in the Mediterranean world. Once established, an olive grove requires neither irrigation nor much cultivation. What foliage feature suggests drought tolerance? (Courtesy Israel Office of Information)

the *Cs* is cut off by the sea coast extension of the Great Central Plateau. Only in Australia, as our map shows, does the *Cs* largely escape the "fenced-in" position. It should not be inferred, however, that over large areas elevations are too high or slopes too steep for some form of human settlement and occupance. As already noted above, the pressure on the use of land has resulted in some terracing of the steeper slopes and otherwise in an adaptation of tree-crop culture to slopes subject to heavy erosion. But another agricultural problem here enters into the picture. A geography student should take note that steep slope land not only is subject to heavy erosion during the rainy season but in rocky areas is likely to be thin and stony as well. Moreover, gravelly and sandy soils are highly porous and do not readily lend themselves to irrigation. Such low water-holding capacity is reflected in the large acreages in the Mediterranean areas sown to barley and other crops adapted to edaphic dryness as well as rainfall deficiency. Where there is deposition of alluvial material by water as at the base of the steeper slopes, a mosaic of many types of soils may occur, from coarse to fine in texture and with varying degrees of fertility. Choice sites, of course, would be found on the silt loams of the alluvial fans whose soils are being continually renewed by deposition, as noted elsewhere in the *B* lands. In Italy, despite very steep volcanic slopes, fields are cultivated up to almost the highest mountain tops to take advantage of the high fertility induced by the weathering of potash-rich lava deposits.

Poor drainage, normally not revealed by the average landform map, severely restricts tillage. Particularly in ancient days, extensive marshes skirted many of the coastal areas of the Mediterranean Basin, presenting conditions unsuited not only for cultivation but also for settlement. Mosquitoes, breeding in such places, have plagued large sections with malaria. Mussolini, once referred to as a leading geographer, is credited with having instituted, among other Italian agrarian rehabilitation programs, extensive reclamation of the coastal marshes of Italy.

A topographic situation such as the above can best be visualized by drawing a cross-section profile from the coast to the plateau or mountain interior. Such a skyline profile is presented in Figure XXIV-5. Hypothetical though it is, this generalized spatial concept of co-ordinated vertical and horizontal components provides not only a cross-section view of the physical profile but also perception of typical associations and adaptations of plant and animal life as well as human forms of occupance. Although there exists considerable variation in the combinations of physical and cultural patterns from region to region, we can obtain a synthetic view of the type of zonation changes: the relegation of the wet and other submarginal areas along the coast in winter to grazing by sheep and goats and possibly some cattle; the summer grazing on the steeper slopes and at the higher altitudes, even above the tree-line, where summer waters from the melting snows may be available; the appropriation of intermediate slope land for vine and tree culture; the reservation of the more level and productive lands for cultivated crops. The topographically limited grazing facilities suggest also a restricted meat diet in the more populated areas of the Mediterranean Basin, the inhabitants depending mostly on vegetal foods having a higher calorie productivity per acre. Protein, in the Mediterranean Basin diet, is largely in the form of beans and fish. Less-populous sections, such as in middle Chile, where more land can be spared for grazing and the raising of forage crops, have more dairy and beef cattle.

Returning to the profile, we find sites along the coast best suited to the raising of figs and dates and perhaps some citrus fruits. Such sea-coast locations reduce the frost hazard. The coastal plains, because of their relative levelness, are best adapted to the cultivation of grain crops, such as wheat and barley, the latter primarily sown on the steeper slopes and on the poorer soils, commonly gravelly or sandy. On the more rugged hillside terrain, extensive groves of olives, fruit orchards, and tree plantations of the nut type are found. Closely associated with this site, or even somewhat higher up the slope, are extensive vineyards, in some cases occupying terraces on the steeper slopes. At about the 3,500-foot level and on somewhat still steeper slopes are remnants of natural forests, including nut trees, such as the chestnut. In Spain and some other sections of the Mediterranean Basin, the chestnut serves as an important source of mast for hogs and diet for humans. Where mountains reach a sufficiently high altitude, summer grazing may be found in the Alps meadows above the timberline, naturally irrigated in some cases by meltwaters of glaciers which cap the mountains. Thus we see a complete zonal utilization of cropland, with goats, sheep and cattle, such as there are, moving up and down the slopes seasonally in transhumance fashion.

Another factor associated with slope and particularly high mountain positions is exposure. Equatorward exposures naturally have the benefit of direct sunshine, sometimes very essential in imparting flavor to fruit, particularly the grape. On the other hand, the shady side of the mountain loses less moisture by evaporation and hence is in a better geographic position for crop production where moisture rather than sunshine is paramount.

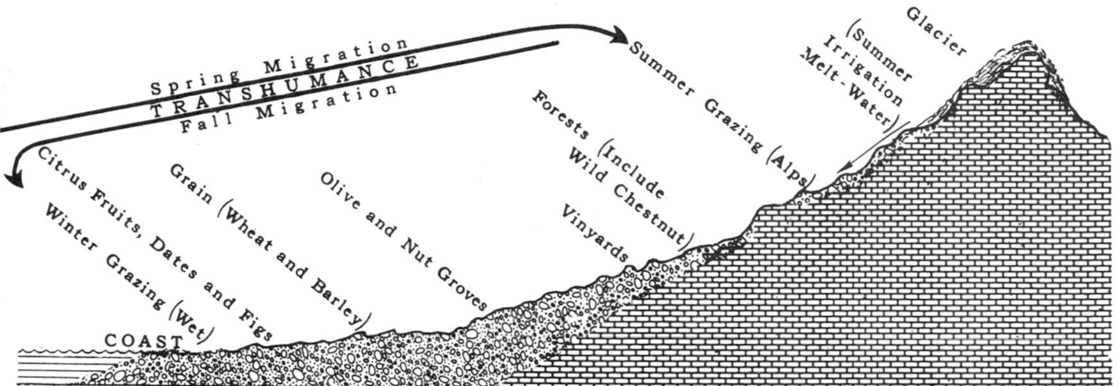

XXIV:5 This is a hypothetical and highly skeletalized *Cs* profile, relating land-use to landform features. Zonation from one section of the Mediterranean world to another varies as to the per cent of slope, differences in slope exposure and soil profiles, and variations in culture.

Old and New Testament geography testifies to a dominant environmental impress on Hebrew life, culture, and worship

Charles Kent, late Professor of Biblical Literature at Yale University, has observed:

¶ No other commentary upon the literature of the Bible is so practical and luminous as biblical geography. Throughout their long history the Hebrews were keenly attentive to the voice of the Eternal speaking to them through nature. Their writings abound in references and figures taken from the picturesque scenes and peculiar life of Palestine. The grim encircling desert, the strange water-courses, losing themselves at times in their rocky beds, fertile Carmel and snow-clad Hermon, the resounding sea and the storm-lashed waters of Galilee are but a few of the many physical characteristics of Palestine that have left their indelible marks upon the Jewish and Christian Scriptures. The same is true of Israel's unique faith and institutions. Biblical geography, therefore, is not a study by itself, but the natural introduction to all other biblical studies.[1]

Palestine indeed assumed world importance out of all proportion to its diminutive size—"The least yet the most of lands." The geographic importance of its situation stems from a complex set of regional factors: Palestine's position in commerce and conquest at the crossroads of three continents of the Old World, where convergence of traffic and breaks in transit were significantly related (1) proximity to five seas —*Mare Internum, Pontus Euxinus, Mare Caspium, Sinus Persicus,* and *Sinus Arabicus,* which the student should have no difficulty in recognizing by their modern toponymy; (2) proximity to the west arm of the Fertile Crescent, extending from the Persian Gulf to the Mediterranean; and (3) areal associations with three major religions—the Jewish, the Christian, and the Moslem.

The purpose of this brief geographic commentary on Palestine is to illustrate geographic influences on Old and New Testament history. Perhaps the best single unified description of the features of the earth, of man's relationship to them, and of man's glorification of God for them, appears in Psalm 104, which might well be called "The Nature Psalm." Here in thirty-five short verses we find references to: (1) planetary relations, "Thou hast made the moon to mark the seasons"; (2) earth tectonics, "The mountains rose, the valleys sank down."; (3) meteorological phenomena, "From thy lofty abode Thou waterest the mountains"; (4) vegetation, "The trees of the Lord are watered abundantly, the cedars of Lebanon which he planted."; (5) animal ecology, "In them (cedars) the birds build their nests; the stork has her home in the fir trees. The high mountains are for the wild

[1] Kent, Charles, *Biblical Geography and History,* Charles Scribner's Sons, New York, 1911, pp. v-vi. Reprinted by permission.

goats; the rocks are a refuge for the badgers." (6) And man's place in the economy and commerce of the earth's resources finds expression in such passages as: "Thou dost cause the grass to grow for the cattle and plants for man to cultivate, that he may bring forth food from the earth," and "There go the ships, and Leviathan which thou didst form to sport in it."

As we know, lessons for living and for life—for both temporal and spiritual (eternal) ends—were psychologically and pedagogically oriented in earth products and patterns. Hence the numerous parables and figures of speech. Thus the parable of the sower and the allusion to soil–crop adaptability (Matthew 13); and the metaphor, "I am the vine, ye are the branches" (John 15: 5).

Climatic references are probably as numerous in the Bible as any other natural allusions. References to environmental hardships are almost always related to water-deficiency. Less commonly recognized by the average Bible reader, or even by some Biblical scholars, is the fact that it is not low annual rainfall (Jerusalem, for example, has approximately 26 inches, which is classified as "humid"), but the desert-like summer (total of only .6 inch for 5 months) which spiritually accents the import of such a passage as, "He leadeth me beside the still waters." Also, unless this is recognized the significance of "first rain and the latter rain" (Deuteronomy 11: 14) cannot be understood in any of the connections in which it appears in the Bible. For unless we understand this climatic regimen of winter-wet and summer-dry seasons, we fail to see why in an otherwise humid land we should have periodic famine.[1]

Have you often wondered about the numerous references to wells and cisterns and the well nomenclature (Esek, Sitnah, Rehoboth; Genesis 26: 18-22)? Such an episode as Christ revealing himself to the woman of Samaria at Jacob's well takes on new environmental as well as spiritual significance, once we recognize not only its life-sustaining water resource, but its role in the Palestine pattern of human circulation and congregation.

So frequent are the references to hills and mountains in Palestine that it would seem the Jews would have been entirely lost without them as a source of perpetual combined natural and spiritual inspiration: "I lift up my eyes to the hills. From whence does my help come?" (Psalm 121: 1); "Those who trust in the Lord are like Mount Zion, which cannot be moved, but abides for ever" (Psalm 125: 1). Worship and sacrifice were nearly always associated with high places: "Joshua built an altar in Mount Ebal to the Lord, the God of Israel" (Joshua 8: 30); "he [Christ] took with him Peter and John and James, and went up on the mountain to pray"; (Luke 9: 28); "The king went to Gibeon to sacrifice there, for that was the great high place" (I Kings 3: 3).

The frequent allusions to caves in the Bible need likewise to be understood, as to their origin, their position, as well as to the uses which they served. Resulting from the solution of limestone formations which dominate the rock structure of Palestine, caves served as sheepcotes (I Samuel 24: 3); as protection of humans against their enemies (I Samuel 13: 6); as dwelling places (Genesis 19: 30); as well as places for burial (Genesis 23: 19, 20). Even the birthplace and burial site of Christ were probably identified with caves.

On the cultural side of Palestine life, perhaps no factor is so instructive of human economy, and at the same time so appropriately spiritual in its applications, as the pastoral setting revealed to us in Psalm 23, the "Pastoral Psalm." It should be apparent by now, that unless this, too, is placed in the proper environmental context, the providential message it is designed to portray is not fully appreciated by people who have never experienced the summer aridity of the Mediterranean realm.

The concept of regionalism and its associated "influence" implications find exemplary expression also in Bible geography. It was a Samaritan woman who engaged Christ in conversation at Jacob's well. After the cleansing of the ten lepers, only one returned thanks, "And he was a Samaritan" (Luke 17). And in Christ's exposition of what constitutes

[1] The "first rain" refers to beginning of the wet season (commonly October); the "latter" rain to the end of the grain-growing period (about end of May). Thus if the former rains fail to materialize, sown grain would fail to sprout; and if the rains terminated too early, grains and other crops would not mature properly.

This view of Jerusalem shows Mount Zion. "They that trust in the Lord shall be as Mount Zion, which cannot be removed, but abideth forever." What elements of the environs suggest "citadel" and "place of peace," said to be the etymological basis for the terms *Zion* and *Jerusalem,* respectively? (Courtesy Consulate General of Israel)

good neighborliness, we have the parable of the Good Samaritan (Luke 10). From such multiple references, the student of geography as well as of the Bible will infer that there must have been something distinctive about the Samaritans. This in turn raises the question about their being different, at least in part, because they lived in a different environment from that of Judea. Here again an observation by Kent is geographically instructive and spiritually illuminating:

¶ Judah is a mountain fortress, with strong natural barriers on every side. Samaria, on the contrary, stands with doors wide open to the foreign trader and invader. . . . The great highways of commerce pass on either side of Judah, while they ran through the heart of Samaria. . . It bred a sturdy, brave race, intensely loyal to their rocks and hills. . . . In contrast, the fertile hills of Samaria, with their plentiful springs and rushing streams, bred a luxury-loving, carefree, tolerant race, who were ready, almost eager, for foreign ideas and cults, as well as customs. Thus that great schism between north and south, between Jew and Samaritan, was not merely the result of later rivalries, but found its primal cause in the physical characteristics that distinguished the land of Judah from that of Samaria.[1]

The Mediterranean Basin as a classical example in witnessing the effects of land–sea design on world affairs

¶ No other part of the world has occupied the forefront of political attention so consistently and so long as the Mediterranean Sea and its coasts. The eventful and intricate history of

[1] *Ibid.*, p. 44. Reprinted by permission.

more than three millennia in this area is traced upon a simple geopolitical pattern. This is the eternal tension between landpower and seapower in a region where, more than elsewhere on the earth, they rest upon a natural environment equally favorable to each. . . . From the dawn of history (which appears to have been cradled in the Nile oasis, that unique adjunct of the Mediterranean) until the oceanic Discoveries of the 15th century, the lands bordering the Middle Sea occupied the center of world affairs. There the political system of Western Europe was born. There raged the battles between the political ideals bred in the maritime atmosphere of the Mediterranean and the concepts brought in by landpowers from desert, steppe, and forest. There the tenuous and indirect contact with the independent civilization of the Orient persisted from classical antiquity, and finally became the incentive of the Discoveries made by way of the Occident. . . . As a persistent theater of world-shaking politics the Mediterranean Sea, with its coasts and surrounding barriers, has no peers. The issues may change in detail, but they remain the same in outline: dominance of narrows and control of smaller or larger bays and basins; rights of free navigation and struggles of maritime states against encroaching landpowers.[1]

This abstract from the preface of Whittlesey's chapter on "The Mediterranean Realm" suggests that we have here the world's leading area in historical and political geography, the understanding of which calls for a most careful examination of the role which space and time elements have played in the various sectors of the eastern and western Mediterranean Sea. To evaluate the geophysical as well as geo-political conditions, the student of geography will likely ponder such questions as: How might the history of the area, or even of the three continents — Europe, Asia, and Africa — have been different had there been no inland seas separating the three continents? How have the various straits and the Suez Canal influenced the course of history? How is the mountain pattern of Greece related to the origin and development of the city-states? What terrain and hinterland handicaps are there on the Eastern Adriatic to the development of seaports by Yugoslavia? Why are good harbor sites generally lacking in the western Mediterranean Basin? Questions such as these are relevant to the study of the retarded development of Mediterranean maritime power on extended coastlines otherwise characterized by numerous deep embayments and smaller inlet areas.

The middle of the twentieth century finds the Mediterranean Basin again the geographic focus of political and military strategy by the world powers. Whatever else Great Britain may be willing to concede in the way of declining colonial control, she is as much concerned as ever in defending her Mediterranean lifeline to the Orient, as was evidenced in 1957 by the joint British-French military attack on Egypt. Next to the Suez Canal's own strategic importance, the island of Cyprus illustrates how strategic a small island can be when viewed in the general perspective of a base for military operations by the British against possible Soviet aggression in the Levant. Similar concern by the United States in restraining further Soviet penetration by way of her satellite countries into this area led to a continental policy in the form of military aid to Turkey and Greece. Occupying its own strategic role by virtue of its geographic position along the Adriatic Sea and at the head of the Danubian Basin is the totalitarian state of Yugoslavia, with its own independent brand of communism. Its proximate position to the Balkan Russian satellites on the one hand, and to the independent countries of Greece and Turkey on the other, helps to explain the otherwise anomalous diplomatic situation of providing loans to a Communist state. In a different geographic context, but again for purposes of strengthening our defense position against the Soviet Union, the United States has negotiated with another totalitarian state — Spain — for the establishment of numerous naval and interior air bases. Spain itself is as much interested as the NATO countries in containing Communism.

Among other problems of international concern is, of course, the perennial conflict between Israel and the neighboring Arab states, as well as between the Arabs and Jews within Israel itself. Here one might say is the most controversial and contested spot on the face of the earth. Apart from the con-

---

[1] Whittlesey, Derwent, *The Earth and the State*, Henry Holt & Co., Inc., New York, 1939, pp. 235-237. Reprinted by permission.

flicting claims to rightful ownership and occupance of the area, the chief issue which concerns the geographer is the adequacy of resources of the country — agricultural and industrial — to satisfy the need of such populations as the country is supposed to accommodate.

Problems of the northwest countries of Africa — French Morocco, Algeria, and Tunisia — form another facet in political geographic study. Moving from an original protectorate status, French Morocco and Tunisia have achieved their independence, and the Arabs in Algeria, who outnumber the French 8 to 1, have likewise agitated for independence. Over half of the Moslem population is said to be indigent, and nearly half of the Moslem population is reportedly unemployed. As few as 25,000 French farmers are said to own as much as one-third of the fertile land. This will at least in part explain why the United States is interested in the Algerian problem. However, a student of geography will recognize that, when regionally analyzed, the Algerian situation is found to be very much unlike most other territories in the world with a dependent status. The French government in this instance has had to deal not only with the Arab but also with the French colonists who think of this trans-Mediterranean territory as their homeland and as part of France itself, and are, therefore, reluctant to see their homes and lands transferred to the Arabs. Improving the lot of the Arab, while at the same time guaranteeing a measure of security to the French colonials, may finally pacify the rival factions.

The Mediterranean regional occupance forms in transition

The *Cs* realm includes some of the most ancient cultures of mankind — the peoples of the Mesopotamian Valley, Palestine and Phoenicia of the Middle East, and the Minoan, Grecian, Roman, and Carthaginian civilizations of latter ancient days. It also involves the various Mohammedan cultures which spilled over from *BS* into the adjacent *Cs* lands of southwestern Asia, of northern Africa, and of the Iberian peninsula of southwestern Europe.

Study of the Mediterranean realm gives insight into the various stages of human occupance inversely considered. Thus among the most recent areas of settlement is that of middle Chile, which lacks the dense types of population found in the earlier settlements of eastern Mediterranean area and where considerable land is devoted to the raising of forage crops and the grazing of animals. Between this sort of pioneer occupance and that of the climactic intensive fruit and grain culture of ancient Mediterranean areas, is our own California with its growing, moderate to dense settlements, where more and more of the land is taken out of grazing and put into intensive agricultural and horticultural production — specialized fruit cultures, such as the orange groves of Los Angeles, the plum-prune country of Santa Clara, and the grape-raisin district of Fresno. "In this home of 'Sunkist' oranges and 'Sunmaid' raisins," as one commentator expresses it, "they eat what they can, and can what they can't."

Modern population relative densities can best be discerned by referring to the population map (see Appendix). Note that the largest area of highest population density occurs in nothern Italy, with a contiguous arm extending along the coast westward through southern France and Spain. Agrarian population densities often allow only 5 to 15 acres for individual farm holdings. In the eastern Mediterranean Basin area, as along the coast of Asia Minor and the eastern extremity of the Mediterranean Sea, population figures frequently range from 100 to 200 per square mile. Similar densities occur along the Tunisian and Algerian coasts. Relatively small areas of California and southwestern Africa vary from 50 to 100, whereas the Chilean and Australian sections more commonly range as low as 10 to 25 per square mile.

The greatly diversified landscape features have resulted in a wide range of density figures as well as types of settlements, both rural and urban. Originally towns were located in the interior rather than on the coast to escape the attacks of pirates, and frequently on mountain sites easy to defend against land attacks; subsequently, in the period of progressive urbanization, more and more towns were established along the coast where some of them became important manufacturing centers and others developed into commercial entrepôts, as we shall see later.

Nearly all major streams of the summer-dry countries are explored for possible irrigation water and hydroelectric power by the construction of huge dams. This view of the Castelo de Bode on Rio Zezere is typical of the "barrages" seen in many parts of Portugal. Note the tree plantings on the hill slopes in the background. (Courtesy Portuguese Consulate, Lisbon)

Fresh water, always the chief asset in the summer-dry areas, attracted settlement to streams, particularly those which did not completely dry up in the summertime. The alluvial fans and deltas were prize attractions for settlement, since such sites not only supplied the much-needed water for domestic use and irrigation but also furnished the most fertile spots for crop culture.

Major settlement deterrents along many of the coasts were swamps and marshes, breeding sites of malaria-spreading mosquitoes.

The development of any economies in the *Cs* world, whether agricultural or industrial, will forever have to take into account the limited water supply conditioned by the dry summers, which, without irrigation in many places, often presents desert-like landscapes. The majority of well-settled areas have now tapped most of the water sources available. Therefore, only distilled sea water, economically feasible perhaps by sun-power or atomic power, as discussed in connection with the drylands regions, can apparently satisfy the further water requirements of expanding communities and industries.

Another factor to be considered is the land problem. Regardless of the land reform programs in each of the Mediterranean Sea countries, it must be emphasized that there simply is not enough land to go around, however equitably divided.

Increasing commercial contacts with the hitherto somewhat isolated Southern Hemisphere Mediterranean lands can be expected to result in more intensive development of such still partially underdeveloped regions.

Southern California, whose stage of occupance may be said to be intermediate between that of Mediterranean Europe and Mediterranean Southern Hemisphere countries, looks to future development under a carefully projected program of extended utilization of water from the Sierra Nevadas and possibly even from the Colorado River.

The future outlook

However glamorous life has often been as associated with pleasure gardens in the Mediterranean world and however glorious has been its past history in providing the roots of our Western culture as well as in the heroic exploits of many of its ancient mariners, Mediterranean lands, as we have seen, have had perennial problems inherent in the summer droughts, winter floods, rocky and rugged terrain, and thin and stony soils. In the sparsely and moderately settled areas of the New World, acute agrarian problems have as yet not arisen; however, in the more densely settled sections of the Mediterranean Basin, as for example in Italy, land reform laws have had to be enacted by the government to cope with the problem. Thus the land reform laws of 1950 are designed to improve cultivation practices and productivity, as pointed out by George Kish in his article on Italy in *Focus:*

¶ These laws represent an integration of several principles: the breakup of large, poorly managed estates; the creation of numerous small peasant farms; the encouragement and long-range support of reclamation; and the introduction of better land use methods through education and agrarian cooperatives. . . . Estates of more than 750 acres (the maximum size now allowed) if poorly run are expropriated; only those managed efficiently and employing a sizeable labor force are exempt. The owners receive adequate compensation based on the 1947 assessed value of their land.

The new owners of small farms, ranging from 7 to 21 acres, are required to pay for their land within 30 years; and they must join a cooperative for 20 years to ensure that they have access to machinery and fertilizers and that their products will be marketed to the best advantage. During the first few years the government provides substantial support in the form of loans, housing, seed, livestock and expert advice on the spot where desirable. In all the land reform districts the land-poor peasants are carefully selected. Only a few of the eligible ones ever receive a farm, however, for the final allocation is made by lot.[1]

Manufacturing features light industries. As in the case of other densely-settled, land-poor sections of the world, countries must look to the development of other resources for sustaining the population. But in most Mediterranean Basin countries industrialization is not feasible on a major scale. For example, Italy, like most of the other Mediterranean countries, "is deficient in many of the economically important minerals. . . . More than 90 per cent of the coal has to be imported . . . and iron ore deposits produce only about half the country's requirements. The only minerals of value to industry that occur in abundant quantity in Italy are sulphur, pyrites and mercury, most of which comes from Sicily and Tuscany. Italy ranks second only to the United States as a world producer of sulphur, and with Spain, has a virtual European monopoly of mercury" (10).[2]

Other areas of significant mineral resources in this realm include Turkey, which produces one-fifth of the world's chromite supply; Greece, which exports iron ore; Algeria, which, in addition to iron ore, exports large quantities of phosphate; Mediterranean Australia, which is said to have the world's richest single iron ore deposit; and California, a leader in petroleum production and refining.

Unlike east-central North America and northwest Europe and western U.S.S.R. with innumerable sites of heavy as well as light industry, Mediterranean lands, with few local exceptions, are weak in industries based largely on metallurgical products. Distinctive industries are those which can exploit to advantage the regional elements for which the *Cs* is famous, as already indicated above, in the form primarily of horticultural and floricultural products: processing of canned, dried, and frozen fruits and vegetables; canning or bottling of fruit juices, wines, and olive oil (centered in California, France and Italy and Spain, respectively); the extraction of perfume oils (Italy and France). The

[1] Kish, George, "Italy," *Focus*, Vol. III, No. 9, May, 1953, pp. 2-3. Reprinted by permission.

[2] Actually the section of Italy most heavily industrialized and dependent for power on its hydroelectric developments is in the Po Valley (*Cfa*) rather than in the *Cs* region.

XXIV:6 Distribution of water from areas of surplus to areas of deficiency preoccupies *Cs* man. Hence, the far-flung aqueduct projects of the Great Valley of California are shown here in relief perspective. (Aqueduct data from "Water: White Gold of California," Department of Water Resources, 1960. Relief map copyright Aero Service Corporation. Both used by permission)

stripping of cork is a distinctive Mediterranean Basin forest industry (Portugal, the leading exporter). Regionally subtropical waters abound in fish, such as pilchard and tuna, whose catches promote several large canning centers (e.g. Monterey, California, "sardine capital of the world.")

Another major industry naturally acclimated is the motion picture industry, which has reached phenomenal development in southern California, where maximal sunshine obtains and, in close proximity, a diversity of landscapes adapted to almost every type of scenario. Predominantly clear skies favor as well the development of the aircraft industry, particularly in the testing of new designs of aircraft.

Will California become our new "Empire State"?

Rated as probably the most homogeneous climatic realm in the world, the Mediterranean lands, widely distributed as they are over six continents, do possess varying individualities. Probably the most individualistic of these regions is California, whose combined physical and cultural elements stand out unique. Among the distinctive natural features are the relatively low annual rainfall, the approximately evenly-divided coastal region with cool summer *(Csb)* and the interior areas with hot summer *(Csa)*, and its frequently fog-enshrouded coast. Unique also is the Great Valley lying between the Coast Ranges and the Sierra Nevadas, occupied by the Sacramento River in the north and the San Joaquin River in the south, where, under irrigation, occurs one of the most productive agricultural regions of the world (Figure XXIV-6). Here on the western slopes of the Sierras are also the magnificent sequoias. Identified with the mountain-building processes in California is the less inviting San Andreas Rift, producing an earthquake zone of marked instability, the basis for height-restricting and other special building codes in a major city such as San Francisco.

California's cultural patterns of occupance comprise: (1) the Spanish missions of the seventeenth and eighteenth centuries, of which relics are still found in the modern landscape; (2) the system of rancho land-grants (minimum 4,500 acres), a legacy from former Mexican occupation; (3) the gold-mining adventures of the "Forty-Niners," with its resultant impetus to the first major American settlements; (4) the annexation of California to the Union in 1850; (5) the subsequent development of subsistence agriculture and stock-raising; (6) diversification and specialization of agricultural and horticultural crop productions; (7) establishment of multifarious industries, fostered particularly by the discovery here of one of the leading petroleum fields in the world; (8) the development of aeronautical and other industries, particularly stimulated by the Second World War; (9) the resultant influx of hundreds of thousands of people, who found in the sunny clime of California the ideal "garden" workshop, and playground. Horticulture-wise, California not only places America in the fruit hierarchy of world climatic realms, but establishes her premiership in fruit-growing, fruit-processing, and fruit-exporting. Observe the regional rating by Clifford Zierer:

¶ Climate and other geographical factors, aided by irrigation and many favorable dynamic social influences, have made California the greatest fruit-growing region, not only in the United States but in the world. . . . Fruits and nuts constitute about 20 per cent of the state's harvested acreage of all crops compared to 10 per cent for the other states. . . . Within half a century, California has converted vast fields of grain into thousands of irrigated citrus groves, orchards, and vineyards and has been transformed from an importer of fruits to the chief commercial fruit producer, fresh shipper, processor, and exporter in the world. . . . The extent and diversity of the state's horticultural output stem from favorable geographical factors of size, climate, soil, and availability of water for irrigation. . . . They have made possible consistently high yields of large quantities of many kinds of fruits of superior quality for drying, canning, crushing, and fresh distribution during long harvesting and shipping seasons. . . . For several decades, California has been the most important and highly commercialized dried-fruit-producing area in the world. It ranks second only to the Mediterranean Basin area in dried-fruit production, accounting for about one-third of the commercial output of the world and over 95 per cent of the United States total. The state is the world's largest producer of every commercially important dried fruit except currants, dates, and figs.[1]

---

[1] Reprinted with permission from Clifford M. Zierer, *California and the Southwest,* 1956, John Wiley & Sons, Inc., New York, pp. 148-154.

Orange groves and citrus area are shown here as seen from Venice Hills, Tulare County, California. Orange groves dominate the citrus fruit areas of the southern San Joaquin valley, this region producing about one-third of the nation's crop. Unlike the olive, the orange tree (*Citrus aurantium*) is not native to the Mediterranean world. Though its original culture is shrouded in antiquity, its native habitat is thought to be southeast Asia. The Arabs are reputedly largely responsible for its transplantation to Europe via the Levant (about ninth century) to Italy (about twelfth century). One of the most naturally variegated and culturally hybridized of all fruits, the orange in its wide longitudinal spread from the Old World to the New is an object uniquely adapted to a historical-geographic study in plant ecology and human cultures intimately identified with the propagation and dissemination of this popular fruit. (Photo by D. A. Hovey, Bureau of Reclamation, U. S. Department of Agriculture)

In the decennium between 1940-1950 California's population increased over 50 per cent. And the population increased another 48 per cent from 1950 to 1960. With th rapidly expanding industries and the increas ing amenity attractions of climate and scenery for the growing number of our population in the retirement class, it is not surprising that in 1962, California surpassed the state of New York in population.

APPLICATION OF GEOGRAPHIC UNDERSTANDING

The "Peddlers of Antiquity" —
The Phoenicians:
A Study in
Historical Commercial Geography

I. The Bible as a Geographic Reference Work.

A. A contemporary geographer once made the observation that Ezekiel 27 gives us the most comprehensive geographic picture of the then known world (*circa.* 600 B.C.), recorded either in sacred or secular history. To aid you in checking this statement, make your own map using an outline base, showing all the "merchants" (trading places) for the various products of commerce here enumerated, and compare this record with other sources of the period.

B. To what extent is Ezekiel's geographic commentary supplemented by other Bible references?

C. Another authority, Wilfred H. Schoff, in *The Ship "Tyre"* (Longmans, Green and Co., 1920), although not questioning the correctness of Ezekiel's sources "so far as they go," observes that only "import" sources—not "export" sources—are named, and "Tyre based her commercial strength upon her manufactures." The thesis of Schoff, accordingly, is that we have here an allegory whose real purpose is to point to the doom of Babylon and Nebuchadrezzar ("King of Tyre"); "The ship 'Tyre' is a symbol of Chaldea; her cargo is a symbol of the institutions of the priesthood and princedom of Judah which Babyon profaned; and her doom is the doom of Babylon herself" (p. 59). In view of this reference, how would you now go about reconstructing a cartographic and commercial view of the ancient world?

D. Compare I Kings 9 with II Chronicles 9, 10, dealing with "Ophir" and "Tarshish" maritime expeditions, respectively. Ophir is supposed to have been in eastern or southern Arabia, and Tarshish in southern Spain. This raises some questions: Does it seem reasonable that the Solomon-Hiram fleet included both these easternmost and westernmost outposts of navigation on the same voyage, or were these scheduled for separate expeditions?

II. However limited your mapped data may seem, the fact remains that the Phoenicians were the leading navigators and traders of their day. How do you account for this commercial supremacy? Here are some criteria for evaluation which a student of geography would normally apply:

A. Position with respect to major sea and land routes of travel.

B. Regional differences of countries traded with (a) in surplus natural and cultural products; (b) in stage of social, economic, and cultural development.

C. Consider the fact that Phoenicia occupied one of the most rugged and rocky sectors of the Mediterranean. Palestine, its neighbor to the south, on the other hand, with better natural endowments, never came to being even a close second in maritime and commercial enterprise, though sharing with Phoenicia the Mediterranean coast and having ready access to the Red Sea as well. How do you account for this? Is there a geographic reason for King Hiram of Phoenicia associating himself with King Solomon's Red Sea fleet project (I Kings 9: 26-28)?

D. In what geographic aspects did the Grecian and the Roman empires differ from the Phoenician and its offspring Carthaginian empires?

III. What commercial or political geographic concepts does the following regional toponymy of the ancient Greek and Roman world suggest:

A. "orbis terrarum"

B. "oecumene"

C. "Mare Internum"

D. "mare nostrum"

IV. The geographic concepts of the world held by the earlier Phoenicians differed from those of the Greeks and Romans. What were they, and what chronologic and chorographic bases can you suggest in possibly accounting for this difference?

References

1 "Mediterranean Leisure Land," *Life,* July 18, 1955, p. 81.

2 *The Bible (Revised Standard Version)*, Thomas Nelson & Sons, New York, 1946-1952.

3 *The Odyssey of Homer,* translation by Theodore A. Buckley, Charles E. Merrill Books, Inc., Columbus, Ohio, 1911, Book VII, p. 37.

4 *The Geography of Strabo,* Vol. IV, translation by Horace L. Jones, 1927, the Loeb Classical Library, Harvard University Press, Cambridge, Mass, p. 49.

5 Semple, Ellen Churchill, *The Geography of the Mediterranean Region,* Henry Holt and Co., Inc., New York, 1931, pp. 297-335, *passim,* pp. 474-479, *passim.*

6 Baly, Denis, *The Geography of the Bible,* Harper & Brothers, New York, 1957, p. 3.

7 Kent, Charles, *Biblical Geography and History,*

Charles Scribner's Sons, New York, 1911, pp. v-vi, p. 44.

8 Whittlesey, Derwent, *The Earth and the State*, Henry Holt and Co., Inc., New York, 1939, pp. 235-237.

9 Hadlow, Leonard, *Climate Vegetation and Man*, Philosophical Library, New York, 1953, p. 191.

10 Kish, George, "Italy," *Focus*, Vol. III, No. 9, May, 1953, pp. 2-3, 4.

11 Zierer, Clifford M., *California and the Southwest*, John Wiley & Sons, Inc., New York, 1956, pp. 148-154.

Chapter 25

The humid, mild winter, forest and prairie realm (Cfa-Cwa)

Cotton is a clear case of an agricultural commodity for which the United States government functions as the world price leader. . . . During the past five seasons [1955-60] we supplied 32 per cent of the cotton which moved in world trade. Of some forty other cotton-exporting countries there was none which could account for even half so much.

Horne, McDonald K., Jr., "Cotton," *The Annals of the American Academy of Political and Social Science,* Vol. CCCXXXI, September, 1960, p. 65. Reprinted by permission.

Chorogram: "King Cotton"

Cotton is grown in some part of each of the major subtropical regions of the world. But the expression "Cotton is King" applies nowhere so aptly as in the South of the United States (Figure XXV-1). Probably no crop in the world, certainly among the fibers, features such concentrated commercial production; nor is there probably another area in the world where a one-crop specialty has had more far-reaching effects on the social, economic, and political life of a nation. Here it was that the cotton plant found one of its most favorite habitats, involving the complex factors of: (1) at least 185 days frost-free season, with hot and humid summers; (2) less than 10 inches of rainfall in the fall—essential in the maturing and harvesting of the crop; (3) virgin soil highly adapted to cotton culture, particularly on the alluvial river bottoms, as those along the lower Mississippi; (4) large extensive tracts of land which could be developed into plantations; originally serviced by Negro slave labor, and, even to this day, benefited by cheaper labor than found elsewhere in the United States. The early invention of the cotton gin by Eli Whitney and the more recent innovation of the cotton picker have further accented cotton culture in the South.

Although contributing greatly not only to the economy of the South but also to the entire nation in strengthening our foreign commerce, since cotton has been for a long time a leading export of the United States, the commercial exploitation of this most important crop of the South has not been an unmitigated blessing. In a certain sense it has directly or indirectly also contributed to major economic and social problems of this country. The one-crop system of agriculture has been responsible for seriously depleting hundreds of thousands of acres of cropland in the South, in some cases almost irreparably damaging the soils, not merely by the exhaustion of nutrient materials, but also by the removal of soils altogether on steeper slopes which should never have been cultivated. The single cotton crop economy has also proved disastrous during times of the invasion of the boll weevil, which crossed the Rio Grande from Mexico. Such insect infestations, as well as crop failures due to abnormal climatic fluctuations, have brought ruin to many a cotton planter. Significantly also, cotton culture, with its exacting labor requirements, along with that of other specialized crops such as tobacco, has contributed to the difficulty in resolving race problems. In the economics of agricultural development, few crops of any area have presented such a challenging surplus disposal problem to any country as has cotton in our economy.

As may be expected, an attack on this Southern problem has come from many fronts; first, from the agricultural extension and soil conservation agents, who have for a long time pointed to the need for much greater diversification of Southern agriculture, including the introduction of animal husbandry. Increases in commercial livestock have introduced new sources of revenue for the farmer. The return of animal manures, as well as the growing of forage and green manure crops such as the legumes, has been instrumental in restoring soil fertility to many hitherto worn-out areas. Notwithstanding the reduction of cotton acreage (almost 50 per cent in the last 25 years), the total production of cotton today as a result of more scientific seed selection, soil adaptations, and cultivation practices is about as high as it was before.

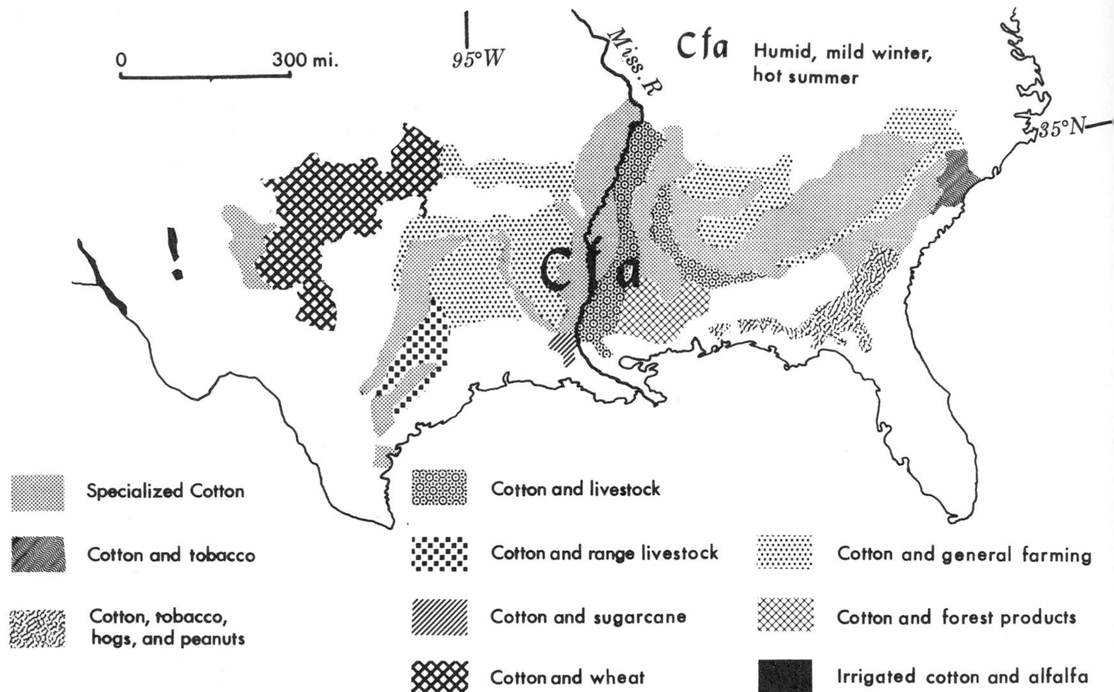

XXV:1 This map shows the classified cotton farming types in the United States. Based on an equal area projection (Albers Conical with standard parallels 29½° and 45½°), this map facilitates areal comparisons. Areally rank each cotton land-use category, and try to account for major differences in size of areas and type of land-use. (Adapted from "Generalized Types of Farming in the United States," Agricultural Research Service, Agricultural Information Bulletin No. 3, U. S. Department of Agriculture, 1950)

Despite our leadership in world production as well as world price leadership in cotton, and despite the natural and cultural conditions which have favored cotton culture as pointed out above, the problem of exporting our surplus, even on an export subsidy basis, remains a critical one. This problem centers about the geography of labor costs, i.e., the disparate cost of cotton production between our South and that of other leading producers, such as India, Egypt, Brazil, and Mexico. As McDonald K. Horne, Chief Economist of the National Cotton Council, points out: "In the cost of production, the great disadvantage of the American cotton farmer is the price of labor. In many other aspects of production, he has a competitive advantage." On the basis of this "cost geography," Horne concludes, with a note of optimism:

¶ If, in the next decade, the technology of cotton production remains rather dormant, it is likely that our genuine economic claim upon a large place in the world cotton market [cotton consumption has doubled in the last fifteen years] will decline. If great technological progress is made, as it can be, the United States farmer probably will achieve a real comparative advantage in the true classical meaning of the term.[1]

The climatic regimen and realm rating

At generally lower latitudes than *Cs* lands, and on the east coast of continents instead of the west coast, lie the subtropical lands, *Cfa*—*Cwa*, whose equatorward extensions normally border the *Aw*. The single continental exception is Europe where the *Cfa* is bounded equatorward by the *Cs* (Figure XXV-2), and does not characteristically classify under the humid subtropic category.

In most areas the equatorward boundary

[1] Horne, *loc. cit.* p. 69. Reprinted by permission.

Cotton is picked mechanically in Mississippi. Mechanical harvesting of cotton has been under experimentation for over a hundred years, but it is about the last major crop production to be so mechanized. Consider the problems involved under the following categories: (1) nature of the plant, (2) technological aspects, (3) economic factors, (4) social conditions (labor, etc.). What advantages and disadvantages result from such mechanization, considering aspects of both systematic and regional geography? (Photo U. S. Department of Agriculture)

cuts across the tropics, and in the case of *Cw* (the monsoon aspect of the mild winter climate) extends within 10° of the Equator. Because of this lower latitude position as well as east coast distribution, the equatorward margins have higher temperatures than the *Cs*, both in summer as well as in winter. But a greater distinction is in the amount and seasonal distribution of rainfall. Most of the *Cf* and *Cw* lands have at least twice as much rain as is commonly found in the *Cs* world; and summers are characteristically wetter than the winters. Particularly is this true under the marked monsoon influence of southeastern Asia and southeastern Africa (Figure XXV-2). Where this disparity in the rainfall regimen reaches such a high figure as ten times or more, with resultant seasonal floods and droughts, we distinguish the *Cw* (winter–dry, summer–wet regimen) (Figure XXV-3) from the *Cf*, with its less contrast in seasonal rains (Figures XXV-4, XXV-5).

During the summer, when low pressures develop in the interior of the continent, tropical air masses bring copious supplies of moisture into the subtropics. Thunderstorms of the thermal convection type or other rains identified with the cyclonic "fronts" often produce heavy local showers. In winter, the rains are of the frontal type from the numerous cyclonic storms which move from west to east across the area. Where monsoons are

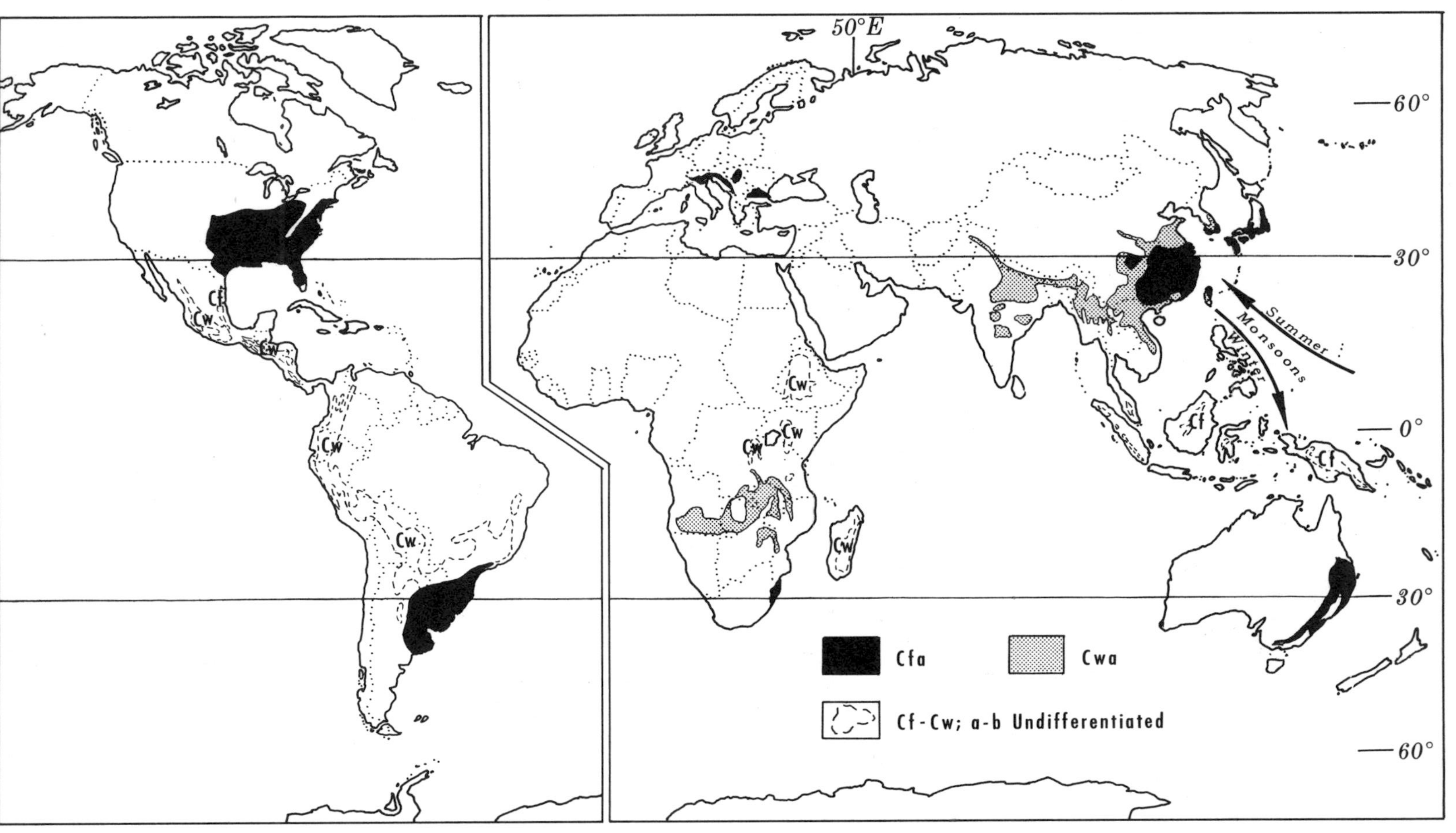
50°E
60°
30°
0°
30°
60°
Summer
Monsoons
Winter
Cf
Cw
Cw
Cw
Cw
Cw
Cw
Cw
Cw
Cf
Cf
Cfa
Cwa
Cf - Cw; a-b Undifferentiated

strongly developed, as in southeastern Asia and parts of Africa, the winter cyclonic storms are overpowered by the strong movement of cold masses of air from the dry inner heart of the continent caused by the high pressure developed there during the season. Obviously such air is dry and incapable of contributing much moisture at this season. In fact, several months may pass without any appreciable rainfall at all. On the other hand, during the summer in-flowing, warm air masses from the tropics bring copious moisture, often resulting in heavy floods. Whereas in the *Cs* world famine may result from excessively long and intensively dry summer seasons, in *Cw* China and India, crops may be destroyed in the field or washed away after the harvest by excessive summer floods. And, just as floods also are often destructive in the *Cs* lands during the winter, so here the reverse meteorologic catastrophe may occur, namely, an unusually long and dry winter where a deficiency of rain and lack of sufficient irrigation water may result in failure of fall- or winter-planted crops.

Except for the seasonally wet and dry extremes of the monsoon *Cw* phase, the humid subtropics, because of its ample rainfall and long growing season, rates close to the top of the leading forest- and food-producing realms of the world.

Forestry versus farming: a characteristic ambivalent realm issue

As pointed out in previous chapters, vegetative cover is the most reflective environmental factor of climate; and forests, covering almost a third of the earth's total land area, form the most dominant aspect of biotic features. Besides supplying wood for construction, paper, and fuel materials, forests are significantly important to mankind in controlling stream flow and checking soil erosion. Their immediate effects on the amelioration of climate is equally, if not even more, significant. Their aesthetic and recreational values, moreover, cannot be measured in monetary terms.

XXV:2 (Left) Several distinctive continental distributions of the *Cf-Cw* are noteworthy: the extensive representation of *Cf* in the Western Hemisphere, especially in the United States Deep South; the extremely restricted *Cf* areas in Europe and Africa; and the combined strong development of *Cf-Cw* in southeast Asia. Account for the strongest representation of *Cw* in Asia and, secondly, in Africa.

The forests of the humid subtropics are distinctive in two important particulars: (1) the extraordinary diversity of the tree species, and (2) the extensive exploitation of forest resources. Equatorward sections include many species typical of the tropical rainforest while the poleward sections incorporate many species typical of temperate, middle-latitude forests. Low-latitude evergreens include both broadleaf and conifers, whereas in the higher latitudes typically deciduous hardwoods occur with local stands of evergreen conifers. The highly varied topographic, meteorologic, and hydrographic conditions, already noted for this part of the world, also add to the diversification, and man himself in these highly populated sections has in many cases transplanted certain types from one region to another to still further diversify the forest lands. Continentwise, major distributional differences also occur: thus in China, Korea, and Japan we have probably the greatest diversity of tree cover in the world, there being reported as many as 1,500 to 2,000 species. In contrast, in the southeastern United States, forests are much more homogeneous in character, as few as only half a dozen trees in places dominating readily distinguishable stands. In the South American area, except for southern Brazil, the region is dominated by grasslands, especially on the *BS* margin, with forests occurring primarily along streams and swampy areas. Prairie herbaceous vegetation in southern United States and southern Africa is restricted largely to the steppe margins. In sum, forests are the dominant natural vegetative cover of this realm.

Regional forest resources differ greatly in the various continental areas. Small remnants of heavily cut-over forest on the lowlands of China indicate that this area once had one of the most dense and diverse forest stands in the world, but it is understandable that as a result of increasing demands on tillage of the soil, with the growing densities of population, extensive deforestation took place.

This poses the general question as to the

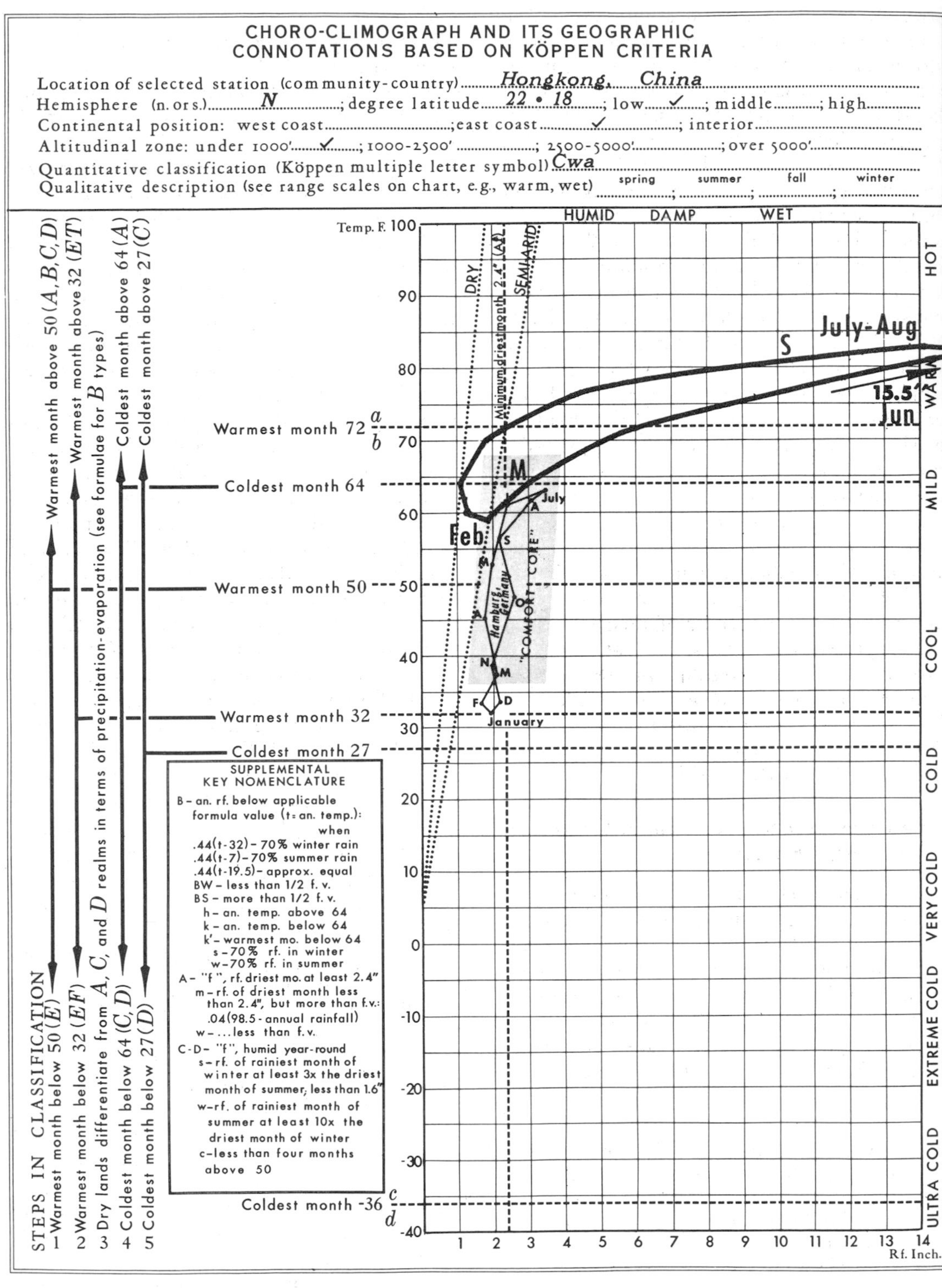
CHORO-CLIMOGRAPH AND ITS GEOGRAPHIC
CONNOTATIONS BASED ON KÖPPEN CRITERIA
Location of selected station (community-country) Hongkong, China
Hemisphere (n. or s.) N; degree latitude 22 • 18; low ✓; middle; high
Continental position: west coast; east coast ✓; interior
Altitudinal zone: under 1000' ✓; 1000-2500'; 2500-5000'; over 5000'
Quantitative classification (Köppen multiple letter symbol) Cwa
Qualitative description (see range scales on chart, e.g., warm, wet) spring; summer; fall; winter
HUMID
DAMP
WET
Temp. F. 100
90
80
70
60
50
40
30
20
10
0
-10
-20
-30
-40
1 2 3 4 5 6 7 8 9 10 11 12 13 14
Rf. Inch.
HOT
WARM
MILD
COOL
COLD
VERY COLD
EXTREME COLD
ULTRA COLD
DRY
Minimum driest month 2.4" (A,L)
SEMIARID
July-Aug
S
15.5"
Jun
M
July
A
Feb
S
O
Hamburg, Germany
"COMFORT CORE"
N
M
F
D
January
Warmest month 72 a b
Coldest month 64
Warmest month 50
Warmest month 32
Coldest month 27
Coldest month -36 c d
STEPS IN CLASSIFICATION
1 Warmest month above 50 (A, B, C, D) — Warmest month below 50 (E)
2 Warmest month above 32 (ET) — Warmest month below 32 (EF)
3 Dry lands differentiate from A, C, and D realms in terms of precipitation-evaporation (see formulae for B types)
4 Coldest month above 64 (A) — Coldest month below 64 (C, D)
5 Coldest month above 27 (C) — Coldest month below 27 (D)
SUPPLEMENTAL
KEY NOMENCLATURE
B – an. rf. below applicable formula value (t = an. temp.): when
.44(t-32) – 70% winter rain
.44(t-7) – 70% summer rain
.44(t-19.5) – approx. equal
BW – less than 1/2 f. v.
BS – more than 1/2 f. v.
h – an. temp. above 64
k – an. temp. below 64
k' – warmest mo. below 64
s – 70% rf. in winter
w – 70% rf. in summer
A – "f", rf. driest mo. at least 2.4"
m – rf. of driest month less than 2.4", but more than f. v.: .04(98.5 - annual rainfall)
w – ... less than f. v.
C-D – "f", humid year-round
s – rf. of rainiest month of winter at least 3x the driest month of summer; less than 1.6"
w – rf. of rainiest month of summer at least 10x the driest month of winter
c – less than four months above 50

relative value of forests in any country's economy. This competitive land feature is well brought out in the observation by Paul Sears:

¶ The forest early assumed an equivocal role in human culture. It was prized for the materials it yielded and for some of the functions it performed, but it was also regarded as a rival for the space needed for crops and flocks. This two-mindedness about the forest has continued to confuse humanity down to the present day, with sorry results.[1]

Since China south of the Yangtze Kiang is dominantly hill country, and even mountainous in large sections, forest stands, chiefly of the conifer type, are still to be found on the uplands. But on the lower slopes where terraced rice cultures and other land tillage were feasible, large timber tracts, of course, were removed. Unless carefully managed, much of the cultivated slopeland of China will be gullied by excessive erosion. Extensive slopeland deforestation has also aggravated the *Cw* flood situation. These conservation considerations again raise the question about the "equivocality" of the use of such lands as between forestry and agriculture.

Despite the fact that the Chinese Botanical Society reports more than 2,000 species of trees in the country, only a very few of these are commercially important. In fact, only two of these are dominant. D. Y. Lin considers the "Chinese fir" (Sha Mu) to be

¶ the most valuable tree in China . . . Sha Mu accounts for more than 90 per cent of the economic timber found in the lumber markets in China, except in the North and Northwest Regions. Bamboo is by far the most useful "timber" in China: those who have lived there will appreciate the multitudinous uses to which it is put. It is used for food, in building houses and bridges, for drilling pipes, for fishing gear and boats, and in the manufacture of paper, furniture, sedan chairs, ropes, umbrellas, mattresses, scrolls, chopsticks, toys, musical instruments, baskets, curtains, combs, undershirts, hats, raincoats, and all kinds of farm implements and household utensils. The West certainly does not possess any tree or shrub which for all around general usefulness can compare with the bamboo of China.[2]

Among the many miscellaneous forest products are also listed the following: tung oil, vegetable tallow, camphor, lacquer, silk, incense, cassia bark (used in medicine), tea, oil, wax, tannin, edible fungi, cork, dyeing materials.

The forest cover of central and southern Japan occupies a similar geographic situation except that because of its more northerly latitude it has a larger percentage of temperate climate types of forest. It appears that more stress has been placed on scientific forestry management in Japan than in China. Despite this fact, Japan has been an importer of forest products from southwestern Canada and northwestern United States—a rather surprising situation for a "hill country."

1. The United States South. Though long exploited for lumber and often with little regard for conservation practices, the timber lands of the South still constitute one-third of our forest resources. Several consociations occur in broad latitudinal belts: oak-hickory dominates the north; loblolly shortleafed pine, the center belt; and the longleafed slash pine, the Gulf coastal section. The central belt veers northeastward along the Atlantic seaboard in the same latitude as the oak-hickory, and in the western sector swamp and bottomland forests follow the Mississippi-Gulf Plain area, transecting all three belts at the confluence of the Ohio and Mississippi rivers. The drier sandy soils along the Atlantic coast and some sections of the Appalachian Piedmont are primarily conifer-covered; the low-lying swamplands along the Gulf and those in the river bottoms feature various species of gum trees and cypress.

---

[1] Sears, Paul, "The Importance of Forests to Man," *A World Geography of Forest Resources,* Edited by Stephen Haden-Guest, John K. Wright, Eileen M. Teclaff; American Geographical Society, Special Publication No. 33. Copyright The Ronald Press Company, New York, 1956, p. 4. Reprinted by permission.

[2] Lin, D. Y., "China," *A World Geography of Forrest Resources,* Edited by Stephen Haden-Guest, John K. Wright, Eileen M. Teclaff; American Geographical Society, Special Publication No. 33. Copyright The Ronald Press Company, New York, 1956, pp. 536-537. Reprinted by permission.

XXV:3 (Left) As you see here, Hong Kong gets out of bounds with its 15.5″ maximum in June. The comet-like sweep of the rain range builds up to 85 inches for the year. Floods in *Cw* regionally may spell famine.

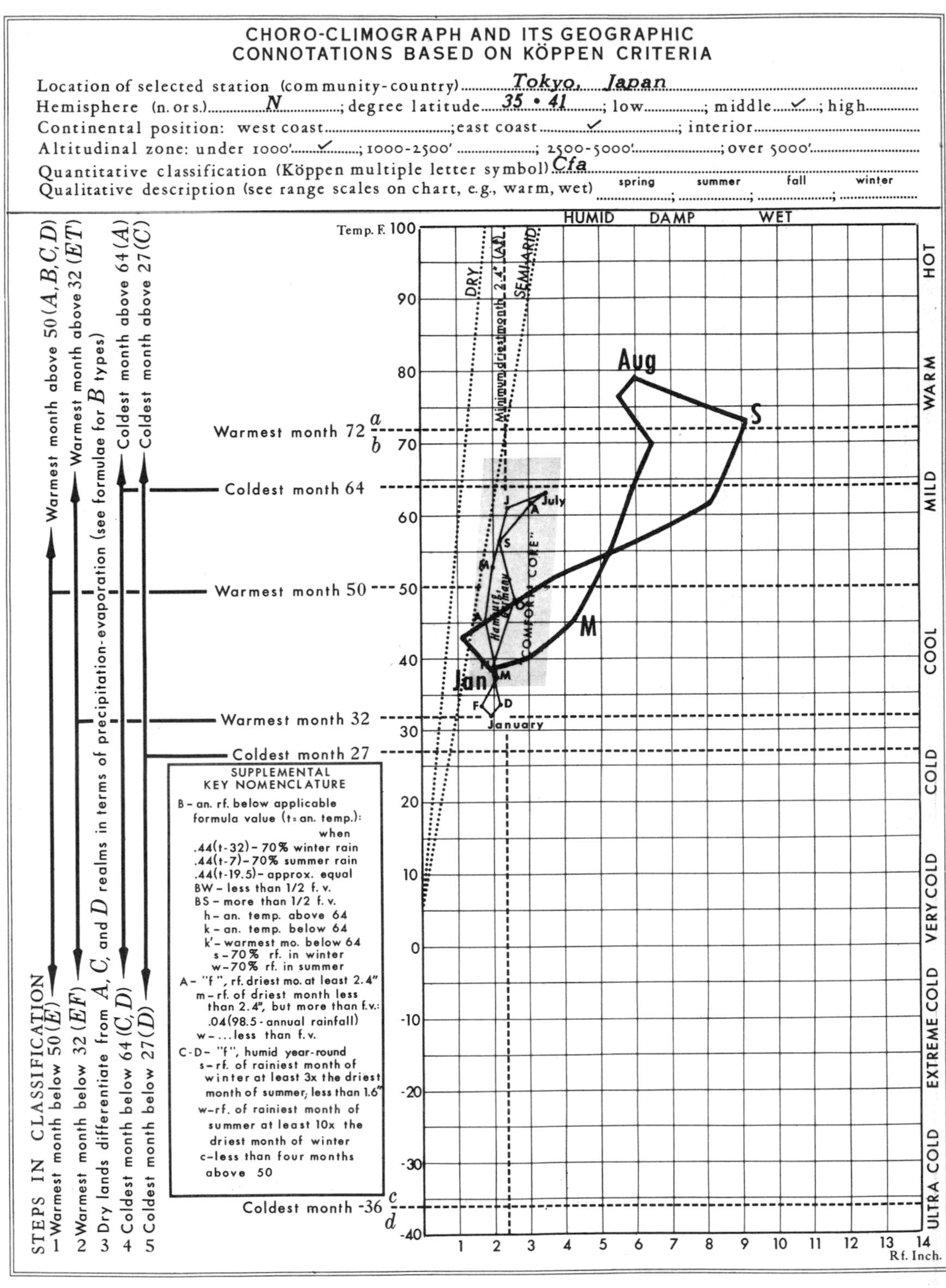

CHORO-CLIMOGRAPH AND ITS GEOGRAPHIC CONNOTATIONS BASED ON KÖPPEN CRITERIA
Location of selected station (community-country) Tokyo, Japan
Hemisphere (n. or s.) N ; degree latitude 35 • 41 ; low ; middle ✓ ; high
Continental position: west coast ; east coast ✓ ; interior
Altitudinal zone: under 1000' ✓ ; 1000-2500' ; 2500-5000' ; over 5000'
Quantitative classification (Köppen multiple letter symbol) Cfa
Qualitative description (see range scales on chart, e.g., warm, wet) spring ; summer ; fall ; winter
STEPS IN CLASSIFICATION
1 Warmest month below 50 (E) — Warmest month above 50 (A, B, C, D)
2 Warmest month below 32 (EF) — Warmest month above 32 (ET)
3 Dry lands differentiate from A, C, and D realms in terms of precipitation-evaporation (see formulae for B types)
4 Coldest month below 64 (C, D) — Coldest month above 64 (A)
5 Coldest month below 27 (D) — Coldest month above 27 (C)
Warmest month 72 a b
Coldest month 64
Warmest month 50
Warmest month 32
Coldest month 27
Coldest month -36 c d
HUMID
DAMP
WET
DRY
Minimum driest month 2.4" (Af)
SEMIARID
"COMFORT CORE"
Hamburg, Germany
Aug
S
M
Jan
July
January
Temp. F.
Rf. Inch.
HOT
WARM
MILD
COOL
COLD
VERY COLD
EXTREME COLD
ULTRA COLD
SUPPLEMENTAL KEY NOMENCLATURE
B - an. rf. below applicable formula value (t = an. temp.): when
.44(t-32) - 70% winter rain
.44(t-7) - 70% summer rain
.44(t-19.5) - approx. equal
BW - less than 1/2 f. v.
BS - more than 1/2 f. v.
h - an. temp. above 64
k - an. temp. below 64
k' - warmest mo. below 64
s - 70% rf. in winter
w - 70% rf. in summer
A - "f", rf. driest mo. at least 2.4"
m - rf. of driest month less than 2.4", but more than f.v.: .04(98.5 - annual rainfall)
w - ...less than f.v.
C-D - "f", humid year-round
s - rf. of rainiest month of winter at least 3x the driest month of summer; less than 1.6"
w - rf. of rainiest month of summer at least 10x the driest month of winter
c - less than four months above 50

Whereas the northern interior uplands supply commercially important lumber from stands of oak, hickory, maple, elm, tulip, and chestnut, the southern pine section with its predominant longleaf, shortleaf, and loblolly pines not only yields lumber products, but also turpentine and other resinous materials. These so-called "naval stores" products were very important in early days in calking seagoing vessels. The southern forests today supply two-thirds of the world's naval stores products. Dating back as far as President John Adams' administration, the exploitation of these resources incidentally provides one of the finest examples in progressive conservation of forest products. Such practices include substituting the new "cup and gutter" method of collecting sap for the old, life-shortening gash tapping; recovering considerable turpentine and rosin also from the "bleeding" of trees in forest thinning, from rotted pine stumps in clearings, from slashings in lumbering operations, and as by-products from paper-pulp manufacturing.

The leading lumbering states in the South today are Alabama, Georgia, North Carolina, followed closely by Texas, Mississippi, Louisiana, Arkansas, and Virginia. The western limit of the forest stand is approximately the 30-inch annual rainfall line. Ranking next to the Pacific coast area (*Cfb*), this section is a leading producer of pine (longleaf, slash) and other lumber and lumber products in the United States, credited with one-third of our annual nation's cut, and supplying also about one-half our wood pulp.

2. ***Australia.*** Sizable forest tracts skirt the coastal areas of southeast Australia, distinguished by the native eucalyptus consociation. Also, at the northern extremity, are notable patches of cypress and pine. The eucalyptus is an evergreen hardwood, most of whose 600 species and varieties are endemic to this island continent. Embracing both hardwood and softwood, the lumber from the many different varieties serves almost all types of construction needs; recent research has also perfected eucalyptus pulp and paper products.

XXV:4 (Left) This "butterfly" profile emphasizes fall maximum rainfall. How near does Tokyo come to being a *Cw* station?

3. ***Southeastern Africa.*** Subtropical to tropical in character, the forests here consist of a mixture of deciduous, semideciduous, and evergreen trees, the first associated with the winter-dry season of the northern section. Dominant species are generally lacking, largely confined in the *Cw* section to river courses, and, in the south, to the very narrow coastal strip hemmed in by the Drakensburg. These limited forest resources have been further depleted by the concentrated settlement of this region; native grazing and cultivation have also been a significant deforestation factor. The indigenous wattle tree has been an important commercial source for tannin products.

4. ***The Pampa-Paraná region.*** In a certain sense, this area is a "geographic anomaly" because, despite its moisture adequacy for the growing of forests, much of the area is largely an extensive grass prairie, interrupted only here and there by gallery forests along the streams and by occasional patches of small groves on the upland. Distinctive among the forest products here are the "Paraguay tea bush," *yerba maté,* source of the leading beverage in this part of South America. Another is the *quebracho*, the leading world source of tanning material, occurring mostly in the Gran Chaco. This most important forest resource of Paraguay is, however, seriously on the decline as a result of over-exploitation and forest fires.

5. ***Po Valley, Italy.*** Intensive pressure of crop culture in the Po Valley has resulted in an almost complete deforestation of the original hardwood forests. The desperate need of forest products, with the least possible competition for the even more needed crop culture, is reflected in a distinctive geographic vegetation pattern, the planting of fast-growing poplars and alders along canals and roadsides.

Farming versus forestry. This is a keynote principle of conflicting land utilization which has come down to us through the ages and which can only rationally be resolved by long-range planning, with due consideration being given to all the challenging aspects of the competing claims for best resource developments for any particular realm or region. As indicated above, the humid subtropics are not only characteristically timberlands, but their forest products have played, and still

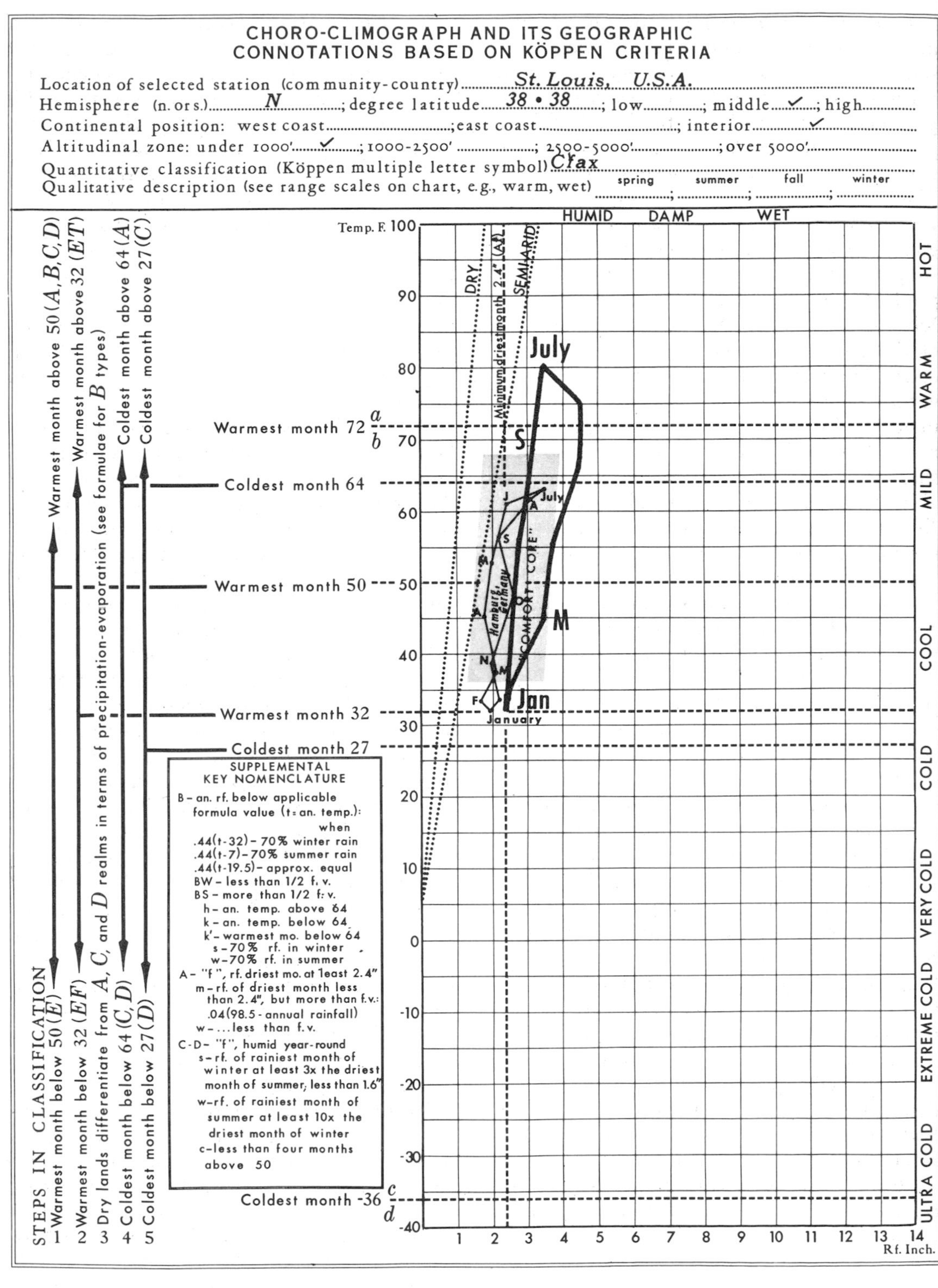

CHORO-CLIMOGRAPH AND ITS GEOGRAPHIC CONNOTATIONS BASED ON KÖPPEN CRITERIA
Location of selected station (community-country) St. Louis, U.S.A.
Hemisphere (n. or s.) N; degree latitude 38 • 38; low; middle ✓; high
Continental position: west coast; east coast; interior ✓
Altitudinal zone: under 1000' ✓; 1000-2500'; 2500-5000'; over 5000'
Quantitative classification (Köppen multiple letter symbol) Cfax
Qualitative description (see range scales on chart, e.g., warm, wet) spring; summer; fall; winter
HUMID
DAMP
WET
Temp. F.
DRY
Minimum driest month 2.4" (A&L)
SEMIARID
July
S
J
July
A
S
Hamburg, Germany
"COMFORT CORE"
O
M
N
M
F
Jan
January
HOT
WARM
MILD
COOL
COLD
VERY COLD
EXTREME COLD
ULTRA COLD
Rf. Inch.
Warmest month 72 a b
Coldest month 64
Warmest month 50
Warmest month 32
Coldest month 27
Coldest month -36 c d
Warmest month above 50 (A, B, C, D)
Warmest month above 32 (ET)
Coldest month above 64 (A)
Coldest month above 27 (C)
Dry lands differentiate from A, C, and D realms in terms of precipitation-evaporation (see formulae for B types)
STEPS IN CLASSIFICATION
1 Warmest month below 50 (E)
2 Warmest month below 32 (EF)
3 Dry lands differentiate from A, C, and D realms in terms of precipitation-evaporation (see formulae for B types)
4 Coldest month below 64 (C, D)
5 Coldest month below 27 (D)
SUPPLEMENTAL KEY NOMENCLATURE
B – an. rf. below applicable formula value (t = an. temp.): when
.44(t-32) – 70% winter rain
.44(t-7) – 70% summer rain
.44(t-19.5) – approx. equal
BW – less than 1/2 f. v.
BS – more than 1/2 f. v.
h – an. temp. above 64
k – an. temp. below 64
k' – warmest mo. below 64
s – 70% rf. in winter
w – 70% rf. in summer
A – "f", rf. driest mo. at least 2.4"
m – rf. of driest month less than 2.4", but more than f.v.: .04(98.5 - annual rainfall)
w – ...less than f.v.
C-D – "f", humid year-round
s – rf. of rainiest month of winter at least 3x the driest month of summer; less than 1.6"
w – rf. of rainiest month of summer at least 10x the driest month of winter
c – less than four months above 50

play, a major role in the economies of nearly all regions of the *Cf–Cw* world. But, as has been noted, many sections, as a result of increasing population, face a distribution food-producing problem, as in over-populated countries—Japan, China, India, and even sections of southern Europe. Increasing croplands in such areas are needed, despite the usefulness of forest resources. The other alternative is the importation of food, paid for in part perhaps by the export of forest products. Encroachments on timber lands elsewhere, as in our own South, result from the proliferation of highway construction, increased urbanization, and various types of industrial and commercial developments. But in this case, large-scale farm abandonments have led in some instances to a natural pasture-forest reversion and in others to extensive pine plantings, together more than offsetting the losses earlier experienced by excessive lumbering.

A sound forestry management program is clearly needed for all these countries of indigenous forest cover, if for no other reason than soil conservation, since, as pointed out elsewhere, a considerable proportion of the *Cf–Cw* lands are in too great relief to prevent erosion on tilled slopes.

Subtropical agriculture viewed in world perspective

The humid subtropics represent truly a mosaic of the greatest number of diverse types of agriculture in the world. This results from a complex set of factors: the latitudinal position which permits a growing season from approximately seven months on the poleward to eleven months on the equatorward side; the diverse landforms which range from extensive low-lying plains (the Pampas and the Gulf and Atlantic coastal plains), mostly below 500 feet elevation to extensive plateaus (Great Central Plateau of south central Africa, which rises between 2,000 to 5,000 feet) and rugged hill and mountain country, reaching altitudes of over 5,000 feet (western China). Here also is a great diversity in vegetation—deciduous, semideciduous, and evergreen forests; broadleaf trees as well as needleleaf trees in varied combinations; prairie and other grasses, herbs, and shrubs.

The widely varying regional combinations of soils, resulting from diversity of climate, relief, vegetative cover, parent material, and variant fertility, do not lend themselves in this brief context to meaningful soil descriptions and technical evaluations as to soil fertility and adaptability to various crops. Let it suffice here to point out a few broad geographic correlations of environmentally-related features dominant in several major regions:

The red-yellow podsolic soil is the dominant type in the American and Japanese sectors. Developed under conifer or mixed conifer and deciduous forests, and hence low in humus, and profiled under humid, largely unfrozen, ground conditions, this type, like most types in this latitude, is heavily leached and acid, with a general rating of from moderate to low fertility.

Probably the next single major area types are the complex mountain soils, including the imperfectly weathered stony lithosols, podsolic in the western part of China and lateritic in the eastern part. As they are commonly developed under considerable relief, the profile is generally poorly developed, if at all; the soils, except in the valleys, are apt to be thin, stony, and of low productivity. This is the broad regional aspect. Of course, in any rugged country, like this section, depositional alluvium on the lower slopes and on the valley floors is prized for its fertility and ease of cultivation.

Collectively continent-wise, the reddish brown soils have the greatest realm spread. Developed in large part under a cover of mixed grasses, these soils are high in humus, and, since they occur under much less humid conditions than those mentioned above, they are only moderately or slightly leached, and hence exhibit calcareous accumulations in relatively shallow horizons on the soil profile. Natural drainage is good, and soil fertility relatively high. The western Pampa, southeastern Africa, and southeastern Australia share in this type.

XXV:5 (Left) What does "x" signify? How is it related to flooded Mississippi and Ohio valleys? According to the chart, which end of the climatic axis is farthest from the "comfort core"?

Where suitable drainage topography obtains, the alluvial type, with its repeatedly renewed mineral and organic material, excels in productivity, as featured along the lower Mississippi flood plain and the Paraná River area.

Topographically, the largest contiguous areas of tillable land occur in the Americas, where coincidentally obtains also the largest area of humus-enriched prairie soils.

If we add to these diverse natural soil-forming factors the contrasting regional conditions of population densities and varied cultures, as already pointed out, it becomes readily understandable that practically every one of the world's major agricultural regions, as mapped and described by Derwent Whittlesey, is here represented. Only two of the thirteen classes (nomadic herding and Mediterranean agriculture) are absent. Thus intensive subsistence tillage is recognized, with rice dominant, characteristic of China and the Ganges Plain in India, with intervening sectors of rudimental sedentary tillage and shifting cultivation. In southeastern United States, the dominant types are: commercial livestock and crop farming with plantation agriculture centered on the lower Mississippi, and specialized horticulture forming a narrow strip along the Gulf and Atlantic coasts. The Pampa and the Paraná regions feature livestock ranching and crop farming, grain or cotton dominant. Southeast Africa and southeast Australia likewise feature livestock ranching, with additional sectors of commercial livestock and crop farming respectively, the latter also featuring commercial dairy farming and specialized horticulture along the immediate coast. Dairy farming is fairly co-extensive with the Po Valley of Italy. Subsistence crop and livestock farming occurs in south central *Cw* Mexico, in the *Cfa* Balkans, and southeastern Africa. Shifting cultivation dominates a very large part of the south central plateau of Africa.

Since this is the first realm with major commercial agricultural production as well as subsistence agriculture, it may seem proper at this point to examine a broad generalized classification, such as is presented by Whittlesey. Attention is directed to this classification not simply to alert the student to its categories, but rather to note the regionally differentiated man–land relationships—the essense of modern geography. The "functioning forms" which Whittlesey recognizes as applying to every type of agriculture are: (1) the type of crop and livestock association; (2) methods of farming; (3) intensive as compared to extensive agriculture; (4) subsistence or commercial production; (5) the types of farmsteads. This classification is intended to be primarily exploratory, subject to further refinements or other revisions. To use Whittlesey's own words, "The classification is largely empirical and qualitative." Thirteen types of agricultural regions are recognized, (See map, pp. 266-7.) of which eleven occur in one form or another, and in one place or another, in the humid subtropics. A number of them also occur in other realms. Only brief excerpts can here be given for the identification of these several types. Major *Cfa-Cwa* regions inclusive of these types and representative of them are indicated in parentheses:

1. Livestock ranching (Pampa; South Africa; Eastern Australia).

¶ The livestock ranch is semisedentary. The ranch house forms a permanent center, where a good deal of capital is fixed in the shape of dipping vats, shearing sheds, and paddocks—facilities calculated to maintain the high quality of the products and to expedite their shipment. Usually the ranch is fenced, a refinement over the pioneer days of the open range. Some land may be tilled to raise forage for winter feeding in cool regions, or against the day of drought. . . . Each region tends to specialize on the animal and the product for which it is best fitted. . . . Livestock ranching is likely to be the mode of occupying an expanding frontier.[1]

2. Shifting cultivation (South Central Plateau; Africa). Though primarily a tropical condition (*A*) due to the heavy year-round rains and the resultant impoverishment of the soil from heavy leaching, this type also extends from *Af* through *Aw* into *Cw* regions, thus into the subtropics as shown on Whittlesey's map.

¶ Tillage is crude, fire being used to clear the ground, with some assistance from hand tools. Many tribes make sticks serve as plows and root

[1] Whittlesey, Derwent, "Major Agricultural Regions of the Earth," *Annals of the Association of American Geographers*, Vol. XXVI, 1936, pp. 199-240, *passim*. Reprinted by permission.

up the plants by way of harvesting them. The return is inevitably very low, and food shortage is common toward the end of the growing period, after the old crop is consumed, and before the new one is ready for gathering.[1]

3. Rudimental sedentary tillage (Northern Burma).

¶ Here and there in regions of shifting cultivation are areas where the inhabitants remain permanently, unless some catastrophe sets them wandering. Some of these districts of rudimental sedentary tillage have become rather densely populated because of special environmental conditions. Such places are likely to be small islands, mountain valleys, and districts where the soil and the climate are favorable above the average.[2]

Conspicuous is the area of this type shown between South China and India. . . .

¶ Where the season is long enough for paddy rice to mature, the highly intensive agricultural system supports the densest rural population found over large areas anywhere on earth. Although three sorts of crops are associated with three types of farmland, the key to this mode of land occupance is the paddy—irrigable deltas, floodplains, coastal plains, and terraces planted to rice.[3]

4. Intensive subsistence tillage with rice dominant (Southern Japan; China; East India).

¶ Rice yields more grain per acre than any other crop. Land out of reach of irrigation, but not too rough, is devoted to varied crops, chiefly grains, oil-seeds, and cotton. Hillslopes too steep to till are planted to trees—mulberry, tea, pepper, and others. . . . All the work is done by hand, except plowing the paddies. . . . It is doubtful if the introduction of farm machinery would increase production. . . . In spite of indefatigable labor, per capita production is not high and the people are abjectly poor. They live in close-set and close-packed villages.[4]

5. Intensive subsistence tillage without patty rice (Northwestern India).

¶ In regions which neighbor the rice country, that crop is ruled out by either lack of moisture or a short growing season, and a good deal of land is out of service during part of the year. These handicaps modify the agricultural system in subtle but profound ways. For the dominant rice, several cereals are substituted, none of them so productive of grain.[5]

6. Commercial plantation crop tillage (United States South).

¶ Nearly every bit of the cash crop is sold outside the region of production, and most of it moves to the middle latitudes. The capital required to develop the business comes from Europe or North America. . . . The plantation is a device to procure in desired quantities and of a standard quality, commodities which cannot be produced in middle latitudes.[6]

7. Commercial grain farming (Pampa; Southeastern Australia).

¶ More than any other type of agriculture, commercial grain farming is the creature of the Industrial Revolution. It has no prototypes and does not antedate the day of the self-scouring steel plow and harvesting machinery, inventions of the 1830's. . . . The crop and stock association is simple and standardized. Wheat is the cash crop, with flax or barley subsidiary at times and in places. . . . Huge acreage separates each farmer from his neighbor's and from town. Towns have a smaller ratio of residences to commercial buildings than in any other landscape.[7]

8. Commercial livestock and crop farming (U.S. South; Southern Brazil; Southeastern Africa).

¶ This mode of agriculture, often called "mixed farming," displays maximum diversity in detail amid essential uniformity in outline. . . . Where the climate is warm enough, wheat, maize, and oats are the principal grains. . . . Hogs and cattle and poultry predominate, with horses, mules, or oxen for draft. . . . Methods include the employment of much machinery.[8]

---

1 *Ibid.* Reprinted by permission.
2 *Ibid.* Reprinted by permission.
3 *Ibid.* Reprinted by permission.
4 *Ibid.* Reprinted by permission.
5 *Ibid.* Reprinted by permission.
6 *Ibid.* Reprinted by permission.
7 *Ibid.* Reprinted by permission.
8 *Ibid.* Reprinted by permission.

9. Subsistence crop and stock farming (Southern Mexico; Balkans).

¶ The farmer produces for his own sustenance and sells little or nothing. Having no cash income he cannot buy expensive machinery nor can he save the best seed from his fields or buy breeding stock. His return is correspondingly low, and he cannot market his rare surpluses in competition with the high-grade and reliable output of commercial regions. Lacking the stimulus of a competitive market, methods are crude.[1]

10. Commercial dairy farming (Po Valley, Italy; Southeastern Coastal Australia).

¶ Commercial dairying pays only where the products can be sold to an urban market. . . . The dairy business is elaborately mechanized, and the capital investment in housing and equipment on high-grade dairy farms exceeds that in any other type of agriculture. Holdings average larger than in adjacent stock and crop farm regions because hay is an extensive crop and there is a good deal of pasture besides, some of it wooded and of low carrying capacity. . . . The return of successful dairy farming is high.[2]

11. Specialized horticulture (Gulf–Atlantic seaboard).

¶ . . . fruit and vegetable growing, if on a large scale, is specialized on exceptionally favored spots. . . . Demand is satisfied in part by market gardens within a few hours trucking of populous cities. There, on the types of land which favor early harvest, intensive labor and consummate skill are devoted to raising the maximum of crops on the minimum of acres. . . . The value of market garden land averages higher per acre than that devoted to any other sort of farming. The crops are vegetables and bush fruits. . . . Farther from the city market, in belts progressing into warmer climates, extend districts of truck farming. Lacking the market garden's advantage of nearness to market, truck farms make up for it by exceptionally favorable soil and by climate, which matures the desired crops earlier than in their competitors' suburban gardens.[3]

---

[1] *Ibid.* Reprinted by permission.

[2] *Ibid.* Reprinted by permission.

[3] *Ibid.* Reprinted by permission.

The diversified agricultural patterns in systematic-regional perspective

1. Oriental muscle compared to occidental machine culture. We have already noted, as you will recall, the dense populations identified with the *Aw* southeastern Asia. Densities become even more pronounced in the neighboring *Cf* and *Cw* areas to the north. Accordingly, the increase in pressure on these lands leads still further to intensification of agriculture. This is perhaps most conspicuously seen by the traveler in the extensive terracing of long slopes as found alike in Japan, China, Thailand, and India.

Conspicuous also are the urban-like densities of population in rural areas, particularly along rivers and in the wetter areas where rice patty irrigation is carried on. It is inconceivable to the Westerner how the Oriental farmer and his family can eke out an existence where acreages generally run under five, and many under three, per family. Compare this with 60 in Great Britain and a quarter section (160) in the United States. Even more startlingly significant is the estimated arable land disparity—1,500 persons per square mile in China; 100 in the United States. Areal arability in China, as in southern Japan, is commonly less than 10-20 per cent. It is knowledge of such geographic concepts as the above which enable one to understand why communism has thrived in China.

It becomes obvious at once that the most intensive and adaptive farm methods are required to utilize the soil resources to the best possible capacity and advantage. The type of agriculture in most cases will be essentially of the subsistence or self-sufficient type—a sort of garden agriculture. Moreover, farms in many areas are fragmented, so that in cultivating his land a farmer has to move from one parcel to another over plots held by other farmers. Every now and then an observer from the West suggests that famine problems in the Orient might be corrected or mitigated if modern agricultural methods, including mechanization, were introduced into these areas. It should be apparent from this garden-type of culture and the surplus labor available, that there could be neither much economy nor efficiency gained by such a practice. Large machinery operations, moreover, would be difficult and impractical in the numerous diked rice-paddies whose irrigation demands the most meticulous care in the distribution of water.

Another concomitant feature of population support in such densely-populated areas is the growing of such subsistence crops as will yield the highest calorie units per acre; rice excels all other cereals in this respect. Moreover, rice cultivation lends itself well to the primitive type of "hoe culture" as distinguished from the mechanized agriculture of the West. It also fits well in multiple-cropping where the growing season is sufficiently long, as in the southern part, and where irrigation waters are available during the dry season. Rice is also, of course, climatically better adapted to the subtropics than are other cereals. Since irrigated rice is planted in water normally about six inches deep, the poorly-drained areas unsuited for other cereals or even other crops may be excellently adapted for rice. Patty rice culture calls not only for a lot of arduous labor and individual responsibility, but also for a form of community co-operativeness as well in order to fully realize the agricultural potential based on irrigation.

Another aspect of intensification of agricultural productivity is reflected in the amount or kind of fertilization of the soil. Practically every conceivable form of fertilizer known to mankind finds application here in one form or another—human as well as animal excreta; vegetable refuse of all types; nitrogen fixed by legumes. Kelp and other sea algae are recovered from the sea by the Japanese and coastal Chinese to reclaim the precious potash found in such marine forms.

Keeping in mind that the winters in the humid subtropics are extremely mild, there is virtually an eleven-month growing season on the equatorward margin, sufficiently warm to grow winter as well as summer crops. Since winter, however, is the dry season, the primary adapted crops are such cereals as wheat and barley. In summer, rice is supplemented by a great variety of vegetables plus soybeans, maize, sugar cane, and sweet potatoes.

Since more calories of food per acre are derived from a vegetal than an animal culture, very few beef and dairy cattle are reared in the Orient. Moreover, religious taboo in some sections against meat eating is another factor; such animals as farmers feel they can afford are primarily draft animals or beasts of burden. The primary vegetable diet is supplemented wherever possible by fish, and fishing on a transoceanic scale has been pushed by the Japanese into the territorial waters of several protesting countries. In lands where the demand for the support of population is so great, food imports rather than exports would be expected; but a few agricultural products from these areas do enter foreign trade, such as tea and raw silk, the latter being the product of the cocoon of the silk worm, whose food is mulberry leaves. Both these products are not only climatologically but also topographically well adapted to southeastern Asia, since most of the region of China is in considerable slope, as is also true of Japan.

2. ***Occidental culture.*** Quite different from the above is the agricultural pattern of the West. An Oriental visiting southeastern United States would probably be impressed by the great empty spaces in the rural country side—the wide unproductive strips along our railroad right-of-ways, the broad unused borders along our highways, the enormous fallow farm fields—acreage which under intense cultivation would go a long way to relieve famines in his country. He would also be impressed by the extensive and specialized crop farms studded with all kinds of agricultural implements and fenced-in fields with large herds of both dairy and beef cattle. He would immediately recognize, too, that not all the vegetal and animal food produced in the area could possibly be consumed by local farmers. Besides realizing the fact that in practically every crop specialty there is a large surplus not only for domestic shipments but also for exports abroad, he will observe also land lying idle, not primarily because of poor soil or fallow fields, but as a result of an over-supply of agricultural products. Thus, it would seem incredible as well as probably most disconcerting to him to know that in our country we have to worry about having too much, rather than too little, agricultural production.

Also, unlike the agricultural pattern of the Orient, the humid subtropic United States, the United States South, comprises three ma-

Table 25.1. Market periods for fresh vegetables for the six months, January to June, and the relative order of the supply from localities and from different types of soil in each locality.

Locality	*First period*	*Second period*	*Third period*	*Fourth period*	*Fifth period*	*Sixth period*
Long Island						Sand
Maryland and Delaware					Sand	Fine sand
Virginia				Sand	Fine sand	Sandy loam
North Carolina			Sand	Fine sand	Sandy loam	Fine sandy loam
South Carolina		Sand	Fine sand	Sandy loam	Fine sandy loam	Loam
Georgia and Florida	Sand	Fine sand	Sandy loam	Fine sandy loam	Loam	Silt loam

SOURCE: Colby, Charles C., *Source Book for the Economic Geography of North America,* The University of Chicago Press, 1926, pp. 249. Reprinted by permission.

jor subtypes of agricultural regions–the Winter Wheat Belt in the north, the Cotton Belt south of the 185-day frost free season (discussed in the introductory chorogram), and the horticulture and vegetable belt fringing the Gulf and Atlantic Coast. Corn is grown extensively throughout the South not only for animal feeding but also locally for human consumption. With the diversification of crop culture, accompanied by an increasing production of forage crops, particularly legumes (soybeans), cattle have assumed an increasing importance in the economy of the South. Other crops include peanuts, tobacco, and the great variety of fruits and vegetables seen in our markets.

The geographic relationship of latitude, season, and soil texture to the production of vegetables for the commercial market is well illustrated in the above table prepared by Colby.

As will be noted in this table, two chief environmental relationships stand out — the production progression from January (Florida) to June (Long Island), and the periodic shifting of local cultivation from the light, well-drained, and easily warmed sandy soils to the heavier loams of later, more substantial productivity. Favored, in addition to the seasonal and soil spread, by the ameliorating winter influence of the Gulf and by the facile Atlantic Coastal Plain trucking, the South has come to have an "early season" near monopoly of daily-delivered fresh vegetables to the major consuming centers of the East and the Midwest.

Tobacco culture is popularly associated regionally with cotton culture in its climatic restrictions. This erroneous view probably arose from the fact that our major tobacco producing areas are in the South—the Carolinas, Virginia, and Kentucky. But its world latitudinal spread extends from the Equator to the 50 degree parallels (into *D* climes). Despite this wide climatic tolerance, however, the sections which lead in world commercial production—that just indicated for the United States and China—are part of the *Cfa–Cwa* category. A "cosmopolitan" crop, in area production and consumption, its culture fits well into the regional diversity of soils which are materially responsible for the diversity of leaf quality. It is also well adapted to the more densely populated areas of the world where labor is plentiful and cheap to meet the exacting demands of intensified tillage and laborious manipulations in curing, grading, and packaging of the product.

The Southern Hemisphere humid subtropical sections, in contrast with those of the Northern Hemisphere areas, are primarily in the earlier geographic stages of settlement with limited regional commercial specialties.

Isolated Australia combines a self-sufficient and commercial agricultural economy with a diversified agriculture similar to that of southeastern United States, but with greater emphasis on the production of beef and dairy cattle. Some tropical and subtropical fruits as well as sugar cane constitute cash crops, a number of fruits being exported.

The agricultural pattern of southeastern Africa is mostly of the subsistence and self-sufficient type, with corn as the leading staple for the dark native and with some commercial emphasis on sugar cane, pineapples, citrus and other fruits. The interior *Cw* plateau region has the most primitive, isolated, and shifting type of agriculture of any of the humid subtropics, this being primarily a pastoral economy in its first stage of occupance, with very little cultivated crop culture.

Ranching, as a dominant form of agriculture, is particularly well developed in southeastern South America. On the extensive natural and planted pastures of this region (Argentina, Uruguay, southern Brazil, and Paraguay) forage large herds of beef cattle and sheep. In addition, large areas are devoted to the growing of wheat, corn, and flax for seed. The region produces not only sufficient amounts of these crops for domestic consumption but also large surpluses for export.

The highland junction of the *Cf–Cw* with the *Af–Aw* in the Tropic of Capricorn São Paulo region is the world's prime area of commercial coffee production. Though the most prominent single commercially productive area is now to be found in the *C* landscape, the cultivation of the coffee bean as a "tropical" product has its widest latitudinal spread in the *A* realm, and its culture was, therefore, described under that category (see Chapter 22).

Case studies of contrasted occidental and oriental cultures

1. Extensive agriculture as exemplified by the Argentine Pampa. The Pampa (Spanish for plain) is not only the most distinguished plain of South America physiographically and economically but also a leader among the agricultural regions of the world in the production of grain and meat for export. With such a distinctive ranking the region deserves more than passing attention. In reading the following brief description and appraisal of the area, the student should be particularly alert to the contrasting commercial relations of this region to Europe and to the United States, keeping particularly in mind the fact that the United States itself is a surplus producer and exporter of grain and meat products and the fact that the Pampa enjoys the commercial advantage of seacoast proximity and hence reduced costs in marketing its products abroad.

¶ To Argentina in particular and to many consuming lands, the Pampa is of supreme importance. The statement "the Pampa is Argentina" has much truth, for the great eastern plain furnishes the major part of the 50[1] per cent of the world's exports of flaxseed which the country ships, the 45 per cent of the corn, the 15 per cent of the wheat and wheat flour, the 28 per cent of the hides and skins, the 30 per cent of the total meat and meat products, and the 50 per cent of the beef and its products. Upon this vast expanse of productive plains, the highly developed industrial regions of northwestern Europe have become increasingly dependent. Moreover, the ease of production and proximity to these send huge quantities of rawstuffs to the United States. As yet this area of approximately 250,000 square miles of the best agricultural land in South America has reached only a primary stage in its economic development, so that for the future the Pampa constitutes a veritable granary for the world.[2]

Now let us take a fleeting airplane view of this landscape. Reconnaissance flights have a great advantage of not only covering large areas in a short period of time but of permitting one to see both the physical and cultural elements of the landscape in broad aerial perspectives not possible by ground travel, a distinct aid in geographic research. Such facility of studying land–life geographic relationships is excellently portrayed in the photographic aerial traverses by John Rich.

¶ The air-line route from Buenos Aires about 400 miles to Cordobá traverses one of the best

---

[1] The percentage figures in this paragraph have been changed to those for recent years.

[2] Jones, Clarence F., *South America*, Henry Holt & Co., Inc., New York, 1947, p. 370. Reprinted by permission.

A

B

parts of the famous Argentine Pampa, where rainfall, though somewhat undependable, is adequate for the growing of corn, wheat, flax, alfalfa, and similar crops. . . . Some 35 miles from Buenos Aires [see facing page], shows a typical landscape. The land is flat and generally unmodified by erosion, although the larger streams . . . have entrenched themselves slightly, and their tributaries are beginning to cut shallow troughs in the plain, like the one crossing the center of the picture. A railroad (lower left to upper right), well graded roads, and scattered farm homes, generally surrounded by a windbreak of trees, constitute a cultural landscape very similar to that of central United States. . . . The greater part of the land in this region is utilized as pasture. Corn appeared to rank second in areal importance followed by wheat, and perhaps also flax. . . . Another view of the Pampa [Photograph B], about 75 miles northwest of Buenos Aires, shows a smooth plain devoted about equally to pasture and to grain. In the center is a typical small railroad town (Duggan), and in the left background what is probably a large cattle hacienda. The identity of the latter is suggested by the large contiguous area devoted to pasture, the groves of trees in distinctive patterns, and the lack of scattered farm homes.[1]

In reading the above sketch the student should be instructively cognizant of those elements of the landscape which can be definitely seen, and those which may reasonably be inferred, as well as such data as are lacking and must be secured from ground mapping, personal interviews, consulting government statistics and the like, if he is to have a complete geographic analysis and evaluation.

2. *Intensive agriculture as exemplified by the Chinese Szechwan Province.* The combination of air photography and detailed field mapping is well illustrated in the accompanying figures on the Province of Szechwan in China. This region was selected to represent high densities of population and intensity of agriculture in the Orient contrasting with the sparsity of population and extensive agriculture of the Pampa. And to pursue our quest for landscape interpretations a bit further, the student is asked to analyze carefully the airplane view (turn to page 544) and the two field sketches (Figure XXV-6 and Figure XXV-7). Before consulting any textual material, try to determine from these visual aids alone the settlement and occupance patterns typical of this area. It would be well in cases like this to check first of all the regional setting on a good relief map. In what manner do any of the figures suggest density of population? How is the settlement pattern revealed? How does the crop pattern reflect the seasonal rainfall regimen of the *Cw*? How are contrasted land surface patterns revealed by the crop culture? What mapped phenomenon indicates a rather unique sociological institution? From the study of figures alone, what would be your tentative conclusion on the food situation? If there is a problem of sustenance, would you say this results from submarginal productivity of the area or from overpopulation?

Now let us fill in the picture to test your tentative evaluations. You will probably have noted on the relief map that the Szechwan Province has elevations commonly rising about 2,000 feet but is dissected by a number of valleys of sufficient low elevations—between 500 and 1,000 feet—to suggest good tillage sites. Prominence of the four streams forming the headwaters of the Yangtze Kiang has suggested the name Szechwan, meaning "four rivers." The following data are quoted from Jen's article to aid us in understanding the two figures quoted above:

¶ ***Chinese Chengtu Plain.*** Chengtu Plain is the richest part of Szechwan Province and one of the most intensively cultivated areas of all China. . . . In the centre of the plain . . . about 75 per cent of the total area is cultivated. That the index of cultivation is not higher is because large areas are occupied by villages and irrigation channels which are especially numerous in the plain. But intensity of land use is clearly shown by the fact that there is practically no waste

[1] Rich, John, *The Face of South America, and an Aerial Traverse*, American Geographical Society, Special Publication No. 26, 1942, pp. 131-132. Reprinted by permission.

(Left) Photos "A" and "B" are of pastoral landscapes northwest of Buenos Aires, briefly described in the text. See if you can identify the features there described. (Courtesy American Geographical Society)

This air view shows Chinese field culture in Szechwan Province. Compare the landscape features here shown with those illustrated cartographically in Figures XXV:6 and XXV:7. What phenomena do they show in common? On the basis of this air-view alone, what land-use concepts are you able to formulate? Point to the comparative advantages and disadvantages of photos and maps in depicting and interpreting such landscape features as are here shown. (U. S. Army Force)

land in the plain [Figure XXV-6]. Detailed field survey by L. P. Yang and others gives the following figures:

Uses		Percentages
Cultivated area		75
patty field	72	
Dry field	3	
Towns and villages		15
Channels and roads		8
Graves and others		2

Here, thanks to the well-managed irrigation system, 95 per cent of the cultivated land is paddy field, which after the summer major crop of rice is capable of producing another crop in the winter. While rapeseed and wheat form principal winter crops, vetch, often plowed under as green manure, is also important . . . two fully reliable crops may be produced from paddy fields. This accounts for the richness of the Chengtu Plain.

The agricultural landscape is dominated by irrigation channels which run straight and wide across the verdant plain.

Towards edges of the plain, low hills about 50-100 m. high rise here and there. . . . The hillocks are equally laboriously cultivated, but chiefly for dry crops instead of rice. As a result, although index of cultivation is still high amounting to 65 per cent, the dominance of dry fields produces a totally different landscape from neighboring Chengtu Plain.

According to L. P. Yang and others, land use

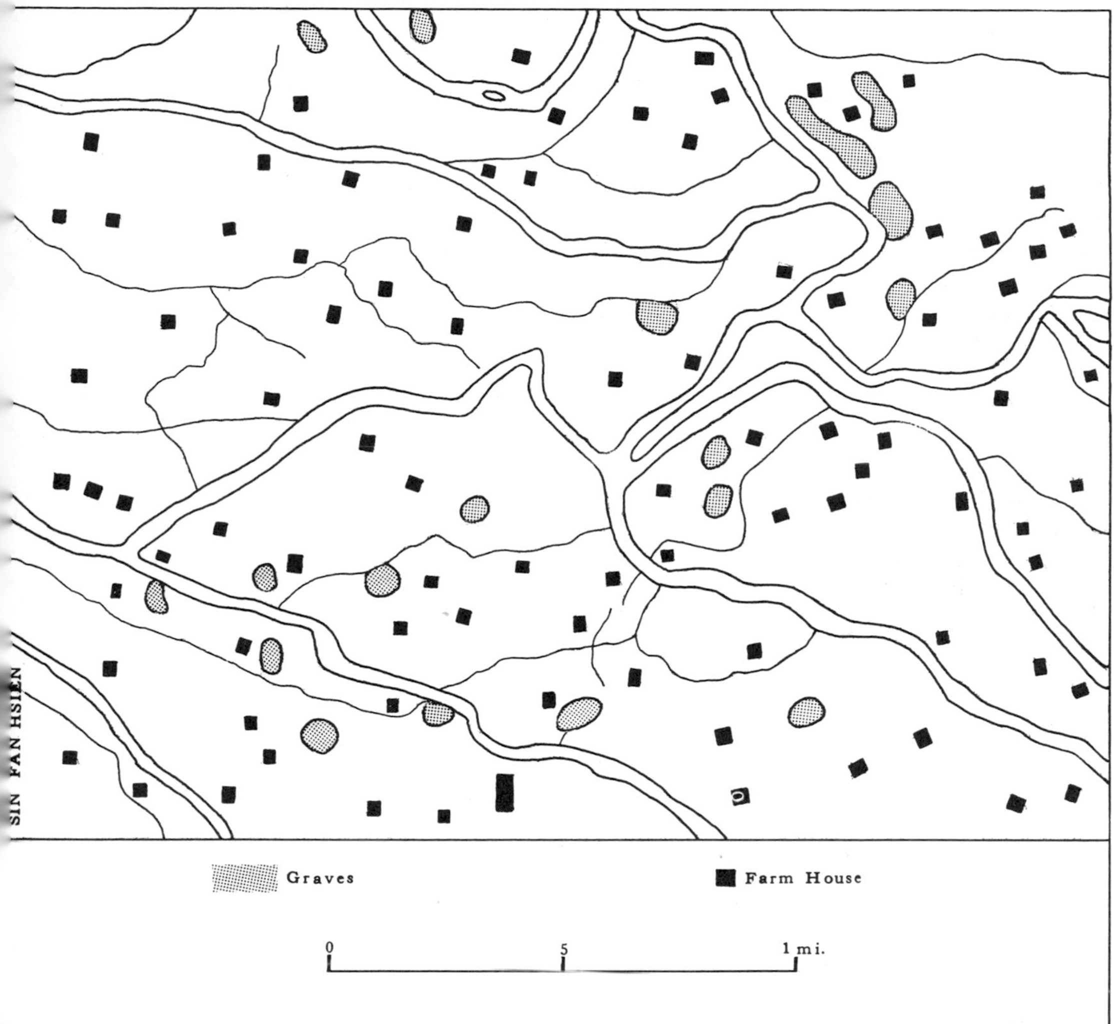

XXV:6 This map shows an irrigated patty field on the Chengtu Plain in southwestern China. Among the most intensely cultivated areas in China, all the land shown here not occupied by farm houses and grave sites is devoted to patty cultivation. (After Yang and others, in "Agricultural Landscape of Southwestern China: A Study in Land Utilization," by Mei-Ngo Jen, published in *Economic Geography,* Vol. XXIV, No. 3, July, 1948)

in the hilly area of Chengtu Plain is distributed in the following percentages:

Uses		Percentages
Cultivated area		65
Patty field	20	
Dry field	45	
Woodland		7
Towns and villages		12
Ponds, roads and channels		8
Graves		1
Waste land		7

Owing to higher location and greater distance from the centre of Chengtu Plain, most paddy fields in the region can hardly be benefited by the Tukiangyen irrigation system; they have to depend on uncertain water supply from rainfall (rain-fed fields) or artificial ponds which are extremely numerous on some hillocks [Figure XXV-7]. Consequently, the paddy fields are lower in yield and incapable of raising winter crops. In dry fields, two crops are generally harvested in a year, wheat and rapeseed as principal winter crops, and maize the most important summer crop.

Diversity of productiveness of the land is readily reflected in density of population, which is roughly arranged in concentric zones, being highest in the centre, with 672 inhabitants per sq. km., but gradually getting lower and lower toward the edge where there are only 258 people per sq. km. In the centre of the plain, as the index of cultivation amounts to 75 per cent, density of population per sq. km. of cultivated land (i.e., nutrition density) reaches 900. However, since some 40 per cent of the population lives in towns, density of rural population is only 400 per sq. km. and the corresponding figure for nutrition density about 530 per sq. km.[1]

Contrasted population patterns and subsistence standards

One and a quarter billions, or half the population of the earth, live in the humid subtropics, with the largest areas of highest concentration in the Orient. Thus, over half of subtropical China has a density of over 250 per square mile, the rest falling only slightly under this figure. The higher density figures are in the thousands. *Cw* India, mostly along the Brahmaputra and the Ganges rivers, averages generally much above 250. Another part of the world which approaches the 250 density category or above is the Po Valley of Italy with its intensive agriculture and extensive manufacturing. Somewhat lesser concentrations occur in the northeastern extremity of the *Cfa* section of the United States, which has a similar combined rural and urban economy. Similar population patterns and densities occur in *Cf* South America centered upon the Buenos Aires region and, to a somewhat lesser extent, in the *Cw* section of Mexico — about Mexico, D.F. Except for the immediate vicinity of relatively large urban communities of southeastern Africa and eastern Australia, sizable areas here average mostly 20-50 per square mile. A similar density obtains for the greater part of our South, with concentration along the major rivers and manufacturing centers where the population in sizable areas may rise to 100 or more.

The *Cw* areas of Africa and South America average generally under 20, with sizable areas in the latter where as few as only one or two persons may be found. Thus, the humid subtropics present great regional contrasts in densities of population. This is a most important factor in regional human geography, alerting the student of geography to other elements in the environment besides climate which must be considered in correlating and evaluating settlements and sustenance.

The great disparity between occidental and oriental densities is related to length of settlement of regions and differences in race and type of culture as well as to regional differences in the physical characteristics of the landscapes. In the Old World the ancient settlements of China and India are built primarily on muscle horsepower, rather than machine horsepower, which dominates Western culture. The people live primarily on a vegetable diet; in the Americas, meat is almost a regular item in the average menu. This in turn reflects a much higher standard of living in the Western world.

In the humid subtropics, hundreds of millions of people live on a substandard diet and periodically experience famine. Under these circumstances one would greet his Oriental friend not by our conventional "How do you do?" but by "Have you eaten?", or "Have you had your rice to-day?"— much more environmentally meaningful salutations, you see.

The Westerner not uncommonly looks upon the hardships of the Oriental as of his own making and accordingly regards his culture with disdain. Priding himself on his own "know-how," the American frequently underrates, or even overlooks entirely, the role that the environment plays in the situation. The history that he has been taught probably reminds him of our great Western European

XXV:7 (Right) These are patty field types in a hilly district, east of Chengtu City. Note the preponderance of dry fields and ponds for water storage. (After Yang and others, in "Agricultural Landscape of Southwestern China: A Study in Land Utilization," by Mei-Ngo Jen, published in *Economic Geography*, Vol. XXIV, No. 3, July, 1948)

---

[1] Jen, Mei-Ngo, "Agricultural Landscape of Southwestern China: A Study in Land Utilization," *Economic Geography*, Vol. XXIV, No. 3, July, 1948, pp. 159-161. Reprinted by permission.

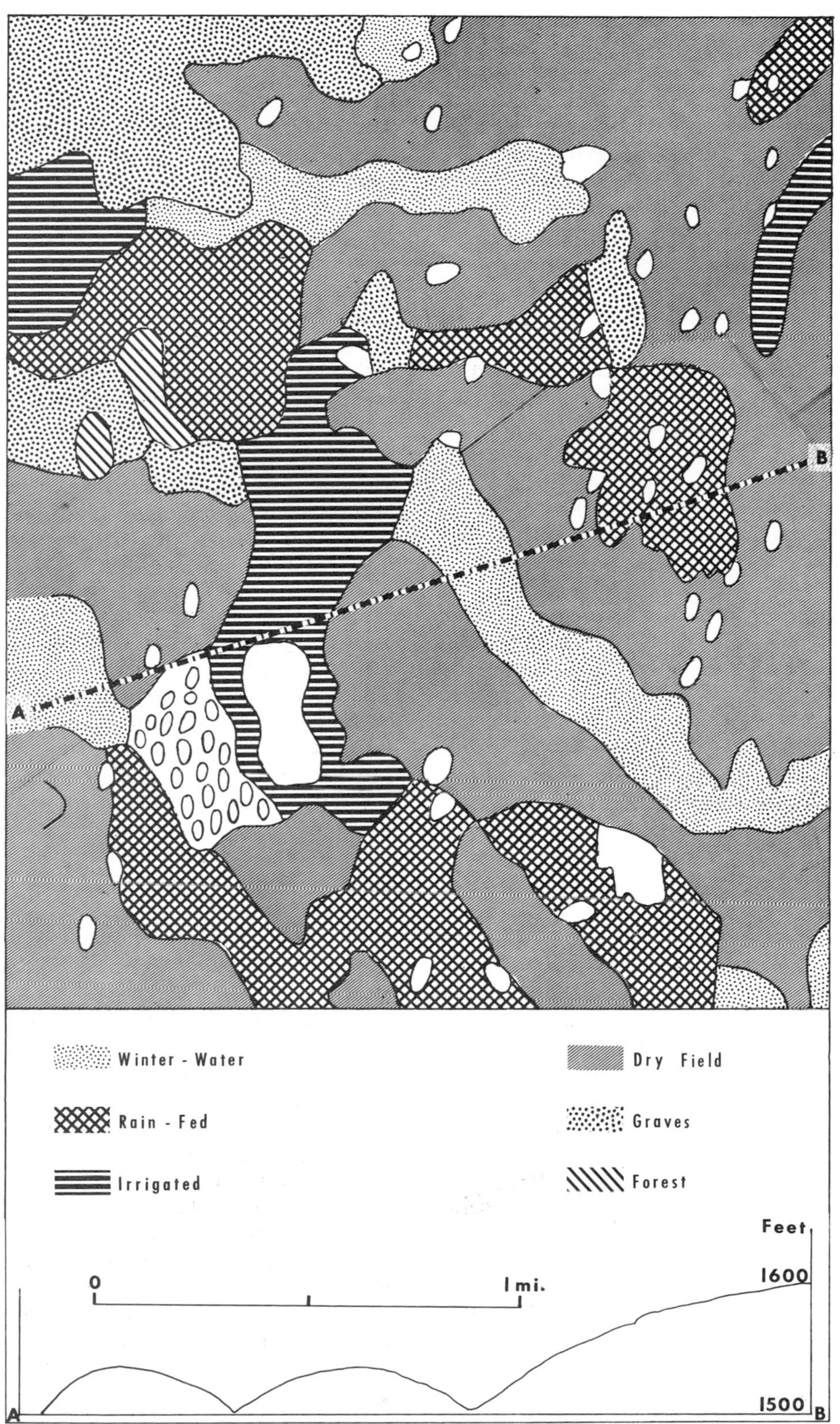

B
A
Winter - Water
Rain - Fed
Irrigated
Dry Field
Graves
Forest
Feet
0
1 mi.
1600
1500
A
B

cultural heritages transplanted to Colonial America (our *Cfa-Cfb* seaboard region)—the resourcefulness of our inventors, the forging ahead of industry and commerce, the aspirations of our "heroes" in religious, educational, and political movements. All these are well and good, because no country can progress without such movements and leadership. But one must not overlook in all such appraisals of human values and achievements that despite some local environmental hardships experienced by the first pioneer colonials, they did not have to contend with *Cw* region-wide regular summer-floods and winter-droughts. The colonial farmer did not have to climb, hoe in hand, the precipitous slopes of hill and mountain lands. He was not compelled to terrace and dike these slopes, or risk the crop-destroying inundations of far-flung flood plains. His "agronomists" were not pressed for experiences to show him how to feed a family of ten or a dozen on 2 to 3 acres of tilled soil. When the American cotton, and especially the tobacco, planter experienced declining yields, all he had to do was to move to a new plot of ground — or indeed into an entirely new province! And why should there be any development of the science of "animal husbandry" in the Orient? There is no room for cattle, except for a limited number as beasts of burden or draft animals; in America, grazing was unlimited.

All this is not to say that if the Oriental rather than the European had settled in America, cultural, economic, and political progress, as normally measured, would have been the same. In fact, it would have been quite different, possibly both in extent and kind. But by the same token, if the west European emigrant had migrated to similarly unoccupied lands in the differently constituted oriental areas as described, their cultural pattern would have been very different.

As lands in the South became exhausted from poor soil management, or as pressure of population increased, or simply as a result of the "urge to move on," the American colonist successively advanced from the "Sea Sand Region" (Coastal Plains) onto the "Blue Mountains" (Piedmont and Blue Ridge provinces); then filtered into the parallel valleys of the "Endless Mountains" (Appalachian Ridge and Valley Province), leaving the last major range of that province via th Cumberland Gap (in the South) and th Mohawk (in the North) as he entered th "Allegheny Ridge" (Appalachian Plateau) whose rivers gave direction westward to th virgin forests, plains, and prairies of th Ohio-Mississippi drainage basin. During th same period, the Chinese and Hindu farme was advancing into his "frontier"— alway seeking higher ground on the mountai slopes of his province, possibly the same on in which his forefathers have tilled the soi for proverbially "forty centuries," and o which he must rely on yields greater than ar found in any of our highly mechanized agri cultural areas.

To what extent can industrial innovations in the Orient narrow the gap between the "sedentary" oriental and the "dynamic" occidental civilizations?

In the previous chapters of this section o areal geography the student will have ob served that very little has been said abou manufacturing, thus possibly leaving the im pression that the type of environmental ele ments favoring the development of manu facturing have not been present to an significant degree. With few major excep tions, this is quite correct, for the establish ment of industry calls for considerable capi tal investments and is at best a complex an speculative venture.

The evaluation of any manufactural pat tern conventionally follows a checklist on th resources immediately available, or at leas readily accessible: fuel, power, metallurgi cal and other minerals; other raw material for processing manufactured goods; capital cheap and efficient labor; sizable areas t allow for possible expansion of industry superior transport facilities; and promisin markets for the manufactured commodities The relative importance of these and othe localizing factors varies greatly as to time an place. Thus in the rise of industry, as in th Industrial Revolution in England and else where, it was essential that steel manufactur ing during the days of poor and costly trans portation would be located as near to th source of raw materials as possible. Thi geographic situation is typified in the Unite States by Birmingham, Alabama, where iro ore, coking coal, and limestone as a flux for smelting all occur together. On the other hand, Gary, Indiana, as the largest steel center in the United States today, has none of these local resources but does have phenomenal transportation and marketing facilities provided by the Great Lakes, the convergence of rails and highways into Chicago, and direct toll-road connections with the East.

Other modern developments show trends away from centralization of industry, particularly accented by the national defense policy of distributing at least the critical defense industries so as to make the nation less vulnerable to a catastrophic attack by the enemy. The development of smokeless and odorless manufacturing processes overcomes objections in some communities against the establishment of at least the heavier industries, while at the same time new types of architecture and landscaping add to, rather than detract from, the beauty of the natural landscape. Modern community planning, moreover, by giving due consideration to the balanced and harmonious development of the residential, commercial, and industrial functions of an area, makes it not only possible but highly desirable for industries in many cases to move out of the larger industrial centers to other areas which have certain distinctive environmental advantages.

*1. **United States South.*** Patently illustrative of the above principles is the South. Once almost strictly an agricultural region, the South is now vying with northeastern United States in cotton manufacturing, producing approximately one-half of the coarser textiles — at one time New England was the chief producer of cotton textiles. Such manufacturing is centered in the southern Appalachian belt from the Carolinas to Alabama. The manufacturing of iron and steel, centered at Birmingham, has already been mentioned. Shipbuilding along the Atlantic and Gulf seaboard also constitutes a major enterprise. Other regional industries include oil refining along the Texas coast and interior, sulfur refining in Louisiana, and food-processing in the horticultural belt, featuring frozen citrus products or concentrates.

The South leads the United States today in the manufacture of rayon; also supplies many lumber products in the form of furniture and paper pulp. Tobacco and cigarette manufacturing are centered in the Carolinas and Virginia. Phosphate fertilizers are produced in Tennessee, Georgia, and Florida from the largest phosphate deposits in the world. More recently, the federal government has established the famous missile station at Cape Canaveral, Florida, and petrochemical works as well as assembly plants for autos and aircraft manufacturing likewise occur.

The accelerated industrialization of the South is attributable to a number of factors: Wages are lower, but this differential is declining in importance as labor in the South is also becoming increasingly organized and unionized. Unquestionably there is a more favorable tax rate in most of the Southern states compared with the Northern. There are other leading economies: lower costs of real estate, and of plant heating. Heavy water-consuming plants will also likely find here more dependable supplies than in the North.

The same factors that attract tourists — climate and scenery — also now operate in attracting industries. Thus scores of the largest industries in the country — manufacturers of electronic equipment, jet engines, missiles — have moved into or near the resort and tourist centers of Florida (e.g., West Palm Beach and St. Petersburg). Characteristically smokeless and odorless, and constructed in harmony with residential landscapes, these industries with their high payrolls have been welcomed rather than resisted. The most diversified manufacturing section in the South is in Texas, where various heavy and light industries are based on the natural oil and gas products of the area.

The accelerated industrial development in the Deep South dispels the commonly held illusion in the past that subtropical types of climate are not conducive to manufacturing; that summers are much too hot and too humid for the high energy potential needed in industrial development. Of course, modern air conditioning has certainly improved working conditions.

*2. **Po Valley, leading European industrial center.*** The headwater areas of the Po River (*Cfa* Italy) are favored by both cheap hydroelectric power as well as an abundance of cheap and skilled labor. Thus, the tri-

THE RESOURCE PATTERN OF MONSOON ASIA (COOLIE)

A vicious (Malthusian) cycle in which too many men try to create capital to support too little land to carry more men to try to.....ad infinitum.

THE RESOURCE PATTERN OF THE UNITED STATES (ROBOT)

An ascending spiral reaching from Nature, manifest in both (*a*) agriculture- and (*b*) industry-supporting aspects, creates capital out of the abundance of natural powers to support man, who gradually becomes the director, planner, and aspirer.

1 Natural aspects ("land")
2 Cultural aspects (capital)
(*a*) agricultural, (*b*) industrial
3 Human aspects (man, labor)

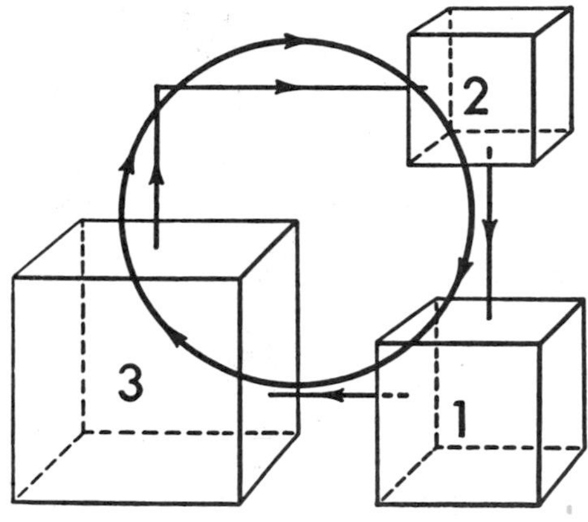

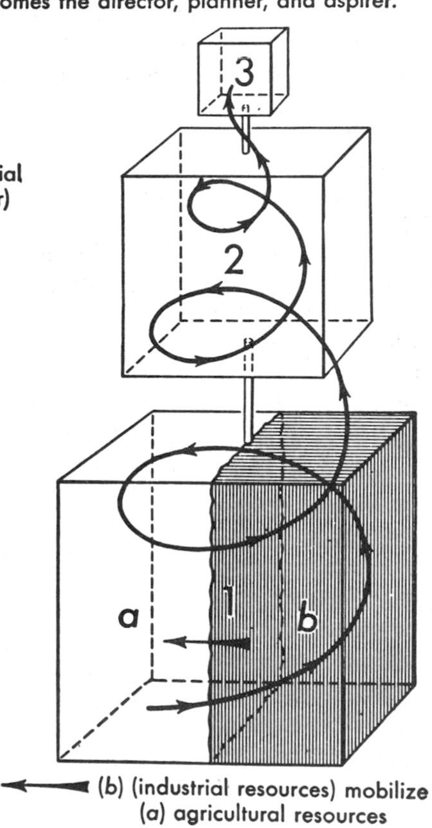

XXV:8 This is a schematic presentation of contrasted "muscle" and "machine" cultures. For further particulars, see text. (From Zimmermann, Erich W., "Culture and Resources," *World Resources and Industries,* Revised Edition, Harper & Brothers, New York, 1951. Reproduction of figure by permission of Harper & Brothers.)

angular region of Milan, Turin, and the port of Genoa constitutes the leading industrial and commercial area of Italy, and ranks as one of the leading machine manufacturing centers of Europe. Incidentally, in this small wedged-in section between the Alps and the Appennines there also have been spawned or sponsored the leading movements in the arts, sciences, and government. This is historic Michael Angelo Italy, Marconi Italy, Cavour Italy: this is the home of one of the most confused panoplies of modern political "isms"—monarchism, republicanism, nationalism, fascism, socialism, and communism.

3. ***"Marginal" manufacturing of Southern Hemisphere.*** The only significant occurrence and exploitation of minerals is in southeast Australia, where some coal and iron occur. But the industries, centered largely in the Sydney and Newcastle region, are primarily established for providing goods for home consumption. On a more limited scale, the same is true of the mineral deposits of Natal of southeast Africa, where again some local industry is established for the manufacture of consumer goods.

Manufacturing in *Cfa* South America is likewise centered chiefly on producing consumer goods—primarily food processing and the manufacture of some textiles. There is also a limited amount of iron smelting—extensive coking coal deposits are lacking. The manufacturing of tannin extracts from quebracho has also become a leading industry.

It will be noted that Southern Hemisphere countries on the whole do not compare favorably with those in the Northern Hemisphere in industrial potential, since they have limited mineral and other natural resources which normally serve as strong backgrounds for industrialization. There are other disadvantages, such as relative commercial isolation and low populations, resulting in relatively weak markets at home for industrial products. A classical example of this is the case of Australian wool enterprises. Although one of the greatest producers of raw wool, Australia is one of the lowest ranking manufacturers of woolen textiles. About 90 per cent of the wool produced in Australia is exported, and by far the larger number of woolen garments worn by native Australians are manufactured abroad, chiefly in England.

4. China's "coolie" resource pattern contrasts with America's "robot" resource pattern. China ranks among the world's leading countries in mineral resources, possessing not only abundant quantities of coal and iron ore, commonly considered prerequisites for heavy industries, but also ferroalloy minerals and others essential for the manufacturing of steel and a great many other metallurgical products. Despite such abundant resources, industries have been largely limited to the household and small workshop type whose products primarily satisfy the home market. Such modern manufacturing as has been established is largely in cotton and silk textiles, concentrated in a few places in the Yangtze Valley and along the coast, China lacking for the most part modern transportation facilities in the interior.

This primitive manufactural-commercial pattern is inherent in the "sedentary" and "vegetable" culture of the Chinese, as Zimmermann so aptly describes and diagrams it in the reproduced Figure XXV-8, in contrast with the American highly mechanized culture. Note the differentiated circular and spiral resource relations between the "natural," "cultural," and "human" categories; the mobilizing relations between the industrial and agricultural resources in the case of the mechanized American culture. Several relevant excerpts from Zimmermann's "Observations on Resource Patterns" will further point up the contrasting civilizations:

¶ The diagram's claim to verisimilitude lies in the size relationships and in the dynamic interrelation of the three cubes representing the three aspects of resourceship—natural, cultural, and human—or the three factors of production, land, labor, and capital. . . . In overpopulated areas of monsoon Asia men create rice terraces to render land more productive, to enable land to support more men. It is a vicious circle which ends in frustration. . . . The vegetable civilization of monsoon Asia is uncommonly immobile. . . . Lack of modern transportation facilities spells isolation and local self-sufficiency. . . . Static nature of vegetable civilization is institutionally reinforced, in the case of China, by special mechanisms assuring the continuity of the social organization. Among these, familism and its corollary, ancestor worship, are the most important.

The contrast with the United States is striking. . . . Inanimate energy, harnessed by metals, mobilizes everything—men, goods, and thoughts—and cuts that fatal nexus between food production and population size that is the curse of monsoon Asia.[1]

5. Japan's twentieth century "feudalism of horsepower." In many ways Japan is a geographic anomaly. Continentally Asian, its present-day culture is not characteristically oriental. Though exhibiting ethnographic earmarks of the Eastern world, its outlook is essentially Western. And when we wish to generalize geographically the manufactural situation, we are in trouble, for it does not well fit either in the oriental or the occidental geographic framework.

Moreover, the unique manufacturing status of this "oriental" dispels a number of commonly held geographic illusions; the kind that a student of geography must learn to guard against, such as (1) Asiatics, including the Japanese, do not possess traits or skills which fit into a machine civilization; (2) subtropical climes — and 32-35 degree latitude manufactural Japan certainly is in this

[1] Zimmerman, Erich W., *World Resources and Industries,* (Revised Edition), Harper & Brothers, New York, 1951, pp. 133-135, *passim.* Reprinted by permission.

category — cannot be expected to incite high energy potential; and (3) that extensive manufacturing, especially the heavier industries, is predicated on the presence of the basic metallic minerals, power fuels, and an abundance of other raw materials. As to this latter, Japan is singularly deficient, as is well illustrated by her chief imports, which include raw cotton and wool, iron and steel, nonferrous metals, machinery and automotive vehicles, petroleum and fertilizers, as well as lumber and rubber. Only one major manufactured material — raw silk — is, one might say, incoherently related to her own home environment. Because of high tariffs in foreign countries, it is moreover difficult to understand how manufactures can be based chiefly on imported materials. Despite its most distinctive manufacturing asset — the combined cheapest and highest skilled labor of any nation in the world, which can, therefore, undersell many countries with its incredibly low-priced articles — it is difficult to see how Japan can establish an enduring place among the leading manufacturers of the world.

Whether the World Power challenges can be continuingly met or not, it is well for us to be reminded how oriental, feudal Japan rose to Western economic and political prestige in the course of less than a century:

¶ The tempo of industrialization sustained in modern Japan over half a century or more is unequalled in the Western World. When Commodore Matthew C. Peary visited the Japanese islands in 1853, he found a nation of approximately 30 million people living in a stage of economic development no more advanced than that of fifteenth-century Europe. . . . By 1940 Japan had transformed herself into a front-rank industrial power. She now supported a population of 73 million people at a standard of living well above anything their grandfathers had known. A quarter of her working population was engaged in industrial pursuits, which had come to furnish 40 per cent or more of her greatly expanded national income. When this industrial potential was mobilized for total war after 1941, Japan quickly overran the entire Far East. She was only brought to her knees when the world's greatest industrial nation was free to project an overwhelming power across the Pacific and to strike against the shipping lanes and inflammable cities which were the arteries and heart of her modern industrial system.[1]

APPLICATION OF GEOGRAPHIC UNDERSTANDING

(N.B.: The student should have no difficulty whatsoever in finding source material on the TVA. One of the most comprehensive treatments is by Gordon R. Clapp, who served as chairman of the board of directors of the TVA for 21 years: *The TVA, An Approach to the Development of a Region,* The University of Chicago Press, 1955. This work also includes a classified bibliography on the various functions of the TVA.)

I. On an outline map trace the Tennessee River and its tributaries. Now draw a line bounding the watershed area. How near does this areal definition coincide with the jurisdictional boundary of the TVA?

What is the area's relative position to (1) *Cfa* U.S.; (2) Mississippi-Ohio River system; (3) inclusive and peripheral physiographic provinces; (4) parts of states within the corporation? Of what geographic significance is each of these relative locative factors?

II. Determine the exact purposes of the TVA Act (very significant in evaluating the effectiveness of this "experimental" and "controversial" government program in socio-economic-political planning). Consult Preamble of Public Law, No. 17—73 Congress, 1st Session (H.R. 5081), May 18, 1933, 48 Stat.58.

III. Of what disciplinary value is a study of the TVA, as related to:

a) The development of the concepts of this particular chapter?

b) The development of interdisciplinary concepts between geography and the other social science disciplines?

IV. Regional Considerations.

Theoretical: Dr. Edward A. Ackerman, one of America's leading research resource geographers, and once Assistant General Man-

[1] Lockwood, William, *Industrial Development, Japan,* Edited by Hugh Barton, Cornell University Press, Ithaca, New York, 1950. Reprinted by permission from The Encyclopedia Americana.

ager of the TVA, observes: "One might say that a region is a particular expression of the attributes and limitations of a culture, observable as they relate to the earth's space and physical composition. . . . One might almost say that the TVA had created a region." Analyze this statement in the context of this areal development and the field of geography.

Practical: Aside from its actual achievements or limitations, would it seem possible that this multiple-purpose project might have been realized by the states acting independently or in concert with each other—without the intervention of a federally organized regional agency? Explain in geographic terms, by comparing a "geographic region" as conceived by Ackerman with a political region.

V. Can you think of any type of a geographic region other than one organized about a river system which would lend itself equally well to the kind of integrated socio-economic-political administration such as is found in the TVA?

VI. Despite impressive rehabilitation and resource developments of the TVA and manifested interest for the establishment of TVA-like enterprises elsewhere in this country (e.g., along the Missouri and Columbia rivers) no new "TVA's" have appeared. Can you give any reasons?

VII. In contemplation of establishing "TVA" agencies along the following rivers in this realm what different types of physiographic, cultural, and political conditions would one have to consider in each case? (1) Rio de la Plata, (2) Kura River (U.S.S.R.), (3) Ganges River, (4) Yangtze Kiang. Carefully distinguish types of rivers and other elements of the hydrography, terrain, rock structure, vegetation, population, settlement, occupance forms.

VIII. In what respects do the Hoover Dam and St. Lawrence Seaway governmental projects differ from the TVA type of project?

IX. "Few subjects in regional or systematic geography lend themselves so readily to resource relationship studies as do those contrived in the context of the TVA." Comment.

X. In TVA, geographers especially distinguished themselves and exemplified the type of professional service they are prepared to render. Postulate the bases for this. Then check your postulates against the services which were actually performed by the geography corps which worked in collaboration with other scientists, engineers, and government agents in initiating and administering the project.

References

1 Horne, McDonald K., Jr., "Cotton," the *Annals of the American Academy of Political and Social Science,* Vol. CCCXXXI, September, 1960, pp. 65, 69.

2 Sears, Paul, "The Importance of Forests to Man," and Lin, D. Y., "China," *A World Geography of Forest Resources,* Edited by Stephen Haden-Guest, John K. Wright, Eileen M. Teclaff; American Geographical Society, Special Publication No. 33, The Ronald Press Company, New York, 1956, pp. 4, 536-537.

3 Whittlesey, Derwent, "Major Agricultural Regions of the Earth, "*Annals of the Association of American Geographers,* Vol. XXVI, 1936, pp. 199-240, *passim.*

4 Jones, Clarence F., *South America,* Henry Holt & Co., Inc., New York, 1947, p. 370.

5 Rich, John, *The Face of South America and an Aerial Traverse,* American Geographical Society, Special Publication No. 26, 1942, pp. 131-132.

6 Jen, Mei-Ngo, "Agricultural Landscape of Southwestern China: A Study in Land Utilization," *Economic Geography,* Vol. XXIV, No. 3, July, 1948, pp. 159-161.

7 Zimmermann, Erich W., *World Resources and Industries,* (Revised Edition), Harper & Brothers, New York, 1951, pp. 133-135, *passim.*

8 Lockwood, William, *Industrial Development, Japan,* Edited by Hugh Barton, Cornell University Press, Ithaca, New York, 1950.

Chapter 26

The humid, mild winter, marine forest lands (*Cfb, Cfc*)

Chorogram: The European coal and steel community

The western European coal and steel community comprises France, West Germany, Netherlands, Belgium, Luxemburg, and Italy. The primary function of the community is to provide "an economy for coal, steel, iron ore, and scrap which operates without national distinctions to eliminate tariffs, customs duties, import quotas, and discriminatory freight rates" (Raymond Vernon, "Launching the European Coal and Steel Community," *U.S. Department of State Bulletin*, June 8, 1953, p. 799). When the community was first initiated in 1952 most prognosticators did not think the union would last very long. They based their doubts upon the fact that western European culture and regional interests are not sufficiently homogeneous to ensure collective and harmonious activity in such a venture. But the idea of a unified market of 165 million consumers, "more rational location of industry, greater productivity, lower prices, and a higher standard of living" appealed to all six of these countries, including the traditional rivals, France and Germany (John Goormaghtigh, "European Coal and Steel Community," *International Conciliation*, May, 1955, p. 347).

Political motives were also likely involved in the founding of the community. It was France's way of maintaining "a certain control over German heavy industry." Germany was making a spectacular economic recovery and France felt that Germany might sooner or later again challenge her industrial and political security. Germany, on her part, detected in this so-called Schumann Plan "the means of rapidly achieving complete equality with its ex-enemies in the West and regaining sovereignty." None of the nations is self-sufficient in the basic resources for steel manufacturing, namely, iron ore and coking coal (Figure XXVI-1). It is recognized, then, that ready exchange of these products is of the utmost necessity for mutual economic and efficient operations. (For a comprehensive treatment of the geographic relations of these mineral deposits to the regional manufacturing enterprises see Norman J. Pounds' *The Ruhr*, Indiana University Press, 1952.)

The success of the integrated manufacturing and "common market" community thus far is attested by the fact that since its inception in 1952 "intra-European trade within the six countries has increased 50 per cent" (Karl Brandt, "Europe, The Emerging Third Power," *Vital Speeches of the Day*, February 15, 1958, p. 265). And the basic industry, steel production, has attained the figure of 57 million tons, second only to that of the United States. Such industrial solidarity augurs well not only for establishing greater economic self-sufficiency for the mainland of western Europe but also for implementing the defense program of the Western democracies against the Communist world.

The preceding chorogram exemplifies a number of basic principles of economic and political geography and stimulates thinking on some of the basic controversial issues which have for years engaged the geographer as he forever explores and evaluates complex environmental relationships in attempting to understand the present pattern of world cultures. How to achieve economic unity out of regional diversity of physical and human resources is one of the basic objectives of modern state diplomacy.

Among the patterns or principles directly mentioned or alluded to by the chorogram are: (1) varying geologic processes in the past have caused a differentiated pattern of mineral distributions, and resulted in large concentrations of one or more ores in one country and a complete absence, or near absence of minerals, in another; (2) few countries are fortunate enough to possess all the basic minerals required for the manufacture of iron and steel; (3) accordingly, facilitating an exchange of surplus products between the surplus-producing iron and coal areas results in mutual manufacturing advantage to all concerned; and (4) the establishment of a common market for the goods of

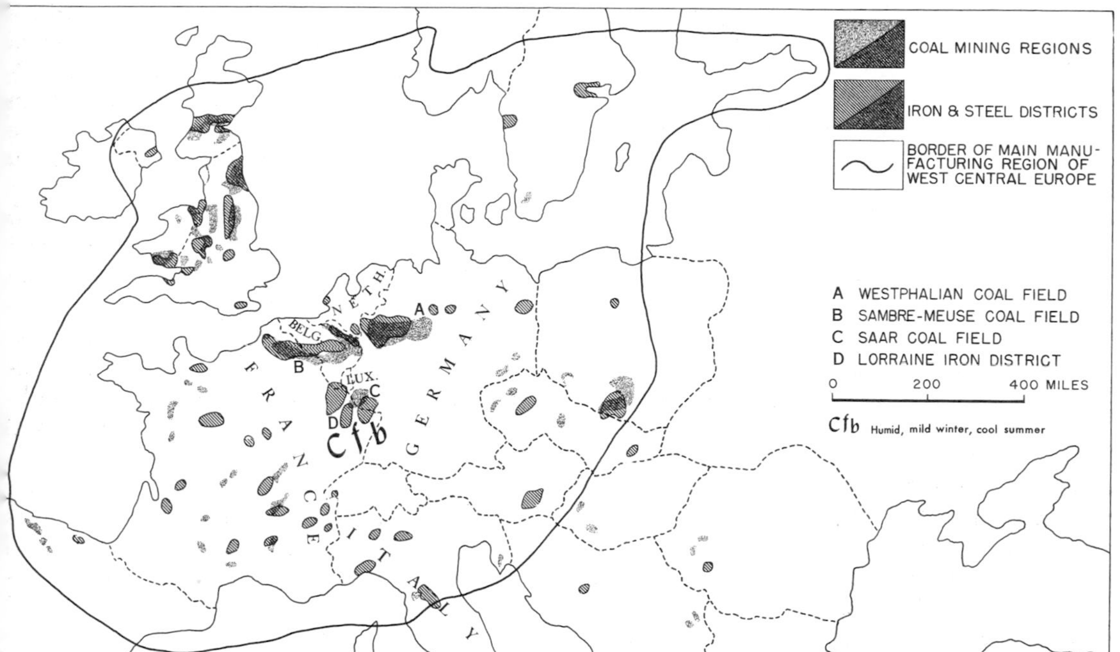

XXVI:1 Basic steel-making materials, mining, manufacturing, and climatic stimulation are key elements in appraising the structure of the Western European Coal and Steel Community, and its relation to the whole Western world. (Composed from two source maps: "Iron and Steel Districts of Europe," and "Coal Mining Regions and Coke Manufacturing by Countries in Europe," by Clarence F. Jones and Gordon G. Darkenwald, in *Economic Geography,* The Macmillan Co., 1954)

the six separate countries not only contributes to economic stability of each, but also promotes political well-being. As former secretary Hull once stated, "Nations will trade or they will fight." Thus, the removal of various restrictions to trade as here mentioned may well suggest the pattern of improved relations among all countries. The application of this latter principle, sometimes called the "Law of Comparative Regional Geographical Advantages," providing for freely-flowing trade between all nations of the world, appears ultimately to be the most effective factor in reducing friction between countries and, therefore, in ensuring a greater measure of world peace.

The subject of this chorogram also poses many questions which are relevant to the present chapter. For example: Why do we have in *Cfb* Europe the most extensive industrial developments in the world? And how did they come to be centered in certain areas, such as the Ruhr district of west-central Europe and the flanks of the Pennine Range of England? What are the ethnographic characteristics which have given impetus and direction to these developments? What are the natural features of western Europe which encouraged the establishment of basic industries? As we shall see presently, Ellsworth Huntington maintained that climate is a major factor as far as the natural environment is concerned. How did Huntington arrive at his conclusions, and how are such conclusions to be appraised? Just what geographic role did the distribution pattern of minerals play in the localization of factory establishments in the two leading manufacturing centers mentioned above? And how are the mineral and industrial patterns related to the organization of nation states and to the recently-formed regional organizations like the European Coal and Steel Community, the European Defense Community, and NATO? In sum, how is the space factor (geography) related to localization of industry?

Cultural-industrial-commercial European pre-eminence viewed in the framework of marinality

The nature of marinality. If marinality is here of focal interest, as the title of this chapter suggests, then we must be certain that this geographic concept and the principles based upon it are properly understood. One of the best ways for a student to learn the meaning and significance of a marine type of climate, classically typified by *Cfb* and *Cfc*, as contrasted with an interior continental or east coast type, is to consult a world isotherm map for January and another for July. Especially instructive is one in which the mean temperatures are reduced to sea level so as to make latitudinal sea–land comparisons independent of temperature changes conditioned by variations in elevation (Figure XXVI-2). Since a marine climate is one influenced by water, we would expect its best development on that part of the globe where the oceans are least interrupted by land masses. This, you will note, occurs in the South Pacific, in the high-middle latitudes, where the *Cfb* forms practically a complete global girdle, flanked poleward by the *Cfc,* almost exclusively an oceanic belt interrupted by only a few score miles of the tapering tip of South America. Here during the southern winter (July) the isotherms generally conform with the parallels of latitude; the 40° F. isotherm for July strikingly coincides with the 50° south latitude. During the Southern Hemisphere summer, the January isotherm of 60° F. closely follows the 40° south latitude. But at points where it crosses land masses, such as in southern South America and the South Island of New Zealand, isotherms first bend equatorward, then sharply poleward, reflecting minor land influences. Whereas coastal Chile at this time has a mean temperature of 60° F., the interior Patagonia region of Argentina directly to the east is crossed by the 70° F. isotherm.

But a much more striking example of this same phenomenon is found in the Northern Hemisphere, particularly in the North Atlantic and during the winter season of this area. Again consulting your isotherm map for January reduced to sea level, you will note successively that on 50° north latitude, passing from the western extremity of the British Isles to the Amur River region of eastern Siberia, you will cross as many as six 10-degree interval isotherm lines. Starting in southwestern Ireland with a temperature mean of 50° F., we note the 40° F. isotherm in southeastern England, the 30° F. in eastern Germany (the eastern limits of our *Cfb* European area), and then successively 20° F., 10° F., 0° F., —10° F., —20° F. from west to east through the U.S.S.R. realm. In other words, during the month of January, there is a temperature range of 70 degrees from the extreme marine condition of southwestern Ireland to the extreme continental condition of interior eastern Siberia.

Tracing a similar course along the Arctic Circle we observe our temperature ranges from 30° F. in marine southwestern Iceland to —50° F. in the "cold pole" region of continental northeastern Siberia—a range of 80 degrees! Such temperature departures from what we would expect as related to "latitude" are known as "temperature anomalies" or "isanomalies."

A similar pattern of marine-continental temperature gradient is observed in northwestern North America, where we cross, for example, four isotherm intervals of 10 degrees each from approximately the position of northwestern Vancouver Island to the southern tip of James Bay in Ontario. Whereas it is 0° F. at the latter point, it is 40° F. in Vancouver. Accordingly, we see by examining the three global areas that the greatest deflections of isotherms occur during the January season in extreme northwestern Europe where the courses of these isotherms are almost at right angles to the parallels of latitude, thus expressing here the greatest positive temperature anomaly in the world—as much as 30-40 degrees.

Analysis of isotherm maps and isanomalies is significant in that it helps to correct some commonplace misconceptions about existing climatic conditions in the high latitudes. It is not uncommon to see people shudder at the news of a serviceman being assigned to a post in Sitka, Alaska or Reykjavik, Iceland during the winter season. Geographically uninformed of the climatic patterns here indicated, such people are amazed when they learn that the actual mean temperature for January is a fraction of a degree higher at

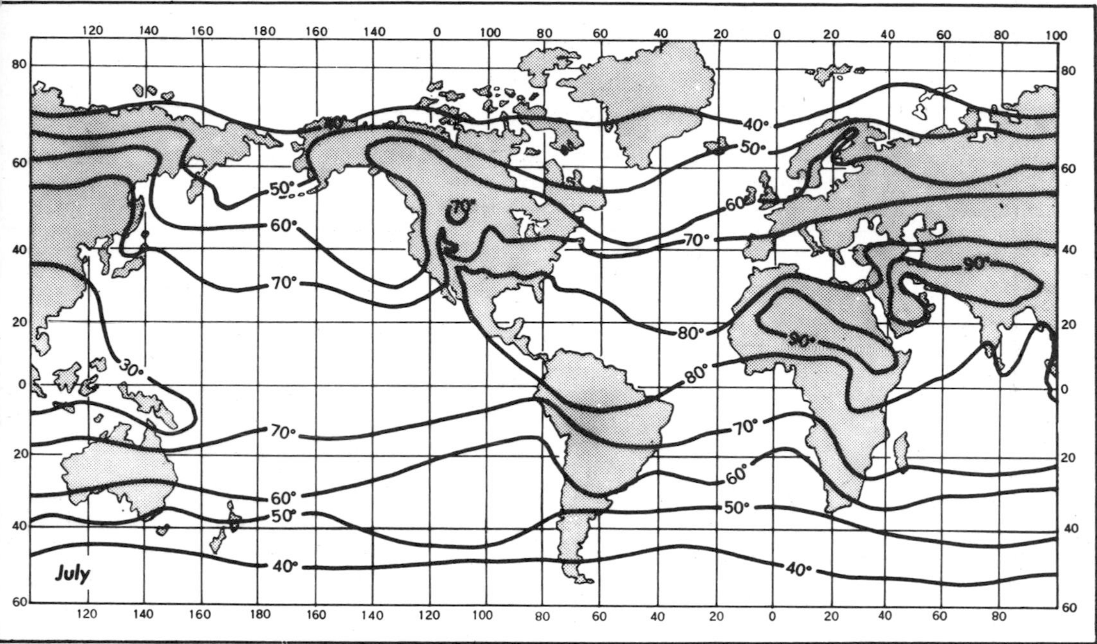

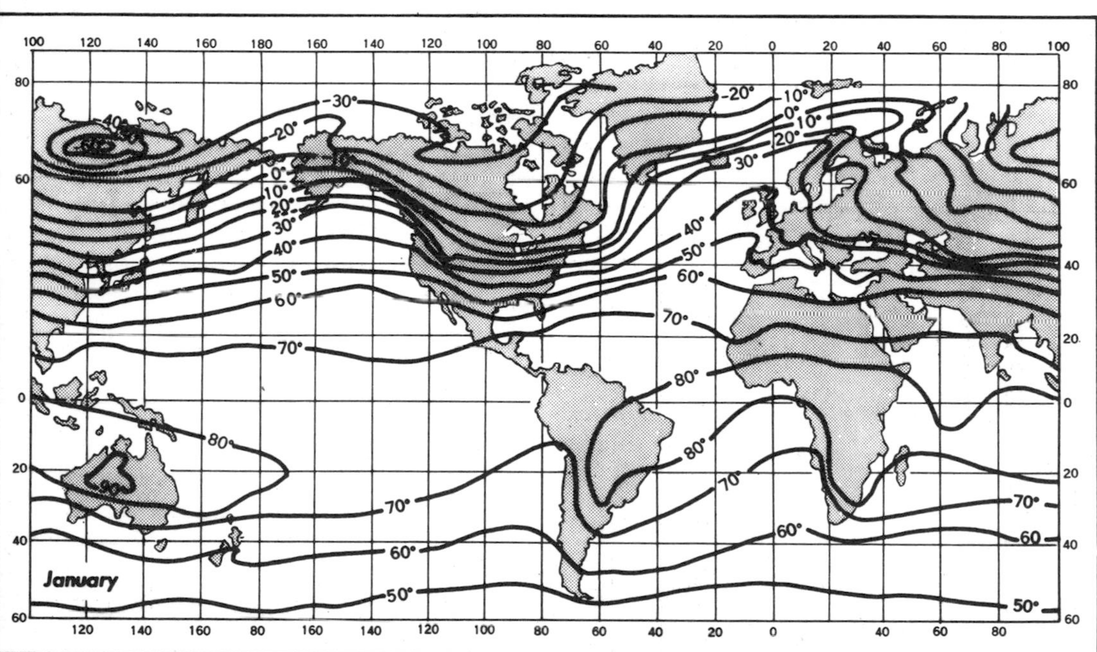

XXVI:2 Here are shown the world isotherm charts for July and January. At least three basic features are to be noted:
(1) the variations corresponding to latitude,
(2) the deflections related to sea-land-wind influences of one type or another,
(3) the seasonal variations.
(From *Pilot's Weather Handbook*, Technical Manual No. 104, published by the Federal Aviation Agency, 1955)

Sitka than it is at St. Louis (32° F. compared to 31.6° F.). Even Reykjavik, only a few degrees latitude from the Arctic Circle, has the extremely mild January mean of only 29.8° F. as compared with 25° F. at Chicago, in 42° north latitude.

Now let us briefly examine in similar fashion the July isotherm patterns for the

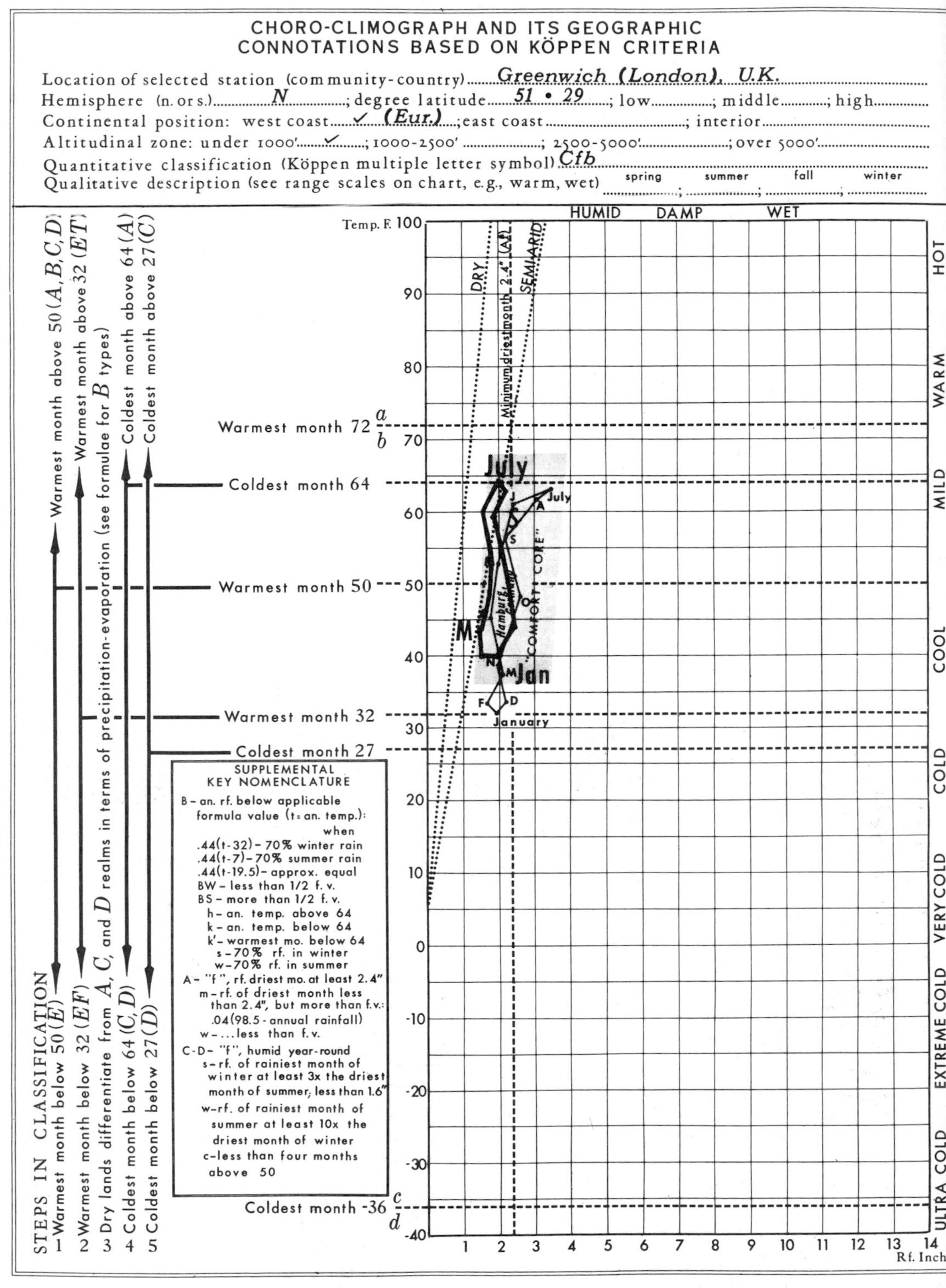
CHORO-CLIMOGRAPH AND ITS GEOGRAPHIC CONNOTATIONS BASED ON KÖPPEN CRITERIA
Location of selected station (community-country) Greenwich (London), U.K.
Hemisphere (n. or s.) N ; degree latitude 51 • 29 ; low ; middle ; high
Continental position: west coast ✓ (Eur.) ; east coast ; interior
Altitudinal zone: under 1000' ✓ ; 1000-2500' ; 2500-5000' ; over 5000'
Quantitative classification (Köppen multiple letter symbol) Cfb
Qualitative description (see range scales on chart, e.g., warm, wet) spring ; summer ; fall ; winter
STEPS IN CLASSIFICATION
1 Warmest month below 50 (E) Warmest month above 50 (A, B, C, D)
2 Warmest month below 32 (EF) Warmest month above 32 (ET)
3 Dry lands differentiate from A, C, and D realms in terms of precipitation-evaporation (see formulae for B types)
4 Coldest month below 64 (C, D) Coldest month above 64 (A)
5 Coldest month below 27 (D) Coldest month above 27 (C)
Warmest month 72
Coldest month 64
Warmest month 50
Warmest month 32
Coldest month 27
Coldest month -36
SUPPLEMENTAL KEY NOMENCLATURE
B - an. rf. below applicable formula value (t = an. temp.): when
.44(t-32) - 70% winter rain
.44(t-7) - 70% summer rain
.44(t-19.5) - approx. equal
BW - less than 1/2 f. v.
BS - more than 1/2 f. v.
h - an. temp. above 64
k - an. temp. below 64
k' - warmest mo. below 64
s - 70% rf. in winter
w - 70% rf. in summer
A - "f", rf. driest mo. at least 2.4"
m - rf. of driest month less than 2.4", but more than f.v.: .04(98.5 - annual rainfall)
w - ... less than f. v.
C-D - "f", humid year-round
s - rf. of rainiest month of winter at least 3x the driest month of summer; less than 1.6"
w - rf. of rainiest month of summer at least 10x the driest month of winter
c - less than four months above 50
Temp. F.
HUMID DAMP WET
DRY
Minimum driest month 2.4" (A.f.)
SEMIARID
HOT
WARM
MILD
COOL
COLD
VERY COLD
EXTREME COLD
ULTRA COLD
July
Jan
January
"COMFORT CORE"
Hamburg
Rf. Inch.

Northern Hemisphere. A comparison of the two seasonal figures shows that the summer isotherms on the whole are less deflected in passing from sea to land than they are in winter; the summer thermal gradient is also much less steep. Thus there is only one 10 degree interval change from Ireland (60° F.) to continental interior Siberia (70° F.). Approximately a similar interval change occurs on the North American continent (e.g., Vancouver compared with the Great Lakes area).

Thus we conclude that the positive temperature anomalies in the world are greatest in winter and find their most anomalous expression in the North Atlantic–western European area.

The west coast areas, being then from 20 to 30 degrees warmer than is called for by the latitude in winter, and about 10 degrees cooler in summer compared with the theoretical latitudinal temperature, are indeed characterized by small annual temperature ranges, and hence are said to have a "temperate clime." In other words, the winters are not uncomfortably cold, nor are the summers unbearably hot (Figures XXVI-3, XXVI-4, XXVI-5). Moreover, diurnal ranges are also correspondingly small. Seasonal temperatures of characteristic areas frequently range from about 60 to 70 degrees in summer and 35 to 45 degrees in winter, both commonly considered as optimal temperatures for physical comfort and high energy potential. Such seasonal temperature means and ranges also conform quite closely to the moderate temperatures regarded by many medical and geographic authorities as physiologically and psychologically the most healthful and stimulating. They likewise appear to be optimal or near-optimal for the domesticated animals most useful to man. In addition, these areas, next to the tropical and Mediterranean climates, have the longest growing season, ranging from six months in the extreme northern and eastern *Cf* European section to nine in the southern and westernmost maritime areas, comparing in these respects most favorably with *Cfa* southeastern United States, described in the previous chapter. However, unlike the hot summers of southeastern United States, the cooler maritime summers of Europe are not adapted to corn culture. But the latter has other cereal-growing advantages, which southeastern United States does not have, namely, in the production of wheat, oats, rye, barley, and root crops, which seem to be seasonally best acclimated in *Cfb* Europe, and in approximately that order poleward.

XXVI:3 (Left) Contrasting types of *Cb* climate occur, hence comparison of this climograph with the two succeeding ones is in order. Strikingly similar to the Hamburg station, you will note, is that of Greenwich.

Heat waves and cold snaps are also conspicuously absent. However, when a very cold air mass from the Arctic does descend on western Europe, both animal and man may suffer greatly because of general unpreparedness for this phenomenon.

Singularly favorable, then, as are the marine temperature characteristics, so also is the precipitation of western Europe. The greater part of the area falls within a range of from 25 inches to 40 inches of annual rainfall. Moreover, it is fairly evenly distributed throughout the year and so does not present the *Cfa* problem of "erosional" rainfall of parts of our Deep South, nor the winter droughts and summer floods of *Cwa* China. Only on the extreme northwestern coastlands do we have excess precipitation, as in the region of Valencia, Ireland, and northwestern Scotland where as much as 75 to a 100 inches or more of rain may fall annually.

Advantageously distributed throughout the year, there is a slight variation in precipitation from a fall or winter maximum on coastal Europe to a summer maximum farther in the interior, where semicontinental influences come to be felt. Thus Valencia's "max" is 6.5 inches in December with a "min" of 3.9 inches in July; whereas for Berlin the "max" is 3.1 in July and the "min" is 1.3 in February. The total rainfall for these two stations is 56.7 and 22.2 in., respectively. Precipitation is primarily of the cyclonic warm-cold frontal type, with maximum storms occurring during the winter season when a pronounced Low forms in the North Atlantic. Convection rains, violent thunderstorms, and especially tornadoes are less common than in *Cfa*. Not only is precipitation usually gentle, but it is also characterized by a high degree of dependability, both seasonally and annually. In fact, the dependability of precipitation in

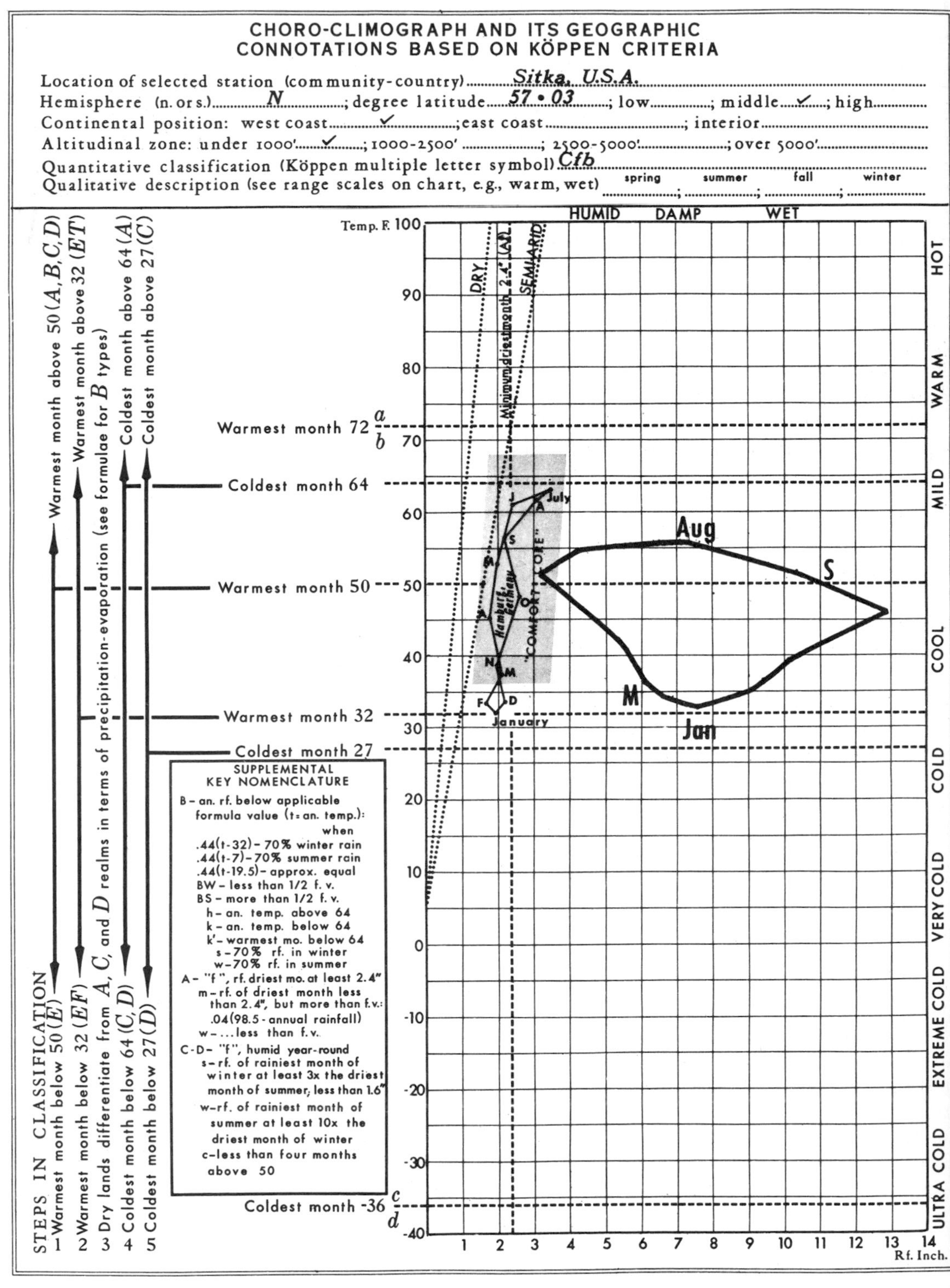

CHORO-CLIMOGRAPH AND ITS GEOGRAPHIC
CONNOTATIONS BASED ON KÖPPEN CRITERIA
Location of selected station (community-country) Sitka, U.S.A.
Hemisphere (n. or s.) N; degree latitude 57 • 03; low; middle ✓; high
Continental position: west coast ✓; east coast; interior
Altitudinal zone: under 1000' ✓; 1000-2500'; 2500-5000'; over 5000'
Quantitative classification (Köppen multiple letter symbol) Cfb
Qualitative description (see range scales on chart, e.g., warm, wet) spring; summer; fall; winter
STEPS IN CLASSIFICATION
1 Warmest month below 50 (E) — Warmest month above 50 (A, B, C, D)
2 Warmest month below 32 (EF) — Warmest month above 32 (ET)
3 Dry lands differentiate from A, C, and D realms in terms of precipitation-evaporation (see formulae for B types)
4 Coldest month below 64 (C, D) — Coldest month above 64 (A)
5 Coldest month below 27 (D) — Coldest month above 27 (C)
Warmest month 72 a b
Coldest month 64
Warmest month 50
Warmest month 32
Coldest month 27
Coldest month -36 c d
Temp. F.
HUMID
DAMP
WET
DRY
SEMIARID
Minimum driest month 2.4" (Af)
"COMFORT CORE"
Hamburg, Bethlehem
July
January
Aug
S
M
Jan
HOT
WARM
MILD
COOL
COLD
VERY COLD
EXTREME COLD
ULTRA COLD
Rf. Inch.
SUPPLEMENTAL KEY NOMENCLATURE
B – an. rf. below applicable formula value (t = an. temp.): when
.44(t-32) – 70% winter rain
.44(t-7) – 70% summer rain
.44(t-19.5) – approx. equal
BW – less than 1/2 f. v.
BS – more than 1/2 f. v.
h – an. temp. above 64
k – an. temp. below 64
k' – warmest mo. below 64
s – 70% rf. in winter
w – 70% rf. in summer
A – "f", rf. driest mo. at least 2.4"
m – rf. of driest month less than 2.4", but more than f.v.: .04(98.5 - annual rainfall)
w – ... less than f.v.
C-D – "f", humid year-round
s – rf. of rainiest month of winter at least 3x the driest month of summer; less than 1.6"
w – rf. of rainiest month of summer at least 10x the driest month of winter
c – less than four months above 50

this region rates as high as in any other area in the world.

Another meteorological advantage accrues from the low percentage of precipitation in the form of snow or hail, except at a few points of higher altitudes or latitudes where there is some accumulation of winter snow. This may result locally in glaciation. But extensive areas of snow are likely to be found as inliers of the *D* rather than of the *C* climatic category, as in the areas bordering the Alps and on the highlands which advance almost all the way to the western coast on the Scandinavian peninsula. The fiord coastline and the hanging valleys with descending waterfalls remind us of climatic changes, in temperature and perhaps precipitation, of the prehistoric past.

But no climate in the world may be said to be perfect—not even the optimal marine climate of western Europe. Coast-wise *Cf* Europe classifies among the cloudiest sections of the world, having a proportionate sky cover of over 50 per cent. Moreover, in addition to relatively little sunshine, frequent fogs and mists, often averaging one day or more per week, occur on the western coastal sections, with all the attendant health hazards and transportation difficulties on both sea and land. In winter, navigation hazards are accentuated by the heavy Atlantic storms of the westerlies, and the resultant turbulent seas which during this season cause many shipwrecks.[1]

The relatively high latitudinal position of these lands (Figure XXVI-6) should predicate cool summers and very cold winters. Among the factors, however, which contribute to mild winters and mild summers are: (1) These lands are exposed windward to a large body of water, the temperature of which is normally higher in winter and lower in summer than adjacent land in the same latitude. (2) Waters of the North Atlantic Drift are an extension of the warm Gulf Stream emanating from the subtropics and continuing as the Norwegian Current, a warm-water drift clear over the northern Scandinavian Peninsula throughout the *Cfb-Cfc* coastal area. In no other part of the world do so-called warm-water currents extend into such high latitudes. (3) The eastward penetration of marine influences is also promoted by insularity (the British Isles) and peninsularity and inland seas especially accented in the North Sea–Baltic Sea area. (4) Unlike the corresponding *Cfb* coastal areas of North America and South America, no mountain wall, excepting in northern Scandinavia, prevents the strong prevailing westerlies from importing interiorward their ameliorating temperatures and moisture-bearing winds. Thus the great Central European Plain and its indented coastal configuration westward combine with the polar deflected windward to establish regional marinality of the first order.

Marinality as mirrored in the vegetation landscape. The primary vegetation cover of western Europe has been, and is, forest—oak-beech forests with increasing numbers of conifers in highland areas. The medieval traveler and settler was enveloped by forests on every side. All the major capitals and centers of industry and trade during this period were literally hewn out of the forest. "The medieval monasteries were not merely centers of learning and the ascetic life; the monks were leaders in the work of cutting down trees, removing stumps, draining swamps, and preparing the fields that have supported later generations."[2]

Very few relict timber stands remain. The present broken cover, especially the oak-beech forests, represents commercial plantings almost throughout. In areas of poor drainage, poor soils, and sandy and rocky highlands, the forests are replaced by heath and moor vegetation. Particularly is this true in the exceptionally rainy highlands of the

[1] It may be well here for the student to review briefly some of the material of Chapter 6 on climate so as to relate the abovementioned meteorological conditions to their basic controls or causes.

[2] Wright, John Kirtland, *The Geographical Basis of European History*, Henry Holt & Co., New York, 1928, p. 67. Reprinted by permission.

XXVI:4 (Left) The "clam" profile of Sitka bears almost no resemblance whatsoever to the simple elongated axis of Greenwich. This raises the question whether such types should be separated into two distinctive categories. As a matter of fact, this has been done by some climatologists, for the environmental habitat is certainly differently conditioned for many forms of life.

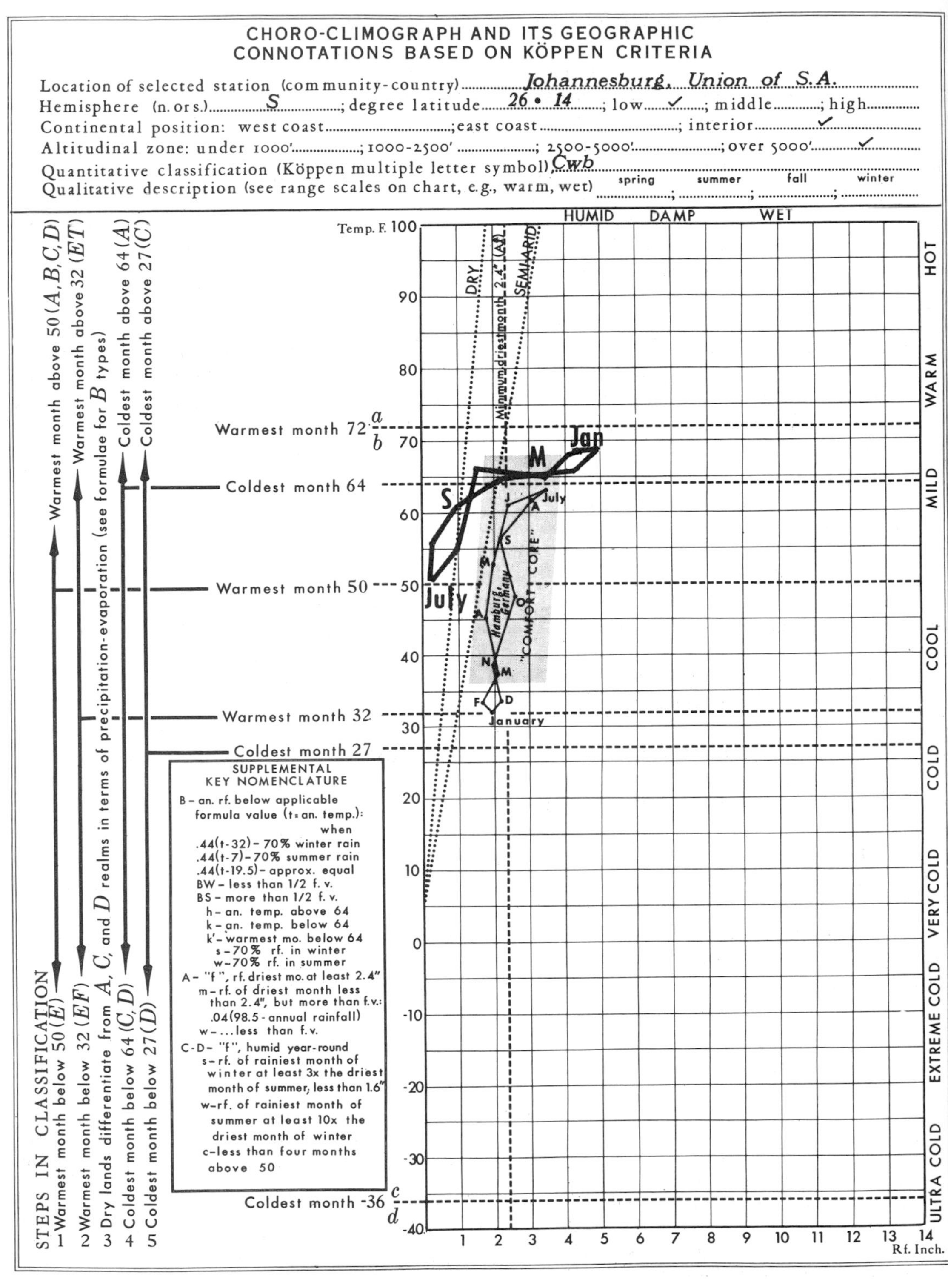

CHORO-CLIMOGRAPH AND ITS GEOGRAPHIC CONNOTATIONS BASED ON KÖPPEN CRITERIA
Location of selected station (community-country) Johannesburg, Union of S.A.
Hemisphere (n. or s.) S; degree latitude 26 • 14; low ✓; middle; high
Continental position: west coast; east coast; interior ✓
Altitudinal zone: under 1000'; 1000-2500'; 2500-5000'; over 5000' ✓
Quantitative classification (Köppen multiple letter symbol) Cwb
Qualitative description (see range scales on chart, e.g., warm, wet) spring; summer; fall; winter
STEPS IN CLASSIFICATION
1 Warmest month below 50 (E) — Warmest month above 50 (A, B, C, D)
2 Warmest month below 32 (EF) — Warmest month above 32 (ET)
3 Dry lands differentiate from A, C, and D realms in terms of precipitation-evaporation (see formulae for B types)
4 Coldest month below 64 (C, D) — Coldest month above 64 (A)
5 Coldest month below 27 (D) — Coldest month above 27 (C)
Warmest month 72 a b
Coldest month 64
Warmest month 50
Warmest month 32
Coldest month 27
Coldest month -36 c d
Temp. F.
HUMID
DAMP
WET
DRY
SEMIARID
Minimum driest month 2.4" (A f)
Jan
July
M
S
Hamburg, Germany
"COMFORT CORE"
January
HOT
WARM
MILD
COOL
COLD
VERY COLD
EXTREME COLD
ULTRA COLD
Rf. Inch.
SUPPLEMENTAL KEY NOMENCLATURE
B – an. rf. below applicable formula value (t = an. temp.): when
.44(t-32) – 70% winter rain
.44(t-7) – 70% summer rain
.44(t-19.5) – approx. equal
BW – less than 1/2 f. v.
BS – more than 1/2 f. v.
h – an. temp. above 64
k – an. temp. below 64
k' – warmest mo. below 64
s – 70% rf. in winter
w – 70% rf. in summer
A – "f", rf. driest mo. at least 2.4"
m – rf. of driest month less than 2.4", but more than f.v.: .04(98.5 - annual rainfall)
w – ... less than f. v.
C-D – "f", humid year-round
s – rf. of rainiest month of winter at least 3x the driest month of summer; less than 1.6"
w – rf. of rainiest month of summer at least 10x the driest month of winter
c – less than four months above 50

northwestern British Isles. Heath vegetation is of the leatherleaf variety, consisting for the most part of low-lying shrubs, including bracken and junipers. The wetter areas are overgrown with moors. Both the heath and the moor, agriculturally forbidding landscapes, have attracted the sportsman bent on hunting grouse, quail, and deer. They also attract the tourist, since the highlands with their many *lochs* provide an aesthetic charm all their own, which incidentally has also been the source of inspiration to many authors and artists. It is a type of landscape that appeals or repels according to one's mood and interests. Thus the ambivalent appraisal:

¶ The Scottish Highlands are undoubtedly attractive on a clear day when the summits, sculptured by the glaciers of the Ice Age, show the purple color of blossoming heather, and many lakes break the monotony of this stern but rather uniform landscape. Nevertheless when clouds lay a dense fog over the hills and rain falls for days and days as frequently happens, the life of the Scottish Highlander caring for his flock of sheep approaches the limit of human endurance, and it requires the ardor of the English deerstalker to wade through the spongy moor without complete disgust.[1]

Marine Europe considered by many geographers the "optimal" climate for human health, energy, and progress. What do the above statistics signify geographically? Up to this point our discussion has been primarily meteorological and climatological. In a work in human geography we are not primarily interested in weather and climate as such, but in the effects they have upon major aspects of the natural landscape which set the stage for man's settlement patterns, land-use designs, and resource developments best befitted to the type of culture that he wishes to establish.

One of the most extensive research programs designed to discern coherent connections between climate and health, human energy, progress, and civilization is that by the late Ellsworth Huntington. His publications on the subject have stirred probably the most intense controversies in the field of geography and in the related social science disciplines concerned with the general problem of accounting for the differentiated regional patterns of civilization, past and present. This subject is introduced into this chapter, and particularly at this point, because of the fact that the Huntington "optimal" climatic criteria of temperature, rainfall, season, and weather variability best seem to coincide with *Cfb* western Europe. It is also for this region, next to that of the United States, that the Huntington data are most adequate in illustrating the techniques and results of his climate-civilization studies. The purpose here in referring in some detail to Huntington's thesis is neither to validate nor to refute the thesis, but rather to bring to the attention of the student (1) the tremendous challenge a complex subject of this kind entails, (2) the wide interest which not only geographers but also many other social scientists have had in the subject, and (3) the opportunity it affords for the student to check the types of evidence and technique or procedure used by Huntington in arriving at his major conclusions. Incidentally, also, the type of maps drawn by Huntington, such as presented here (Figures XXVI-7A, XXVI-7B, and XXVI-7C) illustrates how complex human data can be reduced to an intelligible isopleth type of representation. Let us briefly refer to these maps with a word of explanation of the titles and of the data on the basis of which the maps were made.

Distribution of health (Figure XXVI-7A). This map is based on normal death rates chosen by Huntington, probably as valid as any other single set of criteria to reflect conditions of health, and statistically regarded as more reliable for Europe than for any other part of the world.

Now what are the implications of a comparative study of mapped data such as these?

---

[1] Reprinted with permission from Samuel Van Valkenburg and Colbert C. Held, *Europe* (second edition), 1952, John Wiley & Sons, Inc., New York, p. 47.

XXVI:5 (Left) To which of the two preceding graphs does this irregularly sprawling curve most nearly conform? What would you consider the most distinguishing feature to be? What would be the general agricultural regimen, as here reflected by the calendar and curve?

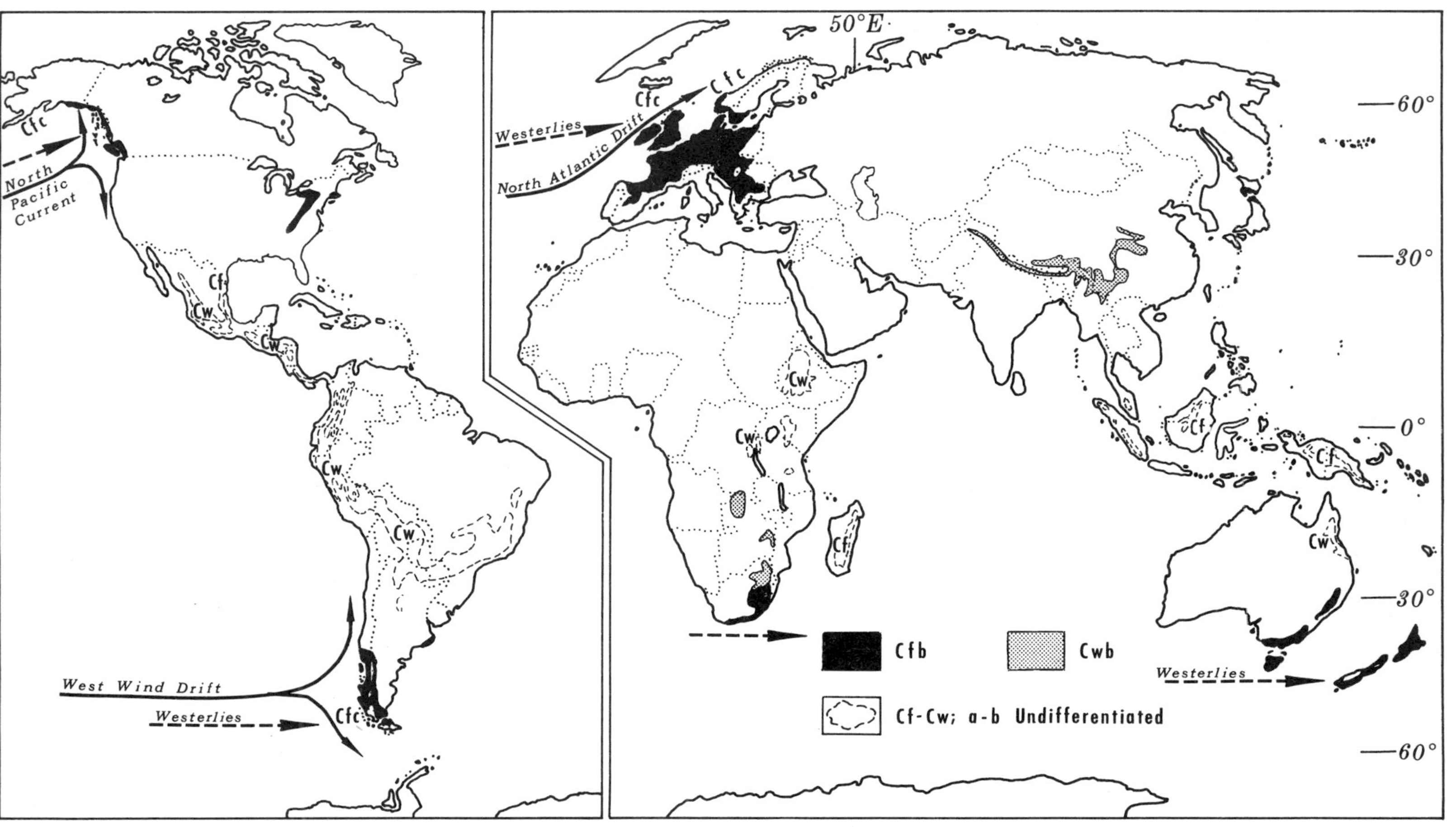
Cfc
North Pacific Current
Cf
Cw
Cw
Cw
Cw
West Wind Drift
Westerlies
Cfc
50°E
Cfc
Cfc
Westerlies
North Atlantic Drift
Cw
Cw
Cf
Cf
Cf
Cw
Westerlies
60°
30°
0°
30°
60°
Cfb
Cwb
Cf-Cw; a-b Undifferentiated

Whatever our evaluations of the several maps may be, the coincidence of patterns, it must be admitted, is striking enough to suggest a close relationship between climate on the one hand, and health, energy, and civilization on the other. The conclusion is drawn that Huntington believes such data make a strong case for exhibiting effects of climate on civilization. But it is also understandable that complex relationships of this kind may be oversimplified, meriting professional criticism. Huntington himself was among the first to recognize the limitations of his climatic thesis. Let us observe representative statements on this point from each of three important Huntington publications:

¶ (1) Climate ranks with racial inheritance and cultural development as one of the three great factors in determining the conditions of civilization. As to which of the three is most important it is impossible to say. The absence of good conditions in any one respect may hold a country back, while all three must rise to a high level if a race is to reach the highest plane of civilization.[1]

(2) Several objections have been raised to the theory that climatic efficiency is basic in setting the geographical pattern of civilization. It is said, for example, that the climatic pattern is frequently overshadowed by isolation, as in Tibet and the southern Appalachians; by innate biological traits, as in Iceland and among the Parsis; by overpopulation, as in Japan; by recent migration within the limits of a single culture, as in Florida; and by the introduction of an advanced culture, as in tropical Hawaii and northern Australia.

This objection disappears when two essential points are remembered. First, climatic efficiency, as we have seen again and again, is only one of the many agencies which influence the geographic pattern of civilization. Indeed it is only a single phase of climate, and its effect is modified by the other phases as well as by soil, minerals, and other physical conditions. The geographic factor, in turn, ranks with heredity and cultural endowment as only one among three major factors that influence the level of civilization. Such being the case, the outstanding fact is not local departures from the cultural level that would be expected on the basis of climatic efficiency, but the broad geographical agreement between the patterns of civilization and climate.

The other essential point is that the theory of climatic efficiency must not be stretched to cover nonclimatic matters. High climatic efficiency does not provide inventive brains; it merely stimulates such brains. It does not supply natural resources, even though the climates that are best for human energy are also admirable for agriculture and animal husbandry, and happen in some cases to be located in regions well supplied with minerals. Climates which promote efficiency merely help in developing the possibilities provided by the geographical environment. In short, *not even the most stimulating climate insures the presence of a high civilization.* It merely *aids* in the attainment of such a civilization (Italics ours).[2]

Huntington also found that the distribution pattern of modern complex manufacturing correlates closely with the pattern of climatic energy the world over, and may be thought of as a sort of civilization criterion on the materialistic side of societal development. A brief comment of his on this point, then, will serve to relate this concept to the preceding and succeeding physical and cultural elements basic to the consideration of complex industrialization as a hallmark of western European culture:

¶ . . . the complex type of manufacturing flourishes only (1) where natural selection and migration have given the inhabitants a racial inheritance of high mental activity and capacity; (2) where the climate is so healthful and stimulating that people possess great energy and perseverance; (3) where a certain degree of skill has been acquired and each generation is

XXVI:6 (Left) The *Cfb* focuses on marinality, with only a remnant here or there of highland inliers usually within the *Cfa*. One other close relative association is the *Cs*, generally equatorward. Western Europe, you will note, is the premier *Cfb* region. Why?

[1] Huntington, Ellsworth, *Civilization and Climate*, Yale University Press, New Haven, Conn. 1924, p. 242. Reprinted by permission.

[2] Reprinted with permission from Ellsworth Huntington, *Mainsprings of Civilization*, 1945, John Wiley and Sons, Inc., New York, pp. 389-390.

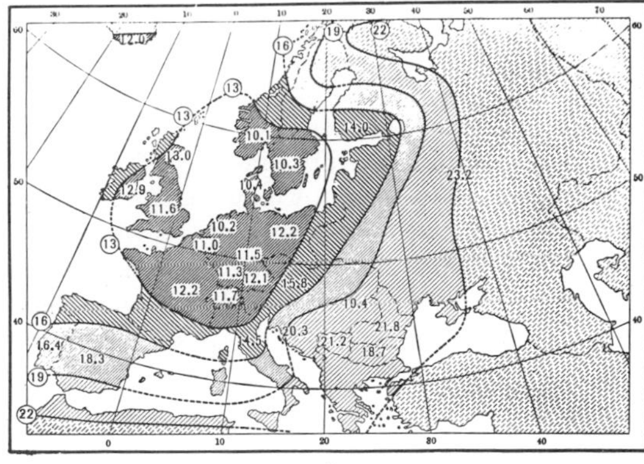

A

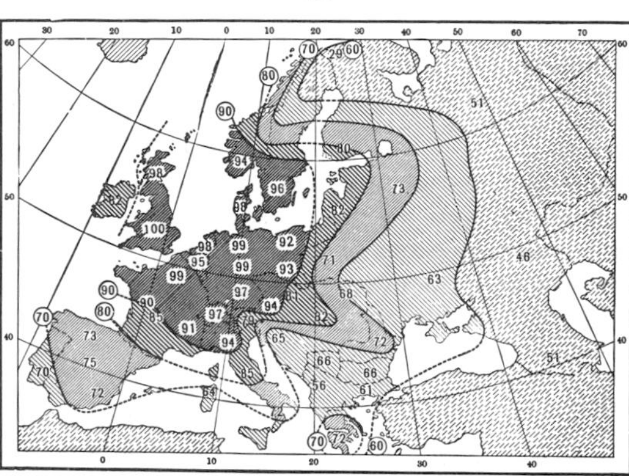

B

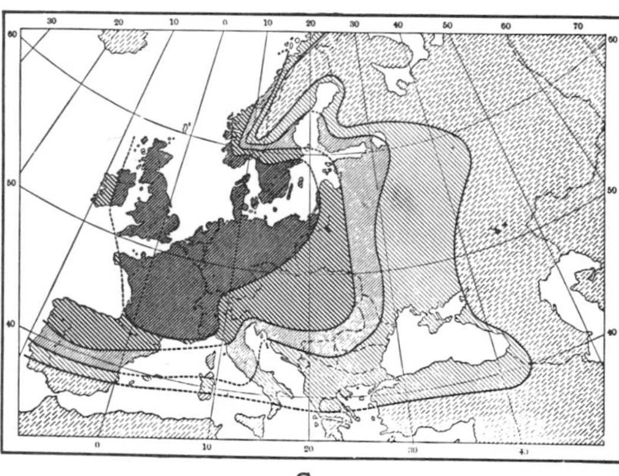

C

XXVI:7 These three Huntington maps are related to health and energy. A. Distribution of health based on death rates. B. Progress and civilization based on the opinions of fifty leading geographers, ethnologists, historians, and other professionals. C. Climatic energy, shading intensity indicating the degree of climatic stimulation. (*Business Geography,* Ellsworth Huntington and Frank E. Williams, John Wiley & Sons, Inc., 1926, used by permission)

able to teach its successor, and (4) where abundant capital is available.[1]

Distribution of civilization (Figure XXVI-7B). In Huntington's questionnaire to those whom he asked to assist in the preparation of this map, he defined civilization as follows:

¶ I mean by this the power of initiative, the capacity for formulating new ideas and for carrying them into effect, the power of self-control, high standards of honesty and morality, the power to lead and to control other races, the capacity for disseminating ideas, and other similar qualities which will readily suggest themselves. These qualities find expression in high ideals, respect for law, inventiveness, ability to develop philosophical systems, stability and honesty of government, a highly developed system of education, the capacity to dominate the less civilized parts of the world, and the ability to carry out far-reaching enterprises covering long periods of time and great areas of the earth's surface.[2]

As indicated in connection with this quoted statement, Huntington recognized two feasible approaches—one, statistical; the other, seeking authoritative opinions. At the very outset, Huntington himself recognized the limited value of the latter approach, but chose this in preference to the former in view of the absence of sufficient data:

¶ Accordingly, in the autumn of 1913, I asked over two hundred people in twenty-seven countries to help in preparing a map. . . . The larger number were geographers whose first duty is to know all parts of the world. Ethnologists in considerable numbers were included for the same reason, but they responded less freely than the geographers. Historians, diplomats, colonial officials, travelers, missionaries, editors, educators, and business men were all included. The only criterion was that each person should possess an extensive knowledge of the world through personal knowledge, or, in a few cases, through reading. Some were selected because of knowl-

[1] Reprinted with permission from Ellsworth Huntington and Frank E. Williams, *Business Geography* (second edition), John Wiley & Sons, Inc., New York, 1926, p. 308.

[2] Huntington, Ellsworth, *Civilization and Climate,* Yale University Press, New Haven, Conn., 1924, p. 242. Reprinted by permission.

edge of special regions not well known to most people and only reached by extensive travel.[1]

The student is invited further to read the letter of instructions Huntington sent out to the interviewees; also the respondents' comments explaining and appraising their own replies as found in the rest of the chapter entitled, "The Distribution of Civilization."

Distribution of climatic energy (Figure XXVI-7C). This map was evolved by Huntington on the basis of physical and mental activities and efficiency as reflected, for example, by factory workers and by students. Huntington found that the optimum summer temperatures range between 60 and 68° F., with winter temperatures from approximately 36 to 44° F.; and with precipitation approximating between two and four inches per month, which also normally provides the most satisfactory conditions of atmospheric humidity. Another indicated optimal factor is the stimulation provided by variability of cyclonic and anticyclonic weather. The student may now determine for himself which parts of the world most nearly approximate this composite type of meteorological or climatological condition, and particularly note how weather station data of the darkest shaded area of the European map compare with the indicated optima.

The North Sea fisherman transformed into sailor-explorer-colonizer-merchant mariner. The sea, no less than land, has entered into the good fortunes of the people of western European. Here the North Sea served as a sort of steppingstone and proving ground for the mariner bent on sea commerce and conquest.

The mild climate, warm seas, insular-peninsular, fiord coast configuration, and shallow continental shelf have been intimately associated with the history of world seamanship. The extensive shallow continental shelf, with its famous Dogger Banks, constitutes the ideal fishing area of the world and has bred a hardy race of fishermen and navigators. Here the North Atlantic Drift, as an extension of the Gulf Stream, maintains a year-round ice-free fishing season; the warm current imports large quantities of plankton fish food, while coastwise the colder currents from the north stimulate spawning. The indented coasts provide proximate sheltered harbors for the large regional population, traditionally short on meat supply. It furnishes a ready local market for haddock, herring, cod, and other fish, besides supplying a large surplus for export.

North Sea fishing has in no small measure served as maritime training for the world sea rovers, dating as far back as the Norsemen, who discovered another famous fishing ground off the coasts of Labrador and Newfoundland. We also are, of course, reminded of the globe-encircling expeditions by the British, initially so well portrayed in the celebrated sixteenth-century epic *Principal Navigations* by Richard Hakluyt. Western Europe also spawned or sponsored the expeditions leading to the discovery of the New World, followed by the Spanish, French, Portuguese, Dutch, and English colonizations in the sixteenth and seventeenth centuries. They were followed in turn by the most celebrated eighteenth-century navigator of the seven seas—Captain James Cook. Nearly all the major empire-building programs are associated with maritime Europe. And though today such overseas empires have all but disappeared, the marine geographic influence is still very much in evidence. Indeed, it is as critically important as ever, for the average western European country must today, and probably always, look overseas for its peacetime life-sustaining commerce and wartime national security.

Ethnography is "dynamic," environment "passive" in a rationale on civilization

Historic Europe. As Huntington has pointed out, there are numerous factors other than climate that must be considered in the evaluation of progress and of civilization. These concern not only other elements of the physical environment besides climate, but also the dynamic ethnographic and historic factors. But such historic factors as we are here committed to consider should, in this context, be treated geo-historically and not in a historical vacuum. This means viewing the major historic events in their physiographic perspective. Here again western Europe is an exemplary area for studying event–environment relationships, since no other similar

[1] *Ibid.*, p. 241. Reprinted by permission.

sized region in the world appears so rich in historic events and at the same time has a landform structure and coastal configuration so diverse.

The earliest civilizations, as we have seen in Chapters 20, 21, and 24, were Asian, African, and Mediterranean Europe—the Babylonian, Egyptian, Arabian, Phoenician, Palestinian, Aegean, Minoan, Greek, and Roman cultures. It is these civilizations that supplied the roots of our Western European culture, which in turn became the mother culture of the entire Occident. Also, just as the Mediterranean Basin is distinguished for its ancient history, so Western Europe is distinguished for its medieval and modern history. Though this is a matter of common knowledge, it is well, perhaps, briefly to note how one of the American leading authorities on Europe (Samuel Van Valkenburg) who at the same time is a native of one of the North Sea countries (the Netherlands) evaluates "Europe as a Continent":

¶ From one viewpoint, Europe is the fountainhead of western civilization, where the landmarks of cultural development are the monuments, museums, cathedrals, and ruins. From another viewpoint, it is a land of relatively small groups of people occupying relatively small states that often war among themselves. It is the focus of political control of much of the world, and it is, still, a center of concentration of much of the world's capital. . . . Finally, wherever Europeans have migrated—and they have gone in large numbers to many lands—they have carried something of Europe with them. Such are the fascinating connotations of Europe. . . . Europe is especially interesting because of the astonishing diversity that it presents in so many of its qualities and because of the influence that it has exerted and still exerts on the rest of the world. No other area of comparable size in the world displays such variable man-and-land relationships. . . . From such an interpretation, Europe emerges as a complex combination of highly diverse peoples, cultures, and natural and cultural landscapes, with the landscapes molded by many different peoples and adapted to their respective modes of occupance through long periods of time. . . . The world's civilization is essentially still largely European. The people of the United States, Canada, and Australia all rightly claim to be European in blood and culture. Those of Latin America make the same claim, but that is true for only part of the population. Other parts of the world have introduced certain elements of European culture or have at least followed the modified European culture of America. Europe is still justly proud of her art and science, her universities and art galleries, her architecture, her rich past; and every summer millions of tourists travel around to inhale the atmosphere of European culture. Nor is the contribution of Europe to the culture, in the broadest sense, of the world merely a thing of the past. In the practical and fine arts, Europe remains a fountainhead of ideas: a good example is found in modern architecture, which combines new applications of engineering and artistic arrangements.[1]

Circulation and settlement. Next to climate itself, the physical landscape and land surface with its detailed relief features is the most essential factor in relating historic events to physical perspective. In this case we are primarily concerned with the major landform features of the continent as presented, for example, cartographically and textually in *Physiographic Diagram of Europe* by A. K. Lobeck (Figure XXVI-8). Here four great physiographic provinces are recognized—the Northwest Highlands with associated Lowlands (most of Scandinavia, Western British Isles, Northwest France); (2) the Great Central Plain (a belt through Central Europe); (3) the Central Massives with Associated Lowlands (blocks of heavily eroded uplands in Spain, France, Germany, and Bohemia); (4) the Alpine System with Associated Massives and Lowlands, forming a more or less continuous formidable travel "barrier" in southern Europe, extending westward to the Pyrenees and eastward to the Caucasus.

In a study in historical geography it is significant to observe among other things how such physical features influenced migrations of people into an area. Recalling the fact that the Mediterranean section was the first to be occupied, the student may therefore ponder how, and by what routes, immigrants entered western Europe from the Mediterranean world via trans-Alpine corridors, as well as from the Orient by the trans-

[1] Van Valkenburg, Samuel, and Held, Colbert C., *op. cit.*, pp. 1-6, *passim.* Reprinted by permission.

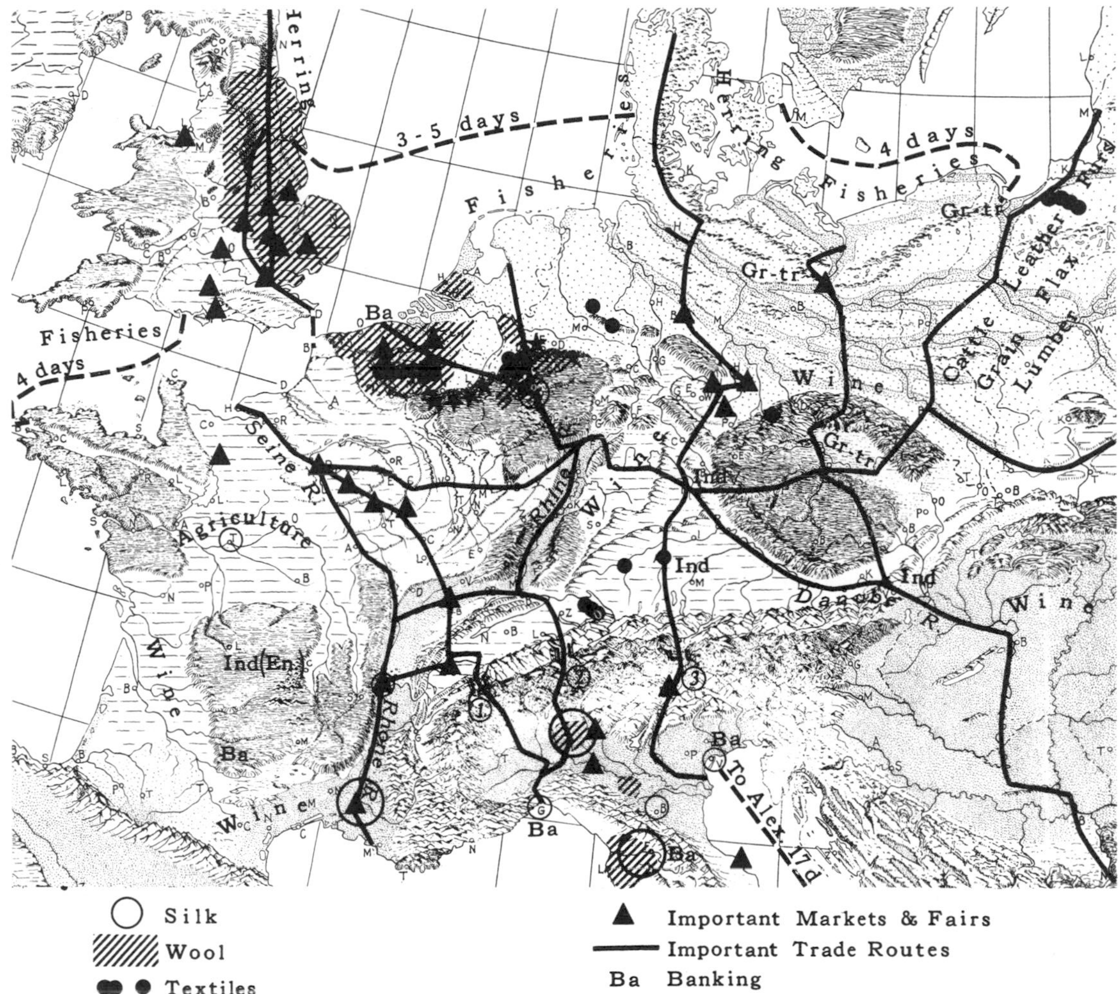

XXVI:8 This map shows the surface configuration of western Europe and its relation to historical geography. (Base map physiogram diagram of Europe, copyright by A. K. Lobeck, reproduced with permission from the publisher, The Geographical Press, a division of C. S. Hammond and Company, Maplewood, New Jersey, U. S. A. Selected superimposed medieval cultural features adapted from *Historical Atlas* by William R. Shepherd, Henry Holt and Company, 1929. Copyright by Velhagen & Klasing, Bielefeld, West Germany, used by permission.)

Caspian steppes. It is expected that here, too, human beings are tempted to follow the line of least resistance in migrating from one region into another; this was especially important in pioneer days of primitive travel, as we have seen in Colonial America (Chapter 25). In advancing the colonial frontier, colonists sought out the navigable streams for such travel and particularly those which breached the highland divides at relatively low altitudes (e.g., the Cumberland Gap and the Mohawk Depression). Now if you turn to the physiographic diagram of Europe you will note the west-to-east trend of folded mountain ranges and associated massives formed a frustrating roadblock to travelers from Mediterranean Europe into central and western Europe. But you will also observe that there are major breaches or gaps. It is such corridor configurations that a geographer will check upon in gaining a true perspective of the circulation and settlement patterns of central and western Europe. Although scores of minor passageways may be traced throughout southern Europe, a half-dozen stand out and are recognized by Griffith Taylor in the following order of geographic significance: Bosporus, the Rhone Gate, the Brenner, the Pear Tree Pass, the Vardar-Morava Gate, and last the Narbonne Gate. The Bosporus is distinctive, for it represents the only sea-level pass and was particularly significant in the early days in furnishing facile navigation facilities between the eastern Mediterranean and the "Euxene" trading areas. The Vardar-Morava Pass was significant, as Taylor points out, in many important migrations of Slavs and Goths, Romans, Serbs, and Turks. This pass is physiographically significant in connecting two rivers. The Pear Tree Pass linked the head of the Adriatic Sea with the Sava branch of the Danube. In ancient days, it served, among others, the Huns, the Ostrogoths and the Visigoths, and has been evaluated by Taylor "as the most attractive on the west of the Balkans, which must inevitably be largely utilized in the future—as, indeed, the growth of Trieste near its western end is some indication." Although there are several passes transecting the Alps, the Brenner Pass, about a half-mile lower in altitude, has been of greatest significance throughout all historic time. As observed by Taylor, "It was one of the main causes of the growth of Venice and Genoa in the south, and of Innsbruck, Munich, and Nuremburg in the north" (6).

On the west, the Rhone Gate opening up on the Mediterranean penetrated the very heart of central Europe and by portage pathways contacted the headwaters of the Rhine, emptying into the North Sea, the Seine headed by the English Channel, and the Loire, coursing through the Brittany Corridor to the Atlantic. Another gateway in southern France, the Carcasonne Gap, named after the city at its eastern end, opened up onto the headwaters of the Garonne River, now connected by the Canal du Midi with the Mediterranean. Toulouse, commanding the west end of the corridor, was the capital of the Visigoths during the fourth century.

Forms of settlement and occupance of western Europe have also been studied by geographers in relation to the various gateways by which immigrants entered the various regions as well as to the landforms into which the gateways penetrated. Thus, Wright observes that

¶ The highlands of Central France, Wales, Scotland, and Norway have always interposed serious obstacles to communication and have supported sparse populations. . . . The lowlands separating the massives from one another are far from uniformly flat and monotonous. . . . These lowlands have been the scene of the most important events and movements of Western life. Indeed, European history is essentially the history of the plains, on which have arisen the main centers of agriculture and industry, the capitals of the greatest nations, and the largest cities.[1]

And Ellen Semple notes:

¶ Each [pass] enacted a different historical role in the great Mediterranean drama. Each facilitated in a different degree the spread of Mediterranean culture into northern Europe, though the character of the inland peoples and of their country decided whether this transplanted culture should take root or die—whether it should flourish, as did the Roman civilization among the agricultural Gauls west of the Rhine, or should be wiped out, as was the older Hellenic culture of the Scythian coast by nomadic inroads from the Asian deserts.[2]

Unlike many other regions of the Western world, western Europe exhibits urban-like rural settlements

"Fields and trees teach me nothing, but the people in a city do." With this statement by Socrates, the geographer may well be in complete disagreement. For however distinguished cities may be in their culture, it is the countryside that forms the economic hinterland of the city, and to which the city must look for the ultimate nurture of its life. More and more it has also become manifest that through "rurban" types of settlements the hiatus between the forms of rural life

[1] Wright, John Kirtland, *op. cit.*, pp. 65-66. Reprinted by permission.

[2] Semple, Ellen, *Geography of the Mediterranean Region*, Henry Holt & Co., New York, 1931, pp. 212-213. Reprinted by permission.

and urban life has progressively been narrowed in many parts of the world. Such features are particularly well revealed in western European historiography. Let us, therefore, consider some of the European characteristic groupings of people and the geo-historical processes which have contributed to a regionally differentiated settlement pattern. To understand fully the evolution of farm settlement types, we should know the dates of their establishment and fit them into the culture of the period; their ancestral or emigrant backgrounds, so as to be able to evaluate the role that transported customs have played in the new environment; their social aspect (individual or colonial type of settlement); the traffic pathways by which immigrants entered the area; and the relevant regional political controls, such as systems of land tenure, inheritance, and the like.

The physical elements here also, of course, enter the picture as they do in the case of settlement of city sites, with a difference, however, in relative emphases. In the case of farmland economy, elements of field culture are paramount. These include, of course, the lay of the land, soil fertility, drainage, regional adaptability to an animal or pasture economy with its normally dispersed type of settlement, and crop culture conducive to more compact types of communities.

Among the regions best suited perhaps to the review of diverse rural settlement types is that of the western part of central Europe. One of the most comprehensive and compressed treatments of such is a research study by Robert E. Dickinson, "Rural Settlements in the German Lands." The following classification by Christaller, cartographically adapted by Dickinson (Figure XXVI-9), greatly aids the student in grasping an historical-geographical perspective of European rural settlements:

1. The Irregular Clustered Village (*Haufen-* or *Gewanndorf*)
   (a) in the old Volksland (the initial areas of German tribal settlement) of Lower Saxony (*Niedersachsen*); the north of each of Westphalia, Hesse, and Thuringia; and Schleswig-Holstein: and
   (b) in the areas of early medieval settlement in south Germany and the Rhineland.
2. Isolated Farmsteads (*Einzelhöfe*)
   (a) irregularly scattered, e.g., Münsterland;
   (b) in groups around a village nucleus (*Schwarmensiedlung*), e.g., Osnabrück district; and
   (c) in linear arrangement, along routeways (*Kettendörfer*).
3. Hamlets (*Weiler*)
   (a) founded by landlords in forest clearings in south Germany;
   (b) grouped around large estate farms (*Gutshöfe*), as in Mecklenburg; and
   (c) emerging through the continual subdivision of holdings (*Erbteilung*) in areas with dispersed farmsteads.
4. Placé villages (*Platzdörfer*) or Rundlings, the primitive Slav settlements of the early medieval period.
5. *Angerdörfer*, the chief village type in the east German (colonized) lands.
6. Street Villages (*Strassendörfer*), the name being used only for those villages which were founded on an existing route; these are widespread in the Slav lands.
7. Linear Villages (*Reihendörfer*) are similar to the villages of groups 2 (*c*) and 6, but are fundamentally different in origin. They include:
   (a) marsh villages (*Marschhufendörfer*);
   (b) forest villages (*Waldhufendörfer*);
   (c) *Fehnkolonien;* and
   (d) estate settlements (*Gutskolonien*).
8. Estate Villages (*Gutshöfe*), both isolated and in combination with villages, e.g., Mecklenburg.
9. Urban Villages, especially mining and industrial settlements.
10. Suburban Settlements.
11. Modern Industrial Settlements.[1]

The technique used by Dickinson in this article on settlement morphology reminds one of that used by Davis in developing his classical geomorphological concepts of "structure, process, and stage."

[1] Dickinson, Robert E., "Rural Settlements in the German Lands," *Annals of the Association of American Geographers*, Vol. XXXIX, No. 4, December, 1949, pp. 260-261. Reprinted by permission.

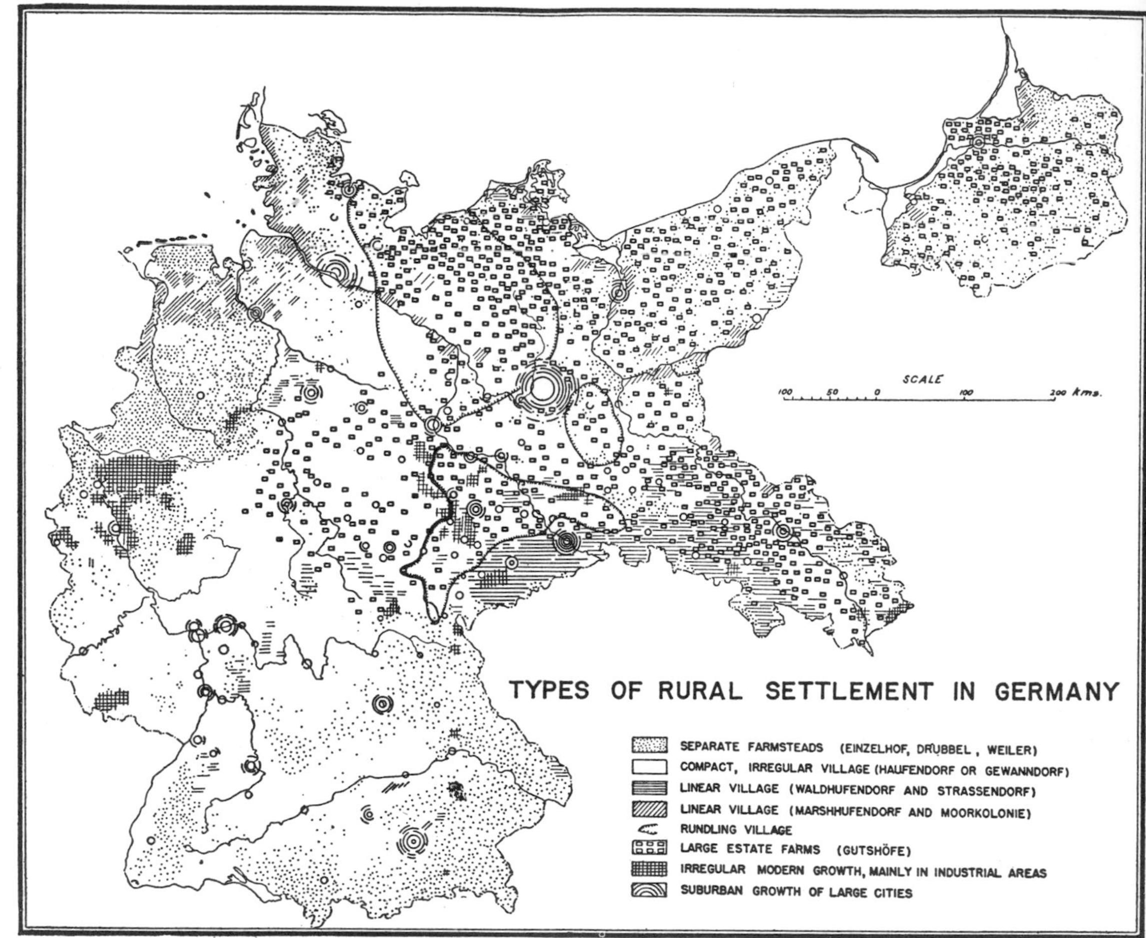

XXVI:9 Study this map of the types of rural settlement in Germany in conjunction with the text. (From "Rural Settlements in the German land," *Annals of the Association of American Geographers,* Vol. XXXIX, No. 4, December, 1949, used by permission)

Mapped types of each of the various agricultural communities here presented indeed prove very instructive, but space does not permit their reproduction. However, a general idea of what farm and field patterns were like, as found for example in the medieval manor, is shown diagrammatically in Figure XXVI-10.[1] Note (1) the complete absence of any suggestion of rectangular field design such as is common today in large sections of the United States; (2) the winding roads, unoriented with reference to any field pattern; (3) a typical "Strassendorf" type of village near a stream, suggesting transportational utility and in proximate position to the manorial estate buildings, including parsonage and church; (4) the far-flung landlord's domain (The Demesne); (5) the fragmented cultivated fields held by the parish church; (6) the peripheral woodlands and wastelands; (7) the dual seasonal plantings in autumn, possibly of wheat, and spring cereal or vegetable planting; (8) a common pasture, jointly shared by landlord and tenants; (9) quite a sizable section of

XXVI:10 (Right) Try to identify on this plan of a medieval manor the nine landscape features outlined in the text. (*Historical Atlas* by William R. Shepherd, Velhagen & Klasing, Ohg., Bingerstr 62, Berlin-Wilmersdorf, Germany, used by permission)

[1] Though a conventional diagram such as this cannot portray regional reality, it does have the advantage of synthesizing regional perspective.

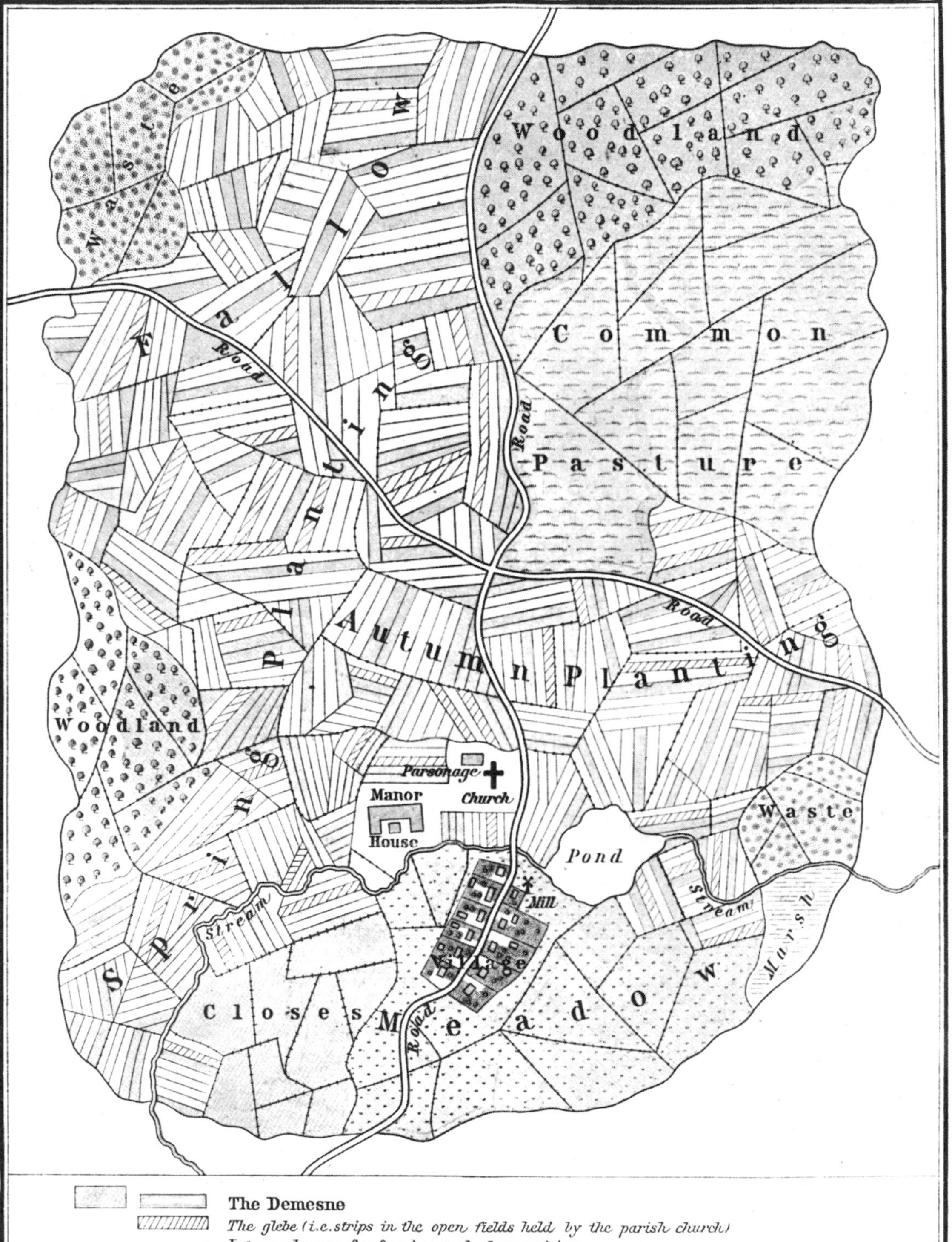

The Demesne

The glebe (i.e. strips in the open fields held by the parish church)

Later enclosures for farming and sheep-raising

This plan of a manor is wholly conventional. It is intended to show: (1) the various features that might be found in English manors (or vills) of the mediaeval period; (2) the more important changes in the agricultural system which occurred in England from the fourteenth century onward. Many of these manorial features, of course, appeared in similar domains on the continent.

fallow in the upper left area of the figure, rotated possibly with seasonal cereal farming.

The French Revolution not only marked the breakaway from the political patterns of governments inherited from the medieval period, but paved the way as well for innovations in agriculture and industry. The emancipation from feudal occupational restrictions on the burgher, serf, and noble alike was responsible more than anything else for the agricultural revolution which occurred in the eighteenth and early part of the nineteenth centuries. Among the agricultural reforms were the following: (1) increasing ownership of homes; (2) replacing of the old-time biennial and extensive fallow with a more scientific system of farming, involving the growing of green manure crops and the application of animal manures; (3) supplementing of cereals with root crops to provide animal winter fodder, and also thereby releasing some pasture lands well-adapted for crop culture; (4) the introduction of scientific breeding of domestic animals for various forms of utility; (5) acquisition of more lands by more peasants; and (6) consolidation of the previously held fragmented units of farm culture.

One of the most far-reaching transformations of field culture resulted from crop and pasture rotation, made possible by the erecting of fences, often in the form of hedges. Already appearing in the latter part of the medieval period, this practice received its greatest impetus from the Enclosure Acts of England in the latter eighteenth century. The present checkerboard or irregular farm field design marked off by stone fences or hedges, rail or board fences, and barbwire, especially in mixed farming areas, had its chief innovation at this time.

The multifunctional European capital

An entire new set of towns and cities developed in western Europe as a result of the agricultural and industrial revolutions. The extension of roadways led to the opening of many backwoods districts for agricultural settlement. Railway transportation greatly modified the traffic pattern here, as it did in America, thus giving rise to new trading and commercial centers at strategic points of intersection. The discovery and subsequent exploitation of ore deposits resulted in the development not only of mining communities but also of large industrial centers in many cases.

One of the most distinctive features of urban development in western Europe is that, unlike the capitals of many other important countries in the world, the capitals of western Europe are almost altogether multifunctional. Situated strategically in terms of trade, as we have already seen on the medieval trade map, such capitals as London, Paris, and Berlin early came to be noted for their pre-eminence in commerce and industry. The relations of qualities of geographic site to this multifunctional development of the major capitals of Europe is well brought out by Wright:

¶ In size and influence the great capitals, pre-eminently London, Paris, and Berlin, have come far to outdistance [the other] urban centers with the exception of Rome. . . . London and Paris . . . became commercial and political towns of the first rank early in the Middle Ages. They both occupy advantageous positions at the crossing of trade routes. The Thames estuary forms a magnificent port, easy of defense against hostile navies. Communication with the interior lowland of England is more direct than from the Channel ports, which are cut off by lines of low hills. Furthermore, London lies almost directly on the seaway that follows the coast of the continental mass of northwestern Europe.

Paris is near the center of the Paris Basin, or lowland of northern France. Connected with the sea by the deep lower course of the Seine, Paris is also a port for barges and vessels of shallow draft. The eastern tributaries of the Seine converge toward the city like spokes around the axle of a wheel, offering avenues northeastward to the Low Countries and German plain, eastward to southern Germany, and southward to the Rhone Valley and Mediterranean. . . .

These natural advantages of situation and site would probably have stimulated the growth of London and Paris even had they not become national capitals, but in the latter case it is doubtful if the immense increase in size that these cities have experienced in modern times would have ensued. . . . The superior position that they early acquired was confirmed by the emergence of England and France as strong, centralized nations at the close of the sixteenth

This is a street scene in Paris, the world culture locus. (Courtesy French Government Tourist Office, Chicago)

century. But it is primarily the Industrial Revolution that has brought about the altogether exceptional growth of the last century.

In the case of Berlin, metropolitan development came much later. The reason lies partly in the late unification of Germany as a nationalistic state and partly in the late appearance of the Industrial Revolution in Germany. During the Middle Ages Berlin was smaller than many of the towns of western and southern Germany and not until the rise of Prussia did it appear as the capital of a powerful state. Berlin illustrates, more strikingly perhaps than London or Paris, the importance of the political factor in the evolution of a great capital. The commercial advantages of its position are not comparable with those of Paris and London. The city stands in the midst of a broad plain, well to the east and north of the principal commercial and industrial regions of Germany. While it is readily reached by roads and railways, it is not a seaport, nor even a river port, although canals connect it with the waterways of the north German plain. And yet, as capital, Berlin has become the focus not only of the nation's governmental administration but of its business and finance. . . . The most striking fact about the great European capitals is their surpassing size.[1]

The traveler in Europe will observe side by side some of the most antique and modern urban sculptures and building architectures. This, of course, is understandable in the light of urban developments dating back to the days of the ancient Roman Empire. Just as the Roman world showed many features of Greek architecture, relict forms of the ancient Roman era are found in the southwestern section of *Cfb* Europe. Other ancient hallmarks, such as urban walls and moats, reflect the importance of defense, almost uni-

[1] Wright, John Kirtland, *op. cit.*, pp. 86-89, *passim.* Reprinted by permission.

versally necessary during the medieval period. Many of the west-central European cities retain the qualities of site, originally inherited from early medieval times—favorable harbor, confluence of navigable streams, mountain passes, productive hinterlands, convergence of trading routes, and the like. Mercantile trading agencies such as the Hanseatic League were instrumental in the establishment of seaports and hinterland trading centers. By the fifteenth century, a number of communities had attained the 100,000 population mark. Largest of these was Paris with a population of approximately 300,000. The largest cluster of industrial centers at this time was to be found in the Flanders area. By 1800, London had surpassed all the cities on the continent, having been the first city to attain the million population mark.

While appreciable urban growth may be dated back to about the thirteenth century, the development of giant cities did not occur until about the nineteenth century, and then was strikingly accentuated in the twentieth century. As many as ten cities of western Europe have now passed the million mark, including the multimillion cities of Berlin (approximately 3½ million), Paris (over 5 million), and Greater London (nearly 9 million).

But the cities of *Cf* Europe are not to be measured simply quantitatively, but qualitatively as well in terms of their industrial, commercial, political, and cultural importance. Suburban satellite communities of acre homesites, as we so commonly find in America, are relatively rare in Europe. On the other hand, smaller towns and villages are much more common in Europe and combine both urban and rural functions. In fact, in many parts, the greater part of the farming population resides in such dual-functional villages. Due to the greater complexities of urban development, city and community planning and regional planning in Europe have long been a pressing issue. It is understandable then that some of the most advanced principles of geographic planning in the world are found here. Emphasis has not only been given to the utilitarian aspect, i.e., to zoning areas for commerce, industry, and residence, but also towards improving the hygienic standards of living and landscape beautification.

West Europe the homeland of the Industrial Revolution

The continent of Europe is the homeland of Western culture, spawned, as we have seen, in the East-Mediterranean area. It is also the continent of revolutions—political revolution (France); the agrarian revolution discussed in the previous section; and the Industrial Revolution, which represents a break with old-time household workshops and the emergence of mechanized, highly-specialized factory establishments. The period of the Industrial Revolution has generally been assigned to the latter half of the eighteenth and the first half of the nineteenth century. Shortly enveloping the entire western European area, its inception occurred in England and may be said to have started in the field of textiles.

Though, as pointed out earlier in this chapter, climate favorably conditioned the setting for such development in this part of the world, mechanization is the product of the inventive genius of man, which includes—and this is often overlooked by nongeographic writers—the *recognition of environmental adaptability* of his inventions. Industrial incentive in the world first became localized in the southern North Sea countries, and it is this locale which witnessed the most phenomenal industrial transformation of all time. The first evidence of this transformation is associated with the labor-saving inventions in the textile industry of England. In the middle of the eighteenth century, the inventions of the flying shuttle, the spinning Jenny, and the carding machine initiated the first step in the acceleration of mechanized clothing manufacturing. This modernization of textile manufacturing, because of earlier machine adaptability, came first in the cotton and then in the woolen textile industries. Since inventions primarily concern effectively operating machinery, there emerged the incentive to discover improved methods first of smelting iron ore and second to find new minerals and perfect new alloy steels. One of the most revolutionary inventions of the Industrial Revolution was the discovery in the early 1730's of the blast furnace process involving the use of coking coal. A second leading invention was that of the steam engine in the 1760's, which presaged the use of steam power as a substitute for hand and water power. In the 1830's, power looms supplanted hand looms, which aroused much opposition, as has commonly been the experience, to labor-saving devices. After the turn of the century, the Watt engine was applied to the first locomotive in England and to the first steamship on the Hudson in America.

The explorations and colonizations overseas in the seventeenth and eighteenth centuries introduced new sources of raw supplies, particularly cotton, which in itself had a revolutionary effect in apparel manufacturing in the gradual substitution of large quantities of cotton for woolen and flax textiles. England, shortly after the turn of the nineteenth century, began to import cotton heavily from America and wool from South Africa and Australia. In the twentieth century, European as well as American corporate specialties of manufacturing emerged, substituting electrical power for steam power, which may in turn be replaced by atomic energy and automation.

Now what does this brief and over simplified discussion of the Industrial Revolution point to concerning the nature of time-space-resource-relationsips? This may perhaps best be answered by referring to one of the best-informed and best-known world geographers, renowned for his research of not only the British Isles and Europe but of all continents —L. Dudley Stamp:

¶ The factors which contributed to the localization of the cotton industry in South Lancashire in the seventeenth century—the existence of linen and woollen industries in the soft-water region of the Pennine flanks, and the settling of foreigners in a non-corporate town—are not sufficiently exclusive or conclusive to explain the present concentration. Numerous other regions had soft water, Flemish weavers, and an atmosphere humid enough for successful spinning. The secret of the expansion of the industry in Lancashire lies in the fact that *as each new development arose, so the natural environment of the region was found capable of being utilized in the desired manner* [italics ours]. When machinery was invented, water power was available; when steam power arrived coal could not have been in closer proximity; the development of chemical bleaching was aided by the presence of the Cheshire salt field, only a few miles away, and by the abundance of soft water; and the need for transport could be satisfied by comparatively easy canal railway construction, and by the enlargement of the existing ports of Liverpool and Manchester. The Industrial Revolution period witnessed all these factors in operation.[1]

The passage italicized impresses us as an apt geographic expression of the nature of man's environmental relationships. In Stamp's succinct statement we note the dynamic character of geography: man, not nature, determines localization of his activities, but man usually does and should utilize his environment in the best possible manner. Moreover, as noted, *time* and *technology* transform environmental qualities—hence the need for evaluating every environmental situation in its appropriate transitory stage.

Thus we have observed that resourceful man in western Europe recognized and appropriated the natural resources to his best advantage. These resources combined with a stimulating climate, a vast plain facilitating land transportation and crop tillage, and a unique pattern of navigable rivers and canals favoring freight and passenger traffic, were instrumental in developing western Europe as a world trading center. Canalization, favored by proximate headwater river courses, makes possible continuous navigation from the Mediterranean to the North Sea by way of the Rhone and Rhine valleys, to the Bay of Biscay via the Loire, to the English Channel via the Seine, to the Black Sea by way of the long and deep Danube. Other major accessory streams in Central Europe supply waterways to the Baltic. Ocean commerce, moreover, here can exploit the many excellent harbors situated on the greatest indentations of bays and seas and estuaries of any continent. And the North Sea area, placed at the center of the World Land Hemisphere, is a natural marine focus of world commerce. The immediate impetus to nineteenth and twentieth century manufacturing was related to minerals, basically coal and iron, without which it is difficult to conceive how even the most resourceful peoples of Europe, or of any other continent,

[1] Stamp, L. Dudley, and Beaver, S. H., *The British Isles*, Longman's, Green and Co., Inc., New York, 1954, p. 494. Reprinted by permission.

could have brought about the Industrial Revolution. And it is in this respect also that western Europe on the whole is singularly blessed. But major regional differences in mineral concentrations do occur, and are discussed in connection with the major powers in chapters 32 and 33.

Western European agricultural production is conspicuously diverse but deficient

Western European countries are commonly considered as primarily manufactural and commercial. This impression has probably resulted from the fact that none of the countries is agriculturally self-sufficient, and most of them are heavy importers of food, much of it from other *Cfb* countries. The reason for this is not low productivity, but rather the heavy population. Let us consider a few round figures. Compare, for example, the lowest populated country, France, of 200 persons per square mile, with that of the United States of only 50—and France is not normally considered densely populated. Nearly all the rest of the western European countries have population densities that are as great as, or even greater than, we find in the Orient. We commonly think of China and Japan, 150 and 500 per square mile, respectively, as overpopulated. But most of the western European population figures eclipse these —Germany, 500; England and Belgium around 750; and Netherlands almost 800! It is not surprising, then, with these high densities, combined with the relative high standard of living as compared with that of the Orient, that the European is faced with a food-import situation, despite the natural assets and the modern efficient land management adapted to make the most of nature's resources.

Actually the European continent is said to have the highest percentage of arable lands of any continent and in general the highest sustained year-by-year yields of cereals and most other crops. Apparently also, Europe has the most favorable temperature-rainfall growing season combination, combined with favorable relief and soil conditions. Still another factor is the great diversity of agricultural products, embracing all the major grains grown in middle-latitude countries, with the exception of corn and rice. The high populations indicated necessitate intensiveness of agriculture; western Europe probably has the most scientific development of agriculture in the world. This is excellently portrayed in the so-called "Farm Adoption," regional sample sketches of typical farms and farmers in the British Isles. These are detailed comprehensive and continuing surveys by the Association of Agriculture in collaboration with various agencies—The National Farmers' Union; The National Federation of Young Farmers' Clubs; various universities, including the London School of Economics Geography Department; and the participating "adopted" farmer, whose correspondence helps keep the farm adoption scheme up-to-date. The selected regional studies give an idea of the great diversity of farm types in the British Isles: (1) A fruit and hop farm in Kent, (2) a cattle and sheep rearing farm on the Welsh border, (3) a cropping and feeding farm in east Perthshire, (4) a west country dairy farm, (5) a mixed farm on the Yorkshire wolds, (6) a small mixed farm in West Wales, (7) a milk and beef farm in Northamptonshire, (8) a sheep farm in the western Highlands, (9) a small dairy farm in South-west Scotland. Note the over-all accent on the animal industry, particularly sheep rearing and dairying.

Because of the pressure of food production, it might be inferred that there is little or no room for engaging in animal industries. However, in this respect western Europe differs markedly from the Orient. In many sections acreages in pasture and forage crops equal or excel those in grain and other crops. This is especially true in the English Channel–North Sea area where the pastoral economy represents a sort of climax development. Optimal climatic conditions apply particularly to the development of the dairy industry. The cool summers, mild winters, and year-round rains favor the growth of luscious grasses and almost year-round grazing. The need for barns to store the large quantities of fodder is thereby reduced, while the much milder winters than in our *Dfb* (Chapter 28) likewise call for less shelter for animals. It should not be surprising, therefore, that several of our most famous dairy cows, such as the Jersey and Guernsey, were originally bred on islands of these names in the English Channel region. In addition to the optimal climate conditions, marketing conditions are likewise most favorable. As already previously indicated, western Europe has by far the highest density of population of Western culture. The delivery of raw milk and other dairy products accordingly finds a ready market in the many metropolitan communities of the area. About the same climatic and marketable situations may be said to obtain for specialized vegetable and fruit cultures whose perishability, like milk, calls for nearby urban consumer populations.

Now let us take a look at the leading food source in the form of the staple grains—wheat, oats, rye, and barley, in about that order of importance. Wheat and rye are primarily bread staples, whereas oats and barley in the main are fed to animals. Like any other plant, each of these has its own optimal conditions of climate and soil for greatest productivity; and again here also, individually or at least in combination, they excel in area productivity. Though all are rather widely tolerant of temperature and moisture range, they seem best acclimated latitudinally in the order indicated: wheat concentrated heavily between the 40-50° latitude, with some extension beyond as in England; oats concentrations primarily from 45° to 60°; rye between 50° and 60°; and barley, about the same latitude as rye. Other considerations for concentrating on growth of certain cereals are, of course, also involved. Wheat is the premier bread cereal of the temperate clime and of Western culture, and ranks among the highest yields for so large a region of western Europe. The highest percentage of rye acreage in the world—in northeastern Germany or along the Baltic—generally reflects the poor, sandy, acid soils to which rye is better adapted than practically any other cereal. The highest percentage of barley acreage is found in Denmark because of her specialized production of hogs for lean and firm bacon and ham. Malting barley for the manufacture of beer, the major European human use of this grain today, finds concentrations in central Germany. Barley is thought by some authorities to have been the most ancient cereal grown for both animal and human consumption. As an excellent dairy feed for animals, high concentrations of it occur in eastern England and other southern North Sea countries.

Some other major considerations for the sowing of the several grains include: The high rainfall tolerance of oats and its high adaptability to acid soils leads to concentrations in the wetter and sandier section of Ireland, Scotland, and the Baltic belt. Rye being the most hardy grain, produces a higher yield of food value than any other grain on highly acid, thin sandy soils, characteristic of the southern Baltic. Also it is one of the most drought-resistant of the grains and, like oats and barley, has a high altitude and latitudinal spread. It is predominantly a European crop.[1]

Despite the most scientific intensive and adaptive farming methods of western Europe, none of its countries has attained self-sufficiency. Even Germany which has utilized to the utmost its sandy soils for the production of potatoes to supplement the grain diet, and most nearly self-sufficient France, with its richly diverse and extensive agricultural tillage and the highest percentage of wheat acreage, must rely in part on food imports. Also, England, with all its surprisingly high arable acreage and pasturage, is not self-sustaining for a period of more than several months and would face catastrophe in a war which isolated it from the rest of the world.

The widely varying cultures of non-European lands

Lands outside western Europe with typical marinal characteristics include the fiorded coastal Anglo-American sections of British Columbia and "Panhandle" Alaska, the island-studded Indian-Spanish Chile, the Dutch-English highlands of Union of South Africa, coastal Victoria and New South Wales, Australia, and their neighboring mountain-ribbed pastoral islands of New Zealand. However, a comparison of marine Europe with the sectors of the Americas and those of the African and Australian segments brings out striking physiographic and economic diversities. Mixed or regionally differentiated racial and other patterns also occur (e.g., the Araucanian Indian–Spanish

[1] For one of the most comprehensive cartographic and textual treatments of cultivated crops, geographically analyzed, see *The Agricultural Resources of the World* by William Van Royen. Prentice-Hall, Inc., 1954.

Exceedingly diverse as is French agriculture, France is pre-eminent in the world in viticulture, and is the leading producer of wine. Note the numerous laborers in the field. Mechanized viticulture is limited. Can you see why? (Courtesy French Government Tourist Office, Chicago)

in south central Chile; the Bantu-Coloured-Dutch-British-Hindu in southeastern Africa).

Let us consider first the climatic contrasts between the American and the eastern Atlantic sectors. Compare, for example, the annual and seasonal rainfall of Los Evangelistas with that of Paris. (See Taxonomic Key in the Appendix.) This Chilean section has almost five times the amount of moisture that the Paris Basin has. Some localities in southern Chile seldom see sunshine (perhaps only one day in five) and record over 200 inches of annual rainfall. The North American counterpart, the next ranking rainy section, records for Sitka 85 inches, and with over a two-fold fall-winter "max," starting in October with the highest monthly rainfall—12 inches (Figure XXVI-4). The *Cf* African-Australian sectors average between 20 and 40 inches total rainfall, and thus are more like western Europe.

*1. **Southern Chile.*** The alert student will be aware at once that geographically these European and American comparisons of climatic station data challenge the applicability of the Köppen *Cfb* nomenclature for such widely divergent variations in moisture. Since Köppen climatic criteria are designed to reflect vegetative distinctions and other ecological areal differentiations, we would indeed expect as much difference between the cover of *Cfb* Chile and *Cfb* France as between, say, *Cfb* France and *Cfa* United States. No one would expect to find nature providing the Paris Basin with the dank, dripping-wet towering Araucaria pine forest, characteristic of the coastal-mountain lands of Chile. By the same token, even the most confirmed critic of the long-discredited "environmentalism" would not seriously disavow the lower cultural potentialities of this area as compared with those of western Europe, especially if he takes into consideration such environmentally restrictive features as the

Andean barrier to communications on its eastern Argentine frontier and the forbidding ports on the seaside, where for the most part, lighters are used to transfer freights, cargoes, and even passengers. Chilean Patagonia is, moreover, in the stormiest section of the "Roaring Forties," encountered first by the global navigator, Magellan, as he navigated the strait in 1520, subsequently named after him. The beginnings of the Chilean nation emerging from the conflict between the Spanish and the natives is dramatized in *La Araucana,* said to be "one of the greatest epics in Spanish-American literature."

This example is a classic caution to the student not to generalize either the natural vegetation or the anthropologic character of a culture on the basis of simply a two-letter or even three-letter climatic symbolism. Such remote "kinships" as *Cfb* Europe and *Cfb* Chile had better be further subdifferentiated into a moderate rainfall phase (*Cf"m"b*)—under 50 inches rainfall, let us say, and an over-50 category (*Gf"h"b*) for the much heavier rainfall. Another striking distinction is temperature range. Los Evangelistas, you will observe, "heats" up to an average of 47° F. in January, and "cools" off to an average of 38° F. in July—a range of only 9 degrees! Paris, on the other hand, has a July temperature of 66° F. and a January temperature of 38° F.—almost three times the range of the Chilean station.

This sunless, summer-less, fog-enshrouded, and rain-drenched forest-desert is home for "the blanketed Indian" and the wilderness-loving shepherd. No wonder that the area scores characteristically under two persons per square mile, and even less in the interior. The accompanying map of the Pan-American Union (Figure XXVI-11) strikingly portrays this cultural vacuum; note the almost complete absence of roads, railroads, and ports.

2. *Fiorded British Columbia and the island-studded Alaska "Panhandle."* These are the North American counterparts of *Cfb* Chile in such physiographic features as indicated. However, the climate of the former,

XXVI:11 (Right) Note the attenuated and articulated structure of Chile, especially the *Cfb* (*Cfc*) section. What problems does this present in unity and security?

despite heavy rain, especially in the fall, is much more hospitable, and its minerals and fisheries are much more valuable. Exceedingly more resourceful also are the timber stands of western hemlock, western red cedar, the northern Sitka spruce, and the southern Douglas fir. In fact, this area has one of the densest stands of merchantable softwood timber in the world. British Columbia possesses almost as much marketable conifer as all the other Canadian provinces together, and almost one-half of the lumber milled in Canada comes from this province. Farther north, the Alaska panhandle produces shingle, pulp, and paper products. The shape and position of the panhandle provides an interesting study in historical and political geography. The map shows that this proruption of southeast Alaska blocks almost half of the British Columbia coast line. Here is an instance in which the map itself arouses a geographer's curiosity, particularly as he observes other "panhandles" in the world (e.g., Burma). See if you can determine the strategic historic-political factor on which this geographic curiosity is based. British Columbia has been frustrated in bringing in machinery to develop mining and water-power enterprises of the area immediately to the east, involving a 350-mile transport over the 10,000-foot-high Babine Mountains to the Canadian port of Prince Rupert, the first port beyond the southern end of the panhandle. Canada has offered to exchange power in return for a leased access directly to the sea across the Alaskan "dangling barrier."

3. Southeastern Union of South Africa. This has climatic components of *C, B,* and *A.*[1] Space will permit focus on only two features which mostly distinguish it from the other *Cfb* non-European areas, namely phenomenal racism and mineral exploitation. Here live side by side (Figure XXVI-12), in the utmost social confusion and economic and political conflict, the black Bantus, dominant native tribe numbering over 8,000,000; some 350,000 Indians (Hindus), mostly sugar plantation workers in Natal replacing the Zulus, about 1860; and over a million Cape Coloureds, a mixed group, constituting about half the population of Cape Town. These "colored," once sharing voting privileges with the whites, now hold themselves aloof from both the whites and the natives. Superimposed upon these native and immigrant cultures and supervising the economic and political affairs is the European, whose first Dutch settlements came about through the refueling and revictualing of the Dutch East India trading expeditions in the middle of the seventeenth century. Subsequently French Huguenots arrived and were integrated with the Dutch into the Afrikaaner or Boer. Then, when the Dutch East India Company collapsed in the Napoleonic era, the British took over the Cape area, the Boers retiring mostly to Natal and the Orange Free State. The British ultimately took over South Africa in the early twentieth century. Thus, the Union became ultimately dominated by the whites, now numbering some two and a half million, about 60 per cent of whom are Afrikaaners; the rest mostly British. Though representing only about a fourth of the total population, the whites have through their Malan Nationalistic Government established what is probably the world's most "classic" example of racial segregation, the so-called policy of "apartheid." Racism, as a breeder of revolt by the nonwhites, has resulted in a notoriously high incidence of crime, thus giving Johannesburg the dubious distinction of being known as the "City of Crime."

But Johannesburg does also have other distinctions—rail focus of the Union, an outstanding mining and manufacturing center—both of which result in her being known also as the "City of Gold." Note in Figure XXVI-13 the extraordinary concentration of industry in and about this community. With a total value of mineral production equal approximately to that of the British Isles, the region, besides having coal and iron, has the additional advantage of rich ferro-alloy deposits of manganese and chromium ores, which, together with limestone flux, makes this a self-sufficient steel-manufacturing center. Just as Britain was the European homeland of the Industrial Revolution, as noted earlier, the Johannesburg area symbolizes the Industrial Revolution of the African continent. Although this in itself betokens material wealth and tech-

[1] The Union of South Africa was formed in 1910 from the colonies of Cape of Good Hope, Natal, Orange Free State, and Transvaal.

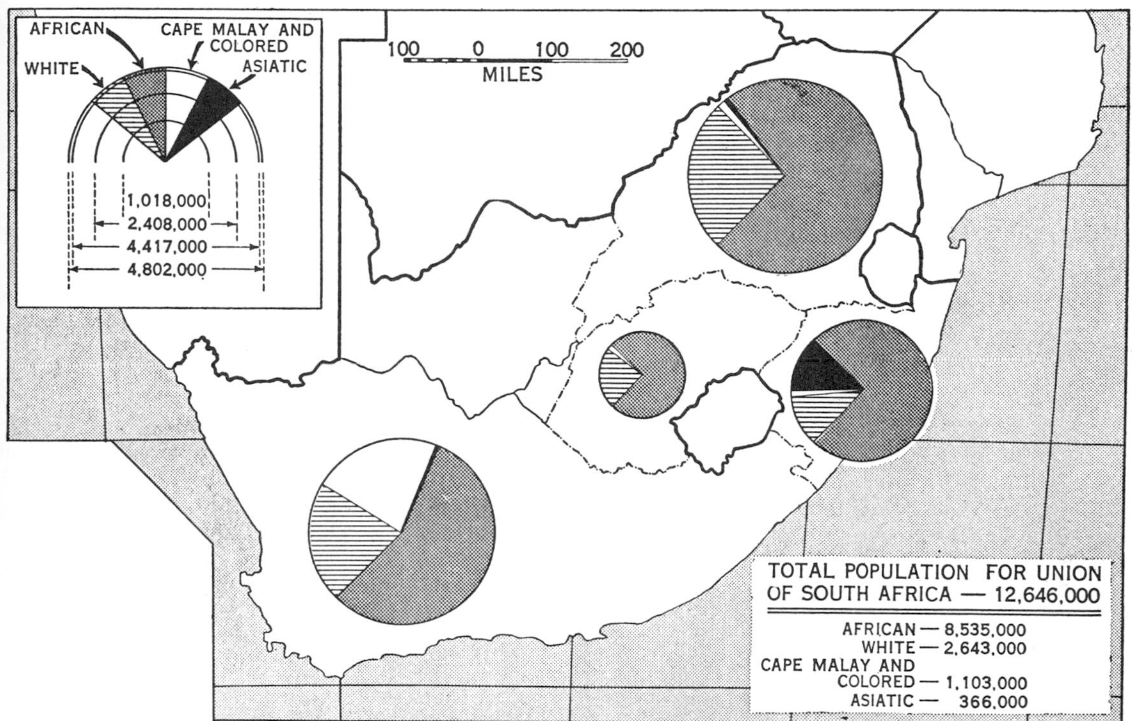

XXVI:12 Observe in this South Africa population pattern both the "pie" segments and insert scale. How do the various racial components vary regionally? (Samuel Thorne, Jr., and Alice Taylor, [Vincent Kotschar, cartographer], *Focus,* American Geographical Society, Vol. IV, No. 2, October, 1953, used by permission)

nological progress, Johannesburg's world famous reserves of diamonds, gold, and steel ironically, on the one hand, have contributed little towards raising the living and literate standards of the native, and on the other hand, have introduced added complications to the whole question of race discrimination and segregation the world over.

4. The "Fertile Crescent," Australia. A comparison of *Cfb* areas of Oceania shows some Australian-African geographic homologues—very similar southeastern coast climatic patterns, many of the same horticultural and other agricultural products, and comparable mineralized and industrialized regions (Figure XXVI-14). Even the areal population design, particularly featuring port concentrations, is similar, except that while the urban and peripheral regions of southeastern Australia have 25-100 persons per square mile, those of southeastern Africa have about twice as much.

The Australian population pattern reflects phenomenally contrasting coherent climatic-settlement associations. Remove *Cf* and *Cs* from Australia, and this island continent virtually disappears from the world scene, for, except for a sprinkling of aborigines, shepherds, and miners in the dry interior, the great desert heart is almost a void.[1] In Figure XXVI-15, Griffith Taylor most effectively portrays in his *isopract* the generalized population densities in relation to regional rainfall and temperature. It should be noted, however, that Taylor recognizes that other factors (e.g., political centers and intensive coal mining) also operate to attract people to the southeastern and to the southwestern Perth region. However, the dominant influence of the *C* climates is beyond dispute, for here intensive crop tillage without irrigation can replace sheep herding.

In the ethnographic setting, this Australian so-called "Fertile Crescent" also differs mark-

[1] Australia became a Commonwealth in 1901, converting into states the colonies of New South Wales, Queensland, South Australia, Tasmania, Victoria, and Western Australia.

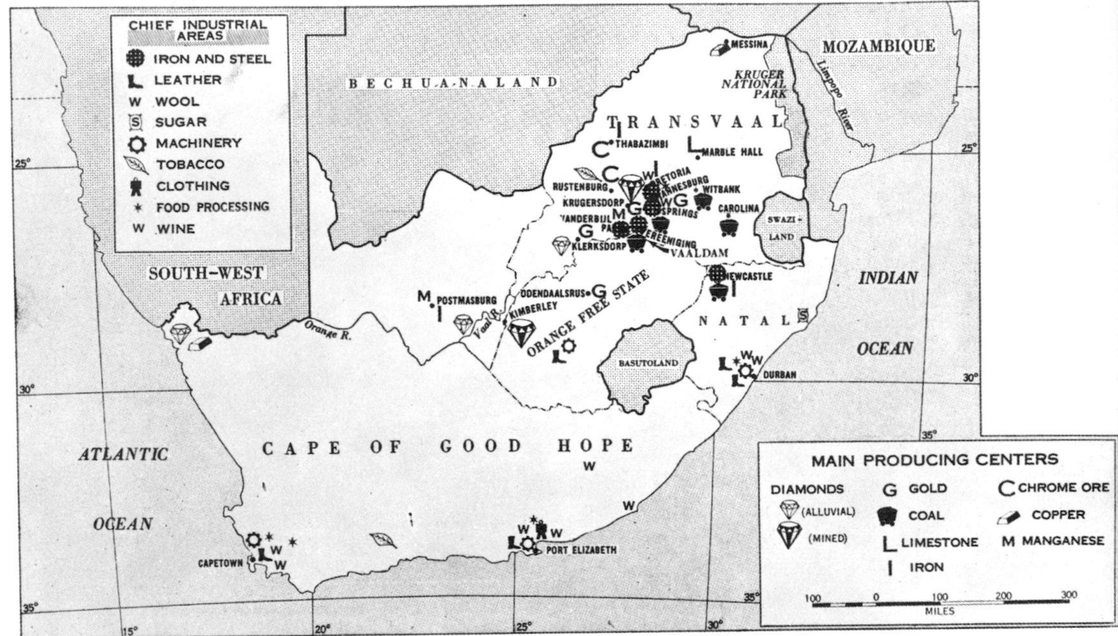

XXVI:13 This map shows the South African leading mining and manufacturing areas. Can you see why Johannesburg has been called the "City of Gold"? (Samuel Thorne, Jr., and Alice Taylor, [Vincent Kotschar, cartographer], *Focus,* American Geographical Society, Vol. IV, No. 2, October, 1953, used by permission)

edly from the African. Though also very much color-conscious, the Australian immigrant did not encounter here a black aboriginal settlement problem. Few in number, about 50,000, the black native occupies primarily the opposite northwestern coast or the interior, where densities are less than two per square mile; only a few aborigines come in contact with white man as herdsmen. But the geography of global destiny has posed for the Australian white a different challenge to his race consciousness — the brown and yellow Asiatic immigrant who came in numbers during the alluvial-gold rush of the middle nineteenth century. This cheap labor threatened white man's standards, which, together with anti-Asian bias, ultimately resulted in the adoption of the White Australia Asiatic exclusion policy.

5. New Zealand challenges American geographic literacy. The average person probably holds more illusions about this three-island "outpost" of civilization — if he has any geographic concepts of this area at all — than about any other white-occupied region of the globe.[1] Thus the uninformed may think: "New Zealand must have an inhospitable climate" (actually shares West Europe "optimum"); "diminutive in size" (larger than Great Britain and Northern Ireland, or about three times the size of Indiana); "lying next door to Australia" (but, as Taylor points out [10], "Wellington is four days away from Sydney by ordinary transport; and in point of fact is nearly as far away from Australia in accessibility as U.S.A. is from England"); "is governed by Great Britain or by Australia" (contrarily, is as much an independent dominion of the British Commonwealth as are Australia and Canada); "has the floral aspect of Australia" (again erroneous—reportedly has the most distinctive indigeneous vegetation of any land its size); "is topographically homogeneous" (actually regionally very diverse, with such striking contrasts as low-lying coastal plains, under 500 ft., and interior volcanic and glaciated mountains which range from several thousand to 10,000 feet, and over).

[1] Discovered by Tasman in 1642, and explored by Captain Cook in 1769, New Zealand's early history is geographically identified with whaling, for which the South Pacific is still noted.

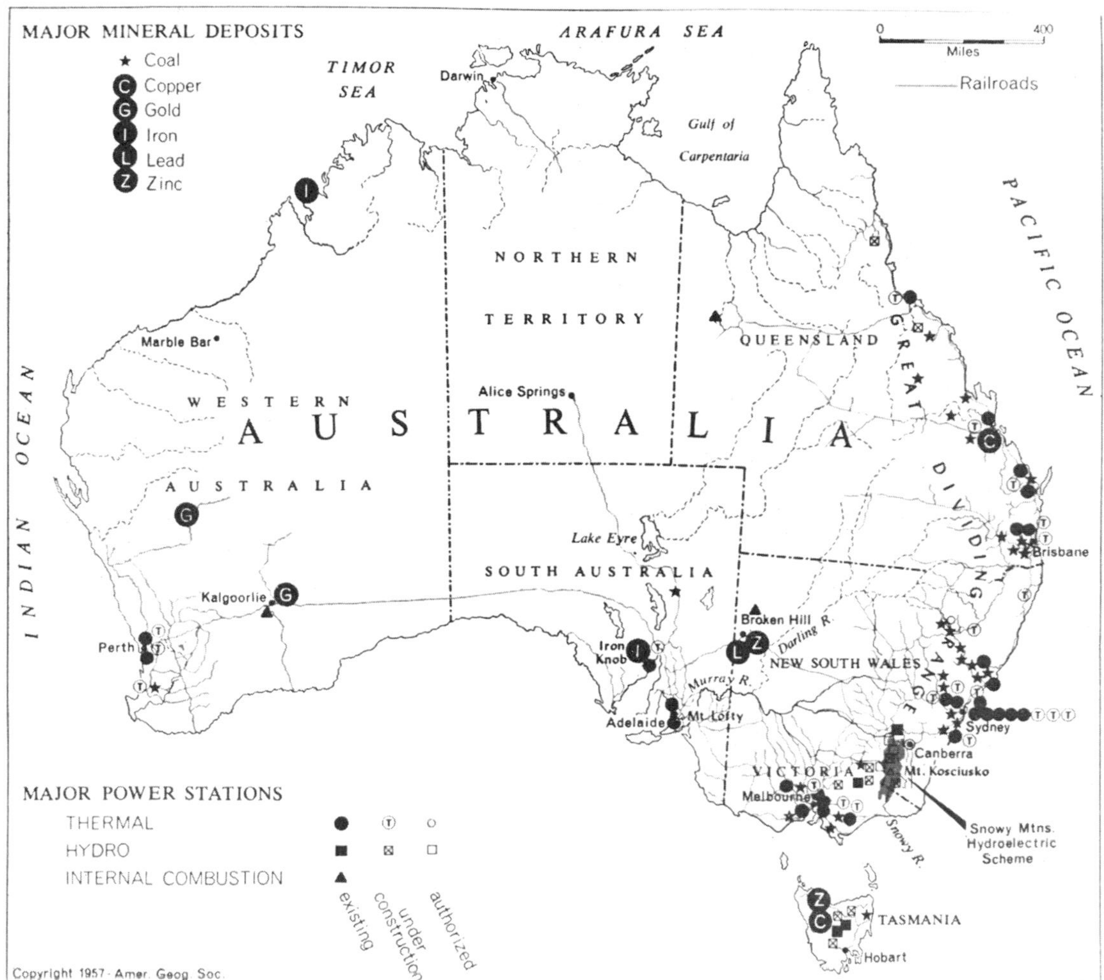

XXVI:14 The mineral deposits and power sites of Australia are shown here. Give all the reasons you can for the concentration of power sites in southeast Australia, the area that coincides primarily with the *Cf* region. ("Australia," Susan Huck, *Focus*, [Vincent Kotschar, cartographer], American Geographical Society, Vol. VII, No. 10, June, 1957, used by permission)

Why do such misconceptions exist? First of all, of course, because of the general paucity of professional geography instruction in American education. As it applies particularly to New Zealand, the misconceptions are somewhat understandable because of the dominion's geographic isolation. Looking at its position in global context, you will observe that it is situated just about in the center of the water-hemisphere, whereas the British Isles, whence came the immigrant settler, though equally marine-oriented, is near the center of the land-hemisphere. From this antipodal relationship derive other antithetical geographic characteristics between the two groups of isles: sea frontier population of the former only 2,200,000 compared with 54,300,000 of the latter; the contrast of extensive paddock grazing with intensive field culture; of isolated urban with conurbanized landscapes; exports of farm products of the one, in exchange for factory products of the other. New Zealand, like the other daughter dominions of the British Commonwealth, still stands as a symbol of long range support for survival of the British, whose own home food and fiber supplies are

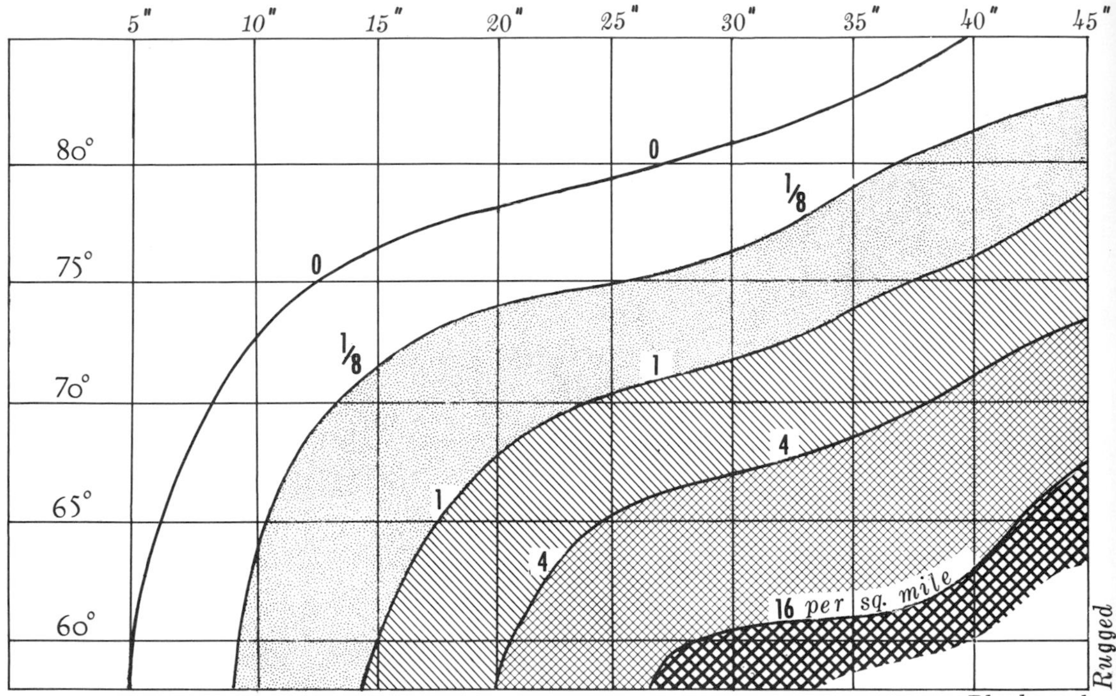

XXVI:15 This graph represents an isopract portrayal of Australian demography. Appraise this graphic method of illustrating the general effect of rainfall and temperature upon settlement in Australia. For more details on Taylor's own concept of this type of graph, see the credit source. (*Australia*, Griffith Taylor, E. P. Dutton & Co., Inc., 1940, used by permission)

in a great measure supplemented by the overseas *Cfb-Cfc* areas considered in this section. The sheep, which supplies both, is an animal common to practically all the *Cfb-Cfc* landscapes here considered. Since sheep breeding, rearing, and marketing have probably reached their highest scientific development in New Zealand in terms of geographic adaptation to environment, we shall present one of the finest models in agricultural geographic writing, namely, the type farm studies, through the courtesy of the British Association of Agriculture.[1]

[1] Unfortunately, this brief abstract, single map, and photo cannot possibly reflect the comprehensive treatment contained in the 18-sheet printed brochure, with 4 maps, 10 photos, plus 12 pages of mineographed farmer correspondence material.

New Zealand—A Fat Lamb Farm in the South Island
Richmond Downs, Amberley, North Canterbury
(Ronald A. Croft Farm)

¶ New Zealand is a small country situated in the South Pacific Ocean about 12,000 miles away from the United Kingdom. Its nearest neighbour is Australia, 1,200 miles to the north-west. There are three main islands—the North Island, the South Island and Stewart Island. The total area of these islands, together with other smaller islets, is roughly 103,400 square miles. This is approximately the same area as the United Kingdom. . . . Most of the South Island is mountainous and hilly country, but unlike the North Island there is no present or recent volcanic activity. . . . Because of these mountain ranges, the eastern side of the South Island is fairly dry and suited to sheep farming and cropping rather than to dairying. . . . The Croft farm, "Richmond Downs," is situated on rolling downs at the edge of the northern end of the Canterbury Plain 6½ miles by road from Amberly. . . . "Richmond Downs" is a fairly typical downland property of close on 790 acres, carrying some 1,600 sheep. . . .

In New Zealand the words "field" and

A tribal ceremony entertaining a Caucasian audience, wherever it may be, is generally symbolic of a relict culture in its last stages of absorption in a world culture. Equalizing factors of geographic change transform aboriginal cultures to modern national or even global patterns. Here Maoris of New Zealand, a truly Polynesian tribe, perform their ceremonial. Because of their intelligence and loyalty to their country, these native antipodeans of the "world down under" have been dubbed the "Britons of the south." What comparable native cultural change situations occur elsewhere in the world? (Courtesy The Canadian Pacific Railways)

"meadow" are practically never used, the great majority of farmers using the term "paddock." A "paddock," however, may vary in size from as little as 4 to as much as 300 acres. On the sheep runs in mountainous tussock country the term "block" is used for the larger enclosed areas, There are often thousands of acres in one block. . . . The layout of the farm [see accompanying photo] is fairly typical for improved properties along the foothills. Paddocks may not always have names and it is very common to refer to them as the "35-acre" or the "40-acre." There is very little level ground on this farm. Paddock No. 21 is still in native tussock grass because it is all fairly steep and impossible to cultivate and reseed. Of the remaining paddocks, some 420 acres are ploughable, but an area of about 150 acres, which consists of gullies with slopes, is too steep for cultivation. These slopes likewise still carry a large amount of the native tussock grasses. The ploughable country carries "English" grasses and clovers. Altogether there are over thirteen miles of fencing on the farm. . . .

The whole of "Richmond Downs" was originally part of the vast tussock grassland which covered nearly 17,000,000 acres of the eastern side of the South Island. Even today some 13,000,000 acres still remain and are the scene of extensive sheep farming. . . . Individual tussocks consist of thick tufts of harsh, wiry leaves adapted to resist drought and strong winds. These tussocks are from 2 to 4 feet high and, in their shelter, where the climate is milder and

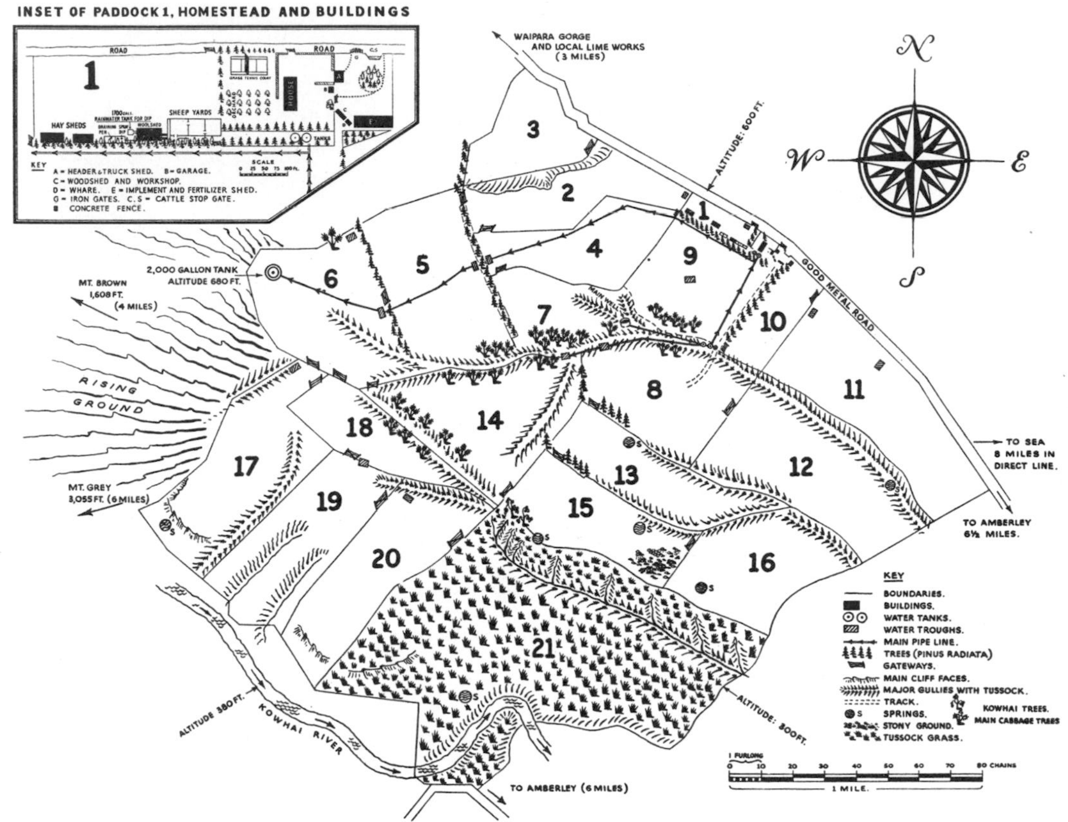

XXVI:16 "Richmond Downs" illustrates a typical paddock (field) layout of a New Zealand farm, near Amberley, North Canterbury. Note all the sketched features and see how much you can infer of the general nature of farming operations. ("New Zealand," *Farming in the Commonwealth,* the Association of Agriculture, London, used by permission)

moister, numerous herbs and smaller grasses grow, many of them palatable and nutritious. . . . Most of the ploughable areas of tussock have long been ploughed and either used for cropping or re-seeded with sown grasses. . . .

Climate, topography and soil fertility will always determine the type of pasture that can be established and the type of animal production that can be carried on, not only in New Zealand but all over the world. At "Richmond Downs" conditions favour the establishment of really first-class pastures. . . .

When the early pioneers settled the tussock grasslands of the South Island, they stocked them with Merino sheep brought in from Australia. . . . This is a breed noted for its fine wool. Later, refrigeration made the export of frozen meat a possibility. The settlers, therefore, concentrated on a dual-purpose animal (that is, one which would not only produce a satisfactory amount of good wool, but a valuable carcass of meat as well). . . . Ultimately, in 1900, by selection and in-breeding, a new breed had emerged and the New Zealand Corriedale took its place among the recognized breeds of the world. . . . The Corriedale was produced for certain conditions in New Zealand, but similar conditions to those in the South Island exist over large areas of the New World with the result that vast flocks of Corriedales have been built up in countries such as the Argentine, Uruguay, Peru, Chile, Brazil, the United States and Australia. As a result, this New Zealand breed is now the second commonest sheep in the world. When fat lamb production began to dominate the scene, the policy of crossing different breeds went a stage further. As a result, in the newly-sown areas of the North

This is a view of the New Zealand fat lamb farm, looking west from Paddock No. 14, diagrammed in Figure XXVI:16. The range is covered with tussock, except for some scrubby bush in the gulleys. Ewes and lambs are of the Corriedale breed. Does this type of terrain suggest any other possible use? (Photo from "New Zealand," *Farming in the Commonwealth,* Association of Agriculture, London, used by permission)

Island and in the flatter, wetter, paddock districts of the South Island, the New Zealand or improved Romney sheep predominates today. . . .

The most valuable animals on the farm, apart from the sheep, are the sheep dogs. . . . No sheep farmer could possibly do without his dogs which are mainly Border or Border-type collies. Long hours are spent in the careful training of a young dog until there grows such a close bond between dog and master that the dog seems to understand by instinct just what his master wants. . . .

Compared to the number of stock on the farm, the buildings may seem to be relatively simple. Sheep do not, of course, need any housing and the winters in New Zealand are not severe enough for it to be necessary to house any other farm animals. On a sheep farm, the only buildings that are really needed are a woolshed and sheds for implements and fertilizers. . . . Shearing machines, wool press and spray dip are permanent equipment in the woolshed and yards. . . .

New Zealand sheep farmers look to Britain to buy most of their meat and wool. Consequently, they try to produce the type and quality which their British purchasers prefer. . . . The vast distance separating New Zealand from her main markets (the fastest liners on the quickest route still take thirty days to reach the British Isles), her well-managed pastures, her favourable climate, the evolution of suitable breeds and crosses of sheep and factors such as refrigeration have developed a unique industry. Nowhere else in the world is there so intensive a system of fat lamb farming and the finest leg of imported lamb today has become more or less synonymous with Canterbury. Since this trade has been built up almost entirely to satisfy the British market, it serves to illustrate just how vital are the links between these two countries of the Commonwealth, which geographically are poles apart (11).

Complementary commercial aspects of Pacific and Atlantic *Cfb* lands contribute to the security of the Western world

We have now noted the essentially homologous coastal and climatic characteristics which suggest a certain *fundament* unitary quality of the world's middle latitude mild winter lands. Let us now, in summary, consider how the economic, commercial, and political aspects fit into the global framework of the several regions, otherwise widely separated. We shall observe particularly how the Dominion sections are economically integrated in the British Commonwealth. Mutually beneficial trade relations constitute, as we have tried to point out in the introductory chorogram, the key to common weal among nations, and this is about as well exemplified by the commerce of these lands as by the trade among any other group of countries in the world.

The Atlantic section, as was noted earlier, is critically "overpopulated"; the Pacific, generally "underpopulated." Western Europe is short on food products; except for certain local heavy industries, based on mining, as in South Africa, the Pacific, on the other hand, is short in supply of factory goods. How the hemispheric sections complement each other's economy is perhaps best illustrated by some round figures in regional trade statistics.[1] The Pacific sector exports are primarily of the extractive and livestock-produce type, whereas the chief imports from Western Europe consist of machinery and motor vehicles. South Chile is in the lowest trading category; its primary export is meat and wool products. Australia's figures are for the entire island, but the "Fertile Crescent" (*C*), comprising *Cf* and *Cs* areas, is by far the prime producer of surplus goods. Exports amounted to 782 million pounds, and imports 821 million. The Union of South Africa exported 331 million African pounds as compared with 482 million imports. New Zealand had a slight export balance—259 million pounds as against 251 million. British Columbia exports chiefly extractive products—minerals, lumber, fish, and considerable fruit. The most interesting fact of the other area exports is that wool leads in value in all of them: In order of value (millions of pounds), leading export products of the several areas rank as follows:

	Union of South Africa	*Australia*	*New Zealand*
wool	59	338	94
butter		29	51
meats		60	37 (lamb)
gold and silver	52		
wheat		46	
atomic energy material ...	30		
uncut diamonds .	24		
flour		19	
cheese			13½

The high wool exports reflect the adaptability of sheep to these regions, the nonperishability of the product, and the facility of transporting overseas a high value product at low cost. Excellently suited to grazing, the areal type becomes commercially significant for beef and mutton production, and for such dairy products as butter and cheese, as again lend themselves to efficient and economical transportation to distant lands. The mineral shipments of the Union of South Africa just about pay for the leading imports — motor cars, 48 million; cotton, rayon and woolen piece goods, 39 million; and drugs and fertilizers, 21 million. In all cases, the trade of the Dominion territories is heaviest with the United Kingdom, both in exports as well as in imports. Chief customers for New Zealand products are, in order: United Kingdom (170); France (15.3); United States (15); German Federal Republic (12.6); Australia (6.7); Italy (4.7); and Netherlands (4.5).

By far the greatest imports of New Zealand are from the United Kingdom (121), with Australia and the United States rating low second and third place (28 and 17, respectively). Australia patronizes primarily the United Kingdom and United States (356 and

[1] Based on Dominion pound values for 1955-56, as reported in *Statesman's Year Book,* Macmillan and Company, 1957.

99, respectively), followed by Germany (35). And the United States competes quite well with the United Kingdom in the markets of the Union of South Africa (100 compared with 167).

While all of these figures, then, reveal the close tie-in of the *Cf* "outposts" with the economy of the Western world, a commercial circumstance which in itself augurs well for its political security, we must not lose sight of the fact that basically the low populations of the non-European marine lands cannot provide the amplitude of markets needed to give more than a partial assist to the western European economy. So we conclude on the note on which we began this chapter — Europe needs to find a common denominator of economic organization with a view to stabilizing production and establishing more freely-flowing trade based upon sound geographic principles of regional agricultural and manufactural resources. Are such regional programs as the European Coal and Steel Community (ECSC), the Organization for European Economic Co-operation (OEECO), and the European Common Market (ECM) the primary answer to Europe's economic dilemma?

APPLICATION OF GEOGRAPHIC UNDERSTANDING

I. Medieval Western Europe (Based on Map, Figure XXVI-8)

A. Industrial "Chorolations"

1. What areas led in industry in medieval times?
2. Within the limited map data and textual reading of this chapter, try to account for each of these.
3. What other historic, economic, political, and geographic facts would you have to know before you could be reasonably certain of your answer?
4. At Limoges, we see the imprint "Ind .A (Enamels)." Recalling what enamels are used for and with the added clue in the map legend, "As a rule the raw materials were manufactured at or near the place of production," what environmental product might be inferred to be associated with this industrial arts center? Check your "geographic guess" against further research.
5. In relation to the previous question, would deposits of raw material have the same influence in localizing industry today as it did in medieval times? Why, or why not?
6. Why do we have exclusively "silk" in Italy? "wool" in England? Is this "geographically" what you would expect, naturally or culturally?
7. Which mineral was most widely exploited? Reasons?
8. Was coal used much industrially at this time?
9. How does the Ruhr-Meuse coal-iron pattern compare with that of modern times as described and illustrated in the chorogram?

B. Mountain Pass — Circulation Co-relations

1. Identify such passes as are mentioned in the text. What other passes do you recognize on the map?
2. How can you in general infer the historic significance of passes in the traffic pattern of this period?
3. In terms of such natural and cultural environmental data as you have obtained, attempt to evaluate the relative commercial importance of the several passes, using the following geographic categories: (a) topography of site; (b) regional situation (political and geographic); (c) hydrographic pattern (navigability of streams, corridor courses, direction of flow, portage connections, etc.); (d) trade route or routes and their connections with the leading markets, fairs, mining and manufacturing centers, as well as their relation to areas of agricultural surplus products which entered into interregional commerce.

C. Trade and Trading Centers

1. Account for the greater number of markets and fairs in England as compared with the much smaller number on the larger area of the continent.
2. Does the map give any regional clues whatsoever to "export" trade?
3. Trade arises from surplus production. In each case conjecture the geographic basis for the production of the following commodities: (a) lumber, (b) grain, (c) furs, (d) fish, (e) cattle.
4. How much information can you de-

rive, or deduce, from the map as to the extent and kind of trade carried on by western Europe with the Levant and the Orient by (a) sea, (b) land.

5. Compare medieval data on navigation time schedules with those of our modern day.

6. Where were the banking centers in medieval times? How and why does their distribution pattern differ from that in modern times?

7. Identify the leading commercial metropolises in relation to (a) the major landform regions, (b) the traffic routes, (c) the agricultural and industrial sections, (d) the political pattern.

II. Modern Western Europe (Your Outline Map)

We have observed in this chapter the integral marinal *Cfb* design based on natural geographic features and interregional commercial interests. But the student will also have noted the complexity of diverse subregional interests. It is one of the main challenges of modern Western diplomacy to establish an integrated pattern of natural and human resource development of western Europe which will serve as the economic counterpart of political NATO in effecting a strong defense of the Western world. Among these, as already pointed out in the introductory chorogram, is the European Coal and Steel Community (ECSC). There are others: The European Atomic Energy Commission (Euratom), Organization of European Economic Co-Operation (OEEC), and the European Economic Community (EEC). The last, organized in 1958, seeks to establish a Common Market among West Germany, France, Italy, and the "Benelux" countries by gradually eliminating customs and other international restrictive trade policies and practices which have hitherto prevented the free flow of commodities between surplus-producing areas and consuming centers of such commodities.

In academic terms, the EEC and all the other regional groupings of states point, on the one hand, to the uneconomic artificiality of political state boundaries, and, on the other hand, to the function which geographic regionalism serves as a basis for recognizing and realizing common areal interests, including improved standards of living and security for all.

How the destinies of each of the nations and of the diverse treaty organizations are related to the several regional programs poses a number of interesting geographic questions:

A. How does the spatial factor differentiate the several programs? Show this on an outline map.

B. What national "togetherness" do the several patterns reveal? Can you detect in these several groupings the basis for regional integration?

C. You will observe that the several regional patterns are not co-extensive. Whatever the geographic validity may be in each case, could the very principle of national prosperity and security possibly be defeated by these several co-existing regions? Apply your answer to the OEEC (17 members) and the EEC (6 members, included in the former).

D. Overseas dependencies of western European nations are integrated in these regional associations. Which political units would that involve? What new trade opportunities would you envision here?

E. Were you surprised to see Great Britain missing from the list of EEC members? Can you guess why? Is there anything in the trade statistics in the concluding sections of this chapter to indicate that the British Commonwealth is a sort of unified commercial region in itself? Can the Pound Sterling exchange in overseas trade be considered a unifying regional factor?

F. Ultimately the commercial goal of western Europe is the establishment of a Free Trade Area. Great Britain, in fact, has proposed this for the OEEC. How would the FTA fit into the geographic ideology of "each area producing agriculturally and industrially essentially such products for which it is naturally and culturally best endowed"?

G. And what interregional relations, if any, does NATO, which includes, as you know, the United States, have to these several economic and commercial regional entities?

H. In "Europe, The Emerging Third Power," *Vital Speeches of the Day*, February 15, 1958, Karl Brandt visualizes the Economic Community as "a decisive gain for American foreign policy." What geographic rationale would support this? Or would you disagree?

I. Do such economic and commercial regional organizations as the OEEC and the EEC portend the ultimate establishment of a "United States of Europe"? Compare such a supranational federation to that of the United States of America. Do you think a "U.S.E." is feasible?

References

1 Wright, John Kirtland, *The Geographical Basis of European History,* Henry Holt & Co., New York, 1928, pp. 65, 66, 67, 86-89.

2 Van Valkenburg, Samuel, and Held, Colbert C., *Europe* (second edition), John Wiley & Sons, 1952, pp. 1-6 *passim,* 47.

3 Huntington, Ellsworth, *Civilization and Climate,* Yale University Press, New Haven, Conn., 1924, pp. 241, 242, 387.

4 Huntington, Ellsworth, *Mainsprings of Civilization,* John Wiley & Sons, Inc., New York, 1945, pp. 389-390.

5 Huntington, Ellsworth, and Williams, Frank E. *Business Geography* (second edition), John Wiley & Sons, Inc., New York, 1926, p. 308.

6 Taylor, Griffith, *Environment and Nation,* The University of Chicago Press, 1936, p. 63.

7 Semple, Ellen, *Geography of the Mediterranean Region,* Henry Holt & Co., New York, 1931, pp. 212-213.

8 Dickinson, Robert E., "Rural Settlements in the German Lands," *Annals of the Association of American Geographers,* Vol. XXXIX, No. 4, December, 1949, pp. 260-261.

9 Stamp, L. Dudley, and Beaver, S. H., *The British Isles,* Longman's, Green & Co., Inc., New York, 1954, p. 494.

10 Taylor, Griffith, *Australia,* E. P. Dutton and Co., Inc., New York, 1940, p. 435.

11 *Farming in the Commonwealth,* The Association of Agriculture (London) in collaboration with the Canterbury Agriculture College, Christchurch, New Zealand, May, 1955.

Chapter 27

The sub-Arctic (Boreal) forest lands (*Dfc-Dfd; Dwc-Dwd*)

Eternal frost is spread over a wide expanse of the land area of our earth. It covers up to 25 per cent of the total surface of the land of our planet.

The zone of perpetual frost in the Northern Hemisphere embraces almost the whole surface from the North Pole Circle (with the exception of some of the areas of the Scandinavian Peninsula), southward to the Asiatic and North American continents (Alaska and the northern part of Canada). . . . In the Soviet Union, the zone of perpetual frost comprises an area of 10.5 million square kilometers, or almost half of the entire territory of the U.S.S.R.

Korol, Nestor, "Agriculture in the Zone of Perpetual Frost," *Science*, October, 1955, p. 680. Reprinted from *Science* by permission.

Chorogram: Farming the Soviet North

The Soviet Union is noteworthy for its large percentage of *permafrost* land with less than a four-month growing season, as suggested by the Köppen symbol *c* (less than four months above 50° F.), and even less than two months growing season in the areas labeled *d*, where the coldest month drops below —36.4° F. Permafrost refers to permanent congelation of certain soil layers and is of great significance geographically since on the one hand it is intimately linked to a chain of cause and effect relationship of natural phenomena, climate–soils–vegetation–animal life, and on the other hand presents a real challenge to the transportation, mining, and construction engineer; to the agriculturist, and the industrialist—in fact, to every person who inhabits or travels the area.

In the Soviet Union, the zone of permafrost, or *merzlota*, as it is called in Russia, comprises nearly half of the entire country (1). It is concentrated in the northeast but extends a considerable distance into the interior of the continent. Representing a large fraction of the Soviet realm, *merzlota* presents a real problem for both the scientist and the government to resolve in the face of a rapidly growing population and the bid for world power. For the geography student, *merzlota* provides an excellent environment medium in which to evaluate man–nature functional relationships. And while *merzlota* presents its own problems of management, yet, upon closer geographical analysis, it is the "effect" rather than the "cause" of the major continental problem. The chief problem is climate rather than *merzlota*.

The major difficulty with agriculture in the zone of perpetual frost is not that the land is too cold but rather that the growing season is too short. It is the brief period between the last frost in the spring and the first freezing days in autumn, rather than the extremely low winter temperatures and the frozen ground, which restricts cultivation. In over half of Siberia, the summer is definitely too short for large-scale commercial agriculture in the present stage of culture.

The growing season problem has been and is being attacked in several ways. One hope is in developing new strains of wheat and other grains which will mature in about 80 days; cultivation may advance northward that way. Expeditions have been sent to the Andes to discover species of frost-resistant wild potatoes which could be crossed with cultivated species to produce a large tuber capable of withstanding 30° F. temperature.

Vernalization, as Gray has pointed out, is another help to northern agriculture. By exposing seeds to heat and moisture before planting them, crops which have requirements of 100 frost-free days can be harvested in areas where now there are only 100 frost-free days on the average (2). Thus science has aided in pushing the agricultural limits northward (Figures XXVII-1 and XXVII-2). And, as Cressey reports, much food is grown artificially to sustain the larger settlements in these permafrost areas. Igarka, a city of 30,000 people, in order to provide fresh vegetables, has acres of greenhouses. To prolong the growing season, the greenhouses are lighted and heated in the spring and fall (3). Less hardy plants are even grown in electrically heated soil. Electrodes are stuck in the ground around the roots. During the long and dark winter months, sheds are artificially

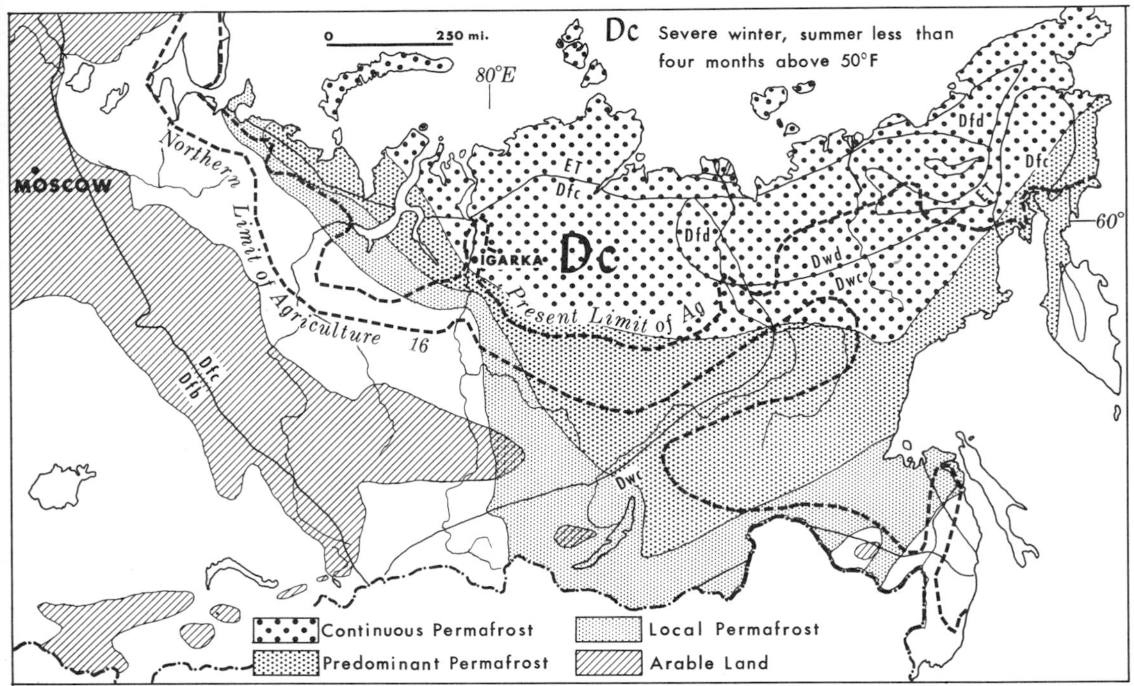

XXVII:1 The *Dc-Dd* challenges the U.S.S.R. scientist and statesman alike. What is here expressly or implicitly indicated as to (1) problems and (2) progress in overcoming environmental handicaps?

lighted to increase the production of dairy and poultry products (2).

In one way, permafrost is an aid to agriculture. Although the Arctic and the Northeast have little precipitation, the six inches of active soil on the top remain moist. The frozen layer acts as an impervious bed and thus prevents loss of water by downward percolation. Loss of moisture by evaporation is also reduced to a minimum as a result of the unusually low temperatures, even during the growing season. But to prepare land for cultivation requires (1) clearing the land of stones and boulders which reappear each year, (2) draining the land, (3) neutralizing the land, and (4) fertilizing it on a large scale. Crops are thus produced at an enormous cost of labor and expense.

There will probably never be any heavy settlement in the permafrost areas. Populations need food, and the Soviet North is not capable of producing the large quantities of food needed. At the present time, it is not feasible to ship food in large quantities to the North. Thus, as Korol observes, unless science comes up with something spectacular, "It would not be a mistake to maintain that agriculture in the zone of perpetual frost will probably never assume any industrial importance" (1).

The above chorogram affords a succinct introduction to what we might call the world's last major challenging frontier of the humid realm. While the areas within the realm — the U.S.S.R., Finland, Sweden, Norway, Canada, Alaska — are commonplace identities, the geographical regions they occupy are probably far less known — or rather less understood — than are those of any other clime. Probably the most popular misconception seems to be that these far-north lands are unsuited to settlement because the winters are too cold; but, as the chorogram points out, it is rather the cool and short summer growing season which is the primary handicap to settlement, particularly in terms of agriculture. In much of the area, even summer frosts must be reckoned with. Thus the small letters *c* and *d* are symbolically

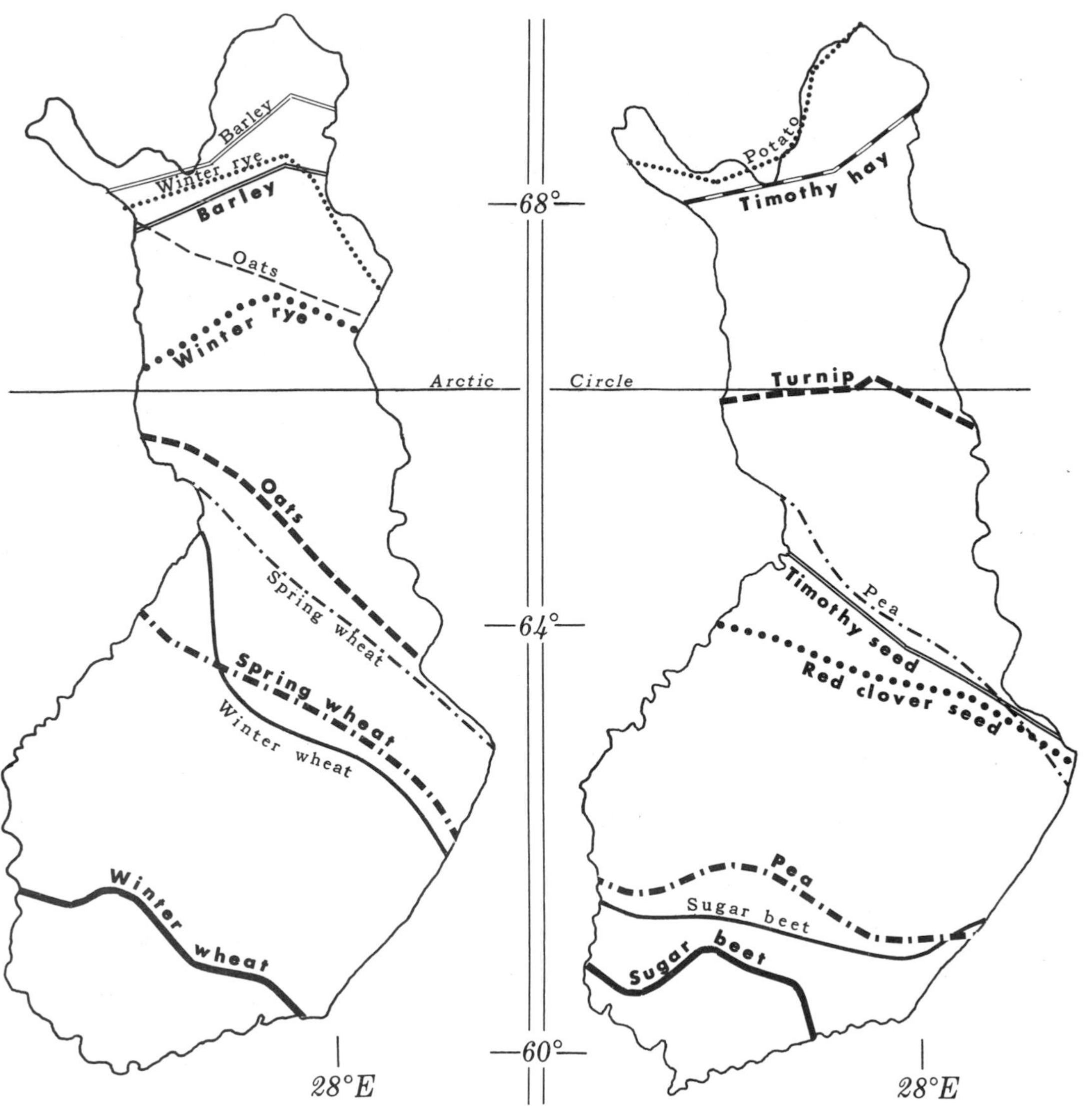

XXVII:2 These maps show the northward march in grain breeding: a study in genetics and geography. Finland's experiment stations and "The Finnish Co-operative Movement" have by seed selection and hybridization succeeded in pushing northward the agricultural limits of crops as shown on this map. (Adaptation after Otto Valle, in Suom. Maan. Käs., as published in *Finland and Its Geography*, by R. R. Platt, Ed., copyright 1955 by Duell, Sloan & Pierce, Inc., an affiliate of Meredith Press. By permission of Duell, Sloan & Pierce).

much more significant in this regional context than the capitals *C* and *D*. We repeat, it is the summer growing season, not the winter dormant season (cold or not so cold), that really counts. In terms of crop culture, the former is critical; the latter is not.

The next feature brought out in the chorogram is that the chief physical correlate of the *c-d* lands is permafrost (Figure XXVII-1). You will note, in the accompanying map of the chorogram, that in almost half the realm, the ground never thaws out, and that in the northern half of the permafrost zone, permafrost is continuous. The resultant problems and challenges which these lands present to the pioneer settling in them are then among the chief concerns of this chapter.

At this point, the student may anticipate some of the things we might want to stress:

How to cope structurally and agriculturally with permafrost. . . . What use, if any, can be made of the muskeg peat? . . . What progress has been made in pushing crop culture northward by developing shorter-season maturing varieties of wheat, barley, potatoes, and other crops? . . . What really are the potentialities of industrial, commercial, and transportational developments as based on the characteristic Boreal native resources of minerals, lumber, and wildlife? . . . What conclusions can be drawn on population growth prospects of the northlands, as, for example, of Alaska, and to what extent does a comparative study of historically prominent settled regions like Sweden and Finland aid us in such prognostications? . . . Can Canada ever become a world power in view of its areally dominant *Dfc-ET* condition, despite the fact that its area is larger than that of continental United States? . . . How does the high-latitude position of a major portion of the U.S.S.R. and its extreme continentality — nearly three-fourths of it over 250 miles from any seacoast — enter into the evaluation of its strength as compared with the United States, less than half the former's size?

Factors such as these very seldom make newspaper headlines; neither are they common topics for editorials, news analysts, or television broadcasts. And to our knowledge no such questions were directed to Premier Khrushchev upon his visit to our country. Yet no evaluation of the comparative strength of the two countries, militarily or otherwise, can be said to be accurate if it ignores basic environmental factors such as these and the geographical concepts developed therefrom.

Continentality is conducive to population paucity

1. Climatic extremes. Just as the *Cfb* (Chapter 26) expressed the best form of marinality of climatic conditions in the world, so the *Dfc-d, Dwc-d* represent the most extreme forms of continentality. Thus in the Arctic Circle latitude of Siberia, the isotherm for January registers —50° F.; whereas maritime western Europe at approximately the same latitude may just experience the freezing mark. Actually, temperatures of individual stations in the *Dw* section of Siberia may annually reach —55° to —60° F., as at Verkhoyansk (Figure XXVII-3), or even on occasion as low as —90° to —100° F., as in the region of Oymyakon.

This "cold pole" of the earth is now recognized to be more widely zonal in character than originally postulated. The greater part of Siberia falls under this category (roughly co-extensive with *Dc-Dd*) (Figure XXVII-4). This phenomenon has thus been explained in a Russian publication:

¶ This zone exists primarily because of its continental location. It is dominated by a stable high-pressure system in winter. It is generally known that the air near the ground in Eastern Siberia is excessively chilled because of calm weather and insignificant cloudiness. The chilling reaches a maximum in those high-pressure areas where reradiation prevails, i.e., which have a polar night of many weeks' duration, twilight or winter day with the sun remaining just above the horizon. The combination of a high-pressure system and a reradiation regime in the high latitudes causes the appearance of a zone of minimum temperatures. . . . Relief also plays a role in the lowering of the temperature. It is obvious that in intermontane basins the conditions for a more frequent and intense chilling of air are more favorable than in exposed localities.[1]

On the other hand, in the summertime a 60°F. isotherm closely follows the Arctic Circle in Eurasia, but drops sharply off the coast—particularly the eastern coast—to the 45° latitude. Mean July temperatures of 60°F. (Figures XXVII-5, XXVII-6) are not uncommon in deep interior Siberia where temperatures of as high as 90-100°F.—uncommon even in some equatorial areas—have been recorded. Annual temperature ranges may thus be of the order of 100°–150°F., and even in extreme cases may exceed 175°F.

The seasonal regimen of this most extreme of climates is reflected in striking landscape changes, as noted for example, by Jorré:

¶ Winter is scarcely over before April. The rivers are set free in an impressive break-up of the ice, which is generally accompanied by terrible floods. The snow melts, and highways, which shortly before were streets of towns like

[1] Parmuzin, Yu. P., "The Zonal Character of the Cold Pole," *Izvestiya Vsesoyuznogo goegrafticheskogo obshchestva*, No. 5, 1958, pp. 472-474. (As translated in *Soviet Geography*, Theodore Shabad, Editor, American Geographical Society, Vol. 1, No. 1-2, 1960, pp. 40-42.) Reprinted by permission.

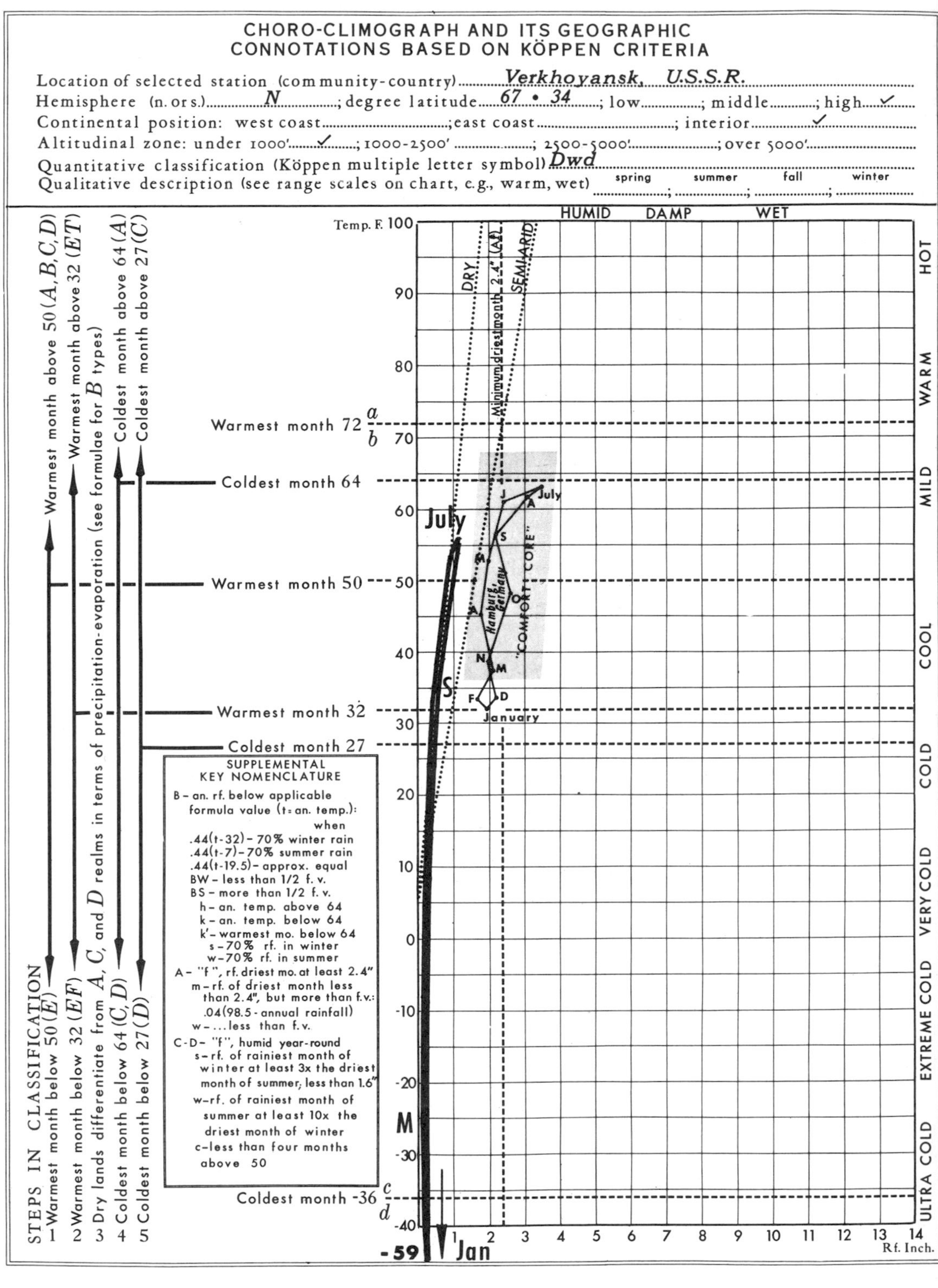
CHORO-CLIMOGRAPH AND ITS GEOGRAPHIC
CONNOTATIONS BASED ON KÖPPEN CRITERIA
Location of selected station (community-country) Verkhoyansk, U.S.S.R.
Hemisphere (n. or s.) N ; degree latitude 67 • 34 ; low ; middle ; high ✓
Continental position: west coast ; east coast ; interior ✓
Altitudinal zone: under 1000' ✓ ; 1000-2500' ; 2500-5000' ; over 5000'
Quantitative classification (Köppen multiple letter symbol) Dwd
Qualitative description (see range scales on chart, e.g., warm, wet) spring ; summer ; fall ; winter
STEPS IN CLASSIFICATION
1 Warmest month below 50 (E) — Warmest month above 50 (A, B, C, D)
2 Warmest month below 32 (EF) — Warmest month above 32 (ET)
3 Dry lands differentiate from A, C, and D realms in terms of precipitation-evaporation (see formulae for B types)
4 Coldest month below 64 (C, D) — Coldest month above 64 (A)
5 Coldest month below 27 (D) — Coldest month above 27 (C)
Temp. F.
Warmest month 72 a b
Coldest month 64
Warmest month 50
Warmest month 32
Coldest month 27
Coldest month -36 c d
HUMID
DAMP
WET
DRY
Minimum driest month 2.4" (Af)
SEMIARID
"COMFORT" CORE
Hamburg, Germany
July
January
Jan
-59
M
S
HOT
WARM
MILD
COOL
COLD
VERY COLD
EXTREME COLD
ULTRA COLD
Rf. Inch.
SUPPLEMENTAL KEY NOMENCLATURE
B – an. rf. below applicable formula value (t = an. temp.): when
.44(t-32) – 70% winter rain
.44(t-7) – 70% summer rain
.44(t-19.5) – approx. equal
BW – less than 1/2 f. v.
BS – more than 1/2 f. v.
h – an. temp. above 64
k – an. temp. below 64
k' – warmest mo. below 64
s – 70% rf. in winter
w – 70% rf. in summer
A – "f", rf. driest mo. at least 2.4"
m – rf. of driest month less than 2.4", but more than f.v.: .04(98.5 - annual rainfall)
w – ... less than f.v.
C-D – "f", humid year-round
s – rf. of rainiest month of winter at least 3x the driest month of summer; less than 1.6"
w – rf. of rainiest month of summer at least 10x the driest month of winter
c – less than four months above 50

Tomsk, are turned into indescribably evil-smelling sloughs and streams of brown mud into which horses sink past their fetlocks, carriages become stuck fast, staggering drunkards are in danger of being engulfed, and cows have been seen to disappear. Then comes a spring which would be delightful but for the too frequent returns of cold weather and which is anyhow extremely short. Summer follows abruptly, is very pronounced, generally as hot as in France, and sometimes scorching; but on the whole is not very pleasant owing to its whirling clouds of dust, its thunder- and hailstorms, and its myriads of mosquitoes which are fierce enough to have discouraged colonization in some places. However, the season does not last long. By August the north and east may have night frosts and slight falls of snow, and the trees begin to shed their leaves. These are the first signs of an autumn which is as short as the spring. At the end of September bits of ice begin to drift down some of the rivers, and a few weeks later winter is back again, frigid and silent.[1]

Again turning to the climate map of Siberia, you will observe that in the eastern highland section the zone of *Dfc* and *Dfd* changes to *Dwc* and *Dwd*. You will recall the earlier use of the small letter *w* in connection with the savannah lands (*Aw*) and again its use in connection with the mild winter *Cw* China, in both instances noting extreme winter dryness and contrasted summer wetness. These were recognized as monsoon characteristics related to the alternating winter high pressure and summer low pressure conditions of eastern Asia. Accordingly, the *Dw* subtype of the severe winter is related to the same phenomena—"the wettest summer month having at least ten times as much rain as the driest winter month." The annual rainfall, however, is much less because of the higher latitude; thus *Dwd* Yakutsk has an average of only 14 inches whereas *Cw* Raipur, India, has a mean annual rainfall of 50 inches.

[1] Jorré, Georges, *The Soviet Union: The Land and Its People*, Translated by E. D. Laborde, Longmans, Green & Co., Inc., New York and London, 1950, p. 21. Reprinted by permission.

XXVII:3 (Left) Verkhoyansk is in the "cold pole" of the Northern Hemisphere. This represents continentality at its best—or worst! Note the extreme range in temperature and the surprisingly high July average. Would the snowfall be heavy in this area?

The most extreme type of climate in the world, then, taking into consideration both seasonal changes in temperature and rainfall would be the *Dwd* type. The combined low annual precipitation and the fact that much the larger part of it comes during the summer season are significant in that the amount of snowfall is correspondingly much less in these regions than is commonly supposed. Unlike that of the more humid Scandinavia and northern North America, Siberia offers little evidence of continental glaciation.

Ultra-cold, then, as are the *Dc-d* regions, it is the short cool summer rather than the rigorous winter which has militated in the past against active settlement. The one prime requisite for the survival of both beast and man is food, and while, as we shall see later, this realm is one of the more heavily populated lands of wildlife, the Caucasian, especially the Westerner, seeks a balanced vegetable–meat diet. Accordingly, pioneers who venture into these lands must anticipate specialized agriculture based on such quick-maturing crops as will mature within three months in the southerly region and within six weeks to two months in the northerly zone. Under the above conditions it is understandable, then, that nature rather than man has given dominant expression to the landscape in the Boreal lands. Here is truly a forest primeval, the stupendous *taiga* studded here and there with innumerable lakes and *muskegs*. Here also is the world's richest realm of the fowl, fish, and fur economy. Much of the forest remains untouched by man, and minerals have been only sporadically mined where fortuitous discoveries of richness of deposit and accessibility of transport facilities have made exploitation profitable. Thus the occupance of the northlands has taken on the usual pioneer form of exploitation. Historically, this has found its most systematic development in the organization and operation of the Hudson Bay Company in its fur-trapping and trading expeditions to the North American continent.

2. *Settlement isolation and insulation.* The Boreal lands are among the most sparsely settled regions of the world, rating only about one-tenth of average world population

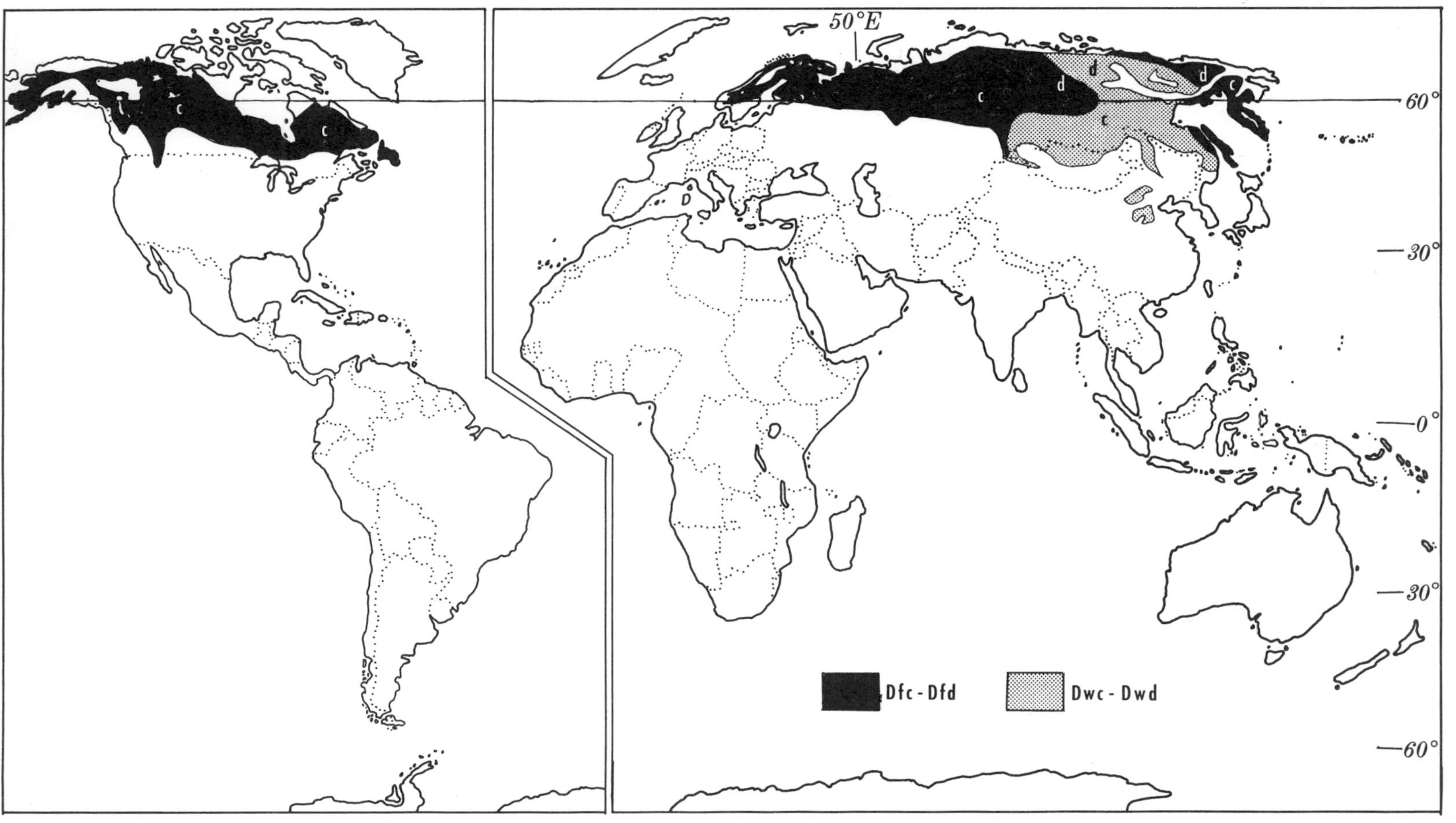
50°E
60°
30°
0°
30°
60°
Dfc - Dfd
Dwc - Dwd

density. In this respect they compare very closely with the broad regional figure of less than two people per square mile, including sizable areal vacua, as reported previously for the desert realm. Normally, densities rise to the order of five, ten, or twenty per square mile in favored settlement sites along the coast lands or inland waterways which favor food supply, some particular resource development, and facilitate transportation; or even a two-score figure, as along sections of railway lines, particularly the Trans-Siberian Railway. Similarly in Canada, only the *Dfb, BS,* and *Cfb* sectors on its southern border, serviced by rail, have sizable populations; otherwise Canada as a whole, one-fifteenth of world area, as Putnam points out, has only one one hundred-fiftieth of its total population. And Alaska, with a total population of only about 170,000 has less than one-sixth as many people as Libya, of comparable size but almost a complete desert. Regional demographic comparisons such as these raise questions which are of far more concern to geographical study than are those that are posed by such publicized exotic epithets of the northland as "Land of the Midnight Sun and Nocturnal Moonlight."

It is to be expected, then, that urban population in general will also be low, and that when sizable cities do occur they are normally the result of some singular magnetic attraction—locus of environmental forces of one combination or another which in this realm more than possibly in any other are highlighted because of the otherwise general environmental unfavorability to dense settlement. Several positional-environmental-resource relationships thus stand out: (1) the concentration of the large cities towards the border of the *Dfb*, reflective of the more hospitable climate and the better transportation facilities (e.g., the Russian cities of Irkutsk and Krasnoyarsk, both outstanding manufacturing and commercial cities in the 300,000 population class); (2) the extraordinary value of ice-free or near ice-free seaports of otherwise ice-locked and landlocked regions (e.g., the warm Gulf Stream open port of Murmansk, a fishing, lumbering, and shipyard center and commercial peacetime and strategic wartime port of 150,000 population; and Arkhangelsk, twice as large and the oldest seaport of Russia, situated near the confluence of the Northern Dvina and the White Sea, kept open by icebreakers, with an industrial and commercial function similar to that of Murmansk); (3) railway and highway termini in an otherwise almost trackless region (e.g., Alaska interior to Fairbanks—6,000—joined by the Alaska Railway to Seward—2,000—, "Gateway to Alaska," and by the Alcan Highway to Canada); and (4) specific local resource and rail transportation focus, such as are based on mining and lumbering (e.g., Canada's Sudbury—45,000—producer of 90 per cent of the world's nickel).

XXVII:4 (Left) Compare the *Dc-Dd* area with the sizes of other realms. What proportion of the Soviet Union belongs to this category?

The overall emptiness of the Boreal lands is perhaps most effectively presented in a space-proportioned population chart such as that by Woytinski (Figure XXVII-7). You will note that Siberia and Canada have all but disappeared from the "map," and the author apparently did not even try to represent Alaska. Only sub-Arctic sections of north European countries show moderately dense population, obviously resulting from their locations proximate to occidental cultures, and also their much longer period of settlement. Though Scandinavia-Finland and Alaska occupy comparable latitudinal positions and similarly extend southward into the *Cf* realm, the former, even smaller than Alaska, has about eight times its population.

The distribution settlement patterns and the morphology of communities are highly reflective of natural environmental conditions predominantly favoring settlements which depend mainly on the so-called *robber economy.* Much of the native occupance—the Yakuts of Siberia, the Lapps of Scandinavia, and the Indians of Canada and Alaska—is even today still migratory in character. The Eurasian Boreal inhabitant characteristically travels with his reindeer herd into and through the tundra lands to the Arctic coast to fish in the summer, and then returns with his herds into the taiga during the winter season, thus establishing a sort of a nomadic transhumance between the

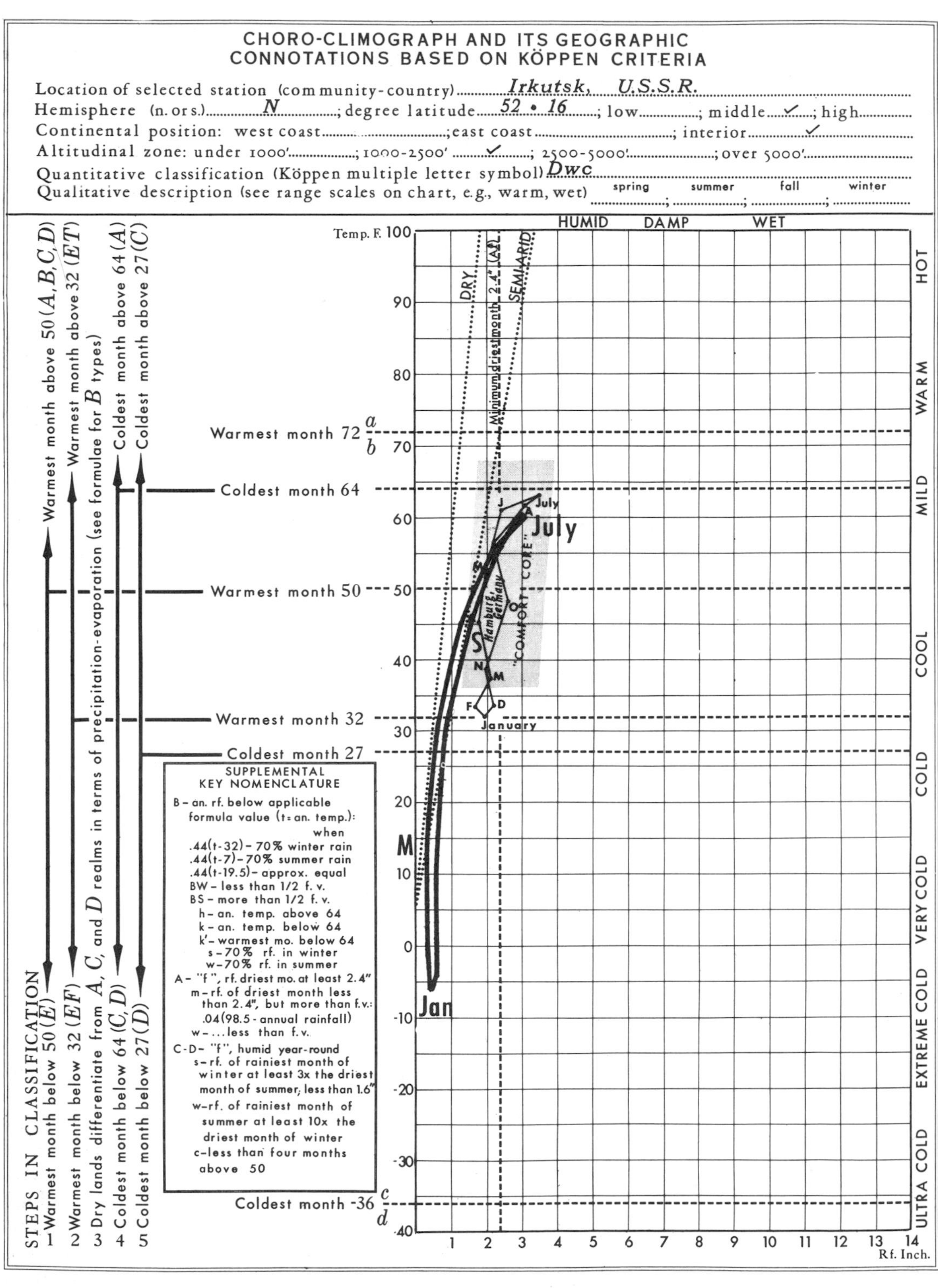

CHORO-CLIMOGRAPH AND ITS GEOGRAPHIC CONNOTATIONS BASED ON KÖPPEN CRITERIA
Location of selected station (community-country) Irkutsk, U.S.S.R.
Hemisphere (n. or s.) N ; degree latitude 52 • 16 ; low ; middle ✓ ; high
Continental position: west coast ; east coast ; interior ✓
Altitudinal zone: under 1000' ; 1000-2500' ✓ ; 2500-5000' ; over 5000'
Quantitative classification (Köppen multiple letter symbol) Dwc
Qualitative description (see range scales on chart, e.g., warm, wet) spring ; summer ; fall ; winter
HUMID
DAMP
WET
Temp. F.
DRY
SEMIARID
Minimum driest month 2.4" (Af)
Hamburg, Germany
"COMFORT CORE"
July
Jan
January
Warmest month 72
Coldest month 64
Warmest month 50
Warmest month 32
Coldest month 27
Coldest month -36
HOT
WARM
MILD
COOL
COLD
VERY COLD
EXTREME COLD
ULTRA COLD
Rf. Inch.
STEPS IN CLASSIFICATION
1 Warmest month below 50 (E) — Warmest month above 50 (A, B, C, D)
2 Warmest month below 32 (EF) — Warmest month above 32 (ET)
3 Dry lands differentiate from A, C, and D realms in terms of precipitation-evaporation (see formulae for B types)
4 Coldest month below 64 (C, D) — Coldest month above 64 (A)
5 Coldest month below 27 (D) — Coldest month above 27 (C)
SUPPLEMENTAL KEY NOMENCLATURE
B - an. rf. below applicable formula value (t = an. temp.): when
.44(t-32) - 70% winter rain
.44(t-7) - 70% summer rain
.44(t-19.5) - approx. equal
BW - less than 1/2 f. v.
BS - more than 1/2 f. v.
h - an. temp. above 64
k - an. temp. below 64
k' - warmest mo. below 64
s - 70% rf. in winter
w - 70% rf. in summer
A - "f", rf. driest mo. at least 2.4"
m - rf. of driest month less than 2.4", but more than f.v.: .04(98.5 - annual rainfall)
w - ... less than f.v.
C-D - "f", humid year-round
s - rf. of rainiest month of winter at least 3x the driest month of summer; less than 1.6"
w - rf. of rainiest month of summer at least 10x the driest month of winter
c - less than four months above 50

northernmost zone of the taiga and the adjacent tundra.

Semipermanent settlements may be established at or near trading posts where the furs of the native are exchanged for trapping equipment or other commodities brought in by the white man. But even such outposts will be of a decidedly dispersed character since animal life, however abundant it may otherwise be, is in itself spotty in distribution, and is, moreover, subject to being exploited faster than the processes of reproduction. And so white man must be prepared physiologically and psychologically to face a frontier life in isolation not unlike that of the North American Indian trapper or his Eurasian nomadic counterpart. Though frontiersmen penetrating the drylands of middle latitudes in years past had to face many experiences of isolation and privation, the long and severe winters of the northlands, particularly in the northern zone, predicate human hibernation in much the same way as animal life.

Not only are settlements widely scattered, but they are also characteristically ephemeral as well, for all subsistence as well as the pioneering economic enterprises are based primarily upon the exploitation of furs, skins, hides, lumber products, and minerals. But fur-bearing animals may be readily overtrapped, and even where animal life may otherwise be sufficient to support a sizable native population, the hunting and fishing economy is normally insufficient inland to support more than a limited population. As we know only too well, in the exploitation of forest products in eastern United States in excess of reproduction capacity, it is only a question of time when the lumber camp must move to stay in business. Unlike the timber of the tropics and the lower middle latitudes, forests of the northlands are extremely slow in reproducing themselves. But, whereas wildlife and timber belong to the category of restorable resources, minerals do not. Thus upon the exhaustion of minerals, the mining community is abandoned, and this adds merely another "ghost" relic to the landscape.

XXVII:5 (Left) By comparison with Verkhoyansk, note the more "amenable" conditions at Irkutsk. Would there be any agricultural possibilities here?

Frontier northland communities are functionally also sporadic. Based on more or less single, or at best two or three, economic resources—and these primarily of the extractive type as indicated above—the smaller urban communities are likely to feel very quickly and keenly the effects of a fluctuating market for their raw resources. Thus a whimsical decision on the part of garment stylists in Paris or New York to feature furs on women's garments may instantly bring a decided boom to the fur trading posts, whereas the discontinuance of use of certain fur products, as was the case years ago of the sealskin cap no longer worn by men, may put a trading post featuring this line out of business. Similarly, the great fluctuation in price of such important minerals in the northlands as copper, gold, platinum, and uranium, and more recently oil, may during times of high prices touch off a rash of new explorations in the most out-of-the-way places. On the other hand, even a slight decline in prices may result in uneconomic exploitations of even normally rich deposits, especially when transportation facilities are prohibitively costly.

For climatological and pedological reasons, as pointed out elsewhere, agricultural productivity is limited, and for the most part takes on the aspect of a pastoral economy, or a garden type of farming, neither of which promotes a dense population. Sizable commercial farming settlements, such as the Peace River locale in Canada, discussed elsewhere, are of the experimental type, supported by a fortuitous combination of natural-cultural circumstances.

The only communities, therefore, with reasonable prospects of permanency and substantial urban growth in the northern parts of the northlands would include those which have a relatively favorable port site coastal position, particularly where streams enter ice-free harbors and where inland connections are made by rail, as in the case of Arkhangelsk on the White Sea, Murmansk on the Kola Peninsula, both in northern Russia; Narvik, Norway, the leading export port of the iron ores of the rich Gällivare district of northern Sweden, or wheat-exporting sites like Churchill of central Canada

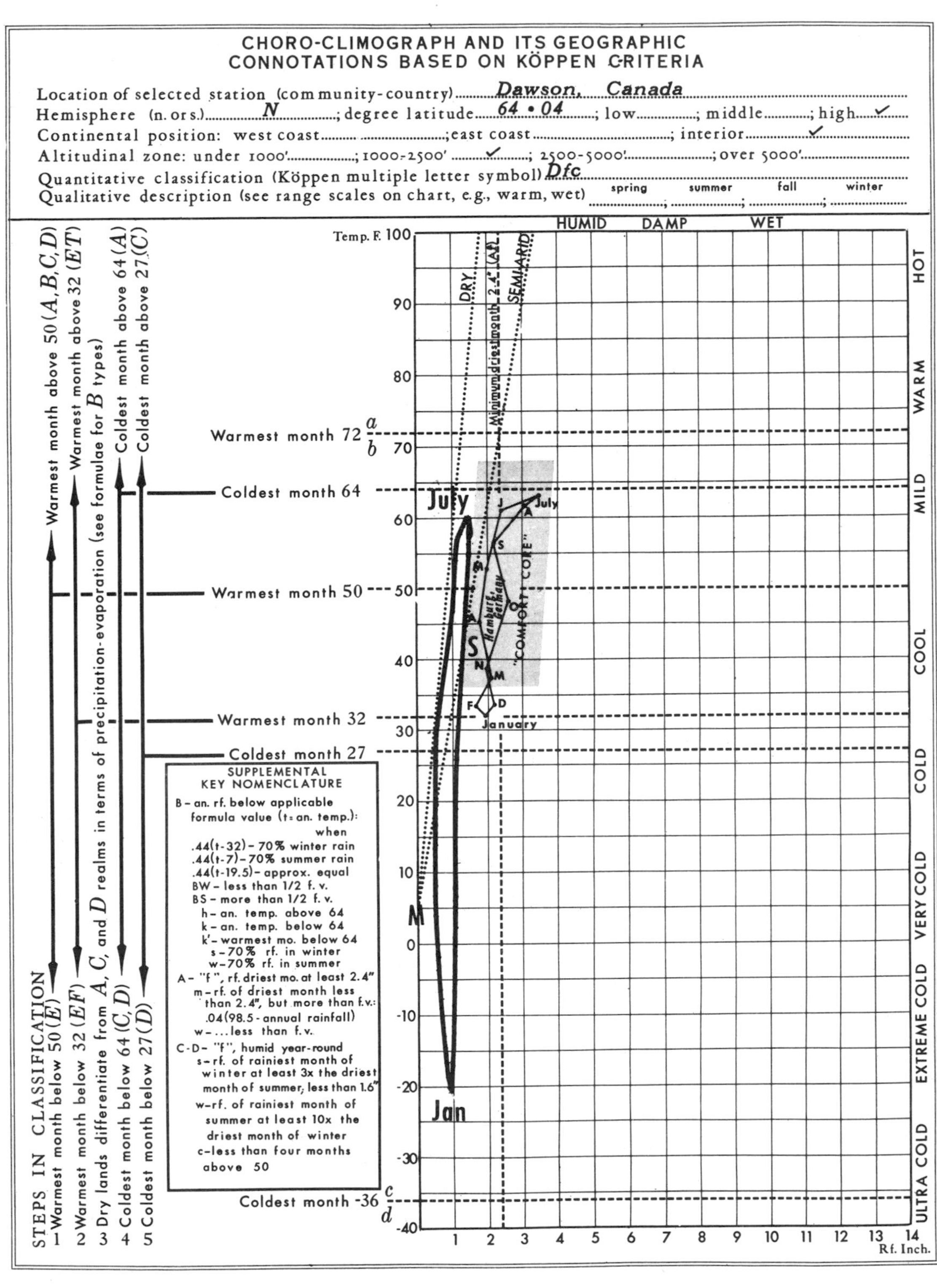
CHORO-CLIMOGRAPH AND ITS GEOGRAPHIC
CONNOTATIONS BASED ON KÖPPEN CRITERIA
Location of selected station (community-country) Dawson, Canada
Hemisphere (n. or s.) N ; degree latitude 64 • 04 ; low ; middle ; high ✓
Continental position: west coast ; east coast ; interior ✓
Altitudinal zone: under 1000' ; 1000-2500' ✓ ; 2500-5000' ; over 5000'
Quantitative classification (Köppen multiple letter symbol) Dfc
Qualitative description (see range scales on chart, e.g., warm, wet) spring ; summer ; fall ; winter
HUMID
DAMP
WET
DRY
SEMIARID
Minimum driest month 2.4" (Af)
Temp. F.
HOT
WARM
MILD
COOL
COLD
VERY COLD
EXTREME COLD
ULTRA COLD
Warmest month 72
Coldest month 64
Warmest month 50
Warmest month 32
Coldest month 27
Coldest month -36
"COMFORT CORE"
Hamburg, Germany
July
Jan
January
Rf. Inch.
STEPS IN CLASSIFICATION
1 Warmest month below 50 (E) — Warmest month above 50 (A, B, C, D)
2 Warmest month below 32 (EF) — Warmest month above 32 (ET)
3 Dry lands differentiate from A, C, and D realms in terms of precipitation-evaporation (see formulae for B types)
4 Coldest month below 64 (C, D) — Coldest month above 64 (A)
5 Coldest month below 27 (D) — Coldest month above 27 (C)
SUPPLEMENTAL
KEY NOMENCLATURE
B - an. rf. below applicable formula value (t = an. temp.): when
.44(t-32) - 70% winter rain
.44(t-7) - 70% summer rain
.44(t-19.5) - approx. equal
BW - less than 1/2 f. v.
BS - more than 1/2 f. v.
h - an. temp. above 64
k - an. temp. below 64
k' - warmest mo. below 64
s - 70% rf. in winter
w - 70% rf. in summer
A - "f", rf. driest mo. at least 2.4"
m - rf. of driest month less than 2.4", but more than f.v.: .04(98.5 - annual rainfall)
w - ... less than f.v.
C-D - "f", humid year-round
s - rf. of rainiest month of winter at least 3x the driest month of summer; less than 1.6"
w - rf. of rainiest month of summer at least 10x the driest month of winter
c - less than four months above 50

on the west shore of Hudson Bay; Coppermine, situated in the rich copper mine district of the Northwest Territories and the only Arctic coast port of this large territory; and Aklavik at the mouth of the Mackenzie, also opening up transport to the Arctic Sea.

Here, perhaps, should be considered the powerful influences of the elements in man's natural environment on his decisions as to type of habitat and habits, supplying needs which themselves have been conditioned hitherto largely by a nature-dominated region. With the increasing intensity of such characteristics, going northward from the zone of three-months' to two-months', and then to one-month's growing season, man must face the problem of a high selectivity of a limited number of crops which will mature in an extremely short growing season, compensated in part by the long sunlight hours, approximating even a full twenty-four hour sunlight day in the extreme northern part. Under these circumstances he may speculate upon the alternative of relying chiefly on forage crops and animal economy. But even for these, beyond subsistence, he must normally look to distant communities for marketing his product and then only to a very limited extent. Only in the transition zone towards the *Dfb* region to the south will he find a market for his goods sufficiently near and stable to give promise of reasonable returns for his arduous labors in an environment which is less naturally co-operative than the agricultural zone favored by at least a four-months' growing season. And it is obvious that unless there is a local market accessible, reasonably good transportation facilities by railroad or highway—again rare in the northlands—are needed.

Although the pioneer farmer of the eighteenth and nineteenth centuries in middle-latitude countries paid very close attention to the degree of soil fertility, forms of cultivable agriculture in the northlands call for even greater perspicacity and soil selectivity. Mature soils generally are mediocre to poor in quality—characteristically thin, stony, acid, and poor in organic materials in the "B" zone—a phenomenon largely attributable to the long permafrost season and to the general lack of earthworm and bacteria activity. Such soils are usually ash-colored beneath a surface layer of dark raw humus, thus the Russian term *podsol.* Topographically also consideration will be given to the more elevated sites, since in the lower depressions water-logged conditions occur, as is attested by numerous bogs, swamps, and lakes.

Under the most favorable conditions, then, of site and culture, wheat and especially barley may be grown where there is at least a three-months' frost-free season. Spring wheat has been extended in its culture even beyond the Arctic Circle. One of the more famous wheat-raising regions of the northlands in North America is the Peace River Valley, located near the end of the northernmost rail line of Alberta (Figure XXVII-8). Many root crops and vegetables of high quality have also been produced in favored locales up to and even beyond the Arctic Circle, particularly in Scandinavia and Finland (Figure XXVII-2). Such areas may have a moderate population and fair circulation.

Historical geography of the Northlands

A study of regional settlement sequences is necessary to an adequate understanding of the population pattern of any realm. Particularly is this significant when we are dealing with challenging environments of the Boreal type. Let us, then, next see how the time and space elements of human occupance are related to each other in the several continental areas.

1. Northern Eurasia. The north country of the Russian realm came into Western consciousness when Richard Chancellor, an English navigator, became interested in exploring for the Northeast Sea Passage to China. As a result of this expedition, the English-Muscovy trading company was formed, and Arkhangelsk was established as a leading trading post in 1584. Already for several centuries this region has been occupied by Russian colonists who had been attracted to this area by the forest with its rich fur resource, and by the availability of ivory of walrus and sealskins in the coastal areas.

XXVII:6 (Left) Dawson is in the North American counterpart of *Dc* Asia. In what respects, however, does the Dawson station differ from the Asiatic stations given?

Fairbanks, in Tanana Valley, the second largest city of Alaska and its only interior metropolis, is located at the terminus of the Alaska Railway. Its geographic distinction, however, is its latitude (about 65° north) rather than its size (comparable to that of an average county seat town in any other state). Temperature of the region may range from 90°F. to 60°F. Note taiga conifer background, with some clearings. What would be the type of economies sustaining a frontier community such as this outpost? (Photo courtesy Alaska Visitors' Association)

Trade in these products had already been organized by the merchants from Novgorod. Also at the beginning of the fourteenth century, salt came to be mined on islands and coasts of the White Sea. By the latter part of the sixteenth century, tradesmen had penetrated what is now Siberia. Gray gives an interesting account of how the trading expeditions pressed on into this new fur frontier:

¶ This use of river transport and short portages was the way by which the gate into Siberia was opened. Apart from adventure for the Cossacks, the great attraction was furs.

It is remarkable to relate that the Pacific was reached as early as 1648 by a Cossack called Deshnev. He actually sailed from the Arctic through the Behring Strait about eighty years before it was re-discovered by Behring himself. However, it must not be thought that, by this time, all Siberia had been discovered. This would not be a true statement even to-day. The real picture is one of pioneering explorers in search of walrus, extinct-mammoth ivory or furs. They made their way from river to river, through tundra and taiga, and occasionally met a small encampment of native tribes living in birch-bark tents, or earth-block houses, and at a Stone Age level of culture.

The rapid conquest of Siberia was due to several reasons:

(a) The new bands of adventurers avoided the relatively more densely populated regions of the steppes and kept to the forest. The natives of Siberia were more backward and presented little organized opposition.

(b) The Russians had not to accustom themselves to new conditions—the Taiga is the same on both sides of the Urals.

(c) Moscow helped the pioneers by manning forts and thus protecting route-ways.

(d) As furs became scarce in one region, there was a hope that there would be plenty further afield.

By the river-routes the Russians settled at Tyumen, 1586, and Mangazeya in 1600. In 1628 the Lena was reached, and the fort (Ostrog) of Yakutsk was founded in 1632. . . . Behring, in addition to sailing in 1728 through the straits that take his name, set off on an expedition in 1714 across the Pacific along with Chivikov. . . . By about 1820, outposts had been established along the coast of North America, as far south as San Francisco. It was in California that the Russians came in contact with Spanish territory but Russia was not destined to occupy much land in North America. She was warned off by the Monroe doctrine which forbade further colonization by any European Power. In any case, it was a great expense to feed the people in these far distant posts. Even Alaska was considered a liability and in 1867 it was sold to the United States for 7,200,000 dollars.[1]

Since the early explorers and fur traders normally followed every navigable stream and coastal water, it is significant to note how the stream drainage pattern of the Great Russian Plain facilitated the exploitation of the fur trade. Nowhere else in a region of similar size in the world do we find so many major river systems whose headwater portages provide transcontinental communications with five major seas: the Arctic Ocean on the north, the Baltic Sea on the west, the Black and Caspian seas to the southwest, and the Sea of Okhotsk, an arm of the Pacific, to the east. Though the U.S.S.R. is handicapped by being largely ice-blocked on the north and has been denied territorial access to the Atlantic and Mediterranean seas by straits controlled by the Western Powers, these were not major problems in the early days of fur trading. The earliest explorations were almost entirely confined to the river systems and the seacoasts. Thus upon entering the White Sea area the journeys by boat proceeded up the Dvina and by headwater portage eastward to the Pechora. In a similar way, the route from the Baltic Sea followed the West Dvina to its headwaters, and crossed over by portage near Moscow to the Volga. This stream system supplied portage connections with the Ob, whose tributaries and portages in turn gave access to the Yenisei. Here the explorers and fur traders had the choice of following the Yenisei northward, back to the Arctic, or tracing the lower Yenisei eastward to a narrow portage of a tributary of the Lena system, which in turn had headwater portage connection with the Amur, which empties into the Sea of Okhotsk, and thus connecting the Ob route with the Pacific Ocean. It is not surprising, then, to find that practically all the early trading posts were to be found along these rivers, their tributaries, and lakes, and along the coastal boundaries of Siberia.

2. *North America Northland.* The chronicles of the northland of North America are very similar to those of the Eurasian counterpart. The first exploratory ventures were likewise directed at finding a short sea route to China. For this purpose, Henry Hudson, an English navigator, was engaged by the Muscovy Company in 1607-1608. Though he did open up the new Spitsbergen area for exploitation, Hudson failed to negotiate a northeast passage. After a third try to find a north passage to India, this time under the auspices of the Dutch East India Company, he finally decided to explore for a northwest passage, having been influenced by a map sent him by his friend, Captain John Smith. His first try at this again failed, but still another attempt (April, 1610) led him into the strait now bearing his name. This was followed by another expedition which led into Hudson Bay (Figure XXVII-9).

[1] Gray, G. D. B., *Soviet Land,* A. and C. Black, Ltd., London, 1947, pp. 124-126, *passim.* Reprinted by permission.

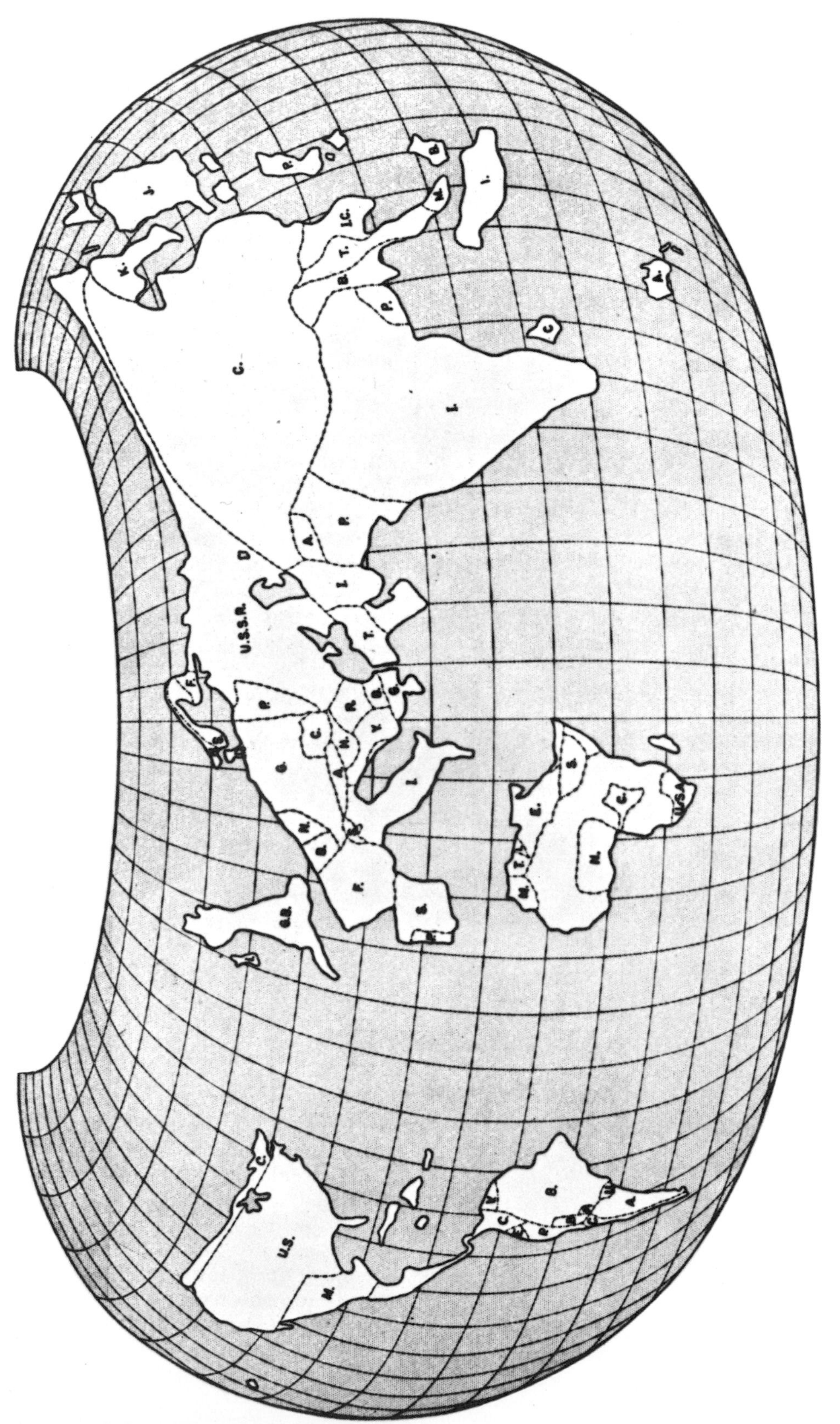

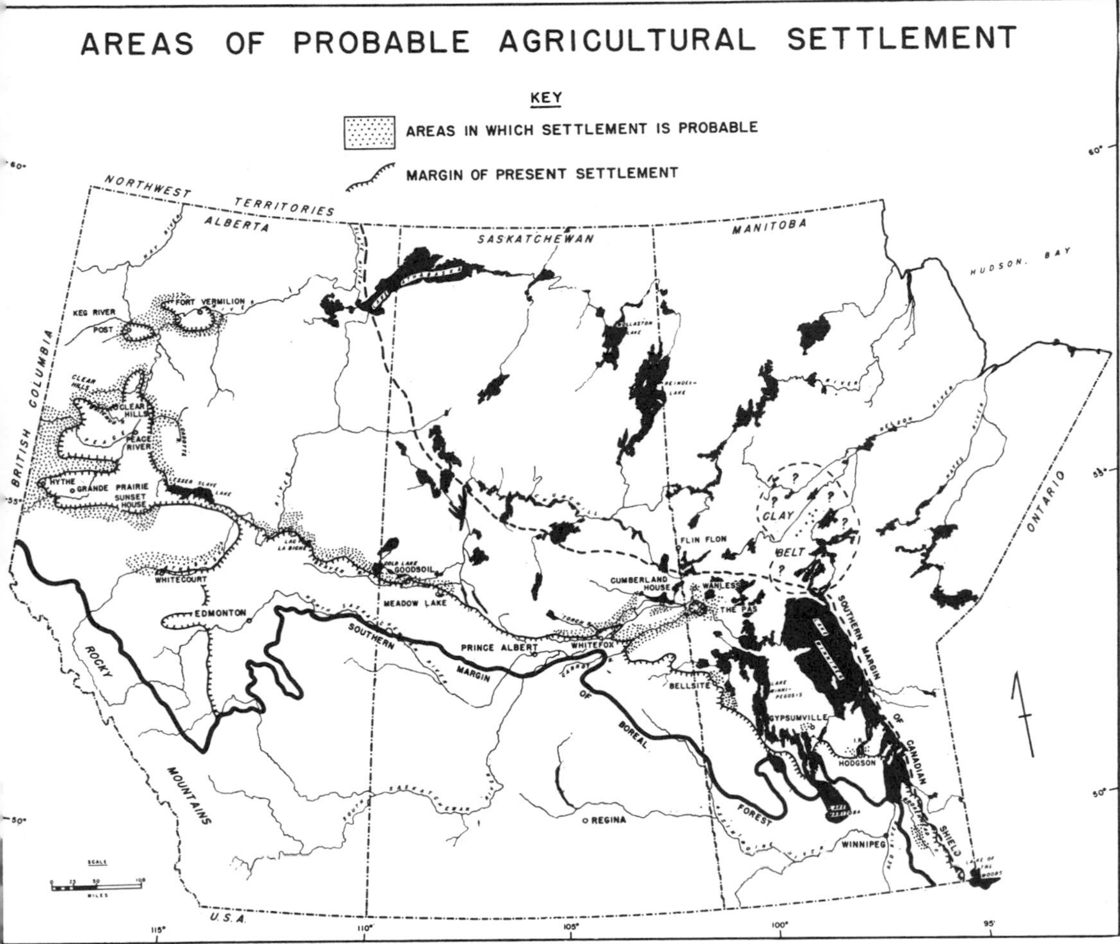

XXVII:8 The prospective agricultural extension of the Canadian Northland Frontier is shown on this map. Account for "outposts" beyond the main advance lines. ("Areas of Probable Agricultural Settlement," Burke G. Vanderhill, *Journal of Geography,* Vol. 58, October, 1959, used by permission)

Though Hudson never realized his dreams of negotiating the Northwest Passage, his high resolve did result in the opening up of the unexploited rich fishing regions of Spitsbergen. He also pointed the way to the development of the lucrative fur industry of the Hudson Bay territory, for which a special organization bearing his name, the Hudson's Bay Company, was chartered in the year 1670 by King Charles II. A charter granted to Prince Rupert, first governor of the company, and a number of other noblemen provided for them

¶ the sole trade and commerce of all those seas, straits, bays, rivers, lakes, creeks and sounds, in whatsoever latitude they shall be, that lie within the entrance of the straits commonly called Hud-

XXVII:7 (Left) Most people know that the northern Siberian and Canadian regions are sparsely inhabited, but how sparse? This distorted "map," scaling the areas proportionate to population, strikingly reveals the empty spaces of the northlands. Yet additional maps are needed to emphasize the disparity between the northern and southern parts. (*World Population and Production,* W. S. Woytinsky and E. S. Woytinsky, The Twentieth Century Fund, 1953, used by permission)

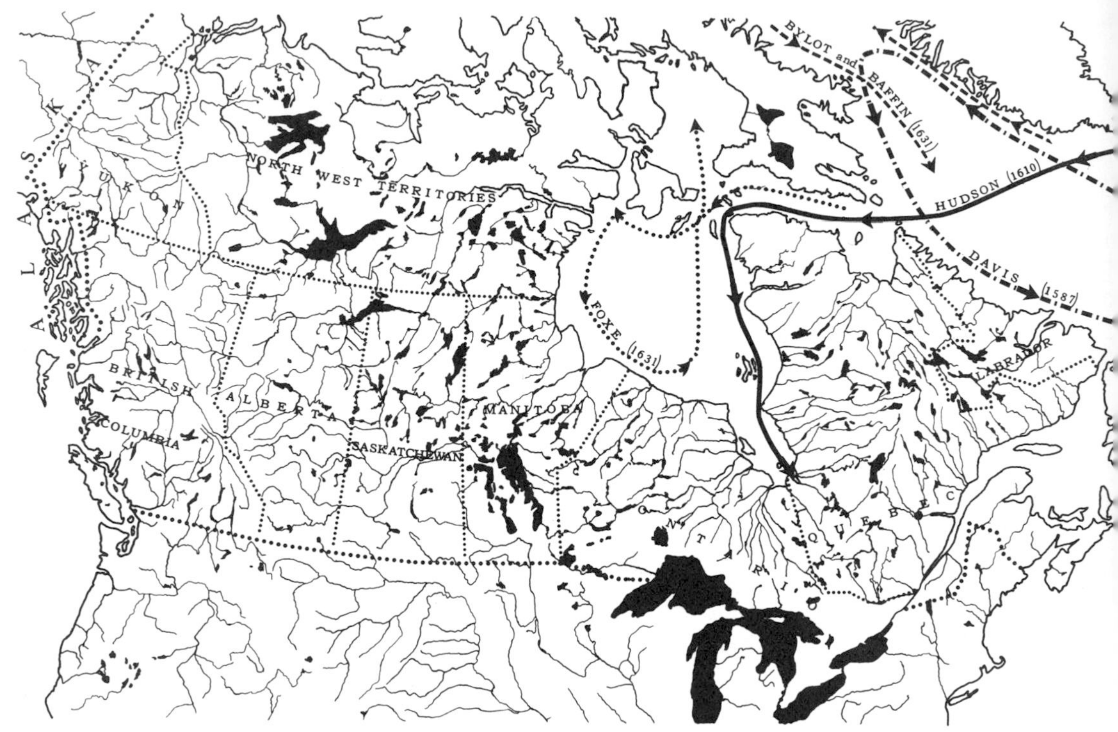

XXVII:9 The quest for the Northwest Passage preoccupied explorers for over three centuries. Here are shown the voyages of several of the original adventurers. (After *A History of Geographical Discovery and Exploration,* J. N. L. Baker, Houghton Mifflin Company, 1931, on Atlas International base)

son's Straits, together with all the lands and territories upon the countries, coasts and confines of the seas, bays, and so forth, aforesaid, that are not already actually possessed by or granted to any of our subjects, or possessed by the subjects of any other Christian prince or state.

The corporation received the right to "the whole and entire trade and traffic to and from all havens, bays, creeks, rivers, lakes and seas into which they shall find entrance or passage by water or land out of the territories, limits or places aforesaid."

The rivalry for exploitation of fur trade in the Northwest Territory became increasingly competitive as Montreal merchants in 1784 organized the North West Company. This had the effect of greatly enlarging the number of trading posts throughout the northwest, the North West Company being the first to enter the Mackenzie Valley. The establishment of a large number of posts and forts in the Great Slave Lake–Great Bear Lake region greatly stabilized the fur trade with the Indian trappers in the area. One of the best chronicles on the Canadian historical geography of fur trapping and trading is that by W. J. and J. L. Robinson, from which the following extract has been taken:

¶ The North West Company was first to enter the Mackenzie Valley. Following Alexander Mackenzie's historic trip to the Arctic, it mapped out fur areas and established posts at Fort Chipewyan (1789), entrance to Mackenzie River (1790), Lac la Martre (1793), eighty miles west of Great Slave Lake on Mackenzie River (1796), Great Bear Lake (1799 and again in 1804), Fort Simpson (1804), Fort Good Hope (1805), and Fort Liard (1805). For the first time traders were in continuous contact with northern Indians and encouraged them to bring furs directly to their posts.

The Hudson's Bay Company attempted to match the expansion of its southern rival and established posts on Slave River, twenty-five miles south of Great Slave Lake (1803), and on

Moose Island in Great Slave Lake (1804). In 1806, however, the Company found that it could not meet the competition and withdrew from Athabasca District. A reorganization of the Company in 1810-11 resulted in renewed expeditions into the North-West. Utilizing its short river supply route to Hudson Bay, the "Honourable Company" was able to regain its share of the fur catch. Finally, in 1821, the two competing companies amalgamated under the name of the Hudson's Bay Company and there followed a more orderly expansion.

During the first half of the nineteenth century the Hudson's Bay Company had a monopoly of the trade of this large area of Canada in which fur was the only known resource. . . . The rule of the Hudson's Bay Company ended in 1869 when Rupert's Land, comprising the vast woodlands and tundra of Northern Canada, was bought from the Company by the newly-federated government of Canada.

Fur-laden ships had been passing through Hudson Strait for 250 years before the first trading-post was established in that area. Beginning in 1909 at Wolstenholme, on the northwest corner of Ungava District (now Quebec), the Hudson's Bay Company started to tap the Eastern Arctic fur resources. White fox is the only economic fur-bearer in the Arctic tundra area, but catches were good and a market was available, enabling the Company to increase the number of its posts and encourage more of the Eskimo inhabitants to become trappers. Revillon Frères, a French-Canadian trading company, established posts in the Eastern Arctic during the nineteen-twenties, but was bought out by the Hudson's Bay Company in 1936.

Posts were opened along the coasts of Hudson Strait and northward in Baffin Island: Lake Harbour (1911), Cape Dorset (1913), Stupart's Bay (1914), Frobisher Bay (1914), Pangnirtung (1921), Pond Inlet (1921), River Clyde (1923), Arctic Bay (1926 and again in 1936), and Fort Ross (1937). The ice-breaker *Nascopie* was built by the Hudson's Bay Company in 1912 to bring annual supplies to these isolated posts, and the sturdy ship has continued to service this ever increasing trade up to the present.

Throughout the years when settlement was spreading across Canada the North West Territories remained a vast fur preserve which annually produced a large fur catch for the scattered native population. These pelts were turned in at the trading-stores for more and more of whiteman's goods until the native life became almost completely centered around trapping. As population spread northward, exploitation of the fur resources of this frontier area increased. Independent fur traders entered the field, but few were able to compete successfully with the efficient organization and widespread service of the Hudson's Bay Company. Competition for furs meant that overtrapping was encouraged and little was done to protect the fur-bearers. This situation was encouraged unfortunately by the false assumption that such vast areas with a sparse population could not be depleted.

The number of white trappers increased rapidly during and after the years of the Klondike gold-rush, when some of the gold-seekers remained in the Territory. A further influx came during World War I when fur prices rose steeply, and another increase, after 1920, followed the collapse of the oil "boom" at Norman Wells. The intensive trapping of the two decades (1900-20) was one of the chief factors in reducing the numbers of certain Mackenzie District fur-bearers.

When the present North West Territories administration was organized in 1921, conservation regulations were immediately instituted to protect the declining fur-bearing animal population.[1]

Toponymy, the study of place names, can itself be a very rewarding geographic technique of analyzing space–time processes of not only the time and type of settlement of a region but also the degree to which man is psychologically influenced by the elements of the natural environment. This is particularly well depicted in the case of Boreal Canada in all aspects of human geography—ethnic, economic, and political. Historically the nomenclature of coast lines, bays, and straits, together with that of the Canadian Arctic, memorializes the leading explorers of the marine approaches to the North Canadian realm. The inland lakes and rivers of the Laurentian Highland, which first carried predominantly Indian or Eskimo names, were subsequently restyled by French names in the southern sector, reflective

[1] Robinson, W. J., and J. L., "Fur Production in the Northwest," *The New Northwest*, Edited by C. A. Dawson, University of Toronto Press, 1947, pp. 133-137. Reprinted from the Canadian Geographical Journal by permission.

of the French pioneer settlements in the Quebec region. The English-occupied sector of Canada, west of the Hudson Bay, though likewise including native nomenclature, features names of prominent explorers or British statesmen. Thus, river nomenclature commemorates Mackenzie, Nelson, and Churchill. Communities, such as Good Hope, Providence, and Resolution, in the Mackenzie drainage basin, reflect a kind of optimistic and deterministic spirit of the explorer and frontiersman. The numerous fort names in this same area and extending southeastward toward the Lake Winnipeg region roughly trace the succession of settlements of trading and military posts established in earlier days by the Hudson's Bay Company. Some of these communities still retain the prefix "fort" such as Fort Vermilion on the Peace River and Fort Nelson on the river by that name, while others such as Good Hope, Simpson, and Providence on the Mackenzie River have dropped this prefix.

Geographically significant also is the mineral toponymy based in part on the most strategic mineral products and geographic situations in the world—Coppermine within the Arctic Circle at the mouth of the river by that name, Port Radium on the east shores of the Great Bear Lake, and Uranium City in a similar topographic situation on the east shore of Lake Athabaska. Because of their diminutive size and single resource, as is also the case with the fur-trading posts, such settlements may be entitled "single enterprise communities."

3. Alaska, the Eskimo's "al-ay-ek-sa" ("The Great Land"). Our first geographic chronicle of Alaska, starts out, as in the case of Boreal U.S.S.R. and Canada, with an exploration to determine continent–sea relationships in the Far North. And, as in the case of the other two, such initial exploration ends up in trading enterprises based initially on furs and skins. There is one primary difference however: in the case of Alaska, "leap-frog" settlements resulted from a series of gold rushes, focused particularly on the Klondike region. But apart from this, the story of "The Great Land" (over twice the size of Texas) is that of the exploratory-adventurous robber economy. Eiteman and Smuts give us one of the briefest and best accounts of the successive gold rushes which epitomize Alaskan historical geography. At the same time, their account provides a summary insight into the potential economic resources as compared with the physical resources of the area. The emphasis on the authors' distinction between these two types of resource adds much to the clarification of the controversial issues which arose at the time Alaska was being considered for statehood. The following excerpts from the authors' article on "Alaska, Land of Opportunity—Limited" should be food for sober thought for all Americans working toward a sound development of Alaskan resources best suited to the nation's economy.

¶ **The First "Gold" Rush**—The Russians were the first to be attracted by the "Devil's lure." Peter the Great planned an expedition to the new world for the purpose of discovering whether or not the western continent was joined to Asia. Intended as a scientific expedition, it ended as a commercial enterprise. The explorers reached the Comador Islands in 1741. Here a storm destroyed the ship and forced the Russians to spend the winter in caves and ravines subsisting on roots, animals, and fish. As a consequence of their enforced stay they were present to witness the coming of the sea otter the following spring. They slaughtered thousands of the little animals and as soon as the weather permitted built a ship and carried the skins back to Russia. The cargo brought such a high price that each crewman made a fortune from the expedition. News of the rich find spread quickly and initiated the first stampede to the Territory. . . . By 1867 the sea otter and the sea cow, which was also hunted extensively, were almost extinct. Not knowing of the gold and copper hidden away in the mountains, the Russians decided that the Territory was no longer worth the cost of defending and sold it to the United States for $7,200,000.

The Second "Gold" Rush—Many Americans considered the purchase of the region as foolish. It was referred to as "Seward's folly" and as "an ice-box." Then, in 1896, a discovery of rich placer deposits in the Klondike led to a second stampede to Alaska. Within a few weeks and months strategically located Alaskan communities of 20 and 30 persons increased to several thousands. Nome grew from practically no population to over 15,000. (It has less than a thousand now.) Practically none of the prospectors planned to settle permanently in Alaska. Most of them expected to loot the region of its gold and then return to the States.

The Third "Gold" Rush—Back in 1898 a party of gold seekers threading their way to the Klondike found a "mountain of red metal" (copper). Although the newly found deposit was unusually rich and easily mined, it was located 190 miles from the coast, requiring transportation of ore over terrain of the most difficult type. The transportation cost of the first metal brought out was $100 per ton. To exploit the deposit, the Kennecott Copper Company built a railroad at a cost of $20,000,000. The huge investment proved profitable, however, for approximately 90 per cent of all Alaskan-produced copper has come from this unique deposit, i.e., more than a half million tons worth in excess of $200,000,000. By 1938 the deposit was exhausted, the mine was closed down, and the railroad was abandoned. Today, the population of the region is dwindling.

The Fourth "Gold" Rush—Even before the gold rush was over salmon fishing was beginning to prove lucrative. In most cases local canneries were owned and financed by absentee owners who opposed the establishment of government in Alaska except insofar as it was to their own interests to have law and order maintained. The fishing industry brought some permanent residents to the Territory, especially to south-eastern Alaska, although even today it is the custom for thousands of fishermen from the States to go to Alaska for the fishing season only.

More of the fortune seekers and adventurers would probably have remained in Alaska if government policy had favored settlers rather than exploiters. In 1898 there were 30,493 white people in Alaska; thirty years later (1929) there were only 28,640 whites. During the decade of the 1930's the white population increased 11,500, chiefly as a result of the depression existing in the States.[1]

How the geography of human occupance operated in the past is significant in the geographical analysis of the present and future of any region. This is particularly significant when we are dealing with potential resources and problems of such a controversial territory as Alaska. The exercises at the conclusion of this chapter are based on those problems.

[1] Eiteman, Wilford J., and Smuts, Alice Boardman, "Alaska, Land of Opportunity—Limited," *Economic Geography*, Vol. XXVII, January, 1951, pp. 35-36. Reprinted by permission.

Taiga timber and lumbering: a Boreal primary resource and industry

Uninviting though the northlands may be to the agriculturalist, the ubiquitous forest cover which dominates almost all the Boreal landscapes may indeed impress the lumberman, who observes here a pioneering opportunity for long-range exploiting of timber products (Figure XXVII-10). But here also, the expansive aspect of the taiga may lead to a miscalculation of the economic potential of the lumbering industry in the realm. As in the case of all other natural resources, forests must be evaluated qualitatively and the areas assayed in terms of accessibility of timber and the feasibility of marketing it. Several illusions are likely to be encountered—for example: the taiga forests are very much like those of the selva, and forestry management may follow much the same practice as that in our middle-latitude areas. Aside from the fact that in both instances the forests are predominantly evergreen, important distinctions in environmental cover and economic exploitation are to be recognized. Whereas the selva forests are primarily broadleaved, those of the taiga are chiefly coniferous; the stands of the former are highly diverse in species consociations, those of the latter primarily characterized by limited tree dominance in each area. In the Eurasian taiga, chiefly in the European section, spruce, cedar, and fir cover over 50 per cent of the area, the rest of the region being dominated largely by pine. In the southeastern part of this area, at somewhat higher elevations, linear strips of birch, basswood, and aspen appear. The larch forms by far the most predominant stand in eastern Siberia, with enclaves and southerly peripheral stands of pine, and locally spruce and fir. The dividing line between the eastern and western dominance may be placed approximately at the Yenisei River.

Broad-leaved trees are favored by river situations, whereas pine and other conifers are found in sandy and rocky topography not well suited for the broad-leaved species. The first trees to replace areas deforested by clearing or fires are aspen and various birches.

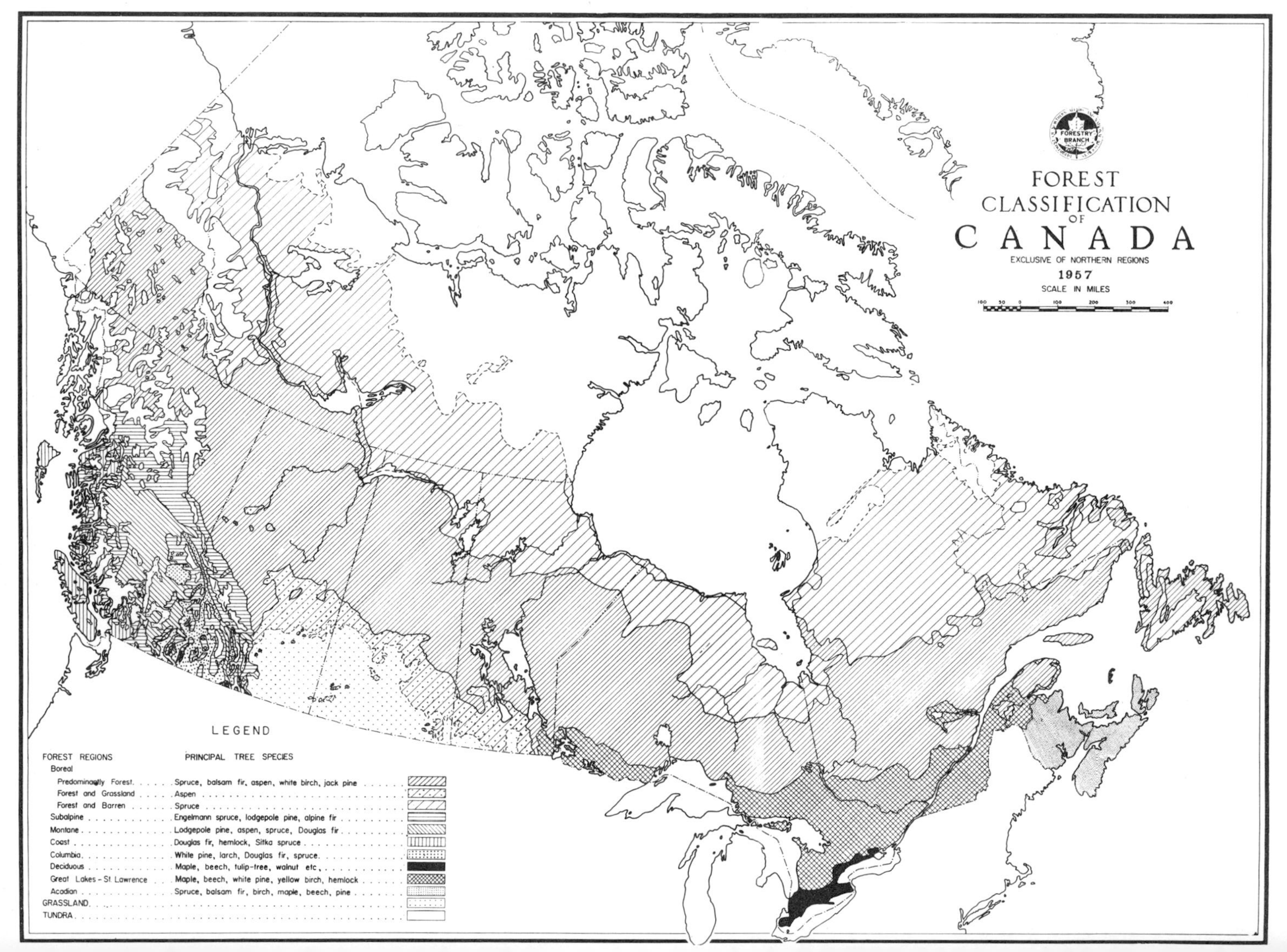
FORESTRY BRANCH
FOREST
CLASSIFICATION
OF
CANADA
EXCLUSIVE OF NORTHERN REGIONS
1957
SCALE IN MILES
100 50 0 100 200 300 400
LEGEND
FOREST REGIONS
PRINCIPAL TREE SPECIES
Boreal
Predominantly Forest . . . . . Spruce, balsam fir, aspen, white birch, jack pine
Forest and Grassland . . . . . Aspen
Forest and Barren . . . . . Spruce
Subalpine . . . . . Engelmann spruce, lodgepole pine, alpine fir
Montane . . . . . Lodgepole pine, aspen, spruce, Douglas fir
Coast . . . . . Douglas fir, hemlock, Sitka spruce
Columbia . . . . . White pine, larch, Douglas fir, spruce.
Deciduous . . . . . Maple, beech, tulip-tree, walnut etc.
Great Lakes - St. Lawrence . . . Maple, beech, white pine, yellow birch, hemlock
Acadian . . . . . Spruce, balsam fir, birch, maple, beech, pine
GRASSLAND . . . . .
TUNDRA . . . . .

Though it must be acknowledged that many of the conifers have considerable merchantable value, the fact must not be overlooked that size and stocking of timber identify differing latitudinal zones of widely carrying capacities. Extraordinarily high latitudes and altitudes with their correspondingly short period of temperatures above 45°F. (normally the minimum temperatures for active growth) have a marked stunting effect on practically all the species. Another reason for the slow growth of timber is edaphic, especially where permafrost exists. Only when the ice thaws in the ground is the water made available to the plants, and this is made possible during only the few months' high-sun period. Thus many of the timbered sections in regions farthest north have nearly a scrub stature. For the same reason, reforestation following a clearing or a burn is a very, very slow process indeed. Also, uncontrolled plantings will normally result in a restocking by undesirable species unsuited for lumbering operations.

Because of the very low population, timber products, like grain, must seek outside markets and ready access to those markets, and do so by the most expeditious and economical transportation. The larger lumber camps and lumber-exporting centers consequently take advantage of coastal and river sites. Most of the urban sites mentioned in the section on population are of this type.

The tremendously increasing demands in recent decades on wood pulp or the manufacture of paper pulp is a highly adaptable enterprise to timber areas once regarded as almost worthless because they were largely stocked with small dimension trees. Boreal forests of this type constitute by far the largest timber reserves in the world, and probably always will.

XXVII:10 (Left) This map shows Canada's forest resources. What geographic correlations are inferrable: (1) between the forest classification and physiographic regions? (2) between the forest-regional classifications and potential forest resources (marketable products)? ("Forest Conservation," *Forest Branch, Department of Northern Affairs and National Resources, Ottawa, Canada*, 1959, p. 10. Published with the permission of the Department of Forestry of Canada)

The taiga harbors the richest fur-bearing fauna in the world

Contrary to popular opinion, Boreal lands harbor a large variety of terrestrial and aquatic forms of animal life. Hoards of insects breed during the summer in the extensive marshes, swamps, and muskegs. Upon them, in turn, feed countless numbers of migratory birds. Flies and mosquitoes make life almost unbearable for man and beast.

Among the ungulates, which browse among the meadows in the forests, are the economically important reindeer and musk ox of Eurasia, and the caribou and moose of the North American realm. Inland streams and lakes, particularly in the southern part, are well stocked with white fish, trout, and many other edible species.

Sub-Arctic seas are proximate to the world's largest sea-fishing grounds, sharing in their benefits as a result of the plankton-laden warm currents which move northward, and the spawning-stimulating cold currents moving southward. Whaling and sealing are here also at their best.

But the animal resources of the largest economic consequence are the fur-bearing animals of the great taiga of Siberia, Canada, and Alaska. In Alaska, fur revenues rank third, exceeded only by those from fishing and mining. Though fur-bearing animals useful for pelt production occur in other climatic realms, the northlands comprise the largest contiguous areas of favorable combinations of climate, vegetative cover, and water features. Another concomitant factor of high animal population is low human population; numerous trading posts and scattered trappers may readily deplete the fur-bearers. Among the more coveted pelts are those of the beaver, muskrat, mink, marten, sable, ermine, otter, wolverine, badger, and fox (Figure XXVII-11).

Most of these species are dependent in large part on the water habitat for their main source of food supply. Significant, therefore, are the numerous bogs, marshes, swamps, lakes, and ramifying rivers characteristic of much of the northlands. Most

Red

White

Black **Cross** **Blue**

FOXES

MINK

BEAVER **MUSKRAT**

XXVII:11 These are the pre-eminent fur bearers of the northland. (*Alaska's Fish and Wildlife,* Clarence J. Rhode, and Will Barker, illustrated by Bob Hines, Circular No. 17, U. S. Department of the Interior)

of the poorly drained areas are identified with continental glaciation, as particularly well typified in the topography and hydrography of Canada and Finland (Figures XXVII-9 and XXVII-12). The latter may be said to be the "lakiest" country of the world. Glacier-formed lake basins may result from ice scour, typically best developed on mountainous terrain (*cirques*) or other highland regions, as, for example, in northern Scandinavia and the Laurentian Highlands; or otherwise result from the irregular deposition of morainic material, blocking the courses of pre-existing river drainage lines or forming *kettle* lakes in the undrained depressions intersecting the groundwater table.

Another feature of hydrography also influencing very decidedly the animal habitat is not normally shown on maps, even of the

MARTEN

OTTER

WOLVERINE

WEASEL

most detailed types. We refer here to the seasonal, overexpanded, miles upon miles of flooded lands adjacent to the major river systems, whose direction of flow is essentially northward. Such a condition is especially accentuated in low coastal plains regions, typified by northern Siberia. Ribbons of ice —which form during long winter months on such streams as the Yenesei, Lena, Ob, and North Dvina of Eurasia, the Mackenzie of Canada, and the Yukon of Alaska—normally first thaw out in the upper southern courses of the streams. Thus the northern unmelted ice blocks the normal drainage line, with the result that in early summer broad expanses of water, normally not mapped because of their transiency, transgress thousands of square miles of low-lying plains. In addition, some of the larger basin lake areas, as in Canada, have resulted from crustal disturbances (diastrophism). Unequal resistance to erosion of the softer and the harder rocks also may result in depressions deep enough for water accumulation. Such are identified in part by the lake basins occupying the less resistant sedimentary formations which bound the Canadian Shield, constructed largely of igneous and metamorphic rocks about the Hudson Bay region. This region experienced heavy continental glaciation during the Pleistocene, to which many of the water-filled basins are attributed. By contrast, unglaciated Siberia for the most part is river-sculptured.

Whatever the cause or source of the numerous lake depressions and rivers may be,

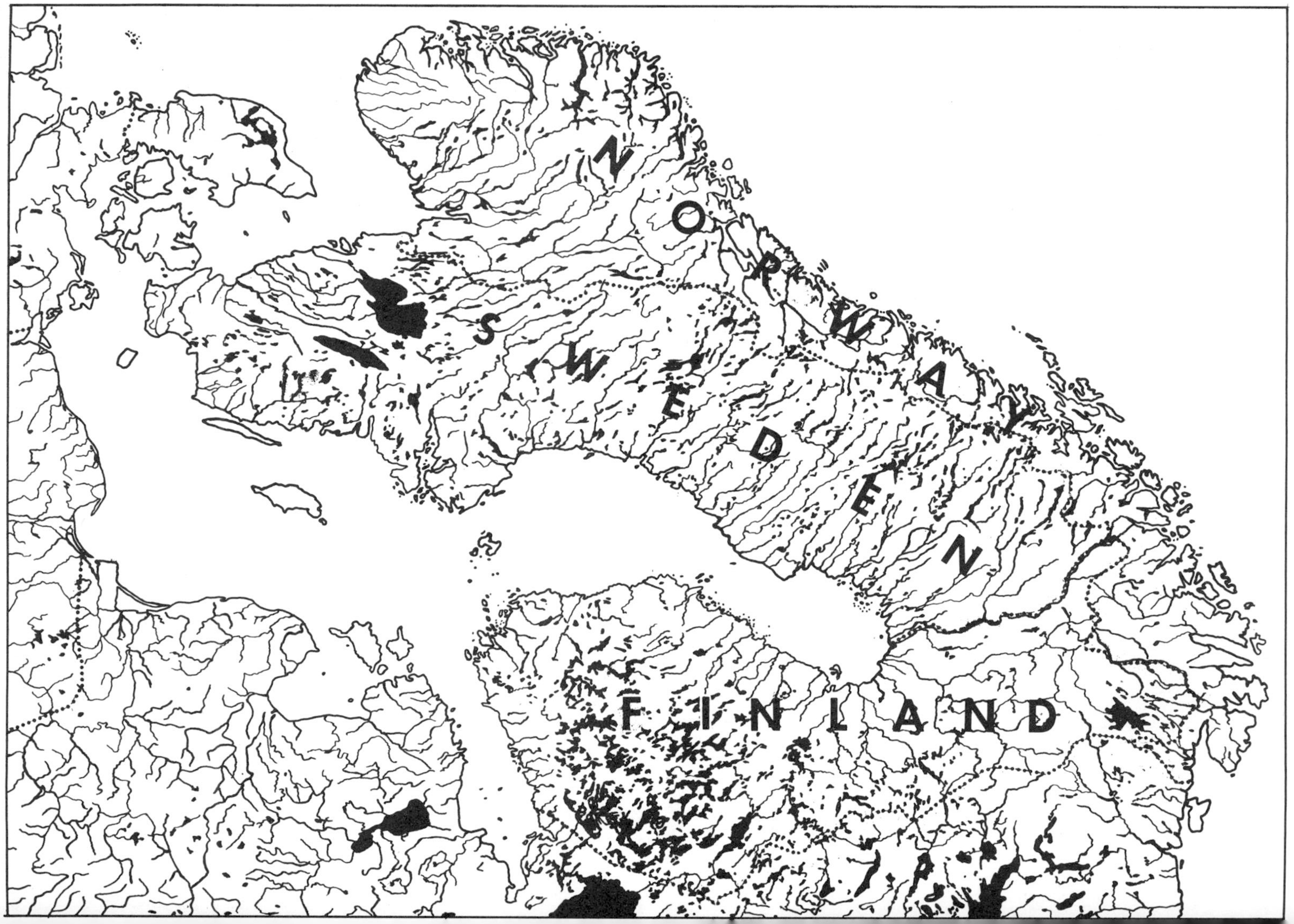
NORWAY
SWEDEN
FINLAND

these are the sites most frequented by the fur-bearers as well as other animals. Therefore, here also we would expect to find the major trapping lines and even many of the trading posts. As was earlier pointed out in the section on historical geography, first the seacoasts and then the interior drainage lines were also the routes of earliest exploration and trading. The chains of rivers and lakes, connected by short portages, enabled the trapper in Canada to move all the way from the Lake Winnipeg region to the mouth of the Mackenzie on the Arctic coast with practically no need to resort to land travel.

Though fur marketing in the total world economy today may not seem to be of primary significance, the commercial fur resource of any one country or geographic region may be of paramount importance, as in the case of Canada. In this country, the value of furs annually approximates $25,000,000, and represents a catch of some 6,500,000 fur-bearers in the following decreasing order of major pelt productivity: beaver, mink, muskrat, and white fox. In addition to these wild forms, ranch animals are reared, primarily mink, whose value alone for the years 1956-58 averaged annually about $15,000,000, or seven times the value from wild mink. The United States by far is Canada's best fur customer, followed by Great Britain (8).

As for the historic trapper himself, his very personality provides a geographic commentary on the type of frontier life identified with the fur, fin, and fowl economy. Greenbie's epic thus dramatizes the character and contribution of the wilderness trappers:

¶ They rise like whitecaps on the sea, appear like mystified deer upon the meadow. They arrive upon the scene as mere cubs of the wilderness, with the gun in their hands as much a part of their reflexes as are the hidden claws of the grizzly, and they use that gun as instinctively as the modern man puts his foot on the accelerator. Yet for all their militant legerdemain, for all their leagues of loneliness, for all the milestones between them and civilization, for all the effacement that watching their traps imposed upon them, for all their want of background, these men emerged from their retirement as real personalities.

The wonder is that with nothing but keen eyes, sharp ears, untrammeled reflexes, and unerring triggers, with nothing else to recommend them to posterity, they should have impressed themselves upon our whole culture with the force of social exploit. . . .

Of personality, our frontiersmen had more than their need. They stood between settlement and its terrors. Singly and unprovisioned, the trapper went into regions where others hesitated to go in groups and fully stocked. Not till he made small of these dangers did the nation make big its advancements. He roamed thousands of circuitous miles while others clung fearfully to his trace and his trail. . . . He was of the wind in the forests and the flow in the rivers, and the rigor of frost on the plains.[1]

XXVII:12 (Left) The drainage pattern of Scandinavia is shown here. Consider particularly the effect of the innumerable lakes in Finland along with the short summers (*Dfc*) on Finland's agricultural development. (After Atlas International Larousse)

Sub-Arctic geomorphology is a geographic guideline to its mineralogy

Geomorphology, the study of earth structure and landforms, can be, and usually is, of marked significance in interpreting the human occupance of a region. This is particularly apparent in Boreal lands for two basic reasons: (1) the high degree of representativeness of world types of physiographic regions in the area, and (2) the contrasting subregional mineralization in which we are here primarily interested.

The geomorphology of the sub-Arctic includes the basic geomorphological forms of shields, massives, plains, plateaus, and cordilleras (Figure XXVII-13). Although normally made up of crystalline rocks (igneous and metamorphic), the shield, a gently downarched landform, is primarily distinguished for its primordiality, representing the "basement-complex" of earth structure. Topographically shields may take the form of low-lying plains, as in the immediate vicinity of the Hudson Bay, or present more ele-

[1] Greenbie, Sydney, *Furs to Furrows (An Epic of Rugged Individualism)*, The Caxton Printers, Ltd., Caldwell, Idaho, 1939. Reprinted by permission.

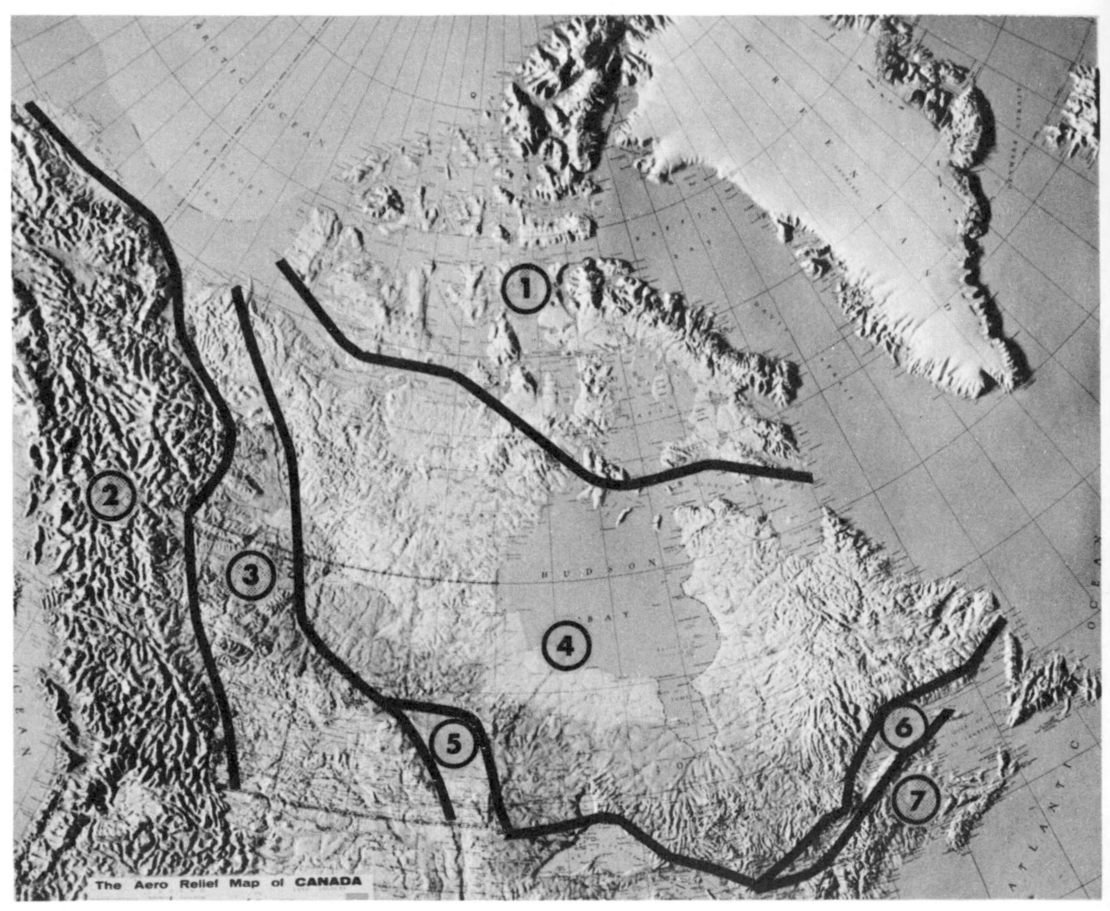

XXVII:13 This map shows the Canadian physiographic provinces: (1) Arctic Archipelago, (2) Cordilleras, (3) Great Plains (plateau), (4) Canadian Shield, (5) Interior Plains, (6) St. Lawrence Lowland, (7) Appalachian Region. The Aero relief base helps to highlight the basic geomorphological structure. (Base from Aero Service Corporation, used by permission)

vated, rugged terrain, as in the Scandinavian highlands. The sub-Arctic thus features three shields: the Canadian Shield about the Hudson Bay, the Scandinavian Shield about the Baltic Sea, and the Angara Shield in North Central Siberia between the Yenesei and the Lena rivers. Strategically situated with regard to Russia's only warm-water port at Murmansk are the Kola Peninsula deposits of nickel, cobalt, chromite, and the phosphorus mineral apatite. These are tremendously significant in a realm otherwise poor in fertilizer materials.

*1. **Mineralogical significance.*** The important thing to recognize here is that while almost any type of rock formation may contain one or more minerals, nearly all the economically important minerals are related in their primary or secondary origin to igneous activity of some type. This is not to say that such minerals are indigenous to the originally formed igneous rocks, but that they may be the result of subsequent hydrothermal action and other igneous-related subsequent processes which have occurred in the parent material itself or in the proximate metamorphic or sedimentary rocks that are in mineralizing contact with the primary source of component mineral-producing elements. Accordingly, then, it is important for the geography student to know that while large areas of the shields themselves may exhibit a lack of original mineralization, many of the more precious minerals in the sub-Arctic are identified with these shield areas. Among these are the noteworthy Kiruna-Gällivare iron deposits of Sweden upon which heavy demands were made in the Second World War by both the Western Allies and the Axis Powers. Also there come to mind the famous multimetalliferous nickel, copper, gold, silver, lead, zinc, platinum deposit in the Sudbury region on the southern border of the Canadian Shield and the iron-rich formations of Labrador, whose potential is fabulously enhanced by the completion of the St. Lawrence Seaway.

2. Plateaus. Plateaus are generally uplands or table lands, flattish to hilly in character, and sometimes characterized by mountainous terrain, in which case they are normally referred to as massifs.[1] A large area of this type in northeastern Siberia attains the highest elevation found in the Eurasian sub-Arctic, the topmost elevation rising well beyond a mile. Gold seems to be the commonest spotty mineral feature.

3. Plains. The northlands embrace one of the largest plains regions in the world, the Eurasian Northern Plain, which extends sub-Arctic-wise from the Gulf of Bothnia to the Yenisei River, whence the higher lands of the provinces previously noted limit the northern plains primarily to the tundra (*ET*) coastal area. The North American Interior Plain is the northern extension of the Great Plains of the United States into the Mackenzie River Basin. The sedimentary rocks of which the plains are chiefly constituted are the normal sites of peat, coal, and oil. The liquid fuels depend upon favorable "trapping" crustal deformation or other concentrating agency for the amassing of commercially exploitable deposits. Such petroleum products occur in the eastern foothills of the cordilleras of Canada and in comparable structural areas in the Eurasian sub-Arctic.

4. Mountains. Mountains are landforms primarily distinguished by terrain rising abruptly to relatively high altitudes, accented by numerous and steep slopes. Most mountains contain components of all the three major classes of rocks — igneous, sedimentary, and metamorphic. Mineralization may then be expected, both because of this fact and the fact that mountains are dominant in regions of crustal disturbances with cores of igneous rocks and flanks of metamorphics. Another associated geographical feature of importance is the weathering and erosion which are normally at a premium, conspicuously exposing the rock components and hence facilitating ore prospecting. The North American Cordillera, forming the westernmost physiographic province of Canada, extends into and through Alaska to Bering Strait beyond which is the Alpine-folded province of northeasternmost Siberia. The cordillera includes the highest and most rugged points of the sub-Arctic. Mineralization and mining in this region, however, are not as widespread or as intensive as some people may think, a misconception commonly resulting from overdramatization of episodes like the gold rushes in the Yukon Valley. Though other important minerals, such as silver, copper, zinc, petroleum, and coal occur locally, their strategic value apparently overshadows their long-range economic importance.

The Ural Mountains of eastern European Russia are considered by some as a part of the Eurasian Northern Plain. While the elevation and ruggedness are not great, the ranges normally not rising over 2000 feet, the Urals extend almost entirely across the plain. The most significant geographic fact about the Ural province is that it probably is, minerally, the most highly diversified mountain area in the world. Besides iron there is an unusual array of ferroalloys such as cobalt, chromite, tungsten, titanium, vanadium, and nickel. Other metals include copper, lead, zinc, and aluminum. Petroleum is likewise found in the vicinity. The value of this high mineralization, of course, is very much enhanced by the proximity of the ores to the more closely settled regions and industrial centers of Russia. However, because of this very fact some of the ores are also nearing exhaustion, as, for example, platinum.

The twentieth century provides new geographic dimensions to sub-Arctic mineral exploration and exploitation

The study of mineral deposits and their exploitation is professionally the province of

[1] Massif—A word of French origin, distinguishing the great Central Massif of France.

the geologist and the mining engineer. The geographer's concern for minerals and mining is primarily one of recognizing the patterns of distribution of each and the role they play in our differentiated regional economies, and in the world at large, as specifically developed in Chapter 11.

The normal procedure for differentiating the sub-Arctic from the other realms of the world in terms of mineralization would be to establish its relative ranking. But a number of geographic forces make this exceedingly difficult. It should already be fairly obvious to the student, in terms of the climatological conditions set forth above, that the prospecting for new ores and the mining operations of mineral deposits already discovered in *Dc-d* lands, are incomparably more difficult and costly than exploration and exploitation in other realms of the *C* or *D* types.

The frozen regolith does not lend itself readily to surface prospecting, and yet the winter is about the only season when penetration of the great plains of the northlands with their numerous muskegs is possible. Moreover, the northern and central areas, underlain by permafrost, create construction problems, if not during the winter season when the surface ground is frozen, then during the summer thaws. Time and again petroleum prospecting machinery had to be abandoned in muskeg country to await the return of freezing weather in order to extricate the equipment.

Moreover, as a result of the general paucity of other natural resources and sparsity of settlement, the sub-Arctic, with the exception of the relatively highly developed region of Scandinavia and the Province of Quebec in North America, is conspicuously devoid of highways and railways and air transportation. Although overcoming obstacles in many ways, air transport is not practical for heavy ore transfer except where the mineral product is relatively pure and its own value high enough to stand the cost of transportation. Furthermore, since minerals are an exhaustible natural resource, even some of the most precious but limited lodes may not justify the building of railways, especially through muskeg or permafrost country. This puts a premium on ore transportation by water. Unfortunately, minerals, unlike animals, have no particular affinity for deep valley watercourses, but are identified normally with just the opposite type of topography, such as inaccessible highlands and mountain ranges with characteristically non-navigable streams. An exception to this, and a rather singular one, however, is the stream gold-placer deposits which are rather surprisingly widespread in both the North American and Eurasian realms of the northland. We have already noted in the historical section how such fluvial deposits in the Yukon Valley of Alaska-Canada were earlier responsible for the first migrations into the Klondike region. Similar placer deposits have been exploited along several of the larger streams of the great Siberian realm.

An interesting example illustrating the normally frustrating ore-transportation problem in the northlands is that of the strategic pitchblende deposit, source of the fissionable material, uranium, near Great Bear Lake in Canada. This ore, which incidentally is also associated with other strategically important minerals, such as nickel, cobalt, and some silver, is concentrated locally and then transported by plane to the nearest rail head at Waterways, whence it proceeds by rail to Port Hope, the refining center, three thousand miles distant from the Port Radium area.

A somewhat similar situation obtains with respect to mining of gold, of which the largest lodes occur in the Siberian sub-Arctic. In earlier days very primitive roads were built to contact some of the richer deposits. But as the five-year plans of the Soviet system exploited such mineral deposits on a larger scale, motor highways were constructed to move the ores to the rail heads of the Trans-Siberian Railroad.

In addition to the geomorphological distinctions of area based on ore genesis, areal differentiations of mineral exploitation suggest themselves, including such as are based on time, transportation, technology, and political control in the development of the various mineralogical regions.

1. ***Time.*** The time factor in the exploration and exploitation of mineral deposits is significant in appraising the mineral production potential of the sub-Arctic compared as a whole with other regions, as well as in evaluating the several subregions of its own realm. Until relatively recent decades, most of the realm was practically entirely unexplored, particularly the Siberian and North Canadian regions. Even isolated and sporadic gold rushes, such as took place in the Klondike area, date back only slightly over 50 years. And not until the second decade of the twentieth century, when the Soviets started to develop their five-year expansion programs, did systematic explorations start in the Siberian region.

The earliest exploitation of mineral deposits in the realm took place in the Scandinavian region, where as early as the second decade in the thirteenth century copper mining and metallurgy were initiated in Sweden. The mineralized sections of the Kiruna-Gällivare district based on iron also were among the sub-Arctic pioneering mining enterprises.

Similarly on the North American continent, the early mining exploits were identified with the earliest frontier settlements of Canada. Although the accelerated reconnaissances by land, and more particularly by air, have now reached the stage where broad geologic evaluations of potential mineralizations have been made, sufficient time has not elapsed to allow for the type of detailed prospecting necessary to form a comprehensive appraisal of the relative regional ranking of Canada as a future mineral producer.

*2. **Transportation.*** Often overlooked in the economic evaluation of an ore deposit is its geographic position with respect to other mineral sites and to ready facilities for exploitation and transportation. The ideal geographic situation for steel manufacturing, for example, would be one that had basic raw materials — iron ores, coking coal, and flux materials.[1] If proximity of such products is not realizable, then available cheap transportation, as provided best by water for heavy cargoes, may be said to be the next best geographic situation for the establishment of metallurgical industries. Such are, for example, the traffic conditions of the Great Lakes in North America and of the Ruhr-Rhine of western Europe. But in sub-Arctic Siberia, numerous coal and iron ore deposits of otherwise high economic value occur far distant from one another and off water-courses. Therefore spur or mainline trans-Siberian hauls over as much as a thousand miles or more are required to bring coal to the iron districts, where the metallurgical establishments are normally set up. And the more northerly fields are today still without any form of transportation. Equally significant is the fact that extensive as are the river systems of the Ob, the Yenesei, the Lena, the Amur, and even the Dvina, in the western part, none of these broad and otherwise navigable streams is exploitable in a major way for bringing iron ore and coking coal together. Commonly overlooked also is the fact that even if iron and coal deposits are strategically situated adjacent to any of these river systems, the sub-Arctic rivers are frozen over a large part of the year and must await the late spring thaws before even the headwaters are open to navigation. Even then, one must wait almost to midsummer before the mouths of these streams are freed from ice. By contrast, the west coast European area, including the very important iron-exporting port of Narvik in the north and the iron-exporting ports of the Biscay of northern Spain, is open the year round. And the St. Lawrence–Great Lakes waterway is frozen over for only a relatively short winter season.

In this connection, it is also geographically significant to note that while such an important iron-ore deposit as the Mesabi hematite and other deposits about the Lake Superior region may relatively soon be depleted, the extensive iron ores of Labrador must await rail connections with the St. Lawrence Seaway to supplement the Lake Superior supply.

*3. **Mining and metallurgy.*** Tying in closely with the preceding are new material-and-energy-conversion processes. Technological advances of our modern age have been particularly noteworthy in smelting and metallurgy. Thus innovations in metallurgical processes in Sweden involve the use of hydroelectric power instead of power based on coal. This is an apt geographic example of how man can substitute one environmental asset for another which is lacking. In this case the expense of long hauls of coal, such as Russia experiences, was overcome. Almost entirely without coal, Sweden is significantly rich in hydroelectric potential based on a topography highly suited to the harnessing

---

[1] The Birmingham region in the United States approaches this ideal, as does the Alsace-Lorraine district of West Europe and the Birmingham district of Great Britain.

of stream power. Swedish technicians have been able to evolve electric smelting processes of high efficiency and economy. This sort of thing also may affect the geographical export pattern of steel, and help put increasing quantities of steel right into the competitive marketing areas of our Great Lakes steel centers. These are now readily accessible via the St. Lawrence Seaway, which on its own part likewise contributes a new geographical dimension to the position of Swedish ore and industrial values.

Newly developed mining and metallurgical processes also make possible economic exploitation of lean and flinty ore-like taconite of the iron-ore district of the northern Lake Superior region and elsewhere. They foretell another change in the mining industrial geographic pattern of the sub-Arctic as well as of other realms. And the new missile and space age into which we have been catapulted will place an additional premium on proven strategic fissionable minerals, such as pitchblende, whose chief American areas of concentration are in the Mackenzie Valley.

4. Political control. All major nations aspire to world power status, and such status is predicated in large measure on outright possession of or ready access to minerals of strategic importance. And so the Soviets immediately upon accession to power recognized that here was one of the major challenges to the industrial and military development of the Soviet Union, if it would aspire to major world powerhood. No other nation in the world, unless it be Canada, faces such environmental challenges in mineral exploration and exploitation over so large a proportion of its domain. The U.S.S.R. has established a record for accelerated attack on this problem. Almost immediately after the revolution in 1917, the Soviets began to organize several hundred expeditions to check on their far-flung sub-Arctic wilderness for promising mineral deposits. Direct discoveries of many mineralized areas were made, and many more prospective areas were geologically mapped for further ground probings. Recognizing that time was of the essence, and that very little had been done in this area, the Soviets resorted primarily to phenomenal air expeditions. Such reconnaissance flights not only helped make up for lost time, so to speak, in pushing toward the goal of a high ranking mineral power, but also overcame much of the weariness of foot travel in the trackless taiga and muskeg country.

From a comparable environmental analysis standpoint, the geography student will recognize that both sub-Arctic Canada and Alaska would benefit from this type of exploration. Actually such geologic expeditions have been inaugurated in both areas, but not nearly to the same extent as they have been by the Soviets in their own northlands. But, as we also know, the Soviets have not only exploited the minerals with a vengeance, but much of their mining labor as well. As has been reported time and again, many of the mining operations are carried out with the aid of slave labor made up largely of German prisoners from the Second World War, and subsequently of other "political" prisoners who have been dispatched to the mining camps, particularly in the northeastern sector. Here continentality and Communism conspire together to effect a unique "concentration camp."

Summation of the basic problems and resource potential of the Northlands

Geography of the Northlands published by the American Geographical Society (1955) is probably as authentic an evaluation of the world northlands as is available to us. Accordingly, the following much abstracted observations from the concluding chapter of this basic sub-Arctic research appear appropriate for concluding our own chapter:

¶ Only a few parts of the Subarctic are attractive to arable farming, and grazing lands are fairly limited, though there is probably room for a large additional number of reindeer herds and herders, and perhaps of musk ox and elk. The hunting and fishing of wildlife must be kept extensive to avoid depletion, and horticulture and truck-gardening in the north have attempted little more than supplying local needs. In the near future, at any rate, the economic incentives drawing immigrants from the south are rather to be found in mining, industry, and services. . . .

The unique advantage of the northlands from the commercial point of view, their position athwart the great circle routes connecting the great metropolitan centers of the old and new worlds, has not yet been exploited to any great extent, but expansion in this field may be very rapid. . . . Surface communication throughout the northlands are improving, but their relative paucity holds back development. Railroads, sea routes kept open by icebreakers, and all-weather motor highways are still inadequate, and their lack, more than any one factor perhaps, restricts the growth of trade, and economic stimulus that goes with it. In many areas local enterprises, canneries, lumber mills, mines, etc., must depend on seasonal water transport.

While wars, cold or hot, continue to threaten, the polar basin, as the nearest approach to an international meeting ground of the greatest military powers, is a primary strategic area. Both sea and land, and inner and outer territories, require protection. . . . But the experts readily admit that in modern warfare no warning system or armed defense can be wholly effective, and still less so over vast frontiers and hinterlands like those of the northlands. On the other hand, a measure of protection against a conventional mass attack from the north is provided by the hard conditions of climate and the dearth of local food supplies, which would render a land invasion onerous in the extreme and a mass air attack most costly.[1]

After considering these and a number of other factors, the author concludes with the final observation:

¶ Venturing to weigh such virtual imponderables as these, we may conclude that the northlands, though almost certain to have greater importance than heretofore, are unlikely to become dominant in the world. A unique region they will remain, with a very special appeal to many as acquaintance with the North becomes more easily obtainable, but probably for the majority still a region to view by preference, from afar.[2]

APPLICATION OF GEOGRAPHIC UNDERSTANDING

I. Controversial Alaska. Commentaries by the press and by Congress itself on the qualifications of Alaskan statehood constitute a classic example of the shortcomings of our nongeographical educational system, which

XXVII:14 The state of Alaska is here superimposed on its sister continental states. This reveals what striking facts of comparative size, shape, and longitudinal extent? (From "Alaska's Fish and Wildlife" Circular 17, U. S. Department of Interior, 1953)

fails to prepare our citizenry to think of area content regionally and systematically in the appraisal of an area's resources, natural and human.

Many of the approaches "pro" and "con" to Alaska's statehood stature still follow the old-fashioned statistical and encyclopedic listing of "facts" of a century ago without discerning the geographic forces which operate in making a country strong or weak, now and in the future. The object of this and other chapter exercises is to have the student fully realize this pedagogical principle and here apply the geographical learning processes of superimposed Alaska (see Fig. XXVII-14).

One way of evaluating the natural and cultural forces of site and situation of a country is to superimpose its map on one of comparable scale of another country — here Alaska on the United States, Figure XXVII-14. Use the categories of geographical regional appraisal commonly employed by geographers, and assuming that Alaska in all its setting took on the characteristics—physical, biological, and human—as now found in the "overlapped" U.S. sections, determine what the new Alaska would be like.

II. Undifferentiated Alaska. "Seward's Folly". . . . "Take Alaska off the Ice". . . . "Bigger than Texas; Better than California; God's country". . . . A territory of anachronistic landscape features: "totem poles intermingled with radio towers; airways overlooking trail-

[1] Good, Dorothy, "Conclusion," *Geography of the Northlands*, George H. T. Kimble and Dorothy Good, Editors, The American Geographical Society, New York, 1955, pp. 499-503, *passim*. Reprinted by permission.

[2] *Ibid.* Reprinted by permission.

Modern aviation has, to an extent, solved the "isolation" problem for many *Dc-d* (and even *E*) communities. As a matter of fact, flying in Alaska has become a popular sport, both in winter and in summer. In snow country, skis replace wheels, and pontoons serve as landing gear. This is one way of visiting North America's highest latitude (only 175 miles from the Arctic Circle) and highest altitude (over 20,000 ft.) in Mount McKinley National Park, shown here. (Courtesy Alaska Visitors Association)

ways; night clubs next to Eskimo huts." Show how statements and features such as these may very well lead to confusing and conflicting appraisals. For one thing: Are we dealing with "one" Alaska, or a number of Alaskas, so to speak? This is the third chapter which deals with an important segment of this "Great Land." Briefly evaluate the geographical characteristics of the several regional units of Alaska.

III. Agricultural Alaska. "The Great Land has every type of climate except tropical." Do you agree?

"Alaska, rugged and primitive, is a land of surprises. . . . Giant strawberries, 50-pound cabbages, delphiniums 9 feet tall." What does all this really mean?

"There is no reason to doubt that on the average wheat culture will be more successful on, and just south of, the Arctic Circle in Alaska . . . than in the same latitudes in Finland. . . . Perhaps the easiest money crop to produce in Alaska, after gold and fish, is reindeer beef." By what geographical criteria would you check the above two statements by former explorer Stefansson, back in 1941?

IV. Comparative Country Analysis. This is an expedient often effective in analyzing a "controversial" territory like Alaska. But as already indicated in the discussion of the various climatic realms, and again now in this chapter, recognized similarities or dissimilarities cannot be the ultimate basis for forming conclusions about the way countries have arrived at their present social and economic status. And especially we cannot use this as a yardstick by which to measure a country's potential. Nevertheless, properly selected and evaluated criteria can serve as useful guidelines in comparative regional study.

Thus one authority, A. H. Brooks, would estimate the future of Alaska by comparing it to the northwestern European geographical counterpart—Finland and Sweden: "Alaska has every advantage over Finland and Sweden both in food resources . . . and in potential energy." How would you go about testing the validity of this observation?

V. Comparing "Economic" and "Natural" Criteria. But authorities like Eiteman point to the problem of commonly confusing natural resources with economic resources (such as the shorter hauls, more efficient transportation, and superior markets for minerals, lumber, and food products in Scandinavia) in comparing regional potential. Do you think that the present statehood status will eventually place Alaska in the rank of Sweden-Finland (about the same size) in resource and population?

Kirk H. Stone, who did a research study on "Populating Alaska" (*The Geographic Review,* 1952) concludes that "new settlements throughout the northern lands generally should not be planned with a view that only agriculture will ensure ultimate permanency." What would you want to know about his researches in order to evaluate the validity of this statement?

VI. Political Geography. Though there was strong endorsement for statehood by Alaskans generally, the Juneau and Ketchican communities were opposed to it. On the other hand, Fairbanks and Anchorage were among the leaders supporting the cause. Do you detect any geographic basis for the diverse regional points of view?

How will the political state status change tourism in Alaska? Imagine you are writing a government bulletin designed to give the American tourist a truly factual and yet alluring account of Alaska's scenic and sports attractions, how would you go about this? Above all, again keep in mind the "diverse Alaskas."

References

1 Korol, Nestor, "Agriculture in the Zone of Perpetual Frost," *Science,* October, 1955, p. 680.

2 Gray, G. D. B., *Soviet Land,* A. and C. Black, Ltd., London, 1947, pp. 124-126, *passim.* 152, 172-173.

3 Cressey, George, *How Strong Is Russia?* Syracuse University Press, N. Y., 1954, p. 62.

4 Parmuzin, Yu. P., "The Zonal Character of the Cold Pole," *Izvestiya Vsesoyuznogo geografticheskogo obshchestva,* No. 5, 1958, pp. 472-474. (As translated in *Soviet Geography,* Theodore Shabad, Editor, American Geographical Society, Vol. I, No. 1-2, 1960, pp. 40-42.)

5 Jorré, Georges, *The Soviet Union: The Land and Its People,* Translated by E. D. Laborde, Longmans, Green & Co., Inc., New York and London, 1950, p. 21.

6 Robinson, W. J. and J. L., "Fur Production in the Northwest," *The New Northwest,* Edited by C. A. Dawson, University of Toronto Press, 1947, pp. 133-137. (Reprinted from the *Canadian Geographical Journal.*)

7 Eiteman, Wilford J., and Smuts, Alice Boardman, "Alaska, Land of Opportunity—Limited," *Economic Geography,* Vol. XXVII, January, 1951, pp. 35-36.

8 Byrnes, Myrtis L., "The Fur Industry Abroad," U. S. Department of Commerce, June, 1959, pp. 5-7.

9 Greenbie, Sydney, *Furs to Furrows (An Epic of Rugged Individualism).* The Caxton Printers, Ltd., Caldwell, Idaho, 1939.

10 Good, Dorothy, "Conclusion," *Geography of the Northlands,* George H. T. Kimble and Dorothy Good, Editors, The American Geographical Society, 1955, pp. 499-503, *passim.*

Chapter 28

The humid, severe winter–short summer, forest and prairie lands *(Dfb-Dwb)*

¶ "Ferme Joanne,"
Paroisse de Ste. Martine,
Comte de Chateauguay,
Province de Quebec,
Canada.
Autumn, 1956.

Chers Amis.

. . . If I may, I should like first of all to go back over the last year and tell you how we fared. Last summer [1955], we had an exceptionally dry year. Temperatures weren't at all favourable to agriculture and we suffered from lack of rain right up until the end of August. The pastures particularly became very parched. Despite everything, however, the harvest wasn't too bad. The rain came on quite well, although the tomatoes ripened with considerable difficulty. The sweet corn was passable and the peas and beans were able to profit from the frequent rains which finally fell towards the close of summer. . . . Most of the cows came into the stable for the winter at the beginning of November. . . . I am afraid that you must sometimes get tired of hearing so much about the weather in these farm reports, but the lives of farmers all over the world, it is no exaggeration to say, are literally dominated by the weather. It doesn't matter if you're in the province of Quebec, the South Island of New Zealand, or the Highlands of Scotland, climate is a factor which either brings success or failure to your farming operations. All you can do is to be philosophical, never despair and put your trust in divine providence! We felt very much like this at Ste.-Martine during the spring of 1956. The cold, wet spring which we experienced greatly retarded our whole seeding programme. We weren't able to *start* sowing until after June 10th, a whole month later than usual. Despite this slow and disappointing start, the grain crops did surprisingly well and were excellent both in quantity and quality, but they couldn't be sold for seed. . . . The hay crop was also abundant, giving us plenty of feed for the winter months, but the harvest of some of the other crops was not at all satisfactory. The sweet corn which we grow for delivery to the Green Giant Canning Company was a total loss—the lack of heat literally prevented it from maturing and developing. Particularly disappointing was the fact that our few arpents of soya beans did not have a happy season for their debut on the farm, for the protein value of the soya bean is important to dairy farmers like ourselves. In a temperate climate, as you know, both animals and humans must keep the protein content of their diet at a healthy level; human beings eat eggs, meat, and cheese, while animals receive their protein largely through the grass they graze. During the long winter months, however, when animals are forced to stay indoors and can no longer get the benefit of the green and growing grass, the beef animal will not fatten so well and the dairy cow will not milk so well without a certain protein supplement, for hay and silage cannot of its very nature contain the same amount of protein as the living crop. . . . You can understand how much we value the five months of the year when the cows [a basic herd of 26 dairy cows] are out to pasture and how much, as a result, we count on the quality and growth of the grass. For this is the time of the year, when animals are out in the field, and when milk can be produced at the minimum cost.[1]

Diverse and complex as is the industry of farming, significant understandings of such, especially by a person who has not been reared on a farm, is most difficult to achieve. Moreover, mere familiarity with the activities of a farm or a farming region, either by direct contact with the land or by reading, inventory fashion, a description of the kind of products a given farm produces, does not render understanding of the significance of farming activities as they vary from region to region. Next to having the experience of

[1] Brault, Henri, "Ferme Joanne" (communication), "A Dairy Farm in French Canada," *Farming in the Commonwealth, Canada*, The Association of Agriculture, London, in collaboration with Le Ministere de L'Agriculture, Province of Quebec, 1956, pp. 1-2, *passim*. Original letter in French. Reprinted by permission.

rural survey training as provided in geography field courses, one of the best ways of obtaining a geographic perspective of the activity of a farm and its role in the total economy of an area is to scrutinize a complete land-use survey of its activities made jointly by the farmer himself and some specialized agency. Such is the type projected by the British Association of Agriculture under the general title "Farming in the Commonwealth," alluded to in a previous chapter. And the *Ferme Joanne,* reported on above by its operator, M. Henri Brault, at Ste. Martine (vicinity of Montreal, Canada) is such a farm study.[1]

The farm is representative of a goodly portion of the St. Lawrence Valley area, itself a component of the so-called Hay and Dairy Region of North America. Besides giving us a unified picture of farmland practices in this type of region, the format as here presented inductively suggests the kind of land-use, inventory, and resource analysis a geography student would consider when making a study of any farm unit which represents the agricultural pattern of the larger region. Such an abridgement must be designed to give primary selectivity to those factors and principles with which the geographer is essentially concerned—both in the collection and in the evaluation of field data.

*1. **Historical background.*** As suggested by the name of the farm and form of address, the farm family is French. The village and parish of Ste. Martine is the *chef-lieu,* or center, of the county (Chateauguay) in French Canada. The village, of some less than 1,000 inhabitants, is situated on the Chateauguay River within 18 miles of Montreal, today the second largest French-speaking city in the world. Connected by highway and railway with Montreal, and with Malone in New York state, the village is the site of a well-established Agricultural School, a thriving farmers' co-operative, and a canning factory.

*2. **The form of the farm.*** Unlike the characteristic rectangular plats of farms which typify most of the midwestern American scene, Brault's farm (Figure XXVIII-1) conforms to the French system of farmstead settlements laid out along the St. Lawrence River on both sides as narrow elongated strips (*cadastrées*) (Figure XXVIII-2). Such a pattern of farm settlements gave each farmer access to the main line of transportation, so significant in the early days when travel facilities by land were extremely limited.

¶ Not only were communities isolated and settlers anxious to build their houses as close together as possible for mutual protection, but the river was their sole means of transport and communication. The strip system also gave to each settler a complete cross-section of the available land: level stretches near the river, uplands for pasture and an area in forest.[2]

But it is obvious that regardless of how narrow the strip might be, the individual farmsteads cannot indefinitely project their holdings away from the river; consequently, a new frontage for the farms farther inland had to be provided and a second tier of farms established:

¶ As time went on and the land beyond the river front was cleared, a second row, or tier, of farms would be established along the frontage of the row, the houses in each row again being grouped together to form a small community. In its extreme form, this system was most impractical and led to bad farming practice. Under the old French code, all sons inherited alike, which meant that farms, already long and narrow, were split again lengthwise into innumerable "ribbons," each son demanding access to the river and a fair share of different types of land.[3]

Any geographer today along the St. Lawrence mapping these ribbon-shaped fields might very well overemphasize the present-day importance of this river farm frontage feature, again signifying the importance of recognizing the fact that these represent a relict structure inherited from the former French *seigneuries* when river transportation was much more significant than it is now.

---

[1] The Commonwealth report—typical of others—consists of about 20 sheets of closely printed legal-size paper, inclusive of seven maps, ten photographs, a diagram, and several letters addressed to the Association by M. Brault.

[2] *Ibid.* Reprinted by permission.

[3] *Ibid.* Reprinted by permission.

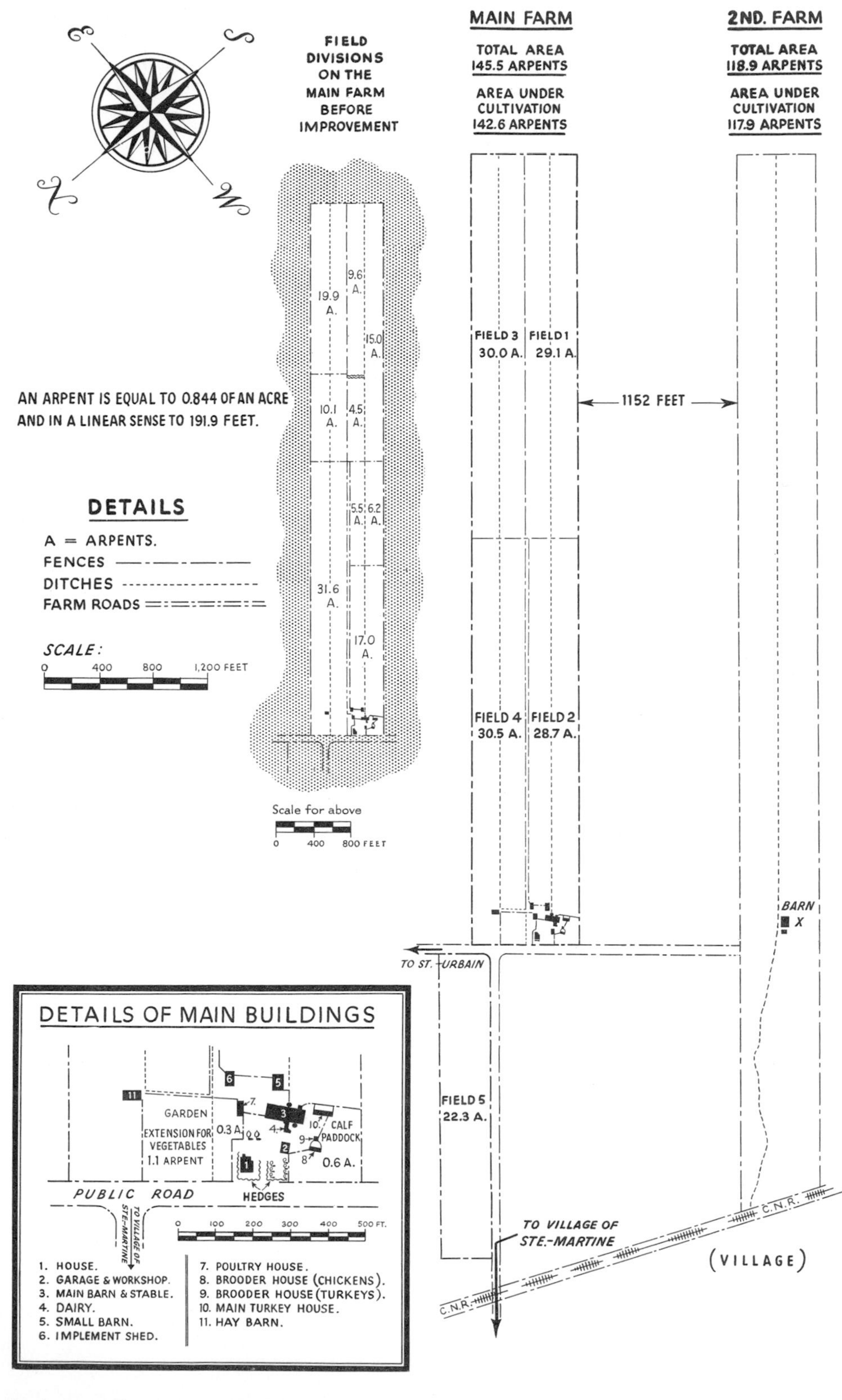

FIELD DIVISIONS ON THE MAIN FARM BEFORE IMPROVEMENT
MAIN FARM
TOTAL AREA 145.5 ARPENTS
AREA UNDER CULTIVATION 142.6 ARPENTS
2ND. FARM
TOTAL AREA 118.9 ARPENTS
AREA UNDER CULTIVATION 117.9 ARPENTS
9.6 A.
19.9 A.
15.0 A.
10.1 A.
4.5 A.
5.5 A.
6.2 A.
31.6 A.
17.0 A.
FIELD 3 30.0 A.
FIELD 1 29.1 A.
FIELD 4 30.5 A.
FIELD 2 28.7 A.
FIELD 5 22.3 A.
1152 FEET
AN ARPENT IS EQUAL TO 0.844 OF AN ACRE AND IN A LINEAR SENSE TO 191.9 FEET.
DETAILS
A = ARPENTS.
FENCES
DITCHES
FARM ROADS
SCALE:
0 400 800 1,200 FEET
Scale for above
0 400 800 FEET
BARN X
TO ST. URBAIN
TO VILLAGE OF STE.-MARTINE
C.N.R.
(VILLAGE)
DETAILS OF MAIN BUILDINGS
GARDEN
EXTENSION FOR VEGETABLES 1.1 ARPENT
0.3 A.
CALF PADDOCK
0.6 A.
PUBLIC ROAD
HEDGES
TO VILLAGE OF STE-MARTINE
0 100 200 300 400 500 FT.
1. HOUSE.
2. GARAGE & WORKSHOP.
3. MAIN BARN & STABLE.
4. DAIRY.
5. SMALL BARN.
6. IMPLEMENT SHED.
7. POULTRY HOUSE.
8. BROODER HOUSE (CHICKENS).
9. BROODER HOUSE (TURKEYS).
10. MAIN TURKEY HOUSE.
11. HAY BARN.

M. Brault's farm measures some 265 *arpents* (both a linear and surface scale measurement).[1] It includes the main homestead, an additional field, and a second small farm of recent acquisition (Figure XXVIII-1). Because of the concentration of the farmsteads along the river front, farm life is integrated with village life, perpetuating a French tradition for a strong desire to live in close communication and fellowship with one's neighbors, as contrasted with other regional settlements of the Scottish and English type, where more or less rectangular and spacious fields separate individual farmsteads.

3. ***Climate and crops.*** As noted in the brochure:

¶ Quebec has a Continental rather than a Maritime climate, the great masses of warm and cold air which sweep across the continent having a very direct influence on its weather. The St. Lawrence Valley lies in one of the regular paths followed by cyclonic storms between the Great Lakes and the Atlantic Ocean. These disturbances give an irregularity to the climate and bring rapid weather changes, storms when they come being violent with torrential rain. In general, the climate of Quebec, even south of the river, is very severe in winter and very hot and humid in summer. Snow generally falls in early December and lies on the ground for nearly four months. . . . Over half the year is cold and the growing season is comparatively short. Few farmers are able to work their land until the first week of May, cattle must be housed for between six and seven months of the year, and substantial provision made for winter feed. Central heating in the houses is an absolute necessity, and the roads have to be kept open with snowplows. The country is, however, very well adapted to its winters and services continue with the utmost efficiency. The county of Chateauguay is situated in the warmest region of the province. . . . The frost-free period in the parish of Ste. Martine is some 133 days, though it can vary from as low as 120 to as high as 150 days. . . . The rainfall is not high, the average being some 31 inches in the year. August is often a dry month and dry spells also come in June and July. . . . The mixed nature of the farming is a big advantage in this region; if weather conditions affect one or more crops adversely, there are always others which succeed.[2]

4. ***Land formation—soil.*** Once covered by the Champlain Sea extending from the Atlantic Ocean into Lake Ontario, the vicinity of Ste. Martine was buried under deep sediments laid down on the low-lying riverine lands. These sediments formed the Rideau clays.

¶ Rideau clay lends itself to intensive arable farming, and in particular to dairying, some of the best herds in the whole province being found around Ste. Martine and Howick. Cereal crops do especially well, ensilage corn and timothy give good yields, alfalfa (lucerne) and clover also suiting the ground. Although the soil is deep and fertile and there are no stones or rocks, its flatness lending it particularly well to arable cultivation, it has a marked deficiency in lime and humus and drainage is a very real problem. Nevertheless, with a well thought-out rotation, ample dressings of farmyard manure, artificial fertilizers and lime, and an effective drainage system, this is very productive land.[3]

Where climate is more favorable to general agriculture as in the *C* climates previously considered and the next—the *Dfa* neighboring climatic region to the south—farm management need not be as exacting as in the higher latitudes where every improved farming technique must be explored to attain the maximum geographic adjustment for both crop and livestock farming. Moreover, where increasing population makes its pressure felt, we may expect, as in the case of this farm, that the best possible cooperation obtains between the

[1] An *arpent* equals approximately 192 feet in linear measurement; and is somewhat larger than 4/5 of an acre. An acre embraces 43,560 square feet; an *arpent*, 36,797 square feet.

[2] *Ibid.* Reprinted by permission.

[3] *Ibid.* Reprinted by permission.

XXVIII:1 (Left) This shows the pattern of a dairy farm in French Canada. Compare the layout of the fields and farmstead buildings of this farm with those of the New Zealand farm figured in the previous chapter. Account for the different structures. (*Farming in the Commonwealth,* The Association of Agriculture, London, used by permission)

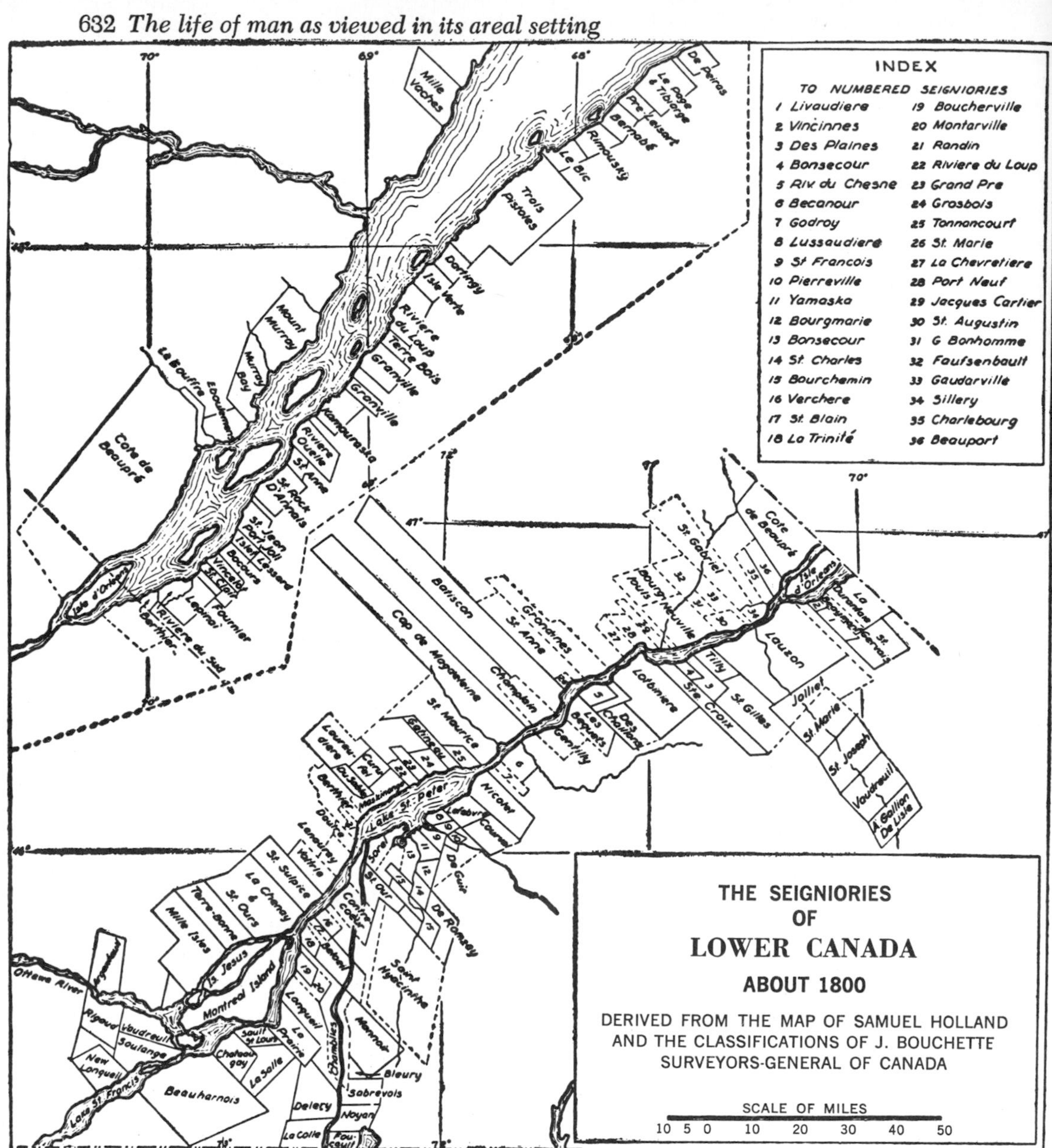

XXVIII:2 Seigniorities, forms of land grants, are narrow "ribbon" farms tied to the St. Lawrence River. A heritage of French feudalism, combined with access to river frontage, the narrow rectilinear pattern (cadastreés) is still a conspicuous present-day feature of this part of Canada. ("Filling up the Land, French and English Settlements," *Historical Geography of the United States,* Ralph H. Brown, Harcourt, Brace, and Company, 1948, used by permission)

farmer and all the governmental agencies concerned with the improvement of farming resources. The problem of effecting adequate drainage of land that is fertile but flat is an example in point. In the program of *Amelioration,* the Field Husbandry Division of the Provincial Department of Agriculture collaborated with the local *L'Ecole d' Agriculture* in completely redesigning Brault's farm with a new crop rotation based upon a reconstructed drainage pattern. This included a central ditch, cross trenches, and a so-called Richard system of plowing, evolved by and named after a former director of the School of Agriculture at Ste. Anne de la

Pocatière. Permanent water furrows lead the water to "dead" furrows, which in turn empty into the cross trenches (*rigoles*), and these finally into the main drainage ditches (*fossés*). The successive plowing ultimately results in a convex configuration of the cultivated components of the farm (*crowns*). As a result of this new drainage and plowing technique, the Brault farm has doubled the yields of many of its crops.

5. *Cropping plans.*

¶ The Brault farm is first and foremost a dairy farm and the rotation is designed to suit the dairy herd. Carefully selected mixtures of grasses, clovers and *alfalfa* (lucerne) are sown for summer pasture and for making into grass silage and hay. These mixtures nearly always contain a proportion of alfalfa (the better drained the ground, the higher the proportion) as, apart from giving excellent quality feed, it has the advantage of being very resistant to drought. *Ensilage corn* (Indian corn specially grown for making into silage) is also included for extra winter feed. In Canada, the winters are long and severe, and the cattle are only able to graze outside for, at most, 5½ months of the year. This means that winter feed on a stock farm is a chief consideration. In addition, a number of *cash* crops is grown for sale off the farm. These include seed oats and barley, sweet corn, flax, peas and beans.[1]

Then the report notes the year-by-year five-field rotation based on a five-year plan, and describes the seasonal geography of the various crops as to space distribution, conditions of planting and harvesting, and the marketing of the several crops, meat, and dairy products.

The above excerpts of the agricultural monograph, together with the introductory letter, supply the kind of survey data and insights needed to appreciate the broader climatic and ecological generalizations to which this chapter addresses itself. It will be well to reread this section and to reflect on the geographic concepts and principles which might emerge from this introduction, as well as to anticipate subregional divergences from the type pattern of land-use here suggested. To sharpen your perspective, it may be well at this point also to scan the concluding topic, "Application of Geographic Understanding," which is a sort of test on how well you have thought out inductively the geographic significance of such facts as are brought out in this introductory farming brochure material.

[1] *Ibid.*, sheets 2, 15, 18, 19, *passim*. Reprinted by permission.

The Köppen "b," rather than "D"—the key to realm agriculture

1. *Temperature.* The *Dfb-Dwb* realm is distinguished from its poleward neighbor (*Dfc-Dwc* of the previous chapter) most significantly by the difference in the length of the growing season. Though vegetation may show signs of life when temperatures reach 40°F., it is not until at about 50° that plant forms, particularly crops, exhibit vigorous growth. Though there is nothing magical about the arbitrary definition which Köppen uses to differentiate *b* from *c* in terms of the number of months above 50°F., such a seasonal growth isotherm does significantly divide zonally the two regions in agricultural productivity.[2] As we have noted in the previous chapter, hardy cereals, such as wheat, barley, and rye, and certain root crops, which gain prominence in the Baltic countries, can be grown under *c* conditions. It is not until we reach the zone where we have at least four months above 50°F. that general farming can be regularly and dependably activated on a commercial scale for competitive production in world markets. Representative are the celebrated grain fields of the Ukraine and areas extending eastward into the chernozem belt of Eurasia, and, in North America, the specialized spring-wheat belt of the Red River of the North, and the dairying, mixed farming, and fruit-vegetable producing sectors of the Great Lakes–St. Lawrence–New England provinces.

The average mean temperatures which approximate the northern and southern boundary of the *b* lands are 30° and 50°F. The January mean isotherm, which approximates a midposition, is about 10°F., rising to about 20°F. in passing from continental

[2] Köppen has on occasion been criticized for using criteria not distinctively correlative for crop culture. It must be kept in mind, however, that each crop has its own maturing season, and the denotation of "at least four months above 50°" is about as good a "growing season" correlative criterion as we can hope to get for *broad* regional differentiation of combined cover and crop culture.

The Brault herd of cattle is shown grazing on Field 2 (see Figure XXVIII:1). What does the picture disclose or suggest: type of breed? size of dairy industry? pastoral and field culture (shape, size, topography, and drainage of fields)? (Photo from *Farming in the Commonwealth, Canada,* Association of Agriculture, London, used by permission)

interiors to the seacoast. Such low annual and extreme January means may seem difficult to correlate with regions of such agricultural and manufacturing prominence as indicated above. This serves to remind us once again, however, that it is not how cold it is in the winter, but rather how warm it gets in the summer which effectively conditions the processes governing productivity and habitability of an area (Figures XXVIII-3 and XXVIII-4). Since the *Db* regions are located primarily in the heart of both the North American and Eurasian continents (Figure XXVIII-5), we should expect that whereas the winters are cold, midsummer days can be quite warm, much of the area averaging a mean July temperature of 70°F. Moreover, the fact that the days are from four to six hours longer in summer at this latitude than in the tropics compensates in part for the relatively short and cool summer season.

The significance of seasonal extremes as compared with average temperature is well expressed by Visher:

¶ The annual average temperature has little significance in regions which possess well-marked seasonal contrasts. The early emphasis on average temperatures reflects the fact that the writers dwelt in a region of moderate seasonal contrasts. (Western Europe, because of the great marine influence, is exceptionally temperate.) What influences living things are actual conditions, not averages. Hence, for example, North Dakota's January average temperature of about 5° and its July average of 68° is vastly more significant than its annual average of 40°. Its summer warmth permits much more agriculture than is possible in various regions having considerably higher annual averages but less seasonal contrast.

Instead of the annual average temperature being highly important, as commonly assumed by persons who know little about climate, it is a minor influence in much of the world. The seasonal temperature is much more significant. In the higher latitudes, the amount of summer warmth counts much more than the degree of winter cold.[1]

2. ***Precipitation.*** Most of the area sectors receive from 20 to 40 inches annual rainfall, ample for most crops, especially when we recall that there is a relatively low loss of moisture by evaporation at this comparatively high latitude and elsewhere where the type occurs at high altitudes. As we advance steppe-ward (westward in North America and eastward in Eurasia), precipitation drops below 20 inches, often as low as 15 and still lower, but adequate for the low temperatures to classify still as humid rather than *B* lands. This again indicates adequate moisture, particularly for such crops as wheat and other moderate-moisture-tolerant grains. As we advance toward the eastern seaboard of North America and Eurasia, the annual rainfall figure gradually rises into the 40-60 inch category. These areas experience primarily summer maxima; especially is this true for eastern Asia where due to monsoon influences "at least ten times as much rain falls in the wettest month of summer as in the driest month of winter," which gives us the symbol *Dwb* instead of *Dfb*.

Realm imagery and regional realities

As is the case of all major areal divisional study in this section of the textbook, realm differentiation is not conditioned solely by simple climatic criteria, but involves a coordinated consideration of all the more salient forms of human occupance that operate in unison in translating man's habitat. Thus, this realm's imagery involves the following major composite characteristics: poleward frontier of the world dense settlement patterns (rural and urban); intense utilization of locally available or economically accessible natural resources (fish, fur, forest, and mineral products); well developed outdoor recreation facilities closely linked to nature; a high energy agricultural potential, focused on a grain-grazing economy; complex manufacturing shared with, or in competition with, the adjacent largest manufacturing belts of the world; and second only to these in world commerce.

Regional differentiation seems best organizable on a continental-cultural basis—with a sector each for North America, Europe, and Asia.

Lands of this realm have primarily an east-west axial distribution, hinging upon the 50° N. L. line and extending some 10° in latitude poleward on the west side of continents (westerly wind marinal influences) and extending likewise approximately 10° equatorward on the east side of continents (continental influences). The general west-to-east wedge is modified by interruptions or extensions as a result not only of continental, marine, or littoral influences, but also of significant variations as well in landform configuration. Thus, at the higher elevations, arcs of *b* lands extend into the Southern Rockies (30°-35° latitude), and at comparable latitudes into the Kurdistan and Pamir ranges of southwest Asia. Extreme continental aridity, as in the dry heart of Eurasia, and orographic rain shadow conditions, as found east of our Rockies, otherwise disrupt areal continuity.

In North America, the province extends almost throughout the entire length of the American-Canadian frontier, including sections of all the southern border provinces of Canada (British Columbia, Alberta, Saskatchewan, Manitoba, Ontario, Quebec, New Brunswick, and Nova Scotia); likewise, it is a partial climatic component of the entire northern tier of states (Washington, Idaho, Montana, North Dakota, Minnesota, Wisconsin, Michigan, New York, Vermont, New Hampshire, Maine). In Eurasia, the province lies primarily in the U.S.S.R. and its satellites (Poland, Czechoslovakia, Hungary, Romania). Sweden and Finland also have small but important sectors included in this type. In the Orient, Hokkaido and about half of Manchuria are *Dfb* and *Dwb* re-

---

[1] Visher, S. S., "Climatic Influences," ***Geography in the Twentieth Century***, Griffith Taylor, Editor, Philosophical Library, New York, 1951, pp. 199-200. Reprinted by permission.

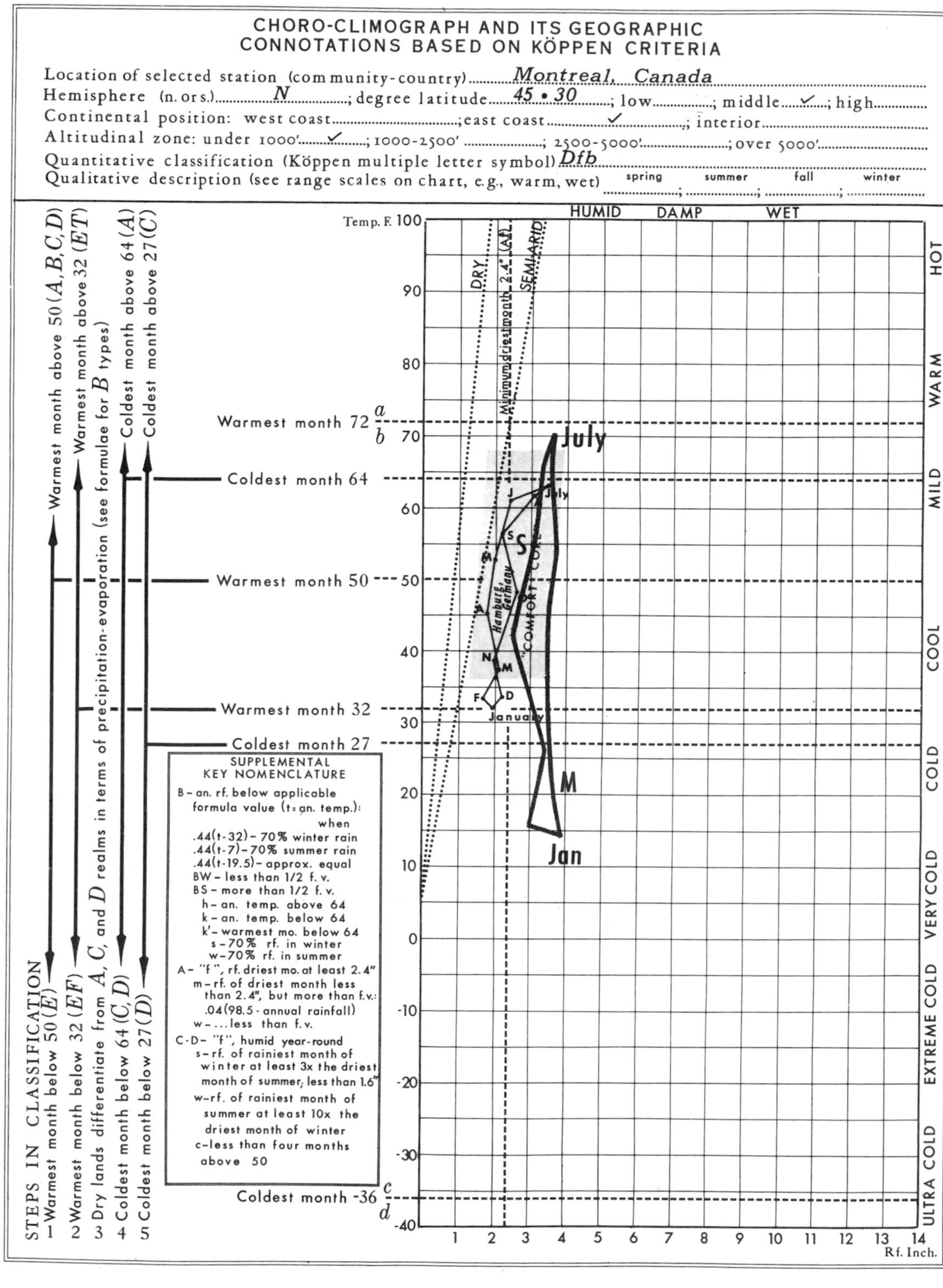
CHORO-CLIMOGRAPH AND ITS GEOGRAPHIC CONNOTATIONS BASED ON KÖPPEN CRITERIA
Location of selected station (community-country) Montreal, Canada
Hemisphere (n. or s.) N; degree latitude 45 • 30; low; middle ✓; high
Continental position: west coast; east coast ✓; interior
Altitudinal zone: under 1000' ✓; 1000-2500'; 2500-5000'; over 5000'
Quantitative classification (Köppen multiple letter symbol) Dfb
Qualitative description (see range scales on chart, e.g., warm, wet) spring; summer; fall; winter
STEPS IN CLASSIFICATION
1 Warmest month below 50 (E) — Warmest month above 50 (A, B, C, D)
2 Warmest month below 32 (EF) — Warmest month above 32 (ET)
3 Dry lands differentiate from A, C, and D realms in terms of precipitation-evaporation (see formulae for B types)
4 Coldest month below 64 (C, D) — Coldest month above 64 (A)
5 Coldest month below 27 (D) — Coldest month above 27 (C)
Temp. F.
Warmest month 72
Coldest month 64
Warmest month 50
Warmest month 32
Coldest month 27
Coldest month -36
HUMID
DAMP
WET
DRY
SEMIARID
Minimum driest month 2.4" (Af)
"COMFORT" CURVE
Hamburg, Germany
July
S
M
Jan
January
HOT
WARM
MILD
COOL
COLD
VERY COLD
EXTREME COLD
ULTRA COLD
Rf. Inch.
SUPPLEMENTAL KEY NOMENCLATURE
B - an. rf. below applicable formula value (t = an. temp.): when
.44(t-32) - 70% winter rain
.44(t-7) - 70% summer rain
.44(t-19.5) - approx. equal
BW - less than 1/2 f. v.
BS - more than 1/2 f. v.
h - an. temp. above 64
k - an. temp. below 64
k' - warmest mo. below 64
s - 70% rf. in winter
w - 70% rf. in summer
A - "f", rf. driest mo. at least 2.4"
m - rf. of driest month less than 2.4", but more than f.v.: .04(98.5 - annual rainfall)
w - ...less than f.v.
C-D - "f", humid year-round
s - rf. of rainiest month of winter at least 3x the driest month of summer; less than 1.6"
w - rf. of rainiest month of summer at least 10x the driest month of winter
c - less than four months above 50

spectively, the latter symbolic of monsoon controls.

The realm includes some of the largest and fastest-growing urban communities of the world—the Russian cities of Moscow and Leningrad, and Poland's Warsaw in the multi-million population class; the "million-plus" of Canada's Greater Toronto and Montreal; the half-million category of America's Minneapolis, Buffalo, Milwaukee; and Sweden's Stockholm. The industrial and commercial significance of some of these will be treated in subsequent sections.

Comparison of the North American, European, and Asian sectors of the realm points to significant region-differentiating principles when one studies the prime patterns of productivity distinguishing the three continental areas.

The hay and dairy belt. The brief survey of the Brault farm already introduced us to the general agricultural characteristics of what the government geographer Baker years ago designated as North America's "Hay and Dairy Region." Over the greater part of the region one-third of the farm income is derived from dairy products (over three-fourths of the farm income being derived from total livestock), with highest concentration in Wisconsin. The average farm size is about 150 acres, and the major plantings are in feed crops —oats, hay, and corn grown primarily for silage. Though considerable milk is marketed directly to consumers, as in the more heavily populated centers to the south and east, most of the western Great Lakes section specializes in manufactured dairy products—cheese, butter, concentrated milk products, and ice cream. Except for the cooler and shorter growing season in summer and the correspondingly longer and more severe winter in North America, the *Dfb* "dairyland" calls to mind many of the dairying features of *Cfb* Europe (Chapter 26). In both regions, major concentrations of population create great demands for fresh milk and processed dairy products.

XXVIII:3 (Left) The kind of climate that M. Brault and other farmers in the Montreal area have to reckon with is illustrated in this graph. Correlate the basic seasonal farming activities described in M. Brault's letter and elsewhere in the Commonwealth brochure material here reported and commented upon, with the seasonal temperature and rainfall co-ordinates here projected.

Place-to-place differences in climate, landform, vegetation, soil, settlement, and, above all, major considerations for the changing pattern of labor, transportation, and markets for the farm products, have resulted in a highly diverse subregionalized economy. Several co-varying areal characteristics and the more significant principles related thereto are based on a high degree of utility and versatility in agricultural production. At least a score of major commercial items involve extensive mechanization of agriculture, scientific farming in the best sense of the term, and a relatively high standard of living of the farmer. Greater over-all regional emphasis on dairy products, particularly of fresh milk, promoted by its proximity to the heavily industrialized and populous centers in the United States and Canada, superior grazing, and feed-producing conditions, results in part from rather high precipitation throughout most of the area. Manufactured milk products—butter, cheese, and various concentrated forms of milk—are primarily centered on the less populous Western Great Lakes States (processed milk products stand transportation costs to distant markets—farther east—better than whole milk). An ethnic factor is of historic significance here also: large-scale cheese and butter manufacturing, especially in Wisconsin and Minnesota respectively, received its initial impetus from the craftsmanshp of Scandinavians, Swiss, and other European immigrants traditionally expert in these arts.[1]

The food and feeding grains. Spring wheat, barley, rye, and buckwheat are comparatively distinctly delimited in their distribution, the first three being largely co-extensive with the drier Western Prairie Province (Red River district), with rye generally relegated to the leaner soils. Similarly, buckwheat and winter wheat are companion components in the Ontario peninsula area,

[1] Regional study may be organized about a prime product or major activity. Of special relevance here is "The American Dairy Region" by Dr. Loyal Durand, Jr., in the *Journal of Geography*, Vol. XLVIII, No. 1, January, 1949, pp. 1-19.

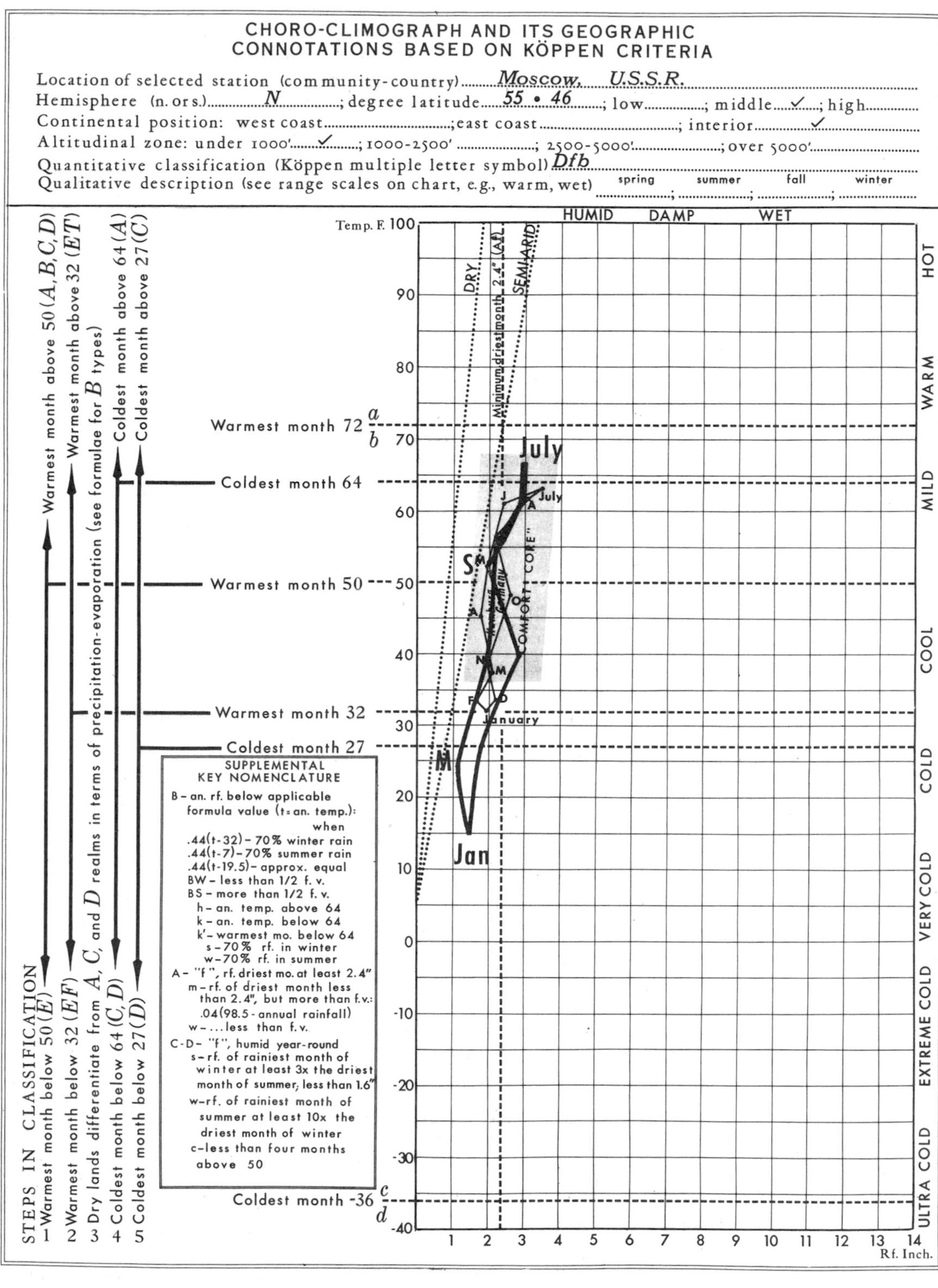
CHORO-CLIMOGRAPH AND ITS GEOGRAPHIC
CONNOTATIONS BASED ON KÖPPEN CRITERIA
Location of selected station (community-country) Moscow, U.S.S.R.
Hemisphere (n. or s.) N; degree latitude 55 • 46; low; middle ✓; high
Continental position: west coast; east coast; interior ✓
Altitudinal zone: under 1000' ✓; 1000-2500'; 2500-5000'; over 5000'
Quantitative classification (Köppen multiple letter symbol) Dfb
Qualitative description (see range scales on chart, e.g., warm, wet) spring; summer; fall; winter
STEPS IN CLASSIFICATION
1 Warmest month below 50 (E) — Warmest month above 50 (A, B, C, D)
2 Warmest month below 32 (EF) — Warmest month above 32 (ET)
3 Dry lands differentiate from A, C, and D realms in terms of precipitation-evaporation (see formulae for B types)
4 Coldest month below 64 (C, D) — Coldest month above 64 (A)
5 Coldest month below 27 (D) — Coldest month above 27 (C)
Warmest month 72
Coldest month 64
Warmest month 50
Warmest month 32
Coldest month 27
Coldest month -36
a
b
c
d
Temp. F.
100
90
80
70
60
50
40
30
20
10
0
-10
-20
-30
-40
HUMID
DAMP
WET
DRY
SEMIARID
Minimum driest month 2.4" (Af)
COMFORT "CORE"
July
Jan
January
HOT
WARM
MILD
COOL
COLD
VERY COLD
EXTREME COLD
ULTRA COLD
1 2 3 4 5 6 7 8 9 10 11 12 13 14
Rf. Inch.
SUPPLEMENTAL
KEY NOMENCLATURE
B - an. rf. below applicable formula value (t = an. temp.): when
.44(t-32) - 70% winter rain
.44(t-7) - 70% summer rain
.44(t-19.5) - approx. equal
BW - less than 1/2 f. v.
BS - more than 1/2 f. v.
h - an. temp. above 64
k - an. temp. below 64
k' - warmest mo. below 64
s - 70% rf. in winter
w - 70% rf. in summer
A - "f", rf. driest mo. at least 2.4"
m - rf. of driest month less than 2.4", but more than f.v.: .04(98.5 - annual rainfall)
w - ... less than f.v.
C-D - "f", humid year-round
s - rf. of rainiest month of winter at least 3x the driest month of summer; less than 1.6"
w - rf. of rainiest month of summer at least 10x the driest month of winter
c - less than four months above 50

the latter, in southern Michigan, forming the northern frontier of the winter wheat belt to the south. Applying the well-known principle that buckwheat is acclimatized to a shorter growing season than most other grains, and is likewise tolerant of lean and droughty soils, farmers sow this crop on many of the hill lands of the East Lakes–St. Lawrence section and extend its culture clear up into the Maritime Provinces.

Corn culture. The growing of both sweet corn and maize also distinguishes the U. S.-Canadian sector. Because of the traditional concept that corn normally requires a long growing season, a hot and humid summer, the "Corn Belt" is commonly identified with the *Dfa* instead of the *Dfb* climate. While region-wise essentially correct, this concept must be modified to recognize the fact that sizable corn acreages do now increasingly appear in the southern Great Lakes section. Corn is grown here as elsewhere primarily for cattle and hog consumption, but progressively used more and more as silage as we advance northeastward into the Ontario peninsula and New York areas.

Old glacial-lake bottoms, particularly the basins of Lakes Huron, Erie, and Michigan, with their deep silts, are favored sites for sugar beets and tobacco. And the "lee" shores of the Great Lakes, particularly the east shore of Lake Michigan and the south shore of Lake Ontario, feature horticulture, berry culture, truck culture, and floriculture. Farmers recognize here the littoral retarded fruit tree blossoming in the spring and the retarded frost-killing as well in the crop-maturing fall season as a major environmental asset. The extended north-southeast shore of Lake Michigan features what is probably the most diverse and extensive fruit-farming of this type. Another exemplary case where the principle of marinality effectively tempers the otherwise long and severe winters of this realm is the Annapolis–Cornwallis

XXVIII:4 (Left) How would the farming operations in the vicinity of Moscow compare with those of Montreal? (Ignore, for the moment, the differences resulting from the contrasted political-economic system.)

Valley skirting the east shore of the Bay of Fundy. Here in the southern Nova Scotia peninsula is found one of the most significant apple-producing regions of the world, supplying a large proportion of the Canadian apple market and the markets of Great Britain as well.

Of all vegetables, the potato is probably the most ubiquitous, found in all sections of the *Dfb* here and abroad (as well as in other realms); however, here also major commercial concentrations occur locally. Perhaps most noteworthy is Aroostook County, Maine, where single farmers plant as much as several hundred acres with potatoes. The establishment here of this "Potato Empire" must be sought in historical as well as geographic factors. Said to be the very oldest of the Western Hemisphere's commercial potato production areas, the enterprise in the early days catered to the cotton textile mills of New England for their starch requirements.

The European sector. This section is distinguished by many factors—the largest contiguous cultivable area, the northernmost extension (latitude 60°), a westward marinal exposure, and a deep interior continental heartland position with both high urban and rural population densities. As in the West, agricultural dominance comprises wheat, oats, barley, rye, buckwheat, potatoes, sugar beets, and cattle, but significant differences do exist in the extensiveness or intensiveness with which the several farm products are produced. For example, rye, potatoes, flax and root crops are generally much more prominent in the European landscape as compared with that of North America. In fact, nowhere else in the world do we find rye and potatoes grown so extensively for human as well as animal consumption. Both of these crops are excellently adapted to the light, sandy, glacial soils which are widely prevalent in this sector. Though the rearing of cattle for dairy and meat products is important, dairying as an industry is not commercially exploited on the same scale as in America. As we advance farther into the interior of Russia, spring wheat becomes increasingly prominent, especially on the drier chernozems, reflecting the same influence as do our drier western *Dfb* regions bounding

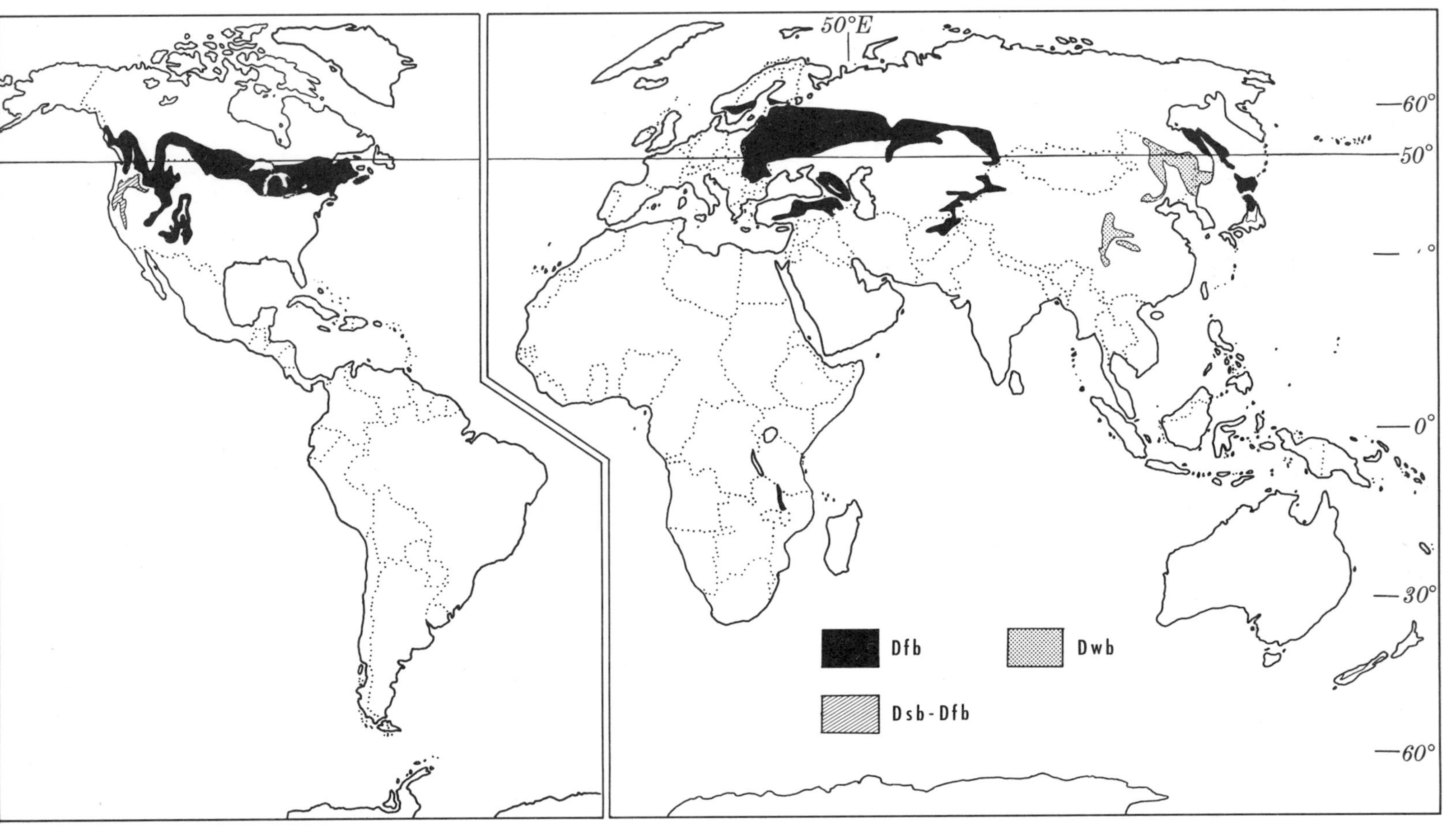
50°E
60°
50°
0°
30°
60°
Dfb
Dwb
Dsb-Dfb

the steppe country. The growing of flax and hemp, and the raising of cattle and swine are important complements in the farming economy.

The East Asian sector. This Pacific areal component, centered upon Hokkaido and Manchuria, is primarily distinguished by the over-all dominance of soybeans, kaoliang (sorghum), and millet—crops tolerant of rather lean soils, hilly terrain, and spells of dryness. Also distinctive is the cultivation of some rice. Of comparatively less importance here than in the other two sectors are wheat, oats, barley, and corn. The relatively high population density precludes a heavy livestock population, products of the vegetable kingdom functioning as versatile substitutes for animal products in the Oriental's diet. Another distinctive regional characteristic is the growing of crops essentially for subsistence, and both the grains and the legumes are consumed by humans and livestock alike. Native to East Asia, the soybean, whose recorded culture dates back some 5,000 years we might say, is a form of nature's subsidization of the whole agrarian economy not only of the Orient but also of large farming sections of the Western world as well. In the Orient where meat and dairy products are ruled out by intensive pressure on the land, the soybean serves as a combined vegetable and animal diet; as a substitute for wheat flour in the manufacture of noodle products; and as a substitute for dairy products, vegetable oil taking the place of animal cream in the manufacturing of butter, and vegetable curds substituting for cheese. Also various oils processed from the bean are used in making soap, paint, and drugs. And the plant, being a legume, extracts free nitrogen from the air with the bacteria nodules on its roots, thus helping farmers to maintain by means of crop rotation permanent fertility of the soil. Though now widely and intensively cultivated in many parts of the world, the soybean is still basically an oriental product and, for the country's size, Manchuria leads in the production and exportation of this product.

XXVIII:5 (Left) Point to the factors genetically related to the distribution pattern of the *Dfb*, *Dwb*, and *Dsb*. How important is the realm space-wise? Position-wise?

Historical resource exploitation

The realm shares with its poleward neighbor a rich natural resource base. At the same time, its position close to the populous and industrial heartland of Canada–United States shares the benefits of the latter's markets which the higher latitude realm does not provide. This "in-between" position is generally always of geographic moment. And so we shall now turn to man's enterprises as environmentally conditioned by this realm.

The fisheries of the Maritime Provinces. The New England region in many respects may be said to be the North American counterpart of the North Sea fisheries of Northwest Europe discussed in Chapter 26. Here, comparable to the North Sea area, we have a large partially enclosed sea (the Gulf of St. Lawrence) with its own multiple embayments and a widened estuary forming the mouth of the submerged St. Lawrence River. It is partially shut off from the Atlantic by major islands (Newfoundland, Cape Breton Island, and Prince Edward Island), flanked by the Nova Scotia peninsula on the south. The Grand Banks off the coast of Newfoundland, varying from 50 to 300 feet in depth and said to provide the most excellent and most important cod fishing in the world, remind us of the famous Dogger Banks off the east shores of Great Britain. Even before there were any settlements in this area, and as early as the beginning of the sixteenth century, directly following the discovery of the Cape Breton Island area by John Cabot (1497), Asia-bound, North Sea fishermen were seen plying their trade across the North Atlantic into this area, as many as fifty ships from Spain, Portugal, France, and Great Britain having been noted at one time returning to Europe loaded with cod.

¶ The first adventurers were poverty-stricken peoples of northern Spain and the Basque country, but these at length withdrew from the northern fishing grounds, the French and English claiming the fishery exclusively, as appurtenances of their adjacent colonies. The American fishery began to thrive early in the last century, gaining

This pastoral scene is in Pepin County, Wisconsin. Do you recognize the breed of dairy cattle? Does the landscape suggest that it is optimal for cattle raising, or that it is of marginal utility for other forms of agriculture? Does it have other land-use possibilities? (Photo by Forsythe, U. S. Department of Agriculture)

ground in proportion as the French lost it, insomuch that about 1755 they are said to have been on a par. Even before the war, however, the American catch never equaled that of the British. Yet, throughout the years of abundant harvest, there appears to have been no diminution of the supply. Possibly five hundred large vessels, and many more small ones, flying many flags but of less variety than formerly, habitually frequent these waters every year.[1]

[1] Brown, Ralph, "The Maritime Interests," *Mirror for Americans*, Edited by Elizabeth T. Platt, American Geographical Society, New York, Special Publication No. 27, 1943, p. 90. Reprinted by permission.

Warm ocean currents from the Caribbean, laden with plankton, sweep northward along the Atlantic coast. And the Gulf Stream mingling with the colder Labrador current from Davis Strait creates optimal spawning conditions. The "banks" are of the proper depth to serve as an ideal habitat for all types of shellfish, upon which the cod and other fish feed. Moreover, the numerous streams that empty into the St. Lawrence River and the Gulf of St. Lawrence provide ideal spawning ground for salmon and other species whose life cycle is complicated by an alternation of salt water, fresh water, and a mixture of the two at various seasons of the year. Here also, as in the case of northwest Europe, major concentration of population, both in southeast Canada and northeast United States, provides excellent markets. Among the numerous species marketed on a commercial scale are cod, mackerel, halibut, herring, haddock, shad, sturgeon, and salmon, the last three being of the sea-and-river species which are seasonally fished for also in the streams which empty into the sea. Shellfish likewise form important items in commercial fisheries. These include lobsters taken from Northumberland Strait, scallops from the Bay of Fundy, and oysters primarily along the coast of New Brunswick and in the vicinity of Prince Edward Island.

Fresh-water fisheries of the Great Lakes are the largest of their type in the world. Though somewhat on the decrease in recent years, partly attributable to the depredations of the sea lamprey which preys heavily on lake trout, annual catches run well over 100,000,000 pounds.

The historic importance of the fur industry in Canada has already been noted in the previous chapter. The far-flung taiga, with its innumerable streams and lakes often interlocked, constitutes the great fur reserve of North America. It will also be recalled that it was the Hudson's Bay Company, chartered in 1670, that operated originally out of the Hudson Bay area to exploit this great fur resource. Then, in 1784, merchants at Montreal organized the Northwest Company competing for the fur trade in the Northwest Territory. In 1800 it set up its western headquarters at Fort William. It soon became obvious that whereas the northern territories were environmentally most favorably conditioned for the production of furs, the actual marketing of furs was elsewhere—the trading posts strung along the articulated water-land transportation routes of the Great Lakes–St. Lawrence Valley. Among such commercially significant trading posts were Michilimackinac (at Mackinac Strait), Detroit, and Fort Niagara, strategic chain collecting centers, respectively, between Lake Superior and Lake Huron, Lake Huron and Lake Erie, and Lake Erie and Lake Ontario. But it was ultimately at tidewater Montreal that furs were finally collected, graded, and processed for export abroad. This is quite understandable, as Brown observes:

¶ Montreal owes its pre-eminence in the fur trade to its situation at the junction of great rivers which offer some conveniences of transport to the interior. The Ottawa River, until recently called the Utawas, having its source in the far interior, unites with the St. Lawrence just above Montreal Island. Thus, by portaging from the Ottawa or the Upper St. Lawrence to other rivers flowing into one or another of the Great Lakes and by portaging also around the many rapids which all these rivers present, it is possible for experienced traders to reach the remoter parts of the fur country within a month's time. They must follow the rivers, preferably the large rivers, since travel through the wilderness, heavily accoutered as they must be with equipment and provisions, is impossible.[1]

It was particularly during the spring three months when Montreal staged a great fair that the Indians and the other trappers hundreds of miles away would converge upon it for the disposition of their pelts in exchange for white man's wares. Statistics by Sir Alexander Mackenzie on the skins collected at Montreal by the Northwest Company in 1798 (as reported by Brown) give us some idea as to the relative importance of the different kinds of pelts marketed: beaver 106,000; marten 32,000; musquash (muskrat) 17,000; lynx 6,000; otter 4,600; kit fox 4,000; wolf 3,800; mink 1,800; fisher 1,650; bear 2,100.

The twentieth century added new distinction to the realm's fur business. The first major experiment in rearing foxes for their pelts took place on Prince Edward Island in 1897. Within a decade or so fabulous profits were realized, which led to further experiments in pedigreed breeding of foxes, mink, and many other fur-bearing animals, producing scores of mutations to satisfy every type of fur market. The fur ranch industry is now centered in Ontario and Manitoba.

Anglo-America recreation resources a unifying bond of friendship

Few peoples in the world outside of this realm are latitudinally so situated that they can motor weekends from their homes in metropolitan communities into areas populated primarily by wildlife in a setting of natural wonders still for the most part untouched by the arts of man. Familiar to all of us are the tourist-promotion pictorial road maps, resort signs, and recreation literature

[1] Brown, *op. cit.*, p. 138. Reprinted by permission.

beckoning us to the shores of the Great Lakes, the inland thousands of smaller lakes and innumerable streams stocked with game fish, and the Maritime-Maine coasts with their salt surfs and salt-water fishing. Aside from the numerous land and water sports provided, summer and winter, scenic and historic attractions hold first rank in these "picture provinces." Up the St. Lawrence came our first inland North American explorers, and Jacques Cartier among them in 1536 pronounced Prince Edward Island as "the fairest land that it may be possible to see." Both in eastern and western Canada and America, national parks and monuments, and provincial and state parks memorialize the handiwork of nature and the historical shrines of man. Ancient historical landmarks have left their imprint to this very day throughout much of French-Canada—in Nova Scotia children can still speak Gaelic. It is not surprising, then, to learn that Canada's visitor industry has attained an importance comparable to its other leading sources of revenue. "If it were considered as a commodity," Canada's Yearbook for 1960 observes, "receipts from its export [$393,000,000] would represent the third largest source of income from external sources, next to exports of newsprint and wheat." Much of this is tourist traffic. Travel bureaus are maintained throughout the provinces to promote tourism. On the American side, similar attention is being directed towards the preservation and expansion of recreation facilities. Thus, according to the Great Lakes News Letter of September, 1960, the Michigan Conservation Commission reports the adoption of an expanded state park program "calling for the addition of some 1,600 acres to land along the shores of three of the Great Lakes. . . . Seven lakeshore parks will be expanded and a new site of 500 acres and having 8,000 feet of Lake Michigan frontage will be established in the Ottawa-Muskegon area to relieve other state parks nearby."

Such a wealth of nature's treasures and historic traditions as here provided naturally then calls for concerted action by governmental authorities and citizens alike to conserve to the utmost these precious landscape attractions that add enchantment to our miles. We need more than roadside incinerator signs and stops to dispose of our car litter, and the litterbug must be taught to appreciate the park sites and beach sites for their intended restful and recreative functions. The hallmark of any culture worth aspiring to is basic education in those attitudes and arts which dedicate man to the conservation and consecration of our geographic and historic heritages, as outlined in the chapter on resource use (Chapter 16). Especially is this of regional significance where, as in Anglo-America "cross-the-border," tourism is a major factor in promoting international comity at its best.

Woodpulp and newsprint empire

The realm is distinctive for its mixed stands of broadleaf and conifer, a greater diversity of species of both types perhaps occurring here than in any other realm outside *A* and *C* regions. Conifers normally dominate the northern sections, and broadleaf the southern. Except for some of the birches, the northern boundary establishes pretty well the zonal limits of the broadleaf species, the northernmost extensions of which would include the sugar maple and white oak. Among the conifers, the white and the red pine approximate the zonal limits. Beyond this zone, the Boreal forest sets in, already described in the previous chapter, dominated by spruce, fir, and jackpine among the conifers, with some representation of birch and poplar and willow of the broadleaf type. On the southern, longer frost-free season boundary, dominant broadleaf forests appear, whereas on the drier sections, forming the western boundary in North America, and the southeastern boundary in Eurasia, the forest gives way to prairie or steppe grassland.

Significant in lumber production both in historic time and still at present, the North American section is the leader in paper pulp production, and the region of southeast Canada, together with that of British Columbia, accounts for Canada's pre-eminent world position in the production of newsprint paper — amounting to more than three-fourths of the world's exports of this product. And over one-half of the world's newspapers are printed on paper manufactured in Canada. Besides wood products of the greatest diversity, other specialized forest productions are

Only some fifty miles from Montreal is this typical French-Canadian village of Ste. Adele. Primarily a tourist center, the Laurentian mountain village caters to skiers in the winter and auto tourists in summer. (Photo from Canadian Government Travel Bureau, Ottawa. Courtesy Trans-Canada Air Lines)

distinctive; for example, New York and Vermont supply well over one-half of the maple syrup of this country and are a major source of Christmas trees sold in northeastern U. S. markets.

Diversity in stocking (climate, soils), accessibility, and demand for forest products are of areal significance in evaluating forest resources. As noted by Putnam, in the Great Lakes–St. Lawrence Forest Region

¶ the dominant conifers are white pine, red pine, hemlock, and white cedar; . . . the dominant hardwood deciduous trees are: sugar maple, beech, yellow birch, red oak, bur oak, and white oak on upland soils; with red maple, silver maple, white elm, white ash, and black ash on the low ground. This forest region has probably more species and a greater number of associations than any other in Canada. It is especially noted for the excellent pine timber and deals which for approximately a century were shipped from the St. Lawrence in great quantities.

[In the cooler and moister Acadian-Forest Region,]

¶ hemlock, white pine and red pine . . . are well represented, as are also the characteristic hardwoods, beech, sugar maple, and yellow birch. Here also are found white spruce, balsam fir, and aspen, reminiscent of the boreal forest. The dominant and characteristic tree, however, is red spruce, which is found throughout this region and apparently, to no great extent anywhere else. This forest was early and most completely exploited. White pine especially was in demand for masts and spars. The old original stands are said to have contained trees six feet in diameter and more than 200 feet high. Lumbering followed, for much of the forest was within easy reach of the long indented coastline. Very large areas were burned over. Nevertheless, except for Prince Edward Island, most of the Acadian forest remains and will remain to produce lumber and pulpwood for the future.[1]

Partly because of the size of the area and partly because of the great diversity of species, the U.S.S.R. sector probably contains the most valuable combined broadleaf–conifer forests in the world. In the westernmost and best-settled section of Russia, the dominant broadleaf pattern includes large enclaves of pine; as we proceed south from Moscow, the pine gives way to increasing stands of oak. Advancing interiorward toward the Urals, oak stands continue in the south along with progressively increasing amounts of spruce, fir, cedar, and pine as we approach and cross the Urals. Spruce, fir, and cedar likewise dominate the monsoon section of southeast Siberia, with larch becoming increasingly prominent and finally dominating the north sector.

Because some conifers tolerate poorly-drained areas, while others tolerate sandy, droughty soils, steep and rocky slopes, and still others tolerate short growing seasons and high altitude exposures, conifer stands occupy areas in which many broadleaf species fail to survive.

Great diversity of species both of the conifer and hardwood types; excellent transportation facilities for most of the area, either by water or rail; and proximate position within and immediately adjacent to the area of heavy populations and industrial developments, combined with a relatively long growing season — all these factors favor exploitation of timber products and the processing of wood products throughout the greater part of the realms of both the European and North American sections. From these factors we would assume, then, that the lumbering industry occupies a very high rank among the other industries, and that this realm is pre-eminent in the world for the production of forest products. While still very significant as a basic natural resource for some of the sections of this realm, particularly for some of the Baltic and Canadian sections, returns from merchantable timber on the whole are smaller than we might expect. This is partly due to the fact that these once virgin timber areas were among the first regions to be settled and exploited following the Industrial Revolution in Europe and the extensive colonization of the New World. Though the forests of southern Norway, Sweden, and Finland have long been managed on a farming rather than a "mining" basis, with rigid conservation policies consistently practiced, western and central Russia have experienced heavy cutovers in the early twentieth century as a result of their rapidly expanding agriculture, urbanization, and industrialization. The First World War, and particularly the Second World War, have also made heavy inroads on the forest resources of this section — to such an extent that today the area is only approximately three-fourths self-sufficient in forest products. And, as every student of American history knows only too well, the settlement of the Maritime Provinces and the rapidly expanding settlements westward along the St. Lawrence and Great Lakes shores of Canada have likewise resulted in large scale deforestation. The same process to an even greater extent has taken place in the United States — first the virtual ravaging of the timber of New England, followed by that of New York; then by that of Michigan, Wisconsin, Minnesota, as the northeastern section of our country made increasing demands upon wood products. With little or no thought given in the nineteenth century to reforestation on a large scale within this area, Americans turned to the Southern Appalachians for both hardwood and conifer timber supplies — and subsequently, now to the distant Northwest for its softwood lumber needs, primarily Douglas fir products. Much of the cutover lands of the northern parts of our Canada-bounding states exhibits a sad spectacle of abandoned scrub-land, productive of neither forest nor farm products, tax-delinquent, and even an eyesore to the tourist.

---

[1] Putnam, Donald F., "Physical Background," *Canadian Regions*, J. M. Dent & Sons (Canada) Ltd., Toronto, 1952, pp. 26-27, *passim*. Reprinted by permission.

Realm shares world manufacturing leadership

The humid continental cool summer realm enjoys companion industrial world leadership with such other areally prominent realms as *Cfb* Europe and *Dfa* United States. Its northern boundary, moreover, expresses the northerly limits of manufacturing in terms of sizable contiguous areas. And within the boundary or at a short distance over into the *Dfc* are the politically or industrially or commercially prominent cities which form what we might call the "northern urban frontier" — in North America: Edmonton, Prince Albert, Winnipeg, Sault Sainte Marie, Toronto, Montreal; in Europe-Asia: Oslo, Stockholm, Helsinki, Leningrad, Chelyabinsk, Omsk, Novosibirsk, Harbin, Vladivostok, and Sapporo. Significant here also are the co-variant relationships between population density, urbanization, and extensiveness of manufacturing enterprises. While heavy populations do not necessarily predicate intense manufactural activity (e.g., southeast Asia), areas of great industrial development almost always cohere with heavy and advanced populations upon which enterprises must necessarily depend for labor and markets. In all the three continental sectors, core population densities of the more concentrated industrial districts rate well over 250 per square mile, scaling down to about 100 per square mile for the outlying industrial districts, and finally to about 25 per square mile in the peripheral areas of primary agricultural settlement. This realm's population and manufacturing may be said definitely to be the heart of the U.S.S.R.

The realm is also a world leader in power and transportation development, phenomenally focused on electrification, increasingly based on waterpower. The U.S.S.R. and Canada, in this order, hold leadership in total waterpower potential; and both the dominant potential and actual power developments are found in this realm, the former centered on the Moscow–Gorki region of central Russia, the latter on the southern sections of Quebec and Ontario.

Whatever other salient linking factors there may be in the manufactural development of any region, transportation is indispensable. In this area of geographic evaluation, the realm is also distinguished by most favorable communication patterns of water, land, and air. All the three major sectors — North American, European, and Asian — have a sea frontier, the first two sharing the advantageous position of the most important transoceanic trade route in the world — the North Atlantic. Nature has blessed the Canadian–U.S. sector with the largest and most used inland water system of the world — the Gulf of St. Lawrence, the St. Lawrence River, and the Great Lakes — which as a consequence of the construction of the St. Lawrence Seaway (about which more will be stated later) converts the major river and lake communities into world seaports (Figure XXVIII-6). Concomitant with this extraordinary navigational facility are the railways, highways, and airways, which together form an integral part of the transportation locus of North America, the most prominent in the world.

Similarly in Europe, the railroad–air route pattern virtually coincides with the outline of the *Dfb* realm, centered on Moscow, whence radiate the main lines of communication westward to all the leading interior and port cities of Europe and eastward by the Trans-Siberian Railway across the Asian sector to the leading Pacific port — Vladivostok. It is not within the scope of this chapter space-wise or purpose-wise to list all the leading manufacturing centers or to inventory the various manufacturing products for which they are noted. However, where a student of geography is faced with the task of making such a comprehensive survey, he could probably do it most expeditiously as well as meaningfully by noting the chief urban centers on the major lines of communication and then proceeding to check the natural and human factors of resource relationships of the hinterland of each of the communities. One of the major sources for the collection of data on manufacturing is, of course, the bureau of statistics of whatever government we are dealing with. Thus, in the North American sector, manufactural statistics are available in Canada from the Dominion of Bureau Statistics; in the United States, from the U. S. Department of Commerce. To make such statistics more meaningful spatially, the leading products for which the respective communities are noted may then be plotted

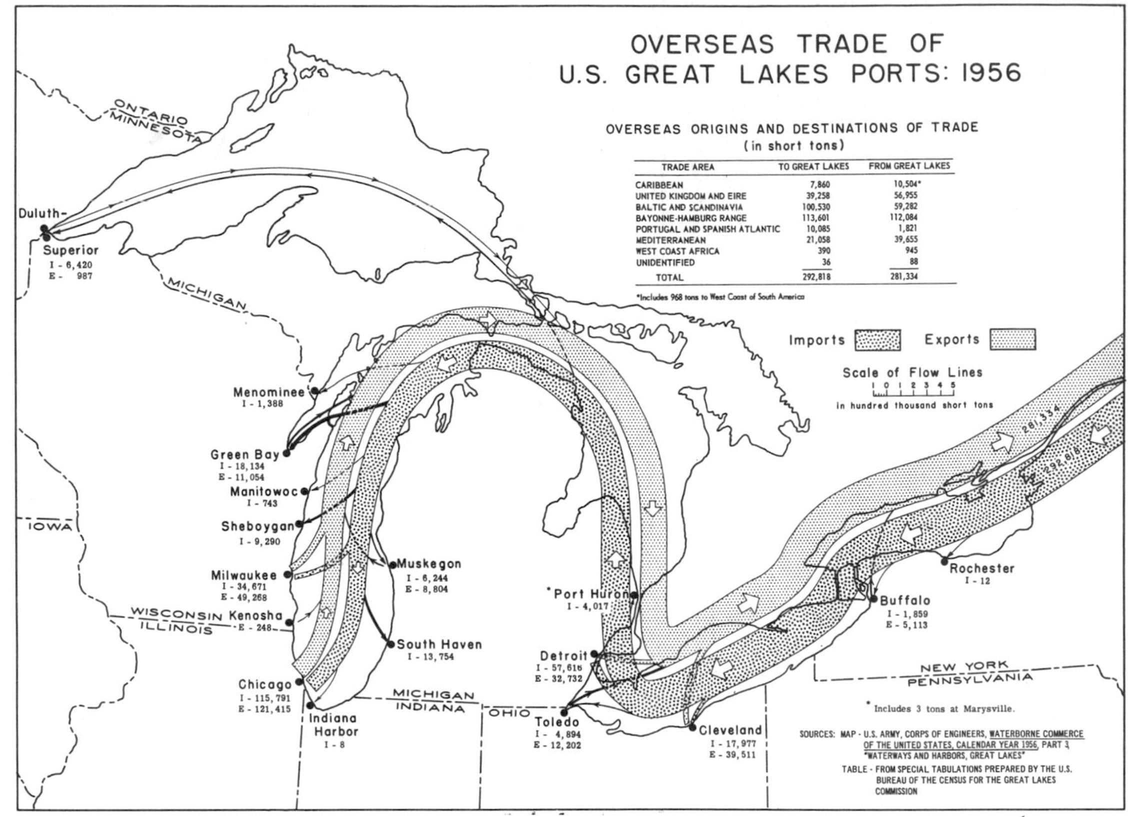

TRADE AREA	TO GREAT LAKES	FROM GREAT LAKES
CARIBBEAN	7,860	10,504*
UNITED KINGDOM AND EIRE	39,258	56,955
BALTIC AND SCANDINAVIA	100,530	59,282
BAYONNE-HAMBURG RANGE	113,601	112,084
PORTUGAL AND SPANISH ATLANTIC	10,085	1,821
MEDITERRANEAN	21,058	39,655
WEST COAST AFRICA	390	945
UNIDENTIFIED	36	88
TOTAL	292,818	281,334

*Includes 968 tons to West Coast of South America

XXVIII:6 Consult data of overseas trade of U. S. Great Lakes ports with those here graphed, and on that basis evaluate the St. Lawrence Seaway.

on a map. Using such detailed distribution of data, then, as the base, subregions, based on one or more criteria which primarily distinguish them, may be demarcated. Thus we see how the various manufactural patterns are identified with the major geographic forces of the region of which the enterprises are a part, as well as of other regions of the world on which the enterprises depend as sources of raw material or markets for their manufactured goods. What does "regionalization" like this mean to a geography student?

In our treatment of the realm's manufactures, only the Russian and Canadian sectors will be considered, since the U. S. segment associated with the latter in many ways duplicates in position and characteristics those of the Canadian counterpart. Furthermore, in our next chapter, basic consideration will be given to the "American Manufacturing Belt," of which this area is also a part.

1. The Russian sector. Russia's struggle for world power rests upon two basic "cold war" geographical principles: (1) the universal utilization of every natural resource with a vengeance, and (2) a rigorous areal planning of regional resources in virtually each administrative province for its own as well as the national welfare. As Cressey points out, the Russian's philosophy of geography is distinctly utilitarian:

¶ Whenever I have asked a Russian geographer to define his subject, he has invariably replied: "The function of geography is to develop the productive resources of the state." As with most Soviet science, there is little room for cultural aspects; geography must be practical.[1]

---

[1] Cressey, George B., "The Soviets Challenge Nature," *How Strong Is Russia?* (A Geographical Appraisal), Syracuse University Press, N.Y., 1954, p. 100. Reprinted by permission.

Thus, certain regional planning principles are basic to each of the five-year planning programs: (1) a wide areal dispersion of industrial establishments for security reasons, even if this means at times an uneconomic duplication, and (2) the development of a high degree of self-sufficiency for each province, just as the U.S.S.R. seeks autarchy on a national level. Thus,

¶ Vasyutin has defined the degree of complexity desired for each major region in these terms: "The problem of complex development of a region is first of all to guarantee the specialized branches of national significance necessary raw materials, fuel, electric power, different raw materials, and in the maximally possible degree satisfy the requirements of the region for fuel, metal, construction materials, chemical fertilizers, agricultural products and consumer goods, in correspondence with the instructions of the 18th Party Congress."[1]

Since the Soviet government has long recognized that it needs to overtake America in the race for industrial supremacy, it has given heavy industry and metallurgical manufacturing prime priority. But such development presupposes access to industrially essential and militarily strategic minerals. And in this area Russia is a world leader. It possesses the greatest variety of minerals of any nation in the world; it occupies a unique position especially in the diverse ferroalloys needed in steel manufacturing; and in total mineral production the U.S.S.R. is second only to the United States. Though diverse ore concentrations have been explored and, in some cases, exploited in widely dispersed areas, a unique variety and quantitative richness distinguishes the Ural area from all other sections of the world. Here in close proximity to one another are rich deposits of iron, copper, gold, platinum, aluminum; ferroalloys such as manganese, chromite, and nickel; and proximate occurrences of fuel minerals: coal, lignite, peat, and petroleum. "Without the Urals," in the judgment of Cressey,

¶ the Soviets could not have won the Second World War; without the Urals, the great industrial shift to the East would have been developed differently. No other mountain range on earth has yielded the wealth of mineral resources produced in the Urals, and the booming cities rival the Ukraine in their industrial output. Due east of Kuibyshev is the magic steel center of Magnitogorsk, comparable in size to Gary, Indiana, and thus one of the two largest steel plants on earth. . . . A dozen other cities, mostly with unfamiliar names, account for the mining or processing of two-score metals.[2]

Soviet planners are now making every attempt to locate industry, particularly heavy industry, as near to the source of metal and fuel minerals as possible. But other factors may lend manufactural prominence to a city. This is particularly well illustrated in the case of Moscow, which city and region is a world leader in manufacturing with only very limited mineral resources. Despite this fact, Moscow is the leading industrial center of Russia, noted for the manufacture of almost every type of product, including steel goods, textiles, foodstuffs, chemical and electrical goods, automobiles and many other goods.

To understand properly the manufactural developments of such interior sites as Moscow, other factors need to be noted: (1) historic impetus, (2) centrality of position, (3) transportation facility, and (4) availability of cheap and abundant power. Moscow, founded during the twelfth century, has had several geographic advantages. Central in position, it early became the focus of trade and therefore the road and rail hub of European Russian. Though lacking the advantages of a seaport, such as Leningrad possesses, "the new Moscow-Volga Canal links the city with Volga commerce and insures adequate municipal water. . . . Moscow is far from the ocean, but the Moscow-Volga Canal has brought visions of transportation something like those with which Chicago views the St. Lawrence and Illinois-Mississippi waterways."[3] Likewise, elsewhere in the area, canalization between the major river systems is effective in alleviating the long-haul transportation problems of heavy goods in a country otherwise generally poor in transporta-

---

1 Harry Swartz, *Russia's Soviet Economy*, © 1950. Prentice-Hall, Inc., Englewood Cliffs, N.J., pp. 555-556. Reprinted by permission.

2 Cressey, *op. cit.*, p. 94. Reprinted by permission.

3 *Ibid.*, p. 76. Reprinted by permission.

tion facilities when compared with western Europe or eastern United States.

One of the other more notable features of areal development concerns the power industry. Unique is the Russian system of using all possible sources of local fuel for development of power: coal, wood, peat, oil, gas. Peat — normally not reclaimed by other countries for power — is used here to a larger extent than all other countries put together. Because of the far-flung enterprises throughout the thousands of miles extent of the U.S.S.R., special attention is given to transmitting power electrically from base power sites as well as by large power systems operated hydroelectrically. The integrated power system based on Moscow-Gorki is said to be "the most efficient system in Soviet Russia" and embraces "the entire central Russian manufacturing district" (7).

2. *The Canadian sector.* Canada is a leading world manufacturer, ranking in sixth place, its manufacturing establishments being almost altogether concentrated in this realm. Supporting directly one-third of the total population, establishments within the last score years have increased almost 50 per cent, and the total workers over 100 per cent. Canadians employed in manufacturing equal those in the combined industries of farming, forestry, fishing, mining and construction; and the value of manufactures — $9,822,000,000 in 1957 — represented almost a third of the gross products. Remarkably little is exported; well over 90 per cent is for home consumption.

Geographers are not in complete agreement as to which statistical criteria measure most accurately the manufactural importance or industrial strength of a country — number of establishments or laborers, amount of capital invested, amount of cost or sales of materials, or value added by manufacture. Each has its own regional significance, but added manufactural value is probably the most all-around meaningful regional index. Using this criterion, the six leading industries of Canada in 1958 were (in descending order): pulp and paper, petroleum products, nonferrous metal smelting and refining, primary iron and steel, aircraft and parts, printing and publishing, sawmilling. For the relative value of each, together with the statistical position of eight other leading industries in this and other categorical measurements, see table 28.1. The same source gives us a comparative provincial base for regional manufactural measurements, for which only a severely abstracted statement must suffice:

¶ Fully one-half of all Canadian manufacturing output is concentrated in Ontario . . . largely influenced by its location on the Great Lakes waterways within easy reach of Pennsylvania's coal and Minnesota's iron ore, both indispensable to Ontario's steel mills. . . . Low cost hydroelectric power resources, the diversity of raw materials . . . one-third of population . . . have been hardly less important factors . . . ; turns out 90 p.c. or more of Canadian production of motor vehicles and parts, agricultural implements . . . ; between 80 and 90 p.c. of rubber goods . . . ; and between 70 and 80 p.c. of primary iron and steel. . . .

Quebec . . . ranks second only to Ontario in manufacturing production and mineral output, as in population . . . accounts for 30 p.c. of the value of Canadian manufactured goods, most manufacturing industries being concentrated in the fertile and strategic valley of the St. Lawrence. The most important single industry is pulp and paper. Other key industries . . . include: petroleum products, non-ferrous metal smelting and refining. . . . The fast growing aluminum industry is also a major factor. . . . Also leads in a number of smaller industries [over a score enumerated].

British Columbia . . . ranks third in manufacturing production, as in area and population. . . . Forest resources, minerals, fisheries, and electric power are the foundation of a rapidly increasing number of manufacturing industries. Chief among these are industries deriving from forest resources . . . accounting among them for more than 40 p.c. of British Columbia's manufacturing employment.[1]

The leading manufacturing centers as of 1958, in the $500,000,000 or over "selling value" class, were: Montreal ($2,266,191,-000), Toronto ($1,825,714,000), Hamilton ($943,304,000), Montreal East ($694,077,-000), Vancouver ($522,600,000).

---

[1] *Manufactures,* Information Services Division, Dominion Bureau of Statistics, Ottawa, Canada, August 31, 1960, pp. 128-137, *passim.* Reprinted by permission.

Table 28.1 Principal statistics of the fifteen leading industries, 1958

Industry	*Estab-lish-ments*	*Em-ployees*	*Salaries and wages*	*Cost at plant of materials used*	*Value added by manu-facture*	*Selling value of factory shipments*
	No.	No.	$'000	$'000	$'000	$'000
Pulp and paper	128	64,084	307,416	597,805	702,951	1,394,679
Petroleum products	71	14,490	76,644	829,920	487,676	1,368,649*
Nonferrous metal smelting and refining	25	26,959	131,081	693,797	378,451	1,135,771
Slaughtering and meat packing	178	25,712	102,677	852,842	196,229	1,050,461
Motor vehicles	15	26,396	129,719	571,501	253,945	847,342
Primary iron and steel	50	30,261	148,023	250,669	304,924	590,318
Sawmills	5,769	47,763	142,700	300,342	236,753	546,299*
Butter and cheese	1,222	20,879	69,034	390,475	118,079	522,793
Aircraft and parts	75	39,932	182,277	176,539	281,132	462,331*
Miscellaneous electrical apparatus and supplies	179	25,116	101,161	164,053	175,828	347,837
Miscellaneous food preparations	299	9,752	34,397	223,012	121,111	345,905
Bread and other bakery products	2,637	35,618	106,969	157,268	172,606	340,918
Sheet metal products	473	19,107	78,135	175,252	154,400	333,265
Printing and publishing	746	30,557	127,741	86,412	238,784	327,687
Machinery, Industrial	379	23,347	95,602	133,424	167,443	311,095
Totals, Fifteen Leading Industries	12,246	439,973	1,833,576	5,603,311	3,990,312	9,925,350
Totals All Industries	36,741	1,289,602	4,802,496	11,821,567	9,792,506	22,163,186

* Reported on a production basis.

SOURCE: *Canada, 1960,* page 131, published by the Information Services Division, Dominion Bureau of Statistics, Ottawa, Canada, 1960. Reprinted by permission.

Brief as the above excerpts are, it is hoped that the reader sees little of value in them merely as statistics but much of value in discerning the geographic matrix responsible for them, partially here expressed, partially of necessity deleted but which the student himself can supply. Among the basic and broader regional phenomena accounting for southern Canada's greatness in manufacturing besides her general high cultural and climatic potential, there should be considered:

(1) The rather unique geographic situation — the neighboring raw frontier to the immediate north from which natural resources for manufacturing are available, and, on the other hand, the immediacy of markets to the south and readily accessible markets abroad.

(2) A rich mineral heritage — In world metal production Canada is a leader in nickel and platinum, and second in aluminum, gold, and zinc. Other leading metals include silver, gold, and copper, and fissionable materials such as pitchblende. Though minerals containing these elements are rather widespread throughout Canada, a major portion of them is concentrated in the southerly section of the Canadian Shield geologic complex so as to be in relatively close proximity to the chief manufacturing areas of Canada.

(3) Optimal geographic conditions for the production of wood commodities, particularly paper manufacturing, include proximity to a wealth of forest and water resources, and economic transportation, particularly by streams accessible for the floating of logs.

Montreal, Canada, is historically the leading fur-exporting port of North America. Modern Montreal, cosmopolitan center of industry and commerce, is reputed to be the world's largest grain port, based largely on export of wheat from the interior prairie province. What commercial changes at Montreal may be contemplated as a result of the development of the St. Lawrence Seaway? (Courtesy Trans-Canada Air Lines)

(4) Concomitant concentrations of power, especially developed waterpower (Figure XXVIII). From this figure you will observe that while extensive undeveloped waterpower sites are widely distributed throughout the *Dfc* realm to the north, only Newfoundland, belonging to this category, can claim extensively developed waterpower sites. Modern technology in developing economic transmission of electric current over relatively long distances, as well as more effective use of local power developments, is of particular significance in relation to the geographic fuel pattern in Canada which is relatively coal-poor and petroleum-poor in the major manufacturing districts. Only in the Prairie Provinces is petroleum production coming to be of primary significance — and this only recently. And the leading coal reserves by far are in the far-off West — Saskatchewan, Alberta, and British Columbia; and in the East — primarily Nova Scotia. Knowledge of this type helps to explain why a country may be both an important producer and importer of the same product. Thus it becomes a matter of geographic expediency for both Canada and the United States to exploit the proximate space-transportation factor to mutual advantage — New England importing Nova Scotia coal, and industrial Ontario and Quebec importing U. S. northern Appalachian coal.

(5) Markets are readily available — in the immediate populous Canadian section itself, in the contiguous U. S. area across the border, and in the trade-favored contacts with Great Britain and other overseas territories made now even more accessible by means of

a deep-draught St. Lawrence Seaway, to which we shall now turn our attention.

Geographic change—America's "fourth seacoast" and the world's "eighth sea," the St. Lawrence Seaway—a new dimension in world affairs

The 27-foot wide St. Lawrence Seaway, officially dedicated on June 26, 1959, by Queen Elizabeth II and President Eisenhower on behalf of Canada and the United States, respectively, memorializes a new landscape in geography as it does a new landmark in history. It is a type of package-project in geographic research which poses in one areal unit all the essential elements and techniques illustrative of the basic principles of conceptual geography: the dynamics of space change (historical geography); the "pro" and "con" evaluation of geo-economic and geo-political factors (systematic geography); analysis of a changed water profile as it affects local ports, regions, provinces-states, countries, the world (regional geography); "prognostic" evaluation.

One of the key principles of geographic study is the analysis and evaluation of the space relationship of earth phenomena transformed by time and technology. And probably no elemental phenomenon is of more moment here than the mobile factor of transportation, any major change of which in routing or in efficacy of service immediately affects the geographic qualities of space, position, and direction in world affairs. Thus, the construction of sea- or ocean-linking canals such as the Suez and the Panama have not only reshaped maritime commercial patterns of the world but also have effected new political and ideological geography concepts as well. Though not in the same category of planetary significance, the deep-draft St. Lawrence Seaway and associated power projects have engrossed the attention not only of Canada and the United States, but of all the leading commercial nations of the world. The ones whose shipping lanes have in the past converged on the east coast, and those which may now consider rerouting from Gulf and west coast to ports of call in the St. Lawrence–Great Lakes basin, are equally interested. It is not surprising, therefore, that numerous geographers, economists, and political scientists have given considerable research study to the prospective changing commercial and industrial potential of this project.

Thus, it is in the area of economic geography rather than in engineering geography (straightening, deepening, widening, and reducing number of locks and canals) that geographic change is of ultimate significance. Among investigators of this project are Harold A. Wood, lecturer in geography at McMaster University, and T. L. Hills, associate professor of geography at McGill University, and geographer Albert G. Ballert, director of research of the Great Lakes Commission. We shall let each of these brief us on several of the abovementioned salient geographic features:

¶ International accord was not easy to reach, because the St. Lawrence has never been of equal importance to Canada and the United States. For Canada this river and its valley form a commercial routeway that not only provides a natural outlet to world markets for much of the central and east-central parts of the country but also forms a direct link between the two leading industrial areas of southern Ontario and southeastern Quebec. A huge volume of passengers and freight moves ceaselessly by road and rail along the north shore, and for seven months of the year small ships crowd the waters of the river.

For the United States, on the other hand, the St. Lawrence is an indirect trade route to the oceans of the world, one which freezes annually for five months and which lies, furthermore, for the most part in foreign territory. Nor does it offer a convenient route for internal United States trade. Even between lake ports and Atlantic seaboard cities, the excellent rail connections are generally preferred to the circuitous water route. The United States flag is rarely seen on the river, and only 2 per cent of the tonnage carried over the St. Lawrence canals moves from one United States port to another; for Canada the corresponding figure is more than 60 per cent.[1]

The Great Circle Route in seaway perspective. As we have learned before, a major competitive space factor in all transportation is to reduce distance to a minimum. And so

[1] Wood, Harold A., "The St. Lawrence Seaway and Urban Geography, Cornwall-Cardinal, Ontario," *The Geographical Review*, Vol. XLV, No. 4, October, 1955, p. 509. Reprinted by permission.

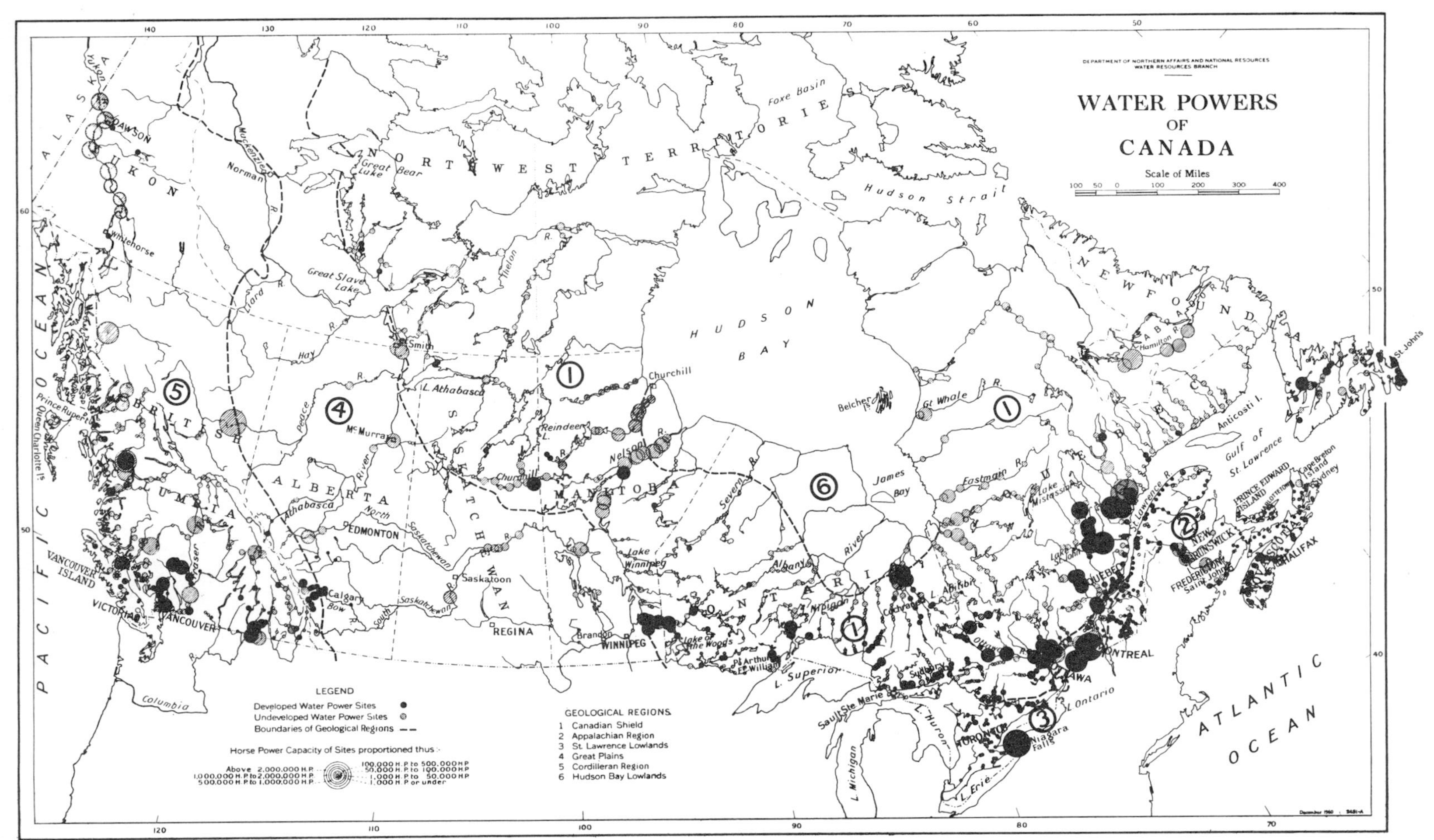
DEPARTMENT OF NORTHERN AFFAIRS AND NATIONAL RESOURCES
WATER RESOURCES BRANCH
WATER POWERS
OF
CANADA
Scale of Miles
100 50 0 100 200 300 400
LEGEND
Developed Water Power Sites
Undeveloped Water Power Sites
Boundaries of Geological Regions
Horse Power Capacity of Sites proportioned thus:-
Above 2,000,000 H.P.
1,000,000 H.P. to 2,000,000 H.P.
500,000 H.P. to 1,000,000 H.P.
100,000 H.P. to 500,000 H.P.
50,000 H.P. to 100,000 H.P.
1,000 H.P. to 50,000 H.P.
1,000 H.P. or under
GEOLOGICAL REGIONS
1 Canadian Shield
2 Appalachian Region
3 St. Lawrence Lowlands
4 Great Plains
5 Cordilleran Region
6 Hudson Bay Lowlands
PACIFIC OCEAN
ATLANTIC OCEAN
HUDSON BAY
NORTHWEST TERRITORIES
YUKON
ALASKA
BRITISH COLUMBIA
ALBERTA
SASKATCHEWAN
MANITOBA
ONTARIO
QUEBEC
NEWFOUNDLAND
LABRADOR
NEW BRUNSWICK
NOVA SCOTIA
PRINCE EDWARD ISLAND
DAWSON
Whitehorse
Great Bear Lake
Great Slave Lake
Norman
Mackenzie R.
Liard R.
Hay R.
Peace R.
Smith
L. Athabasca
McMurray
Athabasca
North Saskatchewan
EDMONTON
Calgary
Bow R.
South Saskatchewan
Saskatoon
REGINA
Churchill
Reindeer L.
Nelson R.
Lake Winnipeg
Brandon
WINNIPEG
Lake of the Woods
Pt. Arthur
Ft. William
L. Superior
L. Nipigon
Albany
Severn R.
River
James Bay
Belcher Is.
Gt. Whale R.
Eastmain R.
Lake Mistassini
Lake St. John
L. Abitibi
Cochrane
Sudbury
Sault Ste. Marie
L. Huron
L. Michigan
L. Erie
L. Ontario
TORONTO
Niagara Falls
OTTAWA
MONTREAL
QUEBEC
St. Lawrence R.
Gulf of St. Lawrence
Anticosti I.
Hamilton R.
FREDERICTON
Saint John
HALIFAX
Cape Breton Island
Sydney
St. John's
Foxe Basin
Hudson Strait
Prince Rupert
Queen Charlotte Is.
VANCOUVER ISLAND
VICTORIA
VANCOUVER
Fraser
Columbia
December 1960

if it is an obvious advantage distance-wise for ocean-going vessels to follow as near as practicable the Great Circle Route from North America to western Europe, such advantage is now accentuated by extending this great circle route to the interior. In this connection, Dr. Ballert notes,

¶ The Seaway route to northwest Europe follows rather closely the great circle—the shortest possible distance. As a result mileages from essentially all ports on the Great Lakes to this major overseas trading area are less via the St. Lawrence route than by rail to the East Coast for transfer to vessels for overseas destinations. Because of the inherent economics in shipping by water, the dollar distances via the St. Lawrence present still greater advantages. From some Great Lakes ports the all-water routes to European trade areas are actually shorter than the transatlantic routes from the East Coast, and all Lake ports are hundreds of miles nearer than are the Gulf Coast ports. From Duluth to Liverpool, for example, the distance is 800 miles less than from New Orleans to this English port. Duluth also is 350 miles nearer to the Strait of Gibralter [sic] than is New Orleans.[1]

Only by a detailed study of the entire historical geography of the St. Lawrence since the beginning to the twentieth century, together with a review of the voluminous literature and legislation published on the subject in both Canada and the United States, can one hope to arrive at an appraisal of the merits and future potential of the project. Extravagant claims "pro" and "con" regionally reflect highly prejudiced interests seldom seen in public projects of this magnitude, as well as objective approaches to proper evaluation of the many-sided controversial issues. Claims for the project include: in general, reduces transportation costs, especially of bulk cargoes (e.g., export of interior prairie grain to Europe); expedites the shipment of heavy ore (e.g., iron ore from the new Quebec-Labrador field to the steel furnaces in the Midwest, to supplement and later supplant the ores from the Mesabi and other American ranges); expands hydroelectric power as a boon to both Ontario and New York industries; consolidates Canadian–U.S. friendship. Some arguments advanced against: favors only limited shippers; regionally is prejudicial to certain ports, railroads, industries, and utilities, especially in the United States; "iceway" is closed to navigation for some five months; is expected to restrict water diversion from Lake Michigan, needed for domestic, industrial, and canal navigational purposes.

Now that the deep-draft navigation is in operation, appraisals of the future of the new "seacoast" are for the most part enthusiastically optimistic. Dr. Hills' summarization may be regarded as quite representative of the general situation:

¶ Undeniably the Seaway has been justified. Cheaper Quebec-Labrador ore is arriving at Middle Western furnaces in ever-increasing quantities. Larger quantities of grain are moving down the cheaper St. Lawrence route, forcing rate reductions on all other major routes. Overseas freighters are venturing into the heart of the continent in sufficient numbers to indicate a definite trend and to bring benefits to those trading with Europe. For those ports that are well located and have adequate facilities and development potential, the prospects are bright. Industry, stimulated by the huge concentration of power along the St. Lawrence and nearby Niagara rivers, said to be the largest concentration in the noncommunist world, is bound to expand, and in turn winter navigation of the Seaway is now more than a possibility.[2]

XXVIII:7 (Left) This map shows an inventory by geologic regions of Canadian developed and undeveloped water power sites as of 1960. From this and other Canadian resource maps determine the factors influential in developing the presently undeveloped areas. ("Water Powers of Canada," Water Resources Branch, Department of Northern Affairs and Natural Resources, 1960, used by permission)

---

1 Ballert, Albert G., "All-Water Economy Route," *Great Lakes Overseas Commerce*, Great Lakes Commission, Ann Arbor, Mich., 1958, p. 4. Reprinted by permission.

2 Hills, Theodore L., "The St. Lawrence Seaway," *Focus*, Vol. XI, No. 4, December, 1960, p. 6. Reprinted by permission.
(For a more detailed exposition by Dr. Hills see his 157-page booklet *The St. Lawrence Seaway*, Frederick A. Praeger, 1959.)

APPLICATION OF GEOGRAPHIC UNDERSTANDING

Now that we have concluded this chapter, recheck the concepts you formed initially in reading the excerpts from Mr. Brault's letter and the Commonwealth commentary.

I. Regional Geography

A. In what respects do the farm data typify (a) this world realm, (b) the Canadian region of which it is a part? (Consider all essential phases of both the natural and cultural elements of geography.)

B. In what important particulars is the farm atypical?

C. What additional data would you seek by (a) field survey; (b) questionnaire or interview?

D. How does one go about resolving field and farm uniqueness of data into an integrated exposition identifying and interpreting the geography of a region?

II. Historical-Demographic Geography

A. Show precisely how a present-day exclusive field survey of Brault's farm is of itself inadequate in explaining (a) its form, (b) its function.

B. What would you want to know about the demographic geography of the region to determine the longevity potential of the French culture?

III. Agricultural Geography

A. What crop and other adaptations *to* the natural environment are recognizable on the Brault farm?

B. What adaptations *of* the natural environment (man-made changes) are also noteworthy?

C. In the attempt to make the best possible productive connections with the land, what do the following activities of the farm family signify? M. Brault is President of the *Union Catholique des Cultivateurs* and of the cattle breeding Artificial Insemination Centre; Mme. Brault is Secretary of the *Cercle de Fermières;* one son is in attendance at *Ecole d'Agriculture;* another, interested in drainage systems, has been working with a surveyor.

IV. Economic-Commercial Geography

Do you think the Brault farm would have any particular interest in the Seaway just discussed? Indicate what local and regional textual and cartographic data you would consider relevant in answering such a question.

References

1 Brault, Henri, "Ferme Joanne" (communication), "A Dairy Farm in French Canada," *Farming in the Commonwealth, Canada,* The Association of Agriculture, London, in collaboration with *Le Ministere de L'Agriculture,* Province of Quebec, 1956, pp. 1-2, *passim;* sheets 2, 15, 18, 19, *passim.*

2 Visher, S. S., "Climatic Influences," *Geography in the Twentieth Century,* Griffith Taylor, Editor, Philosophical Library, New York, 1951, pp. 199-200.

3 Brown, Ralph, "The Maritime Interests," *Mirror for Americans,* Edited by Elizabeth T. Platt, American Geographical Society, New York, Special Publication No. 27, 1943, pp. 90, 138.

4 Putnam, Donald F., "Physical Background," *Canadian Regions,* J. M. Dent & Sons (Canada) Ltd., Toronto, 1952, pp. 26-27, *passim.*

5 Cressey, George B., "The Soviets Challenge Nature," *How Strong Is Russia?* (A Geographical Appraisal), Syracuse University Press, N. Y., [954, pp. 76, 94, 100.

6 Swartz, Harry, *Russia's Soviet Economy,* (quoting Izvestia Akademii Nauk SSSR, *Pravda,* 1950, p. 190), Prentice-Hall, Inc., Englewood Cliffs, N. J., 1950, pp. 555-556.

7 Thiel, Eric, "The Power Industry in the Soviet Union," *Economic Geography,* Vol. XXVII, No. 2, April, 1951, p. 112.

8 *Manufactures,* Canada, 1960, Dominion Bureau of Statistics, Ottawa, August 31, 1960, pp. 128-137, *passim.*

9 Wood, Harold A., "The St. Lawrence Seaway and Urban Geography, Cornwall-Cardinal, Ontario," *The Geographical Review,* Vol. XLV, No. 4, October, 1955, p. 509.

10 Ballert, Albert G., "All-Water Economy Route," *Great Lakes Overseas Commerce,* Great Lakes Commission, Ann Arbor, Michigan, 1958, p. 4.

11 Hills, Theodore L., "The St. Lawrence Seaway," *Focus,* Vol. XI, No. 4, December, 1960, p. 6.

Chapter 29

The humid, severe winter–long summer, forest and prairie lands (*Dfa*); and monsoon phase (*Dwa*)

Manufactural geography questionnaire: geographic commentary

IDENTIFICATION-CLASSIFICATION

Name of establishment; location of main plant, branch plants; classification code, U. S. Census of Manufacturers, MC 202 (to be omitted by respondent); acreage covered by plant and premises; . . .

HISTORICAL DATA

When founded; original location; Were *locational* advantages considered in selecting the site as regards any geographic facility, economic factor, or political consideration (e.g., space, topography, water bodies, water supply, drainage, waste disposal, raw materials, power, labor storage, transportation, markets, regional position to accessory industries, taxes, laws, national defense, etc.)? Please explain and evaluate the relative importance of each influential locative factor; Why located in this particular city? On this particular site? Were locational advantages of alternative sites considered? What and where were their considered advantages? Have there been any changes in geographic location of the plant? If so, basic reasons. What effects have new techniques of manufacturing, such as shift to a new type of transportation, new sources or substitutes of raw materials, the opening of new markets, and the like, had upon the relocation or development of your industry?

RAW MATERIALS USED

Kinds and amounts used (dollar value); geographic sources; owned by your industry or by another concern; alternate sources, should present source be cut off; possibilities of substitutes, sources; changes in geographic sources within the last ten years. What considerations determine the present source of raw materials (specifically, what *locational* factors are involved, if any)?

PROCESSED MATERIALS

What materials, processed in whole or in part, are received by the plant for assembling or servicing? Geographic sources?

EMPLOYMENT

Number employed: men, women; geographic distribution of sources of labor by such residential categories as you may have available; . . . What are the primary transportation facilities and routes used to reach the plant?

UTILITIES

Power: kinds and amounts, sources, reliability of sources, possible substitutes; Water: sources, quality and quantity, use; Sewerage and industrial waste disposal: means and adequacy.

PRODUCT MARKETED

Nature of product and by-products marketed; value (dollars) added by manufacturing; volume and value of sales by states, counties, cities, or foreign countries, by years or last year (use the smallest practicable unit); . . . What geographic, economic, cultural or political factors affect sales? Changes in geographic distribution of markets within the last ten years?

TRANSPORTATION

How are raw materials received? How are products shipped? What is the basis of determining whether truck, train, ship, or plane will be used to transport goods to and from the plant? . . .

PROBLEMS

What geonomic problems are characteristically identified with your type of industry? Approaches considered in attacking them. Do you recognize any industrial land-use problems in your area (e.g., deficiency in quality or quantity of land, etc.)? Explain. Can your community and your industry, in your judgment, effectively share joint responsibility in eliminating geographic maladjustments? Observations. What local, regional, national, or foreign geographic data do you consider essential in helping understand and solve problems related to your type of industry?

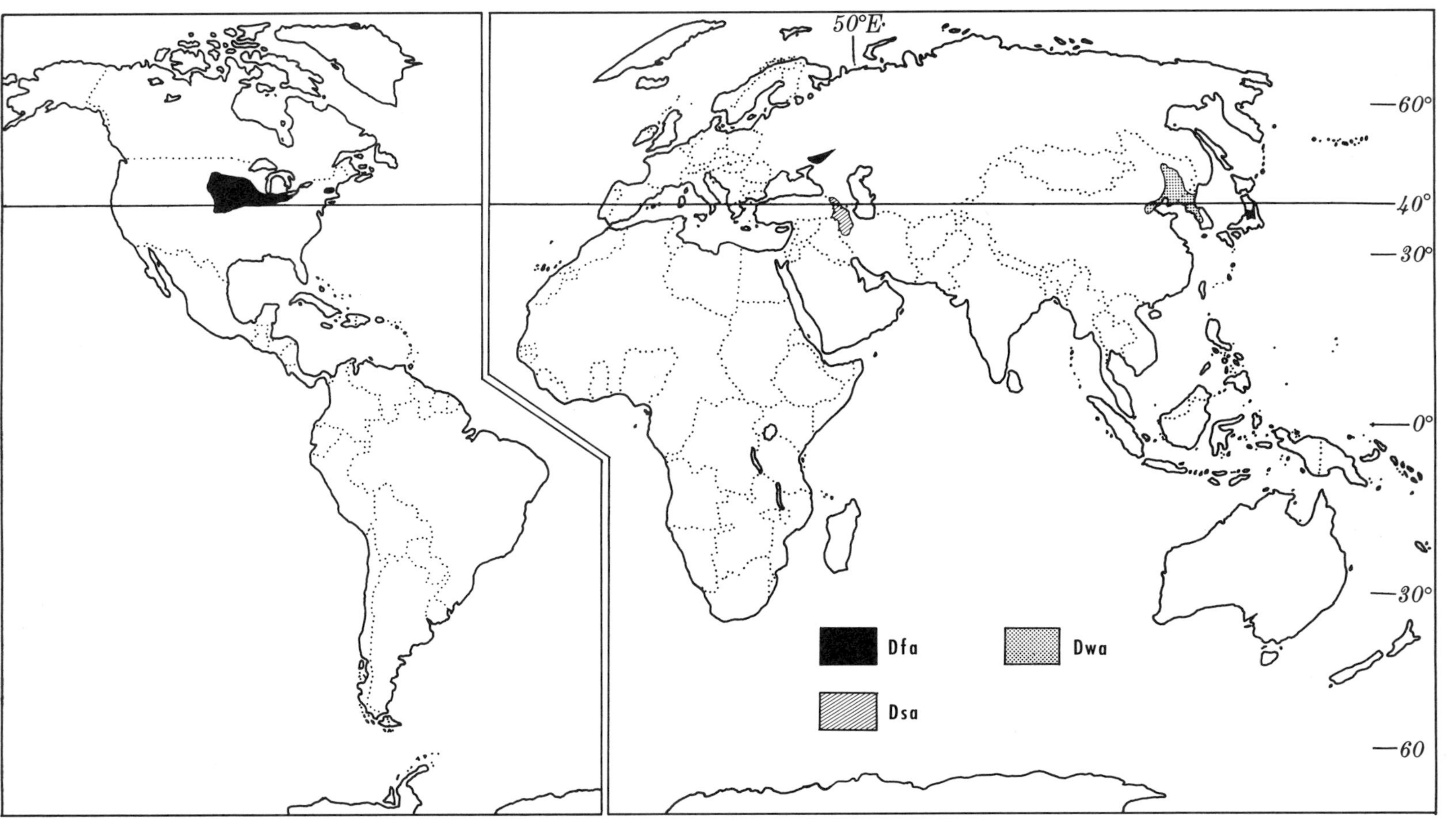
50°E
60°
40°
30°
0°
30°
60
Dfa
Dwa
Dsa

LEGAL CONSIDERATIONS

What legislative restrictive measures, if any, add to the cost of operating expenses? Are local and regional zoning and geographic planning ordinances adequate to meet all the needs of your plant for present operations? For anticipated future expansion? Comments.

PUBLIC RELATIONS

Besides constituting the economic backbone of a community, industries perform social services of great value to the public. Just how, would you say, does your enterprise make a distinctive contribution to the welfare of your immediate community? To the future development of the Calumet region? What future trends may be anticipated in the development of your industry? . . . How would an Indiana Lake Port affect your industry if located at: Michigan City; Burn's Ditch; Lake Calumet? Of what specific advantage to you is the Toll Road? What benefits may derive from the Tri-State Highway?

You will recall, in the previous chapter, a farm letter was used to introduce the agricultural geography of the realm. In this chapter our introduction to manufactural geography is by way of a questionnaire, exploring inductively the characteristics of the world-celebrated "North American manufacturing belt," focused on this realm of severe winters and long summers, as contrasted with the colder winters and cooler summers of the preceding continental climate. The Köppen symbol *a* signifies that the warmest month averages above 72°F. with a correspondingly longer summer than in *Dfb*. The realm in the United States coincides in part not only with the leading manufacturing belt of the United States but with the leading U. S. agricultural belt as well (compare Figure XXIX-1 with Figure XXIX-2). Together, the *Dfa-Dfb-Cfb* manufacturing area suggests the corresponding position of the *Cfb* high energy climate coinciding with industrial western Europe, considered in Chapter 26. The *Dfa* departs only slightly from the commonly considered ideal energy or "comfort" climate as shown in the accompanying graph (Figure XXIX-3). However, as earlier indicated, climate is only one of a number of major factors which condition an area for the creativeness expressed in the arts and industries of mid-latitude North America, Europe, insular Japan, and corresponding Southern Hemisphere sections. We must look, therefore, to other factors for localization of industry.

As in other areas of geographic study, there is wide divergence of opinion among geographers as to the best approach to an understanding of the processes which make for industrial centralization and expansion. Collection of manufactural data and criteria of evaluating their importance can become a much more complicated process than is the analysis of agricultural activity, such as we considered in detail in the previous chapter. There, you will recall, the quest for farm data started with an individual farm, from which we proceeded areally to expand our knowledge of the countryside with the object of determining how often and in what way many of the characteristic features of M. Brault's farm repeat themselves in the landscape, thus affording clues to geographical processes operative on a regional scale. This same type of inductive procedure is now used here to discover the more significant developments of the North American manufacturing belt. The questionnaire introducing this chapter was designed with this in mind, and was actually used in a somewhat more expanded form in the study of some half-dozen Calumet industrial communities in northwest Indiana–northeast Illinois. The student should keep in mind, of course, that not all such questions as here included are equally relevant to all communities or even to all manufactural respondents. But review

XXIX:1 (Left) Of very limited distribution, the *Da* assumes regional prominence only in the form of two major wedges—one (*Dfa*) in the interior Corn Belt of the United States, the other (*Dwa*) on the east coast soy belt of Manchuria and Korea. Now that all the realms have been cartographically considered individually, the space relations of the entire ensemble should be reviewed (see climate map in the Appendix). Genetic considerations should also be inquiringly reviewed. For example, why is there no *D* in the Southern Hemisphere? In what respect is the sea climate pattern different from that of the land pattern (see Köppen-Geiger map)?

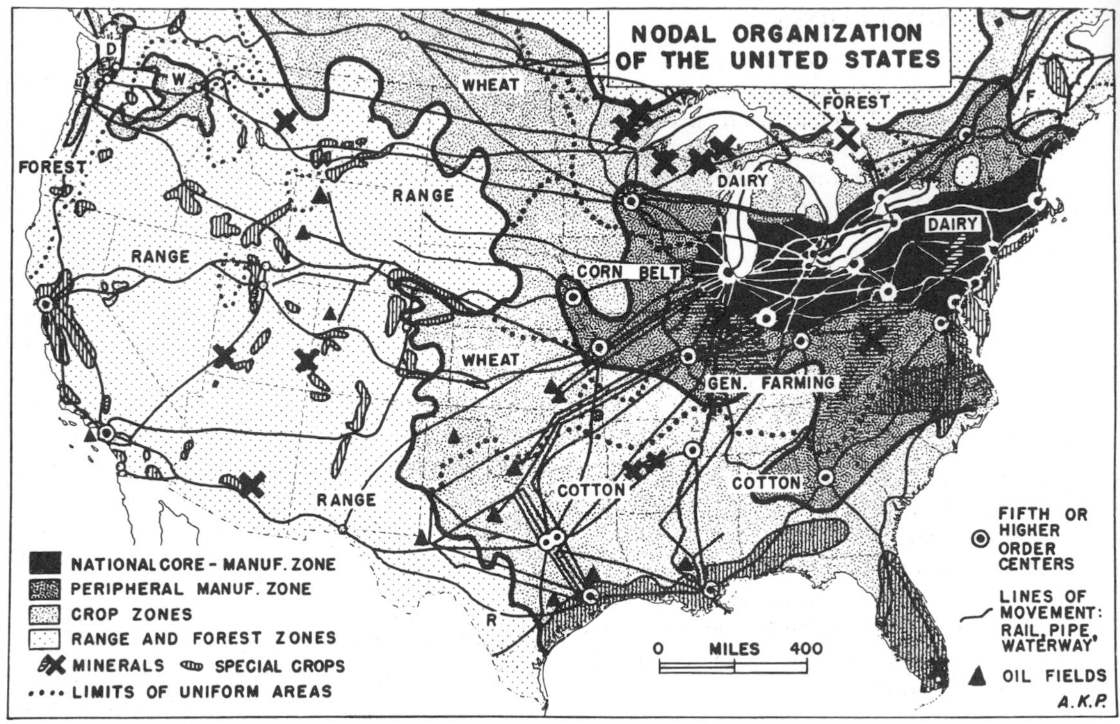

XXIX:2 Compare the areal distribution of the agricultural-manufactural-commercial pattern, centered upon Chicago, with the climatic pattern shown in the previous figure. (Map by Allen K. Philbrick, *Economic Geography,* Vol. XXXIII, No. 4, October, 1957, used by permission)

of these questions under the several categories should afford some idea, at least, of the type of data considered significant in a manufactural, geographic study. You will note that among the features stressed are the topographic sites and regional situations of the plants themselves, of raw materials, of processed materials, of labor, of utilities, of markets, and of transportation. What may easily be overlooked are such factors as are broadly related, we might say, to the temperamental "climate" of the community, i.e., how hospitable and aggressive the people in the community are in attracting industries to the community, and in organizing such groups as the Chamber of Commerce, City Planning Commission, and special industrial and businessmen's associations. This aspect may not seem geographic at all, and yet the very appeals and offers made by such organizations to attract industries must be based on inventory of areal reality and of the resources of the community which of themselves distinctively call for geographic evaluation.

The next major task, of course, is to assimilate the questionnaire data into meaningful categories from which, in turn, one can identify and measure the geographic processes primarily responsible for the manufactural structure of the community. Let us now take a look at one such study of a community whose prominent position in the U. S. steel economy is well known to all.

Gary: leader in "big steel"

¶ Thirteen United States steel manufacturing districts are recognized for which regional steel production statistics have been published by the American Iron and Steel Institute. Such data reveal that the Chicago District, of which Gary is a part, leads in percentage of U. S. steel ingot capacity—19.24 per cent; followed in order by Pittsburgh (17.35); Philadelphia (14.17); Valley (Youngstown) (10.84). The remaining districts—West, Cleveland, Buffalo, Detroit; South, South Ohio River, Upper Ohio River, St. Louis; and Northeast—range from 5.5 down to .45 per cent.

Gary is the leading steel community in the

Chicago District [Figure XXIX-4]. Its mills have an annual capacity of 7,204,000 net tons, followed closely by those of Indiana Harbor (5,800,000), and Chicago (5,441,000) (*The Iron Age,* February 13, 1958). Thus we see the commanding position of the Chicago District and Gary's own strategic position in the Calumet Region and in the United States steel economy.[1]

Are Gary industrialists aware of the importance of regional and topographic locative factors in the localization of industry? Of the thirty-seven manufacturing establishments contacted by the questionnaire and interviewed on this point, thirty-three responded with at least one, more commonly a number of, reasons for locating on the Gary site. Arranged in the order of descending frequency of reference were: land-building availability, market, transportation, and proximity to raw steel. Over one-half of the respondents stressed the first-mentioned factor; namely, the importance of sizable tracts of vacant land obtainable at reasonable prices. This factor itself recalls the selection of this site by Judge Elbert H. Gary, then chairman of the board of United States Steel, who recognized the availability here of 120,000 acres of unoccupied dunes and marsh wasteland at a strategic point on the southern end of Lake Michigan. Though the main raw materials—iron and coal — were lacking in the area, Judge Gary and other officers of the steel company immediately sensed the excellent transport facility of the Great Lakes in shipping Mesabi ore from northern Minnesota, and limestone flux from northern Michigan, supplemented by excellent rail facility for transporting steel coal from relatively nearby fields in Illinois and Indiana, and coking coal from Kentucky and West Virginia. The proximate position of Gary to Chicago which is the chief market for its steel products, as well as the greatest railway center in the country, along with other recognized superior features, led to the development here of what is now the greatest unified steel industrial plant in the United States (Figure XXIX-5). In more modern times, the enterprising citizens of Gary have been interested in seeking diversification of industry, aware of the relative insecurity of industrial and community welfare based essentially upon one major industry — steel. As a result, in 1945 the Gary Industrial Foundation, Inc., was organized

¶ To promote, foster and encourage post-war industrial development in and about the city of Gary, Indiana; to solicit and receive contributions of money and property, real and personal; to assist by means of loans or otherwise manufacturing plants and other employers of labor not located within the Gary district or desirous of so locating; to aid in the creation of employment opportunities for returning servicemen and women; and to operate and function as a civic organization for the general betterment and welfare of Gary, Indiana, and its citizens (2).

The Foundation has followed up its objectives with acquisition of industrial real estate to assist in the expansion of industrial sites for the multiplication of industrial enterprises.

The student will further note that considerable emphasis in the latter part of the questionnaire is placed upon determining the extent of the activities of the planning and zoning and other future development plans of the community. Among the recommendations for the planning of this expanding industrialization program, we note the following observation by the Evert Kincaid Associates, employed by the Gary City Council:

¶ Fortunately there is an abundance of *gross* space within the city which, through appropriate reclaiming, servicing and zoning, can be brought into use for manufacturing and industrial sites. The manufacturing plants here contemplated would, in general, be one-story extended type structures designed to blend well with the immediate physical environment, and they should be "nonnuisance" operationally, in order not to affect adversely any residential areas they might initially or in future adjoin. In order to achieve as much geographical dispersion as possible in the location of new industries, land should be reclaimed, serviced, and otherwise improved in the southern reaches of the city of the general area traversed by the Little Calumet River, and in the southern part of the western limb of the city. These are both population-growth sections and would orient well to localized employment sources.

[1] Meyer, Alfred H., and Hess, Elmer B., "Gary 'Big Steel'—Geographic Design and Destiny," *Proceedings of the Indiana Academy of Science,* Vol. LXVIII, 1958, p. 237. Reprinted by permission.

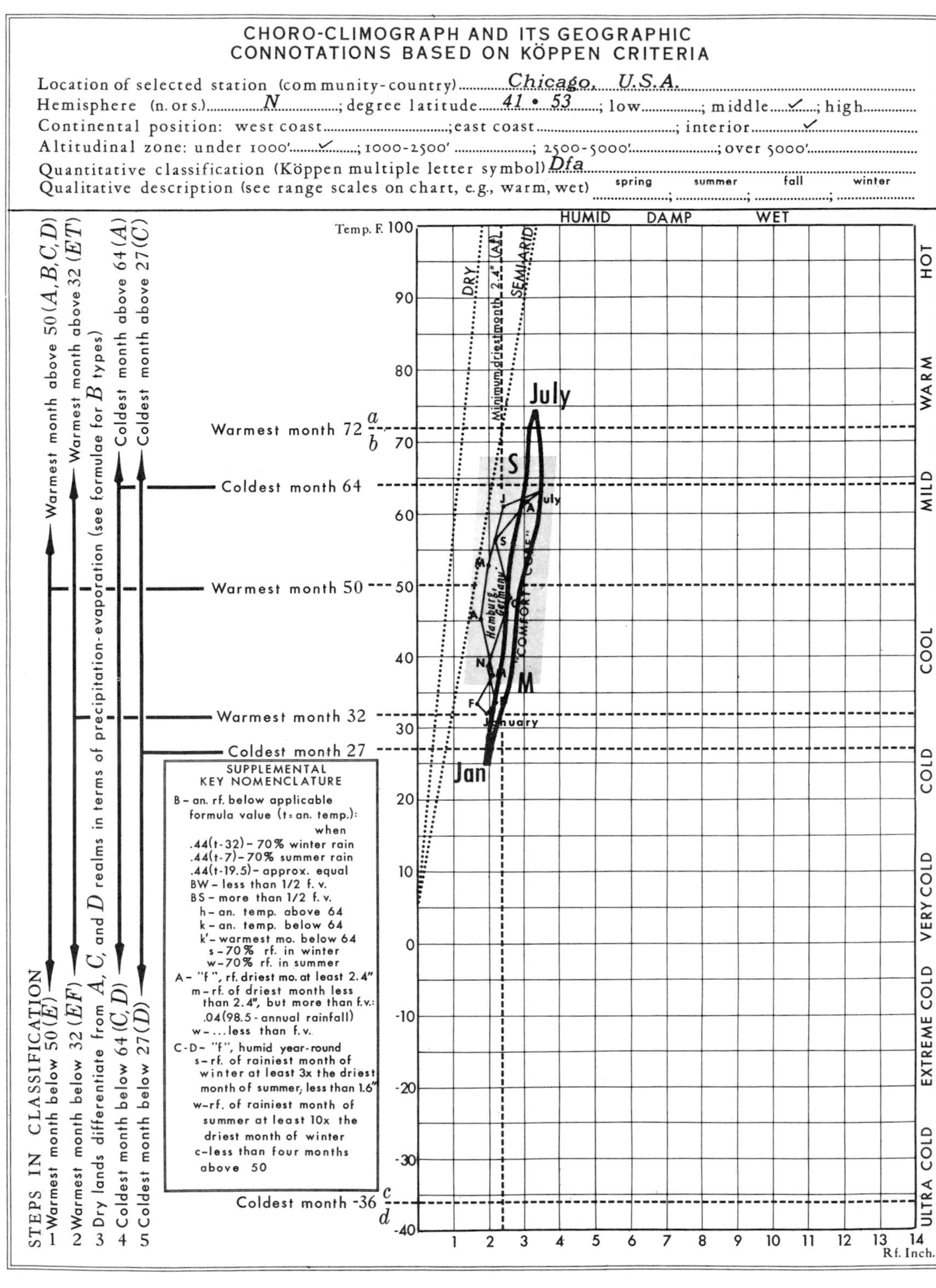
CHORO-CLIMOGRAPH AND ITS GEOGRAPHIC
CONNOTATIONS BASED ON KÖPPEN CRITERIA
Location of selected station (community-country) Chicago, U.S.A.
Hemisphere (n. or s.) N; degree latitude 41 • 53; low; middle ✓; high
Continental position: west coast; east coast; interior ✓
Altitudinal zone: under 1000' ✓; 1000-2500'; 2500-5000'; over 5000'
Quantitative classification (Köppen multiple letter symbol) Dfa
Qualitative description (see range scales on chart, e.g., warm, wet) spring; summer; fall; winter
HUMID
DAMP
WET
Temp. F.
DRY
SEMIARID
Minimum driest month 2.4" (Af)
HOT
WARM
MILD
COOL
COLD
VERY COLD
EXTREME COLD
ULTRA COLD
July
Jan
January
Hamburg, Germany
"COMFORT CORE"
Warmest month 72
Coldest month 64
Warmest month 50
Warmest month 32
Coldest month 27
Coldest month -36
STEPS IN CLASSIFICATION
1 Warmest month below 50 (E) — Warmest month above 50 (A, B, C, D)
2 Warmest month below 32 (EF) — Warmest month above 32 (ET)
3 Dry lands differentiate from A, C, and D realms in terms of precipitation-evaporation (see formulae for B types)
4 Coldest month below 64 (C, D) — Coldest month above 64 (A)
5 Coldest month below 27 (D) — Coldest month above 27 (C)
SUPPLEMENTAL KEY NOMENCLATURE
B – an. rf. below applicable formula value (t = an. temp.): when
.44(t-32) – 70% winter rain
.44(t-7) – 70% summer rain
.44(t-19.5) – approx. equal
BW – less than 1/2 f. v.
BS – more than 1/2 f. v.
h – an. temp. above 64
k – an. temp. below 64
k' – warmest mo. below 64
s – 70% rf. in winter
w – 70% rf. in summer
A – "f", rf. driest mo. at least 2.4"
m – rf. of driest month less than 2.4", but more than f.v.: .04(98.5 - annual rainfall)
w – ... less than f.v.
C-D – "f", humid year-round
s – rf. of rainiest month of winter at least 3x the driest month of summer; less than 1.6"
w – rf. of rainiest month of summer at least 10x the driest month of winter
c – less than four months above 50
Rf. Inch.

To gain the employment objectives through future industrial growth and to promote its geographical dispersion, approximately 250 acres of industrial sites will be required by 1970, in addition to the tracts presently owned by the Gary Industrial Foundation. By 1980, it is estimated that 450 more acres may be needed for industrial and manufacturing uses (3).

The planning pattern and principle of Gary are illustrated in Figure XXIX-5.

Important as is the study of the topographic site of a manufacturing community, to understand the pre-eminence of a manufactural community such as Gary, one must look much farther afield regionally. Though Gary steel products are distributed nationwide, major markets occur within steel-fabricating Indiana satellite communities only five miles distant, such as Hammond, East Chicago, and Whiting (the last oriented to oil refining); and on the Illinois side, Chicago Heights, Harvey, Blue Island, and metropolitan Chicago itself, where industries within only twenty or thirty miles have direct access to Gary steel (Figure XXIX-4). All these communities and other smaller centers among them form an almost contiguous manufactural district centered upon the western Calumet area, each with its own unique industrial development and with relative advantages and disadvantages as compared with one another. So let us now look at one of these briefly to see how communities as close as a dozen miles from one another can present most striking contrasts in manufactural structure.

Chicago Heights: a study in manufactural diversity

Chicago Heights, some five miles to the west of the Indiana–Illinois line and about fifteen miles from the shore of Lake Michigan, with less than one-fourth the population of the city of Gary, has approximately twice as many industrial establishments. An attempt has here been made to follow essentially a standard classification of manufacturing, such as is presented by the U. S. Census of Manufactures. This facilitates study of comparative similarities or dissimilarities of plant classification between communities. Among other striking differences in community structure is the exclusively land-oriented transportation pattern of Chicago Heights as compared with the combined lake–land circulation of the Gary community.

As in the case of Gary, it is interesting to note that industrial development in Chicago Heights was inspired by outside leadership, in this case in the person of Charles H. Wacker, who subsequently became the first president of the Chicago Plan Commission. Mr. Wacker headed an organization which in 1890 purchased some 1,200 acres of land in the area and attracted industry by various concessions, including even the offering of some free land. In the year following, the Chicago Heights Land Association was organized with the specific objective of developing industrially some 4,000 acres of land. The announced policies for such development already at this early date recommended two basic principles of sound geographical development for any community; namely, to seek from the very start diversification, instead of one line of industry, and secondly, to segregate the factory district from the residential section of the community. Thus, the small community today is distinguished by some four-score manufactural industries, with an estimated annual value of manufactural products of some $125 million, and with a labor force estimated at between 12,000 and 13,000. But land alone, even as here allocated for strictly industrial use, cannot of itself ensure successful industrial establishments. Major industries in numbers for such a small community as this must obviously, as in the case of Gary, have good transportation facilities. But as you will note again from the comparison of the two maps, Chicago Heights' "inland" position with respect to Lake Michigan presents an entirely different transportational pattern. Moreover, the railroad pattern originally was linked directly

XXIX:3 (Left) Chicago's climograph is virtually a simple axis, indicating almost a uniform gradual rise of one co-ordinate value with the other from January to July and similarly with a slightly less regular profile, declining values from July to January. The range (50°) is comparatively striking, revealing a high degree of continentality, and suggesting a marked seasonal regimen in man's activities.

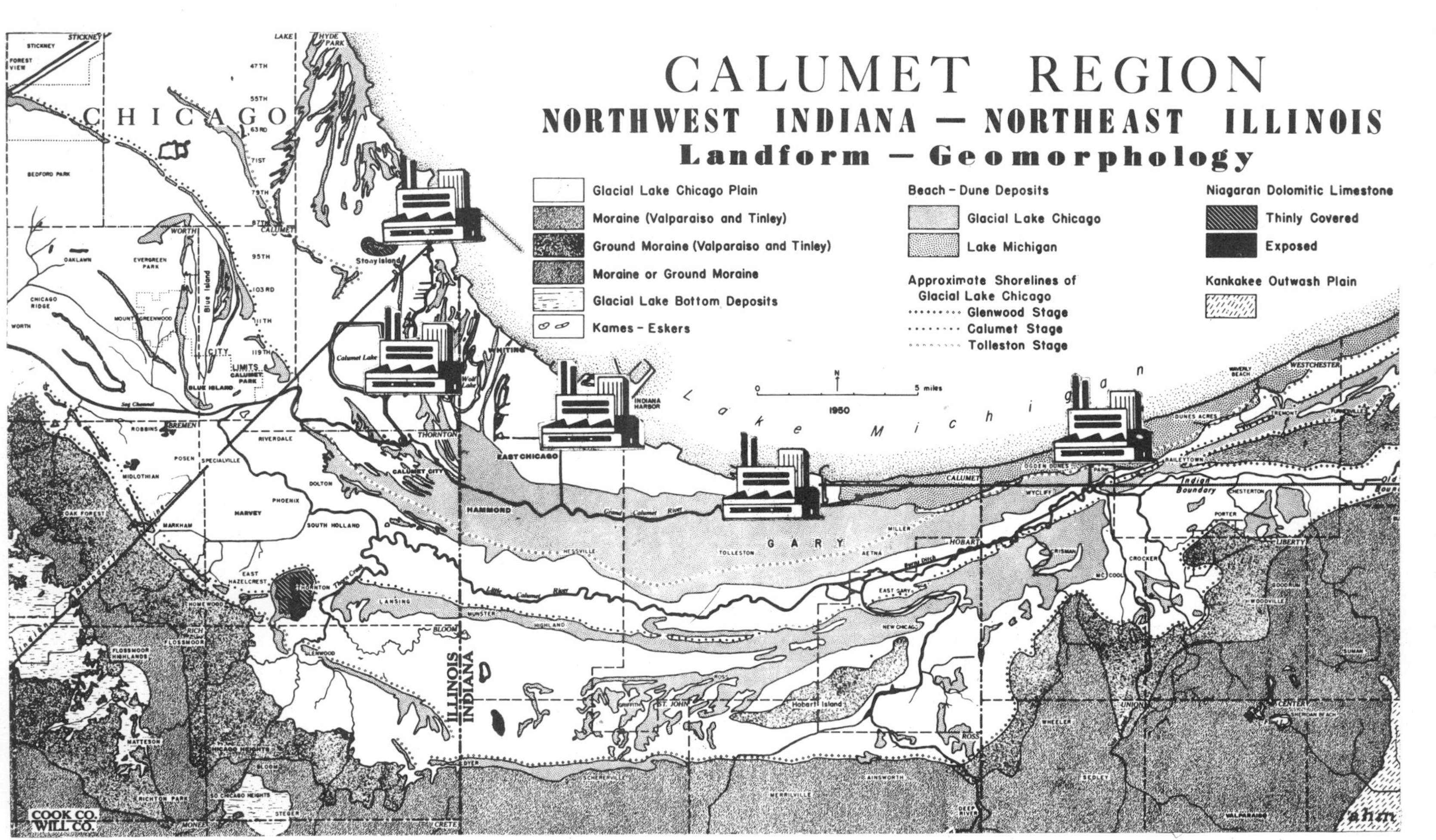

CALUMET REGION
NORTHWEST INDIANA — NORTHEAST ILLINOIS
Landform — Geomorphology
Glacial Lake Chicago Plain
Moraine (Valparaiso and Tinley)
Ground Moraine (Valparaiso and Tinley)
Moraine or Ground Moraine
Glacial Lake Bottom Deposits
Kames - Eskers
Beach - Dune Deposits
Glacial Lake Chicago
Lake Michigan
Approximate Shorelines of Glacial Lake Chicago
Glenwood Stage
Calumet Stage
Tolleston Stage
Niagaran Dolomitic Limestone
Thinly Covered
Exposed
Kankakee Outwash Plain
5 miles
1950
Lake Michigan
CHICAGO
GARY
HAMMOND
EAST CHICAGO
INDIANA HARBOR
WHITING
HARVEY
ILLINOIS
INDIANA
COOK CO.
WILL CO.

into the industrially owned land, with special provision for terminal transfers.

The questionnaire revealed that only as few as 15 per cent of the industrialists were unaware of any specific factor or combination of factors instrumental in influencing management to locate in this region. The high percentage of location awareness apparently is closely linked to the fact that the community has not one, but three major organizations alerted to the significance of locative factors; namely, the Manufacturers Association, the Committee on Chicago Heights, and the City Planning Commission.

¶ Over half of the respondents indicate regionality to be a leading factor in industrial location. In terms of general regional considerations we note the following observations: centrally located; centrally located to the best industrial cities of the areas; near the railroad lines and the railroad center of the U. S. A.; proximity to Chicago; close to Chicago and east Chicago; near southside plants; steel mills nearby; near residential area. . . . Transportation . . . is the leading single reported locative consideration, about forty per cent of the respondents noting this factor. . . . Quantity and quality of site for the placement of buildings constitutes a leading category in locational consideration, almost identical in rank with transportation. . . . Approximately thirty-eight per cent gave focal emphasis to this environmental factor.[1]

The North American manufactural hierarchy

By continuing the same process of studying one manufacturing community after another, we ultimately determine the unifying factors which establish regional identity, as in this case of the industrial pattern of the Calumet region. The communities of other areas whose geographic factors have their own distinctive regional focus should likewise be studied until the various industrial areas have been covered. From the local regional level we may move to the next higher level of the manufactural hierarchy, which we might call the province, consisting of two or more regions; next we consider the areal associations of the several manufactural provinces which compose the main manufacturing belt of North America.

In Figure XXIX-6 we have a representation of the subdivisions that comprise the "belt." Space permits reference here to only several of the most relevant to our realm, designated by Dr. Dicken as the Chicago-Milwaukee Subregion (11); the Southeastern Michigan Subregion (9); and the Pittsburgh-Cleveland Subregion (8):

¶ The Chicago-Milwaukee Subregion—Along the southern shores of Lake Michigan, in Wisconsin, Illinois, Indiana, and Michigan, and in the immediate hinterland of Chicago is a zone of intensive manufacturing. By means of the lake ready access to iron ore, coal, and limestone for the steel mills at Gary (Indiana) and vicinity is available. This subregion is the one place in the United States where steel is produced where none of the bulky raw materials are found within the subregion. The various industries in the district, however, provide a large market for steel, and the excellent water and rail transportation is favorable to the movement of the raw materials as well as of the finished product. Many excellent sites for factories are available along the lake plain. . . .

The Southeastern Michigan Subregion—To most of the people of North America the most familiar manufacturing district is in southeastern Michigan and parts of Ohio and Indiana, the Automobile Subregion. . . . The location of the industry, an accident of invention, is nevertheless justified by the good transportation of the Great Lakes and the many railroads, by nearness to the Pittsburgh-Cleveland steel producing subregion, and by easy access to a profitable market.

Once the early inventors, such as Ford, Haynes, and Olds, had decided to locate here, and the

[1] Meyer, Alfred H., and Miller, Paul F., "Manufactural Geography of Chicago Heights," *Proceedings of the Indiana Academy of Science,* Vol. LXVI, 1957, pp. 217-218. Reprinted by permission.

XXIX:4 (Left) The Chicago district leads the nation in steel ingot capacity, and Gary, Indiana, leads the district. A new steel plant has been constructed at Burns Ditch, near Odgen Dunes, by Midwest Steel Corporation (a subsidiary of National), and another plant is contemplated by Bethlehem Steel Corporation on an adjacent site. The state of Indiana is now promoting a public deep-water harbor project at the Burns Ditch site.

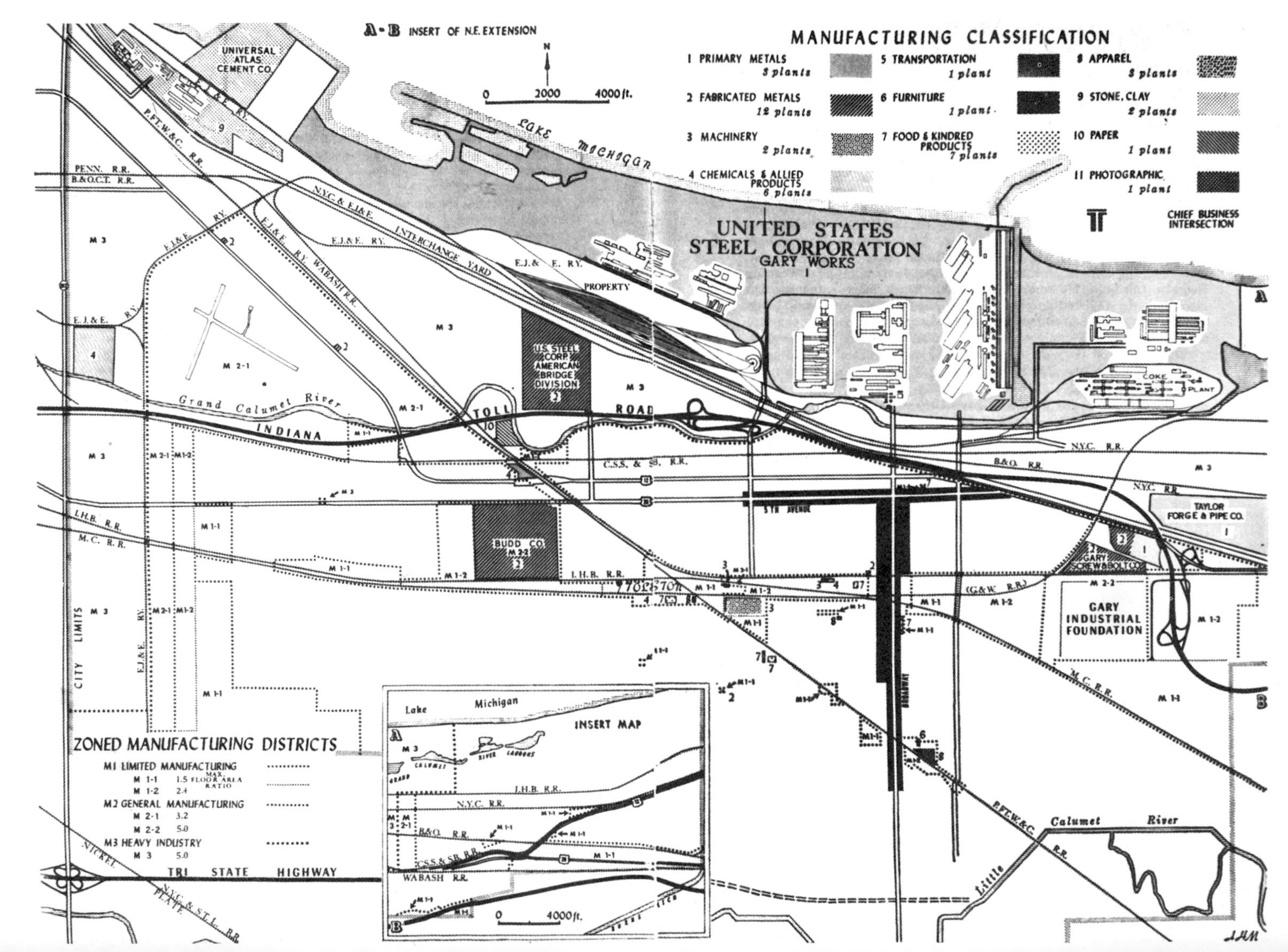

A-B INSERT OF N.E. EXTENSION
N
0 2000 4000 ft.
MANUFACTURING CLASSIFICATION
1 PRIMARY METALS 3 plants
2 FABRICATED METALS 12 plants
3 MACHINERY 2 plants
4 CHEMICALS & ALLIED PRODUCTS 6 plants
5 TRANSPORTATION 1 plant
6 FURNITURE 1 plant
7 FOOD & KINDRED PRODUCTS 7 plants
8 APPAREL 3 plants
9 STONE, CLAY 2 plants
10 PAPER 1 plant
11 PHOTOGRAPHIC 1 plant
CHIEF BUSINESS INTERSECTION
UNIVERSAL ATLAS CEMENT CO.
LAKE MICHIGAN
UNITED STATES STEEL CORPORATION GARY WORKS
COKE PLANT
PROPERTY
INTERCHANGE YARD
U.S. STEEL CORP. AMERICAN BRIDGE DIVISION
BUDD CO.
TAYLOR FORGE & PIPE CO.
GARY SCREW & BOLT CO.
GARY INDUSTRIAL FOUNDATION
INDIANA TOLL ROAD
Grand Calumet River
Little Calumet River
5TH AVENUE
BROADWAY
PENN. R.R.
B.&O.C.T. R.R.
P.F.T.W.&C. R.R.
N.Y.C. & E.J.&E.
E.J.&E. RY.
WABASH R.R.
N.Y.C. R.R.
B.&O. R.R.
C.S.S. & S.B. R.R.
I.H.B. R.R.
M.C. R.R.
G.&W. R.R.
CITY LIMITS
ZONED MANUFACTURING DISTRICTS
M1 LIMITED MANUFACTURING
M 1-1 1.5 MAX. FLOOR AREA RATIO
M 1-2 2.4
M2 GENERAL MANUFACTURING
M 2-1 3.2
M 2-2 5.0
M3 HEAVY INDUSTRY
M 3 5.0
TRI STATE HIGHWAY
NICKEL PLATE
N.Y.C. & ST.L. R.R.
INSERT MAP
Lake Michigan
CALUMET
RIVER LAGOONS
0 4000 ft.

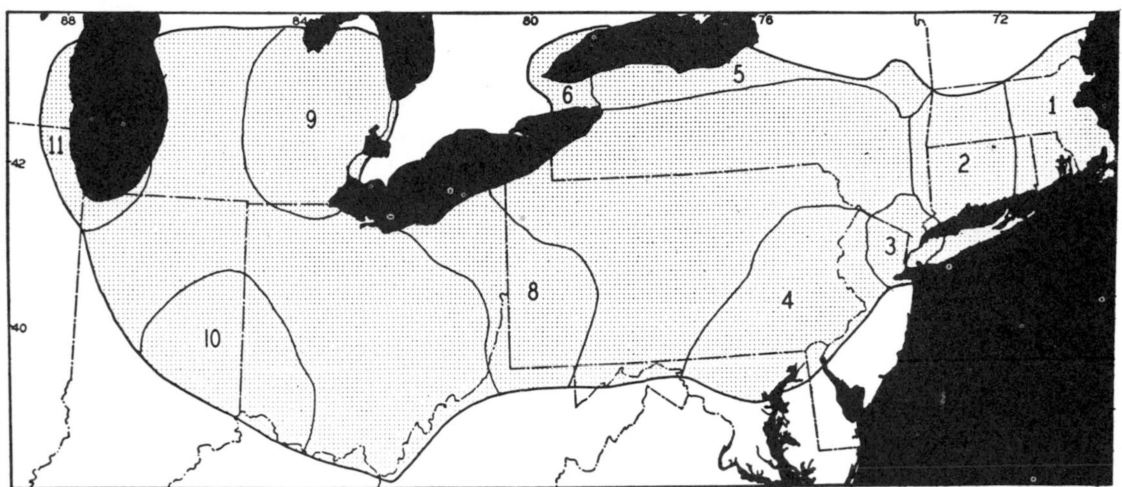

XXIX:6 Here is shown the chief manufacturing belt of North America, and its subdivisions: (1) Eastern New England, (2) Southwestern New England, (3) New York Metropolitan Area, (4) Southeastern Pennsylvania, (5) Albany-Buffalo, (6) Southern Ontario, (7) Montreal-Ottawa (not shown), (8) Pittsburgh-Cleveland, (9) Southwestern Michigan, (10) Inland Ohio-Indiana, (11) Chicago-Milwaukee. (Modified from map by Richard Hartshorne by Samuel N. Dicken, in *Economic Geography*, D. C. Heath & Company, 1955, used by permission)

industry became well established, it was difficult if not impossible to produce automobiles on a competitive basis at any great distance from Detroit. . . . In the early days of the industry, a half century ago, Detroit and vicinity possessed certain advantages because of industries already established. The vehicle industry was turning out buggies, carriages, and wagons of many kinds. On the shores of Lake St. Clair there were small factories producing motor boats. It required no great stretch of the imagination for someone to adapt the boat motor for use on a land vehicle, the buggy.

The Pittsburgh-Cleveland Subregion—The Pittsburgh-Cleveland Subregion is the most vital part of the Manufacturing Belt of North America. Because of the central location and the diversity of the basic industries of this subregion, partially fabricated materials are transported from it to all the other subregions. It is dominant as a metallurgical center, but there are also chemicals, glass, ceramic, rubber, paint, machine tool, and electrical industries. The major resource of this subregion [is] coal. . . . Water transportation on the Great Lakes is of great significance as are also the many railroads crossing the subregion in every direction.

The basic industry is iron and steel. Of the three raw materials needed in large quantities for iron and steel manufacture, two, coking coal and limestone, are found in the Pittsburgh-Cleveland Subregion. The third, iron ore, can be cheaply transported from the Upper Lakes Region.[1]

XXIX:5 (Left) This close-up view of Gary, Indiana, shows what a steel-fabricating community looks like. Planning and zoning (note inserted legend of classified manufacturing districts) help ensure orderly development with some measure of industrial diversification. (Planning-zoning data adapted from maps by Evert Kincaid and Associates, Chicago, consultants for the city of Gary Planning Commission, used by their permission and that of the Gary Planning Commission)

The manufacturing belt belongs to the world. As pointed out previously, major manufacturing communities, such as Gary and Chicago Heights, depend upon interregional raw materials and markets. And the various manufacturing provinces are complexly in-

[1] Dicken, Samuel Newton, *Economic Geography*, D. C. Heath and Company, Boston, 1955, p. 460. Reprinted by permission.

terrelated one to another as well as to the manufacturing belt as a whole. The ultimate significance of this belt cannot be fully understood, then, without comparing it with other leading manufactural regions — of our country, of North America, and of the world. As Dicken so well has said, "The region occupies a comparatively small area of North America but from the standpoint of raw material uses, as well as markets, it belongs to the world."

The kingdom of corn

The previous examples of community studies of manufactural geography illustrate how important human vision and leadership can be in determining the destiny of area development. Without considering, then, the historic facts of the founding of Gary and Chicago Heights by Judge Gary and Mr. Wacker, respectively, and of associated promotional agencies in the area, our understanding would be imperfect. Moreover, the consideration of the complex forces of the manufacturing belt cannot be complete without reference to the integration into the area of the skilled artisans, semiskilled workers, and mass labor immigrants, mostly from European nations, particularly the British Isles, Central Europe, and Scandinavia. Geographers continually ask themselves why people individually and collectively are attracted more to some areas than to others; and so here, too, we learn that this most extraordinary economic development, parallelling that of western Europe, is not merely the result of human inventiveness and industry. The European immigrants and others, as well as the American colonials, were attracted here obviously by what they thought was an environment superior to that which they were ready to leave behind. As often happens in such cases, comparative evaluation may not always be intelligently arrived at. Nevertheless, to start with, here was a climatic situation not too radically different from what they were accustomed to. Except for the more severe winters and the somewhat warmer summers, there was significant comparability (Compare graphs for Chicago and Hamburg in Figure XXIX-3). Originally establishing themselves in large numbers on the Atlantic seaboard, many of the early immigrants, and subsequently the descendents of these, decided to strike out for the interior to pioneer homesteads on highly fertile land, obtainable often at less than two dollars an acre from the federal government, to which the land had been ceded by the Indians. But such frontier farm occupance early beckoned the artisan or craftsman to settle first in the countryside and there establish small service shops directly related to the farm clientele; and, as we have seen in connection with the discussion of the previous realm, the frontier of forest, water, and farm products resulted in progressively greater concentration of mills and factories, and commercial development based upon them. Nature had set the main lines of least resistance to migration—in the South through the Cumberland Gap and then by flatboat down the Ohio and its tributaries northward; in the North, up the Hudson and through the Erie Canal into the Great Lakes area; and from the Maritime Canadian Regions, via the St. Lawrence River. Once the Appalachian "barrier" had been negotiated, stagecoach traffic found its way into the interior and was largely facilitated by the gently rolling forest lands of the eastern and the flat prairie lands of the western section of this region. Though the first railroad was built in Maryland (1830), it soon became obvious that the chief railway net of this country was destined to link the metropolises of New York and Boston to the early lake-port sites—Buffalo, Cleveland, Detroit, and Chicago. Moreover, this region has come to be the most populous in North America, and ranks with the world's most densely populated areas. What is even more significant is that its people, whether farm or factory workers, generally enjoy standards of income and living second to none in the world.

How is all this to be explained? However enterprising a farmer or industrialist may be, material success in this highly competitive world calls for wise selection of sites and resources for remunerative operation. And in this connection particularly, it is significant to point out the regional linkage between manufactural and commercial preeminence and the resource base. Important as are the considerations of such factors as capital and labor in the manufacturing-commercial enterprise, factories must have raw

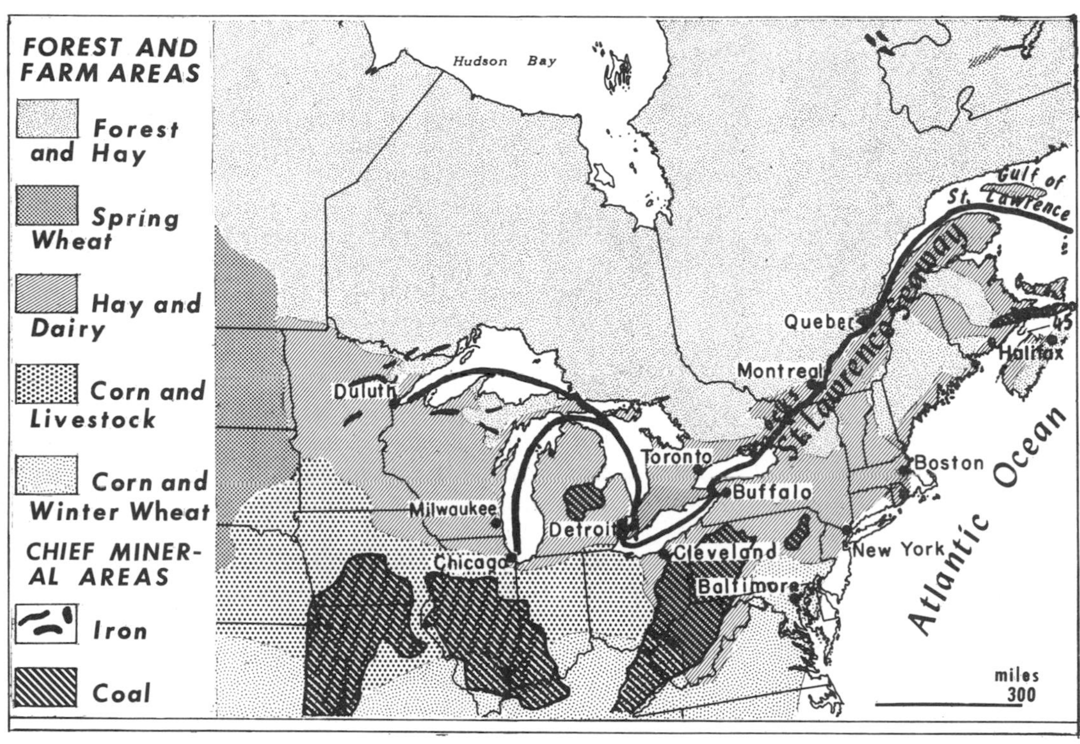

XXIX:7 The position of midwest resources is an index to regional greatness.

materials to process goods, and workers must have food. The composite regional resources supporting both of these are obviously too complex to present here in either textual or cartographic form. About all we can do in this brief context is to note the broad subregional distribution of our most basic resources, as suggestively indicated in Figure XXIX-7. Here you will note the Great Lakes steel manufacturing sites oriented to the iron ore fields of western Lake Superior, the steam coal fields of Indiana, Illinois, and Missouri; the coking coal areas of the upper Ohio River; and the anthracite of Pennsylvania. Many of the manufactures likewise are directly related to agricultural production of a large list of products based on grain and livestock, as well as fruits and vegetables. Peripheral, but directly contributory to the manufacturing of the area, are the farm products from the winter wheat belt to the south and the spring wheat belt to the west. Partly inclusive within the manufacturing belt itself are the hay and dairy belt in the northern and eastern parts, and the corn and livestock belt in the southwesterly section. It is this last-named region, whose pre-eminence in agriculture parallels the leadership of the manufacturing belt in American enterprise, that has brought to this area regional leadership in combined agriculture and manufacturing second to none in the world. Let us, then, take a more detailed look at what Haystead and Fite have designated "The corn-soy belt; feedbag of Democracy":

¶ It is no chauvinism, no misplaced chamber of commerce boasting, no exaggeration to call this area the richest farm on earth. Other, smaller areas have a higher gross production and income per acre. Others show greater unit tonnage. Others produce greater variety. But in no place in the world is the production of food per man hour so high. Nor can any place else make the impact on world agricultural-political economy that this region does. Probably no other combination of areas could so nearly implement a Marshall Plan, even with the aid of the United States Treasury, as this vast triangle. It is hog and cattle rich. Iowa generally ranks from first to third among the states in total farm income. In both 1950 and 1951, when cash receipts from farm marketings were $2,120,266,000 and $2,360,995,000, it fell behind only California. Illinois usually ranks fourth in farm income.

Although all forty-eight states and the offshore territories made their valued contributions to World War II, it was the Corn-Soy Belt that proved to be the real backbone of food defense. Without it, we would surely have had a more difficult time gaining victory. It was not merely food for soldiers, for allies, but most important, a powerful diet high in human TDN (total digestible nutrients), strong in animal proteins, for our industrial workers that gave us a sure edge over our enemies. . . .

The Ukraine rightly deserves admiration, but it is limited in the number and quality of its crops. It has inconvenient climatic restrictions. Its best use is for wheat—a crop that cannot compare to corn in optimum land use. Denmark and the Lowlands can and do produce more per acre, both in crop tonnage and in number of livestock, but at a huge cost in human labor. Moreover, they are dependent on the importation of feeds. By themselves they are not self-sufficient. Australia's very small eastern coastal strip of arable lands is not comparable. Argentina, great though its possible output of grains may be, again does not have comparable virtues. In 1950, Iowa alone produced over five times as much corn as Argentina, 579,000,000 bushels to 103,000,000, although Iowa's acreage was only about twice as large.[1]

The corn regime in American history

To understand the historic economic importance of such an area as the Corn Belt, one must know the properties of corn itself and the geographic principles underlying its culture. Corn (*Zea mays*) is one of the most diversified and widely distributed cereals in this world. Of the thousands of varieties extant, some half-dozen are of world regional prominence. Essentially only three are important in America: dent corn, primarily feed for livestock; and sweet corn and popcorn, for human consumption. It is the predominantly American dent corn (*Zea mays indentata*), basic feeding grain for hogs and cattle, that we shall here be particularly concerned about.

Numerous factors, both environmental and economic, contribute to the present-day world pre-eminence of corn, a gift of the New World to the Old: 1. Corn is the most prolific of all grains. Though commercial production of corn areally reflects rather sensitively the more favorable factors of production in terms of climate, soils, and relief, the corn plant exhibits considerable versatility and tolerance of environmental factors, its geographical range extending from the Equator to 50° latitude. 2. It is readily fed to animals as ear corn, or ground corn, as silage for winter feeding, as fodder, or animal-harvested directly in the field. 3. Scores of food products are derived from corn, and even the corncob and the cornstalk are the source of many industrial products. 4. Corn, a carbohydrate, with some oil, is a grain that can be shipped readily and stores well.

Limits and optima. Though spreading out from its original tropical South American highland habitat to practically every habitable realm of the world, corn does have climatic limits; as a matter of fact, corn is more restricted in its poleward limits than are the other basic grains, such as wheat, oats, barley, and rye. And corn yields decline rapidly with moisture deficiency; precipitation is much more critical for corn than for the other grains.

Because of the importance of corn for qualities already indicated, its culture has probably involved more agricultural experimentation in determining the optimal criteria favoring highest productivity than has that of perhaps any other grain. Length of the growing season is particularly significant.

¶ The optimum length of the growing season is from 150 to 180 days, and summer temperatures should average about 75° F. (23.9° C.), with warm nights—average night temperatures over 58° F. (14.4° C.). Rainfall should be fairly abundant, from 18 to 24 inches (about 460 to 600 mm.) during the growing period, and during the summer months it should be of the thundershower type, with periods of clear, warm weather in between.[2]

---

[1] Haystead, Ladd, and Fite, Gilbert C., *The Agricultural Regions of the United States*, University of Oklahoma Press, 1955, pp. 140-143, *passim*. Reprinted by permission.

[2] William Van Royen, *Atlas of the World's Resources: Agricultural Resources of the World*, © 1954, Prentice-Hall, Inc., Englewood Cliffs, N.J., p. 56.

This is a corn–oats field culture on the periphery of a town in Iowa. Normally, crops assume a rectangular pattern. Why this deviation of strip cropping? (Photo, U. S. Department of Agriculture)

Soils and drainage also are important factors for optimal yields. A broad areal coincidence is recognizable between highest areal productivity of corn and the humid grayish-brown podsolic and prairie soils, particularly the latter, with normally good tilth and drainage. Commercialized corn culture also seemingly does best when integrated with other grain cultures and livestock rearing in a system of rotation farming, so well exemplified again in the Corn Belt.

Hybridization promotes quality, yields, acreage. In probably no other area of plant breeding has the science of genetics yielded such far-reaching results in expanding the commercial opportunities of agriculture, as in corn culture. If the student has traveled through the midwestern countryside, he must have noted the innumerable road signs advertising the various hybrid corn seeds, particularly in Ohio, Indiana, Illinois, and Iowa. As pointed out by Henry A. Wallace, former Secretary of Agriculture and in his own right a theoretical and practical breeder of hybrid corn:

¶ Ninety-nine per cent of the corn of the Cornbelt is the product of hybrid seed. Because of hybrid corn it is now possible to produce, on eighty-five million acres, more corn than could be produced on one hundred and ten million acres in the old days. The net gain is fully one half billion bushels annually.[1]

In this article, Wallace presents a most interesting account of what we might call

[1] Wallace, H. A., "Corn and the Midwestern Farmer," *Landscape*, Spring 1957, Vol. VI, No. 3, p. 12. Reprinted by permission.

the historical geography of the Midwest as based primarily on the evolvement of "Reid Yellow Dent" and other hybrid varieties from the original Indian corn found growing here at the close of the American Revolution:

¶ The drama opens in 1783 with one hundred thousand Indians in the Midwest growing less than three hundred thousand bushels on less than fifteen thousand acres of land. Nearly all of this corn of the pre-white era had eight or ten rows of shallow, hard kernels. Indians preferred to grow this kind of corn, first because it was early and, second because they thought it had a superior flavor, especially when parched.

The scene suddenly shifted when white men from Virginia and the Carolinas came over the mountains bringing with them, to Tennessee, Kentucky, and southern Ohio, the corn which they had grown back home — corn with fourteen to thirty rows of deep, soft kernels. . . . For the first thirty or forty years after the American revolution, Virginia and North Carolina were the two top corn states; and then gradually Tennessee and Kentucky replaced them and remained the two top corn states until about 1845. . . .

The white man had accomplished miracles in the Midwest during the sixty years prior to 1840 but they paled into insignificance when compared with the sixty years from 1840 to 1900. During this extraordinary period the population of the thirteen Midwest states increased by five times, corn production by ten times, hog numbers by four times, and railroads jumped from two hundred and thirty miles to eighty-eight thousand miles. . . . By 1900 the main outlines of the Cornbelt had been defined. Just one great change remained to be made. The relatively moist weather of the eighties and nineties attracted too large an acreage of corn into Kansas. With the drier weather of the first half of the XX Century, Kansas, which had been in third place in 1899, dropped to eleventh place. . . . The hot, dry weather which forced much of Kansas out of corn favored Minnesota. Moreover, Minnesota was the last frontier of the Cornbelt and profited by the sudden introduction of early types of hybrid corn and new types of machinery adapted to the large farms of southwestern Minnesota.[1]

Mr. Wallace then proceeds to point to numerous agencies, including the Department of Agriculture and state experimentation stations, which may spend as much as a million dollars annually to effect a billion dollar increase in corn productivity. How important this corn culture can be in the total geographic appraisal of the past and future development of the area is indicated in Mr. Wallace's concluding remarks:

¶ In summary let me make it clear that the Cornbelt is a complex—first, of a unique soil and climate; second, of good transportation; third, of well-adapted machinery and fertilizer; fourth, of corn scientifically crossed for specific purposes; fifth, of an ever improving type of livestock to turn the corn into high quality human food; and sixth and most important of all, men and women from Scandinavia, Germany, Ireland, England, Scotland, Holland, and all the rest of western Europe together with the old-fashioned Americans from the eastern seaboard. These men of varied backgrounds utilized the soil, transportation, fertilizer, machinery, and high-powered corn to build, in terms of output per man hour, the most productive agricultural civilization the world has ever seen. An efficient Iowa farmer can, with the help of one man, grow the corn to produce enough meat and livestock products to feed three or four hundred people in town. Abundant, high quality animal protein is the basis of the energetic, vital living which is the outstanding characteristic of the people of the United States. Therefore, we may say that for the foreseeable future the prosperity of the city people of the United States and the Midwestern farmer will rise and fall together.[2]

Principles. Several important geographic principles emerge from this brief account of the history of corn: (1) Nature sets its own original pattern of geographic distribution of plants. The original low latitude Indian corn (maize) no doubt found its earliest habitat where it was most hospitable, or at least, favorable. In the course of natural hybridization, corn acclimatized itself in time to new environs—with or without the assistance of the Indian. Upon its discovery by white man as a premier food staple, cross-fertilization followed, rapidly accelerating both the quality and quantity characteristics so as now to give us virtually not hundreds but thousands of varieties. (2) Corn breed-

[1] *Ibid.*, pp. 9-12, *passim.* Reprinted by permission.

[2] *Ibid.*, p. 12. Reprinted by permission.

ing on strictly modern scientific genetic principles has not only extended materially the corn limits into areas with cooler and shorter summers and increasingly minimum rainfall areas, but also has led to the discovery that many cultivated plants, particularly corn, seem to thrive best (when seasons are at all favorable) close to their "poleward limits." Thus, today the optimal climatic conditions of corn culture are in the latitudes of the southern Great Lakes area, only about 200 miles from the northern corn frontier, where corn can be successfully and dependably grown only on a green silage and dry fodder basis. It appears that here, too, there is some broad climatological correlation between the changeable seasonal and diurnal climatological pattern and high yields. At least, it is certain that the hybrid corns now developed in the Corn Belt do best where the winters are severe enough to kill off many of the insect pests that otherwise plague the corn belt in the tropics and subtropics, while at the same time, corn growing is promoted by the relatively long and warm humid summers typical of the *Dfa*. Not only are the seasons optimal, but a highly changeable weather regimen of "sunshine and shower," as found here in the cyclonic belt, is optimal as well.

The cyclonic belt and its cultural implications

A proper conception of the mid-latitude *cyclone* and its counterpart, the *anticyclone*, is essential to the understanding of alternating sunshine and showers, and variable temperatures of the weather pattern so characteristic of the populous and prosperous corn and manufacturing belt. Indeed, since the paths of cyclones and anticyclones converge upon northeastern United States, this has also become known, then, as the cyclonic belt. The mid-latitude cyclone is a barometric depression (rising air) commonly designated a *Low*, of some 1,000 miles in diameter, generally advancing eastward at some twenty miles per hour.[1] The anticyclone registers high pressure (descending air), designated on weather maps as a *High*. The behavior of cyclonic storms is, of course, an intrinsic part of every daily newspaper and television weather forecast. But the mere recital or the plotting on the map of pressure, temperature, humidity, and precipitation data for different sections of the country usually leaves us without meaningful concepts—spatially and meteorologically—as to what shapes our weather, and what this really signifies in relation to man's well-being. Just what does it mean, for example, when a forecaster posts on the screen a figure of atmospheric sea level pressure? Who cares? So, if there is a Low moving in from the southwest of us, or a High approaching us from the northwest, what has all this got to do with the life of "Zea mays" or our own behavior? Like the television weather forecaster who cites a few facts and figures that augur tomorrow's weather, as he moves his Low and High symbols from west to east (the way weather-making phenomena generally travel), we can here only briefly present a bare outline of how weather is made, and what it means.[2]

Weather analysis starts with the collection of pressure and many other data at both low and high altitudes for as wide a region as it is possible to get. With such data at hand, the weatherman attempts to construct the positions of Lows and Highs, and to determine the direction of movement and speed of travel. Air naturally moves from high to low pressure areas; consequently, winds move into the center of a Low, and due to rotation of the earth will normally move inward counterclockwise in the Northern Hemisphere (in the Southern Hemisphere, clockwise), subject to deflections due to various earth surface phenomena. In a High, air currents will follow a generalized clockwise pattern in the Northern Hemisphere (counterclockwise in the Southern Hemisphere). In a High, air descends; in a Low, ascends. Since air gets warmer in descending into a denser atmospheric level, the increasing higher temperature results in greater capacity for air to hold moisture, resulting, therefore, more or less in clear weather. On the other hand,

[1] The cyclonic "storm" of the mid-latitudes is not to be confused with the destructive high-wind velocity of the *tornado* twister (also a depression center, but with a steep barometric gradient); nor with the violent tropical *hurricanes* of the West Indies and the *typhoons* of the East Indies.

[2] Numerous publications on meteorology and climatology, as well as government bulletins, are available. A very inexpensive bulletin may be secured from the Superintendent of Documents, U. S. Government Printing Office, Washington, entitled "Weather Forecasting," 1952.

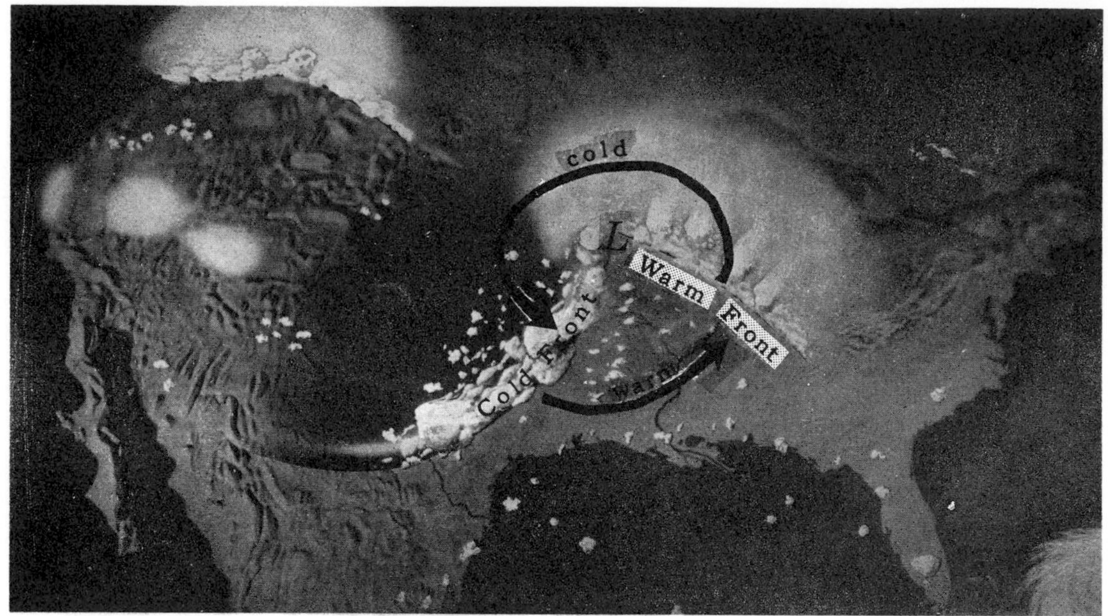

XXIX:8 Here is an astronaut's view of a *Low* or cyclonic storm, moving from west to east across the United States. You will recognize that it is such a weather-making and moving structure that preoccupies the forecaster as he outlines the weather drama on television. (An adaptation from Figure 1 in *Weather Forecasting*, Weather Bureau, U. S. Department of Commerce, 1952)

cloudiness and precipitation may be expected in a Low where air rises and becomes more rarified, the lower pressure resulting in cooling, and hence increasing relative humidity. If sufficient water vapor is present, clouds form and precipitation may be expected. Reference to Figure XXIX-8 and Figure XXIX-9 discloses the same basic meterological structural elements involved in rain making. You will observe in Figure XXIX-8 two well-marked lines, the *warm front* and *cold front,* identifying the discontinuous surface which separates the warm airmass moving in from the South from the cold airmass moving in from the North. Actually, the meeting of this tropical or subtropical airmass with the cold airmass from the polar regions is the basis for the Low. We normally think of two kinds of gases as becoming diffused upon contact, but it should be here noted that a fairly sharp discontinuity between the two airmasses actually exists on the two fronts. Now the principle of rain making is focused on the concept that when warm air carrying moisture is forced upward to higher altitudes for any reason at all—whether against another mass of air or against a mountain—precipitation results if there is sufficient water vapor present and chilling of the atmosphere to raise the relative humidity to the saturation level (*dew point*). Here you will notice on the warm front the warm air rides over the cold air with the resultant formation of *nimbus* clouds and possible rain. Similarly, rain is falling on the cold front to the west —the cold air pushing in and lifting the warm air.

Next principle: You will note in the center of the diagram and to the right an arrow graphically portraying the general direction of storm movement. This, as stated previously, in mid-latitudes is normally from west to east, or at least, from a westerly to an easterly component. Accordingly, in the general eastward flow of air the passing of the center of a Low to the north of us may normally bring two showers, first along the long warm slope, in more or less drizzling and fairly long continued rains; the latter in the form of more violent showers, locally restricted.

The entire airmass moves forward, but the cold front normally advances toward the

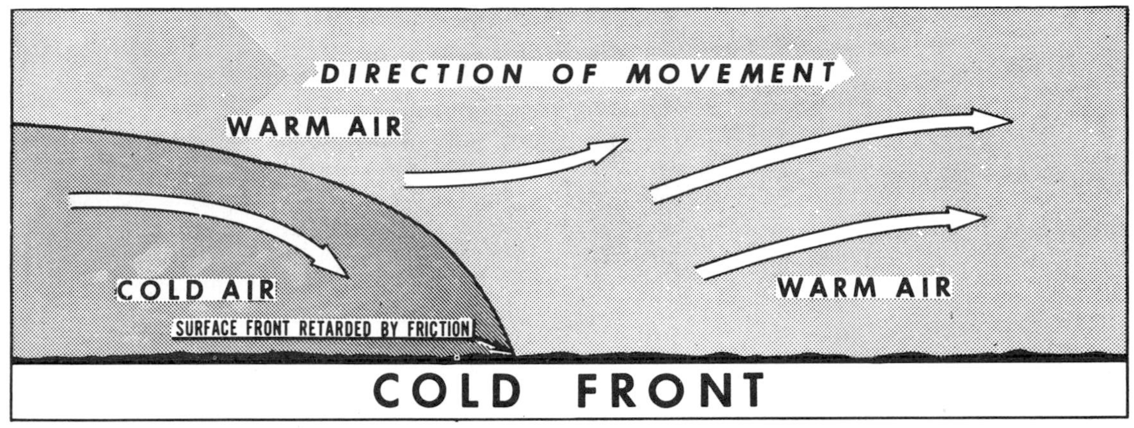

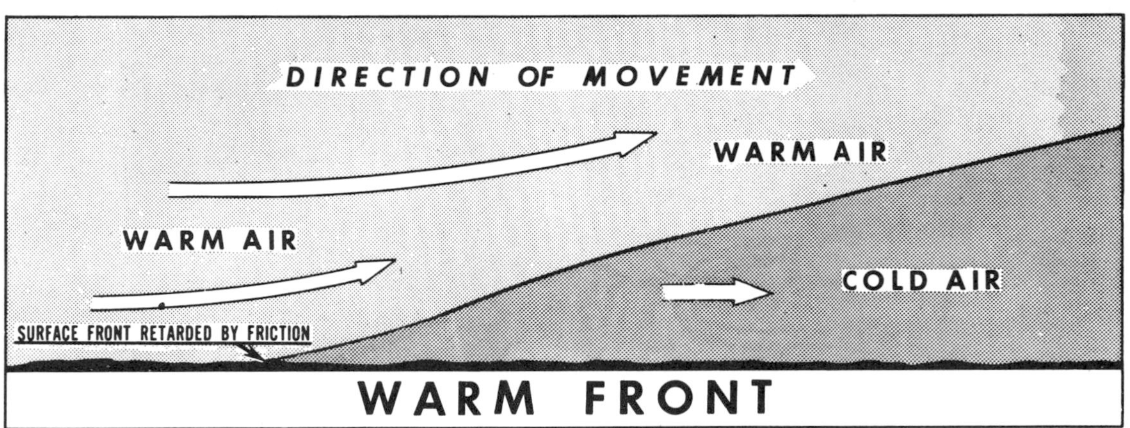

TRUE VERTICAL SCALE OF FRONT - 1 to 100

XXIX:9 This illustration shows a cross-section view (vertical dimensions exaggerated) of the fronts labeled in the previous figure. Note the differences in the slopes of the cold front and the warm front. On the cold front rainfall is apt to be more intense and localized as contrasted with the more gentle and general rains with the passing of the warm front. (Figure 76, from *Pilot's Weather Handbook*, Technical Manual No. 104, published by the Federal Aviation Agency, 1955)

warm front and eventually overtakes it, pushing the entire warm airmass into the upper atmosphere, again a rain conducing process, unless, of course, the absolute water vapor of the atmosphere has been reduced below the saturation point. The point of contact, where the cold front overtakes the warm front, is referred to as the point of occlusion. This generally forms at the center of the Low and progressively moves towards the periphery, presaging the close of the airmass drama.

Although possessing manifest earmarks of considerable oversimplification, the above sketch should at least convey some of the basic principles involved in temperature and moisture changes with the passing of Lows and Highs. This in turn should lead to a better appreciation of the use of such terms as *frontal weather* and *cyclonic belt* in referring to the daily, almost hourly, weather changes in this storm belt of the United

States. It should above all create an awareness of the meteorological basis of our resources—the seasonal and diurnal temperature changes to which in part has been attributed the stimulation reflected in the high energy creativeness and industry in the Western world; the rhythmical sunshine of the Highs and the showers of the Lows that assure food and feed for man and beast in an area epitomized as the "Breadbasket of the World."

America's "cornucopia" based on environmentally adapted crop-combinations

A systematic geography treatment of a single agricultural element, such as corn, has its place in focusing attention on the universal principle of ecological relationships of both natural and cultivated forms of plant life. But regardless of how much we know about the genetics and ecology of corn pedigrees and production, as applied here to discussion of the Corn Belt, such knowledge of itself is far from understanding the agricultural landscape of the Corn Belt, to say nothing about the inadequacy in perceiving the total rural-urban complex of the region. In fact, the very common use of the term "Corn Belt" has probably generated as many misconceptions as it has otherwise contributed constructive concepts of the region. Among such misconceptions are that corn itself occupies a larger percentage of acreage than all other crops put together, or that it is the primary crop, at least, in practically each county in the area. Both of these concepts are far from the facts. In many counties, and even in sizable subregions of multiple counties, other grain crops, or even forage crops, or pasture, may vie for first place of areal occupance. Accordingly, some other grain, such as wheat, oats, barley, or rye, may individually, or as several crops in combination, be of much greater importance than corn. In other instances, soybeans or cowpeas and other forage crops of the hay family may be the dominant crop. In still others, specialized crops, such as potatoes or other vegetables, sugar beets, or fruit or orchard products, may displace corn in whole or in part. In fact, such subregional diversity exists in various sections of the Corn Belt that some sections within it are more like sections outside, whereas other field cultures, as in the *Cfa*, may more nearly resemble those typifying the *Dfa*.

It is thus obvious that the geographer must know much more than corn ecology to understand the Corn Belt. In much the same way as we have briefly considered corn in its habitat relationships, we should consider every major crop in the area. Even so, complete encyclopedic knowledge of the growth habits of each of the major crops and a statistical map showing the relative acreage distribution would still fall far short of an intelligent appraisal of the agricultural virtues of the Corn Belt. We always need to remind ourselves in geography over and over again that proper resource evalutions and geographic processes that concern resource development involve consideration of total landscape phenomenology. This means the study of all farm products in their spatial setting. This is especially important in a region like the Corn Belt, where the extent of diversification and combination of crop and livestock culture may determine farm solvency.

What crops enter into combination with corn? What is the relative acreage percentage? Size of fields? Relation to terrain and soils? What are the systems of rotation and other management practices to maintain farm productivity? What is the farmstead pattern, and how is the rural settlement pattern related morphologically and economically to the urban communities of which the farming region is a part? These and many other questions need to be asked and answered as best we can if we want to understand the rural culture of any area. Total mapping is usually not required, but transects of sufficient frequency are basic in determining continuity and discontinuity of areal features and associations. Then, if we wish, we can calculate areal percentages of significant varying associations and sketch a *synoptic cartogram* which simulates a regularly scaled and oriented map representing a real synthesis (unified view) of regional reality. Such is the "map" in Figure XXIX-10. Crop soil and other associative phenomena are here based on a quantitative analysis of 32 transect surveys embracing approximately 25 per cent of one of the regions of the Corn Belt — the marsh-reclaimed Kankakee. You

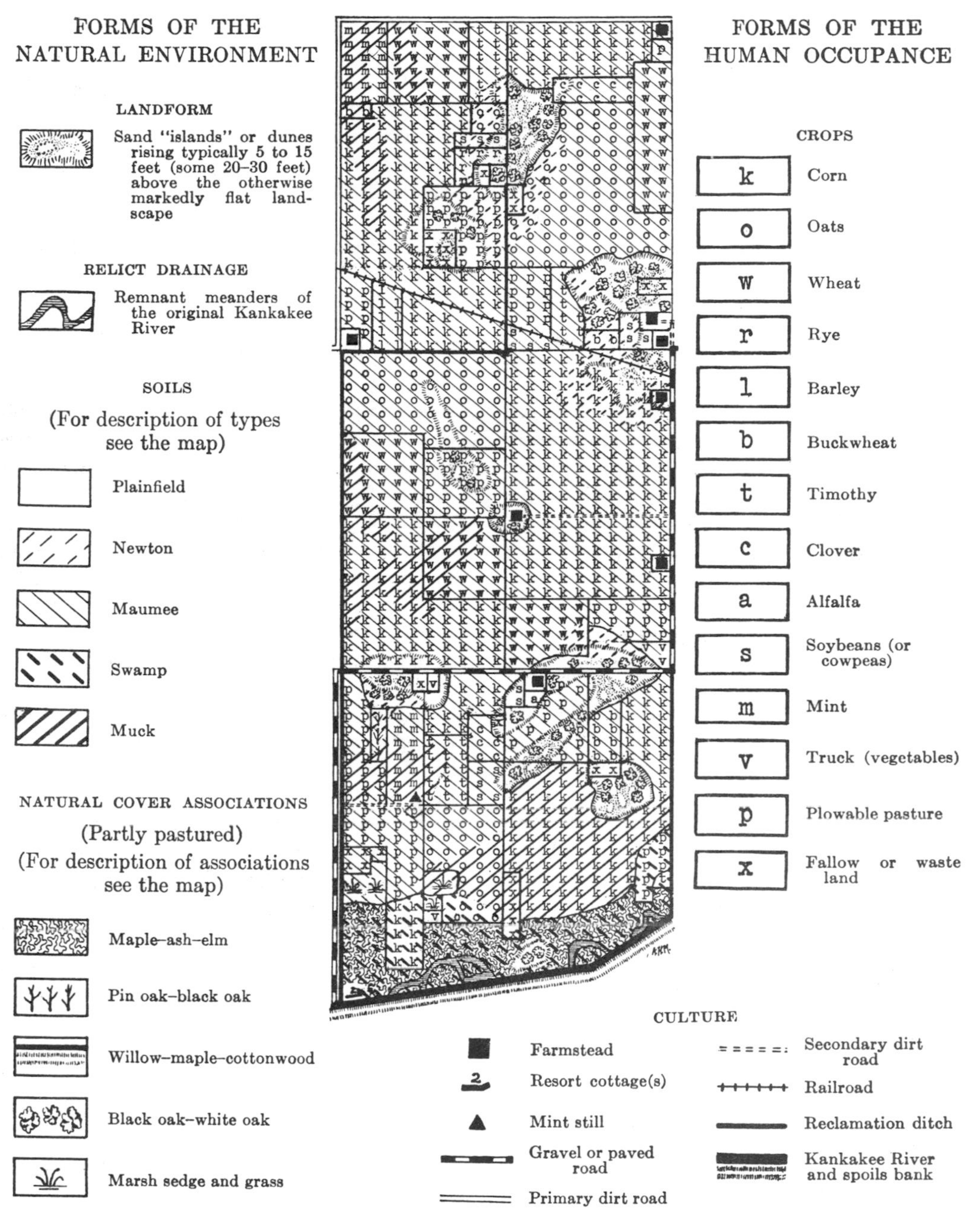

XXIX:10 This regional synthesis (Kankakee) is a statistical-spatial construct to portray proportionate area-soil-topographic associations with leading crop culture. What association characteristics seem to repeat themselves more than others? Give a possible explanation. (Published originally in the proceedings of the Michigan Academy of Science, Arts, and Letters, Vol. XXI, 1936. Copyright by University of Michigan. Re-used by permission)

will note a high percentage coincidence of soybeans, rye, and natural pasture on the Plainfield and Newton soils; corn, oats, and wheat on the Maumee silts; corn and mint on Muck soils; and pasture and corn on swampland, invading the progressively cleared timber swamp next to the river. Notice also the strong repeating associations of pasture, soybeans, and wood lots, together with the site of the typical farmstead itself on the elevated sandy and dunal "islands" which rise from 5 to 30 feet above the otherwise almost perfectly flat terrain throughout the area where mechanized tillage is adapted for large fields and farms. By inference, if not by direct expression, this original lake-bottom terrain also suggests the ready feasibility of crop rotation k - o - w, which happens, in this instance, to fall more or less in the grain pattern, in rotation with a hay, pasture, or a soybean crop.

Statistical approach to regionality

Area-association analysis, such as that of the Kankakee presented above, may give us a reasonably good picture of what the geographic processes consist of in a microgeographic study. But when we go to a larger unit area, such as the commonly defined Corn Belt, or to a still larger region, such as the Middle West, we are faced with more diversified crop combinations. Moreover, because of greater subregional diversities based on differences in climate, landforms, soils, ethnographic heritage, to say nothing of the complex variations in industrial and cultural patterns, we face a more complicated challenge. At this point, then, it may be well to bring out the fact that one of the more recent developments in geographic analysis is a statistical approach based on one or more mathematical formulae to achieve some integrated association evaluation of a region as a whole and of subregions within the larger region. One of the more classical and involved studies of this type, dealing directly with the Midwest (1,081 counties), is that by John C. Weaver.[1] In an article of some twenty-five pages, including a featured colored map of crop combinations, together with two dozen crop percentage distribution maps, Weaver seeks to explore the forces that make for geographic change in crop combination patterns in the Midwest. To state it in Weaver's own words:

¶ The primary goal of the research program in agricultural geography from which the present preliminary and partial progress report has evolved is a systematized and enlarged understanding of the dynamic forces that both initiate and give impetus to change in the patterns of cropland use. Since the attainment of this objective obviously calls for an introductory attempt to define the basic behavior of such change geographically, and since neither individual crop performance nor cropland-use patterns as a whole can be adequately understood without the perspective afforded by some knowledge of existing crop combinations, an effort has been made to devise a workable method for the delineation of crop-combination regions.[2]

Using primary data from the Federal Census of Agriculture, Weaver proceeds to plot various agriculture values and to measure such values in terms of the various differences in crop combinations by means of a self-designed theoretical curve based on a derived deviation formula, expressed as follows: $\sigma\ 2 = \frac{\Sigma\ d^2}{n}$.[3] No attempt will here be made to present the rationale or the application of the formula as developed in this procedure. Suffice it here to report, some ten major crops and thirteen other specialty crops are symbolized, defined, and mapped, and the total evaluated by the process indicated. From this, various observations are derived, significant among which is the conclusion "that the traditionally established agricultural regions of this part of the world, which were probably oversimplified generalizations in the first place, are in need of complete re-evaluation and redefinition."[4]

[1] Dr. Weaver, formerly professor of geography at the University of Minnesota, is now Dean of the School of Arts and Sciences, Kansas State College. The researches were supported by a grant from the Geography Branch of the Office of Naval Research, a governmental agency which has been very active in supporting other geographic projects.

[2] Weaver, John C., "Crop-Combination Regions in the Middle West," *The Geographical Review,* Vol. XLIV, No. 2, April, 1954, p. 176. Reprinted by permission.

[3] "d" is the difference between actual crop percentage in a given county and the appropriate percentage in the theoretical curve, and "n" is the number of crops in a given combination."

[4] Weaver, *op. cit.,* p. 200.

This is an aerial view of Chicago's railroad yards and freight terminals west of the Chicago River. The Chicago Terminal District is the leading global traffic center. Besides featuring the world's busiest airport, the district is the world's largest rail center: thirty-seven railroads, twenty-two trunk line carriers, seven belt and switching railroads, eight industrial railroads, 3,000 to 35,000 freight cars handled daily (nearly one-fifteenth of all the nation's freight car loadings). (Photo, courtesy of the Department of City Planning, City of Chicago; statistics from *Planning the Region of Chicago* [1956], the Chicago Regional Planning Association, now merged into the Northeastern Illinois Metropolitan Area Planning Commission, used by permission)

"Areal functional organization" as a unifying interregional world principle

The ultimate essence of all geographic study is to see how the smaller unit of human occupance, say a farm or a factory, is progressively linked up in some significant geographic pattern with its focal trading center; this in turn to a cluster of focal points; this in turn to a "cluster of clusters" of focal places; this in turn to a major urban or metropolitan region; and this ultimately linked to a regional–world space basis. By classifying each farming and industrial community in such a progressive hierarchy of classified parallel space relationships, we pass through the various orders of integrated functional activities. The study of diverse homogeneous regions may thus be brought together largely by the analysis of movement (transportation) focused on commercial centers of various orders of magnitude. Such a study is that of Allen K. Philbrick, who recognizes seven orders of "areal functional organization" in the United States, the fifth or higher order centers being concentrated in the com-

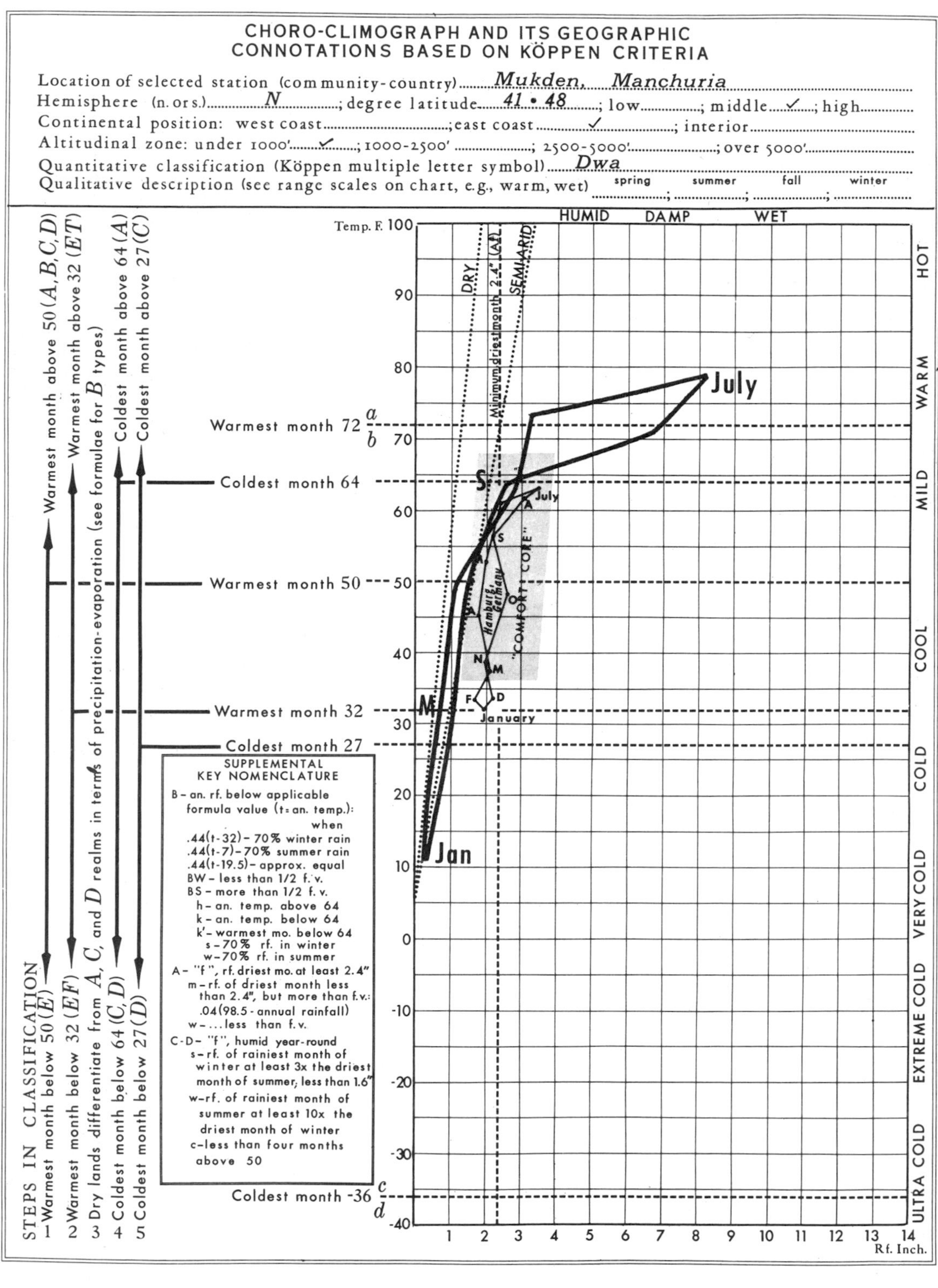

CHORO-CLIMOGRAPH AND ITS GEOGRAPHIC CONNOTATIONS BASED ON KÖPPEN CRITERIA
Location of selected station (community-country) Mukden, Manchuria
Hemisphere (n. or s.) N; degree latitude 41 • 48; low; middle ✓; high
Continental position: west coast; east coast ✓; interior
Altitudinal zone: under 1000' ✓; 1000-2500'; 2500-5000'; over 5000'
Quantitative classification (Köppen multiple letter symbol) Dwa
Qualitative description (see range scales on chart, e.g., warm, wet) spring; summer; fall; winter
STEPS IN CLASSIFICATION
1 Warmest month below 50 (E) — Warmest month above 50 (A, B, C, D)
2 Warmest month below 32 (EF) — Warmest month above 32 (ET)
3 Dry lands differentiate from A, C, and D realms in terms of precipitation-evaporation (see formulae for B types)
4 Coldest month below 64 (C, D) — Coldest month above 64 (A)
5 Coldest month below 27 (D) — Coldest month above 27 (C)
Warmest month 72 a b
Coldest month 64
Warmest month 50
Warmest month 32
Coldest month 27
Coldest month -36 c d
Temp. F.
HUMID
DAMP
WET
DRY
Minimum driest month 2.4" (Af)
SEMIARID
"COMFORT CORE"
Hamburg, Germany
July
Jan
January
HOT
WARM
MILD
COOL
COLD
VERY COLD
EXTREME COLD
ULTRA COLD
Rf. Inch.
SUPPLEMENTAL KEY NOMENCLATURE
B - an. rf. below applicable formula value (t = an. temp.): when
.44(t-32) - 70% winter rain
.44(t-7) - 70% summer rain
.44(t-19.5) - approx. equal
BW - less than 1/2 f. v.
BS - more than 1/2 f. v.
h - an. temp. above 64
k - an. temp. below 64
k' - warmest mo. below 64
s - 70% rf. in winter
w - 70% rf. in summer
A - "f", rf. driest mo. at least 2.4"
m - rf. of driest month less than 2.4", but more than f.v.: .04(98.5 - annual rainfall)
w - ... less than f. v.
C-D - "f", humid year-round
s - rf. of rainiest month of winter at least 3x the driest month of summer; less than 1.6"
w - rf. of rainiest month of summer at least 10x the driest month of winter
c - less than four months above 50

bined corn and manufactural belt, as shown in Philbrick's map (Figure XXIX-2). Nodal circulation evaluation of mobile criteria embraces land, water, and air media—transportation by railroad, motor vehicles, ship, and plane. Chicago is thus determined to occupy a prime position: "Chicago is probably the world's best-developed and clearest example of a transportational focus for a quasi-continental grouping of clusters of clusters of central places." Continuing the hierarchical order of nodal progression, the leading American manufactural and agricultural belt is finally integrated into the word nodal organization:

¶ The repetition of nodal organization of the United States, of the nations of Western Europe, and of the Soviet Union at a scale on the order of 1/300,000,000, demonstrates the parallel relationship of national units of occupied surface into a single core region characterized as the industrially developed Northern Hemisphere, based upon modern technology and interconnection of a highly developed regional division of labor. At the same time as this huge industrialized region can be considered an area of uniformity, it is so in a setting of the rest of the world. . . . The nodal organization of the world focuses upon the major industrial world-core region in the Northern Hemisphere. It is interconnected locally, regionally, nationally, internationally, and intercontinentally by all forms of land, water, and air transportation and communication.[1]

Philbrick shows how the sea lanes integrate the Northern Hemisphere industrial core with the Southern Hemisphere to form the *integrated commercial world,* with its varied subsistence and exchange types of occupance.

[1] Philbrick, Allen K., "Principles of Areal Functional Organization in Regional Human Geography," *Economic Geography,* Vol. XXXIII, No. 4, October, 1957, pp. 329-336, *passim.* Reprinted by permission.

XXIX:11 (Left) Of all the climographs we have pictured, this *Dwa* (Mukden) profile seems to arrest our attention most. Note the far-flung ranges of both seasonal temperature and rainfall, reflective of the strong monsoonal influence. Does winter drought create any problem? How about the summer rains?

European and Asian coregions

The severe winter, long summer, as in the case of the previous realm of short summer, has a sector both in Europe and in Asia. The former extends through the southern Ukraine from Lake Stalingrad on the east to the vicinity of Bucharest, Romania, on the southwest. In Asia, the mainland section is centered upon the Manchuria triangle, with the cities of Harbin, Mukden (Shenyang), and Seoul in Korea forming the northern, western, and southeastern apexes. The other Asiatic section is northern Honshu, Japan, coextensive with the interior highlands. Climatically, the Ukraine and Honshu are quite similar to the American Corn Belt, but Manchuria, as illustrated in the climograph for Mukden (Figure XXIX-11), has a monsoon pattern, with contrasting wet summers and dry winters. Landforms and soils vary from the chernozem plains of the Ukraine to the podsolic highlands of Manchuria and Honshu, much of which exhibits considerable relief. This latter feature contrasts with the gently rolling to flattish plains of the podsolic and prairie soils of the eastern and western sections, respectively, of America's Corn Belt.

Though corn, oats, barley, and the raising of livestock are significant in the southern Ukraine, wheat, instead of corn, is the kingpin cereal. And in the Manchurian-Korean sector, the soybean and sorghum (kaoliang) reign supreme, along with some grains and a heavy concentration of vegetables. Though rice is primarily a tropical and subtropical product, considerable acreages of it are found in *Dwa* Korea and *Dfa* Japan on a one-year crop basis.

Major differences among the three continental sectors, as in the case of the other agricultural realms previously considered, emerge chiefly from varying demographic and political patterns—Russia with its expansive and mechanized collectivist and state farms, as contrasted with the small-sized farms of the Orient—(in Manchuria-Korea as well as in Japan)—where by muscle rather than machine energy a family normally ekes out a subsistence on less than five acres.

In some ways the manufactural and commercial patterns of the Ukraine and southern Manchuria region show considerable resemblance to our own American manufacturing belt. In the Ukraine we find some half-dozen cities of the half-million population class, highly industrialized. With iron, coal, oil shale, and other mineral deposits, plus the rich agricultural resources, most of these cities have developed iron and steel industries, metallurgical and chemical establishments, oil and sugar refining, and other miscellaneous industries. The Black Sea port of Odessa, with over a million inhabitants, is a leading manufacturing and shipbuilding center, terminally tied into one of Russia's chief rail nets. Besides, it is celebrated for its rich historic and culture tradition, forming at one time (1824) the capital of New Russia. Stalingrad, on the Lower Volga, acquired particular military prominence in the Second World War.

Considering the very low development of manufacturing generally on the Asiatic mainland, Manchuria stands out as a real leader. Here, as in the Ukraine, are some half-dozen communities of prominence — population-, industry-, and commerce-wise. And, as in the Ukraine also, metallurgical establishments based on iron, coal, oil shale, and other minerals have given impetus to heavy industry and the manufacture of machines and chemical goods on a relatively large scale. With the resources just mentioned and with rail termini of the leading transportation system to the interior—the Trans-Siberian Railway—as well as to China, via Peking, and with seaport contact with the Pacific, Manchuria must be reckoned with in calculating the future expansion of world trade in North Pacific Asia.

APPLICATION OF GEOGRAPHIC UNDERSTANDING

(Summary Observations on Part IV)

I. Realm Differentiation.

Global differentiating criteria, as you have observed, are climate, and its nearest correlate, vegetation.

A. What unifying functions of human geography derive from such a pattern? What limitations do you recognize? Can you think of a more functional plan in organizing and integrating areally differentiated phenomena—natural and cultural—on a global scale?

B. With the above pattern in mind, what types of landscapes would you successively encounter in traveling from the mouth of the Niger River to the Strait of Gibralter? How would the population patterns change from one realm to another, and what would you expect in the way of contrasted indigenous problems in land-use?

II. Demographic Geography.

Australia, Canada, Brazil, and the United States are of comparable size (approximately 3,000,000, 3,800,000, 3,300,000, and 3,600,000 square miles, respectively). Their populations in round figures are 10,000,000, 17,000,-000, 65,000,000, and 181,000,000, respectively. Thus, the striking demographic ratios: 3, 4.5, 19, and 50, per square mile.

A. On the basis *only* of the realm criteria and resources discussed in Part IV, how do you account for these disparate figures?

B. What other factors of physical geography, demographic and social geography, economic and commercial geography, and historical and political geography would you want to examine to establish tenable conclusions?

III. Comparative Geography.

How strong or weak a region or a country may be is a "relative" matter, in respect to both space and time. Applying principles developed thus far in this text:

A. Compare the grazing resource potential of the Great Plains steppe (*BS*) with the Llanos savannah (*Aw*).

B. Compare the general farming potential of any underdeveloped region of one continent, say Africa, with that of another, say South America. Indicate the geographical criteria you would use in each case in determining the kind of aid most needed and most effective in promoting productivity.

C. Compare the industrial northeast of the United States with the industrial southwest in terms of (a) climate, (b) basic natural resources, (c) actual and potential population, (d) domestic and overseas trade expansion programs. How do our industries in the South fare by comparison?

D. Which country possesses by nature the most resourceful realms: the U. S. or the U. S. S. R.? In what ways are the challenges in realm resource development similar in the two countries? Dissimilar?

IV. Political-Military Geography.

The next part (Part V) focuses attention on political-military regimes of nation states, where viability, security, and power are key geographic concepts.

A. What climatic, space, and resource criteria of Part IV serve as a general framework for the development of such concepts?

B. On the basis of such criteria, evaluate the relative strength and weakness of the newly formed nations in Africa: Cameroon, Central African Republic, Chad, The Congo, Dahomey, Gabon, Ghana, Guinea, Ivory Coast, Malagasay, Mali, Mauritania, Niger, Nigeria, Senegal, Sierra Leone, Somalia, Togo, Upper Volta, Algeria.

C. By what geographical criteria would you measure the political and military importance of these "infant" states to the 'East" vs. "West" world power alliances?

References

1 Meyer, Alfred H., and Hess, Elmer B., "Gary 'Big Steel' — Geographic Design and Destiny," *Proceedings of the Indiana Academy of Science,* Vol. LXVIII, 1958, p. 237.

2 *Eleventh Annual Report,* Gary Industrial Foundation, Inc., 1954-55.

3 *Ordinance for the Comprehensive Amendment of the Zoning Ordinance for the City of Gary* (Evert Kincaid and Associates, consultants, Chicago, Illinois) June 25, 1957.

4 Meyer, Alfred H., and Miller, Paul F., "Manufactural Geography of Chicago Heights," *Proceedings of the Indiana Academy of Science,* Vol. LXVI, 1957, pp. 217-218.

5 Dicken, Samuel Newton, *Economic Geography,* D. C. Heath and Company, Boston, 1955, p. 460.

6 Haystead, Ladd, and Fite, Gilbert C., *The Agricultural Regions of the United States,* University of Oklahoma Press, 1955, pp. 140-143, *passim.*

7 Van Royen, William, *Atlas of World Resources: The Agricultural Resources of the World,* Prentice-Hall, Inc., Englewood Cliffs, N. J., for the University of Maryland, 1954, p. 56.

8 Wallace, H. A., "Corn and the Midwestern Farmer," *Landscape,* Spring, 1957, Vol. VI, No. 3, pp. 9-12, *passim.*

9 Weaver, John C., "Crop-Combination Regions in the Middle West," *The Geographical Review,* Vol. XLIV, No. 2, April, 1954, pp. 176, 200.

10 Philbrick, Allen K., "Principles of Areal Functional Organization in Regional Human Geography," *Economic Geography,* Vol. XXXIII, No. 4, October, 1957, pp. 329-336, *passim.*

Part V

The regional and resource factors of nation-states

In Part IV the complex global matrix of interrelated natural and human phenomena was treated areally by recognizing realms or regions of essential homogeneity in several fundamental environmental categories. Thus, you will recall, southern Canada and northern United States shared unit treatment in the *Dfb* realm, geographical processes within which on both the American and Canadian sides suggest unity — not separateness — of cultural and economic interests. Such "geographic" regions in effect, then, disregard boundaries which separate countries politically. It is the geographer's unique way of trying to keep area-association of things intact so as better to detect the processes responsible for such association. But "artificial" though it may seem, arbitrary lines have been drawn by man on the earth's surface from time immemorial to demarcate the territorial domain of a province, a state, or a nation, for purposes of governmental administration. Such political entities are, after a fashion, "regions" also, but since they are organized on a legislative rather than man–environment relation basis they do not correspond to truly "geographic" regions. Yet, because of their spatial, demographic, and resource characteristics, such areal units also lend themselves to geographic analysis by examining the regional composition of the political unit itself, as well as noting how one political unit compares with another in world affairs when assessed by criteria basically geographic. Such geo-political criteria are illustrated in the figure below.

Though there is no set pattern or stereotyped order of criteria treatment in works of political geography, nor in this part, some attempt has been made to show close linkages of area-resource concepts useful in relationship study. Using this as a sort of checklist, contrast the criteria used by the political geographer with those of the political scientist in assessing the viability and security of a nation-state. Do you see any areas here which suggest a close partnership of the two fields in viewing the world order?

Chapter 30

China and India: reborn nations in an ancient landscape

The heart of Asia is a high plateau, the highest in the world, fringed by mountains, also among the highest in the world. Great rivers flow outward from this highland complex, eastward toward the Pacific and southward toward the Indian Ocean. The lands through which these rivers flow have alternating flood and drought — flood during the summer rainy season, drought during the winter dry season. The seasonality of rainfall accounts for the name by which these lands are commonly called, the monsoonal lands. In the Köppen climatic symbolism, they are the *Aw*, the *Am*, the *Cw*, and the *Dw* lands of Asia.

Physiographically, monsoonal Asia is a region of broad river valleys which have been carved across the face of ancient plateaus. In India, the plateau (the Deccan) is relatively flat, bordered on its eastern and western edges by steep, maturely-dissected escarpments (the Eastern and Western Ghats) which, from the sea, look like mountains. In China, the plateau has undergone such severe erosion that the original plateau surface survives today only as summits of one of the world's most extensive regions of hill country (the South China Hills). The greatest of the rivers, laden with the rock and silt which they have stripped from the plateau surface in the course of widening and deepening their valleys, have used this material to build broad flood plains in the valleys and great deltas into the sea (2).

These broad river valleys — especially the valleys of the Hwang, the Yangtze, the Si, and the Ganges — have served for at least 4,000 years as great natural stages on which successive civilizations and empires and religions have come and gone, waxed and waned. They have served as gateways through which wave upon invading wave has surged out of the dry interior of Asia — driven, as some geographers suspect, by recurring cycles of drought in the central Asiatic steppes. They have served as highways for armies, commanded by some of the most famous or notorious conquerors of all time. Eventually, they became nuclei around which states developed. India, today, is built around the Ganges Valley. China's long history is, to a very large extent, the story of how its three nuclei in the Hwang, Yangtze, and Si valleys were brought under one central authority from time to time and how, when this central authority became weak or tired, China would fall apart into its component nuclear regions.

It would obviously be impossible to trace, in these few brief pages, the long and complicated histories of the monsoonal nations. Our interest is in that most recent brief hour of their histories which we have shared with them and which has bound us to each other, in hope or in fear, for all of the predictable future.

East meets West in monsoonal Asia

The earliest contacts between oriental and occidental civilization are lost in the mists of history. As early as 326 B.C., Alexander the Great fought a mighty battle in what is now India at the Hydaspes (Jhelum) River, and within less than a century Chinese scholars were making diagrammatic illustrations of the Pythagorean theorem, presumably traceable to direct or indirect contacts with Alexander's armies. From at least that time on, there were frequent, although intermittent, contacts between China and the Mediterranean world. India was in even closer touch with the West — one of the most ancient Christian churches, the Mar Thoma Church, was established in India during the first century of the Christian Era, possibly by St. Thomas — and this association continued to be close until Islamic conquests in the Middle East closed the passageway between the Mediterranean and the Ganges Valley. It was, indeed, these very conquests which prompted European traders and explorers to look for alternative routes to China and India. In the twelfth and thirteenth centuries, a number of travelers, among them the Polo brothers, reached China by way of an overland route which led through the steppe lands of modern Russia to the oases of the central Asian deserts and thence into the headwaters of the Hwang Ho system. Meanwhile others, notably the Portuguese, were seeking a water route to the Far East, a quest which culminated successfully in Vasco da Gama's voyage to the Malabar Coast of India (1497). And, of course, every schoolboy knows that many of the early voyages to America were undertaken in the hope of finding a direct route westward from Europe to Cathay (China).

1. Why Western man went to the Orient. What was it that Europe wanted from the Orient? Since the days of the Roman Empire, Chinese silk had been a much-valued status symbol among wealthy Europeans, and the silk trade had become a major element in East-West commerce. There was also a brisk trade in Far Eastern spices, and legend had invested China with an abundance of precious metals and jewels which appealed to the cupidity of the European. Added to these economic motivations was a lust for adventure which characterized the dawn years of the Renaissance and a very important political consideration: with most of Asia, the Near East, and Slavic Europe united under a powerful Mongol Empire, some of the rulers of Western Europe saw the possibility of forming an alliance with the Mongols against the hated Moslems.

The discovery that the Americas were continents in their own right and not outliers of the coast of Cathay redirected the interests of Western Europe, for a while, from the Orient to the New World.

¶ In 1750 (a full 250 years after the Portuguese arrival) [the mercantilist powers of Western Europe] still held only scattered trading factories on the coast, or at best dominated a few petty client-states; these posts, however, though scattered, were not isolated, but rather links in a chain which secured the bulk of overseas commerce. . . .

The Industrial Revolution, however, with its insatiable demand for raw materials and markets, greatly accelerated the development of the maritime empires, so that by 1900 Southern Asia was all but completely under European control, while America had just supplanted Spain in the Philippines. The Turkish Empire, Persia, and Afghanistan were nominally free from this domination (though not from "peaceful penetration"), but this was more by reason of the jealousies between the Great Powers than by their own strength. The same was very obviously true of Siam, and might even be said with some plausibility of China. In 1907 Persia was virtually partitioned economically between Britain and Russia, and after the first world war the core of South-west Asia, from Palestine to Iraq, was parcelled out into French and British Mandates. In the east China was powerless to prevent her Manchurian territory from being the theatre of the full-scale Russo-Japanese War, in which she herself was neutral.[1]

Note how much is implied in these two brief paragraphs. There is, in the first place, the basic European view of Asia as a source of raw materials and a market for the cheap products of European industry. The European was little interested in learning to appreciate any of the Asiatic cultures; it was taken for granted that they were inferior. A few Europeans were interested enough in the peoples of Asia to want to bring them the benefits of European religion, education, medicine, and law, but they did so with little direct support from the colonial administrators. Even fewer Europeans had any intentions of settling permanently in any of the countries of Asia; they were there to rule or to trade or to educate or to evangelize for a period of time, and then to go back home. Meanwhile, they had no intention of subjecting themselves to local laws or governments. They brought these with them as colonial administrations (India) or as consular courts (China).

2. The unifying impact of the West on India. The reasons for European behavior in monsoonal Asia were not all ignoble nor were their consequences all bad. It happened that the European came to China and India in one of the deepest troughs of their cultural cycles. India, at the time the first Europeans arrived, was in one of its recurrent periods of political and cultural anarchy. The Mongols, at that time, were trying to build an empire, but their attempt ran afoul,

[1] Spate, O. H. K., "The Resurgence of Asia," *The Changing World*, Edited by W. Gordon East and A. E. Moodie, Harcourt, Brace & World, Inc., 1956, pp. 465-467. Reprinted by permission.

as had so many previous attempts, of the essential heterogeneity of the Indian subcontinent. As one writer has put it,

> ¶ If the history of India reads with a bewildering change of pace and locality, it in part is owing to the lack of regional definition in the landscape of India and in part to the fact that new competitors were constantly surging through the Mountain Wall to engage in the struggle for some part of India. Often the Punjab, the Ganges Valley, or the Deccan was the scene of a mad scramble during a whole century, producing a regional anarchy and a wild struggle for paramountcy which failed to produce a positive result. Sometimes in widely separated parts of India two regions stood out above the remainder at the same time. If this happened side by side there ensued a bitter struggle, often resulting in the dominance of one contestant. On the other hand, the contest sometimes ran for centuries. . . . Significantly, too, there are negative spots of rough hill country, desert, or overwet mountain fringe that never have been the seat of a leading culture or group.
>
> The struggle for regional dominance, as a natural part of things, is a segment of Hindu political philosophy. As an undercurrent in Indian life it has been present as far back as any record can be read. . . . Always before one group could bring the whole of India together and cement the unity into a fixed pattern, its energy or its resources ran out or some new invasion came to overwhelm the waning leaders.[1]

Upon this pattern of ethnic, religious, cultural, and geographical diversity the British gradually imposed, over a period of almost 400 years, a measure of political unity. It was this achievement that prompted one of India's most prominent contemporary journalists, Frank Moraes, to say that "the concept of India is really a British creation."

It was not the policy of the British in India to interfere with ancient customs or established authority any more than was necessary to maintain peace and order for profitable trade. For the first 300 years of British involvement in India, the effective government of the subcontinent was not even carried on by a department of the British government but by a chartered trading company, the British East India Company. Not until 1858, did India come under the direct control of the British government. And even when that happened, the day-to-day administration of India continued to be carried on by civil servants responsible, at least nominally, to local rulers, who enjoyed a greater or lesser measure of autonomy. Thus, at the same time Britain was unconsciously creating an India, she was just as unconsciously perpetuating the old demon of regional disunity (Figure XXX-1).

More effective, perhaps, than government policy in creating Indian unity was the pervasive influence of the several hundred thousand Englishmen who were scattered across the subcontinent at any given time as civil servants, soldiers, merchants, schoolmasters, missionaries, and engineers. Their language became the nearest thing multilingual India had to a *lingua franca.* Their standards of etiquette and sportsmanship were imposed, by way of their schools, upon the children of the Indian upper classes. Their theories and forms of government, validated by centuries of political stability at home and by capable administration in India itself, appealed strongly to thoughtful Indians who realized how much political turbulence had cost their people through the centuries. Their religion, particularly in its ethical emphasis, seemed much closer to pristine Hinduism and Buddhism and Jainism than did the superstition-encrusted forms of these religions which were being practiced by the Indian masses.

When contrasting cultures meet, the leaders of the less vigorous culture tend to adopt what they consider the best elements of the more vigorous one. In the first generation, this adoption process can be a very painful one, for those who become involved in it tend to become alienated from their own culture without being fully at home in the new. This has been true of India. Tagore, Gandhi, Prasad, Radhakrishnan, Nehru, Krishna Menon—each has sought, in his own way, to accept what he found best in the new European culture without abandoning what he considered best in the culture of his own people. In the process, each has had occasion to experience something of the lost feeling of a man without a country. Nor is this surprising, for the Indian

[1] Reprinted with permission from J. E. Spencer, *Asia East by South,* 1954, John Wiley & Sons, Inc., New York, p. 180.

himself is as much a British creation as is the concept of India. Less than a hundred years ago, there were no Indians—only Urdus and Bengalis and Gujaratis and Punjabis and Telugus; Moslems, Hindus, Jains, and Sikhs; Brahmans, Kshatriyas, Vaisyas, and Sudras. Men defined themselves in terms of some linguistic, religious, or caste affiliation. Britain provided, in the first instance, a framework of unity and, later, a common enemy, which made it possible for men of diverse linguistic, religious, and caste loyalties to recognize themselves and each other as Indians, and India as the larger to which all lesser loyalties had to be subordinated. But both India and the Indian are still in the process of creation.

Here, then, is geography in action. The modern educated Indian stands with one foot firmly planted in the valley of the Indus or the Ganges and with the other foot just as firmly planted in the valley of the Thames. Clad in sari and bearing on her forehead an ancient good-luck mark, an Indian university professor lectures to her class, in faultless Oxford English, on Locke and Hume. In her, and in thousands of Indians like her, Europe and Asia meet, merge or conflict, and produce a cultural hybrid.

3. *The shattering impact of the West on China.* Out of the encounter of Europe and Asia in sub-Himalayan Asia came India and the Indian. When Europe and Asia met in China, the impact shattered that ancient empire, setting the stage for half a century of near anarchy, which has only recently been resolved by the establishment of a new tyranny.

It was China's misfortune that no one European country ever succeeded in establishing suzerainty over her; if that had happened, the unity of the country might have remained intact, however hateful foreign rule might have been. Instead, China became an economic and political and cultural battleground.

¶ The Chinese realm was too big a series of geographic regions to be taken over by any one European power. The situation turned into a political-economic race for spheres of influence among Britain, Germany, Russia, and Japan. A series of political treaties were exacted from China, under various kinds of military pressure, giving European powers special concessions of an economic and political nature, usually accompanied by the lease of small areas of land in port cities along the coast of China and the Yangtze River. The first such "treaty port" arrangements occurred in 1842; the last such exaction was in 1898. Just before the close of the nineteenth century the drive of imperialism became more frantic. France held economic claim to most of southwest China, Britain to the Yangtze Valley, Germany wanted Shantung, Japan had Korea, and Russia was interested in Manchuria. The United States had no regional unit in mind, but held the newly acquired Philippine Islands. And in a spell of self-interested altruism the United States set forth the open-door doctrine which proposed an end to regional, political imperialism in China. Its real effect, however, was to sanction economic imperialism for everyone, since the treaty ports and treaties giving the Europeans special rights were not canceled. . . .

As the years of the twentieth century have passed the obvious occidental imperialism has slackened. More subtle and pernicious undercurrents in the form of financial loans, and large-scale commercial dealings protected by unequal treaties, have continued. And with the slackening of occidental imperialism there arose Japan

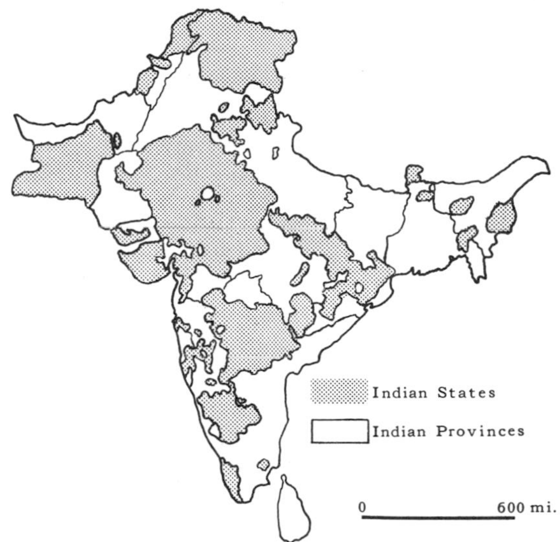

XXX:1 The confusing boundaries of Indian political subdivisions are shown as they were in 1939. (From *An Historical Atlas of the Indian Peninsula* by C. Collin Davies, the Oxford University Press, 1957, used by permission)

XXX:2 This map of the provinces of China reflects the considerable reorganization of political units that has taken place under the Communist government. (From *Land of the 500 Million* by George B. Cressey, McGraw-Hill Book Co., Inc., 1955, used by permission)

ese imperialism, a century late in the race, even more seriously to plague Chinese society. Commencing with the seizure of the southern Ryukyu Islands in the late 1870's and reaching its disastrous climax in the 8 years of the Sino-Japanese War, the Japanese effort exceeded any of the illustrative examples set by the Occident. There are those who hold that the economic imperialism of the outside world was rapidly beating China down to the role of an economic slave producing volumes of low-cost materials at the price of a steadily lowering Chinese standard of life. In the eighteenth century China possibly had the highest standard of living in the world, whereas in the early 1930's China was a rival for the questionable rank of "one of the lowest standards of living in the world."[1]

How was it possible for so great an empire to allow its territories and its wealth to be nibbled away by outsiders? A large part of the answer is implicit in Spencer's phrase, "a series of geographic regions." China was an empire—not so much, as one writer has put it, a state, as a state of mind. Within China proper, as we have noted, there were three nuclei—one in northern China (the Hwang Valley and the North China Plain, centered upon the ancient capital of Peking), one in middle China (the Yangtze Valley and Delta, centering upon Nanking and Shanghai), and one in southern China (the Si Valley, centering upon Canton) (Figure XXX-2). There are

[1] Spencer, *op. cit.*, p. 315. Reprinted by permission.

fundamental linguistic, economic, and cultural differences between North China and South China, the boundary between the two lying somewhere in the Yangtze Valley. North China has cold winters (*D*), suffers from cycles of flood and drought, raises wheat, inclines toward the old ways, and looks inland toward the Eurasian drylands, from which successive waves of invaders have come to rule and to settle the land. South China is subtropical (*C*) and hilly, raises rice, receives periodic infusions of new ideas from contacts with other lands, and looks outward toward the sea and toward Southeast Asia, from which many of its earliest peoples came. The northern Chinese have shown little tendency to migrate, even into such relatively open adjacent lands as Manchuria. The southern Chinese have migrated into every part of the world.

Whole millennia of Chinese history were required to unite these two disparate parts of China proper into one country. Strong dynasties managed to hold them together. Weak dynasties lost control to regional and local warlords. Thus divided within itself, China might seem to possess few of the qualifications for an imperial power. But strong rulers managed to bind their country together by a fine system of roads and canals and an efficient administration functioning through a highly-competent civil service. Under such rulers, China reached out to bring under her control the thinly-populated, "backward" desert and steppe lands along her western and northern boundaries. The effectiveness of this control varied with the strength of the central government, but in recent centuries it has extended, to some degree, to Tibet, Sinkiang, Mongolia, and Manchuria.

The essential point to bear in mind is that China is and always has been "a series of geographic regions." We may say that it is basically a centrifugal state, in which all of the pressures are toward dismemberment. To compensate for these centrifugal tendencies, a strong central government is absolutely necessary.

This leads us to the second aspect of our answer to the question: How could China have allowed its territories and its wealth to be nibbled away by outsiders in the past hundred years? Simply stated, these were years of political decay. By the middle of the nineteenth century, the once-mighty Manchu dynasty was suffering from a case of advanced senility. It lasted until 1912, an archaic symbol rather than a government, and with its fall China fell apart politically. A central republican government in Nanking, under Sun Yat-Sen and later Chiang Kai-Shek, struggled valiantly to reconstruct the shattered country, but their task was rendered nearly hopeless by the natural centrifugal tendencies that were rooted in the geography of China, by continued foreign interference in the internal affairs of their country, and finally by Japanese aggression. Thus, for almost forty years after 1912, China was politically in a state of near anarchy.

In the absence of an effective central government, China allowed its roads and canals to deteriorate until at last they were unusable. Half-hearted attempts at railroad building failed to provide any new links between its various regions. Civil administration collapsed and local governments fell into the hands of local warlords. Trade, transportation, and communication within the country withered and died, and the economy was shattered into a multitude of local economies, most of them incapable of supporting the burgeoning population. The basic unit of Chinese life, the family, began to break down as natural calamities of flood and drought and social evils such as usurious interest rates and uncontrolled inflation forced people off the land and into the big cities. It is no wonder that, in such a desperate hour, the Japanese thought they saw a chance to bring all of China under their control without having to do serious battle for it. The wonder is that, weak as she was, China found the strength to resist the Japanese advance inch by inch for more than a decade.

New nations

Present-day India and China are both products of the political upheaval that partly coincided with but chiefly followed the Second World War—India less so than China, for India's independence was the culmination of a process which had been going on for years before the war and which was probably only hastened by the war. China, on the other

Here is a modern solution to an old problem. Contrary to the ideas of many people, India is not a rainforest land with heavy rain the year round. It is a monsoonal land, with a distinct and often severe drought season in the summer. Water is stored in reservoirs called "tanks" and carried, often, some distance to the home. This is still the practice in many parts of the country, but the water truck is making life a bit easier in those places where it has been introduced. (Allis-Chalmers)

hand, experienced a convulsive rebirth which shattered the political, economic, and social patterns of her past.

1. India discovers her identity. However true it may be to say that the concept of India is a British creation, it is at least equally true to say that India is a geographic reality, although there are many significant elements in the Indian landscape which tend to obscure that reality. A physical map of Asia shows how the Indian subcontinent is set apart from the rest of Asia by a high mountain wall (the Himalayas) on the north and the east. Within the area thus set apart, there is the heavily-populated heartland of the Ganges Basin. Into it, rivers drain from the Himalayan foothills to the north and the northern half of the Deccan plateau to the south. If the Ganges Basin is taken as the base of a triangle, the other two sides are formed by the shoreline of the Bay of Bengal and the Arabian Sea. Thus defined by seas and high mountains, India is a kind of huge island—diverse enough within itself but distinctly set off from the rest of the continent.

Climatically, also, India is a kind of world unto itself. Its monsoonal climates (*Aw* and *Cw*) impart a high degree of climatic homogeneity to the subcontinent: dry, dusty winters offset by rainy, oppressively humid summers. Climatically, also, India is the creature of its rimming mountains and seas. The mountains to the north are effective barriers to any strong climatic influences from central Asia. The differential heating of land and water produces strong indrafts of air during the summer, when the intense heating of the land creates low-pressure conditions favoring the flow of air from the cooler seas onto the land. During the winter, there is a greater equalization of land temperature and sea temperatures and the flow of air is cut off, leaving India dry.

We must now note one very important exception to both of the patterns which we have discussed. Topographically, the sea and mountain rim within which India is contained is breached to the west, where nothing more than a very low divide separates the Ganges Valley from the valley of the Indus River. So low is this divide that it has never served as an effective deterrent to movement between the drylands of southwestern Asia and the monsoonal lands of southern Asia. Pre-war political India extended westward to the Iranian and Afghan boundaries, incorporating within its territory the predominantly Moslem, dryland (*B*) Indus Basin. So long as Britain remained as a referee and a common enemy, Moslem and Hindu managed to accommodate to each other and even to work together for independence. Once independence became an imminent reality, this marriage of convenience fell apart, and British India became two states: The Union of India and the Dominion (later Republic) of Pakistan.

Partition was radical, but apparently necessary, surgery for the subcontinent as it passed from colonialism to nationhood. Hindu, Jain, Sikh, Christian, and Animist managed to get along with each other, but the Moslem, perhaps because he represented the largest single group next to the Hindu, proved an unassimilable exception to the rule. In 1933, while Gandhi and others were agitating for an independent India, Moslem students at Cambridge coined the name which became the rallying cry for Moslem demands for a separate state: Pakistan. The P stands for the Punjab, the A for the Afghan borderlands, the K for Kashmir, the I for Islam, the S for Sind, and the "tan" is the final syllable of Baluchistan. In geographical terms, the name, Pakistan, represented a demand for the drylands of northwestern India. When independence and partition finally came in 1947, the Moslem minority achieved this goal and more. As finally constituted, Pakistan included the drylands of the northwest (excluding Kashmir, whose status is still not settled) and an area of some 55,000 square miles in former East Bengal. Thus Pakistan today consists of two parts, separated from each other by a thousand miles of India.

The travail of partition is something which both Indians and Pakistani prefer to forget. While the great majority of the Moslem population lived before partition in the areas which later became Pakistan, there were significantly large numbers of Moslems scattered through Hindu India; indeed, even today Moslems are the second largest religious group in the Union of India, accounting for a tenth of its total population. Unscrambling the religious omelet of India was not, therefore, an easy thing in 1947. There were migrations both ways, Hindus out of Pakistan into India and Moslems out of India into Pakistan. Many of those who migrated did so less than voluntarily: they were driven out, either in the face of bloody rioting or under the compulsion of economic sanctions.

Ultimately, however, boundary lines were drawn and national areas defined, with one important and vexing exception. The state of Kashmir, reputedly one of the most beautiful places on earth, became a bone of contention between India and Pakistan. Its Hindu maharajah ceded it to India, an act which incensed the 77 per cent of his subjects who were Moslems. Time after time, the "Kashmir problem" threatened to erupt into war, but wise statesmanship in both India and Pakistan, reinforced by timely United Nations intervention, has so far succeeded in keeping the situation under control.

Necessary as partition undoubtedly was to solve the otherwise apparently insoluble religious question, it was a costly solution for both countries.

¶ By the partition, both India and Pakistan gained some advantages from each other. For instance, Pakistan profited in that much of the land she gained was irrigated from canals that had been constructed by the British, especially the canal tracts of the Punjab and the Sind, and thus India was deprived of some of the more valuable tracts of irrigated lands. On the other hand, as a result of the partition, India received the lion's share of the mineral resources of the subcontinent; for example, the iron and coal deposits and the attendant steel industry of southern Bihar have no counterpart in Pakistan.

By the boundary line fixed by the partition between India and Pakistan, the irrigation system was actually dismembered. To illustrate: three tributaries of the Indus River—the Ravi, the Beas, and the Sutlej—have their lower reaches in West Pakistan; but the upper reaches are in the parts of Kashmir which presently are under the control of India. Moreover, the sources of the Punjab canal system, which utilizes the waters of these rivers, is also in Indian territory. West Pakistan must depend, therefore, upon the good will of India for the maintenance of a uniform and regular supply of water.

. . . India depends on Pakistan for cotton and jute; she is also dependent on Pakistan for raw materials for her leather industries. On the other hand Pakistan in some instances depends on India for electrical energy from the Mandi powerhouse and for coal, cotton goods, and supplies of mustard oil. In the field of communication, partition cut across established networks. The East Pakistan frontier cuts across the railway system that was constructed to link the outer parts of Bengal with Calcutta, thus leaving East Bengal with no outlet and West Bengal with no through and direct route to Assam. Both of these disadvantages arising from severed communications systems have now been overcome, the former by the further development of Chittagong as a port, and the latter by the construction of new rail lines bypassing Pakistan territory.[1]

Kuriyan makes the further point that partition has left India in a particularly unhappy defensive posture, with Pakistan controlling the western approaches to India and, to a lesser extent, the eastern approaches. He notes further that both the capital of India (New Delhi) and its largest city (Calcutta) are uncomfortably close to Pakistan boundaries and would, therefore, be very vulnerable in the event of an outbreak of war between the two countries.

2. China takes on a new identity. We have already noted the centrifugal forces which tend to pull China apart. After the overthrow of the imperial government in 1912, there was a long period of political confusion in China, compounded after 1931 by Japanese adventures on Chinese territory culminating in an invasion of China proper in 1937. Between 1937 and the end of the war in 1945, Japan extended its control over most of coastal China, forcing the government and many of the people and industries of China to migrate westward to Szechwan, where a new capital was established at Chungking. Thus, between 1912 and 1945 these centrifugal forces were in full sway, aided and abetted by political turmoil within and invasion from without.

The defeat of Japan seemed to promise a new day for China. During the war, the legal Chinese government of Generalissimo Chiang Kai-Shek had held a very influential position in the counsels of the Western Alliance and, at the organization of the United Nations, was given a permanent seat on the Security Council with the right of veto. The re-establishment of Chiang's government in Nanking at the close of the war gave China one effective central government for the first time since the overthrow of the Manchu dynasty.

The new day was fated to be short-lived. By October, 1948, a Communist movement under Mao Tse-tung had seized Manchuria, and within two years it established its control over the rest of mainland China, forcing Chiang's government to establish an exile regime on the island of Formosa. Since the establishment of this government-in-exile on December 8, 1949, there have been two Chinas — the Republic of China (Chiang's regime), which presently exercises effective control only over the island of Formosa, but which still holds China's seat in the United Nations; and the People's Republic of China (the Communist regime), which is the *de facto* government of mainland China, but still unrecognized by the United Nations or the United States.

It would be venturing into an emotion-charged area of still-unsettled controversy to attempt to suggest reasons for the swift collapse of the Chiang regime and its supplantation by the Communists. This much, however, can be said: With a few notable exceptions, there were few leaders or scholars in the West who seemed, at the time, to have any clear conception of what was happening in China or of the implications of what was

---

[1] Kuriyan, George, "India and Pakistan," *World Political Geography* (second edition), edited by Etzel G. Pearcy and Associates, Thomas Y. Crowell Company, New York, 1957, pp. 537-538. Reprinted by permission.

happening for the total world picture. One might say that Communism took over China while the West was, as usual, looking the other way. We were preoccupied with what was going on in Europe, particularly with the job of reconstruction and the countering of Soviet threats in Germany and the Aegean area. Our geography, based upon flat-world maps, placed China far over on the right-hand side of the map, as remote as any part of the world could be from our interests and concerns. Few Westerners really knew China, and fewer still really cared much about it. And so we were gullible enough to swallow a number of comforting myths — the Chinese Communists were "agrarian reformers"; even if they succeeded in taking over power in China they could not fundamentally change the attitudes or the behavior of the people, for "China has absorbed every invader"; the Chinese Communists were "Chinese first and Communists only secondarily"; and, in any case, communism was "a Western philosophy which could not be transplanted to the ancient Chinese culture." There were even those who suggested that an honest, efficient Communist government would serve China better than the allegedly "corrupt," "ineffectual" Chiang regime.

For this geographical and ideological naïveté we have paid heavily. All other considerations aside, China has the geographic potential of a major world power. It has the size, the resources, the location, the people, and the sense of nationhood (sometimes latent) that are the requisites of a major power. All that it lacked was strong, purposive leadership, capable of organizing all of these assets and directing them toward the accomplishment of national goals. If the West had given more attention to the study of political geography, it would have known that, laying all other considerations aside, it could not allow the tremendous power potential of China to fall into the hands of an anti-Western regime. But Western man has, for centuries, considered the whole world east and south of the Mediterranean "exotic," not quite real, and certainly incapable of posing any serious threat to the West's military and technological position.

And so China became Communist: 669,000,000 people, coal reserves so large that they may be the greatest on earth, good supplies of iron ore, one of the world's major sources of antimony and tungsten, and perhaps yet-to-be discovered sources of other minerals — all of these came under the control of a small but dedicated group of Marxists whose program envisioned nothing less than a complete reconstruction of Chinese society and culture.

Despite the huge populations of China's great cities, the country always has been, and still is today, predominantly rural. Any thoroughgoing communization of the country had, therefore, to begin with the communization of the peasant. The family, which throughout Chinese history had constituted the basic social unit, was systematically attacked. Farmers and their families were herded into communes where, for all practical purposes, they became slave-laborers.

¶ The engineers of change throughout China's rural scene have been the cadres (*kan pu*), those fanatically indoctrinated, harsh young harbingers of the totalitarian future numbering several million. They were those who followed the conquering Red armies to "turn over the society." First, they classified all peasants in gradations from landlords to rich peasants, poor farmers, and farm laborers. Then the mass of more dissatisfied including tenants and rural laborers were assembled into "farmers associations" that destroyed the gentry and others who had held status under the old order through "wiping slates clean" meetings where excess rentals and interest were returned, "land reform," and "people's trials." Under constant guidance and prodding from Peking, they successively took the peasants into "mutual labor teams," cooperative farms and collectives. They alternately cajoled, lectured, threatened, and sometimes pleaded with peasants to "follow the new way." When, late in the summer of 1958, Peking announced the "irresistible nationwide demand" of the peasantry for joining the communes—about which few had ever heard before—the cadres staged the "big blooming and big contending" assemblies. There peasants had to argue themselves and each other into this new order where they exchanged a measure of independent action for a place in a labor brigade and a seat in one of the new communal mess halls.

The cadres also were charged with ensuring peasant use of new technology in agriculture;

Wing Lock Street in Hong Kong shows that the people of heavily-populated China are gregarious. These characteristics are evident in their cities where well-ordered crowds mill through the narrow streets. Unfortunately, the authentic China survives today chiefly in such peripheral places as Hong Kong and Formosa. (Canadian Pacific Railway)

they have made one really great contribution in reforestation. But the very thoroughness of the authorization controls they had forged permitted of some disastrous consequences. In 1956-57, when the planners in Peking apparently realized that China must secure an almost immediate jump in farm output to meet their ambitious targets, the word went down that this would be achieved with maximum mobilization of human labor. The "Great Leap Forward" resulted, preceding by a year and continuing with establishment of the communes. While there was renewed attention to digging more mud from pond bottoms and streams for fertilizer, making compost, etc., and the abortive backyard blast furnace campaign, the emphasis was upon extending irrigation systems and water control. The aim was to intensify use of and enlarge that portion of China's arable land which is double-cropped—about 60%—while also bringing water to dry regions. The arguments for this were strong. For example, Japanese experiments in North China during World War II had shown that wheat production could be doubled by only irrigating at the two stages when the plant was "tillering" and "booting." Claimed achievements for this human mobilization are extraordinary by any standard; Peking reported that water had been brought to an additional 80 million acres. But it is now apparent, and inferentially admitted by the Chinese press, that much of this rush irrigation construction was faulty. Hastily thrown up dikes often did not withstand the next summer's rains. Fragments of evidence suggest the water table over much of the North China Plain had been seriously disturbed. And alkali is beginning to blight fields irrigated without adequate soil surveys and provision for drainage.[1]

We shall come back to some of the problems of present-day Chinese agriculture a little later. At this point, what we are trying to illustrate is the fact that the Chinese Communists were not content with modest objectives. The campaign to "turn over the society" was intended to produce nothing less than a new China. Traditional virtues, values, and ways of doing things were methodically attacked, and leaders of the state called for a new spirit of "hard work and frugality" because, they alleged, China was a poor country and "it will take scores of years to turn China into a rich country" (6). A kind of Puritanism became the official philosophy of life. Young people were sent out from the cities to work on the land. High priority was given to railroad building in the hope that a better transportation system would soften the consequences of local crop failures by allowing for the better distribution of foodstuffs. The cities were cleaned up, beggars and idlers were put to work, and a strong emphasis was placed upon industrialization. How many opponents or reluctant co-operators with the new order were put to death is not known, but certainly their number ran into the hundreds of thousands.

Because the United States does not have diplomatic relations with the Communist regime in China, it is hard to get first-hand information on what is actually happening there. It is known that the government has undertaken some large hydroelectric and irrigation projects, the most notable of them being the Sanmen Gorge Project on the Hwang in the province of Honan. A new canal-building program, announced in 1959, calls for the construction of four trunk canals running north and south to connect the Yangtze with the Hwang. The government claims that impressive increases have taken place in steel production (from eight million metric tons in 1958 to 13,350,000 in 1959), in coal production (an increase of 29 per cent in 1959 over 1958), and in pig iron production (up 115 per cent in 1959 over 1958).

The Achilles heel of the Chinese economy remains agriculture. (Note map of agricultural regions, Figure XXX-3.) Bureaucratic bungling plus two successive years of bad weather in 1959 and 1960 resulted in two harvests which fell far short of stated goals. The consequences of these failures are significant for the whole economy, for China had counted on the sale of surplus agricultural production to finance its program of industrialization and modernization. In a desperate attempt to increase production, the government has recently shipped tens of thousands of its own bureaucrats into the countryside to help

[1] Ravenholt, Albert, "Red China's Food Crisis," East Asia Series, American Universities Field Staff Reports Service, New York, Vol. IX, No. 2, January, 1961, pp. 10-11. Reprinted by permission.

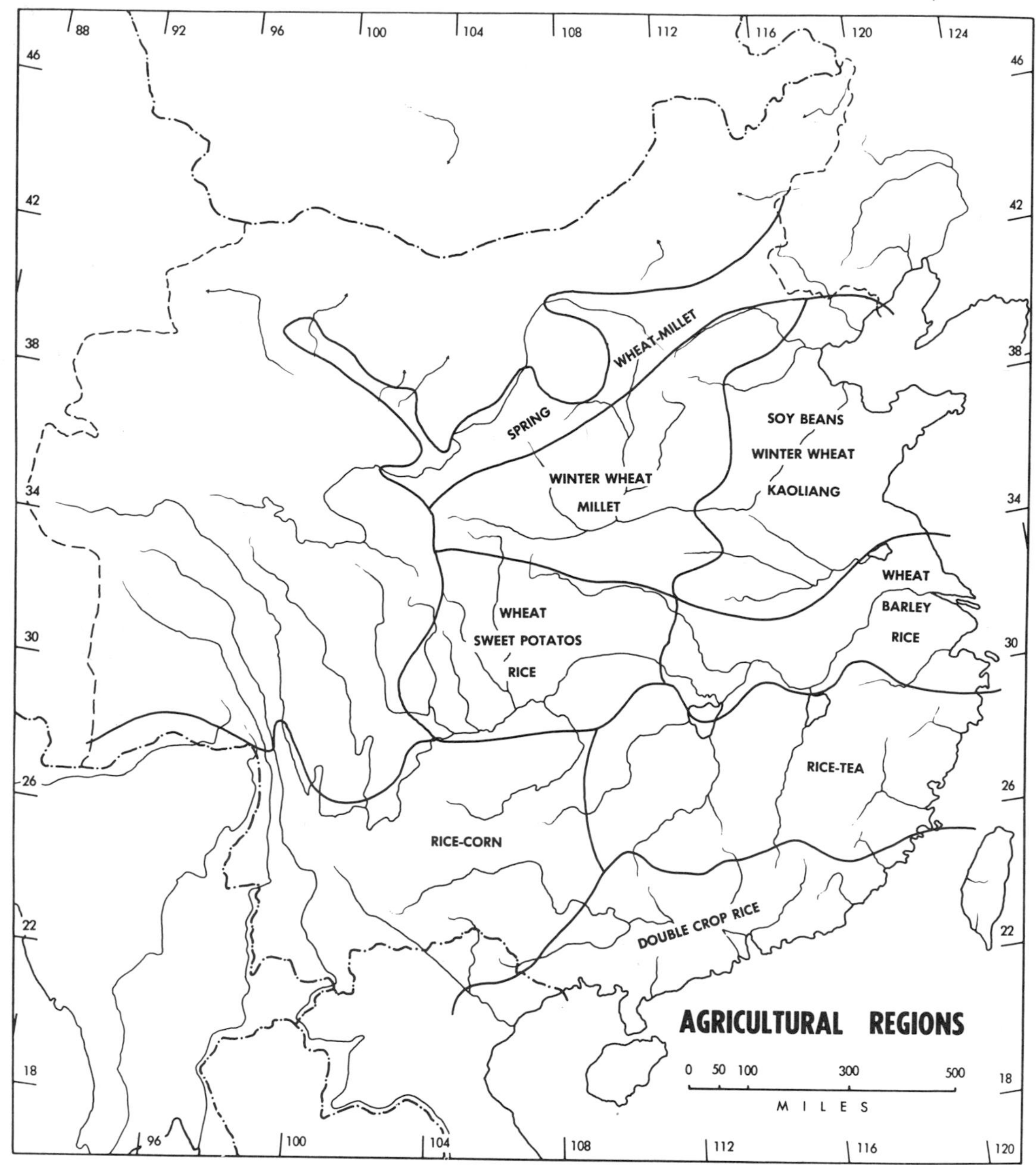

XXX:3 Here are shown the agricultural regions of China. (Modified from J. Lossing Buck by J. B. Spencer in *Asia, East by South,* John Wiley & Sons, Inc., 1954, used by permission)

work the land, and it has attempted to court the friendship of the peasants by restoring to them private garden plots. Meanwhile, to solve the immediate problem of a food shortage, it has been importing wheat from Canada and Australia. And still the food problem is a long way from solution.

¶ There are three innovations that make a major difference in Asian agriculture: water, improved seed, and chemical fertilizer. Red China has expanded herself to the limit to provide the first. Seed selection is encouraged and Peking has a core of able scientists who have been helped by the Russians. But this cannot be done rapidly. And certainly the cadres with their obtuse devotion to "politics must lead" are ill-equipped to manage delicate hybridizing of seed such as spurred the great jump in American corn yields. Chemical fertilizing offers the quickest and greatest means to expanding output on the land. But of this China is miserably short, due in substantial measure to insignificant attention to constructing fertilizer capacity during the first Five-Year Plan (1952-57). The mainland now uses some three million tons of chemical fertilizer annually, of which about one-half is imported. But if China is to provide for its present and anticipated population, yearly chemical fertilizer needs are of the order of 40 to 45 million tons; Peking today admits it should have 20 million tons. The consequences of revamping industrial plans to build such capacity would substantially alter Red China's role in world affairs. For the men who today manage the "good earth" it is not a simple choice to forgo their dreams of revolutionary grandeur in favor of such provision for production by the peasants, that traditional basis for Chinese survival, individually and nationally, in a land affording only the slimmest margin for error.[1]

With the agricultural crisis still a long way from solution, the population of China continues to increase at a net annual rate of 2½ per cent to 3 per cent, and the rate may rise as the government's energetic program of public health begins to make a significant impact upon the death rate. With insufficient food to feed its present population, China must find some way either to increase food production or to stabilize population. There are no present indications that either of these is being effectively done.

Forces to reckon with

Legend has it that giants get tired more easily than do ordinary people, and therefore have to sleep more. It is also said that, when they do awake, they are hungry and irritable. Without pursuing the analogy too far, it may be that our age is an age of the awaking of giants — first Russia, and now China. It is obvious that both India and China are hungry, and that China is certainly irritable. What dislocations these giants may cause in the house of mankind when they are fully aroused we can not yet know. But we do know, by their very size and potential, that they are forces to be reckoned with.

1. The Indian tight-rope trick. India, as the 1960's opened, could be described as a country which was united but not yet unified. Differences rooted deep in her geography and history are still a long way from being obliterated; the economic situation is still far less than satisfactory; and India is caught up, as are all nations, in the power struggle that is going on all around her.

Despite heroic efforts to minimize the importance of linguistic, religious, and caste lines, these continue to disturb Indian life and militate against true national unity. Roughly through the center of the Deccan Plateau a major language boundary runs east-west, separating the Indo-European languages of the north from the Dravidian languages of the south. Some fourteen main languages are spoken in the Republic, some of the more important of which are Hindi, Bengali, Sindhi, and Gujarati. These languages, in turn, are broken down into several hundred dialects. About half the people of India speak Hindi, which is the language of central India. It has been adopted as the national language and is scheduled to become official in 1965. This has brought strong opposition in southern India where Hindi is as much a foreign language to the Dravidian peoples as Japanese would be. English, which is widely known and widely used among educated Indians, has been given the status of a second official language in the colleges.

How important the language factor still is in India is perhaps best indicated by the fact that, in the process of consolidating the multitude of political units which existed in British India into states of the Indian Republic, the state boundaries have been drawn very largely along linguistic lines (Figure XXX-4). Necessary as such a concession to linguistic loyalties may have been in the practical sense, it would seem that this consolidation of linguistic groups behind the protective walls of political boundaries would tend to hinder the acceptance of any one national language.

Religious differences, which erupted in bloody riots at the partition of 1947, continue to break out from time to time in actual conflict between religious groups, particularly

[1] Ravenholt, *op. cit.*, p. 14. Reprinted by permission.

Table 30.1 Progress in India, 1950-1961. A Record of Production and Development

Item	*Unit*	*1950-51*	*1960-61 (anticipated)*	*Target for 1965-66: % up from 1960-61*
Foodgrains	million tons	52.2	75.0	33-40%
Cotton	million bales	2.9	5.4	33%
Sugar cane, *gur*	million tons	5.6	7.2	25-28%
Oilseeds	million tons	5.1	7.2	28-32%
Jute	million bales	3.3	5.5	18%
Tea	million lbs.	613	725	17%
Tobacco	thousand tons	257	300	8%
Milk	million maunds (of 82 lbs.)	466	600	15%
Wool	million lbs.	60	72	25%
Area irrigated	million acres	51.5	70	29%
Nitrogenous fertilizers consumed	thousand tons	55	360	178%
Electricity generated	million kw-hr	6,575	20,700	104%
Towns and villages electrified	thousands	3.7	19	79%
Iron ore	million tons	3	12	167%
Coal	million tons	32	53	83%
Finished steel	million tons	1	2.6	165%
Pig iron (for sale)	million tons	0.35	0.90	67%
Aluminum	thousand tons	3.7	17	341%
Machine tools	Rs. 100,000 value	29	550	445%
Diesel engines	thousands	5.5	33	100%
Electric motors	thousand h.p.	100	800	213%
Sewing machines (organized sector only)	thousands	33	300	50%
Bicycles (organized sector only)	thousands	101	1,050	90%
Automobiles	thousands	16.5	53.5	87%
Cement	million tons	2.7	8.8	48%
Paper and paperboard	thousand tons	114	320	119%
Railway freight carried	million tons	91	162	45%
Surfaced roads	thousand miles	97.5	144	14%
Post offices	thousands	36	75	27%
Telephones	thousands	168	475	42%
Students in schools	millions	23.5	41.1	58%
Hospital beds	thousands	113	160	19%
Family planning centers	number	—	1,797	356%
Registered doctors	thousands	59	84	23%
Registered nurses	thousands	17	32.5	62%

SOURCE: Excerpted from Government of India Planning Commission, *Third Five-Year Plan—A Draft Outline*, June 1960, pp. 38-42. Figures for 1960-61 and targets for 1965-66 are provisional. Reprinted by permission from Talbot, Phillips, "India, 1961," American Universities Field Staff Reports Service, South Asia Series, Vol. V, No. 1, p. 4.

between the majority Hindu group and the largest of the minority groups, the Moslems. A recent report from India noted that

¶ Despite occasional violence, the minorities in both countries [India and Pakistan] generally live peacefully. Discord is vociferously condemned by national leaders. Yet beneath the surface there appears to be little peace of mind.

Many a Hindu, even one who considers himself most tolerant, will think twice before giving a Moslem a job, renting him an apartment or inviting him to his club. Many Moslems, meanwhile, appear inhibited by a feeling that they are not wanted.

"You just can't trust them," a Hindu business man told an American recently. A week earlier, a Moslem in Pakistan had said the same thing about Hindus. Both had difficulty explaining why.

Some Hindu extremists are still angry, nearly fourteen years after partition, that Pakistan was created. Indian leaders agreed to partition, however, in the hope that it would end Hindu-Moslem conflicts. The extremists reason, despite repeated denials and lack of proof, that religious ties must make Indian Moslems feel more loyal to Pakistan than to their own country.[1]

Associated with the religious differences are caste differences. Technically, these no longer exist, having been outlawed by the constitution under which the Republic is now governed. But, as Americans have special reason to know, it takes more than laws to outlaw forms of discrimination which have deep historical roots and are embedded in a culture. One reason for the vitality of the caste system is that it has, for generations, defined occupational groups. Depending upon how far one is willing to go in subdividing the castes, one can identify as many as 2,400 of them, each defined by certain rights, privileges, occupations, beliefs, patron deities, traditions, and limitations. Completely outside the caste structure are some fifty million "untouchables," the very shadow of whom, falling upon a Brahman, is considered a defilement.

It is out of such diversity that the leaders of India work patiently to forge a unified nation. Meanwhile, they must also give attention to making this nation a viable economic unit, capable not only of supplying its present needs but of raising the desperately low standard of living of a people whose numbers increased by 21.5 per cent between 1951 and 1961. Economically, therefore, her problem is two-fold: (1) to win the race to keep her food production ahead of her population growth of eight million a year, and (2) to bring her industrial economy up to the breakthrough point where it becomes self-generating without requiring heavy infusions of foreign aid (6).

XXX:4 The boundaries of Indian states are shown here as they were in 1961. Since the achievement of independence, the government of India has been attempting to consolidate small political units into larger, more rational units, based largely on linguistic lines. (Courtesy Information Service of India)

The climates of India (*Af, Am, Aw,* and *Cwa*) leave much to be desired, but do allow intensive agriculture. She has the good soils of the Ganges-Brahmaputra lowlands and vast rolling plains which are good for crops that can tolerate the severe winter drought. However, excessive summer rains regionally produce flood conditions. Intensive subsistence tillage is the usual practice and under it a considerable variety of crops is raised: rice, wheat, sugar cane, cotton, peanuts, tobacco, vegetables, and fruits, to name only the more prominent ones. The great agricultural menace is the unpredictable southwest monsoon which often brings flood conditions to one part of the country while others are choked in dusty drought. To compensate for this

[1] *The New York Times*, Sunday, March 19, 1961. Reprinted by permission.

handicap, India is developing a system of canals and wells for irrigation.

Industrialization, which is already well advanced, can be further developed by a greater utilization of resources which are present, although still little developed, within India itself. Among the vast reserves still waiting to be exploited are chromite, iron ore, manganese, mica, titanium, and coal. She also has a great hydroelectric potential and some petroleum. Both road and railroad systems are well developed. Labor, of course, is no problem in a country which, in 1961, was still 82 per cent rural.

India, in the first decade of independence, took giant strides toward the development of her economy. Between the censuses of 1951 and 1961, industrial production increased by 70 per cent, agricultural output by almost a third, national income by 40 per cent, and per capita income by 19 per cent (7). But good is not good enough in a country where millions still are subsisting on a near-starvation diet and where extremes of wealth and poverty are among the greatest on earth.

Politically, India has enjoyed a long period of good government under its first prime minister, Pandit Jawaharlal Nehru. Recognized as a kind of elder statesman among the leaders of the formerly colonial countries which have achieved independence since the end of the Second World War, Nehru has been influential far beyond India. Himself a disciple of Gandhi and of his policy of nonviolence, Nehru has sought to pursue a policy of neutralism in the conflict between East and West. Perhaps his ideological bent toward neutralism has been reinforced by the situation in which India has found herself since she became independent. Sharing a common frontier with Red China, and separated only by a narrow appendix of Afghanistan from the Soviet Union, India has not been anxious to stir up any trouble with her Communist neighbors at a time when she needed to devote all of her energies to building up her own internal strength. Moreover, as the largest and most powerful of the free nonwhite countries, she has gained a certain recognition as their unofficial spokesman. There may be some changes in the offing, however. One writer has reported that:

¶ . . . Thanks to Communist China's continued belligerence, the earlier virtually unanimous public support for the world view and policies of Jawaharlal Nehru has given way to a spectrum of response that includes open, hostile criticism. "People used to accept everything he had to say on foreign policy," a close associate comments. "Now they are quite ready to challenge him aggressively." As if to buttress this observation, a retired Indian diplomat admits privately that "our faith was really shaken when we discovered that the Chinese had been encroaching on our territory for more than five years before he told Parliament and the public anything about it."

. . . By contrast, Indian relations with the Soviet Union are excellent at the moment—though some commentators point out, as A. D. Gorwala has put it, that "The Soviet Union poses as our friend and assists the Communist Chinese in every way possible." Whatever validity there may be to the Indian belief (or hope?) that Moscow is urging Peking to moderate its dispute with India, both political and economic relations with the Soviet Union continue to flourish for the reason that Indians, at least, see no evident conflict between the two countries' immediate national interests. Many say that each country can use the other's support in key policy areas, including Laos, possibly Communist China, and perhaps such wider issues as colonialism and disarmament.[1]

Prophecy is, at best, an uncertain art. It becomes a form of recklessness when one attempts to forecast the future course of a nation whose recent history has been dictated by one great man, now entering his seventies. Geographically, India is neither of the East nor of the West. Within her borders, East and West meet. The encounter in the past has been a fruitful one and has left India with a distinctly Western veneer. How thick and durable that veneer is we shall not know until it has been subjected to pressures from within and without which would seek to destroy it. There are those who believe that India, in its policy of neutralism, will be able to work out her own national destiny without joining sides with either of the great forces that are presently contending for world leadership. If she succeeds, she will have performed the greatest tight-rope trick on record.

[1] Talbot, Phillips, "India, 1961," South Asia Series, American Universities Field Staff Reports Service, New York, Vol. V, No. 1, p. 16. Reprinted by permission.

"Lest we forget." Colonialism has come to be a dirty word in many parts of the world. Some of the newly-independent countries of the world might remember, though, that their onetime masters gave while they were taking and that some of what they gave has enduring value. This train, shown here crossing the Western Ghats, is symbolic of those useful elements in Western civilization that Britain brought to India. An even better testimonial to the success of British rule in India is the fact that, when the British left, there was a cadre of Indians competent to take over and manage the structures and enterprises that Britain had established in India. (Press Information Bureau, Government of India)

2. *The Chinese puzzle.* We are witnessing, in modern China, the attempt of a group of Moscow-trained Chinese to apply principles which a German Jew set down in organized form in England. These principles, enunciated in their present form only a little more than a hundred years ago, are being pitted against a tradition which goes back at least four thousand years and which, on almost every point, is in conflict with them. The battle is between Marx and Confucius, and a decade is hardly long enough to allow us any clear picture of how the battle is going.

In a more profound sense, though, the battle is between ideology and geography. Marxism was developed as one man's answer to the problems of an industrial society. In China it is being applied to a society which is still overwhelmingly rural. One of the stated objectives of Communism is the ultimate liberation of the individual by bringing about social and economic conditions which will permit the "withering away of the state." In China, it is being applied to a state which, in very recent history, had come perilously close to withering away and which needed more than anything else to be re-established as a political and economic entity. In Europe, communists have long been concerned

A road cuts through a rice land in Szechwan province, China. Note that the flat land is totally given to rice. Trees are restricted to slopes and to watercourses. In the upper right corner of the picture is a portion of a farm village. (U. S. Army Air Forces Photo No. 339-AO-182-19 in the National Archives)

that the low costs of machine labor would produce a large jobless and bankrupt working class. In China, the pitifully low cost of human labor — a reflection, in large part, of the huge and growing population — tends to make machines uneconomical and thus inhibit industrialization. The philosophical background out of which Communism sprouted was Western-style individualism, against which it was necessary for Communist theoreticians to oppose the concept of socialist co-operation. In China, the social unit of the family is one of the major roadblocks in the way of the achievement of the socialist state.

That the Communist government has enjoyed some notable successes in the achievement of its program is undeniable. An economic and technological renascence is taking place which has brought expressions of concern not only from Western leaders but, by implication at least, from the leaders of the Soviet Union. But even the Communists have, as yet, found no way to undo nature. So far as agriculture is concerned, floods, droughts, and typhoons still imperil every season's crops in greater or lesser measure. The amount of arable land seems incapable of any large-scale increase. All in all, Cressey's conclusion still seems to be valid:

¶ The second half of the twentieth century will doubtless see notable changes in agriculture. Transportation will open markets to the isolated interior producer, and new skills will improve production. But whether all the needed changes are feasible and adequate is an open question.

Although an increased production of 25 per cent would be of conspicuous value, what China needs in order to take her place as a world power is an increase in her per capita income of several hundred per cent. It does not appear that agriculture holds the key to such a change.[1]

As for industrialization, Cressey has this to say:

¶ It is clear that China has mineral wealth adequate for a considerable industrial expansion. A decade of peace will bring spectacular developments in a number of places. At the same time there appear to be major limitations in oil, copper, and several essential minerals. Any tendency toward optimism should be weighed against an appreciation of vast area, the great number of people to be supplied, and the present low level of economic prosperity. Improvement over the present is one thing, catching up with the West quite another matter. Per capita equality, economically, with Japan is a big enough objective for the present century.[2]

Politically, the question which engrosses and perplexes Western statesmen is that of the relationship between Communist China and the U.S.S.R. It would appear that the Chinese Marxists are more "orthodox" in their Marxism than are the present rulers of the U.S.S.R. Hopeful Western commentators have seen in the divergent Chinese and Russian readings of Marxist philosophy the prospect of a rift between these two great Communist powers. While more cautious opinion tends not to share this view, there seems to be general agreement among the experts that Red China is no mere Russian satellite — that it is at least an equal partner in the Communist alliance and, perhaps, the more influential of the two partners.

Thus, in India and in China, the world must reckon with two potentially great forces, both of too recent origin to permit reliable prediction of their future courses. Neither state has yet achieved maturity and stability; both still face a tremendous job of internal organization and of economic development. In India, an attempt is being made to fit democratic ideals to the geographical realities of a society divided along linguistic, religious, and caste lines. In China, the attempt is to impose a Communist ideology upon an individualistic peasant people whose primary loyalties for centuries have been to family and to region. What will come of these attempts we do not know, but since they involve almost a third of the world's population their consequences will be worldwide and, perhaps, world-shaking.

APPLICATION OF GEOGRAPHIC UNDERSTANDING

I. What is the geographic reasoning behind the statement that "in some ways, the problem of unifying India can be compared to the problem of unifying Europe"?

II. One Indian university professor has said that the average Indian knew and cared less about China than about Europe or the United States. How could this be, in view of the fact that the two countries share a common boundary?

III. What is the importance of Kashmir to India? To Pakistan? What would be the arguments for and against setting the Kashmir up as an independent, neutral state?

IV. The Chiang regime on Formosa has never abandoned its intention someday to launch a counterattack upon the Red Chinese mainland. From the geographical point of view, what are the prospects of success for such a venture?

V. What geographical reasons are there for expecting a greater amount of friction between the U.S.S.R. and Red China? What reasons are there for supposing that this friction would not become serious?

VI. How does the physiology of China encourage the development of regionalism at the expense of national unity? How could a Chinese government go about minimizing the divisive effects of the topography?

VII. What does Ravenholt mean when he says that China is a land which affords "only the slimmest margin for error" to the economic planner? How does this fact help to explain the traditional conservatism of the Chinese peasant?

---

[1] By permission from *Asia's Lands and Peoples,* by George B. Cressey, Copyright 1951. McGraw-Hill Book Company, Inc., New York, p. 93.

[2] By permission from *Land of the 500 Million,* by George B. Cressey, Copyright 1955. McGraw-Hill Book Company, Inc., New York, p. 351.

VIII. What reasons are there for suspecting that, despite the Indian government's attempt to make Hindi the national language, English might become the actual functioning language of commerce and communication in India?

IX. India raises more sugar cane than any other single country on earth. Why, then, does she not figure in the world cane-sugar trade?

X. In the light of what has been said in this chapter, how effective do you consider the Southeast Asia Treaty Organization as a defender of the peace in southern and eastern Asia? How would India's joining the Organization affect its strength?

References

1 Spate, O. H. K., "The Resurgence of Asia," *The Changing World,* Edited by W. Gordon East and A. E. Moodie, Harcourt, Brace & World, Inc., New York, 1956, pp. 465-467.

2 Spencer, J. E., *Asia East by South,* John Wiley & Sons, Inc., New York, 1954, pp. 180, 315.

3 Kuriyan, George, "India and Pakistan," *World Political Geography* (second edition), edited by Etzel G. Pearcy and Associates, Thomas Y. Crowell Company, New York, 1957, pp. 537-538.

4 Ravenholt, Albert, "Red China's Food Crisis," East Asia Series, American Universities Field Staff Reports Service, Vol. IX, No. 2, January, 1961, pp. 10-11, 14.

5 *The New York Times,* Sunday, March 19, 1961, p. 33.

6 *Newsweek,* December 12, 1960, p. 46.

7 *The New York Times,* Sunday, April 2, 1961, p. 6.

8 Talbot, Phillips, "India, 1961," South Asia Series, American Universities Field Staff Reports Service, Vol. V, No. 1, p. 16.

9 Cressey, George B., *Asia's Lands and Peoples,* McGraw-Hill Book Company, Inc., New York, 1951, p. 93.

10 Cressey, George B., *Land of the 500 Million,* McGraw-Hill Book Company, Inc., 1955, p. 351.

Chapter 31

Japan: a case of topographic frustration

It is now more than two decades since Japanese planes came whining out of the dawn upon elements of the American fleet anchored in Pearl Harbor. In retrospect, the indignation which that attack occasioned has given place, among thoughtful Americans, to a series of incredulous questions: Why did Japan thus seek to provoke a war which might have been avoided? How could the Japanese ever have seriously supposed that they could match their limited strength against the overwhelmingly greater strength of the United States? What could Japan have hoped to gain from a war which, even if she had won it, would have cost her enormously in lives and resources? Can Japan ever hope to solve her problems by resorting to war?

The answers to these questions require more than a superficial knowledge of Japan. And yet some useful clues to the answers can be found in even a relatively sketchy survey of her physical geography. For Japan, perhaps more than any other nation, can be described as a frustrated nation. And the two primary sources of her frustration are (1) the rugged topography of her land base and, (2) the paucity of those resources which are essential to national power in the modern world.

The land of quaking mountains

A map of the Pacific Basin will show that this greatest of the world's oceans is almost completely encircled by mountains which extend in the form of a great arc from Cape Horn at the southernmost tip of South America all along the west coast of the Americas, then down the eastern margins of Asia into New Guinea, New Zealand, and ultimately Antarctica (Figure XXXI-1). Included in the mountain masses which form parts of this vast system are some of the youngest and most rugged mountains on earth. Many of these mountains are volcanic, dormant for the most part in the Americas but still active on the western side of the Pacific Basin. Japan has some 500 volcanic peaks, the most famous of them being the lovely Mt. Fuji. About 10 per cent of these peaks have been active within historic time, half of these being still active at the present time. Many of the ranges within this circum-Pacific system are still young, which means that they are still in the process of building. Frequent and sometimes very intense earthquakes result from the dislocations that accompany the building process. Japan experiences about 15,000 earthquakes a year. Many of these quakes are submarine and set deadly seismic (tidal) waves in action. On September 1, 1923, half a million dwellings were demolished and 91,000 people were killed in an earthquake and its resulting fires which struck the Tokyo-Yokohama area.

Japan lies off the east coast of Asia in approximately the same latitudes as those of the lower Mississippi Valley. It is a part of this mountain rim and consists of four large mountain masses and a great many small islands. Geologically a part of the Eurasian land mass, these segments are separated from the mainland by the shallow, recently-drowned basin of the Sea of Japan. Altogether, these islands have an area of 142,644 square miles, just a little less than the area of the state of Montana. The largest of the islands, Honshu (Hondo), contains 87,500 square miles, an area slightly larger than the state of Idaho. The next largest, Hokkaido (Yezo), is about the size of South Carolina. The third largest, Kyushu, is a little smaller than the combined areas of Massachusetts, Connecticut, and Rhode Island. The smallest of the main islands, Shikoku, is a little smaller than Vermont. In addition to these larger islands, there are many smaller islands, ranging in size from several square miles to mere rocks sticking up out of the sea.

The map (Figure XXXI-2), reproduced from Watanabe, will give some idea of the complexity of Japan's surface forms. At least six independent insular and submarine mountain arcs meet in Japan, and much of the surface irregularity is the product of the differing ways these arcs coalesce. Watanabe's original map divides the islands into four

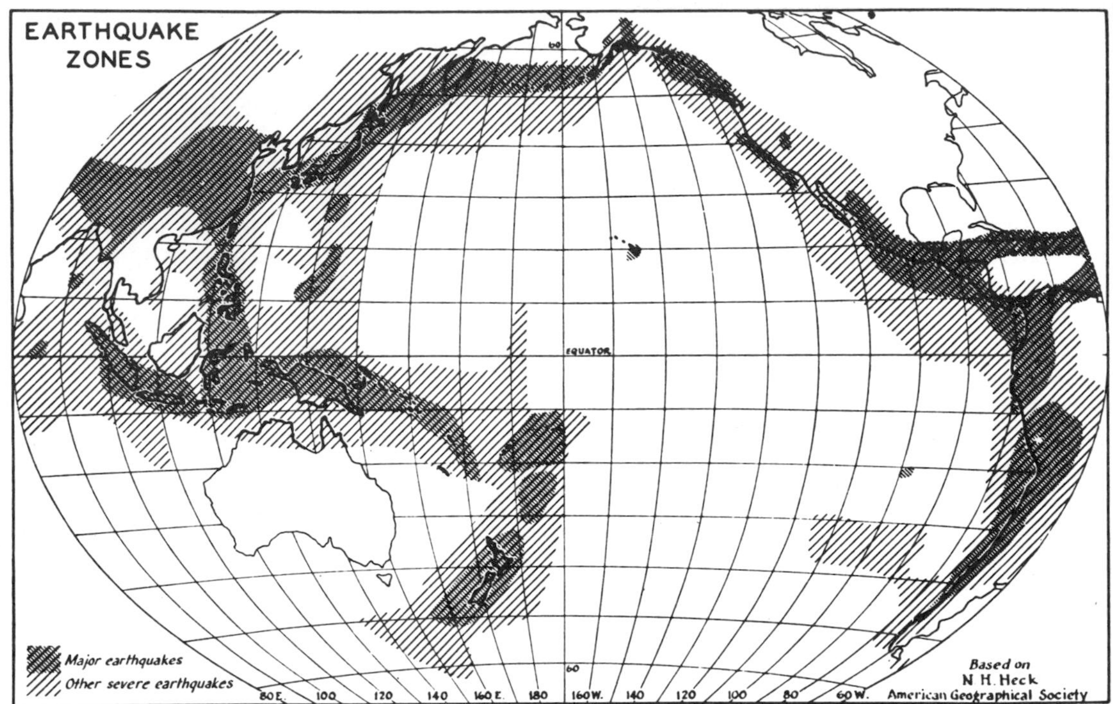

XXXI:1 This map shows the circum-Pacific earthquake belt. (From *Pacific Ocean Handbook* by Eliot G. Mears. Published and copyrighted by James Ladd Delkin, 1944, used by permission)

primary landform divisions, these in turn into ten subregions, these subregions into fifty "districts" and these districts into 229 "sections."

To the geologist, such a multiplicity of landform divisions suggests a highly heterogeneous surface. To the geographer it is perhaps more meaningful simply to note that three-fourths of the surface of Japan lies at an angle of ten degrees or more—too steep for cultivation, too steep, indeed, for most other economic uses of the land. In terms of productive area, therefore, Japan must be conceived of as many small patches of relatively level land in narrow belts of coastal plain or in fingerlike projections extending up the short, steep river valleys. Altogether, these small patches add up to about 25,000 square miles or roughly 17 per cent of the area of Japan. And even this area includes considerable areas of largely useless land, such as rocky valley floors and wet coastal marshland. Yet it is on this very small area that by far the greater number of Japan's 90,000,000 people must live and make their living.

The largest of these plains areas is the Kanto (Kwanto) Plain which lies inland toward the north from Tokyo Bay. The Kanto Plain is only a little larger than Connecticut and hardly more than a hundred miles broad in any direction, yet it contains over 15,000,000 people. South of the Kanto Plain, and separated from it by mountain country, lies the much smaller coastal lowland of Tokai. West of this lowland, and fringing the Inland Sea, lies the very much fragmented Setouchi Depression, the cradle-land of the Japanese state. Northwestern Kyushu contains a number of infaulted depressions separated from each other by block mountains, and Hokkaido has three relatively large plains areas—the Tokachi Plain, the Nemuro Uplands, and the Ishikari-Yufutsu Lowlands. These plains and lowlands make up what might be called "occupiable Japan."

The lowlands—incubators of civilization

It was in these small patches of lowlands that Japanese civilization began, quite some

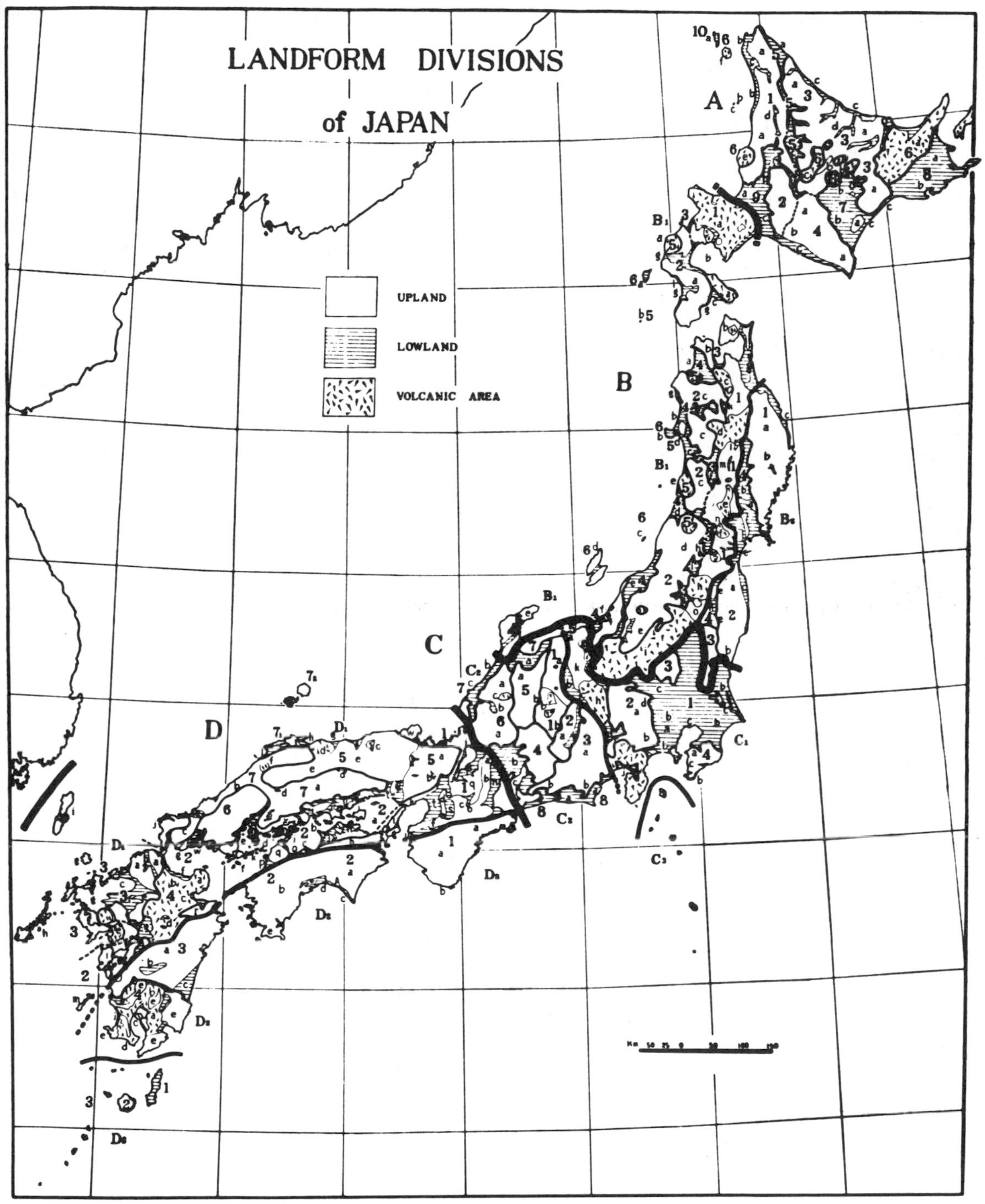

XXXI:2 The purpose of this map of Japan's surface forms is to show the great variety which exists within the relatively small area of Japan. Note how very small a percentage of the total area is lowland.

(Map by Akira Watanabe from *Proceedings of the Eighth General Assembly and Seventeenth International Congress of the International Geographical Union,* used by permission) time before the beginning of the Christian era. The aboriginal people of the islands were of Caucasoid stock. The Ainu ("hairy barbarians"), of whom only about 15,000 are left today, are a remnant of this earlier stock. Around 1500 B.C. Kyushu was invaded by a short, thick-set people with large heads and short legs that tended to bow. Where these people came from we do not know with any certainty, but the best evidence suggests that they probably came from two directions: one strain from northeast Asia by way of Korea and the other from southeast Asia by way of the China Coast. The combining of these strains into one people in Northern Kyushu produced the Yamato people, the ancestors of the modern Japanese.

Spreading northward from Kyushu, the Yamato people filtered through the coastal lowlands along the Inland Sea, eventually establishing a second major center of power west and south of Lake Biwa, near Kyoto ("eastern capital"). By about 500 B.C. the aborigines had been pushed into cold, inhospitable Hokkaido, the many small tribal chieftains had been brought under some measure of control, and the tradition of imperial rule had become established in the lands bordering the Inland Sea. But the long years of conquest and tribal warfare were to leave their mark upon the Japanese character. A military tradition was created during this time which was to become one of the enduring marks of Japanese civilization.

Located as she is off the Asiatic mainland, separated only by narrow straits from the vigorous Chinese civilization, it is not surprising that often in her history Japan has come under strong influence from the mainland. Her script was borrowed from the Chinese, many of her arts and crafts were adapted from those of China and Korea, and the Buddhist religion became the religion of many of her people. But even after Japan had achieved the outward forms of political and cultural unity it still took quite a long time for true national unity to develop. Great noble families, descended from earlier tribal chieftains, fought each other for control of the government until finally one such noble seized power in 1192 and assumed the title of Shogun, or military governor. For almost 700 years the Shogun was the actual ruler of Japan, the emperor falling into the role of a quasi-divine, but altogether powerless, figurehead.

Two factors seem to have been of major significance in unifying Japan. The first of these was involvement in foreign wars, particularly in Korea. As so often happens, the struggle against a common enemy forced men to look beyond the boundaries of their little mountain-girt plains to the larger identity of their islands. And the second unifying event was the introduction of Buddhism, which forced the issue between the old conservative and centrifugal forces on the one hand and the more progressive centripetal forces on the other. The struggle for power between these two culminated in a short, bloody civil war in which Buddhism gained the upper hand. By 710 the first permanent capital of all Japan was established at Nara. This capital was later moved to Nagaoka and then, in 794, to the site of modern Kyoto where it was to remain for more than a thousand years.

It is important for an understanding of recent Japanese history to recognize the importance of the warrior class which developed in these early days of Japanese nationhood. Although separated from Western Europe by the great breadth of Eurasia, Japan developed a feudal system very similar in some respects to that of Europe. One of the classes in this system was the warrior, or *samurai,* class schooled, as were the Prussian Junkers, to bear pain and hardship without complaint, to serve their feudal masters without questioning, and to devote their lives to the military service of their country. These samurai obeyed a stern code called "Bushido," a set of prescriptions very closely related to the nationalistic religion called "Shinto." Shinto taught, in the words of a modern Japanese historian, that "Great Yamato is a divine country. It is only our land whose foundations were first laid by the divine ancestors. It alone has been transmitted by the Sun Goddess to a long line of her descendants. There is nothing of this kind in foreign countries, therefore it is called the divine land." Bearing in mind that the code of the samurai dominated the thinking of the Japanese military down to our own day, it is perhaps not surprising that Japanese leaders at the time of Pearl Harbor gave greater weight to what they considered Japan's

Japan is an ancient country, with a history of the kind of violence through which most vigorous people have passed. Osaka Castle is today, of course, as anachronistic as the castles of England or of the Rhine Valley. But it is a reminder of a feudal age which, in Japan, lasted much longer than in Western Europe, partly because of Japan's long isolation from the rest of the world. (Courtesy Consulate General of Japan)

divinely-ordained destiny than they did to the apparent physical superiority of the United States.

Increasing numbers but stable patterns

It is interesting to note that while densities of population have increased greatly in Japan since those earliest days of her history, the pattern of population distribution seems not to have changed greatly. Now, as then, the people are crowded into the lowlands, and the mountains are still only very sparsely settled (Figure XXXI-3). The major population centers are the larger plains areas, such as the Kanto Plain (Tokyo), the alluvial coastal lowland of Tokai (Nagoya), the Setouchi Depression, and the interrupted lowlands of western Kyushu. Even on Hokkaido, still relatively lightly populated, the people have concentrated within the lowlands.

During the past century especially, Japan's population has grown so rapidly that these lowlands have been crowded to what would appear to be almost their capacity. When Japan reopened her ports to foreign commerce in 1853, her population was probably about 30,000,000. Twenty years later it was estimated at 33,000,000. After that time, the rise was rapid: 42,400,000 in 1897; 54,134,000 in 1917; 73,114,000 in 1940. Today it is a little over 90,000,000. Within another

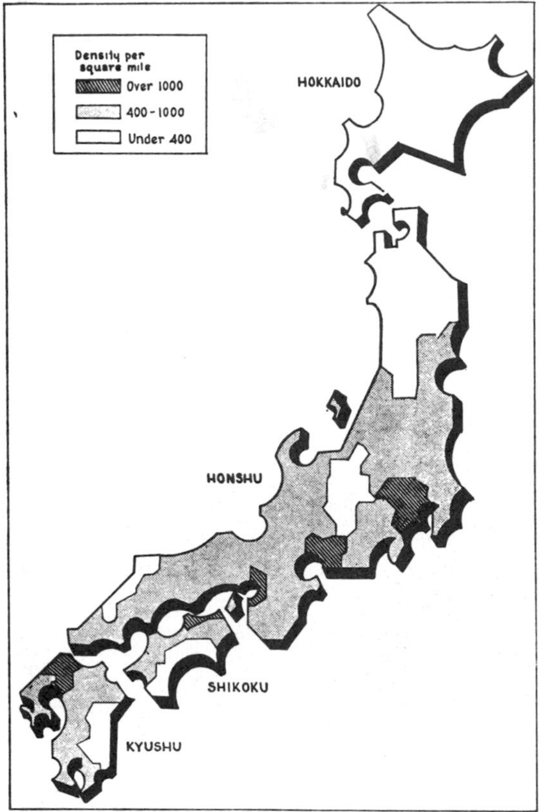

XXXI:3 This map shows the distribution of population in Japan. Significantly, the Japanese author of this map reserves the lowest category of population density for those "open" lands where there are fewer than four hundred persons per square mile —a density which would be considered dense in any part of the Western world except built-up metropolitan areas. (Map from *The New Japan*, Mainichi Press, 1959. Reprinted in *Population Bulletin*, Vol. XV, No. 7, November, 1959, published by Population Reference Bureau, Inc., used by permission)

decade, if present trends continue, Japan's population will have passed the 100,000,000 mark (4,000 per square mile of usable land). Fortunately there seem to be some indications of a leveling-off of population growth. But even a leveling-off would mean only that an almost hopeless problem may not become any more hopeless.

How shall we account for this dramatic increase in population in a country whose population seems to have been practically static for centuries prior to the 1850's? The essence of the answer may lie in the nature of modern Japan, a nation still basically Asiatic in its culture but strongly influenced by Western science and technology. Her high birthrate is a legacy from an Asiatic culture which until very recently placed a high value upon hands to till the fields and bodies to bear the burdens and do the work of an unmechanized society. Her constantly declining deathrate, on the other hand, is ascribable largely to the introduction of Western medicine, hygiene, and surgical techniques. Thus the spread between births and deaths has constantly increased and, in the absence of any real opportunities to emigrate, the Japanese have had to accumulate in their own small territory.

What has happened in Japan is essentially the same thing that had happened generations earlier in Europe. But whereas the great increases in Europe's population could be siphoned off by migration into the vast new lands opened up in the Age of Discoveries, the Japanese have had no such outlet. Even today Japanese are barred by the policies of most of the more prosperous nations of the world from immigrating to them. Nor was it possible for Japan to assert economic suzerainty over any wealthy underdeveloped lands. These had already been absorbed into the economic empires of nations which had, long before Japan's entry upon the international scene, skimmed off the cream of the world's great resource areas. And so Japan was left with no very likely choice but to intensify the use of her own national area by developing all of the potentialities of her agriculture and by establishing industries which could absorb her growing labor force. When her best efforts along these lines failed to raise Japanese prosperity to the level of the nations of the West, it was probably inevitable that there would be demands for more land and more resources, acquired, if need be, by force.

To all that has been said about the very limited habitable area of Japan must be added the fact that nature has been niggardly, indeed, in her allotment of resources to the Japanese. The high degree of industrialization which Japan has achieved in the past seventy-five years has given rise to a widespread misconception that Japan is well endowed with the materials and fuels needed for modern industry. This is far from being the case. It was the determination, discipline, and hard work of the Japanese people, rather than any natural advantage, that enabled them within the space of one generation's life span to convert their country from a feudal, agricultural state to one of the great industrial powers of the modern world.

Not much to do with

Japan's deficiency in industrial raw materials has sometimes been likened to that of Great Britain. What must be remembered is that Britain, however deficient she may have been in other materials, was blessed with abundant supplies of high-grade coking coal. Japan has enjoyed no such advantage. Estimates of Japanese coal reserves place these resources at a little more than nine billion tons. Annual coal production in the United States averages around 560 million tons. Thus if Japan were to use as much coal as we do each year she would run out of coal in about sixteen years. As a matter of fact, Japan does not use nearly as much coal per year as we do. Practically all of her coal goes to industry. Homes are heated by charcoal. Thus by carefully allotting her scarce coal to the most essential uses Japan may extend the life of her reserves for as long as 200 years. But even so, prospects are not bright. Less than 10 per cent of Japanese coal is satisfactory for conversion into coke, the coal seams are generally narrow and discontinuous (thus effectively ruling out the mechanization of her mining), and the costs of mining are constantly increasing as the coal must be sought at lower depths. Indeed, it may actually prove advantageous for Japan to import lower-cost coal than to absorb the prospective still-higher costs of her own production.

Japan's iron ore situation is even more critical. Her total ore reserve is estimated at 80,000,000 tons, of which only half is believed to be good enough for industrial use. (Annual production in the United States was 118,000,000 tons in 1953.) Japan is thus forced to supplement her very meager production with imports of both ore and scrap iron. She prefers to import scrap iron, since it requires less fuel to process scrap.

One of Japan's most serious deficiencies is her almost total lack of petroleum. Her total annual production of two million barrels is about the equivalent of eight hours' production in the United States.

It is true that Japan has a considerable variety of other minerals, although most of these occur in small, scattered deposits. Among those which are present in significant quantities are:

(1) Magnesium, available in unlimited quantities from the sea; (2) sulphur, important as the base for sulphuric acid and various fertilizers and quite abundant because of the volcanic nature of the Japanese islands, but cheaper to import from the United States than to produce at home; (3) copper, still barely sufficient for normal peacetime needs but rapidly approaching the point of exhaustion; (4) gold and silver, enough to meet Japan's very limited needs; and (5) waterpower, available in every part of Japan, but by now, for all practical purposes, fully developed.

As one examines this list of minerals, however, one is immediately impressed by the fact that they are of comparatively little value to a country which lacks adequate supplies of metallurgical coal and iron ore to furnish a solid undergirding for modern large-scale industrial development.

It is not surprising, therefore, that even today between a third and a half of Japan's people make their livings off the 25,000 square miles of cultivable land that constitute the real homeland of the Japanese people. Surprisingly, on this very small amount of land they manage to raise over 80 per cent of their country's food requirements. Obviously such huge production from such a small area of land can be achieved only by the most painstaking methods of cultivation, especially since the land is not highly fertile to begin with.

Complex patterns of soil and climate

In a general way, Japan's soils can be regionalized both latitudinally and altitudinally. The better soils are in the southeastern parts of the country and in the low-lying plains and deltas. The poorer soils are in the northwestern parts of the country and in the mountains and uplands. Thus the soils

These terraced fields are in the Japan Alps. The pressure of people on the land is great in Japan. When the small areas of level land were filled up, it became necessary for the Japanese to begin, quite literally, to level the hills. Usable land cannot be wasted, so the village has been pushed up to the base of the higher slopes which are too steep for terracing. (Courtesy Consulate General of Japan)

of Hokkaido and western Honshu are generally infertile gray soils, developed under a cover of forest and moor. The soils of eastern Honshu and the South, while still not notably fertile, are much better, ranging from brown forest soils in the vicinity of Tokyo Bay to red and yellow semilaterites on Kyushu. Upland soils are generally deficient in calcium, nitrogen, and humus and, where the forest cover is removed, are subject to very rapid and very profound erosion.

Offsetting somewhat the serious limitations of the soils is the favorable climate for agriculture throughout most of Japan. In the Köppen symbolism Japan south of middle Honshu is *Cfa*, northern Honshu is *Dfa*, and Hokkaido is *Dfb*. But Japan's climates are not really quite that simple, since the extreme irregularity of the surface tends to make the islands a compound of microclimates, and the nature and location of the islands impart to Japan's climates subtle peculiarities which are easily concealed beneath the Köppen symbolism.

Japan is, first of all, an island group; thus her climates tend to be basically marine. But she is an island group off the east coast of the world's broadest land mass in the belt of the westerly winds; thus there is in her climates a very considerable element of continentality. Latitudinally Japan stands within that zone in which warm currents bearing equatorial waters northward encounter cold currents bearing polar waters southward. Largely because of the shape of the Japanese islands and the Island of

Karafuto to the north (Figure XXXI-4), both of these currents bifurcate so that a branch of each flows on either side of the Japanese islands. But since moving bodies in the Northern Hemisphere are deflected toward the right, the cold Okhotsk Current has comparatively little influence on the climates of the islands except in northern Honshu and in Hokkaido. On the west side of the islands, the Okhotsk Current is deflected toward the coast of the mainland and the islands are washed by the warmer waters of the west branch of the Kuro Shio. The east side of the islands south of Tokyo is washed by the east branch of the Kuro Shio. Finally, Japan lies on the edge of the East Asian monsoonal system. Therefore, winds in the winter are dominantly from the northwest over Japan, whereas in summer they are principally from the southeast.

Seasonally the climates of Japan fall into the following patterns:

1. *Winter*—long, hard, and damp on Hokkaido; not so long, not so hard, and relatively dry on eastern Honshu; warmer and very snowy on western Honshu; mild and drizzly in southern Honshu and Kyushu.
2. *Summer* — Heavy rainfall throughout the islands, especially on the south and southeast coasts and particularly in June and in September. The June rains, called the *Bai-u* or "plum rains," are all-important for the rice. The September rains, or *Tsuyu*, are associated with the typhoons which are especially common at this season. Temperatures range from moderately warm in Hokkaido to warm in Kyushu.

Except for the typhoons, then, Japanese climates are generally favorable to agriculture. And climate and man, working together, manage to do wonders with the mediocre soils.

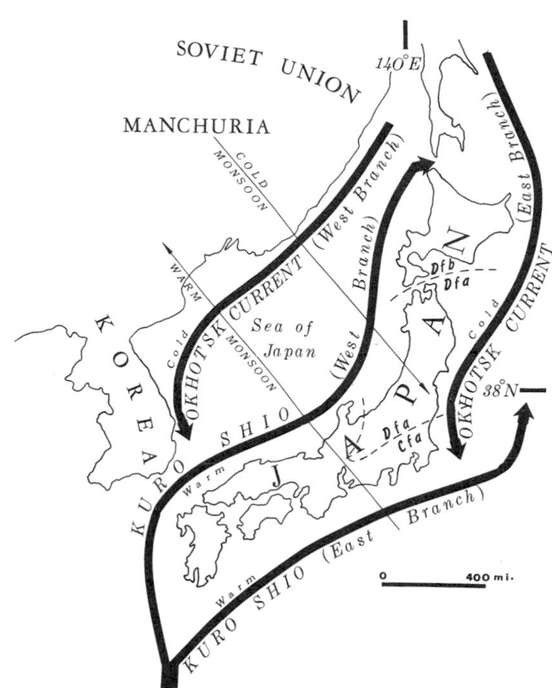

XXXI:4 Here are illustrated some of the controls over Japan's climates. In winter, a great pressure dome builds up over eastern Siberia, sending strong winds southeastward over Japan. In summer, a weak low-pressure system develops over the interior of Asia, drawing gentle winds into it from the ocean.

"Garden" farms

Japanese agriculture is the world's most intensive agriculture. The average farm in Japan contains about two and a half acres, but much larger (ten-acre) farms are in Hokkaido and considerably smaller (acre-and-a-half) farms are along the Inland Sea. And even these acreages are normally not in one unit. Rather they are made up of several garden-size, noncontiguous patches. By American standards, therefore, it would be altogether proper to call a Japanese "field" a garden and it should not be surprising to find that Japanese tools and cultivation methods are in some ways similar to gardening tools and methods in our own country. Little modern farm machinery is used. The hand and the hoe, with sometimes an assist from the draft ox, do the work.

Perhaps nothing impresses the outsider so strongly in Japanese farming practice as does the tremendous emphasis upon soil conservation and fertilization. Soil is the life of the Japanese farmer, and its destruction, whether by erosion or depletion, means disaster to himself and to his children. Where cultivation takes place at all, the landscape is likely to be wholly artificial, a mosaic of channels to carry water where it is needed, of ridges and low dykes to hold it where it is wanted, of terraces in broad, flat steps up the lower slopes. More than half of the cultivated land is in rice, almost all of which is grown under irrigation and all of which is produced at a huge cost in human effort.

By far the greater part of Japan's rice is raised in the lowlands. Here, late in spring, irrigation water is brought onto the land and the soil is worked into a thick mud into which the seedlings are set by hand. Fertilizers, both natural and chemical, are applied by hand directly to each plant. Not a single weed is permitted to grow in the patty. When extra water is needed, it is carried, again by hand, in buckets. Even the children are kept busy during the growing season scaring off the birds which might otherwise steal a few of the grains. In some of the warmer portions of southern and southeastern Japan, two or even three crops of rice may be taken off the same land in the same year. Where this is not possible, the land will certainly be planted with some dry-season crop after the rice harvest: wheat or barley most probably, although possibly clover or a legume or rape.

Rice is raised also in the uplands, usually in rotation with wheat and barley. The tendency has been for rice to take over as much of the upland acreage as physical conditions permit, since people must eat, while the acreages of other upland crops have tended to decrease proportionately. This economic fact of life and certain climatic requirements of the plant and the silkworm which feeds upon it define the area of mulberry production in Japan.

For decades until very recently, mulberry ranked next to rice and wheat in acreage and silk ranked next to rice in value in Japan. Even today, about half of Japan's farmers engage in the production of silk, the chief producing district lying in central Honshu where the land is too hilly for rice and too poor for tea. The development of the many synthetic fibers has greatly reduced the world market for silk and the acreage under mulberry culture today is less than half what it was in 1940. A considerable part of the land which has been withdrawn from mulberry has been planted with orchards.

Japanese tea production, on the other hand, has benefited since the Second World War from the reluctance of many Western nations to trade with Communist China. Encouraged by the help of government experiment stations, Japanese farmers have adopted the most modern methods of production and grading, and have succeeded in capturing the larger part of the world's export market in green tea. The chief tea-producing areas in Japan are the hill country between Tokyo and Nagoya and the hilly sections of the islands of Kyushu and Shikoku.

Too many people, too little land

Until the end of the Second World War, less than a third of Japan's farmers owned the land that they worked. By far the greater number of farmers were landless tenants or part-tenants. One of the first acts of the American occupation authority was to issue a directive ordering the Japanese government to "take measures to ensure that those who till the soil of Japan shall have a more equal opportunity to enjoy the fruits of their labor." In conformity to this directive, the Japanese government enacted a land reform law in 1946 which provided (1) that absentee landlords be required to sell their land to the government for redistribution by sale to tenants; (2) that the size of owner-cultivated holdings be limited so as to make more land available to more people; (3) that rentals in the form of crops be eliminated; and (4) that cash rentals be regulated so as not to exceed 20 per cent of the value of the rice crop or 15 per cent of the value of other crops. These last two provisions, although they may sound like dull economic legislation, meant much to tenant farmers who, in the past, had provided their own houses, outbuildings, tools, seeds, and fertilizers and still had to hand over half of their rice crop to the landlord. To such farmers it represented an opportunity, for the first time in the lives of many of them, to get out from under a staggering load of debt which made it impossible for them to prosper on the farm and equally impossible to leave the farm. By 1951, more than three million farmers had bought land under the easy terms of the reform law and tenancy had been cut by 12 per cent.

Even with these improvements, however, the Japanese farmer still ekes out a precarious living. Yields are thought to be very close to their practical limits. Ackerman sum-

During the season for patty-field planting the lowlands swarm with people. The men drive the oxen while the women take care of the plants. From this kind of intensive cultivation come high yields of rice, the highest in the world. Would it be advantageous to the Japanese to mechanize their farming? (Courtesy Consulate General of Japan)

marizes this aspect of Japan's agricultural picture as follows:

¶ On the one hand, the basic climatic features favor a much higher production per unit area than in western Europe or in the greater part of North American agricultural land. The length of the growing season, growing-season temperatures, and normal abundance of water supply during the summer months in combination encourage the growth of crops of relatively high calorie yield per unit area, like irrigated rice or corn. A mild winter and long frost-free season encourage multiple cropping. On the other hand, high yields depend on unstinted labor and heavy application of fertilizers. Topography will not permit a high degree of mechanization. In addition, the country must expect from natural sources recurring and consistent damages which always lower production below the theoretical maximum. The same climate which encourages high yields also favors somewhat higher disease and insect losses among crops than in cooler regions. Localized but recurrent losses of significance must be expected from floods, typhoon winds, earthquakes, tidal waves, and even occasional droughts. Thus, while the theoretical production maximum is high, normal losses from natural causes also are higher than in most middle-latitude areas. High production also is contingent upon liberal application of human effort, through the requirements for fertilizer supply, terrace tillage, intertilling, multiple cropping, erosion control, and other devices which add to the effectiveness of the land.[1]

As for expansion of acreage, Shiroshi Nasu noted as early as 1941 in his *Aspects of Japanese Agriculture* (Institute of Pacific Relations) that "It will be seen that the exploitation of arable land in Japan Proper has virtually reached the limit, leaving little room for further reclamation even with highly expensive and thoughtful assistance from the government." Ackerman, however, in his much more recent study, considers the Japanese government's postwar program designed to reclaim almost four million acres of hitherto unused land by 1965 feasible to the extent of about 80 per cent. But any significant increase in the nation's over-all food production will most likely have to be accomplished on land already under intensive cultivation.

Meat and dairy products have not, in the past, been important in the Japanese diet, and livestock are surprisingly rare in a country which, at first glance, might seem to be well-suited for a grazing industry because of the great amount of slope land. Many factors, however, tend to militate against stockraising, among them the following:

1. In the lowlands, the preferred use of the land must necessarily be for crops if Japan is to feed her large population.
2. In the uplands, the native grasses are not good pasture grasses and their replacement by cultivated grasses would be difficult and very expensive.
3. The Buddhist religion disapproves of the taking of life.
4. Traditional Japanese dietary patterns have no place for meat or dairy products.
5. The initial investment in land and animals for stockraising would prove prohibitive to all except a very small number of the wealthiest farmers.

Except, therefore, for some oxen that are used as draft animals and for a small but growing number of dairy cattle, Japan keeps few animals. Even hogs and chickens, which are scavengers and are everywhere under foot in nearby China, are fairly uncommon in Japan. Meat in the Japanese diet is largely fish, and the fishing industry is one of the most important of all Japanese industries.

The world's greatest fishing nation

The mixing of warm and cold currents on either side of the Japanese islands makes the coastal waters of Japan especially rich in food for fish. This advantage is somewhat offset by the extreme narrowness of the zone of shallow water surrounding the islands, but even so Japan has been able to keep a thriving fishing industry going in her own coastal waters. Almost every village has its small fleet. Sometimes fishing boats are found in small coves where there is not even a village. Among the fish taken in the coastal waters are sardines, cuttlefish, and shellfish. In addition a great deal of seaweed is gathered and used as fertilizer or as food for man and animals.

Japan's enormous demand for fish cannot, however, be supplied from its own coastal waters. Japanese fishermen, have, therefore, ranged the seas, particularly north and east of the islands. From the cold northerly seas they bring herring, cod, salmon, and crab. From warmer waters they bring sardines, bonito, tuna, yellowtail (a fish similar to tuna), shark, and mackerel. In recent years American tests of atomic weapons in the

---

[1] Ackerman, E. A., *Japan's National Resources*, The University of Chicago Press, pp. 49-50. Copyright 1953 by the University of Chicago.

Japanese fish for yellowtail. Japan can afford to "waste" very little of its land on meat animals. Fish, therefore, are important in the Japanese diet, and Japan's fishing industry is one of the world's most important. Notice that the land in the background looks exactly like what it is, a mountain range mostly submerged in the sea. (Courtesy Consulate General of Japan)

Trust Territory of the Pacific have greatly alarmed Japanese fishermen who fear contamination of the waters in a fishing area which is all-important to them. That this fear is not a groundless one is best indicated by the quarantining and destruction of catches brought into Japanese ports from time to time and discovered to be dangerously radioactive.

Japan is the world's greatest fishing nation, and while the greater part of her catch is intended for human consumption, a rather large percentage of it goes into other uses. Many inedible fish, for instance, are caught for use in the making of fertilizers, and one of the world's major whaling fleets operates in the waters off Antarctica.

About a million and half Japanese engage in fishing. Only about half of these are full-time fishermen, the other half consisting of farmers who look to both land and sea for a living.

Industrialization under handicaps

In a recent U.S. government publication designed to supply basic information for United States businessmen, Japan's economic handicaps and possibilities were summed up as follows:

¶ The small mountainous area comprising Japan is poorly endowed with many of the more important natural resources required for industrial production and most of those present are being fully exploited. However, some key resources are available, most significantly a large and skilled labor force, water power for hydroelectric development, and coal — although the last-named is of a generally poor quality and, to a considerable degree, is not suitable for metallurgical purposes. Japan's population density per square mile of cultivated area is among the highest in the world. Limited expansion of cultivable area is possible and is being explored by the Japanese Government. Plans also are being considered for expansion of electric power. Possibilities may exist for increasing the recovery of other resources, but the extent of such expansion is circumscribed by the natural environment.

Barring a major scientific revolution, Japan's resources will be insufficient for its needs. Consequently, it will have to depend on utilizing imports, as it has for nearly a century, for the production of semimanufactures and manufactures to provide sufficient earnings to maintain a reasonable level of living for its large and growing population. In 1953, per capita national income was about $160, one-fourth that of the United Kingdom and France, less than one-third that of West Germany, and only about one-eleventh that of the United States. However, it is considerably higher than that of most Far Eastern countries (2).

Japan came late upon the world's industrial scene. As a result, it enjoyed the major advantage of being able to start off with an efficient industrial plant patterned after the best that older industrial countries had arrived at by a costly system of trial and error. But Japan started off also with a major handicap, for by the time she began serious industrialization (after 1868) almost all of the principal sources of raw materials and all of the most promising markets had been appropriated by American or European interests.

It is obvious that a high degree of industrialization is essential to the maintenance of Japan's huge population on a relatively high level of living. But it was not, at the outset, a concern to supply an economic base for a growing population that brought about the establishment of industry in Japan. Rather it was a concern to maintain Japan's independence in a world which, quite obviously, was dominated by the great manufacturing nations. This early association of industry with considerations of national security helps to explain the several peculiar characteristics of Japanese industry which serve to differentiate it from the industries of other great manufacturing countries.

Since there was little private capital available for investment in the early days of modern Japan, the government furnished practically the entire initial capital investment in plant and equipment. The managerial group was also furnished by the government, chiefly from the ranks of its own civil servants. And since, especially in its early days, Japanese industry could not compete with the lower-cost industries of the older manufacturing nations, the government bolstered it with an elaborate system of direct and indirect subsidies. One of the most notable of these subsidies was the purchase, by the military and by the nationalized railways, of Japanese industrial products at prices far higher than they would have had to pay for comparable goods imported from Europe or the United States.

The Japanese were temperamentally disinclined toward socialized industry, but the essential poverty of their resource base made it impossible for them to develop a system of free (and therefore wasteful) competition. And so the pattern which developed from about 1900 on was a pattern of monopolistic private control in the hands of politically powerful industrial groups known collectively as the *Zaibatsu*. By 1937, these groups held more than two-thirds of Japan's trust deposits, conducted a third of Japan's foreign trade, for all practical purposes completely controlled her factory industry, and dominated the government. Three of the *Zaibatsu* controlled half of the coal output and owned nearly half the merchant ship tonnage registered in Japan. Two of the *Zaibatsu* controlled two of the major political parties and, through them, largely influenced national policy. In Japan as in Germany, the concentration of power in the hands of a small industrial-military oligarchy made it impossible for truly representative government to function.

A second peculiar characteristic of Japanese industry which serves to differentiate it from the industries of other great manufacturing countries is its dependence upon foreign sources of raw materials and fuels. It must be remembered that in Japan industry did not, as in Europe and the United States, develop "naturally" from the combination of national resources and the skills of the people. Rather it was developed as an element in national policy, designed not primarily to advance the economy of the state or its people but to provide a foundation of military power against a still vigorously expanding Western colonialism. And so among the first industries established were those which seemed most necessary to the military security of the state, whether Japan possessed the resources to pursue such industries profitably or not.

This concern for national security largely explains the establishment and rapid expansion of an iron and steel industry in a country which, as we have seen, possesses little coal and less iron. It helps to explain the early establishment of such industries as shipbuilding and armaments. Viewed realistically, a very large section of Japanese industry from the 1860's down to the period of allied occupation at the end of the Second World War could best be described as war industry, conforming to the general pattern of war industries in its dependence upon military purchases, in its relative freedom from "normal" economic controls, and in its tendency to grow far beyond the ordinary peacetime needs of the nation.

Had this large section of Japanese industry been compelled to justify itself in purely economic terms, it would surely never have grown as enormously as it did. Indeed even with government subsidy it is doubtful whether Japan could have remained a manufacturer of heavy goods, importing both the raw materials and a large part of the fuel for their production, had it not been for two very valuable resources which the Japanese possessed and which, in the postwar period, have enabled Japanese industries not only to survive but to grow in spite of the loss of the military market.

The first of these assets is waterpower, present in every part of Japan and almost fully developed in the industrial sections of Japan. The rivers of Japan are short, precipitous, and swift because they descend in a very short distance from the mountainous spine to the sea. Thanks to Japan's climates, they never lack sufficient water to generate power. Developed as they have been by the Japanese, they supply more than half of the country's power needs, even allowing for a degree of rural electrification which compares favorably with that of the world's wealthiest nations. In this respect, at least, Japan's rough topography is not a limitation but an advantage.

The second, and undoubtedly even greater, asset that Japan enjoys is a cheap but skilled labor force. The large population tends to keep wages low, but for centuries the Japanese farmer had supplied many of the things that he needed by manufacturing them in his own home. Even today, side by side with factory-type industries there exist thousands of small shops, each employing only a few workers, which turn out vast quantities of consumer goods for the home market. From this reservoir of skilled workers, Japanese factories have been able to draw their hard-working, highly skilled labor forces.

Apart from that large segment of industry that had its origins in the government's quest for military security, there exist many factory-type industries which are solidly based upon Japan's resources and the needs of her people. Chief among these, and one of the first to develop, is the textile industry. The generally mild climate of Japan and her continental neighbors, coupled with very low per-capita purchasing power, made it profitable for Japan to import raw cotton and export low-priced cotton cloth to markets throughout the Far East. And until the war and its attendant large-scale development of synthetic fibers, the Japanese found a huge market for raw silk (and even some silk textiles) in the United States and in western Europe. Besides, there was a demand in Japan for a wide range of consumer goods ranging from books and furniture to food products and beverages.

In its earliest days, much of Japanese manufacturing was imitative. Faced with the necessity of converting within one generation from an agricultural and fishing economy to a complex agricultural and manufacturing economy, Japan had no time to wait for the distinctive genius of its own people to set its stamp upon Japanese production. Instead, foreign experts were imported and bright young Japanese were sent abroad to gather up the best examples of goods which the Japanese wanted to manufacture and which, in their production, they often slavishly imitated. But already by the time of the First World War Japan had ceased to be merely imitative and while she continued to flood the markets of the world with cheap novelty items, she was also finding a place in the quality market for fine products which exhibited the good taste and pleasing simplicity of traditional Japanese craftsmanship.

The distribution of industry

The Japanese manufacturing belt extends from northern Kyushu northeastward along both sides of the Inland Sea and along the south coast of Honshu into the Kanto Plain. Within this belt there are concentrations of industry on the north coast of Kyushu, at the east end of the Inland Sea, around Nagoya, and inland from Tokyo Bay. The most important of these concentrations is at the east end of the Inland Sea, with Osaka as its principal center. The types of industries found here run the whole gamut of modern manufacturing. At first textiles were dominant. They are still a very significant part of the pattern, but the district has also become an important center of the metals industries and manufactures machines, tools, and chemicals. In the process of developing its industries, this district has become as congested, as grimy and sooty, as squalid and as characterless as have most of the world's great manufacturing centers. Fortunately the old and charming city of Kyoto has managed to remain a center for the craft industries and has thus been able to preserve some of the grace and beauty of the older Japan. But Osaka and its port town, Kobe, are new and rather ugly introductions into the Japanese landscape.

On about the same level of importance as this district is the great manufacturing district inland from Tokyo Bay. Like Berlin, Tokyo is an old town but a very young city, and its explosive growth in recent decades derives largely from its function as capital of a country which has developed along lines of political and economic centralization. Here, in the largest of Japan's plains areas, are a heavy population, furnishing both a large market and an abundant supply of labor; good power supplies from the harnessed rivers of the neighboring mountains and the nearby Joban coal field; one of the world's finest harbors, giving easy access to sources of raw materials and to markets; relatively large areas of flat land for factory sites and residential development; and the focal point of Japan's railroad and highway systems. Originally the industries of this district were relatively small, but the wartime intensification of industry brought large factories into the district and today the Kanto Plain displays all of the good and bad characteristics of a boom area. Tokyo, except for the quiet and feudal precincts of the Imperial Palace, is a great, sprawling, formless new city, starkly modern downtown and depressingly drab in its residential sections. Since the danger of earthquakes prohibited its upward growth, it spread out onto lowlands which Japan could ill afford to take out of agricultural production. Yokohama, its port town, is even more modern in its present appearance, having been almost completely rebuilt after the 1923 earthquake.

The Nagoya district is the only one of Japan's industrial concentrations in which textiles are still the most important products. Probably the chief reason for this is that the district has no important resources and lacks the kind of transportation facilities which would make it possible to import them advantageously. The environmental advantages on which this district has capitalized are waterpower from the adjacent mountains, a fairly large area of flat lands suitable for factory construction, and a good labor supply. Apart from textiles, the Nagoya district manufactures principally machines, tools, metals, foodstuffs, and chemicals. Most of these are small-scale industries carried on in relatively small plants.

The last of Japan's major industrial centers, the iron and steel district of northern Kyushu, is also the most "American" of her industrial areas. Fukuoka, the most important steel town, reminds the Western visitor of Gary, and the kinds of industry found in this district are essentially the kinds found in the Calumet district of the United States —iron and steel, cement, glass, flour, all manufactured in large, drab mills and factories. Unlike the three districts already discussed, the northern Kyushu district does not have much land for industrial expansion, but this handicap is more than offset by the presence of Japan's largest coal field nearby. No one city dominates this district, but Fukuoka is the largest city and Nagasaki is a famous old port town.

"Trade or die"

Almost from the outset, Japanese industry has had to look overseas both for raw materials and for markets. As a result, Japan has long been involved in maritime trade. Prior to the Second World War she had one of the world's great merchant fleets, and this fleet, in turn, was backed up by an important shipbuilding industry which, since 1957, has been the world's largest. At the same time, prewar Japan sought to secure her economic position by expanding politically into certain areas which she considered necessary to her long-range economic security. Thus, in the 1930's she created the puppet state of Manchukuo out of the territory of coal-and-iron-rich Manchuria. From there she penetrated down along the China coast, almost succeeding in bringing all of China under her suzerainty. With the outbreak of the Second World War, she moved quickly to seize the Indo-Chinese territories, the Malay Peninsula, Burma, the Philippines, the islands of Indonesia, and some of the islands of Melanesia. Apparently her goal was consolidation of these territories into a political and economic empire which would furnish her with a dependable flow of fuels and raw materials and would, in return, accept the finished products of her factories. Whether or not Japan intended to make Australia a part of this "Greater East Asia Co-Prosperity Sphere" has been long debated. But there is no doubt that Australia was a prime military objective in the strategy of the war.

With the end of the war, and with the collapse of Japan's short-lived empire, Japan did not return to some earlier status quo. Essentially, she found herself in the awkward position of a badly-battered heavyweight boxer who has been stripped of all of his possessions except for his fifth-grade school clothes. Not only had Japan lost her political empire; she had lost practically all of her merchant fleet, her fishing fleet, her investments on the mainland and in the islands. At home her industry had been overbuilt to meet the war emergency and both her political leadership and the best brains of her industry had been compromised by their roles in the planning and execution of the war. Worst of all, she had incurred the enmity of the very nations whose friendship and good will she most needed. No nation in recent history has had to face a future as potentially disastrous as did Japan at the end of the Second World War.

What saved Japan at this critical juncture was the new crisis in world affairs that developed soon after the war ended. Before the victorious nations could even agree on terms of peace for Japan, they became involved in a bitter and protracted struggle among themselves, a struggle in which practically all of eastern Asia fell under Communist control, leaving Japan in a highly advantageous position to bargain with the anti-Communist powers. As a matter of fact, it was not even necessary for Japan to press any demands upon her former enemies, so eager were they to rebuild her strength and undergird her economic and political stability. Recovery was, therefore, very rapid from the effects of the war, and by 1951 the index of production already stood higher than it had in the immediate prewar period. Increases in population and labor supply must, of course, be taken into account in such comparisons, and when these are allowed for the picture is not quite so bright. Adjusted for these factors, the 1951 production index stood at only 86 per cent of the prewar figure. But since 1951 Japan has enjoyed unprecedented prosperity, and her present economic condition is the best it has ever been.

But her prosperity is a very fragile thing. It is still based very largely upon the unhealthily inflated needs of a world preparing for war, and it is still very largely supported by the expectation of outside assistance if such assistance should prove necessary. There is still not a sufficiently large domestic market in terms of purchasing power to absorb the products of Japanese industry, let alone its potential production. And the war has left its aftermath of suspicions so that many countries, particularly in the Far East, are still reluctant suppliers and customers to the Japanese.

It is not very difficult for the American or the European to understand the many problems which Japan's physical geography imposes upon her, for these are problems which have to do with such universal needs as food, clothing, and shelter. It is much more difficult for Western man to understand the psychological problems of a people whose cultural roots lie deep in a civilization as old as, but quite different from, his own. The Japanese are not a primitive people who need only to be "civilized." They are a people of

This modern housing development is in Tokyo. Except for the precincts of the imperial palace, there is nothing quaint about modern Tokyo. The city epitomizes the series of revolutions which Japan has undergone in the past century: a fantastic growth in population, industrialization under forced draft, partial absorption of Western culture, and a notable rise in the standard of living. Tokyo may be the largest city in the world today. Certainly it is still growing at what some Japanese consider an alarming rate. Why do the Japanese let their capital city sprawl like this instead of following the example of New York, i.e., building upward? (Courtesy Consulate General of Japan)

ancient culture who, since they cannot afford to isolate themselves from the rest of the world, find themselves torn between two powerful forces: on the one hand, a strong attachment to their own heritage with all that implies in terms of national pride, military tradition, reverence for a great past, and devotion to ancestral ways; and on the other hand, a vigorous desire to match the other great nations of the world in power, in wealth, in intellectual accomplishment, in standard of living, and in world influence.

The role of the recent arrival is always a hard one. One who has nothing to be proud of in his past may find it relatively easy to accept the standards and norms of the group into which he has moved, but one who honors and respects his own past finds himself torn inevitably between the desire to remain what he has been and the necessity to become something else. This tension is likely to exhibit itself in what appears to others to be highly erratic behavior. The Western visitor is baffled by the Japanese businessman who, in his office, is practically indistinguishable from his counterpart in Chicago or Manchester but who, in his home, "reverts" to the ceremonial life of feudal Japan. Western statesmen are sometimes exasperated by Japanese statesmen who deal in subtleties allegedly incomprehensible to the "practical" Western mind. Even long-time friends of Japan often find themselves hard put to it to understand how so much grace and dignity can exist side by side with so much modern shabbiness in one small country. Japan has suffered greatly both from the exaggerated enthusiasms of her friends and from the unwarranted criticisms of her detractors.

The need for understanding

Perhaps the first step toward understanding Japan must be the realization that she is a nation in cultural transition. This is perhaps most apparent in the appearance and function of her cities and towns. Prior to industrialization, Japan was overwhelmingly rural, and the rural population has remained essentially stable since the beginnings of industrialization. Lacking additional land to occupy and use, Japan's surplus population has been accumulated in urban areas until today Japan has six cities with populations in excess of one million. These are Tokyo, Osaka, Nagoya, Kyoto, Kobe, and Yokohama. Cities of such size are characteristic of the great powers in the modern world. What are lacking are cities in the intermediate size range, between half a million and a million. Their absence may be ascribed to the lack of sufficiently large agricultural or industrial hinterlands as a result of the segmented topography. Even the small towns have tended to lose population to the larger cities until, by now, it is estimated that more than twenty million Japanese live in cities of more than 100,000 population.

The great cities are strikingly modern downtown and traditionally Japanese in their residential districts. The danger of earthquakes limits the heights of buildings even in the downtown areas and it has discouraged the building of apartment houses in the residential areas. Typically, the smaller cities and towns and the residential districts of the major cities present a low, flat skyline; sprawl formlessly out into the surrounding countryside; consist of unpainted wooden structures which constitute a major fire hazard whenever, as always happens in connection with an earthquake, fires break out and water lines are snapped; and display an irregular pattern of narrow streets. Here and there the pattern is broken by a colorful temple or shrine, sometimes surrounded by gardens, which rises above the otherwise rather drab landscape.

Notably lacking in Japanese cities, as indeed in the whole Japanese social structure, is any evidence of a middle class. This is, in itself, an indication of the transitional character of present-day Japan. The great majority of the people, while their condition is far better than that of the bulk of the lower economic groups on the mainland, are very poor and have little reason to hope for any considerable improvement in their lot. A very small group of high officials, military leaders, and wealthy industrialists enjoy a high level of material comfort. But in between these extremes there is only a very small middle class of teachers, professional men, civil servants, and small businessmen. As in other nations, the lot of this group has been a difficult one in the postwar period of inflation.

There persists also in Japan, although it is no longer legally recognized, an outcaste group, the *Eta*, whose ancestors slaughtered animals or dealt in flesh or hides. Such occupations are, of course, inconsistent with traditional Buddhist teachings about the sanctity of life, and those who carried on such occupations were considered unclean.

It is interesting to note that in Japan, as in other countries, birth rates have tended to decline in urban areas, and it is believed that Japan's cities, too, would cease to grow if they were not constantly being replenished from the countryside. As Japan becomes constantly more urban, and as urban reproduction rates come more and more into line with urban reproduction rates in the cities of Europe and North America, it may be anticipated that population growth will be slowed down and perhaps eventually cease altogether.

Rural Japan is still basically oriental. Land is at so great a premium that it cannot be spared for broad highways, except between the major cities. Roads, therefore, are mostly narrow foot paths. Fences are a rarity, their place being taken by hedgerows or ditches or dikes. Field sizes are too small to allow for the economical use of mechanized equipment, so much of the work is done by hand with perhaps an occasional assist from ox or horse. Except on Hokkaido, rural settlement usually clusters in villages in houses built of bamboo. These villages are commonly built on land which, for one reason or another, is not prime agricultural land so as to save the good land for crops. On Hokkaido a pattern of dispersed settlement on individual farms has developed, partly because Hokkaido is largely devoted to extensive wheat farming rather than intensive rice farming; partly because population densities are not nearly so great in this cold northerly island as in the more temperate islands to the south; and partly because technical advisers from the United States were invited by the Japanese government to assist in the planning of Hokkaido's agricultural development in the early decades of the twentieth century.

The future?

What does the future hold for Japan? The answer to that question hinges on how Japan meets her most pressing problem of adjusting her population to the limitations of size and resources which presently handicap her development. The experience of other nations that have faced a similar problem would seem to suggest that its solution must be sought along one or more of five lines: (1) more intensive agriculture; (2) a lowering of the standard of living; (3) the creation of wealth-producing industry; (4) an extension of political and/or economic empire; or (5) a check on population growth. It should be apparent from our discussion that any considerable intensification of agriculture in Japan is probably impossible. The experience of other nations would indicate that no country accepts a lowering of its standard of living unless it is forced to it by inability to prevent it. The industries which Japan has managed to build on the basis of its meager resources can already be described, without undue exaggeration, as miracles of Japanese resourcefulness and hard work, and while some further development may be anticipated, it is not likely that the pace of future industrialization can match anticipated population growth. The remedy of imperial expansion, in either the political or the economic sense, would hardly seem to be a realistic remedy in view of the debacle of the Second World War. It cannot, however, be entirely ruled out as a possible strategy of desperation.

This would leave a check on population growth as Japan's apparent best bet for the long-run solution of her problem. And this is not such an unlikely solution, either. Put very bluntly, birthrates tend to decline when children cease to be economic assets and become economic liabilities. In rural, agricultural areas children may be valuable as additional hands to work the land. In cities they make little contribution to the family income and occupy space which is already badly limited. In impoverished lands where living standards are low, it is hardly possible for children to depress the family's level of living below its already rock-bottom level. In lands where the standard of living is high, or where there is a promise of a rise in the level of living, children constitute a threat to a hoped-for improvement in the family's level of living. Birthrates tend to level off or decline at the point where significantly large numbers of parents must choose whether to have another child or to add to their material comforts and conveniences. Japan has reached the point where significantly large numbers of her people are now in a position to make that decision. It may be anticipated that before too long Japan will have stabilized its population at a figure probably somewhat in excess of one hundred million. But even this number would press heavily upon the limited land and resource base of Japan.

APPLICATION OF GEOGRAPHIC UNDERSTANDING

I. How might Japan be different from what it is if

A. It were a group of relatively flat islands instead of a partially-submerged mountain range?

B. It were five hundred miles east of its present location?

C. It were five hundred miles south of its present location?

D. It were all one island rather than a number of small islands?

E. It had been discovered and settled by Europeans rather than Asiatics?

II. Would the organization of Japan's farms into larger units of ownership and management be advantageous or disadvantageous to the country's social and economic welfare?

III. What would be the arguments for and against the establishment of a free-trade area involving Japan, China, the Philippines, southeast Asia, and Indonesia? Consider not only local regional interests but the larger world picture.

IV. Switzerland, Denmark, and the Netherlands are also countries with large populations and meager resources. Why could Japan not seek a solution to its problems along lines that these countries have pursued (e.g., investments, specialization of agriculture, tourist trade, development of craft industries?)

V. If Japan were wholly free to determine her own foreign policy, would you expect a Japanese government to favor or oppose the admission of Communist China into the United Nations? Why? (Bear in mind not only economic considerations but also strategic interests.)

References

1 Ackerman, E. A., *Japan's Natural Resources,* The University of Chicago Press, 1953, pp. 49-50.

2 *Investment in Japan,* United States Dept. of Commerce (The Superintendent of Documents, 1956).

Chapter 32

The changing face of Western Europe—Germany, France, Italy

How many loved your moments of glad grace,
And loved your beauty with love false or true;
But one man loved the pilgrim soul in you,
And loved the sorrows of your changing face.
—William Butler Yeats

It is perhaps not altogether inappropriate to introduce a chapter on Western Europe with a stanza from one of the great love poems of modern times. Many of us who live in the New World still have at least vague recollections of an earlier home, and there are ties of affection and concern that bind us to it. Few of us, probably, would want to return to it permanently, and yet a growing number of us returns from time to time, drawn by those "moments of glad grace" which have provided the themes of some of our popular songs or by those deeply-etched sorrows which give personality and character to the constantly changing face of the continent.

We shall be dealing in this chapter with Western Europe, that part of the continent which traces its cultural ancestry back through Rome to Athens and Jerusalem. For more than a millennium this was Catholic Europe, much of it loosely confederated in the Holy Roman Empire, all of it culturally organized around the Roman Catholic Church. In the past five hundred years, the political unity has all but disappeared, and the religious unity has been shattered both by schism and by the growth of secularism. And yet a large residue of cultural unity remains—enough, at least, to provide a foundation upon which new attempts to restore the unity of the region are being based.

The axis of Western Europe extends north and south from the Scandinavian Peninsula to Italy. Its core area includes the Benelux Countries (Belgium, the Netherlands, and Luxemburg), France, Germany, Switzerland, Austria, and northern Italy. Toward the east, there is a transition through Poland, Czechoslovakia, Hungary, and Yugoslavia into Slavic, Orthodox Europe. To the south, there is another transition through the Iberian Peninsula to the dryland culture of North Africa. Toward the north and west there is not so much a transition as a gradation into the insular and peninsular cultures of Scandinavia and the British Isles. Finally, to complicate matters, there are the special cases of Finland, culturally Western but necessarily cautious not to offend its Russian neighbor; and Greece, culturally Eastern and Orthodox but politically and economically bound to the West.

Since all boundaries must, in the final analysis, be arbitrary, we shall arbitrarily define Western Europe as that part of the continent which lies north of the Mediterranean Sea and west or north of the so-called "Iron Curtain." Our primary focus will be upon the core of this region — France, the Benelux Countries, Germany, Austria, Switzerland, and Italy — with only so much reference to its borderlands as may be necessary to illuminate our discussion of this core.

Background: the Second World War, its devastation and its consequences

May 8, 1945, makes a convenient historical watershed for purposes of comparing Europe as it is today with the Europe that existed at the outbreak of the Second World War. On that day, V-E Day, the travail of six long years of war ended, and for the first time it was possible to see the continental dimensions of the war's devastation. It was not a pretty sight. Hitler's Thousand-Year Reich lay in a mass of blasted, smoking ruins. A large part of the Netherlands lay under water, flooded by the Dutch in a last desperate effort to stem the German blitzkrieg; and the great port city of Rotterdam, all but leveled by the Germans in reprisal for Dutch resistance, had all of the aspects of an ancient ruin. Belgium and France, relatively untouched by the physical destruction of war, bore the livid emotional scars of a long and hateful occupation. Italy, bankrupt and leaderless, teetered on the brink of anarchy.

How long would it take the prostrated continent to recover from the shock and the destruction of the war? There were sober-

A big dike is being constructed for the Zuiderzee Works. The European landscape is the product of more than a thousand years of co-operation between man and nature. Often enough, nature's co-operation was only grudgingly given. The Dutch have even wrested a large part of their national area from the sea, but in less dramatic ways, other Europeans have had to build their own lands from marshes and swamps and fens and dunes. To what extent may the greatness of Europe be a reflection of the difficulties her people have had to overcome? (Courtesy The Netherlands Information Service)

minded experts who said that it would take at least a generation merely to recover from the physical effects of the war. Germany, so some of the experts said, might need a century to regain her former strength; and when it became apparent that she was to be divided indefinitely into two states, this prediction was revised upwards. It seemed almost certain that the hatreds engendered and reinforced by the war would so completely alienate the great nations of the continent from each other that it would be impossible to restore even such limited co-operation among them as had existed before the war. In short, the war seemed, if not the deathblow, at least something close to it for the continent which had dominated the stage of history for so many centuries.

At this moment of its greatest extremity, Europe suffered what seemed to be the final, crushing blow. Hard on the heels of the war, a cataclysm of awakening nationalism shook and shattered the colonial empires which had so heavily subsidized the domestic economies of the maritime powers of Western Europe for so many centuries. The Netherlands lost its fabulously wealthy empire in Indonesia, and France its colonies in Indochina. Italy, too, lost its colonies, although the loss was not a great one since they consisted mostly of vast tracts of African desert. The Belgians, the French, and the Portuguese were able to delay for a while the inevitable loss of their African holdings, but by the end of 1960 the Belgian and French empires were "one with Nineveh and Tyre," and ominous cracks were developing in the once-monolithic Portuguese empire.

But despite all this devastation and loss, no one would deny that, as the Sixties dawned, Europe was thriving. Economically, it was enjoying a "boom" of unprecedented proportions. Socially, it seemed sounder than it had been since at least before the First World War. Politically, it was stable internally and influential in world affairs. The scars of war remain, but it is not so much the scars that impress the visitor as it is the great amount of new construction. The not-yet-forgotten past still returns in nightmares and in abortive attempts to resurrect fascism, but Europe looks not so much to the past as to its prosperous present and toward a future which could be very hopeful if it were not overshadowed by the menace of a third World War. And the hatreds engendered by the war, if they have not altogether died, have at least been allowed no voice in the councils of European statesmanship.

How shall we explain this postwar European renascence? Certainly much of the credit must go to brilliant leadership; the names of Adenauer, DeGaulle, and DeGasperi have been engraved into the history not only of our times but of their nations. Beyond all doubt, the generous outpouring of American aid to these countries immediately after the war was the transfusion without which they might not have survived the profound economic shock of the war and the financial drain of reconstruction. But leadership and timely aid do not tell the whole story. It has been said that the best way for a man to ensure his longevity is to choose the right ancestors. It might be said with equal accuracy that the best way for a nation or a region to ensure its longevity is to choose the right geography. The geography of Western Europe is conducive to national and cultural longevity.

The changing economic face of Western Europe

Borrowing a device from accounting, we might cast a balance sheet for Western Europe somewhat along the following lines:

ASSETS	LIABILITIES
Climatic	
Plentiful, year-round rainfall (except in *Cs* Italy)	Cool summers limit variety of crops (except in Italy)
Mild summers with cool (but not cold) winters	
Few severe storms or droughts	
Mineral	
Abundant coal, easily accessible (Britain, West Germany)	No petroleum to speak of
Abundant iron ore (Britain, France, Belgium)	Almost total lack of ferroalloys
Large supplies of bauxite (France)	Some iron resources approaching exhaustion
Large supplies of potash (Germany)	
Important supplies of sulphur (Italy)	
Two-thirds of the world's mercury (Italy and Spain)	
Good supplies of lead (Spain, West Germany, Yugoslavia)	
Pedologic	
Highest proportion of agricultural land of all of the continents	Much draining and liming necessary because of relatively heavy rainfall and low relief

ASSETS	LIABILITIES
	Geodetic and Topographic
Location near center of land hemisphere Location at eastern terminus of North Atlantic sea lane Vast plains area extending from Ireland and central France to the Yenisei River Longest coast line in relation to its area of all of the continents Many excellent harbors Seas penetrate deep into the heart of the continent Location at end of the Gulf Stream in westerly wind belt produces marine climate	As a peninsula of Eurasia, Europe has been wide open to repeated invasion from the East Mingling of warm and cold ocean currents off its western coast give Europe frequent and extended fogs High-latitude position reduces intensity of solar radiation Low relief frequently causes problems of drainage
	Hydrographic
Many important rivers flowing from the heart of the continent to the sea Dependable volume of water in the rivers the year around Many rivers widen into tidal estuaries as they approach the sea Divides between the great rivers often low, narrow, easily canalized Abundant ground water	Some rivers require dredging for navigation Locally large areas of wet land
	Cultural
Vigorous, inventive people A religious tradition which emphasizes individual freedom and responsibility A political tradition which emphasizes the rule of law and the rights of the individual A great heritage of the arts and the sciences	Political fragmentation Mutual jealousies, fears, and animosities among the nations Economic fragmentation along political boundary lines Social stratification which, in the past, often produced gross inequities in the distribution of wealth Recurrent periods of war, civil unrest, and dictatorship Growing economic and political competition from other parts of the world

It would seem fair to say that, on this balance sheet, the assets outweigh the liabilities in all of the categories with perhaps one exception, the cultural. For centuries, the political and economic fragmentation of Europe has fostered wars and kept the continent in turmoil as nations sought to supply their resource deficiencies by attempting to seize them from their neighbors. The classic example is the century-long conflict between Germany and France in which one of Germany's objectives was always to get control of the Lorraine ores while France was equally covetous of the coal in the Saar Basin. Indeed, the troubled history of the Saar in the past eighty years epitomizes the politico-economic struggles that have resulted from the rampant nationalisms of the continent:

¶ . . . Until about 1880 it had little economic significance, but thereafter its coal deposits were intensively developed in association with Lorraine iron ore. Saar coal was sent to Lorraine, and ore from that region was smelted at the Rochling works at Volklingen and at those of Stum at Dillingen and Neunkirchen. German capital and labour were largely responsible for the industrial development of an area which was, and still is, predominantly German-speaking. After the first world war the treaty makers attempted a compromise settlement; they established the Saar Territory to be ruled by a commission of the League of Nations from January 1920 for fifteen years, gave the Saar coal mines to France for that period as part of German reparations, and arranged for a plebiscite to decide the future of the Territory at the end of the period. In 1935 the Saarlanders voted overwhelmingly for return to Germany, but this political arrangement did not solve their economic problems. The Saar was still dependent on neighboring French territory for food and labour supplies, and, because of its distance from the important industrial regions of Germany, it did not fit as conveniently into the economy of that country as it had done into that of France.

Immediately after the second world war the Saar formed a part of the French Zone of Germany. A plan for economic union with France and political autonomy was put forward by the French government. When the western zones of Germany were fused together in 1947, a Franco-Saar customs and currency union was established, and the Saarlanders retained their political autonomy on a territory which had been enlarged in 1946 by 942 square kilometres and the population of which was 20 per cent greater than that of the former Saar Territory. As a result of Anglo-American protests, this area was reduced to 2,559 square kilometres in 1947, and a further slight adjustment was made in 1949, thus giving the Saar its present area of 2,567 square kilometres. In the meantime British and American spokesmen had made it abundantly clear that a permanent settlement of the Saar problem must await the conclusion of a peace treaty with Germany. . . .

In October 1954 a new agreement was reached between France and Germany which "shows that a new territorial conception has been introduced, establishing something that is neither a State, nor a protectorate, nor a condominium." This agreement provided for the "Europeanization" of the Saar—i.e., it would have been given a European statute within the framework of Western European Union, and a European commission appointed by W.E.U. would have undertaken representation of Saar interests in foreign affairs and defence; internal affairs would have been the responsibility of an elected parliament, and the coal mines and iron and steel works would have been in the hands of Saarlanders. These ingenious arrangements marked a new stage in Franco-German relationships connected with the Saar, but they were subject to approval, or otherwise, by a referendum among the Saarlanders. . . .

. . . The Saarlanders, however, rejected the Statute.[1]

Such a lot of trouble — and all because long ago someone drew a political boundary line between a coal field and an iron deposit!

Fortunately, there are signs that Europe's postwar leadership takes the intelligent position that what man has done man can undo. It may not be altogether accidental that the two "fathers" of European economic union both come from the Franco-German borderlands and thus know, at first hand, that any boundary through this borderland must be unsatisfactory to one side or the other. Robert Schumann comes from Luxembourg, Konrad Adenauer from the Rhineland. Together, they have done much to minimize the political boundary between France and Germany and to open it to the free movement of people and goods. In so doing, they have made some fundamental changes in the economic face of Western Europe.

The new pattern of regional economic associations is discussed in Chapter 15. At the present time, all of the countries of Western Europe except Spain hold membership in one or the other of two such associations, the European Economic Community (EEC) or the European Free Trade Association (EFTA). These associations are, on the one hand, confessions of the inherent weaknesses that had existed in the national economies of the past and, on the other hand, practical attempts to capitalize on the advantages to be gained from regional co-operation. The fact that there are two such associations rather than only one reflects not so much a dis-

[1] Moodie, A. E., "Britain, France, and the Benelux Countries," *The Changing World*, edited by W. Gordon East and A. E. Moodie, Harcourt, Brace & World, Inc., New York, 1956, pp. 105-106. Reprinted by permission.

More so than in most other parts of the world, the works of man give character and personality to the landscape of Western Europe. Less permanent than hills and mountains, the great architectural masterpieces of the continent, such as the Brussels City Hall, are nevertheless centuries old and provide a link between the present and the remote past. This sense of continuity is a stabilizing factor in European civilization and culture.

agreement over the desirability of European economic integration as a difference in judgment as to the best methods of achieving it. The nature of this difference has been stated by Professor Walter Hallstein, president of the Commission of the EEC:

¶ In a very real sense, he said, the Community was one unit. Although its most publicised actions hitherto have been in the field of tariffs and quotas, it in fact contained many more radical features. Its aim was to set up a single home market in which capital, labour, and services, as well as goods, would circulate freely as in a national home market. It meant the harmonisation of legal systems and the application of common rules. It meant common policies for agriculture and for transport, where free competition, for various reasons, could only be a distant goal. It meant co-ordination in matters of monetary policy, and common responsibility for regional development and social policies designed to ensure harmonious development of the economy.

The unity of the Seven [EFTA], Professor Hallstein continued, was of a less advanced order. He said: "By this I do not mean any slight upon the European Free Trade Association or its members. Its Scandinavian members, in fact, were talking about the possibility of a Nordic Customs Union three years before the members of the European Economic Community signed the Rome Treaty. And if the countries of the Seven have found it easier to establish among themselves a less thorough-going degree of unity, this clearly reflects their particular situation as individual countries."[1]

The "particular situation" to which Professor Hallstein refers involves a complex of many factors, some of them quite subtle. Perhaps the most apparent characteristic of the EFTA countries, by contrast with those of the EEC, is their greater reluctance to submerge any part of their national identity in a larger association. The EFTA countries are old countries clearly defined by boundaries which, except in the case of Austria, have been among the most stable in the world. Each of the EFTA countries is, therefore, very much aware of itself as a culture, a society, a state. This is undoubtedly true also of such EEC countries as France and Italy, but one of the striking characteristics of all of the EEC countries is the presence within them of relatively large groups that are aware of themselves first of all as Europeans and only secondarily as citizens of a particular country. Put in geographical terms, EFTA is a loose association of political, sociological, ethnic, and even physical islands. EEC is a step toward the reunion of a Europe which, in the days of the Holy Roman Empire, actually was a kind of super-state.

There is another significant difference between the EFTA states and those of EEC. The EEC states — France, Germany, Italy, Belgium, the Netherlands, and Luxemburg — are either primarily or distinctively industrial; the presence of constricting national boundaries has the effect of a number of tourniquets blocking the economic arteries of what is really one industrial organism. The removal — or at least the loosening — of these tourniquets would benefit every part of the organism. Of the EFTA states, on the other hand, only Great Britain (which late in 1961 took the first steps toward joining the EEC) is primarily industrial. The other six—Norway, Sweden, Denmark, Austria, Switzerland, and Portugal—are industrialized to various degrees, but none of them is primarily or distinctively industrial. The need which they feel is therefore a need for co-operation among separate organisms, rather than healthy circulation within one organism. Sweden, for instance, may derive certain advantages from co-operating economically with Norway; France and Germany have come to realize that mere co-operation is not enough, that neither country can enjoy maximum economic health without some degree of integration of their economies.

For both the EFTA and the EEC, however, the ultimate goal is the same: the eventual amalgamation of "the Seven" and "the Six" into one economic union. Great Britain's Prime Minister Macmillan stated this goal clearly in a speech to the Political and Economic Conference in London in November, 1960:

¶ Both EFTA and the European Community of the Six are manifestations of the same theme, striving toward European unity. As such, both are to be welcomed. But we and the Six have a responsibility to ensure that in breaking down the barriers within our own groups we do not create new ones, new and formidable ones, between the Six and the Seven. We must all be conscious of something wider than these economic groups. All of us from Scandinavia to Iberia share a common heritage. We are all part of Europe. . . .

I have said that our purpose first is to expand

[1] EFTA *Bulletin*, Vol. I, No. 3, December, 1960, pp. 3, 8, 11. Reprinted by permission.

the trade between us in the Seven, and, secondly, to reach agreement with the Six. But that is not enough. . . . Our purpose and aim must be to expand the trade of the whole world, and if we have Europe as our first objective it is not from the narrow view of trying to make some little world where we can live on our own, it is to make it a firm base on which we can place our duty in the whole world and play our part in the whole world. . . .

Therefore, I think we must always keep in mind the double purpose, the strength of our Seven, to join up and make a great unified Europe within the thirteen, but not, as I say, of a narrow constricted selfish view.[1]

Meanwhile, with ultimate goals still reserved for realization in the future, Europe's new economic regionalism is paying off in terms of trade expansion within the continent. The 1960 annual report of the secretariat of GATT (The General Agreement on Tariffs and Trade) showed a growth in intra-European trade in 1959 of 2,300 million dollars, or 11 per cent. Trade within the EEC increased by 1,300 million dollars (19 per cent), while trade within the EFTA increased by 200 million dollars (7 per cent). The report concludes that

¶ E.E.C. is likely to be beneficial for world trade if it can be assumed that the establishment of the Common Market will contribute to maintain and even accelerate an uninterrupted growth of production in the six countries as a whole. EFTA, with its goal of internal free trade in all but agricultural products, can also be expected to make a positive contribution to growth. The two areas are therefore likely to experience a more rapid development than if integration had not taken place. If so, this would lead to higher imports of primary products from non-European countries, since for many primary products the possibilities for supplies from European sources are quite limited (3).

The changing political face of Western Europe

No less dramatic than the changes in the economic face of Western Europe have been the changes in its political face. The maps (Fig. XXXII-1) tell a story of fragmentation

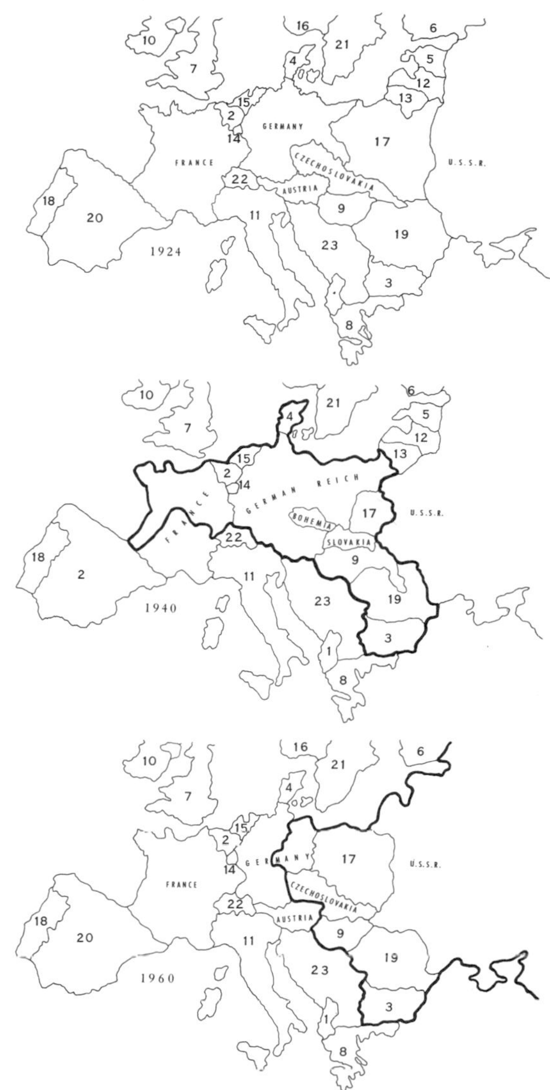

XXXII:1 This map shows the political boundaries within Europe in 1924, 1940, and 1960. The 1924 boundaries represent the attempted stabilization of the continent after the First World War. Note the possibilities for dissension implicit in the division of Germany by the Polish Corridor and by the proliferation of small states between the German and the Russian spheres of interest. The 1940 boundaries represent the high tide of German power under Hitler. The 1960 boundaries (some of them, as in the case of the boundary between the two Germanys, still unrecognized in international law) represent the high tide of Russian power.

---

[1] *Ibid.*, pp. 3, 8. Reprinted by permission.

in the peace settlements following the First World War; of a voracious, expanding Germany in the late 1930's; and of fragmentation at the end of the Second World War.

The most significant political changes, at the end of both World Wars, took place in the belt of states which runs southward from Poland to Bulgaria. At the end of the First World War, many of these states regained their independence after having been partitioned between Germany and Russia or incorporated into the Austro-Hungarian Empire. At the end of the Second World War, many of these same states were re-established after having been incorporated into Hitler's "Third Reich." This cycle of conquest and liberation has been going on for centuries. Speaking of these states, one geographer writes:

¶ All are well-known geographical entities, even though their political boundaries have often changed. Other terms are also used to designate the region: "Shatter Belt," for instance, which is a political expression depicting the fragmentation of the region into many small countries. "Devil's Belt" is a term used by the peoples of East Central Europe to reflect their expectation of being overrun, destroyed, or exterminated at any time by the great powers which border them. . . .

. . . the name "East Central Europe," while in a way arbitrary, is perhaps the most satisfactory from the general geographical point of view. An additional circumstance which arose after World War II gives the area a completely unified aspect: East Central Europe is at present the major zone of interest of the Soviet Union. It is communist ruled, and has a new political, social, and economic face. Despite Yugoslavia's defection, East Central Europe can still be considered as the western security belt of the Soviet Union. . . .

Nothing is stable in the area: everything is mixed and changing, unconsolidated in space as well as in time. Shifts are felt in races, peoples, clans, and individuals, ideals and languages, the way of thinking, the habits, the religions, and customs. Not the least variable, as a result, are East Central Europe's political life and the political boundaries.[1]

[1] Teleki, Geza, "East Central Europe," *A Geography of Europe*, edited by George W. Hoffman. Copyright The Ronald Press Company, New York, 1953, pp. 509-510. Reprinted by permission.

The most obvious example of this instability is Poland. The impression that one gets from a comparison of the maps is that Poland, at the end of the Second World War, was lifted up bodily and set down west of its prewar location. Actually, what happened was that the U.S.S.R. pre-empted the whole eastern third of the prewar Polish state, and compensated the Poles for this loss by giving them a broad slice of Germany, including the excellent coal deposits of Silesia.

The westward thrust of Slavic power pushed the boundaries of Germany all the way back to the Oder River — actually some 175 miles west of the Oder, because the German Democratic Republic (East Germany) is a member of the Communist bloc. The old German capital, Berlin, was divided between East and West, the western portion being given access by highway and air corridor to the German Federal Republic (West Germany). The purposes of these arrangements are obvious: divided, Germany is hardly likely for some time to come to be able to launch any empire-building drives toward the east; and Berlin, divided and isolated, epitomizes the instability of all of central Europe. In the absence of any settlement of "the German question" it is impossible to conceive of any permanent structure of peace and order in central Europe.

Apart from the radical revisions of Germany's eastern boundaries, there were only a few minor changes in boundaries within Western Europe at the end of the Second World War. The most important change—one which did not, however, involve any actual relocation of boundaries—was the liberation of Austria from its forced union with Germany. Among the minor changes were some adjustments of the Franco-Italian boundary, which transferred certain watershed areas to France, and a very slight modification of the boundary between Germany and the Netherlands.

Within Western Europe itself, the most important consequence of postwar political changes was the creation of a tremendous refugee problem. West Germany, for instance, has absorbed some ten million displaced persons from Poland, Czechoslovakia, and East Germany since the war, and the migration has not yet ended; the state of Schleswig-Holstein alone received almost a million of these refugees, a number which represents 38 per cent of its normal population. Austria, in 1951, had more than 300,000 displaced persons crowded into its small area. Jews in large numbers have migrated from central and eastern Europe to Israel, and Poles have migrated from prewar eastern Poland into prewar eastern Germany. The incorporation of the small Baltic republics of Esthonia, Latvia, and Lithuania into the Soviet Union produced a wave of refugees to Great Britain, North America, and Australia; and the failure of the democratic uprising in Hungary in 1956 sent thousands of Hungarians in search of asylum in Austria and Italy and overseas.

The plight of the refugee has occasioned justified concern. The lot of the sick, the aged, and the infirm has been particularly desperate because practically every country sets high standards of physical fitness for admission. Those who cannot meet these standards become, in effect, stateless persons, doomed to spend the rest of their lives in the "temporary" accommodations of the refugee camps.

In the new world power situation that has developed since the end of the Second World War, Western Europe has found itself "in the middle" between the two great continental powers, the United States and the U.S.S.R. Firmly committed to the Western alliance organized around the United States, the countries of Western Europe have nevertheless refused to become mere American satellites. In every country there are influential elements which believe that a united Europe could act as a "third force," charting its own course between the giants. Most thinking Europeans are aware of the realities of geostrategy: placed as it is between the North American power center and the Eurasian power center, Western Europe could all too easily become the theater of operations if the two power centers should come to blows. To the Germans, threatened as they are by the presence of Russian power on their eastern boundary and restricted as they still are in their own defense, the situation seems to call for the closest possible military and political association with the United States. The Swedes and the Swiss, encouraged by the success of their neutral stances in both World Wars, hope to remain neutral in any future conflicts, and have been joined by the Austrians. France, remembering the glories of its past, accepts, but not without some resentment, its role as a junior partner in the Western alliance, but from time to time pursues an independent course of action. Understandably, the French are not eager to see their country become again a beachhead in another European war. A considerable body of British opinion holds reservations similar to those of the French.

For many Europeans the matter comes down, therefore, to a conflict between sentiment and geography. Long accustomed to dominating the world scene, the great nations of Western Europe must now hitch their wagon, so to speak, to one of the new "upstart" stars of the power firmament. Never again can either France or Germany hope to dominate all of Europe by the brilliant deployment of land armies across the North European Plain and into the Danubian lowland. Never again can Great Britain hope to secure her own safety and control large portions of the earth with her navy. Important as land power and sea power may still be, the ultimate power in the modern world is in the air and in space. Small countries today can all too easily be obliterated before they are even fully aware that they are under attack. The European knows this, and he sees his only hope for survival in somehow preventing a showdown between his powerful neighbors to the east and to the west.

The Second World War shattered once and for all the myth of European invincibility. And once the myth was shattered, there was no holding together the vast empires which the great colonial powers of Europe had built, particularly in Asia and in Africa. But the process of empire dissolution had begun long before that.

¶ The cataclysmic event which ushered in the modern period of declining colonialism was the outbreak in Europe of the first World War. It is true that the colonial powers came out of that war with their empires essentially intact, except for the defeated Germans and Turks, but the nature of these empires was quite different from what it had been.

The war had forced the European powers to concentrate their attention and their energies upon the defense of their home territories. Except, therefore, for certain colonies which possessed some unusual strategic importance, the colonies generally were beneficiaries of a policy of what Dr. Spock might call "wholesome neglect," which is just another way of saying that while the cat was away the mice played. The most notable product of the war situation was the loosening of ties which had held colonial systems together, particularly within the British Empire and Commonwealth. It was at this time that the dominions became, for all practical purposes, self-governing nations.

But the war did more than strain the resources and manpower of Europe. It shook Europe's thought and faith to their very foundations. Europeans had taken it for granted that war, as an instrument for the settlement of disputes, had disappeared from the civilized world along with such other "evidences of primitiveness" as absolute monarchy and child labor. Now, all of a sudden, here was civilized Europe, engaged in a bitter war which was being fought more viciously, more savagely, than any waged by the so-called backward peoples of Asia and Africa. Was Europe really so advanced, so skilled in statecraft that she could claim some presumptive right to rule less advanced, less experienced peoples? The question ate away at that inner assurance which had long been one of the European's chief defenses against self-doubt and criticism.

Something else had happened, too. Of necessity, European colonial powers had found it expedient to make one kind of concession or another to certain of their colonial peoples during the war so as to keep them from stirring up trouble while the major issues of the war were being threshed out on the continent of Europe. Indeed, in the heat of the conflict individual European powers were not above offering certain lures and attractions to the colonies of hostile powers in an attempt to stir up trouble in each other's colonial back yards. A number of formerly colonial areas achieved at least the formal status of self-governing nations in the pay-offs that followed the end of the first World War.

Surprisingly enough, though, while European *political* control over non-European lands was somewhat relaxed during and after the first World War, European (including American) economic control spread both horizontally and vertically; that is, economic involvements became more significant in those areas where Europeans had already been operating, and new areas were brought into the realm of European and American economic colonialism. The reasons for this are many and complex but two reasons stand out as especially significant: (1) the tremendous drain upon natural resources that accompanied the industrialization of the European and American economies, and that had continued under those industrialized economies, had depleted or threatened to deplete many important natural resources in the home territories; and (2) the invention of new machines, new materials, new weapons, new processes had made the Western world dependent upon materials which it had never had any great use for before and many of which it did not produce at all at home. One thinks immediately of the petroleum of the Near East and Venezuela, of the rubber of Malaya and Indonesia, of the iron ore of North Africa, of the copper of the Belgian Congo and Chile, of the bauxite of the Guianas. To this list could be added many more commodities which we bring, or need to bring, from the far corners of the world.

To ensure the continuing flow of these materials to their factories and forges, the nations of Europe were willing to make fairly generous political concessions to their colonial peoples. The record of the 1920's and 1930's is, accordingly, one of growing native influence in the political and cultural life of their countries, culminating in individual instances in the acceptance of certain highly Europeanized natives on the highest social levels. The last governor-general of the Dutch East Indies was partly of native extraction.

During this same post-war period, the colonial lands began to feel the effects of another development which had been going on for some time. Kipling had written that "East is East and West is West and never the twain shall meet," but as a matter of fact they had met in the persons of bright young men and women who had gone from the colonial lands to the great universities and technical schools of Europe and the United States. They had gone with the permission, and sometimes with the support, of the colonial administrations who calculated that a native accepted by and immersed in the culture of the West would be both a living example of the virtues of the colonial system and a valuable supporter of the colonial government. As it turned out, these latter-day Moseses also "chose not to be called the sons of Pharaoh's daughter," but identified themselves with their own people, often with a special virulence nourished by snubs and indignities which they had experienced or fancied they had experienced in the white man's world. Among these Europeanized rebels against

European rule one might mention the late Mahatma Gandhi, Prime Minister Nehru, Mr. Krishna Menon, Prime Minister Kwame Nkrumah, Premier Ngo Dinh Diem, Mr. David Marshall, and a host of less famous men and women who have spent half their lives in jail and the other half in high political office.

In the late 1920's, there occurred yet another event which was to jar the stability of the colonial system. This was the Great Depression, which humbled the pride of the greatest powers and sent shock-waves of unrest and revolt through the whole world. The colonial powers, finding themselves unable to finance necessary public works projects in their own home territories, were more and more forced to ask their colonials to take on the burden of maintaining their own public works. Unable to solve the employment problem in their own home territories, the colonial powers were self-admittedly incapable of solving the growing problems of poverty in the colonial world. In short, a world war plus a depression made it more and more obvious that even if there was such a thing as the White Man's Burden, the white man was no longer capable of carrying it. He had failed to enforce peace in 1914. He had failed to maintain economic stability in 1929. The only question that remained to be answered was: could he enforce his sovereignty over the areas which he claimed the right to govern? As we shall see, World War II answered that question.

Meanwhile, there had been unleashed in the aftermath of World War I a force which was actively hostile to the established order of things in all of the countries of the world. This was Russian Communism, a movement whose idealistic roots we find it difficult to recall as we look back upon its bloody record of the past four decades. Young men and women, particularly, influenced by Western political philosophers and by ideas which had been implicit in the teachings of the missionaries, despaired of achieving social justice and ethnic recognition by the slow process of Western parliamentary reform and looked to the leaders of the Russian revolution for examples of reform triumphant. Thus there developed, at least in local instances, that very strange and illogical identification of nationalist aspirations with Communist ideology.

At the outbreak of World War II, then, we find the colonial system still apparently dominant through most of the non-white world. But while it was a very impressive facade, it was nothing more than a facade. How fragile it was even those most directly involved in it did not realize until the lightning-swift advance of Japanese forces down the Asiatic coast and into the islands smashed the system beyond all hope of repair in most of Asia and the Far East (5).

The maps (Figs. XXXII-2 and XXXII-3) tell their own story. Within fifteen years from the end of the Second World War, only scraps of the old empires remained, except for the Portuguese empire in Africa. The liquidation of the old empires proceeded fast and, on the whole, remarkably painlessly, except for one case — the long, bitter, frustrating war in Algeria which brought the Fourth French Republic to an ignominious end and brought Charles DeGaulle back to power as president of the Fifth Republic.

¶ Algeria was, indeed, a special case.

The French began to occupy Algeria in 1830 during a period of their history when they were looking for some foreign achievement to offset the sense of frustration which existed at home. Their policy was one of *refoulement,* of driving back the native Berbers into the mountains and of occupying their former lands with white people. In this process the French aroused the deep hostility of the native peoples. Official policy came, especially after 1870, to recognize Algeria as an integral part of France and to settle there groups of French peasants who would lead the same sort of life and grow the same kind of crops as their ancestors had done in France. . . . The area of Algeria is about 847,500 square miles. The total population is about 8,876,000, of whom no more than a million are Europeans. . . . Algeria is an integral part of France. Northern Algeria is constituted as three *departements* of the Republic, but owing to the sparse population and the unsettled conditions, the huge interior of Algeria is subject to a special military administration. Its trade is overwhelmingly with European France, which takes four-fifths of Algeria's exports and supplies three-quarters of its imports.[1]

The question of whether Algeria was actually an integral part of France or a French colony was one that has been debated for years. To the French settlers in Algeria,

[1] By permission from *Europe and the Mediterranean,* by Norman J. G. Pounds, Copyright 1953. McGraw-Hill Book Company, Inc., New York, pp. 366-367.

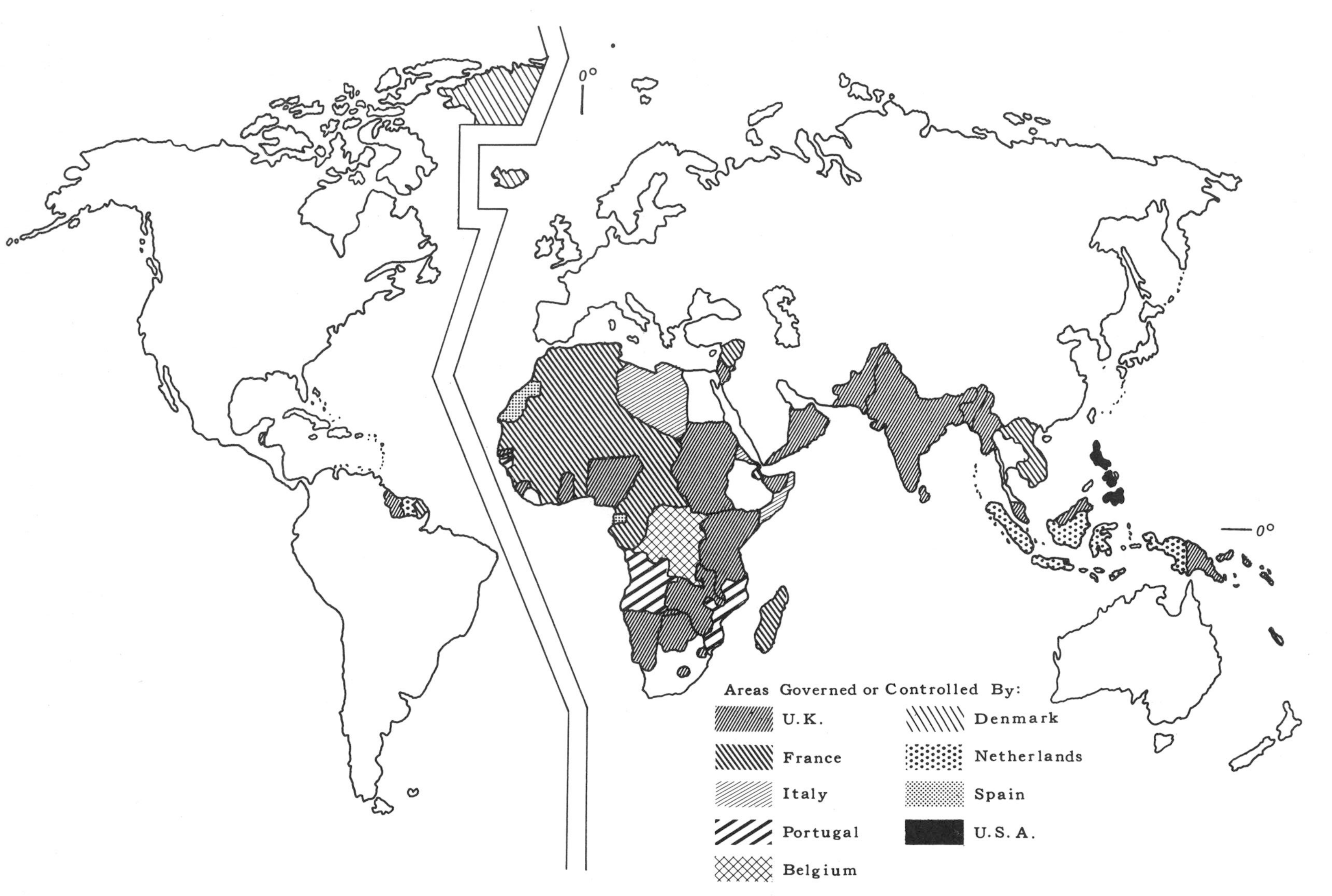
0°
0°
Areas Governed or Controlled By:
U.K.
France
Italy
Portugal
Belgium
Denmark
Netherlands
Spain
U.S.A.

the *colons,* there was no question about it; their ancestors had come to Algeria more than a century before and had never ceased to be Frenchmen. To the successive governments of the Fourth Republic, it was equally clear that the conflict in Algeria was essentially a civil war, over which such outside agencies as the United Nations had no jurisdiction. But to the Arab nations, Algeria was no more an integral part of France than was Tunisia or Morocco; it was a colony, held in unwilling bondage by a European colonial power. And with the discovery of oil in the southern desert of Algeria, the Arabs came more and more to explain French refusal to leave Algeria as just another example of the European's economic exploitation of non-European peoples.

The same difficult problem, though on a somewhat smaller scale, has presented itself in other parts of Africa where Europeans have settled in large numbers — notably the Union of South Africa, the Federation of the Rhodesias and Nyasaland, and Kenya. Throughout the continent the cry has been, "Africa for the Africans!" But once the native African and the European have been baked into the same omelet, it is not easy to devise any solution which will ensure each the supremacy that he demands. Britain and France, especially, have learned that it is as difficult to close out an empire as it is to build one. But they have been left no choice but to close out their empires.

The changing cultural face of Western Europe

The changing position of Western Europe in world affairs has been chronicled day by day on the front pages of every newspaper. But while these changes were taking place, other changes, no less significant, were taking place within the continent itself. One of the most interesting and unexpected of these changes has been the reversal of prewar trends toward stable or even declining populations. To some extent, this reversal may be accounted for on the basis of steadily declining death rates, resulting from the dramatic medical discoveries and the more widespread access to medical treatment that have characterized the postwar years. But what surprised the demographers was the sudden rise in the birth rate immediately following the war and its persistence since that time.

The effects of these trends in both the birth rate and the death rate can be seen in a comparison of the populations of the countries of Western Europe in 1947 and in 1960:

	Population (in millions)	
Country[1]	*1947*	*1960*
Austria	6.910	6.934
Belgium	8.453	8.798
Denmark	4.169	4.388
France	40.518	42.774
Italy	44.530	49.363
Luxemburg	.287	.291
The Netherlands	9.714	10.551
Norway	3.124	3.343
Sweden	6.842	7.290
Switzerland	4.580	4.950
The United Kingdom	50.027	50.785

To an American, who sees nothing unusual in his country's growing by twenty million people or more between censuses, these figures may not seem particularly impressive. After all, none of them comes close to matching our own rate of population growth. But to population experts these figures provide a considerable surprise. Take, for example, France. Here is a country which had maintained a steady population figure of about forty million for almost a century; now, in the space of a little more than a decade, the population spurts upward by almost two million. Or take such a stable, strongly-Protestant country as Sweden where there are no religious scruples to prevent the limitation of family size; here, also, there is a population increase of almost half a million in a period of thirteen years.

It may be that this reversal of trends toward stabilized or declining populations will prove a temporary phenomenon, a reflection of postwar prosperity and of a *Zeitgeist*

[1] Germany is omitted from these comparisons because the heavy influx of refugees obscures the rate of natural increase. To a certain, but far lesser, extent, this is true of other countries.

XXXII:2 (Left) This map shows the non-self-governing world in the last year of the colonial era, 1946. From this year on, the empires began to break up.

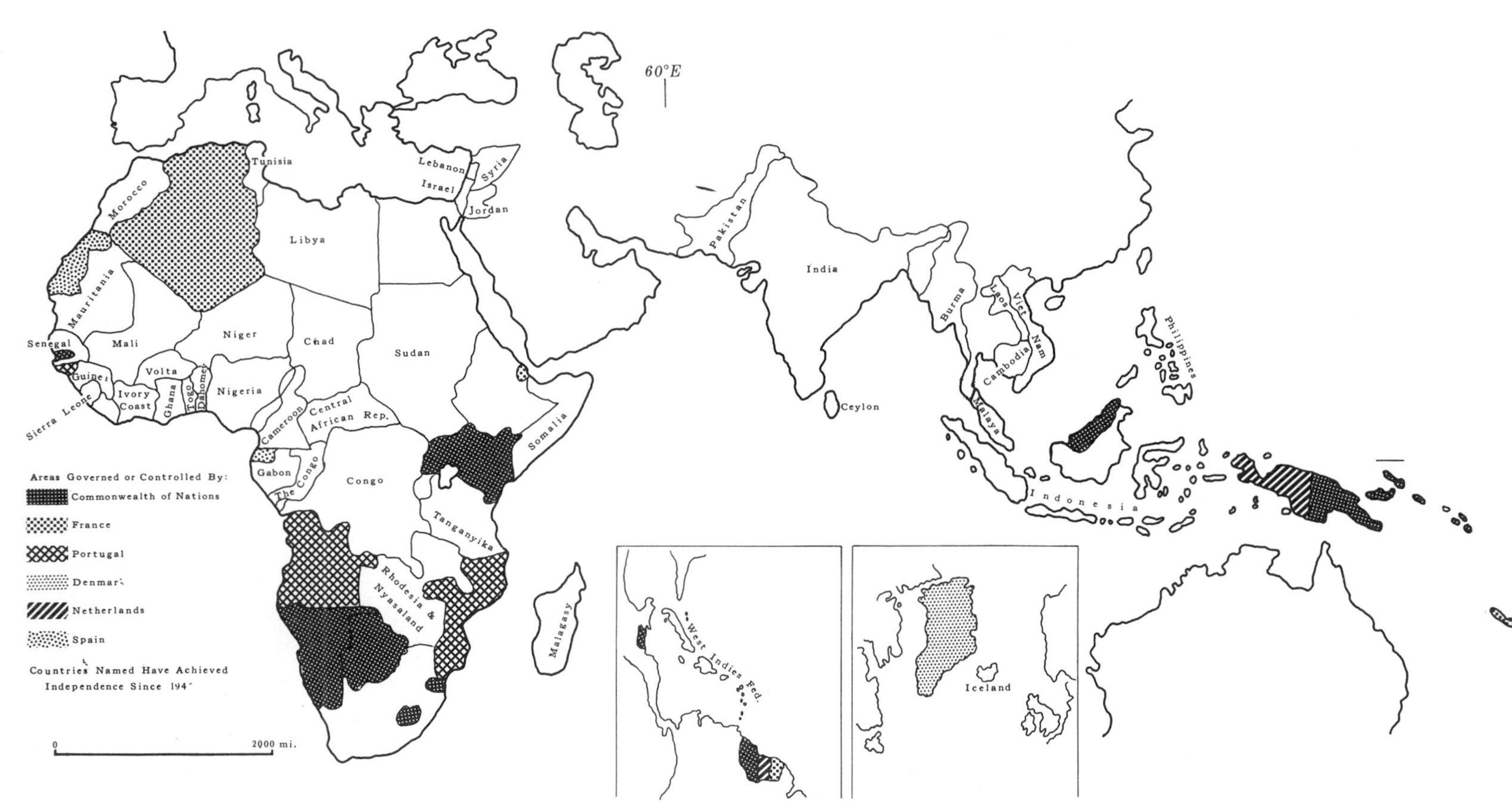
60°E
Tunisia
Morocco
Lebanon
Israel
Syria
Jordan
Libya
Mauritania
Senegal
Mali
Niger
Chad
Sudan
Volta
Guinea
Ivory Coast
Ghana
Togo
Dahomey
Nigeria
Sierra Leone
Cameroon
Central African Rep.
Somalia
Gabon
The Congo
Congo
Tanganyika
Rhodesia & Nyasaland
Malagasy
Pakistan
India
Ceylon
Burma
Laos
Viet Nam
Cambodia
Malaya
Philippines
Indonesia
West Indies Fed.
Iceland
Areas Governed or Controlled By:
Commonwealth of Nations
France
Portugal
Denmark
Netherlands
Spain
Countries Named Have Achieved Independence Since 194
0
2000 mi.

Beilstein, a village on the Mosel, is shown with its vineyards and ruined castle. Europe is changing, but the past still lives, especially in the countryside. The terracing of these vineyard slopes was not primarily an attempt to add to the available agricultural land but rather to expose the vines to more direct sunlight in this far northern latitude. The European did not adopt the oriental expedient of attempting to match population growth with land carved out of hillsides. He turned instead to commerce and industry at home and to migration overseas. (Courtesy German Embassy, Washington)

which has favored larger families in almost every country of the world since the war. But temporary or not, it reflects a notable reversal of previous trends, and may help to account for a new spirit of youthfulness which so many competent observers say is abroad in old Europe these days.

A geographer would not pretend to have any one neat, pat answer to the question of why this increase has occurred. He is impressed, however, by the fact that it coincides with (a) one of the most remarkable periods of prosperity that Europe has ever known; (b) a period of political liberalism which has produced, among other things, generous medical and welfare programs; and (c) a period of large-scale migration from the land to the cities.

XXXII:3 (Left) The retreat of colonialism is shown here. Note that, except for the Portuguese territories (which may be the next to achieve self-rule) most remaining colonial areas are either expanses of desert or very primitive areas of tropical rainforest.

It may seem strange to associate a trend toward urbanization with increasing population. Normally, urban populations tend to produce smaller families than do rural populations. But two offsetting considerations need to be kept in mind. In the first place, one of the remarkable features of the postwar "baby boom" in all of the Western countries has been the trend toward more children in urban middle- and upper-class families where the prewar fashion was for one or two children. In the second place, in rural Europe, where farm sizes have long been small, the desire to hand down the farm intact to the next generation tended to discourage large families. One male heir sufficed to ensure the continuity of the family on the land. Any additional male children meant either dividing the already small inheritance or imposing upon one of the children the heavy economic burden of buying out his coheirs. For the time being, at least, there seems to be a relationship in Western Europe between increasing urbanization and a rising birth rate. On the basis of past experience, we would expect this to be a temporary phenomenon.

This trend from the land to the city is the second of the significant characteristics of postwar Europe. Actually, of course, it had been going on for a century or more, but there has been a noticeable acceleration since the end of the Second World War. Three reasons might be singled out for special emphasis in explaining this trend:

1. The growing mechanization of European agriculture, resulting in a need for fewer human workers to accomplish a given measure of production and in a trend toward larger farm units to make the most effective use of machinery.

2. The postwar economic boom and the rapidly expanding demand for industrial workers that has resulted from it.

3. Manpower losses, particularly in the younger and most vigorous age groups, resulting from military and civilian casualties in the Second World War.

Taken together, these factors have produced a situation which, in some countries, created a serious labor shortage. Great Britain, for instance, found it necessary in the early fifties to bring in workers from eastern Europe and the Caribbean area to supplement its inadequate labor force. Germany found the stream of refugees which poured across her borders not so much a problem as the solution to a problem of an inadequate labor force.

As a result of this migration, Europe, already for the most part highly urban before the Second World War, is today even more so. Great Britain, with more than 80 per cent of its population living in urban areas, and Germany, with more than 70 per cent, are the prime examples of this new urbanization. France, on the other hand, maintains an even balance between urban and rural, although even there the trend has been slowly away from the land to the cities.

What does this trend portend for the future? One writer has noted that "the theory that cities are a source of instability and weakness is at least as old as Thomas Jefferson and as new as Communist revolutionary doctrine." But he contends that:

> ¶ In the long sweep of history it may be that modern urban society is insufficiently stable to provide the enduring social institutions and cultural traditions necessary for a lasting civilization. But in the short run, it is clear that those who fear the urban mobs as revolutionary forces have been refuted by recent history. The most urbanized countries are at the same time the most stable politically. The twelve countries having one-fourth or more of their people in cities of a hundred thousand or over is a roster of countries that have been characterized by stable governments since World War II. . . .
>
> It is fair to say that in the modern world internal political stability is more likely to be found with a high degree of urbanization than in a peasant economy and society. It is precisely the countries undergoing transition from the old self-contained rural peasant world that are experiencing the most acute political disorder.[1]

Is any country more stable than Great Britain, any city more orderly than London?

A third significant characteristic of postwar Europe is the trend away from certain occupations toward others. We have already noted the decline in the number of workers required by agriculture and have ascribed it primarily to the increasing mechanization of agriculture. Similar declines have characterized other primary or extractive industries (e.g., mining and fisheries). At the same time, there has been a notable increase in the

[1] ***Principles of Political Geography***, by Hans W. Weigert, *et al.*, Copyright © 1957, Appleton-Century-Crofts, Inc., New York, pp. 307, 308. Reprinted by permission.

Here is a view of Koenigs-Allee in Düsseldorf, Germany. The European is a city dweller and has been for centuries. What began perhaps as a matter of necessity has survived as a matter of preference, and urbanism as a way of life is nowhere more highly developed than in Western Europe. Many of the cities (Düsseldorf is a good example) are relatively young in their present form, although they may have developed out of ancient villages. Particularly in Germany, the downtown districts of even the oldest cities appear disappointingly new to American tourists who had hoped to immerse themselves in the medieval. But a distinguishing characteristic of most of the great cities of Europe is the obvious evidence that they were designed to be lived in, not merely worked in. (Courtesy German Embassy, Washington)

number of workers engaged in the chemical industries, the building trades, and the heavy industries. The professional classes have also shown a remarkable growth since the war. Better schooling and the automation of the manual-labor occupations — the latter reflecting an actual labor shortage in certain industries — have helped to bring about these trends.

A fourth very obvious trend has produced some significant changes in the European landscape. The combination of extensive war damage and growing populations has necessitated extensive rebuilding in the cities, and the building of new towns in what was formerly the countryside. Some of the oldest cities of Europe are, as a result, very young in appearance. Examples that come immediately to mind are Rotterdam and Coventry, both of which were heavily damaged during the war. In the Ruhr, severe damage to industrial facilities necessitated the building of new plants after the war and these new plants are the latest word in efficiency. Social changes have also brought about much new building. The combination of post-war prosperity with welfare-oriented governments has fostered a movement toward better housing for the lower economic groups, a movement away from urban slums toward housing developments of the high-rise type within cities or of the detached-residence type on the urban fringes. American tourists sometimes express surprise that some of the ancient cities of Europe have a more modern appearance than do some of the young cities of our own country.

Europeans, at the same time, sometimes express concern that the new Europe may be in the process of becoming only a carbon copy of the United States. They note, for example, the ubiquitousness of certain American soft drinks, the "intrusion" of American slang into their languages, the importation of American standards and values by way of the films, the introduction of such American institutions as the supermarket, the coffee break, and certain kinds of popular music. Whether these fears are well-founded is hard to say. Certainly it would seem likely that as new and faster means of communications develop both within Europe and between Europe and the New World, a certain homogenization of culture could be expected to take place. Distinctive local cultures are usually the product of some degree of isolation, and as the walls of isolation fall throughout the Western world it is only to be expected that local cultures will tend to become absorbed in a larger culture. This is, perhaps, to be regretted, but certainly not feared. The best in European culture is graven deep in Europe's history and geography and can be expected to survive. Superficial forms have always been fluid and have reflected whatever contacts Europeans have had at any given time. If, today, Europe seems to be borrowing a great deal from North America, it may be recalled that, at times in the past, Europe has borrowed from the Romans, the Moors, and the Chinese without ever ceasing to be Europe. It is a kind of law of cultural geography that all things tend to be drawn toward their center, and Europe is the best illustration of this law. But in that center is a unique geographical matrix which tends to modify and Europeanize whatever is drawn into it, and this seems to be happening today in Europe.

APPLICATION OF GEOGRAPHIC UNDERSTANDING

I. What are the geographic reasons for and implications of the statement that Great Britain is in Europe but not of Europe? To what extent and in what ways is this statement false?

II. What are the geographic reasons for saying that the continent of Europe is organized around Germany? If this statement is true, what are the implications of a divided Germany for Europe?

III. Suggest reasons for and against including the Scandinavian states and Denmark in Western Europe. What elements in their physical geography tend to differentiate them from the continental "core" of Western Europe?

IV. What is the significance of the statement that, to a very large extent, the greatness of Europe is a product of its deficiencies?

V. How might European history have been different if (a) there had been an Alpine mountain range along the valley of the Rhine? (b) Buddhism had been introduced into Europe by way of the North European Plain rather than Christianity from the Mediterranean world? (c) Emperor Louis the Pious (814-840) had had only two sons? (Consult any good standard reference in history for the significance of the Treaty of Verdun in 843.)

VI. What role has the peninsular character of Europe played in the development of its history and in the "tone" of its culture?

VII. What centripetal forces tend to draw Western Europe together? What centrifugal forces tend to fragment it into small states and competing economies?

VIII. Geographically speaking, what are the chances that Europe could constitute itself a "third force," holding the balance of power between East and West?

IX. European agriculture has shown a steady trend away from general farming toward some type of specialized use of the land. How do you account for this trend?

X. Suggest reasons for the popularity of the "small car" (e.g., Volkswagen, Morris, Fiat) and the motor-scooter in Western Europe.

References

1 Moodie, A. E., "Britain, France, and the Benelux Countries," *The Changing World,* Edited by W. Gordon East and A. E. Moodie, Harcourt, Brace and World, Inc., New York, 1956, pp. 105-106.

2 EFTA *Bulletin,* Vol. I, No. 3, December, 1960, pp. 3, 8, 11.

3 An official summary issued with "International Trade 1960," the GATT Annual Report, 1960.

4 Teleki, Geza, "East Central Europe," *A Geography of Europe,* Edited by George W. Hoffman, The Ronald Press Company, New York, 1953, pp. 509-510.

5 Strietelmeier, John, "Some Reflections on the Passing of European Imperialism," *Proceedings* of the Valparaiso University Institute on Human Relations, the Lutheran Human Relations Association of America, Valparaiso, Indiana, 1956, pp. 16-18.

6 Pounds, Norman J. G., *Europe and the Mediterranean,* McGraw-Hill Book Company, Inc., New York, 1953, pp. 366-367.

7 Weigert, Hans W., *et al., Principles of Political Geography,* Appleton-Century-Crofts, Inc., New York, 1957, pp. 307, 308.

Chapter 33

Great Britain from Empire to Commonwealth

For almost a century, a process has been going on which is wholly without precedent in recorded human history — the peaceful and largely voluntary dissolution of a great empire. Peaceful may be too strong a word, for there have been episodes of violence, but the violence was never so great that it could not have been put down if the British had wished to use the stern repressive measures by which great empires in the past have attempted to stave off disintegration and by which the new Communist empires maintain control at the present time. That this process has been largely voluntary is not only a tribute to the humanitarianism and the political sagacity of the British people and their rulers but also an indication of their sensitivity to the significance of geographic change. For the British Empire, in all its manifestations and permutations, was a politico-economic response to geographical realities, and nowhere is this fact more evident than in its transition, during the past century, from something like the old, classical model of empire to the new, unprecedented association of free nations which is today's Commonwealth of Nations.

The geography of empire

It is not, perhaps, quite accurate to speak of *the* British Empire. As Carrington has pointed out, there were at least five British Empires: an empire of settlement, an empire of trade, an empire of finance, an empire of conquest, and an empire of ideas (1). The five were not always coterminous in the past; they are even less so today. Thus, at one time the United States was a member of all five of these empires. Today it is still at least an associate member of the empire of ideas. Ghana, on the other hand, was never a member of the empire of settlement, but it is a member of the other four. In any case, the term "empire," with its connotations of centralized authority and enforced submission to a foreign power, is no longer an appropriate symbol of the voluntary association of free nations, some of them republics, which is the Commonwealth. It would be more appropriate to speak of the Commonwealth as a community of trade, of finance, and of ideas. The bond which holds the Commonwealth together is partly economic, partly ideological, partly cultural, and partly sentimental. The symbol of this bond is the Queen, in her role as Head of the Commonwealth. The Commonwealth is, however, the outgrowth of the old Empire, and it is necessary, therefore, to look back into the geography of the Empire to understand the geography of the Commonwealth.

1. The empire of settlement. Great Britain is an island, small and relatively poor in resources other than coal and iron ore. Until the Industrial Revolution of the eighteenth century, even these resources were of only limited importance in her economy. Most of her people derived their livings, directly or indirectly, from her very limited areas of arable land, from her constantly-diminishing forests, or from the fishing grounds of the surrounding seas. Pestilence, civil war, and foreign adventures acted as controls upon population growth which would otherwise have far outrun the island's meager resources. This tendency toward a natural population surplus was aggravated by a system of land ownership which concentrated most of what was worth owning in the hands of the King, the aristocracy, and (until the dissolution of the monasteries under Henry VIII) the Church. The English common man was, therefore, land-hungry. There was room for a limited number of tenants on the great estates and for a small yeomanry on some of the less desirable land, but the very limited opportunities in agriculture made it necessary for surplus populations to find other ways of making a living or to migrate from the land into the towns and cities.

When, therefore, new worlds were opened up in the Americas and the Antipodes during and after the Age of Discoveries, there were significantly large numbers of people in Great Britain who welcomed the chance to leave their overcrowded island and seek opportunity overseas. They went, taking with them the language, the culture, and the institutions of the home country. Typically these migrations were to lands where the aboriginal populations were small and primitive, easily dispossessed.

In Britain, as in the rest of northern Europe, the Age of Discoveries was contemporaneous with an age of religious tumult. For something like 175 years, from the early years of the reign of Henry VIII (1509-1547) until the accession of William and Mary (1689), England was torn by a bitter struggle between Protestants and Roman Catholics and by a struggle within Protestantism between the Anglican Church and the various nonconforming groups, such as the Congregationalists and the Friends. During this period, each of the contending groups found itself cast at times in the role of the persecutor and at other times in the role of the persecuted. The Atlantic seaboard of North America became during these troubled times a trophy to be awarded to those who happened to be, for the moment, on the victorious side, and a haven of refuge for the defeated and oppressed. Generally speaking, the royal favorites were granted the warmer lands from Maryland southward while the unpopular groups (Congregationalists and Friends) were permitted to settle in the cooler lands. Thus, from the very beginnings of English settlement in North America a strong equalitarian tradition in the north has been matched against an equally strong aristocratic tradition in the south.

A third impetus to migration was provided by the Draconian English legal and penal systems which meted out severe penalties for even the most minor infractions of the law. The Oglethorpe colony in Georgia was established to give a new start to petty offenders. Australia was, for a long time, a penal colony, populated by prisoners who had been sentenced to "transportation" and by their guards.

In North America, as later in Australia and New Zealand, the British proved to be successful settlers. Too remote from the mother country to receive any substantial assistance from her, the colonists evolved political and social institutions based upon British prototypes but adapted to the needs of new environments. Australia, vast and sunny and populated by immigrants drawn chiefly from the overcrowded slums of Britain's cities, came eventually to bear only a faint family resemblance to small, insular, cloudy New Zealand with its population descended largely from middle- and upper-class Anglican families. In the thirteen seaboard colonies of North America, the differences between mother and daughter became so pronounced that the family relationship was broken. In Canada, the presence of a large Roman Catholic, French-speaking citizenry required the improvisation of a bilingual state with special safeguards for the historic interests of one of its provinces. In South Africa, a similar attempt at accommodationism among Afrikaans, English, and Bantu elements in the population failed.

The empire of settlement evolved very rapidly into an association of free nations. The pattern for this new association was set by the confederation of Upper and Lower Canada and its subsequent development, in 1867, into a dominion. Within half a century, all of the major units in the empire of settlement achieved dominion status—Australia in 1901, the Union of South Africa in 1910, and New Zealand in 1907. Thus, in the very heyday of empire, the process of dissolution was going on. The basis of this process of dissolution was essentially geographical. London was too remote from the wheat fields of Alberta, the sheep stations of Australia, the diamond mines of the Rand, the dairy farms of New Zealand to legislate intelligently for their peoples. Moreover, each of the great units of the empire of settlement possessed within its own territory the ingredients of nationhood, both physically, in terms of area and resources, and culturally, in terms of a common history and distinctive cultural responses to distinctive physical environments. The fact of Canadian and Australian and New Zealander and South African nationhood was evident at least by the beginning of the twentieth century. Legal recognition of this fact came in 1931 when the Statute of Westminster defined these dominions as "autonomous communities within the British Empire equal in status, in no way subordinate one to another in any aspect of their domestic or external affairs, though united by a common allegiance to the Crown and freely associated as members of the British Commonwealth of Nations." Since

Halfway around the world from London, another great city stands—English in appearance and in language and bearing the name of a British prime minister: Melbourne. This picture epitomizes what Carrington means when he talks about the empire of settlement. (Canadian Pacific Railway photograph)

1931, two modifications of this definition have been made:

1. The acceptance of India, a republic, into the Commonwealth has effectively cancelled out the common allegiance to the Crown as a requirement in the Commonwealth.

2. The accession of Queen Elizabeth II was proclaimed in terms which make it clear that she reigns in her various realms as queen of each of those nations, rather than as Queen of the United Kingdom. Thus, even in the unlikely event that she were to be deposed as Queen of the United Kingdom, she would remain Queen of Canada and Australia and each of the other monarchies within the Commonwealth unless they chose also to depose her.

2. The empire of trade. The old slogan that "trade follows the flag" was true in Great Britain's case from the earliest days of her involvement in discovery and colonization. A strong argument could be made for the contention that, through most of her imperial history, Britain was far more interested in the commercial benefits of empire than in the trappings and prestige of empire. Britain is, in many ways, a poor country. Climatic homogeneity severely limits the range of crops that her people can grow. Highlands in Scotland and Wales and the Pennine Chain running down through the heart of England restrict the amount of arable land. Apart from coal and some iron, she has no important mineral deposits. Historically, therefore, she has had to depend upon trade both for foodstuffs and raw materials and for markets for her industries. One recent writer has put it well:

¶ The vital character of our sea routes is dinned into us from the nursery age. That is quite different from the outlook in Continental countries —and here the United States can be classed with them—which have a plentiful agriculture of their own. I do not suppose that American, any more than French boys, are brought up on a book of ships to remind them that "the bread which you eat and the biscuits you nibble" are brought to the country by sea. Sea power, then, is not a luxury for us, as for Germany or Russia, but essential to our existence.[1]

The products which cool, humid, mineral-poor Britain has most needed may be grouped under three major headings: (1) products such as wheat, wool, and mutton which, while they can be, and are, produced also in humid lands, are more economically produced in dry or subhumid lands; (2) tropical or subtropical products such as cotton, sugar, tea, spices, and more recently rubber; and (3) almost every kind of mineral except coal. If one were unacquainted with the facts of British colonial expansion, one might interpret the present pattern of commonwealth nations and territories as the fulfillment of some great master plan worked out centuries ago, for this pattern seems to have been tailor-made to supply the deficiencies of the home country. Canada and Australia, with their vast areas of the *BS* type of climate, have some of the world's best wheatlands and rangelands. India, Pakistan, Nigeria, Ghana, and many other territories large and small within the Commonwealth are capable of producing any kind of crop that can be grown in the tropics. Australia, Canada, the Rhodesias, and many other territories are rich in minerals.

Actually, of course, there was no master plan. While it may not be altogether true that the Empire was accumulated, as one wag has put it, "in a fit of forgetfulness," much of it was accumulated by accident or in response to some particular need of the moment. Above all else, the empire of trade was an improvisation patched together under the compulsions of geography. Britain's experience in India, while a unique one, may serve as an example of how, in the process of attempting to ensure the safety of her trade, she quite unintentionally found herself creating an empire.

British involvement in India began as a strictly private affair when John Mildenhall, representing the English East India Company, secured a trade concession in 1608. In the following years, additional concessions were obtained by the company, and it carried on a thriving business buying and selling goods which were carried in its ships. Unfortunately, there was a great deal of civil disorder in India during these years, and other European powers, particularly France and Portugal, were actively interested in the India trade. The company, by astute diplomacy and by military power—and primarily for the sake of maintaining the peace and order necessary for profitable trade—enforced order in its trading territories but otherwise interfered relatively little in the affairs of the people. As its business spread, the area of supervised order was extended. At the same time it managed through diplomacy, force, and strategic alliances with native states to squeeze out or force out rival European companies. Eventually the company became, for all practical purposes, the government of India, and not until it was rocked by a series of disturbances culminating in the Great Mutiny did the British government as such take over the rule of India. This was in 1858—250 years after Mildenhall's arrival in India.

Not glory, therefore, but commerce was the spur to most of Britain's imperial expansion. By the time the Empire had reached its fullest flowering, immediately prior to the outbreak of the First World War, it resembled a cluster of four large islands (Canada, trans-Saharan Africa, India, and Australasia) clustered around a small island (Great Britain), and connected with it by stepping-stones. Binding the whole together was the Royal Navy, whose mission it was to ensure safe and unimpeded movement from one part of the Empire to the other. To ensure the safety of her shipping lanes, it was essential that Britain control any bottlenecks along the way and that she establish coaling-stations for the ships that plied them. Accordingly, she had acquired a large number of small and strategically-located islands and peninsulas. From such small and easily-

[1] Clarke, C. F. O., *Britain Today,* The Harvard University Press, Cambridge, Mass., 1951, p. 217.

defended bases, her fleet could control vast areas of ocean. Thus, from Gibraltar, she commanded the passageway from the Atlantic Ocean into the western Mediterranean. From Malta she controlled movement from the western Mediterranean into the eastern Mediterranean. After the Suez Canal had been dug to link the Mediterranean with the Indian Ocean, she controlled passage through the canal from bases at Alexandria, on Cyprus, and in the Aden Protectorate. In the North Atlantic, an unwritten understanding with the United States ensured the safety of the vital sea lanes which linked Britain with Canada, her Caribbean possessions, and South Africa. In the Far East, movement from the Indian Ocean into the Pacific Ocean was controlled from the great British base at Singapore and protected by an alliance with the Dutch who at that time still held possession of Indonesia.

This control of the seas was a chief factor in making Britain the carrier of the world's commerce during the nineteenth century and the first half of the twentieth century. Another important factor was her great wealth of coal; for while Britain imported chiefly bulky raw materials, she exported less bulky manufactured goods. Outgoing ships thus usually had room to spare in their holds. Such extra space was filled with coal, which was carried as ballast and either sold at a profit to foreign countries or deposited at the fueling stations to be used by British ships or to be sold to the vessels of friendly foreign powers. Thus much of the cost of British marine transportation was defrayed by the sale of coal, and British shipping lines could, accordingly, offer low freight rates. Such a world-wide operation also furnished the British with much "inside" trade information.

The empire of trade was, therefore, a broader empire than the empire of settlement. Those portions of it which were not also parts of the empire of settlement were, for the most part, tropical or subtropical lands which were already either overcrowded or climatically unsuited to large-scale European settlement or both. When this fact is borne in mind, it is not difficult to see why Britain could face with equanimity the loss of immediate political control over these possessions when they ceased to be profitable operations or when it became obvious that there would be no economic loss involved in granting them political freedom.

3. The empire of finance. The British standard of living was, for a long time—and especially in the nineteenth century—the highest in the world; so high that even her manufacturing and commerce could not offset her expenditures for food, for raw materials, and for other imports. It was, therefore, the usual thing for Great Britain to show an "unfavorable balance of trade," i.e., an excess of imports over exports. The difference she made up on income from "invisibles," i.e., such services as insurance, investments in overseas enterprises, and governmental and private loans. She built up, therefore, an empire of finance which was broader and more inclusive than either the empire of settlement or the empire of trade.

It was British capital, for instance, which underwrote a considerable part of American railroad building in the latter part of the nineteenth century. It was British capital that built many of the public utilities of Argentina during this same time. And, of course, it was British capital that made possible much of the internal economic development of the dominions. British insurance companies, e.g., Lloyd's, operated throughout the Empire and beyond it and for generations did the bulk of the world's underwriting business.

Any one explanation of Britain's pre-eminence as a supplier of capital in the nineteenth and early twentieth centuries would be an oversimplification. It can be said, though, that among the reasons for this pre-eminence certain geographical considerations undoubtedly played a significant part. Capital tends to flee before the danger of internal disorder or enemy attack. The British, secure behind their watery moat and the protection of the Royal Navy, had little reason until the First World War to fear enemy invasion; and the stability of their political institutions minimized the risk of internal disorder. Situated near the heart of the land hemisphere, London was the crossroads of the world's commerce, and whatever wealth passed through this crossroads left a portion of itself behind to be added to the capital fund. Political control over large portions of the world's surface gave Britain something approaching a monopoly in the development of its resources. Finally, and this is a very important consideration, for well over a century Britain had no effective competition. Europe was disorganized and still economically anemic from the drain of the Napoleonic wars, North America was wholly preoccupied in the gigantic task of exploring and settling a continent; southern and eastern Asia were turned in upon themselves and engaged in a futile attempt to remain isolated from the rest of the world.

The First World War began, the Great Depression accelerated, and the Second World War capped a process of liquidation of Britain's empire of finance. During the Second World War, Britain was forced to dispose of many of her investments in foreign countries, including some of her most profitable ones. The financial leadership of the world was taken over by the United States, which emerged from the Second World War as the world's leading creditor nation, a role long played by Britain. Meanwhile Britain, with many of her former sources of income gone, had her own home territory to rebuild after the devastation of the war. In order to rebuild, she had to buy materials from overseas. But she had nothing with which to buy. She had had to liquidate some 850 million pound sterling of overseas investment during the First World War. During the Second World War the cost was even higher:

¶ In the six years of war the United Kingdom drew on external resources in excess of income to the extent of £10,000 millions. Of this £7,500 millions was met by grants and aid from the United States and Canada (offset in part by £2,100 millions in reciprocal aid provided by the United Kingdom), £1,100 millions by selling overseas investments, and £3,500 millions by the accumulation of sterling balances.[1]

Among Britain's creditors at the end of the Second World War were some of the Commonwealth nations which had, through all of their prior history, been her debtors. To the political independence which they had achieved a generation earlier was added the economic independence which they achieved during the Second World War. More than that, certain of them—notably Canada and Australia—found it expedient to ally themselves more closely, economically and militarily, with the United States than with Great Britain.

4. The empire of conquest. When one considers the enormous extent of the British Empire on the eve of the First World War, it is amazing how little of it was acquired by conquest. By far the greater part of it was acquired by purchase, by treaty, by invitation of local rulers, or by the mere occupation of essentially open lands. The three most striking exceptions to this general rule were French Canada, for which Wolfe died on the Plains of Abraham; South Africa, which Britain seized in a war which was strongly opposed by a large and influential segment of her own people; and India, where Britain was only one—but by far the strongest—of several forces contending for control of the subcontinent.

To these conquests some would add the partition of Africa in the latter decades of the nineteenth century. It is true that the vast colonial possessions which European powers acquired in Africa at this time were not acquired by purchase or by treaty or by the invitation of local rulers, nor were they in most cases open, unpopulated lands. But neither were they, except in rare cases, occupied by force of arms. They were merely parceled out by Europeans sitting around bargaining tables, with no particular reference to any such geographical realities as natural regions or tribal units. Until fairly recently, the African himself knew little and cared less about these boundaries. The real world for him continued to be the world of his tribe and of its traditional ranging area which sometimes cut across colonial boundaries. Not until a considerable number of Africans had become detribalized by being drafted for mine work or lured into the new cities as a cheap labor supply did the colonial units begin to have meaning for them as units of administration. When that happened, they began to question why they should not have some voice in the administration, and this question ultimately led to an insistence upon self-government. Unfortunately, with the coming of self-government the arbitrariness of colonial boundaries stood

[1] Devens, Ely, "The Financial Burden of World War II," A review in *The Manchester Guardian,* October 3, 1956, of *Financial Policy 1939-1945* by R. S. Sayers, Longmans, Green and Co., Ltd., London, 1956. Reprinted by permission of the Controller of Her Britannic Majesty's Stationery Office.

fully manifest, and many of the African nations have experienced the hardships of trying to create political realities out of heterogeneous natural regions and ethnic groups which happened to be lumped together within the old colonial boundaries.

It seems probable that one reason why Great Britain depended so little on force of arms in the building of her Empire was that her geography had ill equipped her for large-scale military operations. Her island people were at home on the sea and knew all of the tricks of seamanship. It was to the Navy, therefore, that Britain looked for her defenses, and the Navy did not fail her. Drake and the weather broke the back of Spanish power in the battle with the Armada; Nelson neutralized the threat of French invasion at Trafalgar. Until the First World War, therefore, land armies were not essential to the defense of Britain and were only occasionally employed for overseas adventures. As a result, the army tended to become a largely ornamental institution, officered by gentleman amateurs who were more adept at parading than at fighting. Only in India did Britain maintain a truly professional, battle-ready army. For military operations elsewhere in the world she had to rely either upon gallant but usually inept soldiers from her home garrisons or upon mercenaries. Not until the development of air power posed the threat of invasion by the huge, well-trained land armies of the continent did Britain begin to give as much attention to her army as she had traditionally given to her navy.

5. The empire of ideas. The most far-flung of all British empires defies all attempts to map it, and yet it is none the less real than any of the four that have been discussed. This is an empire of ideas, of which Carrington has written:

¶ Another mode of expansion may yet prove more lasting than trade, finance, or annexation. "There is an Empire," said Macaulay in 1833, "exempt from all natural causes of decay, the imperishable empire of our arts and our morals, our literature and our laws." At every trading-station in the world the British commercial colony became, more or less consciously, a centre of British culture, not because there was an intention to propagate it, but because all other nations wanted to share the benefits of British industrial supremacy. Macaulay's minute on education would have been written in vain if the *babus* of Bengal had not been determined to learn the language of the masters of India. In a more debased form even than babu-English the language of the nation of shopkeepers spread along the shipping-routes until, in all ports of the Old World from Sierra Leone to Tientsin, pidgin-English became the *lingua franca.* Britain really ruled the waves when half the world's sea-going trade sailed under the Red Ensign and the other half was equally dependent on British cable-stations, British coaling-stations, and the use of a few corrupted words from the English language.

Industrial civilization is highly infectious. All nations, from the polished Chinese to the primitive Central Africans, agreed in recognising it as an advantage which the white men from the West should not be allowed to monopolise. The simplest savage, having once seen the technical accomplishments of the trader, can soon discover that the secret of the white man's magic lies in book-learning. And the same age that brought the trader brought the missionary; in many cases the latter came first and penetrated farthest. Whatever else they achieved, one thing is certain; the Protestant missionaries everywhere founded schools at which some instruction was given in reading the English Bible. For many millions of the most intelligent boys and girls of half the world, the mission school was, and is, the first means of approach to Western civilization. There only can they learn English, the first step for the few who can aspire to technical, scientific, or political progress. In this respect the English-speaking missionaries, in the nineteenth century, staked out a claim for British ideals over the most populous regions in the world. The English language is spreading more rapidly than ever before and may in time become, perhaps in some rationalised form, the universal means of communication, carrying with it some notions that are implicit in its vocabulary.[1]

It was, indeed, some notions that are implicit in the vocabulary and literature of the English language that made it impossible for Britain to build a monolithic empire on the order of the old Near Eastern and Mediterranean empires. The same missionary educa-

[1] Carrington, C. E., *The British Overseas,* The Cambridge University Press, New York, 1950, pp. 1032-1033. Reprinted by permission.

tion that opened the English Bible to Indians and Africans also gave them access to Milton's *Areopagitica,* to John Stuart Mill's essay *On Liberty,* to John Locke's treatise *On Civil Government,* to Adam Smith's *The Wealth of Nations,* and to the whole voluminous literature which was, both in letter and in spirit, subversive of despotic rule. The "rights of Englishmen" claimed a universality rooted in universal moral principles that forbade their being restricted to any one race or national group. Thus, paradoxically, the more British the Empire became in spirit, the less British it became politically.

The crisis of empire

Geography has been defined as the study of the stage upon which the drama of human history is played out. Such a definition is satisfactory only if one allows for the fact that the stage is in a constant process of rearrangement, influencing and being influenced by the drama as it unfolds. From time to time, the process of rearrangement moves so rapidly and makes such radical changes in the stage settings that the drama which is being played upon it must either take a radical new turn or become altogether incongruous. The drama of empire has been in such a moment of crisis since about 1914.

By 1914, Britain's daughter nations in the empire of settlement had developed their own identities and had become mistresses in their own houses. When the First World War broke out, it was not compulsion from London but their own free choice that brought them into the war alongside the mother country. Economically, however, they were still very closely tied to Great Britain, both because of British investments in their industries and transportation networks and because of their dependence on Britain as a market for the products of their mines, forests, and agriculture.

Through the years, these economic ties have also tended to loosen. Canada, for instance, has long been a member of the "dollar bloc" rather than the "sterling bloc," and 1959 trade statistics show that the value of her imports from the United States is more than six times the value of her imports from the United Kingdom, while the value of her exports to the United States is four times that of her exports to the United Kingdom. Australia still depends very strongly upon trade with Britain, but Zierer considers it "likely that Australian trade relationships in the future will become closer with her near neighbors in southeast Asia and perhaps shift from the Atlantic to the Pacific basin" (4). Implicit in this prediction is the assumption that Australia, which has taken giant strides in industrialization since the end of the Second World War, will become even more industrialized and, thus, even less dependent upon British manufactured goods. New Zealand—still confined by isolation, by relatively small area, and by a limited range of resources to the role of an agricultural and pastoral economy—remains closely tied to Britain economically, although she looks to Australia and the United States for assistance in regional defense. South Africa, a special case, has remained economically close to the United Kingdom even while it was becoming more and more alienated from it politically.

The crisis of empire precipitated by the coming-of-age of Britain's daughters in the empire of settlement was followed by a second crisis in (to carry the household analogy a bit farther) her domestic staff—the tributary states and territories in her empire of trade. Well-treated as these "servants" had been in the imperial household, they began to become discontented with the role of a servant. Passive resistance in India and an insistent demand for "Africa for the Africans" were manifestations of this discontent, which rumbled beneath the surface during the years between the two world wars and erupted at the end of the Second World War.

There are many ways to explain this awakening of nationalism in the tropical territories of the Empire. The geographer, from his particular vantage point, can see at least two contributory factors. The first of these is the shift of the world power center, at the end of the First World War, from Western Europe to the United States, a shift which dealt a severe blow to the myth of European superiority and tended to create a new myth that what Britain's former American colonies had achieved in their relatively short period of independence would be achievable by any colonial area that could once rid itself of outside control. The second contributory factor was the rapid development and ex-

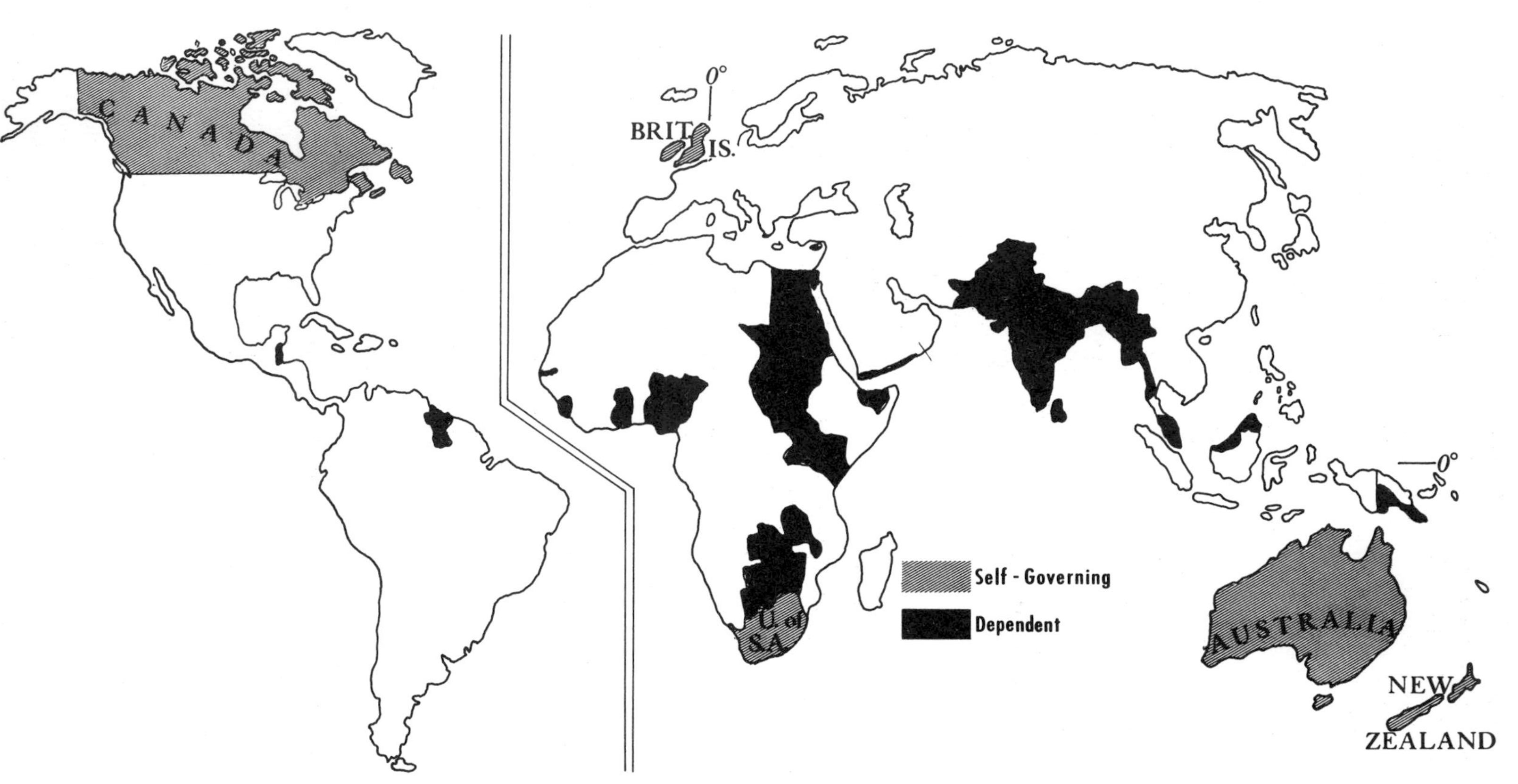

CANADA
0°
BRIT. IS.
U. of S.A.
Self - Governing
Dependent
0°
AUSTRALIA
NEW ZEALAND

pansion of new, fast, and efficient means of communication, which thrust many of these long-isolated lands suddenly into the mainstream of twentieth-century life and thought. The airplane gave man, for the first time, a means of transportation which was not seriously affected by such obstacles as deserts, mountains, and rainforests. Radio made possible the almost instantaneous transmission of ideas from one place on earth to any other place on earth. Between them, the airplane and the radio largely eliminated the two great isolating factors of man's previous history—space and time.

Infected by ideas to which, for the first time, they were exposed, the peoples of the colonial tropics developed a severe and virulent case of nationalism. The intelligent youth, particularly, agitated for independence, quoting as arguments for their freedom those classic statements on human rights which Englishmen for centuries had been adducing in defense of their own freedoms. A new geography was at work, the geography of the Air Age in which both men and their ideas moved freely and swiftly through the air without serious hindrance by surface obstacles.

The crisis which the British Empire faced in its tropical empire of trade has been succinctly described by one of her greatest and most far-sighted viceroys of India, Lord Halifax:

¶ I have often pondered an apparent paradox which must assuredly puzzle the future historian of these times. Will he not think it a strange thing that Great Britain, after developing such overwhelming strength in war,[1] should within a few years of the war's conclusion have been passively content to accept an apparent reduction in power and importance that would have been more appropriate to defeat? Of her own free will she allowed herself to be quietly extruded from India and Burma and from her former position of control in one of the strategic areas of the world, Egypt. These had all been rallying points in Imperial strength, which had lost none of their importance in the new distribution of world-power and carried with them an assembly of associations, political, historical, and cultural, that no nation could have been willing lightly to discard. . . .

The explanation of these events, of which the historian will presumably be aware, but to which he may find it difficult to give adequate weight, no doubt largely lies in the new order of political ideas that, emanating from President Wilson at the end of the 1914 war, had confused and conquered the Western world. The assertion of the principle of self-determination had, as it was bound to do, greatly stimulated popular movements in favour of self-government, where such were not already in existence, and to this general drift India was no exception. The doctrine of trusteeship, which had inspired British administration in India, as it still inspires British administration in the Colonies, was the expression of an honourable resolution to govern for the good of the governed and to make it one of the principal objects of government to train the temporarily subject people to govern themselves.[2]

Out of these two crises the future outline of the British Commonwealth began to emerge. For the English-speaking nations of the empire of settlement there would be full and unconditional acceptance of the fact that they had already become mistresses in their own houses and adult members of the Commonwealth family, free to come or go as they pleased. For the non-English-speaking peoples, there would be tutelage toward independence with the promise of its grant as soon as they were competent to assume the responsibilities of adult nations. The argument thereafter was not over purposes but over timing. British governments tended to fear that individual colonies were "not yet quite ready" for independence, while colonial nationalists tended to feel that independence was being unnecessarily delayed.

The geography of the Commonwealth

The Commonwealth as it exists today is a post-World War II creation, although its roots, as we have seen, go much farther

XXXIII:1 (Left) This was the British Empire in 1914. Those were the days when Englishmen could boast quite properly that the sun never set on their Empire.

[1] The reference here is to the First World War.

[2] Reprinted by permission of Dodd, Mead & Company from *Fullness of Days* by Lord Halifax. Copyright 1956, 1957, by Edward Frederick Lindley Wood, 1st Earl of Halifax.

back. The beginnings of what Sir Winston Churchill caustically referred to as "the liquidation of the British Empire" can be traced to the accession of the Labour Party to power in Great Britain in July, 1945. One of the campaign pledges of the Labour Party had been to hasten the preparation of colonial peoples for freedom and nationhood.

The first decisive implementation of this policy was the partition of India and the creation, out of its former territory, of the two dominions of India and Pakistan, both of which became formally independent on August 14, 1947. Both later became republics, but without sacrificing their membership in the Commonwealth. Once this epochal event had shattered the tradition that full nationhood within the Commonwealth was restricted to English-speaking, "white" nations of the empire of settlement, the pressure for independence within "colored" nations of the old empire of trade built up rapidly. The consequences may be briefly summarized chronologically:

1948—Jan. 4, Burma became an independent republic and withdrew from the Commonwealth.

1948—Feb. 1, The Federation of Malaya came into being with complete home rule. The Federation became a self-governing dominion within the Commonwealth on August 31, 1957.

1948—Feb. 4, Ceylon became a self-governing dominion within the Commonwealth.

1953—Aug. 1, Northern and Southern Rhodesia and the Protectorate of Nyasaland were federated in the Federation of Rhodesia and Nyasaland and given virtual self-government.

1956—Aug. 2, Jamaica, Trinidad, and the lesser islands of the British West Indies were federated in the West Indies Federation and given home rule.

1957—March 6, the Colony of the Gold Coast became the self-governing dominion of Ghana. On July 1, 1960, Ghana became a republic but remained within the Commonwealth.

1960—June 26, British Somaliland was released to join the new independent Somalia Republic.

1960—Aug. 16, Cyprus became a self-governing republic, its relations to the Commonwealth still to be determined.

1960—Oct. 1, Nigeria became a self-governing dominion within the Commonwealth.

1961—April 27, Sierra Leone became a self-governing dominion within the Commonwealth.

1961—May 31, the Union of South Africa became a republic and withdrew from the Commonwealth.

1961—December, Tanganyika became a self-governing dominion within the Commonwealth.

This chronology touches only the high points. It would be difficult and, for the purposes of our discussion unnecessary, to detail the special arrangements which have been made for ensuring a larger measure of self-government to such small territories as Bermuda, Malta, and Singapore. The essential point is that in all of her colonies and possessions Britain has followed the same policy, a policy of giving them as large a measure of self-government as they are capable of handling. Of the old Empire, therefore, very little remains today, and most of what still remains is scheduled for liquidation. In its place stands the Commonwealth, a voluntary association of free, self-governing nations, the majority of which are not British by language or ancestry and three of which (India, Pakistan, and Ghana) do not recognize the Queen as their sovereign.

The Commonwealth and Empire consisted, as of January 1, 1962, of the following units:

Self-Governing Nations

The United Kingdom of Great Britain and Northern Ireland

Canada

The Commonwealth of Australia and its dependencies:

- The Cocos Islands
- Norfolk Island
- Papua
- The Trust Territory of Nauru

New Zealand and its dependencies:
- Island Territories
- Western Samoa Trust Territory

The Union of India
Pakistan
Ceylon
The West Indies Federation
Ghana
The Federation of Malaya
The Federation of Rhodesia and Nyasaland
Nigeria
Sierra Leone
Tanganyika

Crown Colonies (Dependencies of the United Kingdom)

In the Americas:
- Bermuda
- The Bahamas
- British Guiana
- British Honduras
- The Falkland Islands

In the Atlantic Ocean:
- St. Helena

In the Mediterranean Sea:
- Gibraltar
- Malta

In West Africa:
- Gambia

In East Africa:
- Kenya

In the Indian Ocean:
- Mauritius
- Seychelles
- Aden

In the Far East:
- Singapore
- Hong Kong
- North Borneo
- Sarawak

In the Western Pacific Ocean:
- Fiji
- Gilbert and Ellice Islands
- Pitcairn Island

Protectorates (Indirectly governed by the United Kingdom through Local Rulers or Administrations)

In Africa:
- Gambia (that portion which is not a colony)
- Uganda
- Zanzibar

In the Indian Ocean:
- Aden (that portion which is not a colony)

In the Far East and the western Pacific Ocean:
- The Sultanate of Brunei
- The Kingdom of Tonga
- The British Solomon Islands

Trusteeships (Administered by Nations of the Commonwealth Under the Supervision of the United Nations)

In Africa:
- Togoland (administered by Ghana)
- The Cameroons (administered by Nigeria)

Condominium (Sovereignty Shared by the United Kingdom and France)

The New Hebrides

What holds this heterogeneous assemblage of sovereign states, crown colonies, protectorates, trusteeships, and condominiums together? Certainly there are bonds of sentiment and affection, of long-shared history and of interwoven culture. But there are also some very important practical advantages to belonging to the Commonwealth, advantages rooted in geography and economics.

The chief of these practical advantages is that each of the units of the Commonwealth, whether self-governing or still dependent, may find within the Commonwealth what Britain herself was seeking in her days of empire building: preferred access to raw materials and to markets. For many years, and still to a lesser extent today, the countries of the Commonwealth granted each other certain tariff concessions under the policy known as "Imperial Preference." The advantages of such an arrangement are readily apparent: Canadian forest products, Rhodesian minerals, Australian wool, New Zealand dairy products, Malayan rubber, British manufactures, Indian jute, West African cocoa, Ceylon tea, and a host of other products are for sale within the Commonwealth to Commonwealth members at what amounts to discount prices. Moreover, within the Commonwealth (except for Canada), the free use of sterling greatly facilitates multilateral trade. Thus, for instance, India can buy Birmingham steel products with sterling balances built up by the sale of its jute to Aus-

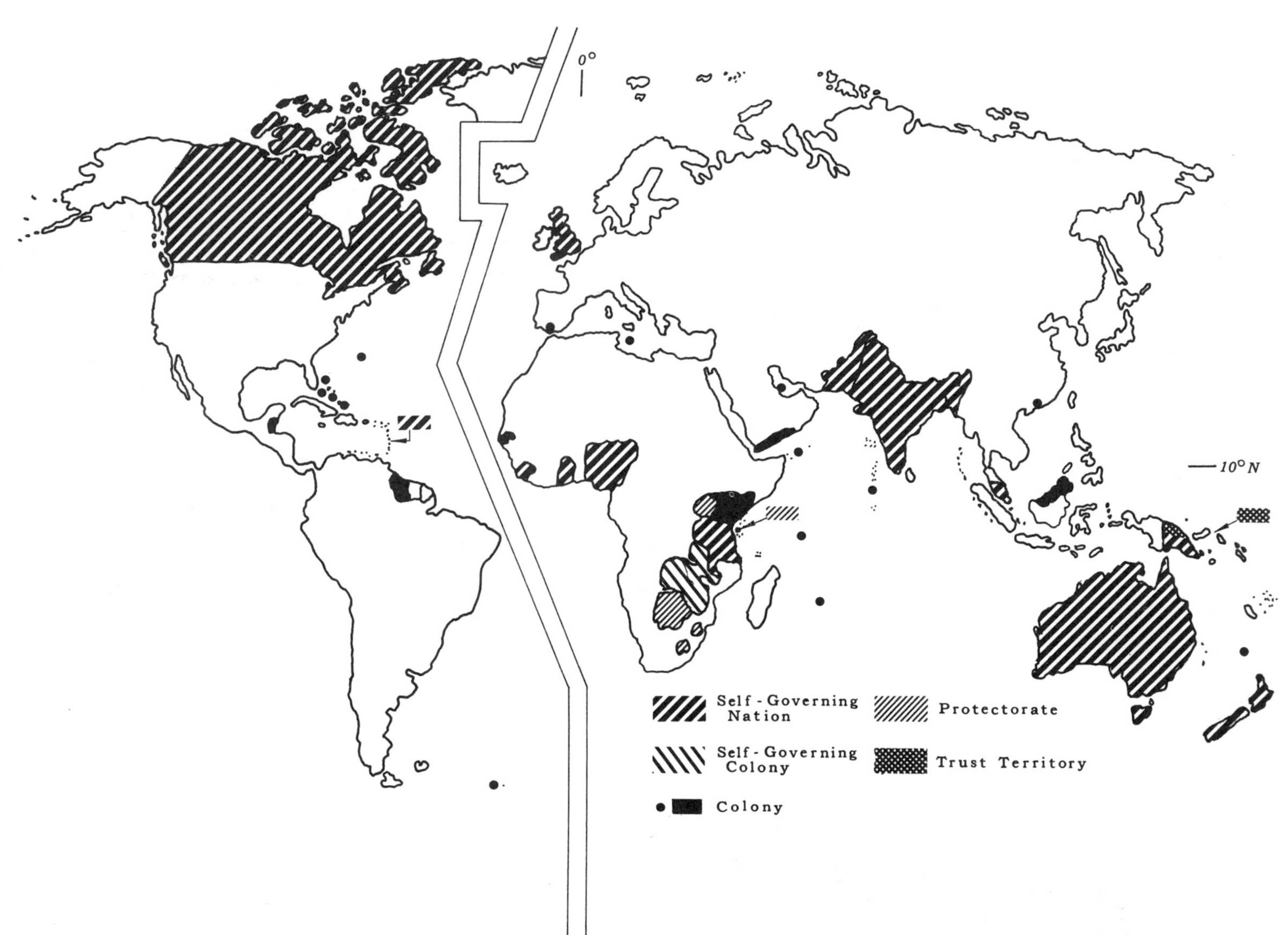
0°
10° N
Self - Governing Nation
Protectorate
Self - Governing Colony
Trust Territory
Colony

Table 33.1 Percentage of Commonwealth countries' trade with other Commonwealth countries in 1957

Australia	55	New Zealand	73
Canada	17	Pakistan	34
Ceylon	50	Rhodesia and Nyasaland	72
Ghana	42	South Africa	47
India	40	The United Kingdom	45
Federation of Malaya	34	U. K. Dependencies	51

tralia. The clearing-house for these transactions is London, where the great banks act as agents for the central banks of the Commonwealth countries in pooling gold and dollar earnings and disbursing them upon demand. Certain non-Commonwealth countries also belong to this "sterling bloc," among them Burma, Iceland, Eire, Jordan, Libya, and the British Protected States in the Persian Gulf area, thus constituting a commonwealth of trade and finance which is even larger than the Commonwealth proper.

That imperial preference and membership in the sterling bloc are of real value to the Commonwealth's member nations is indicated by the fact that "nearly half of the Commonwealth's trade—which in turn is nearly one-quarter of the world total—is 'within the family'"(6).

This trade reflects, in turn, the important role which Commonwealth nations and dependencies still play in the production of the world's primary commodities.

Besides providing for what is still, despite growing restrictions, essentially a world-wide free-trade area, the Commonwealth serves as the framework for many other types of cooperative activities among its member nations: in agriculture, in science, in air and ocean transport, in telecommunications, and in education. Finally, while each of the sovereign nations within the Commonwealth defines the citizenship and nationality of its own people and determines the status of other nationals within its boundaries, the following member nations have enacted legislation which, in effect, preserves the common status of British subject or its equivalent, Commonwealth citizen: Canada, the United Kingdom, New Zealand, Australia, Ceylon, Rhodesia and Nyasaland, Pakistan, India, and Ghana. The recognition of this common status in so many lands permits great freedom of movement to the citizens of the individual member countries and encourages migration among them.

XXXIII:2 (Left) This shows the Commonwealth of Nations in 1961. Of the old Empire only a few small colonies are left.

Can such a tenuous, voluntary association as the Commonwealth survive? Only time will tell. In the Spring of 1961, the Union of South Africa, irked by criticism of its racial policies by representatives of its sister nations in the Commonwealth, withdrew and proclaimed itself an independent republic outside the Commonwealth. There is nothing to prevent any other member nation from following the same course if it should choose to do so. Militarily and in terms of national defense, no nation of the Commonwealth derives any great advantage from membership in it: individual nations seek their security in regional defensive associations (NATO or SEATO) or in a policy of neutralism, rather than in any kind of Commonwealth-wide association. The Commonweath tie has held remarkably fast, though, through an extended period of world crisis, and it may be its very flexibility and tenuousness which keeps it from snapping under the tensions and pressures that have been brought to bear upon it.

Table 33.2 Commonwealth share in world production of primary commodities

	Proportion of free world output
Gold, platinum, nickel, titanium, asbestos; wool, jute, tea, pepper	Half or more
Tin, bauxite, columbite; natural rubber, sisal, rice, peanuts, cocoa	Between one-third and one-half
Copper, lead, zinc, silver, diamonds, chrome, manganese; wheat, oats, barley, cane sugar, vegetable oils and oilseeds, butter, copra, woodpulp	Between one-fifth and one-third
Coal, iron ore, cobalt; cotton, meat, cheese, tobacco	Between one-tenth and one-fifth

SOURCE: *The Commonwealth in Brief*, British Information Services, 1959, p. 26.

APPLICATION OF GEOGRAPHIC UNDERSTANDING

I. What geographic reasons are there for the fact that Australia and New Zealand are two nations rather than one?

II. What factors were important in persuading the Canadians to confederate into a nation of their own rather than seek admission to the United States? How does the presence of the United States inhibit the full development of Canadian nationhood?

III. Why were no large tropical or subtropical areas included in Britain's empire of settlement? Why no large oriental areas?

IV. What geographical and historical justification would there be for calling the American Revolutionary War an Imperial Civil War? What might the future of the United States have been if that revolution had not succeeded? How might the future development of the British Empire have been different if the Revolution had not succeeded?

V. Why was it to Britain's advantage, during the late nineteenth century, to try to maintain firmer control over its empire of trade than over its empire of settlement?

VI. Why was Great Britain so interested in the digging of the Suez Canal? In America's Open Door policy in China? In the reorganization of the political structure in the Near East following the breakup of the old Ottoman Empire after the First World War?

VII. What are the possibilities that Britain could become as dominant in air power in the twentieth century as she was in sea power during the nineteenth?

VIII. For each of the primary products listed in Table 33.2, name at least one important producing area within the Commonwealth.

IX. Australia has long followed a "White Australia" policy which, in effect, forbids "colored" migration to or settlement in Australia. Ignoring the ethical and ideological implications of this policy, what geographical considerations may account for it?

X. Thinking in terms of economic geography, what is the logic behind the statement that "Britain has preserved her Empire by dissolving it"?

References

1 Carrington, C. E., *The British Overseas*, The Cambridge University Press, New York, 1950, pp. 1032-1033.
2 Clarke, C. F. O., *Britain Today*, The Harvard University Press, Cambridge, Mass., 1951, p. 217.
3 Devens, Ely, "The Financial Burden of World War II," a review in *The Manchester Guardian*, October 3, 1956, of *Financial Policy 1939-1945* by R. S. Sayers, Longmans, Green and Co., Ltd., London, 1956.
4 Zierer, Clifford M., "Australia: the Cultural Development," *Geography of the Pacific*, Otis W. Freeman, Ed., John Wiley & Sons, Inc., N. Y., 1951, p. 149.
5 Lord Halifax, *Fullness of Days*, Dodd, Mead & Co., New York, 1957, pp. 108, 109-110.
6 *The Commonwealth in Brief*, British Information Services, October, 1959, p. 28.

Chapter 34

The geography of the Cold War

In a brief speech following the signing of the Anglo-Soviet treaty of alliance on May 26, 1942, the then British foreign secretary, Anthony Eden, commented that "upon the co-operation of the Soviet Union, the United States of America, and the British Commonwealth the future of mankind will largely depend." This comment was, of course, no more than a statement of sober fact. But as the war moved into its climactic stages there developed, at least in the West, a disposition to believe that, since the future of mankind depended upon the co-operation of the three great wartime allies, this somehow assured that there would be such co-operation in the new era that would dawn with the war's ending. To the hope was added the wish for such co-operation, grounded at least in part in the admiration which was felt everywhere in the West for the gallantry that the Soviet people and their armies displayed in such remarkable measure at Leningrad and at Stalingrad. Forgiven, if not altogether forgotten, were the reiterated incitements to world revolution that had emanated from Moscow in the past. That masterpiece of amoral cynicism, the Russo-German nonaggression pact of 1939, was allowed to fade into the limbo of a past best forgotten. United against the same bitter enemy, West and East seemed to be finding a community of interest and understanding which would ensure their working together in the reconstruction of the world after victory had been won.

True, there were ominous signs. As early as 1944, Russia's "liberation" of Poland brought from the *Polish Daily News* in Chicago the editorial question whether it was actually a liberation or an occupation. In that same year, Prime Minister Churchill was obliged to admit to the House of Commons that Britain had been unable to get from the Russians a satisfactory answer on her intentions in Poland. But in spite of growing misgivings the West proceeded to construct the peace and the chief instrument for maintaining it, the United Nations, upon the assumption that the wartime allies constituted an association of peace-loving peoples. Such doubts as there were about the peaceful intentions of the Soviet Union were assuaged by the apparently logical contention that the Soviet Union needed a long period of peace to recover from the catastrophic human and material losses of the war.

What actually followed is history too recent and too well-known to require lengthy rehearsal at this time. By May of 1948, when Churchill reviewed the events of the then-recent past in his famous reference to the "Iron Curtain," it was evident to all but the purblind that one war had ended only to be succeeded by another. This "Cold War" is still going on, and its issue is still in doubt.

Background to conflict

To the vast majority of Americans, the theories and practices of Marxism are repugnant. Since the expansionist policies of the Soviet Union have been equally repugnant the temptation to relate Marxism to Russian expansionism as a simple matter of cause and effect has been a particularly attractive one, and the logic of such an association seems to be validated by certain key concepts in Marxist ideology. But even the most cursory study of the historico-political geography of the state which is now the Soviet Union will cause one to question whether ideology is the only—or even the most important—consideration in explaining the aggressive and expansionist policies of the Soviet government.

Similarities between the history of Russian expansionism and the history of our own national growth are interesting, and somewhat embarrassing. The course of American empire made its way westward from a nucleus, the Thirteen Colonies, along the Atlantic seaboard. Eastward and southward the course of Russian empire has made its way from a nucleus, the Principality of Muscovy, at the headwaters of the Volga River. In both cases, the pattern of expansion was primarily one of mere penetration into essentially empty lands, interspersed with occa-

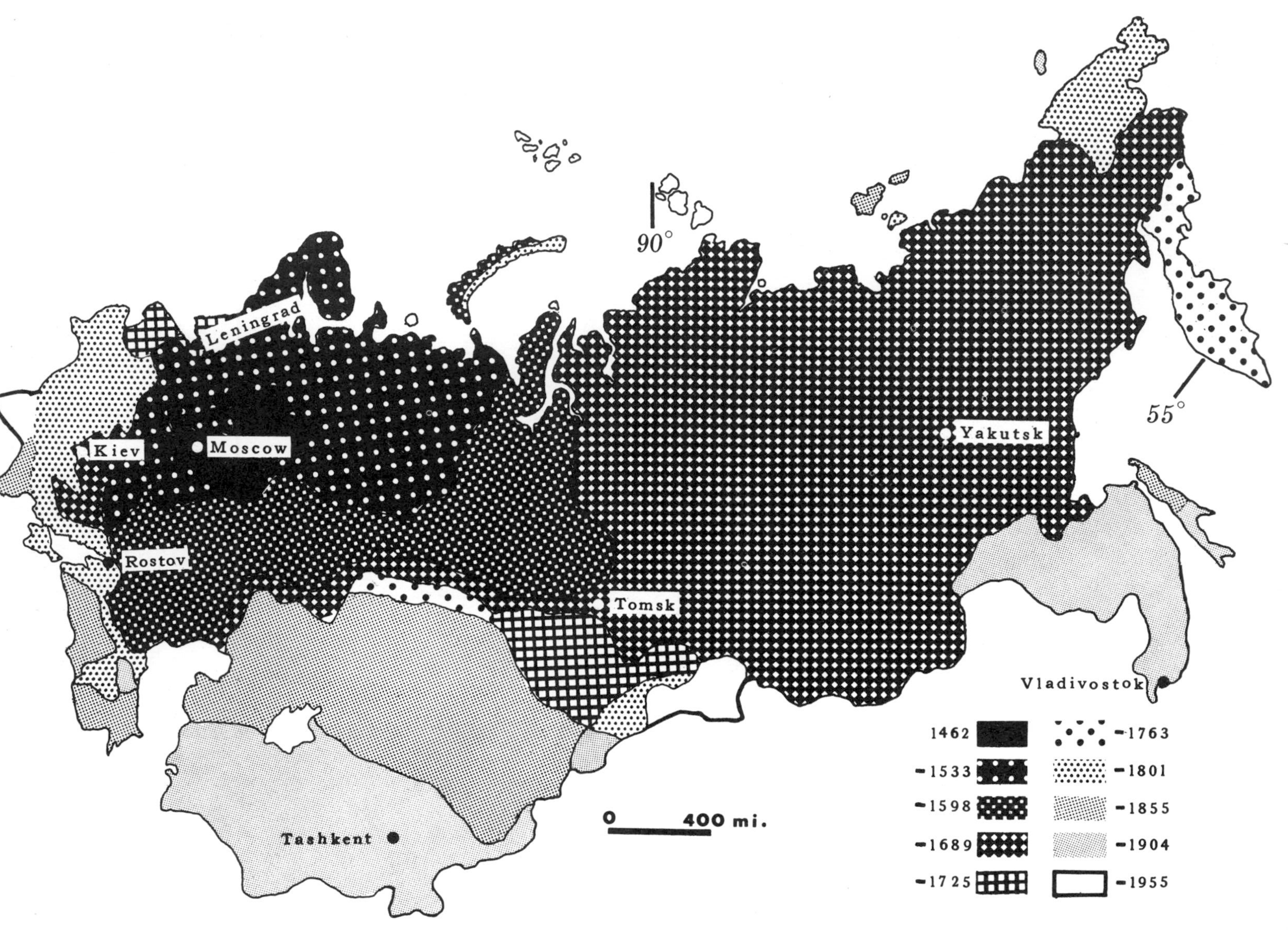

Leningrad
Kiev
Moscow
Rostov
Tomsk
Yakutsk
Vladivostok
Tashkent
90°
55°
0
400 mi.
1462
-1533
-1598
-1689
-1725
-1763
-1801
-1855
-1904
-1955

sional clashes with small, essentially nomadic, aboriginal populations. To a certain extent, American expansionism, at least until the time of the Civil War, was motivated by considerations of self-defense—against the possible encroachment of British power from the north and Spanish or Mexican power from the south. Russian expansionism, likewise, has from time to time been dictated by considerations of self-defense—against Tartar threats to the south, against the encroachments of Swedes and Lithuanians and Poles and Teutonic Knights from the west, against Mongol invasions from the east. Against such threats, the Russians learned early in their history that a good offense is the best defense.

The basic reality underlying Russian expansionism was and is geographical:

¶ The theatre of operations was an interminable plain with no natural boundaries against invasion. It had to be filled up; and in this long process was born the peculiar Russian method of defence by attack. The Russian voyaged across the plain, much as Tudor seamen explored the oceans. It was hard to know where to stop. If the Muscovites themselves had not expanded outwards from their centre and deep into the plain, their neighbors would have done so in their place. And for ever afterwards the plain was to prove a source of danger—up to our own days when the German Armour overran the western levels. The problem permanently facing the Russians was very much like the problem which faced the Eighth Army in the western desert: Benghazi could not be held without command of the desert for a thousand miles on either side. In the last resort, to secure Cairo you had to hold Tripoli and all the land between. So the Russians went to Vladivostok, to Samarkand, to Kamchatka, to the White Sea and the Baltic, to the Caucasus and the Crimea. And this habit, at one time stark necessity, became, as it were, part of an unconscious principle of life. Russia forgot how to stop. She even expanded across the Bering Sea into Alaska before she realized quite what she had done. And then, thinking better of it, and suddenly realizing that the only way to hold Alaska was to continue her expansion across the whole North American continent, she sold Alaska and withdrew across the water.[1]

Translated into the American experience, here is, again, a familiar story—the story of our own thrust toward such remote points as New Orleans, San Antonio, Sante Fe, and San Francisco, points which gave us command over the vast intervening empty lands. The rationale for our expansionism was the idea of Manifest Destiny. The Russians, although they did not employ the same term, were motivated by much the same combination of hope and ambition and fear.

Two other aspects of Russian expansion which Crankshaw notes—the economic and the missionary—have their counterparts in American history. For our forefathers, trans-Appalachian America held the promise of fertile land, valuable furs, and perhaps (they had no way of knowing) precious minerals. So also for the Russian there was the unexplored frontier, the new lands where factual information set, as yet, no boundaries to fantasy. We had our frontier forts and our fur-trading posts in the Northwest Territories, in the Great Plains and later as far west as Pacific shores. The Russians had theirs in cis-Ural Russia and later in Siberia. At the western end of our rainbow we found gold—in California. At the eastern end of their rainbow they, too, found gold—in Lenaland.

The missionary aspect of Russian expansionism is a bit more difficult to explain. To understand it, one needs to recall the small, isolated Muscovite principality, cut off from Europe by the Tartars and by a defensive line running through eastern Europe against the Tartars. Thus isolated, the Russians came to look upon themselves as a kind of chosen people, an outpost of Christianity in a pagan world, the authentic successors to the Christian Empire in the East which had been destroyed by the Moslems in the fourteenth century. The pious people called their country "Holy Russia," and their rulers assumed a title (Tsar = Caesar) which accorded with their claim to the throne of the conquered Christian empire of the East. And so, beyond the narrow limits of Muscovy lay not merely

XXXIV:1 (Left) This shows the growth of the Russian State. (Based on a map in the *Oxford Regional Economic Atlas—The U.S.S.R. and Eastern Europe,* Oxford University Press, 1956, used by permission)

[1] From *Cracks in the Kremlin Wall* by Edward Crankshaw. Copywright 1951 by Edward Crankshaw. Reprinted by permission of The Viking Press, Inc.

open land to be had for the taking nor merely a new economic frontier to be colonized, but also vast territories to be claimed for the Cross, or at least denied to the Moslem destroyers of the Christian East. And when Moslem power swept northward and westward into Slavic Eastern Europe, the Russian defenders of the faith accepted the additional moral obligation of championing their Slavic brethren against the heathen invader.

Much of the vigor of our early expansionism derived from a simple faith in democracy as a system of life and government rooted not only in practicality but in "the laws of Nature and of Nature's God," and armed with that faith we set out to make the New World secure for democracy. Our determination to secure the benefits of democracy for our little brothers in the Americas found expression in the Monroe Doctrine. Much of the vigor of Russian expansionism derived from a simple faith in Orthodox Christianity, and armed with that faith they set out to make northern Eurasia safe for Christianity. Their determination to secure the benefits of this faith for their little Slavic brothers found expression in Pan-Slavism, the idea of a Slavic world dominated and protected by the Slavic heirs of Constantinople.

But if these parallels are valid, why is the Soviet Union still aggressively expansionist while the United States asks nothing more than the preservation of a reasonable status quo? There is no simple answer, but to a geographer it is both interesting and suggestive that the complex of hopes and ambitions and fears which we Americans comprehended under the term "Manifest Destiny" was capable of satisfaction within the framework of the geographical realities of North America. There were boundaries beyond which we either could not or need not press in building a secure and compact state. East and west, we had the two great oceans. North and South, we had weak and ultimately friendly neighbors. We were, politically speaking, an island, impregnable on all sides. At the same time, we had access to the two greatest oceanic market-places in the world, the North Atlantic and the North Pacific.

It was quite otherwise with the Russians. Natural frontiers of a sort there were, on the north and on the south. But the northern frontier was the frozen Arctic Ocean, and the most natural southern frontier was the mountain backbone of central Asia, remote from the nucleus of the Russian state and long since transgressed by Turkic and other peoples. And where was the natural boundary to the East? At the Urals, hardly more than good-size hills? At the Yenisei? At the Amur?

But the real problem was in the West. No barrier of any consequence breaks the broad sweep of the North European Plain between the Urals and the Atlantic. Somewhere—no one knows where, with any certainty—the Slavic world ends and the Germanic world begins. A Germany intent upon expansion must look eastward. A Russia intent upon safeguarding its western frontier must press it as far westward as possible. Only a Pole, perhaps, can appreciate the utter fluidity of this boundary. Whichever way the tide runs, it engulfs his country.

Add to this "frontier frustration" yet another problem. For all practical purposes, Russia is landlocked. Only at the remotest extreme of her territory does she have direct access to the open ocean, and that to the relatively unimportant Pacific. All of her other ports lead either to the frozen Arctic or to inland seas. The American, with his "don't fence me in" attitude, can understand better than perhaps most people how frustrating it would be to have his comings and goings prescribed by neighbors who might or might not be friendly toward him.

All this is said by way of explanation, rather than justification, of historic attitudes which have developed out of the Russian geo-political situation. The purpose of saying it is to emphasize the fact that Russian expansionism has roots that go back much farther than 1917; that are, in fact, imbedded in what Russia is and where it is.

The Russian Revolution of 1917 provided new fuel for the fire of Russian expansionism by giving it a powerful ideological motivation. The victorious Bolsheviks under V. I. Lenin saw themselves not merely as the liberators of Russia but also as the vanguard of a movement which would sweep over the earth, ultimately to fulfill the prophecy of Communism's battle hymn, *The Internationale:* "The International Soviet shall be the human race." Engels had written that:

¶ . . . in reality the State is nothing else than a machine for the oppression of one class by another class, and that no less in the democratic republic than under the monarchy. At the very best it is an inheritance of evil, bound to be transmitted to the proletariat when it has become victorious in its struggle for class supremacy, and the worst features of which it will have to lop off at once, as the Commune did, until a new race, grown up under new, free social conditions, will be in a position to shake off from itself this state rubbish in its entirety.[1]

The established governments of every state became, in this view, oppressors of mankind, to be displaced, as opportunity permitted, by dictatorships of the working classes. What had formerly been mere Russian expansionism now took on the aspects of a holy war, a crusade, for the realization of a new world order, Marxism's "International Soviet."

There has thus been loose in the world during the past three decades a vigorously expansive force reminiscent of the Spain of four centuries ago. The conquistadores sailed from the ports of Spain motivated both by dreams of national glory and by a missionary fervor to plant the Holy Cross in the newly-discovered and still-to-be-discovered lands of the New World. The Red Conquistadores of the twentieth century have expanded from the Soviet homeland motivated both by dreams of national glory and by a missionary fervor to raise the hammer and sickle over lands which, in their view, still groan under the economic heathenism of capitalism. The hour of opportunity came at the end of the Second World War.

The matrix of conflict

In the years between the world wars, Russian expansionism had been effectively contained by a ring of power along her borders. In the Far East, there was Japan, itself an expansionist power which had already secured control over Korea and Manchuria and posed a constant threat to Soviet Far Eastern territories. On the south, Britain still held firm control of India and had effective, although indirect, control of the Moslem states of southwest Asia. On the west, there was renascent Germany, still threatening a *Drang nach Osten*, a surge toward the East; and there was, in addition, a system of alliances between France and the Slavic countries—Poland, Czechoslovakia, and Romania—which had been deliberately planned to establish a *cordon sanitaire,* a belt of safety, between Russia and the West. Internally, the Soviet Union was still nursing the wounds of revolution, still from time to time shaking with massive internal convulsions, and very slowly building its economic strength.

The Second World War changed all of that. First of all, faced with an actual assault upon their homeland, the peoples of the U.S.S.R. found common cause in the defense, not of Marxism or of the Communist government, but of "Mother Russia." There were defections, particularly in the Westernized Ukraine, and these were dealt with mercilessly. But at Leningrad and at Stalingrad the Russian people made stands which won—and properly so—the admiration of the world. And it was in the glow of this admiration that Western leaders—all except Churchill—forgot that the roots of Soviet expansionism lay not in the shallow ground of a particular dictatorial regime but in the deep soil of Russian geography and history and of communist ideology. The Russians were treated as allies having a common purpose with the West, rather than as co-belligerents whose interests, at the moment, could best be served by co-operating with the West.

What were these interests? The same that they had been under the Tsars: to break down whatever power dams stood in the way of further Russian expansion, to establish suzerainty over the Slavic nations on its western border, to destroy the threat of German power, to break through to warm-water ports. All of these objectives were accomplished either in the closing days of the war or in the interim peace settlements which followed the war.

In Europe, Russian troops, against Churchill's urgent advice, were allowed to "liberate" the Slavic countries of the old "*cordon sanitaire*" and to press westward through Germany as far as the Elbe, thus ensuring a divided Germany. A wider buffer zone

[1] Engels, Frederick, "Introduction to the German Edition of the Addresses of the General Council of the International Workingmen's Association Concerning the Civil War in France," *Capital,* Max Eastman, Editor, The Modern Library, Random House, Inc., New York, 1932, p. 381. Reprinted by permission.

against possible future attack from the west was incorporated into the Soviet Union itself, primarily at the expense of Poland, which was compensated for its losses with territory taken from Germany. The old *cordon sanitaire* was reconstituted, this time as a Russian belt of safety against the West. The former French allies became Russian satellites. Germany, whose position makes it, for good or for ill, the power center of Europe, would have been left a complete power vacuum if the Western powers had not awakened, just in time, to the fact that this was the key to Soviet grand strategy for the domination of the whole continent; as it was, Germany became two countries and Berlin was left as a festering sore which could, at any time, by Russian prodding, be made to radiate pain and infection through all of Europe.

In eastern Asia, a similar power vacuum was created when Japan was demilitarized and shorn of its continental holdings in Korea and Manchuria. With Japan out of the picture, with China torn by civil war, with the United States demobilizing as fast as men could be run through its separation centers, there was nothing to bar Russian expansionism in the Far East. Inevitably the Chinese Nationalist government fell before the combined power of the Soviet Union and its own Chinese Communist opposition. A later attempt to incorporate Korea into the Communist sphere was fought to a stalemate which resulted in another partition on the German model. Thus, within five years from the end of the Second World War, the Communist world empire had surged outward from the prewar boundaries of the Soviet Union to the Elbe on the west and the South China Sea on the east.

Meanwhile, British power no longer opposed any thrust toward the south. The Indian subcontinent had been divided into a Western-oriented but largely impotent Pakistan and a neutralist India. In Indo-China, the French empire collapsed into three weak, disorganized states. Burma received its independence from Britain and opted for the neutralist policies of its Indian neighbor. The Middle East, no longer policed by British power, erupted into a series of wars and revolutions which seemed to invite third-party intervention. A new and aggressive regime in Egypt threatened for some time to cast its lot with the Soviet bloc and take all or most of the Middle East with it.

Important in the Communist strategy of expansion was the factor of timing. Practically all of the Soviet Union's permanent gains were made within five years immediately following the war when its recent allies were either (1) exhausted, as in the case of Great Britain, or (2) torn by internal troubles, as was France, or (3) preoccupied with colonial troubles, as were Britain, France, and the Netherlands, or (4) anxious to return as fast as possible to prewar "normalcy," as was the United States, or (5) prostrated by the effects of the war, as were the Slavic countries of Europe, Germany, China, and Japan. Understandably but tragically, the statesmen of the Western world, by and large, ignored the first rule of political geography: that a power vacuum will not remain unfilled. This is particularly true when the vacuum exists along the borders of a strong and aggressive power. They ignored also the first rule of international diplomacy: that great nations have no friends, only interests. The Soviet Union was a courageous and gallant ally of the West in the War, but her long-term interests precluded any lasting friendship or even co-operation.

Geo-strategical implications of the new weapons

On August 6, 1945, an American plane dropped an atomic bomb on the Japanese city of Hiroshima, obliterating within seconds three-fifths of that city. Shortly thereafter, another such bomb was dropped on Nagasaki, with like effect. Staggered and terrified by these blows, the Japanese cabinet on August 10 made an offer of surrender, and the Second World War ended on a note of somber warning that it might be the last world war from which mankind could emerge with civilization more or less intact.

The warning has become all the more somber as the passing years have brought newer and more destructive weapons and more efficient ways of employing them. The Hiroshima bomb has long since become "conventional" and been replaced as a strategic weapon by the hydrogen bomb, with even more destructive cobalt and bacterial bombs in prospect. Missiles and atomic-powered submarines have been perfected to deliver these bombs precisely on target at speeds which have raised serious questions as to the value of warning or retaliatory systems.

The geostrategic significance of these new weapons is immense. For the first time in man's history, our earth is spherical strategically as well as geodetically, i.e., military operations are no longer limited either by surface conditions or by the weather conditions of the troposphere. A nuclear warhead can be dispatched as readily through the Arctic as it can across the Atlantic. One way of putting it would be to say that missiles carrying nuclear warheads have brought about a neutralization of the space separating an aggressor from his intended victim. As a result, the tundras and taigas and frozen ocean which until now would have prohibited any transpolar attack of the United States and the Soviet Union upon each other no longer serve as effective buffers between these two great power centers. We who have become accustomed by long usage to think of the world in terms of a map with the Equator at its center are now compelled to think of it as a globe with the great powers deployed around a center in the Arctic Ocean.

The new weapons have also virtually eliminated distance as a factor in military strategy. The newest missiles are capable of making the trip from Chicago to Novosibirsk in minutes. For the Soviet Union, this means that its traditional strategy of defense in depth, employed with such telling effectiveness against both Napoleon and Hitler, is outmoded. For the United States, it means that neither its oceanic moats nor the vast wastelands of the Arctic serve any longer to insulate it against attack. Hostile action in any future major war must be expected to be launched directly against the centers of population, industry, and government. Overland operations must be expected to follow, rather than precede, action against the prime targets.

A third profoundly significant characteristic of the new weapons is their capacity for regional devastation. "An atomic war, as atomic tests have revealed, will destroy most of the industrial sectors of the globe. A single hydrogen bomb can obliterate a metropolis of any size" (3). To a small nation such as Great Britain, this fact is a disturbing fact of life which must weigh heavily in any decisions that she is called upon to make concerning her own role in the struggle between East and West. Faithful as she has been to the Western grand alliance, "there is a great deal more anti-Bomb agitation in Britain than elsewhere on the continent. . . . England is the only country in the world that has already been subjected to missile bombardment; Hitler's V-2 rockets killed almost 3,000 men, women, and children. Premier Khrushchev's warnings that 'the unsinkable aircraft carrier of Britain would cease to exist the first day of an atomic war' are taken very seriously."[1] A 1960 Pentagon statement to the Armed Forces Committee of the Senate estimated that the first twenty-four hours of a Russo-American thermonuclear war would cost between fifty million and seventy-five million American lives.

It has been often suggested that the possession by both sides of such devastating weapons could produce a balance of terror which might minimize the possibility that such weapons would ever be used. If this is true, the Soviet Union possesses certain ideological and geographical advantages which would enable her to do, against the background of the constant threat of thermonuclear war, certain things which the West would neither wish to do, profit from doing, nor be in a favorable position to do. Strung all along the boundaries of the Soviet world (including her satellites) are weak nations which invite conquest for their own sake or as passageways into lands beyond. In the past decade, we have seen thrusts into Korea, Viet Nam, and Laos. In none of these instances have thermonuclear weapons been used—but the threat was always there.

For the West, this has posed two problems: (1) since its ideology does not permit, as does the Communist ideology, the initiating of aggressive action, it has been forced to equip itself to fight whatever kind of war, local or general, the Communist bloc might choose to fight, with whatever type of weapons, conventional or nuclear, its adversaries might choose to employ; and (2) since the trouble areas, actual and potential, lie along

[1] Newman, Peter C., "The Nuclear Dilemma of the Western Peoples," *Maclean's*, December 3, 1960, p. 67. Reprinted by permission.

the periphery of the Communist world, the West has been forced to establish a costly chain of advance bases from which it can move quickly to challenge Communist thrusts into this periphery. In essence, the West finds itself in the position of a forest ranger forbidden to enter the forest but responsible for putting out the fires that are set by a pyromaniac operating from the heart of the forest: no sooner has a fire been put out along one sector of the forest border than another breaks out in another sector.

Finally, these new weapons have tremendous propaganda and blackmail significance. From time to time, Soviet leaders warn such small, close-by countries as Denmark and Norway of the reprisals they might expect if they co-operated too closely with the West; and in the "uncommitted" countries, particularly of Asia, the Communist stockpile of almost-ultimate weapons is pointed to both as a warning not to risk the Red wrath and as proof of the enormous technological strides that backward nations can make under a Communist system. Both by blackmail and by propaganda they seek to weaken the Western systems of alliances and to bring the "uncommitted" nations more closely into the Communist orbit.

The surge from the Heartland

We have seen that Russian expansionism, while it has received strong reinforcement from a new and vigorous ideology in the past forty years, follows a general pattern which can be traced far back into the history of the old Russian Empire. The national psychology which motivates this expansionism is not within the geographer's competence to explain. The geographical realities which have permitted this psychology to express itself in a long history of empire building can, however, be identified and described. The logic of these realities is embodied in the "Heartland" concept.

The word "Heartland" was first introduced into geographical literature in 1904 by the late Sir Halford Mackinder, one of the greatest of British political geographers. It became a key concept in his epoch-making study of the organization of peace after the First World War, *Democratic Ideals and Reality*—a book which was, alas, little read in the West but avidly studied by Dr. Karl Haushofer who, with his disciples, created the pseudo-science of geopolitics as a support and apology for the aggressive designs of the Nazi state. In the last years of the Second World War, Sir Halford returned to the Heartland theme, defining the Heartland as follows:

¶ The Heartland is the northern part and the interior of Euro-Asia. It extends from the Arctic coast to the central deserts, and westward to the broad isthmus between the Baltic and the Black Seas. . . . For our present purpose it is sufficiently accurate to say that the territory of the U.S.S.R. is equivalent to the Heartland, except in one direction. . . . [Here Sir Halford excludes that part of Soviet territory which lies east of the Yenisei River—Lenaland, as he calls it]. . . . In the present war the Russian army is aligned across that open [western] frontier. In its rear is the vast plain of the Heartland, available for defense in depth and for strategic retreat. Away back, this plain recedes eastward into the natural bulwarks constituted by the "inaccessible" Arctic coast, the Lenaland wilderness behind the Yenisei, and the fringe of mountains from the Altai to the Hindu Kush, backed by the Gobi, Tibetan and Iranian deserts. These barriers have breadth and substance, and far excel in defensive value the coasts and mountains which engird France. . . .

The vast potentialities of the Heartland, . . . to say nothing of the natural reserves in Lenaland, are strategically well placed. Industries have grown rapidly in such localities as the southern Urals, in the very pivot of the pivot area, and in the rich Kuznetsk coal basin in the lee of the great natural barriers east of the upper Yenisei River. . . . Except in a very few commodities the country is capable of producing everything which it requires.[1]

Mackinder's concept of the Heartland as an interior fortress practically invulnerable to successful land attack probably requires some modification in our age of supersonic aircraft and missiles. And yet it retains a great deal of its validity. The boy inside a well-provisioned snow fort is still at an ad-

---

[1] Mackinder, Sir Halford J., "The Round World and the Winning of the Peace," *Compass of the World*, Weigert and Stefansson, editors, New York, 1945, pp. 164-167, *passim*. Reprinted by permission of The Macmillan Company.

vantage over his attackers from outside, and the Russians are inside one of nature's finest fortresses.

Rimming the Euro-Asian landmass are states which, historically, have looked out to the sea and many of these states have, from time to time, dominated the seas, making themselves great empires. In earlier days the Greeks, the Italians, the Phoenicians, the Portuguese, and the Spanish enjoyed such suzerainty. In more recent times, Britain, France, and the Netherlands built great overseas empires, making themselves rich and strong far beyond what the limited resources of their own small national areas would have permitted. To this group, in very recent times, could be added Japan.

¶ . . . with the organization of the heartland and the sea powers a crush zone of small states has gradually come into existence between them. These states are largely survivals from an earlier time when political and economic organizations were on a smaller scale, and each has characteristics, partly acquired in that earlier time and partly natural. With sufficient individuality to withstand absorptions, but unable or unwilling to unite with others to form any larger whole, they remain in the unsatisfactory position of buffer states, precariously independent politically, and more surely dependent economically. This zone of states, with small populations, has varied in position from time to time with changing conditions, but it has included Finland, Sweden, Norway, Denmark, Holland, Belgium, Luxemburg, Switzerland, Poland, the Balkan States, Iran, Afghanistan, Siam and Korea. . . . In some sense, Germany and even China belong to this belt.[1]

It is into this "crush zone" (Hartshorne calls it the "shatter zone") that the surge from the Heartland has swept in the postwar years. Call the roll: Finland, relatively free but under Soviet domination and forbidden free contact with the West; Sweden, neutralized; Norway and Denmark, periodically threatened; Poland, a Soviet satellite; the Balkan States (Czechoslovakia, Hungary, Romania, Bulgaria), all Soviet satellites; Iran, tenuously held to the West by its pro-Western Shah, but constantly threatened; Afghanistan, neutral but much influenced by its Soviet neighbor; Korea, divided between East and West; Germany, divided between East and West; China, the Soviet Union's junior (or is it senior?) partner in the Communist world conspiracy.

With every passing year, Communist control over the countries of the crush zone becomes more firmly consolidated by the "liquidation" of whole groups and classes that might act as nuclei of resistance or revolt, by the natural dying off of an older generation that can still remember another way of life, and by the careful nurture of the rising generations in the Communist world view. Once this consolidation is accomplished, the next surge may reasonably be expected to follow.

This surge would carry Communist power into the politically and economically unstable lands of Africa and Latin America, in the process reducing Anglo-America (the United States and Canada) and Western Europe to the status of islands in a Communist sea. The way for this surge has already been prepared. Well-trained, strongly disciplined Communist cadres have been active for years in the Latin American republics, blocking every effort of legally-elected governments to bring about necessary reforms and, at the same time, fixing the blame for these failures upon those governments. In Africa, Communist leaders who are clear on their objectives take full advantage of the inexperienced leaders of the newly-independent states and exploit to the full the rivalrics for power that develop with the withdrawal of European control. On both continents, the strategy is one of encouraging the maximum amount of turmoil internally, of blocking any effective solutions of economic and social problems, and of casting the West in the role of the villain who is responsible for all of these difficulties.

Unfortunately, there is just enough truth in Communist allegations against the West to make them seem plausible. That there was exploitation of people and resources in the former colonial areas no American or European would now deny. The travail of the Congolese people is of too recent memory to allow for any glib excusing of European irresponsibility. In Latin America, there has

[1] Fairgrieve, James, *Geography and World Power,* E. P. Dutton & Co., Inc., New York, 1941, pp. 329-330, 331. Reprinted by permission.

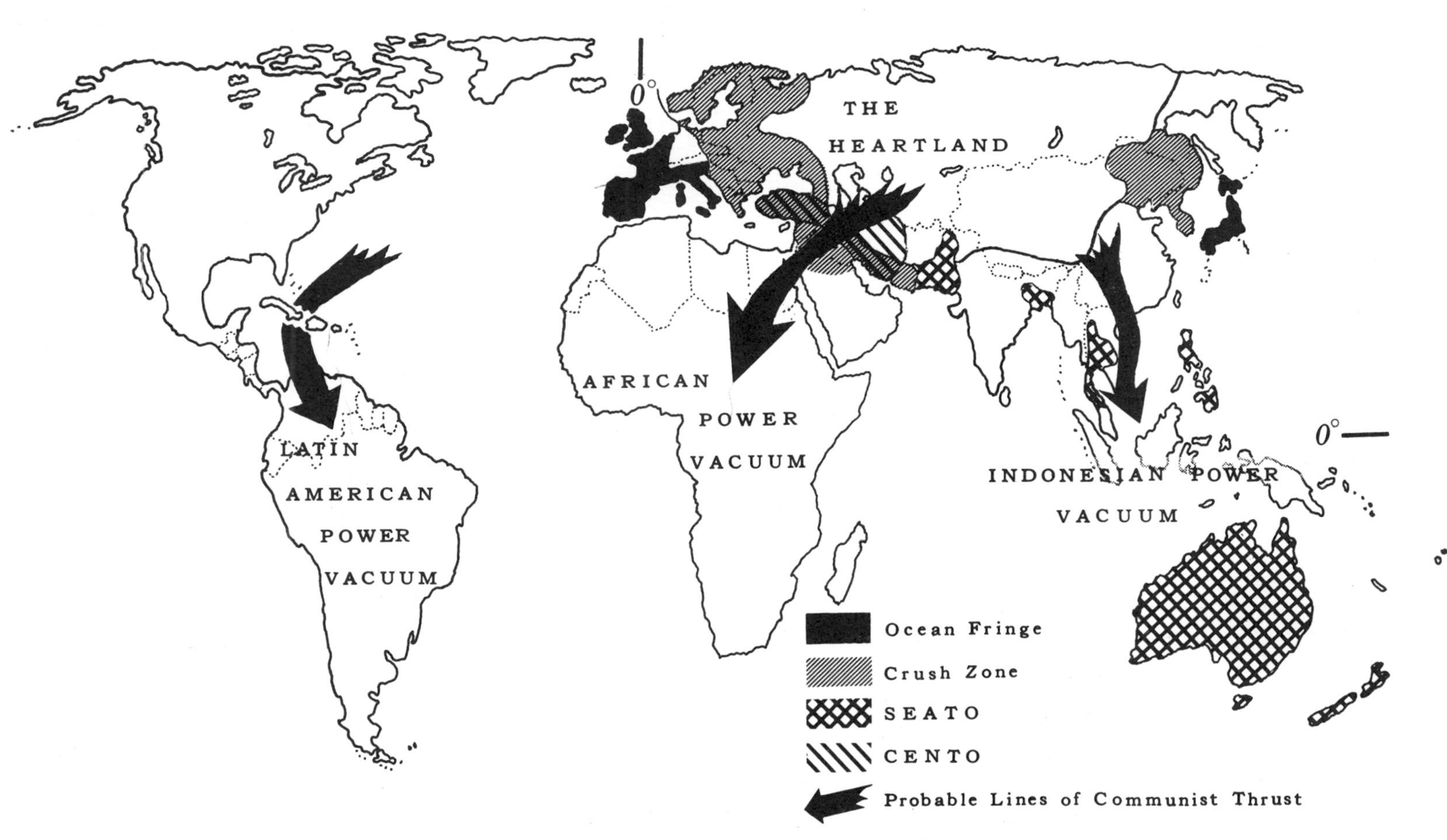
THE
HEARTLAND
0°
0°
AFRICAN
POWER
VACUUM
LATIN
AMERICAN
POWER
VACUUM
INDONESIAN POWER
VACUUM
Ocean Fringe
Crush Zone
SEATO
CENTO
Probable Lines of Communist Thrust

been unconscionable exploitation of the masses by a wealthy minority, and there were long years when America's Latin American policy reflected something less than respect for her sister republics in the Western Hemisphere. The question before the peoples of the contested lands of Africa and Latin America is not whether they have been dealt with unjustly in the past; that they were is now freely conceded by those who once oppressed them. The question is whether they would profit most from friendship with those whose oppression is now a thing of a genuinely-regretted past or those who, for all their protestations of friendship, propose a new and even more efficient oppression. It might help these "neutral" countries to remember that the U.S.S.R. and China have never yet emulated the good example which the United States set years ago in giving the Philippines and Cuba their freedom, and which Britain has followed in its policy of empire liquidation for almost a century.

To recapitulate at this point, we have seen how Russian expansionism from its nucleus in Muscovy pushed outward in all directions until it eventually made the Russian state coterminous with the Euro-Asian Heartland; this had already been accomplished by the beginning of the present century. Reinforced by a new and dynamic ideology, the Russian state after 1917 consolidated its strength within the Heartland during the quarter-century ending with the Allied victory in the Second World War. In its next phase, this same expansionism surged outward from the Heartland into the "crush zone," and the gains which were made in this surge are now in the process of consolidation. We seem now to be in the preliminary stages of Phase 3, the "softening up" of the unstable countries of Africa and Latin America for a surge which, if it should succeed, would leave the North Atlantic Basin surrounded by Soviet power; isolate Japan, Australia, and New Zealand from the power centers of their alliances; and leave the "uncommitted" nations to face, one by one, the necessity of coming to terms with the new world power situation.

XXXIV:2 (Left) Here are shown the Heartland, the "Crush Zone," the Ocean Fringe, and the important power vacuums into which Russian power might seek to thrust.

Western strategy for containing the Red Surge

To this Red Surge from the Euro-Asian Heartland, the nations of the West have opposed a strategy based essentially upon two assumptions: (1) that the North Atlantic Basin constitutes a second world Heartland which is as powerful as, and no more vulnerable than, the Euro-Asian Heartland; and (2) that enough of the "crush" zone still remains to allow for the construction of effective "dikes" against further Soviet expansion. These assumptions have been given practical expression in a system of alliances for mutual defense.

The key alliance is that which binds together the nations of the North Atlantic Basin. This is NATO, the North Atlantic Treaty Organization. Its present membership consists of the United States, Canada, the United Kingdom, Iceland, Norway, Denmark, the Netherlands, Belgium, Luxembourg, France, Portugal, West Germany, Italy, Greece, and Turkey, all of which, with the exception of West Germany, are also members of the United Nations. The industrial and military power of NATO, rooted solidly in its geographic resources, is formidable. Its major weakness as a power structure is that its member nations are free, which means that its energies are always in danger of being vitiated by differences of opinion, the "touchiness" of individual member states, and economic rivalries. Nevertheless, on the great issue of defending the freedom of what still remains of the free world, it has shown a capacity for firm and concerted action. NATO may be conceived of as a strong dam which has been built across the natural channel of the Russian power flow across the North European Plain into Western Europe. The point of impact, i.e., the point at which the full force of this flow strikes most heavily against the dam, is in Germany. A danger which must be constantly watched is that the Russians might, by a diversion of power toward either the Scandinavian or Aegean ends of this dam,

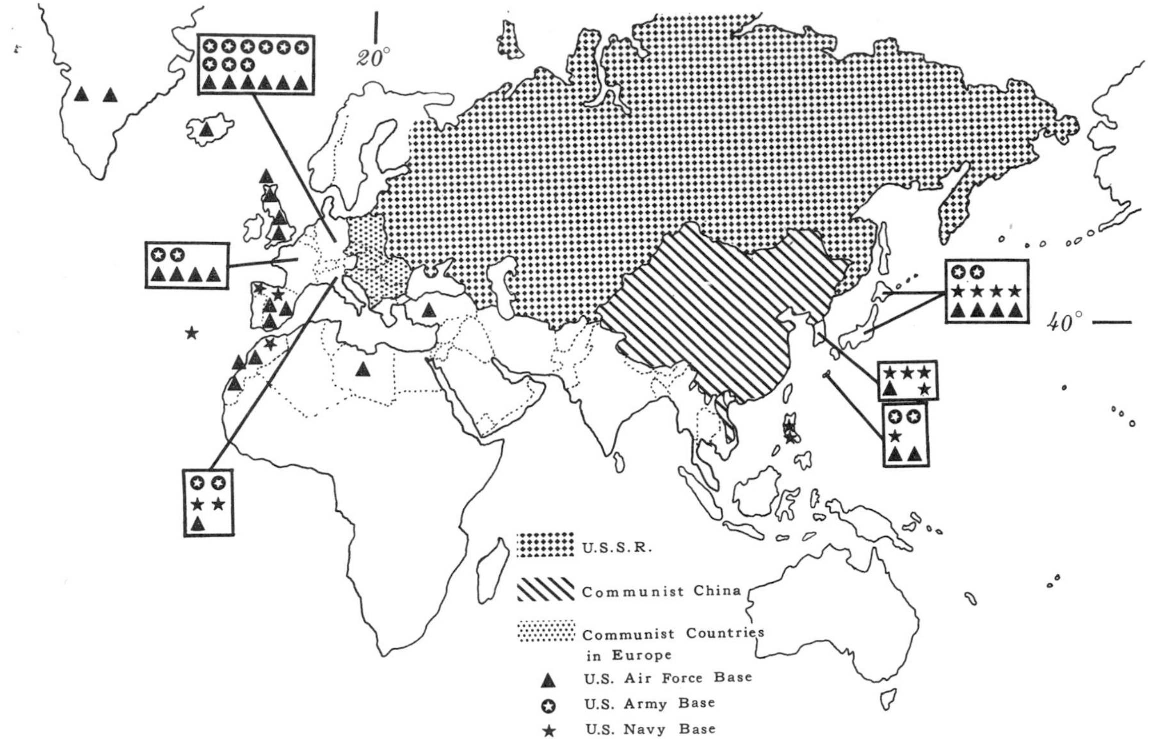

XXXIV:3 These are the major United States bases within the "Rim of Containment." (Based upon a map in *The Chicago Daily News* of May 8, 1961)

achieve a breakthrough which would threaten to undermine it from the rear.

Beyond the NATO dam, toward the east, the Western system of alliances might be compared to a series of hastily-constructed, temporary levees which are always in danger of giving way and occasionally do break down under the massive pressure of the Red Surge. The Far Eastern levee is SEATO, the Southeast Asia Treaty Organization, consisting of Australia, New Zealand, the Philippines, Pakistan, Thailand, the United States, the United Kingdom, and France. Conspicuous by their absence from this organization are the two great regional powers which could assure the effectiveness of this levee —India and Indonesia. The power flood which threatens to breach this levee is that of Communist China, whose aggressive designs may be beyond the ability even of the Soviet Union to curb. The main channel along which this flood appears to be moving runs through Indo-China toward the power vacuum which seems almost certain to develop if the unifying presence of President Sukarno should be removed from the polyglot Republic of Indonesia, where economic, geographic, and cultural diversities have created enormous centrifugal forces.

Between the NATO dam and the SEATO levee stands the weakest of the Western defense-works, the association originally known as the Baghdad Pact Community. Since the withdrawal of Iraq following the 1958 revolution, this alliance has included Pakistan, Iran, Turkey, and The United Kingdom. This levee is threatened both frontally and from its rear. To the north, the flood of Russian power builds up for a possible breakthrough into an already strongly developed power vacuum in Africa. To the rear, a combination of Egyptian nationalism and Arab hostility to Israel threatens to provide the break through which the Red Surge could pour.

Is this system of dams and levees strong enough to hold back the Red Surge from the Heartland? History has not yet given us the answer. Meanwhile, the United States and, to a lesser extent, its allies, work feverishly to strengthen this "rim of containment" by shoring it up with economic aid, with technical assistance, and with strategically located bases. Much will depend upon whether the great power vacuums in Indonesia, Africa, and South America can be filled to the point where, if breaks should occur in these defensive works, the Surge will not be able to flow unimpeded or, as at present, even accelerated by the powerful attractive force of these vacuums. Certainly the defensive system would be vastly strengthened if such powerful uncommitted nations as India could be persuaded that they, too, face the prospect of Communist engulfment unless they build powerful barriers against it, either on their own or in concert with other nations.

Of particular concern to Americans is the instability which has long existed in Latin America and which, for a number of reasons, could be capitalized upon by enemies of the United States. We have seen just this sort of thing happening, on a small scale, in Cuba. The latent anti-Yankee feeling which Premier Castro has so adroitly exploited there exists throughout Latin America. The instrument upon which we rely both for the mutual defense of the Western hemisphere and for the improvement of understanding among its nations is the Organization of American States.

The "balance of terror"

So delicately balanced is the world power situation in our day that all of mankind walks the razor's edge of oblivion. To the American, upon whose shoulders rests the primary responsibility for resisting any further advances of Russian imperialism, the Heartland of Europe and Asia looks like a great restless lake, pressing against the dams and levees that have been hurriedly thrown up to contain it. The question is: will the levees hold, will the dam stand fast? To the Western European, and perhaps to the liberal Japanese, every threat, every harsh word from the Heartland, is, or may be, an ominous warning that the defenses may not be high enough or strong enough to hold back the awful power which, if it should ever break through, would pour down with fullest fury upon them; they seek, but have not yet found, some better method of containment than is offered to them by military alliances. To the Russian and to the Chinese, our world is still the battleground of a universal class struggle which can be resolved only by an extension of the radical Marxist remedies to its farthest corners; they do not shrink from the "holy war" that might be necessary to achieve the worldwide triumph of the workers and the peasants. To the uncommitted peoples, the struggle is the old familiar story of a battle of the giants, from which prudent third parties do well to stand aloof; they hope that, by avoiding overt offense to either giant, they can avoid being involved in the struggle.

Given such an explosive situation, is there any hope of preventing the outbreak of a Third World War? Obviously there is, or it would have been pointless for the authors to have written this book or for the student to have read it. There is, first of all, for most people, the hope that man is not wholly free to determine his destiny, that there is still some overriding Power in the universe who could, and probably would, veto any human program of self-destruction. And there is, secondly, the fact that people on both sides of the Iron Curtain are people—capable of rationally appraising the probable consequences of a nuclear war and at least concerned enough about self-survival to refuse the risks that would be implicit in any such war. Obviously neither of these considerations gives any strong support to hopes for genuine peace, but perhaps they leave as little rational excuse for despair. And while the stalemate goes on, there is always the possibility that the great universal law of change may work on both sides of the Iron Curtain to produce new understandings and new attitudes which will create a new climate for the resolution of international difficulties.

APPLICATION OF GEOGRAPHIC UNDERSTANDING

I. In the light of the power posture outlined in this chapter, what is the significance of Berlin in the East-West struggle?

II. How does the participation of the United States in NATO affect the "image" of our country among the newly-independent nations of Africa and Asia?

III. What strategic advantages might the Communist powers hope to derive from stirring up unrest in (a) Panama? (b) Singapore? (c) Jordan?

IV. Assess each of the major regional defense associations (NATO, SEATO, Baghdad Pact) in terms of (a) resources, (b) population, (c) military striking power, (d) capacity for concerted action.

V. What is the significance of the American base at Thule, Greenland, in the present world power struggle? What other American or Allied bases are important for this same purpose?

VI. What arguments could you offer for the assertion that the Soviet Union itself is, properly speaking, a Russian empire?

VII. What geographical reasons are there for suspecting that the U.S.S.R. and Communist China might find themselves someday no longer allies but enemies?

VIII. Where would you fit each of the following into the power pattern that is outlined in this chapter: Japan? Yugoslavia? Egypt (the United Arab Republic)?

IX. What consequences might a policy of racial segregation such as the *apartheid* policy of the Union of South Africa have in the world power situation?

X. What would be the arguments for and against the establishment of a demilitarized zone through the whole belt of countries which Fairgrieve includes in the crush zone?

References

1 Crankshaw, Edward, *Cracks in the Kremlin Wall,* The Viking Press, New York, 1951, pp. 59-60.

2 Engels, Frederick, "Introduction to the German Edition of the Addresses of the General Council of the International Workingmen's Association Concerning the Civil War in France," *Capital,* Max Eastman, Editor, The Modern Library, 1932, p. 381.

3 Pearcy, G. Etzel, and Associates, *World Political Geography,* Second edition, Thomas Y. Crowell Company, New York, 1957, p. 675.

4 Newman, Peter C., "The Nuclear Dilemma of the Western Peoples," *Maclean's,* December 3, 1960, p. 67.

5 Mackinder, Sir Halford J., "The Round World and the Winning of the Peace," *Compass of the World,* Weigert and Stefansson, Editors, The Macmillan Company, N. Y., 1945, pp. 164-167, *passim.*

6 Fairgrieve, James, *Geography and World Power,* E. P. Dutton & Co., New York, 1941, pp. 329-330, 331.

Part VI

Summary observations on man's relations to space in time

Since neither space nor time in our earthly existence has meaning apart from each other, the quintessence of all geography — whether social, economic, or political — resides in the unitary formulation of concepts in the combined perspective of these two dimensions, a field properly denoted as historical geography. We cannot understand the geography of the present without some reflection on the geographies of the past. And without geographical intelligence of the present, we cannot wisely plan for the geography of the future.

In Part V, a check list of geo-political factors was presented as a guideline for conceptual thinking of world affairs in the framework of national and international relations. Here in concluding Part VI, the figure at the lower right symbolizes the primary human occupance forms as guideposts in examining the geography of culture in transition. Despite the fact that historic cultures from place to place and time to time do not progress according to a uniform pattern, movement, or direction, categorical stages of cultural development do differentiate places and peoples in time and place. It is this geohistory (sequent occupance) that needs to be reconstructed to point the way to harmonious and effective living among all the peoples of the earth. Accordingly, in the two remaining chapters we summarize the basic concepts and principles of geographic methodology of space and time in both their theoretical and applicational aspects, with some concluding observations on "Planning the Geography of the Future."

Chapter 35

Conceptual geography in historical perspective

For as Geographie without Historie seemeth a carkasse without motion, so Historie without Geographie, wandreth as a Vagrant without a certaine habitation.

John Smith, *Generall Historie of Virginia*, London, 1624, p. 169.

At this point we are prepared to summarize the leading principles and concepts developed in the previous five sections and reevaluate some of them in the context of the changing value of space.

You will recall that in Chapter 1 we presented a cursory review of the changing concepts of geography throughout the historic period of man. Such concepts varied not only because of the different backgrounds of scholars in the field, but because of geographic changes as well in earth landscapes and in man's exploration of new horizons of such landscapes in the world.

As was pointed out in Chapter 2, if we want to understand properly the history of mankind, we must unify our knowledge of earth realities in terms of all subject matter areas with particular emphasis on such historical studies as will give geographic change the proper kind of perspective. In Chapter 3, glimpses of past world geography were presented in cartographic form, and finally in Chapter 4, the demographic factors in geography were assayed, especially in terms of the future significance of the so-called "population explosion."

In Part II, the earth domain over which man exercises dominion was considered in terms of the various natural processes which operate as natural laws producing the varied physical and biologic forms that characterize present-day landscapes. Generic principles of landforms and minerals, of soils and waters, and of the various ecologies of vegetable and animal life were considered. As there indicated, land as well as life is in a constant state of flux, and man's own planning for his terrestrial habitat must always take this into consideration if he is to realize maximal values of earth resources.

How man's own processes of acculturization transform the products of the fundament into economic resources to supply his daily needs is covered in Part III (Chapters 12, 13, 14, and 15). Here under the various systematic branches of geography, are considered the various types of processes by which man as artificer adjusts to the earth conditioning factors and forces through the various inventions and discoveries of science and technological applications. Though not all cultural forms will leave their imprint in a material way on the landscape, many of the cultural changes will be so reflected. In the various systematic divisions of geography, then, the geographer seeks to indicate how the changing cultural landscape is generically and genetically related to the face of the earth.

In Part IV the textual focus shifts from the systematic to the regional form of treatment of world affairs. The contemporary regional geography of the world is introduced by a significant event from contemporary history in the form of a chorogram followed by a geographic commentary. Though based on what may very well appear to be an ephemeral chronicle of a given affair, the major criterion for selecting the topics is their relatively stable value in introducing patent principles of combined history-geography analysis of world events.

In Part V, an attempt was made to show how man's "architectonics" of the various regions of the earth must be finally interpreted in the political structure under which they have developed. Different political systems, whether of the oligarchical or of the democratic type, often reflect radically different philosophical views on the geographic aspects of national unity and security, and on the different types and degrees of development of natural resources and the varying employment of geographic strategy for developing world power. Not all government policies will, of course, be reflected in the landscape, but many of them can be so detected; even a change in party leadership in a country such as ours may result in radical regional transformations of geography, as exemplified in the case of the Tennessee Valley Authority.

However, then, we may approach the study of man's occupance of the earth, and in whatever geographic form, whether systematic, regional, or political in its treatment, one universal feature stands out, namely, the dynamic or changing aspect of geography of landscapes. It is this to which we now turn our major attention in this concluding part of our book.

Where have we come from? Where are we going?

Literally, in terms of place, and figuratively, in terms of our life's destinies, these are the time-revered questions which every stratum of mankind in every order of society has asked itself since time immemorial. In these commonplace terms reside all life's philosophies from the simplest to the most sophisticated. In the space-time continuum of these two questions must be determined the geography and history of mankind. Geographic changes of historic moment are of essentially two different forms: (1) changes which result from man's migration from one place to another, and (2) residual changes within the same area as the result of man's changing technology, or as we generally say, progressive change in culture.

The primary geographic agencies responsible for landform and land-use changes, whether by immigration of new cultures into the area or by residual cultures within the region, are: (1) fire, (2) deforestation, (3) grazing, (4) irrigation, (5) drainage, (6) soil management, (7) plant and animal cultures, (8) mining, (9) manufacturing, (10) commerce, and (11) all constructions incident to settlement — rural and urban.

In a very rough way, this order of classified forms of occupance suggests sequent developments of man's historical-cultural pattern. Naturally, each region and each culture is unique, but practically all archaeological and anthropological records indicate the dominance of the earth resource factor in the early stages of occupance of the area, followed by the dominance of the human resource factor in the latter stages of more complex societal developments. Essential to recognize also is the principle that all these agencies lend themselves to areal inventory and mapping; thus, the many institutions of societies and man's ideas in back of them can be directly observed and assayed. In fact, it is from this content of area that the most distinctive contribution of the study of geography to the understanding of human society emerge.

The primacy of these nature-conditioning and man-controlling patterns and processes were focally treated in Part III. A few additional historic observations are in order. Omer C. Stewart considers fire as the first great force employed by man:

¶ Use of fire and manufactured implements of stone are the cultural achievements recorded in ancient strata of the earth as indicators of the beginning of humanity. . . . To rouse or drive game during hunting was the reason most frequently recorded over the world. A hundred different Indian groups of North America, as well as natives of South America, Africa, Tasmania, Australia, New Guinea, China, and Turkestan set fire to drive game. . . . There are numerous examples of the passage of land from cultivation into pasture and thereafter of the maintenance of the grazing area by fire.[1]

Deforestation, whether by fire or other means, is regarded by H. C. Darby as "perhaps the greatest single factor in the evolution of the European landscapes." Once almost a universal cover,

¶ The presence of woodland, and the effort to use it or subdue it has been a constant motif throughout the history of successive centuries; and the struggle has left a mark, often upon the form and intensity of human settlement, and always upon the general character of the landscape.[2]

Darby then proceeds to show how the clearing took on different forms in each of the three regions of Europe—southern, central, western, and eastern. As has been previously noted, clearings were often effected

[1] Reprinted from *Man's Role in Changing the Face of the Earth,* edited by William L. Thomas, Jr., by permission of The University of Chicago Press. © The University of Chicago, 1956. Published 1956, composed and printed by The University of Chicago Press, Chicago, Illinois, U.S.A.

[2] *Ibid.* Used by permission.

by primitive or early cultures to promote hunting and grazing. In modern times, forests have been exploited primarily for their lumber products. Virgin timber is today practically unknown in the United States. Reckless deforestation practices have become the themes of virtually hundreds of articles deploring this depreciation of one of nature's bounteous gifts. As Sauer observes:

¶ Man, nurtured in the woodlands, has been of old the enemy of trees. He has exploited them, destroyed them, rarely favored them. His simplest skills were adequate to overcome the tree, for which he needed no ax, only the immemorial arts of setting fire and stripping bark. In the wood and brush lands in which most of mankind has lived over most of its span, the woody cover was progressively thinned and the ground more and more fully exposed to sun and air. Sun-requiring herbaceous plants increased at the expense of shade-tolerant ones.[1]

1. Agricultural forms. Here are included all the processes that deal with food production — soil management, including irrigation, drainage, and fertilization, the rearing of animals, and the cultivation of crops. Despite the increasing complexities of modern society, agriculture, in all its forms the world over, still constitutes man's basic industry. It is upon this that man has to rely, as he always has throughout history, for food, shelter, and clothing. It has been commonly assumed historically in the development of land cultures that the husbandman emerged from the herdsman. "The classical view carried down from Roman authors, that mankind progresses on a general sequence of stages, beginning as collectors through hunting and pastural nomadism to agriculture, is still current in serious writing," as Sauer reminds us. But this leading anthropological geographer, a specialized authority in civilization and antecedents, reverses the order of sequence:

¶ Agriculture began in wooded lands. Primitive cultivators could readily open spaces for planting by deadening trees; they could not dig in sod or eradicate vigorous stoloniferous grasses. . . . The inventors of agriculture had previously acquired special skills in other directions that predisposed them to agriculture experiments. Of all peoples those most given to hunting were least apt to incline to work domestication and breeding of plants, or, I think, of animals. . . . Above all, the founders of agriculture were sedentary folk. I have already said that groups move as little as the needs of food, water, fuel, and shelter require. Mobility as a dominant character goes with specialized hunting economies or with life in meager environment. Growing crops require constant attention. . . . The domestication of herd animals by sedentary folk who were seed farmers and who arose out of one common way of life is still most acceptable, culturally and biologically. The hearth of domestication of herd animals lies in Southwest Asia. To the myth of the wolf that became a dog by joining the campfire of hunters and the one that hungry collectors began to sow and thus originated the noble grains, we may add the fancy that enclosure of game animals by hunters was the means by which herd animals came to be.[2]

Questions related to food production are paramount to the history of mankind. As pointed out in connection with the population explosion problem in Chapter 4, the imminent question for the future is not concerned with astronautics, but again with the science of agriculture: Can food production keep pace with the anticipated accelerated population growth of the latter twentieth century? To what extent can undeveloped and underdeveloped countries be aided to increase their own food supplies? In the United States, how can we reconcile governmental policies which, on the one hand, extend farming acreage by drainage and irrigation, and, on the other hand, are concerned with the general problem of overproduction of agricultural commodities?

2. Manufactural-commercial forms. Technological revolutionary developments in the twentieth century identified with mining and other extractive industries, with manufacturing, simple and complex, with commerce and trade by land, sea, and air, and the resultant phenomenal metropolitan growth of communities challenge our imagination of future geographic changes. From a geo-historical point of view a most significant change will

[1] Sauer, Carl O., *Agricultural Origins and Dispersals,* Bowman Memorial Lectures, The American Geographical Society, New York, 1952, *passim.* Reprinted by permission.

[2] *Ibid.,* pp. 21, 22, 85, *passim.* Reprinted by permission.

unquestionably be the narrowing of the economic gap between the advanced and underdeveloped countries or cultures. Of course, place-to-place differences will always persist as long as the earth endures, and regional resource developments, occupation- and industrywise, will vary in pattern because of the universal space–time principle of different regions lending themselves best to distinctive types of cultural progress. The chorogrammic studies of contemporary history which introduce various chapters of Part IV are illustrative of the effects of technological changes on social, economic, and political geographic patterns.

In a very illuminating historical essay on "Changing Ideas of the Habitable World," C. J. Glacken reviews some threescore authorities on the significance of geographic changes in human history. Representative of its revealing concepts, attitudes, and insights are:

¶ Human history was in part the history of environmental changes (Plato); difficulties of distinguishing a natural from a cultural landscape (Mencius); conception of nature as a divinely created order for the well-being of all life (Lovejoy, et al.); the task of human art was to improve the primeval aspects of the earth through tillage and in other ways (Ray, et al.); man has failed in his appointed role as a steward of God and man's vast changes are upsetting the balance and the harmony of nature by ruining the earth (Marsh).[1]

The subject of geographic change invariably brings up the questions of why and how cultural processes and natural processes are related. The student will recall that philosophical viewpoints on the matter were discussed in Chapter 1. A summary reference from C. J. Glacken may assist the student at this point in reappraising the basic concepts held with respect to possibilism and environmentalism. Glacken writes:

¶ There were two general kinds of environmental theory: (1) the older tradition concerned with the influence of such factors as climate, location, and relief which originated in antiquity and was revived in modern times by such thinkers as Bodin, Montesquieu, and Karl Ritter, followed by (2) a more rigid determinism owing to the application of the Darwinian theory to human society. Cultures succeeded in the struggle for existence because of their ability to adapt themselves to limitations enforced by the physical environment. It was the Malthusian theory applied to human society, but in the form which Darwin in the *Origin of Species* had given it by applying Malthus' principle of population to the whole realm of organic nature. The older environmentalism led to an emphasis on geographical factors, influences, and controls, and the newer to an emphasis on the survival value of environmental adaptations. Environmentalism completely overshadows the idea of man as a geographic agent, and the subject, instead of becoming a vital part of the study of man, was relegated to the technical and scientific literature.

The doctrine of [possibilism] was the fusion of three sets of ideas: (1) the idea of man as a geographic agent, emphasizing, that is, the role of man in changing the physical environment; (2) the significance of historical factors in the development of a culture; and (3) a concept of resources based on the idea of plant and animal associations, derived from the growing science of plant ecology.[2]

The importance of the study of our geographic past and man's ideas concerning it is expressed by Glacken in these concluding words:

¶ The earth has felt the touch of man in ways which can be understood only by following the devious paths he has taken. The ideas and observations of the past suggest what these paths were—and where they led—and therefore will be a continuing source of new insights into the historical processes which have brought the earth to its present condition.[3]

Illusory concepts of historical geography

Before defining the nature and delimiting the objectives of the study of historical geography, some common illusions must be dispelled:

(1) "Geography deals with things of the

[1] Reprinted from *Man's Role in Changing the Face of the Earth,* edited by William L. Thomas, Jr., by permission of The University of Chicago Press. © The University of Chicago, 1956. Published 1956, composed and printed by The University of Chicago Press, Chicago, Illinois, U.S.A.

[2] *Ibid.* Reprinted by permission.

[3] *Ibid.*, pp. 85-88, *passim.* Reprinted by permission.

earth, whereas history deals with events." Just as the objective of history is not simply the study of dates, so the objective of geography is not simply the study of objects.

(2) "History deals with earth's changes; geography with fixed phenomena." As indicated above and throughout the text, both geography and history continually deal with change, and both are concerned with changes related to natural history as well as human history.

(3) "History deals with 'chaps' [biographies]; geography with maps." This would also seem to imply that history deals primarily with people; geography with places. As indicated in Chapter 3, such a distinction is not supported by the study of the history of geography or by the study of the history of history. As pointed out earlier, this illusion is based on another illusion that "Geography deals with the physical or natural earth, and history with the cultural earth." Historians from Herodotus and Strabo on down to our most distinguished modern historians, including Toynbee, have held that places and people have no meaning apart from each other.

(4) "Geography begins where history ends." Such distinction is likewise untenable. Just as there has always been a geography in the past, so history is being made every day. Examples from contemporary history have served as motifs for chapter introductions in Part IV of this text to illustrate the unity of history and geography in contemporary world affairs.

(5) "In explaining our present-day cultures, the role of historic heritage is often distinguished from the genetic processes of present-day man–land relationships." Though such a distinction has its value in a critical analysis of the mergence of cultures in a landscape, heritages in this context must be presumed to be related not only to "past history," but also to "past geography" as well.

A false dichotomy has thus come to exist between the functions of geography and history. Consideration of the field of historical geography may thus help to illustrate the essential unitary relationships of the two disciplines.

Definition and scope of geo-historical study

Historical geography is an analysis or evaluation of the areal significance of geographic processes of any given period or sequent periods of history. Geo-historical investigations assume various forms, a brief outline of which may help the student better to understand what is meant by the previous definition:

1. Geography of a single special period. The motif for such a project may derive from a historic event of special importance, or particular familiarity with a segment of history, or from the availability of documented material which lends itself well to geographic research in this area. An excellent example of this is Darby's *Domesday England* (1957—), which attempts a reconstruction of the geography of England in 1086. Here, in a set of six volumes, are treated the effects of woodland and other natural factors of the early Middle Ages of England and their bearing on settlement of the English landscapes after the Norman conquest. An American example of the periodic study type is that of Klimm's on "The Relation Between Certain Population Changes and the Physical Environment in Hampden, Hampshire, and Franklin Counties, Massachusetts, 1790-1925" (1933).

2. Historical geographies of continents, countries, states or provinces, or geographic regions. This category includes the larger number of publications of political units primarily in book form; the regional studies primarily in professional journals. Representative of this prolific area of publications are Wright's *Geographic Bases of European History* (1928), Semple's *The Geography of the Mediterranean Region and Its Relation to Ancient History* (1931), Brown's *Historical Geography of the United States* (1948), Smith's *Historical Geography of the Holy Land* (1894), Clark's *Three Centuries and the Island—Prince Edward, Canada* (1959), Dodge's "Sequent Occupance of the Illinois Prairie" (1931), Kniffen's "The Primitive Cultural Landscape of the Colorado Delta" (1931), and Broek's "The Santa Clara Valley in California: A Study in Landscape Change" (1932).

3. Systematic historical geography. Titles such as the following suggest that any topic of natural or human geography interest which plays a significant role in understanding the historical records of man–land relationships is appropriate material for geo-historic study: Davis' "The Geographic

Cycle" (1899), Russell's "Climatic Change Through the Ages" (1941), Weaver's crop study, "Barley in the United States: A Historical Sketch" (1943). Similarly in the area of explorations, circulation, migration, and settlement, title sampling includes the following: Raup's "The German Colonization of Anaheim, California" (1932), Baker's *A History of Geographical Discovery and Exploration* (1937), Taylor's *Environment, Race and Migration* (1937).

4. Principles of geographic change. One of the most philosophical of all works in this area is "Man and Nature" (1864) and other writings by Marsh, in which a strong pessimistic note is voiced by the author in man's dominance in destroying the ecological balance in nature. This writing, it may be said, has set the pattern for conservational thinking and writing for almost a century. The early twentieth century produced a number of writings of the geographic influence type, of which Brigham's *Influence in American History* (1903) is an example. Along the same general line but of a broader scope is Huntington's *Mainsprings of Civilization* (1945). Striking out in a very different direction in explaining modern cultural forms is Sauer's *Agricultural Origins and Dispersals,* mentioned earlier, in which Sauer looks upon man as an "ecologic dominant" and observes that the geographer "properly is engaged in charting the distribution over the earth of the arts and artifacts of man, to learn whence they came, and how they spread, what their contacts are in cultural and political environments."[1]

5. The history of geography. The development of geographic concepts in time is sometimes also identified with historical geography. But within this context its inclusion is justified only because of the psychological principle that what man has thought of his environment and his relation to it has, as we have noted in Part One of this book, had itself much to do with the modification of earth landscapes, both on a local and world scale. Sometimes this can be as important as or even more important than learning what the landscapes were like at a given period in history. Here again, numerous works exist which deal with the history of geographic thought on wider or narrower spatial and temporal bases. Included, for example, are Bunbury's *A History of Ancient Geography* (1883), Kimble's *Geography in the Middle Ages* (1938), Wright's *The Geographical Lore of the Time of the Crusades* (1925). For a single summary source reviewing and comparing the geographer's own views of geography in its chronological development Hartshorne's classic *The Nature of Geography* still is the most comprehensive source of such information.

The purpose and province of historical geography

As the French historian Jules Michelet has said, "Without a geographical basis, the people, makers of history, appear to be walking on air, as in those Chinese pictures where the ground is lacking." It is clearly, then, the distinctive function of the geographer to supply the "ground" on which man has lived, moved, and had his being ever since he was primordially committed to act as steward of the earth. Only by bringing our historical studies down to earth, as it were, can we intelligibly grasp the mission of man, his history—adjustments and maladjustments to earth's resources—and his destiny, with all that this implies in the way of man's spiritual and moral responsibilities. Specifically, where, how, and why has man succeeded (or failed) to establish cultures most conducive to his material and spiritual well-being? Why have some nations prospered and others declined? What lessons can be learned from geo-history to avoid repetition of calamitous mistakes? To what extent does differentiated areal reality knowledge equip us in freeing us from geographic provincialisms which retard progress and unified thinking and action in world affairs?

To attain the proper insights into such matters, we must comprehend the processes of nature and the processes of cultural growth as well as the principles by which man can most effectively operate in maintaining a harmonious relationship between the two. The geographic principle of determining the most pleasant occupance form and most profitable utilization of space may well be considered a space–time universal.

[1] Sauer, *op. cit.*, p. 1. Reprinted by permission.

Ankara has been capital of the Republic of Turkey since 1923. Geo-historic landscape study, based as it is on sequent occupance, is not readily, if at all, illustratable photographically. But the historical geographer is ever alert in detecting relict architectural and other ancient structural forms which have survived modern innovations. A classic example is that of Ankara. One of the fastest growing cities of the world (from about 30,000 in 1925 to almost half a million in 1960), Ankara has been dominated successively by many diverse cultures which have left their landmarks on this hill site—ruins of the original citadel crowning the hill, together with the remains of Graeco-Roman, Byzantine, and other architectural forms here hidden by the distinctly modern urban structures. (Courtesy Turkish Information Office)

It is related to that timeless controversial subject of "balance of nature," the philosophy of which comprehends man as a part of nature rather than apart from nature. Or to put it in another form somewhat more philosophically, the ultimate terrestrial aim is to establish proper environmental relationships of man's prudence to God's providence. And so with each epoch of history, questions like the following come through the minds of the investigators in historical geography: Where did people settle—and why? Where did they come from, and why did they migrate? By what route or routes did they come into the area? What were the original forms of occupance and utilization of resources? To what extent are these forms related to cultural heritages and to what extent was man sensitive toward modifying his earlier cultural patterns to better adjust himself to the new environmental structure? Are relict forms still manifest in present-day landscapes? What evidence of the total environment ensemble indicates a trend towards a further transformation of the landscape in the future?

Historical geographers can, of course, attempt only a partial answer to such questions, as is so well stated by Clark:

¶ Geographers do not make the absurd claim that research in historical geography can reach definitive, all-inclusive answers to such problems, but they do suggest that such research can make a contribution and can throw light that is not gained from any other perspective. Imbalance of population and resources, cultural receptivity and cultural lag, rapid changes in techniques and population, indeed most of the themes arising in the present problems have recurred again and again in the past. Today we are faced with a world that is changing rapidly because of new technical devices. Geographers may wish with great fervor to give direction to the change, or, if that is impossible, to make some intelligent guesses as to where the changes may lead. Many of the desired insights are to be gained from past experience. There is no dearth of problems; only of curiosity to see them and of industry to solve them.[1]

How does historical geography differ from history?

Historical geography differs from history primarily in its methodology. It is next in order, therefore, to discuss some of the primary techniques commonly considered in a space-time study. In doing this, we must reconstruct the patterns of the trails that men have trod, the tasks at which they have toiled, the successive sites where man has settled. Unlike the historian who identifies the changing events primarily with the historic characters responsible for them, the geographer's primary concern is to show how the facts and principles of cultural history are related to the facts and principles of natural history. The manner in which the historical geographer proceeds to do this will vary with his own background training and the type of philosophy which he holds concerning the critiques and techniques which he thinks most relevant to the particular study.

Then also, as in the case of pursuing other branches of geography, the *modus operandi* will vary as between the systematic approach and the regional approach. Illustrative of the former is Olmstead's "People, Time, Space, and Ideas in the Economic Core Region of Anglo-America." Here, as illustrated in Figure XXXV-1, Olmstead develops the topic of the economic core of Anglo-America with respect to internal as well as external conditions of expansion. This particular article emerged from the author's conviction that concepts of the type here developed are essential if we are to make both history and geography meaningful in our classroom curricula: "I believe that it is so basic to the study of human society at any time or scale that it might well be the central concept in the organization of the school curriculum in the social studies, thus developing a curriculum equally based in geography and history." Without such conceptual training, as the author points out, there is justifiably a "fear that [the student] may be full of facts and figures about places and will never understand the geographic structure of the American economy and society and its basis in people, time, space, and ideas."[2]

In the regional approach to geo-history, complete areal content of the significant factors of the environmental ensemble is considered. As previously indicated, the geographic region may be studied simply in terms of the "geography of the past" of a particular epoch, or, as is more commonly done, in a form of sequent occupance through significant periods which reveal successive areal heritages.

Principles and practices in a historical geographic study with special reference to sequent occupance

Though the mode of attack of a geo-historical study varies with author and purpose, general guidelines are suggested by the practitioners specializing in this area, several of which are here noted:

1. Develop familiarity with all present-day field evidence and statistical-historical docu-

[1] Clark, Andrew H., Chairman of the Committee on "Historical Geography," *American Geography, Inventory and Prospect,* Preston E. James and Clarence F. Jones, editors, Syracuse University Press, N.Y., 1954, pp. 92-93. Reprinted by permission.

[2] Olmstead, Clarence W., "The Application of a Concept to the Understanding of a Region: People, Time, Space, and Ideas in the Economic Core Region of Anglo-America," *The Journal of Geography,* Vol. LIX, No. 2, February, 1960, pp. 54, 61. (Also published in *Social Education,* Vol. XXII, 1958.) Reprinted by permission.

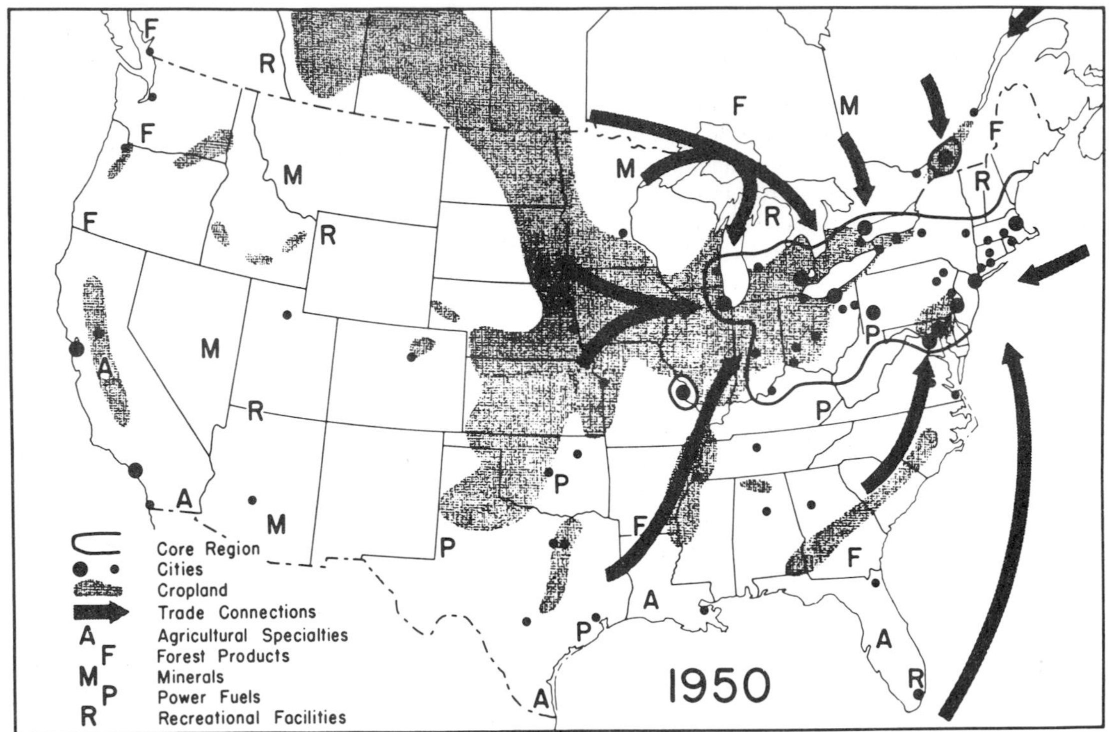

XXXV:1 This map shows the areal-functional relationships of the economic core region, 1950. It is a cartographic design in a textual context which treats of the basic elements of people, time, space, and ideas related to the economic core region of Anglo-America. (By Clarence W. Olmstead in *Journal of Geography,* Vol. LIX, No. 2, 1960, used by permission)

mented material of direct relevance to the project.

2. Determine the significant epochal transitions and establish the stages you wish to differentiate.

3. Select the inventory items to which are related the most significant geographic changes. It is well to consult published check lists, such as Wellington Jones' "Procedures." Here in comprehensive—if not all-inclusive—form are "catalogued" basic phenomena (regional and interregional) of primary concern in exploring human occupance patterns: "pattern of distribution, areal extent, operations, disposal of products or services, operational units" (7).

4. Select the items most germane to the project, scrutinizing all significant lines of evidence as gathered from field observations, interviews, and examination of archival and historical textual and cartographic material.

5. Analyze the relative significance of the occupance forms for each stage of culture, noting the processes (geographic changes) operative in both the forms of the natural landscape and the cultural environment.

6. Synchronize the interperiod as well as interregional relationships. This is the most challenging aspect of the study. Meaningful geo-historical integration involves (1) recognizing the chief genetic geographic factors for each stage, and (2) distinguishing those which have left vestiges in successive stages from those leaving no apparent relict forms. In these two principles lies the essence of purposeful retrospective geographic study, which has for its objective the understanding of the processes and principles of geographic heritages of the past with which the present stage of occupance is linked.

7. Graphically portray in the most expeditious manner all the salient landscape changes from one stage to the next. In perhaps no other area of geography is the portrayal of geographic forces so essential and

effective. Geographic change from region to region, or within the same region, is graphically illustrated in Figure XXXV-2.

8. Finally, a note of caution. The student must keep in mind not only that history does "not repeat itself" but that geography does "not repeat itself" either, except in a most generalized institutional way. There can be no formula, then, for outlining uniform occupance change. The geonomic sequence of world cultures is sometimes represented as conforming successively to the following pattern: primitive hunting and fishing; nomadic pastoralism (in grassland areas); commercial trapping and lumbering (in timber regions); general agriculture; mining and manufacturing; water, land, and air commerce. But, as stated, such progression from the simpler to the more complex cultural forms must not be construed as a specific guideline to be followed in any one regional study. One or another of these "conventional" stages of economy may be skipped or several of them reversed. These broad sequence categories suggest merely the general global principle that as population increases and there is more pressure on resources, there is a progressive intensification of land-use from the aboriginal "exploitative" economy to the most complex manufacturing and commercial forms introduced by successive technological inventions.

Whittlesey, who introduced the term "sequence occupance" as applied to a fifteen-square mile region in northern New England, recognizes a certain degree of constancy in occupance forms, but rarity of "normal sequences":

¶ . . . alterations as evolve from the inherent character of a particular mode of occupance follow a normal pattern and at length usher in a new and consequent mode of occupance. Strictly speaking, normal sequences are rare, perhaps only ideal, because extraneous forces are likely to interfere with the normal course, altering either its direction or rate, or both. These may be so-called acts of God, whereby one or another element of the natural complex becomes abruptly and profoundly modified. Such are severe earthquakes, windstorms, tidal waves, floods, volcanic eruptions, landslides, insect or other biological pests, pestilence, and the like. Interruptions of the cultural order engendered by man occur even more commonly: shifts in political boundaries, revolutions, or often mere enactment of laws; movements of population which carry with them mores and attitudes novel to their new habitat, or create social friction; the introduction of new technology; changes in means of communication which alter physical and mental contact with outside regions; all these are capable of breaking or knotting the thread of sequent occupance. When once the new forces begin to operate, however, the dynamic march is resumed, but according to new orders of the day.[1]

Regional case study of sequent occupance—microgeography

Definition and description of sequent occupance at best can only vaguely stress the idea and import of this unique contribution of geography to the understanding of human geo-history. Accordingly, a brief version of such a study is here presented, followed by some questions on geographic understandings.[2]

Circulation and settlement patterns of the Calumet–South Chicago region of northwest Indiana and northeast Illinois

Identity and significance of the region. The Calumet derives its name from the chief drainage forms, the Grand Calumet and Little Calumet rivers and Lake Calumet. In reality, the Calumet rivers and their tributaries quite well express the "natural" basis of delimitation and unity of the region as here defined. In terms of human occupance and activities, the area as delimited on the map corresponds approximately to the area in which commuter service to Chicago is common (Figure XXIX-4). Thus, a very large percentage of the residents in the Calumet Region are industrially or commercially employed in the Chicago–East Chicago–Whiting–Gary centers. To outsiders as well as residents of the area, the Calumet stands out as a leading industrial region of the United States and, for that matter, of the world.

---

[1] Whittlesey, Derwent, "Sequent Occupance," *Annals of the Association of American Geographers*, Vol. XIX, No. 3, September, 1929, pp. 164-165. Reprinted by permission.

[2] This section is reproduced (with minor editing) from the writer's article appearing in the *Proceedings of the XVIIth Congress, International Geographical Union.*

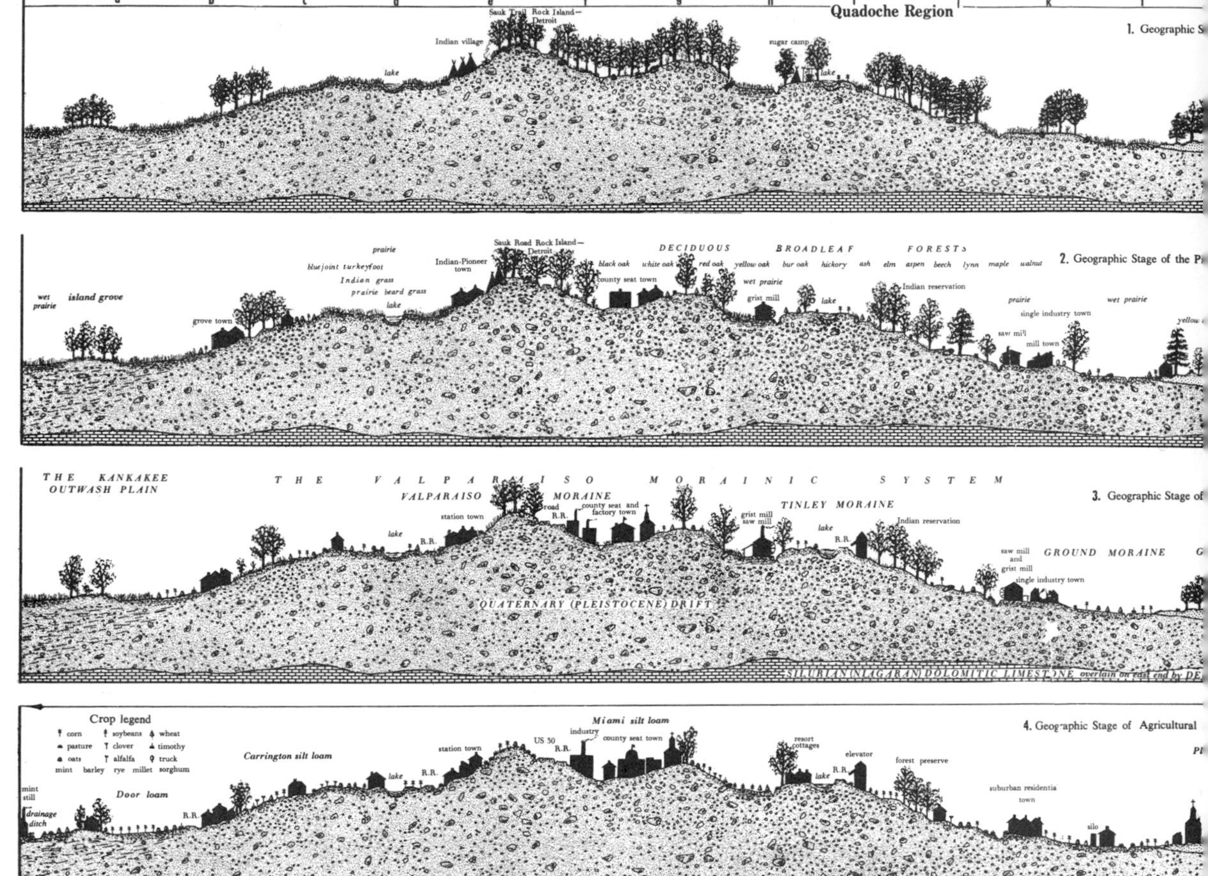

XXXV:2 Silhouette skyline sketches trace geographic changes in place and time: a regional synthesis of the Calumet-southern Chicago, Indiana-Illinois landscape. (Published originally in *Proceedings*, VIIIth General Assembly, XVIIth Congress, International Geographical Union, Washington, 1952, used by permission)

Objectives and techniques. Our purpose is to describe and explain the circulation and settlement patterns as they evolved through four stages of occupance (Figure XXXV-2).[1] Natural factors and cultural forces significant in understanding the human adjustments made within each stage are explored, and heritages carried over into succeeding stages are noted. This affords a basis for evaluating the reciprocal role which man as the actor and the milieu as the stage have played in the evolution of the modern Calumet landscape.

One of the chief problems in a chronologic-chorographic study of this kind is to present a unified stage and story. Investigation of the geographic factors of the several periods reveals that the progression of natural and cultural heritages from one period to the next can be most effectively integrated by using the pattern of circulation as a unifying bond of expressing interperiod as well as interregion relations. Thus the Indian trail evolves successively into the pioneer's dirt road, the improved farm road, and the present-day paved arterial superhighway.

Situation and nature of the region. As indicated in Figure III-15, the *cul-de-sac* situation of the Calumet at the head of Lake

[1] An alphabetical index is provided at the head of the figure by means of which the reader may readily find the illustrated profile features referred to in the original text. To facilitate further identification, italics are used for natural phenomena to distinguish them from the cultural forms. Different styles of typography help to differentiate the various classes of natural and cultural phenomena.

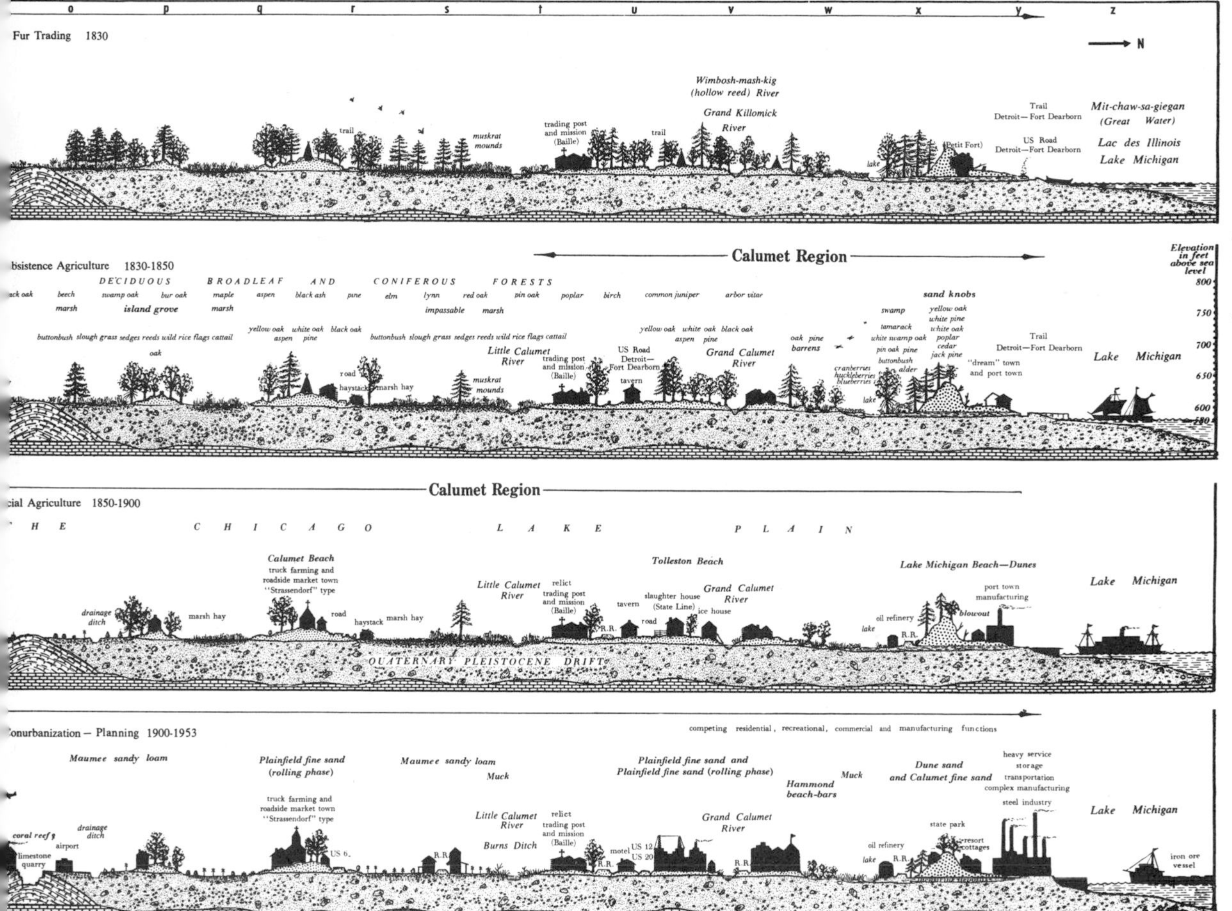

Michigan has exerted a powerful converging and veering influence on transportation and traffic in the region and in adjacent areas. Its position with reference to the early portages between the rivers tributary to Lake Michigan and those of the Illinois waterway has been a significant factor in man's settlement and economic development of this region.

Two major physiographic units dominate the region—the Lake Chicago plain and the Valparaiso–Tinley morainic system. On the periphery to the south and east is the Kankakee outwash plain. Most of the Lake Chicago plain is level, rising generally only 20 feet above the level of Lake Michigan (580-600 feet above sea level). The level terrain has favored road and building construction but has also created serious drainage and sewerage problems. Three ancient shore line beaches—the Tolleston, the Calumet, and the Glenwood, each rising successively about twenty feet higher above lake level—are noteworthy for their effect upon the human circulation and settlement patterns. Two streams, the Grand Calumet and the Little Calumet rivers, constitute the basic drainage system. Marsh-bound and meandering, they had limited utility until dredged and ditched.

Stage 1: Pottawatomie Indian — fur trading (—1830)

Just what did the aboriginal landscape of the Calumet look like? And of what significance is such information to the understanding of subsequent occupance forms down to the present? To help answer these questions the writer constructed a fundament map from field notes and some forty of the original federal township survey plats. Among the most noteworthy landscape features at this early date were the far-flung wet prairies, marshes, and swamps (Figure XXXV-2; 1. n,s).[1] These made lakeward travel from the south particularly difficult; east-west travel sought out the sandy, high and dry old lake shore beaches. The spatial relations of these water and land features are essential to the understanding of the trail pattern of the Pottawatomies (1. e-f, m-n, r, u, y) and in turn the basic pattern of our present-day east-west arterial highway system, for example US 30, US 6, US 12 and US 20 (4. e-f, m-n, r, u). At the more prominent trail termini and junctions, Indian encampments were established, and subsequently there appeared white man's settlements such as Michigan City, Valparaiso, and Merrillville (Figure III-15).

Like the neighboring Kankakee region to the south, the Calumet was famous for its wild fowl and fur-bearing animals (1. o-p, r-t). The wild rice marshes, particularly the Cady and the Calumet of northern Lake County, ranked as one of the leading hunting and trapping areas of the Great Lakes region. The first to enter the trapping and trading business here were the French *voyageurs* and *coreurs de bois,* who followed up on the exploratory voyages of Joliet, Marquette, and LaSalle. Trading based on fundament exploitation of fur-bearing animals rarely leaves geographic vestiges in the modern landscape. The Calumet, however, does present such a relict form in the Bailly homestead (1. t). Here in 1822 M. Bailly, one of the French fur traders in the employ of John Jacob Astor, founded the leading fur-trading post of northern Indiana.

Stage 2: pioneer settler — land survey — subsistence agriculture (1830-1850)

The immigration of the first white settlers into LaPorte County (1829), the Federal Land Survey (1829-34), the establishment of the LaPorte county government (1830), the charting of its first mail route through the Calumet from Chicago to Detroit along the lake shore Fort Dearborn trail in 1831 (2. y), the relinquishment of the Indian lands by the Pottawatomie in 1832, and the founding of Michigan City in the same year are events which demarcate the transition from the Pottawatomie to the Pioneer stage of occupance.

Location at the southwesternmost extension of the Great Lakes within the heart of agricultural America should have favored early settlement of this region, but settlement maps of the period reveal that this was one of the last Midwest regions to be occupied. Factors retarding settlement were: (1) the Pottawatomies were not removed till 1832, after which the ceded lands were surveyed; (2) there were numerous handicaps to circulation and cultivation—one-third of the land was covered with dense timber, mostly on the Indiana side, prairies were often too wet to work, and marshes and swamps covered about one-fourth of the region,[2] (3) pronounced sedimentation on the *cul-de-sac* shoreline of Lake Michigan interfered with harbor and port developments; (4) railroads did not enter the region till the close of the Pioneer period (1850).

The favored sites of pioneer rural settlement were the small timber groves on the Illinois prairies (2. b). The first urban settlements have been differentiated by the writer into four fundamental categories, several with overlapping functions: (1) the pioneer Indian campsite town (2. e); (2) the grist- and sawmill town (2. k); (3) the county seat town (2. f-g); and (4) the "dream" town (2. y). The latter represented real-estate promotions hardly advancing beyond the paper platting stage.

Local sawmills and gristmills, mostly on the tributary streams of the Little Calumet, furnished lumber and flour (2. h, j-k). The forests, both the broadleaf and conifer, supplied not only the lumber needs of the local community but also constituted the source of much of the lumber which went into the construction of the early frame buildings of Chicago.[3] It is interesting to note also that settlers came all the way from Chicago, Rock-

---

[1] Hereafter references to the silhouette features of the figure will be simply designated by the stage numeral and the feature letter (example: 1. n,s).

[2] In the pioneer silhouette the author has attempted an inventory representation of the basic types of natural vegetation, determined mostly from the original federal surveyor's notes recording "bearing" trees along section lines.

[3] The kind of lumber available may be determined from the tree stocking labels in the silhouette, listed in order of dominance as far as the writer could determine from the relative frequency of their recordings as "bearing" trees in the federal surveyor's notes made on section lines.

ford, Joliet, and Galena, Illinois to purchase flour from Michigan City mills.

The diversified timber, prairie, and water forms provided a rich variety of foods, readily accessible or easy to produce. Agriculture was almost altogether of the subsistence type, centering around wheat, corn, oats, and potatoes as the principal crops (2. b, c, g, k, l). Such trade as there was with outside regions was nearly all of the import type, handled by Chicago for the west end of the Calumet and by Michigan City for the east end (port town, 2. y).

Stage 3: Corn Belt farmer—commercial agriculture (1850-1900)

Next to clearing the land of thick timber (mostly on the Indiana side) and breaking the heavy prairie sod (predominantly on the Illinois side), one of the main tasks of the third period of occupance was the ditching and tiling of wet land, particularly on the lake plain. The construction of the Illinois-Michigan Canal in 1848 (Lyons, Stickney Townships), the excavation of the Sag Channel (Worth Township), and the straightening of the Little Calumet (Calumet Township) advanced the regional reclamation program. Locally, reclamation was promoted by large land speculators, as for example, A. N. Hart of the East, who bought 6,000 acres of the Cady marsh lands (3. o-p; vicinity Dyer and Highland).

But nothing is more noteworthy in this period than the construction of railways. Practically all the major trunk lines which now traverse the area and make it the greatest railway center in the world were established between 1848 and 1906. Waterway and harbor developments also figured prominently in transportation. The Illinois and Michigan Canal and its Calumet river-lake connections by way of the Calumet feeder made available an extensive market for goods forwarded from Chicago. It also established a market for Calumet maize at St. Louis, then more important than the Chicago market. Extensive government harbor developments at the mouths of Trail Creek (Michigan Township), Calumet River, and Chicago River promoted the shipment of farmer products to the far eastern markets.

Agricultural statistics for Lake County for 1882 may be taken as representative of the agricultural production of this period. The products in descending order of value were: corn, beef cattle, timothy hay, oats, mixed hay, stock cattle, milk, hogs, horses, butter, wool, and potatoes. The crop symbols in silhouette study 3 roughly suggest the dominant field culture of this period.

The urban and rural settlement pattern of this period is most significantly related to the phenomenal railroad development and the related establishment of post offices and post roads. Station depots (3. e, n), at first simply train stops for passengers, mail, or merchandise, frequently served as nuclei for community settlement (e.g., Schererville). In addition to these station towns we recognize truck towns (3. u-r; e.g., Highland and Munster), whose specialized form of agriculture led to concentrated settlement. Then there is the single-industry type of town built up usually about gristmilling or sawmilling (3. k; e.g., Deep River, Waterford). And finally we have the town of complex manufacturing (3. y; e.g., Michigan City).

Two manufacturing characteristics of the period are noteworthy ; (1) the prominence of manufacturing in small towns (e.g., Valparaiso had some score industries, now nearly all extinct); (2) the first establishment of heavy industries for which the Calumet today is world famous, steel making at South Chicago, oil refining at Whiting, Pullman car manufacturing at Pullman, and the livestock slaughtering at the State Line Slaughter House (now Hammond). At the latter place also originated the world's first refrigerated transportation of meat products.

Stage 4: agricultural and industrial specialization — conurbanization — planning (1900-1953)

Industry. The most remarkable phenomenon of settlement of the modern period of occupance is the expansion of the western Calumet communities into one large Chicago metropolitan region. . . . This reflects the phenomenal twentieth century development of the steel and related industries centered about the Gary–East Chicago–Indiana Harbor–South Chicago region.

During the previous period, heavy industries had already recognized the need for wide open spaces not any longer available in Chicago proper. On the beach-dune sand of northern Lake County and adjacent Cook County, inhabitants were few and land was cheap. Moreover, the Calumet River with harbor and river improvements formed a superior waterway for navigation and waste disposal. The marsh wastelands solved the problem of such nuisances as smoke and fumes from the steel and cement plants, the obnoxious odors of oil refineries, and hazards of powder works. Today some 200 industries, manufacturing over 1,000 products, are located in this beach-dune sand region (4. t-y), which was the haven of countless wild fowl and fur-bearing animals.

The major industries are grouped in the conurban Chicago–Gary area on sites especially favored by rail and/or water transportation facilities—along the shore of Lake Michigan, on both sides of the Grand Calumet River and especially in its lower course, in the vicinity of Lake Calumet, and along the course of the Indiana Harbor Canal. Sizeable industries of the lighter type are also found beyond the conurban area in Michigan City, LaPorte, Valparaiso, Crown Point, and Chicago Heights, where the sites combine excellent suburban living conditions with good railway and highway transportation, and in the case of Michigan City, lake port facilities as well. The phenomenal expansion in industrialization has resulted in the establishment of three new harbors in addition to those founded in the previous period, namely South Chicago (Indiana Harbor), Gary, and Buffington, the latter two developed by private enterprise.

Agriculture. The opening of this period witnessed the maximum number of Calumet farms. The phenomenal expansion of industrialization and urban development resulted in a corresponding contraction in farmland acreage, but total productivity of cereals has been maintained and a sharp increase is noted in truck and dairy products, particularly the former. Oats, corn for grain, hay, corn for silage, and wheat, in descending order, dominated the agricultural scene at the middle of the period.

More recently, the writer made a field survey of farmland to determine the relative acreage of crops and cover identified with each of the four physiographic units of the region. Some 57,000 acres were mapped. From this survey, the order of acreage dominance of each of the leading crops and cover was determined for each of the four physiographic units: for the moraine—corn, pasture, oats, timber, soybeans, fallow or waste; for the lake plain, exclusive of beach deposits —corn, fallow or waste, truck, timber, pasture, oats; for the beach deposits—timber, fallow or waste, wild grass, corn, pasture, truck; for the outwash plain—corn, fallow or waste, oats, pasture, wheat, timber.[1]

Another survey of Calumet crops was made by the writer using the unpublished township statistics of 1945, U. S. Bureau of the Census. With the aid of T. M. Bushnell, a soils specialist, the numerous soil types were reduced to six major soil groupings, which are shown on silhouette 4. From these areal and statistical surveys together with the adapted soil groupings, the following brief generalizations are drawn:

The more numerous and smaller-sized farms are found in Lyons, Worth, Thornton, and other townships on the periphery of the conurban area where urban expansion is encroaching upon the farmland. Many of these are devoted in whole or in part to truck or fruit farming. Potato acreage is highest in the Jackson-Springfield area. In general, on the moraine, the Illinois prairie farms are larger than the Indiana timber farms. By far the largest farms of all are on the outwash plain, the flatness of which favors extensive agricultural operations. The highest percentage of farms operated by full owners is found in the Indiana morainic section, particularly in the belt from Center Township (Porter County) to Springfield Township. Here also is found the greatest percentage of idle cropland. Part ownership is highest in Thornton, Liberty, and New Durham Townships. Highest farm tenancy is found in the southwestern, south-central (especially Ross Township), and southeastern sections, where farmsteads for the most part are of the highest value. These areas also have the highest acreage in cropland harvested.

The large barns and numerous silos and the extensiveness of pasturage and forage crops of the Calumet, together with the dom-

[1] The acreage percentage of these and several additional items is regionally expressed symbolically on the silhouette profile.

inance of corn and oats as grain crops, reflect the importance of the livestock industry. Dairy husbandry has capitalized on the advantages offered by the area's peripheral position to America's second largest metropolitan community. The highest acreages in woodland pasture are in the sandy areas of Portage and Pine Townships. The largest contiguous area of other high-acreage pasturages is central Lake County and adjacent Union and Porter Townships in Porter County. This area and the two adjacent townships of Crete and Monee in Will County to the west also produce the most clover and timothy hay, but alfalfa is grown more extensively in Frankfort Township and in the Porter-LaPorte morainic section. Soybeans are quite well distributed throughout the area. The distribution patterns of cows and beef cattle are very widespread and similar, the animal concentration conforming in varying degrees to the grain, forage, and pasture acreages. Hogs also are rather widely scattered over the area with little noticeable correlation locally to corn, the chief crop of the region.

Calumet problems and geographic planning

We have tried to show how the present Calumet in the course of a little over a century has been transformed from a wild marshy plain and thickly timbered moraine into an industrial and commercial empire. This has been made possible by man's ingenuity in exploiting the advantages of geographic site and situation and in applying his own resourcefulness in developing the potential resources of the region. But geographic growth and progress have their own peculiar way of posing problems. In terms of suburban life such as characterizes the Calumet, residents strive to combine the living advantages of the country with the working advantages of the city. This "Problem of Peripheral Population in Pursuit of Propinquity," as Stanley Berge, Professor of Transportation at Northwestern University, has facetiously yet aptly characterized it, presents a set of challenging settlement and circulation issues. These must be resolved if past mistakes in occupance of the region are to be at least partially rectified and future environmental maladjustments reduced to the minimum.

First of all, it is to be recognized that the Calumet region is one of the fastest growing sections of the United States, demographically and industrially. Very revealing on this point, for example, are the settlement data on the Tolleston, Indiana, topographic map issued by the government at about the time of the opening of our fourth stage of occupance. It is noted that the entire area of northern Lake County east of Whiting and East Chicago was almost wholly devoid of rural homes. Gary did not come into existence until 1906, when the area was surveyed for the U. S. Steel Corporation. The only urban street platted communities shown in the vicinity of modern Gary were two hamlets of some 8-12 blocks in extent, Calumet and Tolleston. Today almost the entire northern section of Lake County is one conurbanized community.

Now it is equally significant to note that within the last decade the population of the metropolitan area outside of Chicago has grown, percentage-wise, more than four times as fast as that within the city. During the same period Chicago has attracted three times as many manufacturing plants as the area outside of the city. Representative of the numerous problems presented by this situation are the following:

(1) Should drainage operations in the region be unlimited, without regard to their effects on the water table, water supply, natural vegetation, and wildlife? (2) Just how far should sand excavations and sand-filling operations be permitted to exploit the geologically instructive shoreline beaches of old Lake Chicago and the recreative dunes of modern Lake Michigan? (3) What state, regional, county, and city measures are needed to prevent substandard housing, to provide adequate sewage disposal and other forms of health protection, and to guarantee equitable tax levies for "rurban" residents both inside and outside of corporate limits? (4) How can industry take advantage of the excellent terrain and transportation facilities afforded by the open spaces and waterways of the Calumet, without unduly encroaching upon the green belt areas of the suburban dweller, the resortist, and the truck gardener? (5) Is an extended

and improved suburban railroad service, rather than a proliferation of highways and superhighways, the primary answer to the Calumet's congested commuter traffic and parking problems? (6) What are the relative merits of the various Calumet waterways —and their present and proposed Lake Michigan harbors—with regard to the projected Great Lakes–St. Lawrence Seaway?

Only through systematic local and regional planning, participated in by citizen and official alike, can such questions as the above be wisely and successfully resolved. According to D. H. Burnham, President of the Chicago Regional Planning Association:

¶ The Calumet-South Chicago District is an important part of the Chicago Region. It has experienced a constant growth of many vital industries and the usual attendant commercial services and residential areas. This growth is expected to continue and should be planned for.

In planning the common facilities necessary for it and the usual zoning and subdivision control of development, governmental agencies, local leaders and their technical consultants have had to cooperatively consider and weigh district and regional factors. In general, a creditable job has been done. The Chicago Regional Planning Association has provided guidance and given assistance in many instances.

Provision has been made in most communities for expansion of industry with due regard for the peculiar local situation and in accordance with local policy. In the years ahead, as county zoning is established over the unincorporated areas, proper provision must be made there for probable industrial growth as has been done within municipalities.

Residential expansion, whether close development or redevelopment within cities, or in the more open form found in the smaller towns and rural areas, must be given zoning protection and should meet the higher standards of subdivision development and building construction that progress and experience have shown to be advisable. Adequate drainage, sewage treatment, and street improvements are especially necessary in rural areas.

Acreage in parks, playgrounds, and school grounds in many communities has not kept up with the growth in population measured against the desirable standard of 10 acres per thousand population, about a third of which should be in evenly distributed playgrounds. The larger sized regional and state parks should be provided in an amount approximating 10 acres per thousand people.

In transportation, expressways must be built, waterway routes and terminals extended and enlarged, and airports established in accordance with traffic needs and appropriate financing (9).

It is a commendable commentary on the farsightedness of the Calumet citizenry that we can report that nearly all the counties and sizable communities within the area have set up planning commissions which have adopted or are in the process of adopting comprehensive planning programs. Conjointly with the planning of the Chicago Regional Planning Association, such may be considered the "blueprint" of the future landscape of the Calumet (10).

APPLICATION OF GEOGRAPHIC UNDERSTANDING

I. Classify the kinds of primary sources of information you think were used for the successive occupance periods in the Calumet study above—government archives, historical documents, questionnaire interviews, field evidence.

II. Essentially, what criteria determined the regional and temporal differentiations?

III. A. List the elements of the natural environment which figure in this survey.

B. List the cultural elements.

IV. Which of the elements you listed appear to be most germane to the appreciation of the genetic processes—natural and cultural —for each period?

V. A. What geographic factor was used to tie together one place with another place and one epoch with another epoch so as to present a unified geo-historical interpretation of the region? Can you think of any other element or elements that might have been so used?

B. What evidence of vestigial heritages is indicated, and of what value are they in understanding the present landscape?

VI. The Calumet map and silhouette sketches: How does this graphical material supply geo-historical perspective which the text fails to do?

VII. In what primary particulars would you expect the history of the areas presented, for example, by county histories to differ from the historical geography of the area as here presented?

References

1 Stewart, Omer C., "Fire as the First Great Force Employed by Man," *Man's Role in Changing the Face of the Earth,* William L. Thomas, Editor, *et al.*, University of Chicago Press, 1956, pp. 115-122, *passim.*

2 Darby, H. C., "The Clearing of the Woodland in Europe," *Man's Role in Changing the Face of the Earth,* William L. Thomas, Editor, *et al.*, University of Chicago Press, 1956, p. 183.

3 Sauer, Carl O., *Agricultural Origins and Dispersals,* Bowman Memorial Lectures, The American Geographical Society, New York, 1952, pp. 1, 18, 21, 22, 85, *passim.*

4 Glacken, Clarence J., "Changing Ideal of the Habitable World," *Man's Role in Changing the Face of the Earth,* William L. Thomas, Editor, *et al.*, University of Chicago Press, 1956, pp. 70-76, 85-88, *passim.*

5 Clark, Andrew H., Chairman of the Committee on "Historical Geography," *American Geography, Inventory and Prospect,* Preston E. James and Clarence F. Jones, Editors, Syracuse University Press, N. Y., 1954, pp. 92-93.

6 Olmstead, Clarence W., "The Application of a Concept to the Understanding of a Region: People, Time, Space, and Ideas in the Economic Core Region of Anglo-America," *The Journal of Geography,* Vol. LIX, No. 2, February, 1960, pp. 54, 61. (Also published in *Social Education,* Vol. 22, 1958.)

7 Jones, Wellington D., "Procedures in Investigating the Human Occupance of a Region," *Annals of the Association of American Geographers,* Vol. 24, 1934.

8 Whittlesey, Derwent, "Sequent Occupance," *Annals of the Association of American Geographers,* Vol. XIX, No. 3, September, 1929, pp. 164-165.

9 Burnham, D. H., Former President of the Chicago Regional Planning Association, Communication.

10 Meyer, Alfred H., "Circulation and Settlement Patterns of the Calumet—South Chicago Region of Northwest Indiana and Northeast Illinois," *Proceedings of the XVIIth Congress,* International Geographical Union, Washington, 1952, pp. 538-544.

Chapter 36

The geographic way of life—planning the geography of the future

It is upon the surface of the land, its natural beauty or its man-made ugliness, that we are compelled to gaze most of our waking hours.
—L. Dudley Stamp

Geographer Stamp of the London School of Economics and Director of the Land Utilization Survey of Britain is the first geographer to be honored by the Honorary Degree of Doctor of Economics, conferred by His Majesty, the King of Sweden, for "fundamental research in regional geography to the benefit of economic life and community planning." Stamp's career signally symbolizes the "bridge" character of a geographer's professional training and services between the road the geographer typically travels and the roads pursued, as in this instance, by other specialized disciplines, such as economics and planning, upon which geography impinges.

Planning as geography aforethought

In our first chapter, "The Geographic Facts of Life," you will recall we pointed to those earth phenomena and world principles by which we live. In this concluding chapter, we shall attempt to show how these facts of area, content, and context are to be used as practical guideposts in planning for effective earth stewardship and enjoyment of life's amenities for all peoples. Despite projecting man into outer space and exploring for possible ecumene of other planets, we submit we still have much to learn about geographic man on the earth in the art of living in harmony with nature and in peace with our fellowmen.

As was pointed out in the previous chapter, to know where we are and where we are going, we must reflect first of all upon those principles of geographic change in historic time which illuminate man's ecologic dominance in the landscape. In our silhouette study we explored the event-environment space-time integrations of an area in order to see what natural and cultural processes were most dominant for the respective epochs—the role each process played in the establishment of the occupance pattern. In following genetic processes and trends of geographic change from one period to the next, we learn to identify and apply principles of geography contributive to pleasant and profitable living. In a sense, this applied unified chorographic-chronologic learning is the essence of all life's planning, which is forever concerned with the age-old space-time questions of "Whence have we come?" "Whither are we going?" and "By what road do we seek to attain our destination?" Whatever else these basic questions of life may imply, one fact is paramount, that man as lord of creation is divinely destined to plan. Planning for the necessities and the amenities of life in terms of spatial and resource realities is, we might say then, basic to all earthly purposeful activity since it expresses intelligent forethought applied to orderly development of areas. The legislative form of planning combined with zoning (e.g., so-called master plans) may then be said to provide a pattern of space design and resource-use policy seeking maximum functional utility and social satisfaction of what we might call the "geographic way of life." Let us see how planning processes progress from our private affairs to matters of public policy.

1. The tourist as an observer of landscape planning. If you are planning a tour, you likely will want a roap map to guide you. But does the map serve only as a guide for destination, distance, and direction? We hope not. If you really want to see something—places of intelligible geographic and historic interest—you will consult maps that indicate the distribution of such educational phenomena. Moreover, if you possess such geographic knowledge, as here presented in the text, you will be alert to the things which most maps do not show—the changing regional patterns which identify and differentiate major scenic and economic landscapes on the roadside. Traveling with this awareness of roadside phenomena must impress any scrutinizing observers with the fact that the pattern of landscape phenomena reflects man's plans in carrying out his life's purposes. And so, one of the very best ways to study a people's culture, whether local or foreign, is to note how such culture expresses itself in the pattern of settlement and resource-use. A traveler trained to see, as he moves from place to place, the significant differences between the size, shape, and character of field, farm, and forest in the countryside; the changing slope patterns of cover and crop as he alternately tours the low valleys and high ridge roads, themselves changing to fit the terrain; the contrast between rural, suburban, and urban settlements—spatially, architecturally, and functionally—is prepared in large measure to understand what we might call the "space behavior" of the inhabitants—their idea of "planning."

2. ***The farmer as planner.*** Despite common views to the contrary, a farm effectively operated is among the most complicated of all industries. A farmer must learn to adapt crops to soil and season, and tillage to terrain. Land-use planning in diversified farming commonly involves scientific crop rotation, combined with animal industry. Moreover, a progressive farmer must plan his crop culture and animal rearing to fit prospectively favorable markets. And so he must keep posted on the transactions of the stock exchange and on the outlook of larger foreign surplus production of the type he himself intends to market. The traditional picture of the modern farmer as a mere sower and stockman is an illusion. He is rather an agronomist; a plant and animal husbandman; a speculator on weather and market. Unless a farmer reasonably well qualifies in these areas and plans his entire farming program along sound geographic and economic principles, his chances for long-time financial survival in our present agrarian economy look very unpromising, in spite of government subsidization of his farm management.

3. ***The citizen as planner.*** All forms of construction—house, school, church, business, and industrial establishment, road and recreational forms—normally call for a blueprint (another name for a special type of map). But the citizen as a geographically-trained individual is not satisfied with merely the blueprint of construction plans; he wants to see a "blueprint" of the topographic site and surrounding regional situation to which his life's activities are related. So if you're contemplating building any structure, or are a participant in a community building project, you will want to examine first of all, in terms of geographic elements, alternate sites, recognizing the major planning principle that both favorable and unfavorable aspects are inherent in almost every site and situation which we geographically explore. This involves an intricate study of the entire landscape mosaic whose spatial arrangement of elements will largely suggest whether any particular landscape is desirable or profitable, or not. The implementation of such space selections and allocations is effected by land-use zoning, a legislative procedure. The major premise of all good geographic planning is to select for all the major functions of a community—residence, recreation, church and school facilities, business, industry, and commerce—the sites best suited for each, and to provide as well the optimum interrelated space facility for the community as a whole.

Public planning may be of any space order of magnitude

1. ***Community (city) planning.*** The geographic know-how of site quality of all landscape elements with which man has to deal—natural and cultural—where gregarious man has chosen to live, as in villages, towns, and cities, assumes a more complicated form of geographic planning than is found where the areal elements are scattered as in the countryside. Planning for urban life is also more imperative, as it was, therefore, also understandably the kind of settlement which first received attention on the part of the neophyte planner. Lack of foresight in properly placing or spacing an individual building may adversely affect only that enterprise; but a multifunctional urban and suburban life which is malfunctional as well, geometrically multiplies areal maladjustments, often beyond repair. Strangely, while nearly everyone is quick to spot a slum neighborhood, as a result of lack of harmonious geographic perspective, people are often slow to observe when communities are without slums as a result of painstaking scientific planning. And so the average citizen simply takes the slumless city for granted without even inquiring whether possibly a city planning commission has had something to do with it.

The rather belated acceptance of community planning in America, and even present-day local reluctance and remonstrations against any form of planning, is a sad commentary on our American educational system. Though the theory of all geographic planning is based on the conservation of the best elements of our spiritual, esthetic, and economic life, many distorted ideas concerning private property rights and personal freedoms in a democracy have militated against any type of programming of a community's structure. As will be pointed out later, only recently has the American educator come to the realization that the understanding of the administration of planning in a democracy is at the very heart of responsible citizenship.

2. County planning. Farmers, though planners in their own right on their own premises, as pointed out above, are traditionally reserved in accepting planning principles and practices when they involve county zoning of rural as well as suburban land. But when it is demonstrated that conservation of land values is inherently a part of the whole program of conservation of natural resources, which is primarily a rural phenomenon, more and more counties, even with a predominantly rural population, have come to view planning as an over-all beneficial program. Within the last decade, for example, the number of counties establishing planning commissions increased from 10 or 20 per cent to as much as 50 per cent or more in various states.

3. State planning. The larger the political unit, the more complicated normally is the administrative machinery required to integrate the over-all city-county-regional planning of the resources of the state. The job of region-resource planning may be administered by a special planning agency (such as we have for the cities and the counties), or it may be "disguised" under another name, e.g., Department of Commerce, and other similar titles. Singly or jointly, state-wide planning includes such general topics as population growth (or decline), industrial and commercial expansion or contraction, and adequacy or inadequacy of transportation and recreational facilities. Specific attention will be paid to drainage and sewage problems, sanitation, port developments, and the like.

State-wide organized planning based on total field inventory of land-use is illustrated in exemplary form by the land-use surveys of Britain and Puerto Rico. In *The Land of Britain—Its Use and Abuse* (1), Stamp, as director of the Land Utilization Survey of Britain, reviews the entire history and structure of the Land Utilization Survey and some of the basic principles of land-use planning, with a final word on the "planning prospect." Figure XXXVI-1 exemplifies "the general system of dividing a county into land-use regions."

In a *Symposium on the Geography of Puerto Rico,*

> ¶ Eight students in a Latin American seminar, under the direction of Clarence F. Jones and G. Donald Hudson, made a study of the available basic information on Puerto Rico, analyzed the appropriateness of various techniques of geographic field mapping, and developed tentative keys for the mapping of landuse and physical characteristics of the land.[1]

This graduate student geography project was inspired by Dr. Rafael Picó, Chairman of the Puerto Rico Planning Board. Figure XXXVI-2 from the survey illustrates the traverse technique effective in generalizing landform–land-use correlations. And Figure XXXVI-3 illustrates how a geographer may go about combining field observation with aerial photography in inventorying natural-cultural unit associations.

4. Regional planning. This normally contemplates the programming of resource development related to a geographic region independent of political boundaries, or only incidental to them. Regional delimitations may be based on a commonness of resource characteristics or for a specific land-use problem of the area, which usually transgresses political boundary lines. Of this type would be the Calumet region study described in the previous chapter, for the greater portion of which area there is now being considered the organization of a Chicago Metropolitan Planning Commission in which both Illinois and Indiana would participate. Among the topics for integrated consideration would be drainage and sewage; growing conurbanization, with its accompanying transportation problems; inter-

[1] Jones, Clarence F., and Picó, Rafael, *Symposium on the Geography of Puerto Rico,* University of Puerto Rico Press, Rio Piedras, P. R., pp. 6, 18. Reprinted by permission.

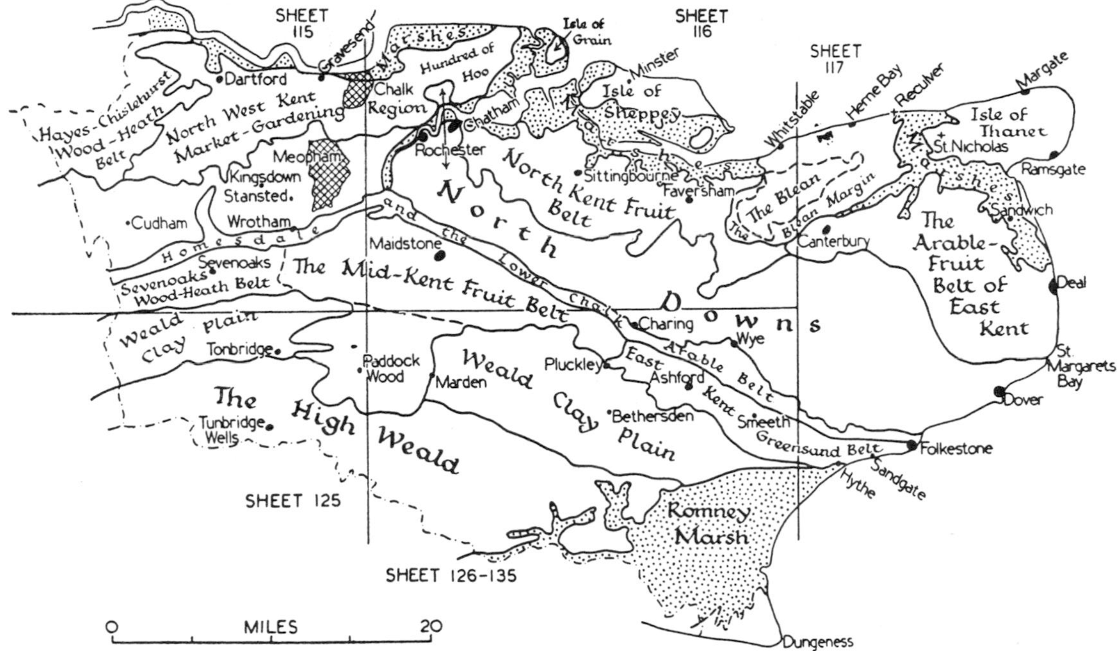

XXXVI:1 This map shows the land-use regions of Kent, England. Planning presupposes adequate land-use inventory against such natural environmental background features as are essential in revealing meaningful nature–man relationships. In this case the general system of dividing the country in land-use region is primarily based on physiography. (From Stamp, "Report on Kent," *The Land of Britain: Its Use and Misuse*, by L. Dudley Stamp, Longmans, Green & Co., Ltd., London, 1950, used by permission)

state port developments as related to the St. Lawrence Seaway; the competitive claims to head of Lake Michigan beach sites by industrial, commercial, recreational, and residential interests; and the like.

On the larger spatial scale, the Tennessee Valley Authority (TVA) exemplifies how a drainage basin serves as the unifying geographic factor for much needed and effective planning. We shall let Gordon Clapp, former chairman of the Board of Directors, state the case and scope of this planning project:

¶ The scene is a great river coursing from its tributaries high in the mountains of Virginia and the Carolinas. From these high slopes it meanders widely through Tennessee, Alabama, Kentucky, where it joins the Ohio. Parts of Mississippi and Georgia contribute their waters to the wide arc of this river. There was a time, less than twenty short years ago, when the river ran wild in flood and destruction during the heavy rains of the winter. When the rains stopped falling, the river ebbed to a lazy, powerless stream. Today the Tennessee River neither destroys nor sinks into idleness. The system of man-made dams, built of concrete and steel, pierced by locks for navigation and penstocks and turbines to transform the energy of falling water into controlled and mobile electricity, has put this river to work for man.

Back on the land that forms the great valley of the Tennessee the heaviest annual average rainfall, except for the Northwest, is being trained to run down to the river a little more slowly. After years of hard work and the practical application of the science of soil fertility by tens of thousands of farmers, grass and pastures and a revived forest cover are beginning to show green the year round. . . . Less and less does the land slip and roll into the streams and into the sea. . . .

The restoration of grass and pastures is the result in part of renewed soil fertility. New chemical processes centered about the development of electric furnaces apply the controlled energy of the river to the phosphate rock ores

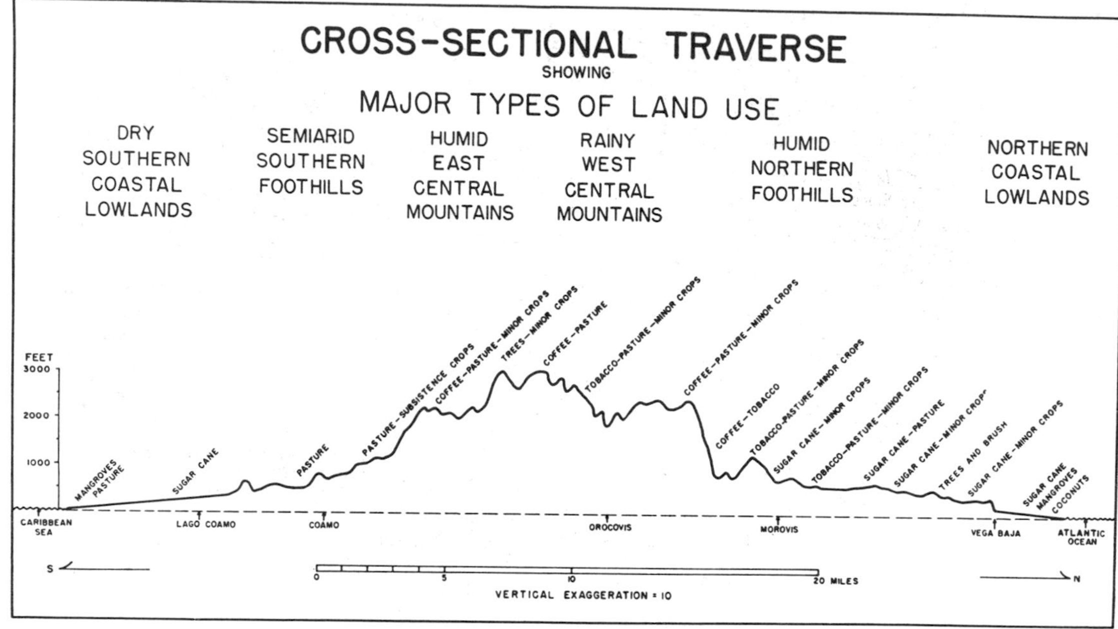

XXXVI:2 This type of survey and profile representation is expedient and effective in reconnaissance work and planning, especially where the surface profiles differentiate distinctive changes in topography and culture, as they do here. The caption to this figure reads: "Nearly all the principle types of land-use and land characteristics are represented in the north-south traverse across plains, foothills, and mountains of the island." (Donald R. Dryer, "The Development of Survey Techniques for the Rural Land Classification Program," *Symposium on the Geography of Puerto Rico*, Edited by Clarence F. Jones and Rafael Pico, University of Puerto Rico Press, 1955, used by permission)

deposited in another geologic era. These chemical processes transform the ores into soil mineral fertilizers upon which the fertility of phosphate-deficient soils depends. . . .

What is going on in the Tennessee Valley is in essence an adventure in faith—faith in man's ability voluntarily to achieve harmony between human pursuits in making a living and nature's fruitful habits of growth and production.[1]

Regional planning on a systematically organized national scale has become a standing major objective with the National Resources Committee. Following the establishment of the TVA Act of 1933, the government recognized the need for consolidating various planning agencies dealing with regional or interstate problems which called for concerted efforts between the state and the Federal government. A noteworthy effort is that of the Pacific Northwest Regional Planning Commission (4). In a 192-page report, the Commission reviews the salient natural and cultural problems and potentialities related to another river basin—the Columbia River. Another volume (5) reviews the general concepts and procedure of effective planning and the joint responsibility of the federal and state systems in initiating and developing the planning programs.

5. *World planning.* The United Nations, apart from representing an international security agency to keep the peace, includes such agencies as UNESCO which are directed to help develop the natural and human resources of particularly those parts of the world commonly referred to as the undeveloped or underdeveloped areas (Figure XXXVI-4). As the alphabetical designation suggests, attention is given to the promotion of educational, scientific, and cultural programs, and in this sense UNESCO may be considered an international planning service

[1] Clapp, Gordon R., *The TVA—An Approach to the Development of a Region,* The University of Chicago Press, pp. vi-vii. Copyright 1955 by The University of Chicago.

for human betterment. Another such agency is WHO, directed at raising the standards of world health, and particularly designed to stamp out the endemic and epidemic types of diseases.

As pointed out in Chapter 4, "population explosion" shares with "atomic population annihilation" the spotlight in our contemporary world. As there pointed out, vital statistics of increasing birth rates and decreasing death rates have little geographic significance in themselves; they must be space-wise and resource-wise, that is geographically, treated. In the last analysis, the question is, "What is the ultimate potential of natural and human resources in providing adequate sustenance and a reasonable standard of living?" And so this also has become a major concern for the United Nations, whose numerous research committees are engaged in studying world resource potentials and methods of aiding overpopulated countries in checking famine or near-famine conditions. The United Nations agencies would do well to consult such global resource surveys as those by geographer Stamp—*Our Underdeveloped World* (6) and *Our Developing World* (7)—which provide a regional perspective of critical resource–population problems, themselves often a threat to world democracy and global peace.

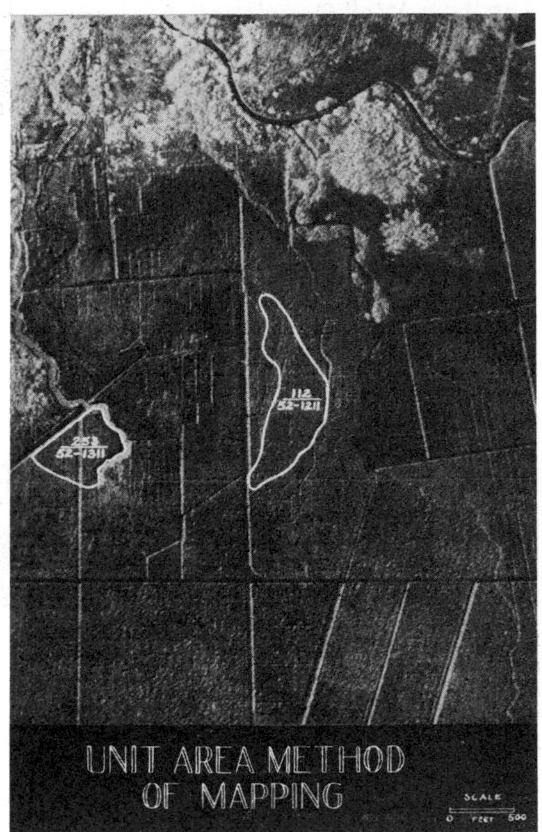

XXXVI:3 This areal photograph illustrates the unit area method of mapping. Note the code used to inventory field data. For example, notation of field in the center reads: "Average quality sugar cane (112) on organic soil, level land that is adequately drained and has no erosion or stone or rock exposure 52-1211. Survey on the ground and from the air go hand in hand in modern geographic field work." (Donald R. Dryer, "The Development of Survey Techniques for the Rural Land Classification Program," *Symposium on the Geography of Puerto Rico,* Edited by Clarence R. Jones and Rafael Pico, University of Puerto Rico Press, 1955, used by permission)

Urbanization and planning

Formal planning had its inception in association with the phenomenal growth of cities in the twentieth century and had its first systematic application in the largest metropolitan centers, where evidences of blighted neighborhoods and substandard living, as in the case of slums, became critical and chronic. This brings us at once to the problem of defining a city as over against the countryside, and an urban community as compared with a rural settlement area. One of the commonest phenomena of a landscape, a concentrated settlement which we call a city is quite difficult to define. When is an agglomerated settlement a town, and when does it become a city? Though the United States Census Bureau, for most statistical purposes, specifies an arbitrary minimum population of 2,500 to classify "urban" as distinct from "rural," a city is not determined by its areal size or by size of its population.

For purposes of urban geographic studies and master planning, a city may be thought of as a focus for a variety of institutional services, usually of a complex character (cultural, economic, administrative, etc.), serving not only the urban dweller but the rural contributary area ("hinterland") as

The Less Well Developed Areas and Their Importance to the United States

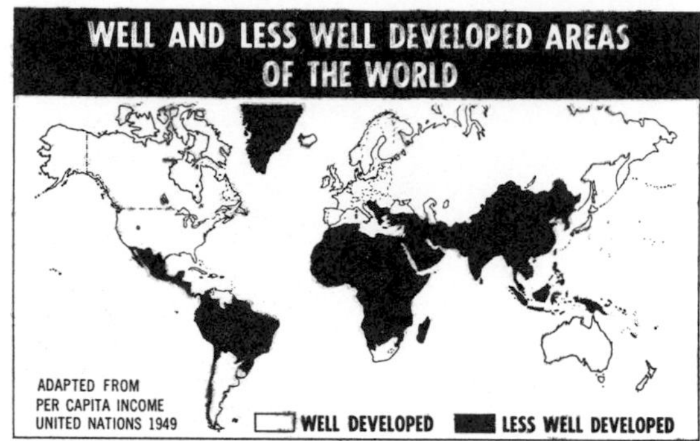

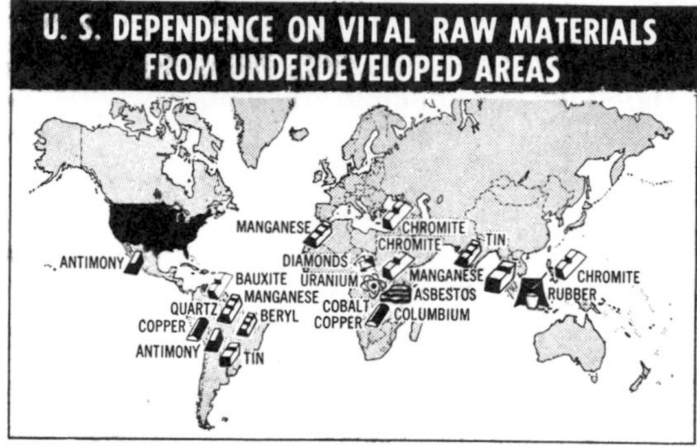

Characteristics of Developed and Underdeveloped Areas of the World

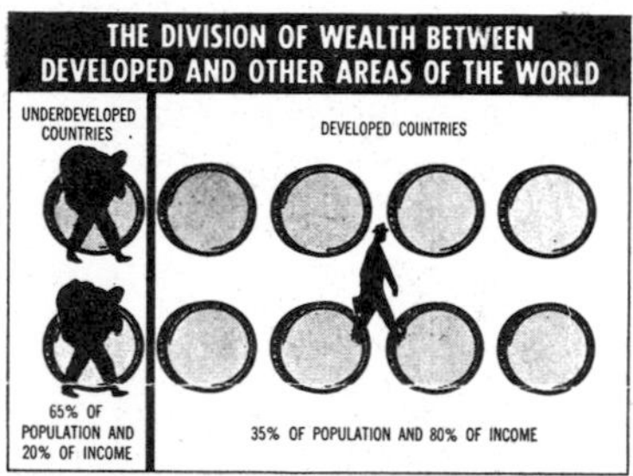

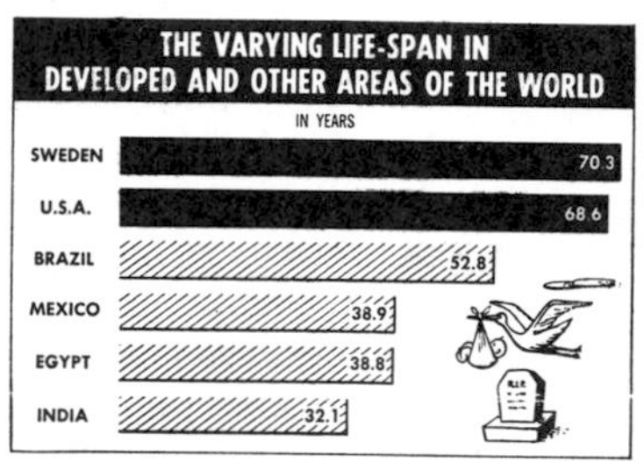

Barriers to Development and Means of Achieving Advancement

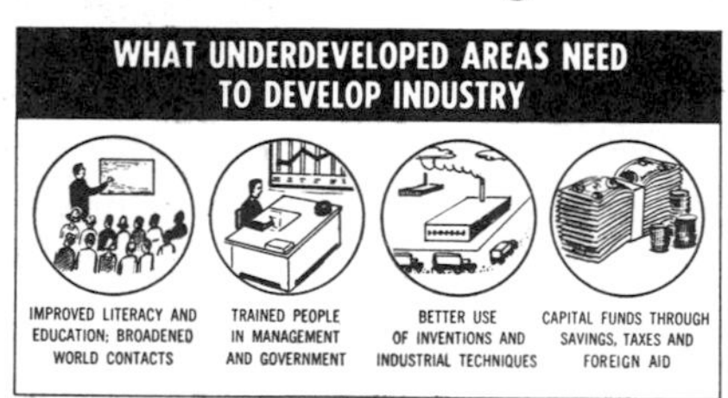

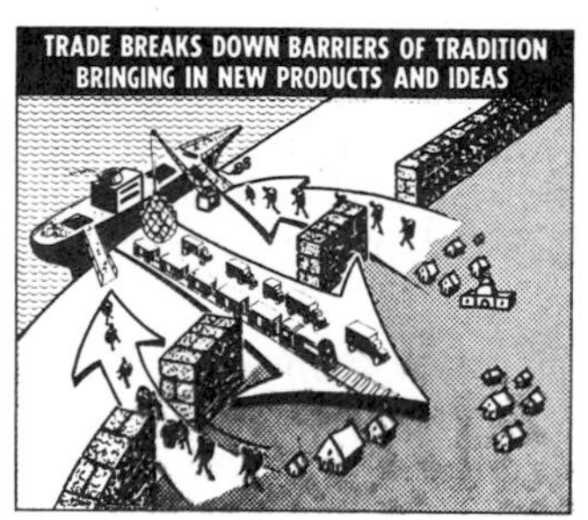

XXXVI:4 From a geographic point of view, the leading principle governing "aid" programs for any region is, "Is man making the best possible connections with the land and its resources—natural and human—of which it is capable?" (From *Newsletter*, The Twentieth Century Fund, No. 29, Spring, 1957, used by permission)

well. Such urban areas have been classified by M. Aurousseau on the basis of their predominant functions as (1) Administration: typically a capital city, desirably with a central location, communication facility, strategic advantages, and climatic favorability. (2) Defense: a fortress, garrison, or naval base town, normally occupying a peripheral position and dating back to antiquity. (3) Culture: centers of religion, education, art, and the like; no regular geographic site pattern is recognized, except frequent associations with old-time road junctions. (4) Production: manufacturing and craft communities, whose placement in many instances was dictated or strongly influenced by local sources of power or raw materials, or climate. (5) Communication: a. "collection" depots for local-regional resources (e.g., farm, forest, mining products); b. "transfer" points, typically sited to favorable marketing of goods or break-in-transit situations; c. "distribution" centers featuring wholesale business, and oriented generally in series to major transportation routes. (6) Recreation:

communities which, because of some attractive natural or cultural feature, cater to tourists or resortists; typically seasonal activity (8).

From such a classification students must not get the impression that the average urban community is characterized by only one of these classified functions. Many of the large cities would indeed be very difficult to classify, not only because of their multifunctional character but also in that they may embrace a number of functions of almost equal prominence.

Also using a functional approach of classification of cities, Harris supplies specific criteria for distinguishing the various types, his classification being based on the activity of greatest importance in each city. The classification comprises the following: manufacturing cities (two subtypes), retail centers, diversified cities, wholesale centers, transportation centers, mining towns, university towns, resort and retirement towns. The author illuminates the classification by indicating not only the critical criteria used as a basis for classification of cities but also the methodology used. Classes are also exemplified by numerous regional cities, and illustrated cartographically. The functional significance of the several classes as related to locative factors is stated thus:

¶ The central-location theory, in which centrality within a productive hinterland is stressed, is illustrated best by the distribution of wholesaling centers, which are usually large cities centrally placed within a wide area, and of retail centers, centrally placed within a smaller area [footnoting Ullman]. By way of contrast, in the rise of mining and resort centers, site factors, either mineral resources or climate, are of greater importance than central location. Industrial cities are intermediate in that both location factors of convenience to markets and raw materials and site factors of power and labor are important; they exhibit diffusion within a clearly defined manufacturing belt.[1]

Related to the preceding is still another type of classification, focused on "service." Thus Nelson, recognizing "that modern cities are performing more and more of the services necessary to the functioning of a modern society," feels that "the proportion of the labor force of a city engaged in performing a service is perhaps the best means of measuring the distribution of that activity," and that the "proportion of the labor force actually employed in a service is of much more direct significance to the economy of the city than the value or volume of sales of goods or of services performed" (10). For his classification, Nelson selected nine of the fifteen categories listed by the U. S. census of population table on "Economic Characteristics of the Population. . . .": mining; manufacturing; transportation and communication; wholesale trade; retail trade; finance, insurance, and real estate; personal service; professional service; and public administration. As in the case of the article by Harris, these various categories are exemplified and their distribution indicated on outline maps of the United States. The analysis of size, spacing, and relative importance of the various classes are commented upon, suggestive of various geographic principles operative in their distribution.

Important as they are to the study of urban geography and to the entire field of geography, articles such as these by Harris and Nelson, among others, dealing with the nature and classification of cities, are paramount to the understanding and the planning of our geographic way of life. Though geographers are interested in both the form (morphology) and function of cities as well as other areal units, more recent rural and urban landscape analysts, as illustrated in the two preceding references, recognize that function rather than form is more expressive of the dynamic quality of the landscape. This also, as the student will recall from what was stated in Part I particularly, conforms to the whole spirit of modern geographic investigations, centered as they are upon geographic "processes" instead of geographic "products." Especially is this true when we are dealing with an area of planning with its continual overtones of geographic change—landscape patterns of the past being transformed into the present morphology and in various transitional stages seeking adjustment to prospective future needs, in both

[1] Harris, Chauncy D., "A Functional Classification of Cities in the United States," *Readings in Urban Geography*, Harold M. Mayer and Clyde F. Kohn, editors, the University of Chicago Press. Copyright, 1959 by the University of Chicago.

New York City, a pioneer in planning (starting in 1925), has published the most extensive urban planning survey in the world: *Regional Plan of New York and Its Environs* (eight volumes). The view is New York Airways Heleport, Hudson River at 30th Street. (Courtesy New York Airways, Inc.)

spatial and constructional aspects. Among traditional considerations for community growth and development are: (1) Clearing the city of slums—and what city of any substantial size does not have them? Slum clearance, as a matter of fact, was the incipient circumstance that led to the first major planning program in urban renewal in America (New York City). What has created the slum in the first place? (2) Maintenance of residence property values by controlling substandard housing and zoning classified residential types as to architectural appointments, single or multiple dwelling units, cost, and the like. How are the elements of race and housing related? (3) Adequate provision for serviceable commercial areas (retail and wholesale)—business core, neighborhood stores, unified peripheral shopping centers. Are parking facilities ample? (4) Zoning of industrial districts for light, intermediate, heavy industries. What are the controlling factors in minimizing certain noxious manufacturing processes? (5) Provision for adequate facilities and suitable sites for the spiritual, educational, and recreational functions of the community. Are the amenities and the aesthetics of life in proper balance with the city's utilitarian forms and functions? (6) Development of a communication and transportation pattern that effectively serves the city and its commercially-contributary hinterland. Are the various services properly co-ordinated?

Planning principles and citizen community concepts themselves change as do the urban landscapes. For example, communities which were at one time or another set against location of industry in their midst as invasion of their "privacy" now welcome them. Much of this change in attitude is the result of two major factors: (1) realization of the fact that along with other modern innovations in industry, the noxious aspects such as smoke and odors have been minimized, if not en-

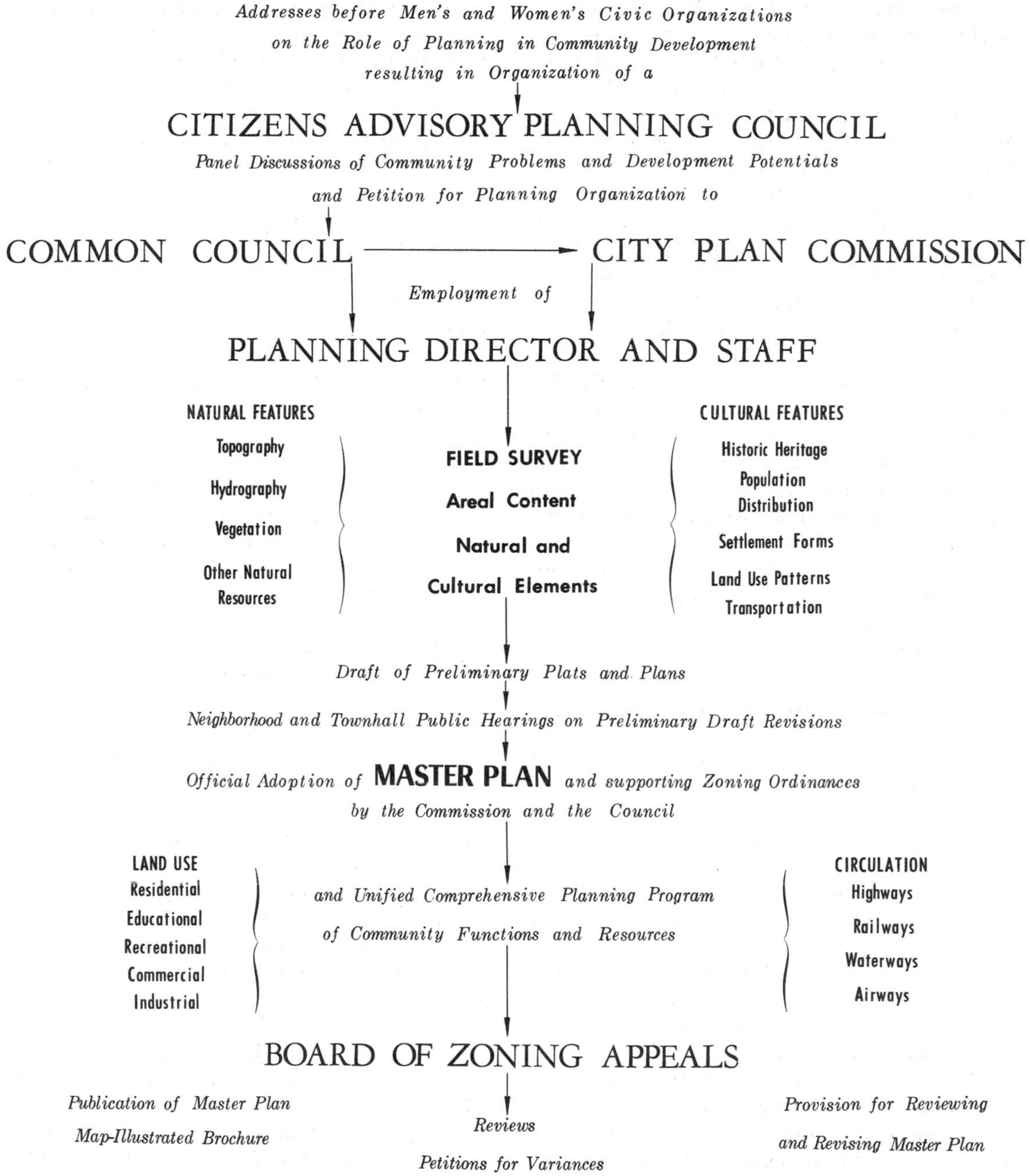

Addresses before Men's and Women's Civic Organizations
on the Role of Planning in Community Development
resulting in Organization of a

CITIZENS ADVISORY PLANNING COUNCIL

Panel Discussions of Community Problems and Development Potentials
and Petition for Planning Organization to

COMMON COUNCIL → CITY PLAN COMMISSION

Employment of

PLANNING DIRECTOR AND STAFF

NATURAL FEATURES
Topography
Hydrography
Vegetation
Other Natural Resources

FIELD SURVEY
Areal Content
Natural and Cultural Elements

CULTURAL FEATURES
Historic Heritage
Population Distribution
Settlement Forms
Land Use Patterns
Transportation

Draft of Preliminary Plats and Plans

Neighborhood and Townhall Public Hearings on Preliminary Draft Revisions

Official Adoption of **MASTER PLAN** *and supporting Zoning Ordinances*
by the Commission and the Council

LAND USE
Residential
Educational
Recreational
Commercial
Industrial

and Unified Comprehensive Planning Program
of Community Functions and Resources

CIRCULATION
Highways
Railways
Waterways
Airways

BOARD OF ZONING APPEALS

Publication of Master Plan
Map-Illustrated Brochure

Reviews
Petitions for Variances

Provision for Reviewing
and Revising Master Plan

XXXVI:5 This chart may be used as an organizational guide to grass-roots planning.

tirely eliminated; (2) many plants have done a better landscaping job of beautifying their premises than have many homes. It is also recognized, of course, that industries are almost indispensable in many communities, not simply to provide employment but also to widen the tax base to help support the many "amenities" the communities demand.

Another major civic change which might be thought of as a natural outgrowth of planning itself is the challenge it presents to the average citizen to make his influence directly felt in the community. Especially has this influence become articulate in the many civic groups which assert themselves in the promotion of specific aspects of community development—e.g., the women's societies interested in city beautification and edification; the men's clubs and the Chamber of Commerce, and perhaps specially-organized industrial enterprises interested in boosting business and in getting new industries to locate in the community. In fact, such agencies are often instrumental in getting formal planning itself started in the community by organizing a citizen's advisory council to help the city council initiate the procedure and the machinery necessary for effective city planning (Figure XXXVI-5). The entire venture is functional democracy at its best—the grass-roots level. But wise planning is predicated on an enlightened citizenry —a citizenry that is familiar with the community structure, its chief historical antecedents, its primary functional classification; a citizenry that has an understanding of those environmental elements and processes which facilitate or retard progress in one direction or another.

Some questions posed for urban planning

Because urban communities — most of them multifunctional — experience more pressure on land-use than is common in rural areas, it should be readily understandable that comprehensive planning of the so-called *master plan* type can be a most perplexing and challenging art, the participants in which—the architect, the economist, the engineer, the geographer, the jurist, the political scientist, the sociologist, and, of course, the city plan commission and city council —each have their role to play under the direction of a professional planner, or rather a planning agency. Such an agency is usually constituted of a sizable personnel, working in part in the field (making areal and other surveys), and in part in the office (organizing collected data, drafting maps, and preparing planning brochure material). In the course of the field "spade" work and especially during the concluding phases of the planning project, various types of meetings—meetings with neighborhood groups, town hall hearings, council-commission sessions — are scheduled to transfer planning intelligence to the public and to the city officials and to consult with them on special problems of community development. As anyone who has had anything to do with urban planning knows only too well, unless the average citizen in the community is "sold" on the idea that properly conceived and administered master planning is oriented towards protection and promotion of property and human values rather than aimed at prohibition of man's freedom in the exercise of property rights, community planning, however expertly engineered, may achieve only very limited success. Therefore, it is essential that the public be given full opportunity to participate in the discussion of questions and policies on planning procedures and objectives.

Many are the questions, indeed, which come up for consideration, and which vary markedly for each community for which contractual services are performed. A few may be hypothetically posed here: What is the general nature of the areal structure of the city (Figure XXXVI-6)? What is the geographic basis for recognizing differentiated communities (actually a form of regionalism) within the urban area? Where are the particularly critical areas of competitive land-uses which need special attention for a type of zonation best fitted to serve not only the private but also the public interest? What principles of quantity and quality of space are considered essential in allocating adequate space for the various forms of city functions—residential, religious, recreational, educational, industrial, and commercial? Are suitable sites available for homes, churches, schools, civic centers, recreational playgrounds, and parks? What should be the guideposts for maintaining the proper balance between the development of a community along the cultural, spiritual, and aesthetic side as compared with the economic and utilitarian aspects of the community? Are the city's utilities adequate in quantity and quality to fit the growing needs of the community? Is the city over-all optimally functional on a scale not only suited to its own needs, but also to that of the surrounding region which is, of itself, necessary to the city's welfare? Are the officers of the City Planning Commission and of the Chamber of Commerce, and above all, we should add, the industrialists themselves, fully aware of the significance of the locative

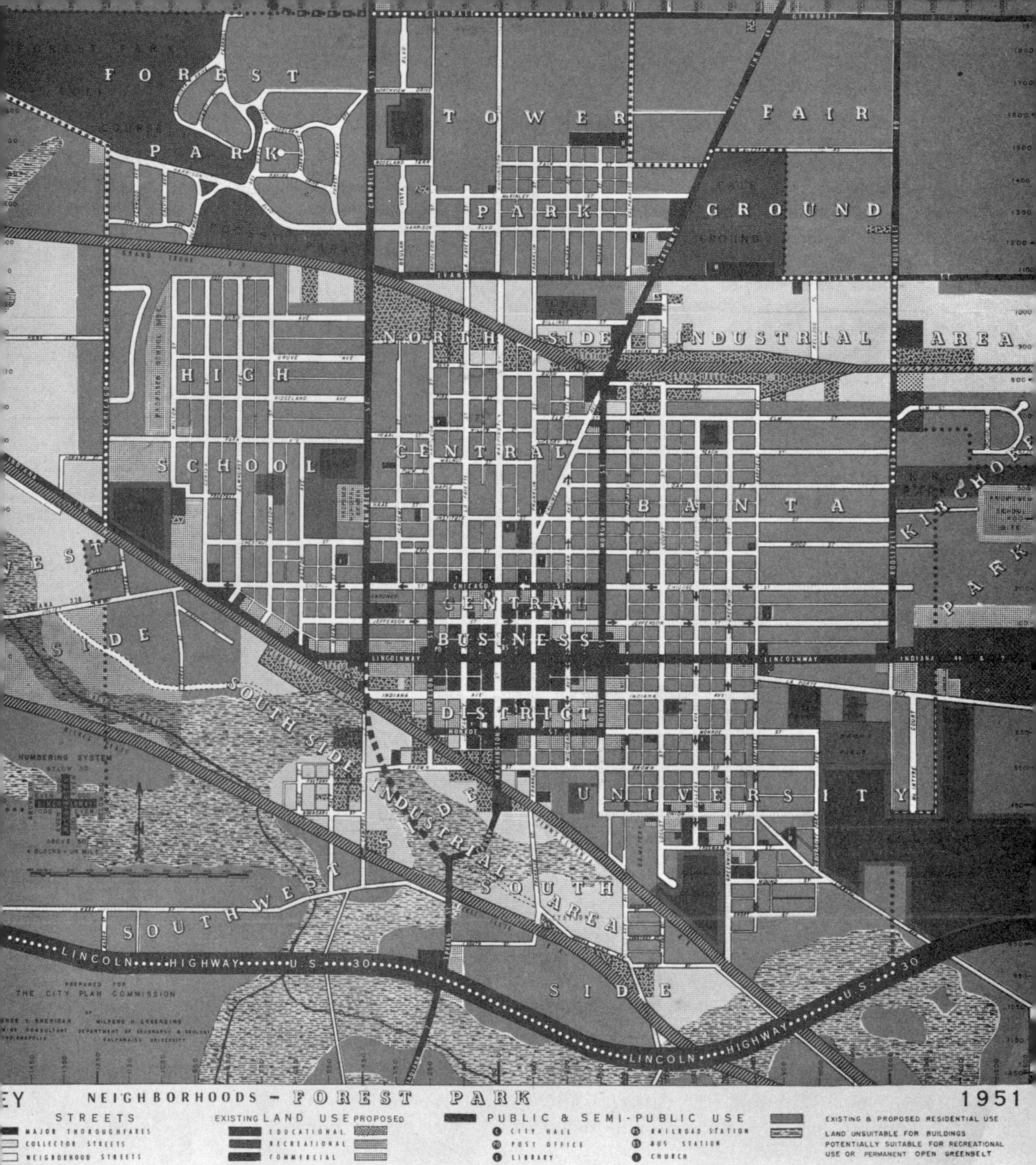

XXXVI:6 On the community level, effective geographic planning starts and ends with comprehensive mapping—preferably with maps covering all relevant phenomena of the community—of our past heritages (if data are available), of the present, of course, embracing all the leading categories that enter into planning considerations; and, finally, zoning and planning maps for future guidance in community development. Here is a specimen of a geographic planning survey of a small university town in the midwest—Valparaiso, Indiana. (From Valparaiso Master Plan, 1951, Revised 1954. Used by permission of Valparaiso City Plan Commission and Lawrence V. Sheridan, Planning Consultant)

factor in the siting and zoning of industrial districts—recognition of the type of space relation existing between industry, business, and residence; among the industrial districts themselves within the city; the distribution pattern of raw materials, of labor, and of markets; and the means of transportation available to integrate the various manufacturing establishments within the community?[1]

What is the size and character of the hinterland which in a significant way economically and commercially contributes to the development of the urban area? How does the economy of the city fit into the major geographic region of which it is economically a part? Is its business oriented competitively or complementarily to the businesses of the other city centers within the region? Do urban expansions and zoning and re-zoning of land-use take into consideration the relative productivity of soils for agricultural use and the areas uniquely designed for recreation or for the conservation of natural and historic phenomena? What types of geographic changes in recent years are considered significant in presaging future trends—clues that are considered very essential in building for the future aesthetics as well as economics of a community?

Only when Mr. Citizen has some understanding of the spatial and other implications of these and related matters involved in directing the future development of his community—of his neighborhood, of his church and school district, of his employment establishment, and of the total enterprises of the community ensemble of which he is a part—is he intelligently prepared to accept and help implement any planned community-betterment program. The Citizens' Advisory Planning Council and the Neighborhood and Town Hall Public Hearings, as outlined in Figure XXXVI-5, have been found very effective in enlightening the public with the structural and functional principles and procedures commonly employed in professional planning. Moreover, these open forums are almost indispensable in obtaining insights of public opinion as to what the citizen himself recognizes as community problems. Unfortunately, there are times—often too common—when only the more vocal but least informed of the citizenry attempt to make their influence felt. Important as is, then, intelligent and aggressive citizen participation in the planning program, with the prospect of increasing demands on such participation as communities become increasingly complex, it behooves our educational authorities to consider geographic planning education as an integral element in every high school and college social science curriculum.

Planning is a co-ordinative and co-operative venture shared by many disciplines

As already pointed out in Chapter 2, planning is an area in the liberal arts college which well fits into an integrated program of liberal arts education, since planning cuts across more disciplines perhaps than does any other single field where theoretical principles of societal structure and practical application of life's activities are involved. As also indicated in an earlier section, the geographer draws upon many related disciplines in analyzing total areal interactions. In other instances, planning services become so specialized as to be delegated to specialists outside the field of geography. As Dickinson observes:

¶ The geographer is not so much concerned with the precise analysis of particular service areas, for this is ultimately the problem of marketing for which the economist is more qualified. . . . It would be obvious . . . that the trained historian is best fitted to deal with the documentary evidence relevant to the formation of cities, and that the art historian can best deal with individual comparative studies of urban architecture. . . . What is of most interest to the sociologist is the distribution of social maladjustment in disorganized areas—delinquency (adult and juvenile), vice, suicide, mental disorders, alcoholism, divorce and desertion, poverty, mortality, and disease.[2]

---

1 Government documents here can prove most helpful. For example, more than a score of environmental and economic factors are treated in a booklet entitled *Data Sources for Plant Location Analysis* (11).

2 Dickinson, Robert E., "The Scope and Status of Urban Geography: An Assessment," *Readings in Urban Geography*, Harold M. Mayer and Clyde F. Kohn, editors, the University of Chicago Press, pp. 18, 24, 25. Copyright 1959 by The University of Chicago.

The interdisciplinary base of both theoretical and factual planning is even more complex than previously indicated. Master planning includes zoning, which has a jurisdictional base. Consequently, professional planners must familiarize themselves not only with local city ordinances but with state planning enactments dealing with planning and zoning legislation as well as court practices validating or invalidating such legislation. At this point, then, enter the political scientist, the attorney, and the jurist. In technical matters of construction, such as transportation lines, traffic control, sewage disposal, and the like, technicians will be needed in the engineering and architectural fields. For the most part, their functions lie outside the area of geography proper.

The distinctive contribution of the geographer to planning

As indicated in Part I of this book, the entire philosophy and practice of the geographic discipline are oriented about the space–resource phenomena of man and his habitat. Here, also, in planning as in other areas of geographic investigation, the geographer plays the role of a systematist generalist—a trained expert in the genetics and principles of space processes and structures. Herein, both on the theoretical and practical side of planning, lies the distinctive contribution of the geographer. As so well pointed out by Mayer, a combined professional geographer and researcher in planning:

¶ Specialists in . . . sociology, anthropology, and political science, engineering, architecture, meteorology, pedology, geomorphology, and even psychology may describe and interpret spatial distribution of those groups of phenomena with which each is especially concerned; only the geographer is concerned with all the interrelationships among them, as they exist within an area and as they differ from one area to another.

The urban geographer is thus concerned with the city as a functional as well as a physical entity. He is concerned with the environments of cities as well as with the environments within cities; with the patterns of distribution of cities on the earth as well as with the pattern of distribution of people, buildings, facilities, institutions, and cultures within cities. He is concerned with the interpretations of these distributions and their differences in occurence and intensity from place to place, in so far as the interpretations may be found in the inter-relationships among the various phenomena thus distributed. . . . The urban geographer, therefore, is concerned with the problems of guiding urban growth and development into set forms and patterns as will further the attainment of a better urban way of life.[1]

Thus we see that the geographer is trained not only in comprehensive land-use inventory, but he develops and applies principles which show the meanings of space context in which the landscape content exists. Accordingly, the geographer also develops a geographic form of planning cartography in which landscape-mapped designs reflect both the problems and potentiality of land-use. This technique of field mapping and laboratory cartography expresses methodology unique to the geographer, who sees landscape phenomena in their "togetherness," the key to all effective planning.

Experience indicates that geography-trained personnel (staff and students) can constructively contribute to practically all levels of the planning operation, especially in field inventory analysis and master-plan formulation. At the same time the geography personnel benefits directly from contacts with the professional planner, the city government, and public forums in the interchange of planning intelligence and experiences.

Geography preparation for the planning profession

At this point, no doubt, the student may be interested to know how a geography major or minor interested in the planning profession qualifies for that profession by general reason of his geography and related subject-matter college training background. What courses especially in geography are planning-wise significant, and what are the prospects for a geography-trained student to be thus employed by a public or private planning agency? This perhaps can best and most briefly be answered by professional geog-

[1] Mayer, Harold M., "Geography and Urbanism," *Readings in Urban Geography*, the University of Chicago Press. Copyright 1959 by The University of Chicago.

raphers who are themselves now engaged in planning or are curricular-wise specifically interested in this area of geographic education, or who have made it a special point of investigation, as has an Association of American Geographers committee. Thus we find Harold V. Miller, a professional geographer and executive director of the East Tennessee office of the Tennessee State Planning Commission, making the following observation:

¶ A competent geographer finds himself with a background to analyze the community, to recognize the functional relationships between its component parts, and, on this basis to assist in location or attraction of industry, expansion of trade and service, and whatever else may be necessary to firm up the local economy. Good training in economic geography will enable him to visualize the relationships and potentialities of the community or region in relation to its resources and even in relation to the remainder of the nation and the world. Thus, he is in a position to deal competently with the economic base of his community or region and in so doing insures the availability of the wherewithal to translate his best plans into facilities or conditions of value to human beings.[1]

And a graduate student of city planning, Mr. Gary M. Cooper, at the Georgia Institute of Technology, recognizes a common denominator of geography education and planning education in that both "deal with design of structures, the arrangement of transportation and communication, and the relations between human constructions and their intended functions." Then Cooper goes on to suggest that:

¶ If a student plans to become a specialist in city planning he should take a general education course prior to specializing at the graduate level. Modern cultural geography appears to be one answer; it is a diverse type of science which is applicable to many fields such as economic, recreation, political, agricultural, transportation, urban, population, resource, and industrial geography.[2]

Motivated by the conviction that "for geography students, planning is an exciting career to those attracted by the problems of concrete spatial expression," Professor Theodore Herman of the Department of Geography of Colgate University addressed a letter "to the chairmen of nine of the leading graduate planning schools, asking them to mark beside each of the 38 even remotely related courses currently offered at Colgate one of the following symbols: B (basic), D (desirable), or N (not needed), for preplanning training." The courses considered by the respondents basic in 7, 8, or 9 designations included as geography, Elements of Geography, Urban Geography, and Cartography and Aerial Photo Interpretations. Those checked as basic in 4, 5, or 6 designations included as geography, Economic Geography, and two other courses, Population Problems and Urban and Rural Communities, sometimes offered in sociology departments and sometimes in geography departments. This latter list includes six other courses in miscellaneous academic departments (16).[3] Recognizing the close academic relationship between geographic training and the planning profession, a number of geography departments have adapted undergraduate curricula as pre-professional background for a planning career.

And finally: How does the percentage of geographers engaged in planning compare with the percentage of geographers engaged in other nonteaching, nonfederal occupations? The most recent data we have access to reports:

¶ Apparently there are more geographers engaged in planning than in any other nonteaching, nonfederal occupations. But planning is to a large degree a governmental function and only 22% of the returned questionnaires are from employees of private planning firms, whereas 16% are from State planning agencies, 34% from County or Regional agencies, and 28% from City agencies. Collectively they are all planners whose function is to organize man's occupance of earth's space, but there are variations within

[1] Miller, Harold V., "Training Geographers for Planning," *Journal of Geography*, Vol. XLVII, May, 1948, p. 179. Reprinted by permission.

[2] Cooper, Gary M., "Geography as a Foundation for City Planning," *Journal of Geography*, Vol. LVIII, No. 9, December, 1959, p. 436. Reprinted by permission.

[3] As for professional planning programs, there were, as of 1958-59, twenty-eight institutions in the United States and four institutions in Canada which offered academic degree programs in the field—9 bachelor's, 30 master's, and 6 doctor's (17).

the groups not only in the ways this objective is approached but also in attitudes, methods, and means whereby they shall be done" (18).[1]

Political and institutional implementation of geographic concepts

Important as is the formulation of anthropo-geographic concepts, and principles growing out of them, testing for the soundness and practicable applicability of such concepts and principles goes hand in hand with the theoretical researches in the field. It is in these phases of the geographic discipline that community and regional planning provides an exemplary testing and proving ground for many of the things geographers claim for geography. And since planning of any area—large or small—to be effective, must be provided for through legislation, the jurisdiction of planning administration resides in city, county, state, or federal government. It follows, therefore, that the planning field, cultivated intercurricular-wise with political science, is one of the very best ways to realize effective implementation of "the geographic way of life." Another way is close identification of geographers or geography departments with government agencies which directly or indirectly sponsor such programs as previously alluded to: The Land Utilization Survey of Britain, the Rural Land Classification of Puerto Rico, the reports of the U. S. National Resources Committee, and the Tennessee Valley Authority Act. Implementation of geography through government planning has its exponents elsewhere also, even in areas generally considered remote from the center of the World Land Hemisphere. Thus, in the Union of South Africa, the Planning Officer of the Natural Resources Development Council, Fair, reports:

¶ That there is considerable scope for geographers in planning in South Africa, provided the opportunities for employment exist, is clear from the nature of the problems with which a planning body such as the N.R.D.C. has to deal. These vary from the study of the use and development of individual resources such as minerals and water, to the study of whole regions, their possibilities and problems of development, whether they be underdeveloped and mainly rural regions or highly developed city regions.[2]

Another geography-implementation procedure is direct participation by geography staff and geography students in a combined "town and gown" venture in college-community planning (20); still another, by program participation in state or institutional conferences on planning (21). Now appearing also are publications which feature integrated considerations of areal investigations and areal planning; for example, the classically written German *Raumforschung und Raumordnung* with its superb cartographic craftsmanship in color (22).

By and large, it appears that American geography, despite some spotty signs of growing interest and intelligence in the planning field and other related applications of geographic services, has not as yet been captivated with the idea that for geography to achieve its loftiest purposes and highest degree of usefulness it must seek more effectively to utilize the talents and training which geographers possess to show how geography can be truly professionally functional beyond the teaching field, important as is this area. It is a challenge that the young geographer may well embrace.

Textual summary—theoretical and applicational geography

This brief summary of textual principles is intended to help in review of the primary objectives, principles, and techniques preparatory to writing an essay on such a title as "Geographic Man." A subtopical outline may well be organized about self-constructed summaries of the major parts or sections of this book.

From the first chapter on "The Geographic Facts of Life" to this concluding one, "The

[1] As the title of this report, "The Nontraditional Jobs of Geographers," suggests in surveying "the experiences of geographers in business," there are other fields of applied geography besides planning—e.g. business and government—where geographers give a good account of themselves. Planning is featured in this chapter since few areas in professional geography can match planning for integrating and implementing the principles and techniques of geography.

[2] Fair, T. J. D., "Geographers and Regional Planning," *Tydskrif vir Aardrykskunde (Journal for Geography)*, Published by The Society for the Teaching of Geography, Department of Geography, University of Stellenbosch, Union of South Africa, Vol. I, No. 1, September, 1957, p. 31. Reprinted by permission.

Geographic Way of Life," you will recall, we have stressed the anthropocentricity of geography as the mother of science. Commissioned to subdue the earth by divine decree, man is geographically represented not as a product of nature, but as a spiritual and creative force above nature. While a part of earth reality to be sure, geographic man is destined not only to live and enjoy the fruits of the earth but to exercise responsibility of world–resource stewardship. In other words, the geographic discipline as here presented embraces the ethos as well as the ecology of man in his natural earth and cultural world relationships. Accordingly, precepts as well as concepts form the basis of motivation, and landscape-descriptive and product–statistical material have been regionally selected to fit as expeditiously as possible the types of geographic processes and their evaluation that modern authorship appears to stress in the best tradition of historic and current literature.

It is hoped that sufficient relevant reference sources have been directly quoted to inspire the enterprising student, particularly the prospective major in the field, to investigate further the wealth of literature on the subject, both the professional journal type as well as the numerous excellent textbooks on the principles of geography and in the various systematic branches of geography. Above all, as illustrated in the present chapter on geographic planning, what one knows is not worth very much unless it is applied —and applied not simply empirically, but scientifically. A plan for one's life, then, as a home builder, as a businessman, or as an aspiring local and world citizen, may raise such questions as: How well am I prepared to perceive and measure the degree to which my understandings of religion, of the humanities, of the social sciences or the natural sciences equip me to understand world realities in a truly "down to earth" geographic context? How does an understanding of the geographic concepts and principles aid me in selecting a desirable homesite and in detecting a promising locale for my business? How does such an understanding, based on space-time continua, unify our knowledge of the various disciplines? How does systematic geography contribute to our awareness of how well or how poorly our geographic behavior is adjusted to a specific (unique) area? And how does the study of the various facets of regional geography give us insights into the diverse problems and potentials of areas and countries, identified as they are with differentiated regional population patterns and pressure, and into the natural and human resources available, within or without, to cope with them?

In the final analysis, then, geographic learning and behavior, through areal planning (personal or professional), aims at realizing man's designed destiny to be an informed and intelligent citizen of world affairs and a good custodian of the world's resources divinely entrusted to him.

"Geographic man"

(Conceptual topical guidelines for writing an essay on the above title, based upon your home region or other area with which you are especially familiar or with which you identify some particular areal interest.)

I. Uniqueness of features that differentiates it as a region in the truly geographic sense. In what significant characteristics of "geographic man" does the "hard core" of this space-unit distinguish itself from other areas adjacent to it? Resource-wise or space-wise, do you recognize significant similarities to other world regions?

II. Totality of areal content of habitat significance. What appear to be the chief environmental criteria upon which area analysis focuses?

III. "Togetherness" of landscape context. What cartographic technique seemingly serves best to illustrate (1) unifying and (2) disunifyng natural and cultural forces in the area?

IV. Correlations of environmental associations within the area which reflect the chief factoral adaptations between the natural–natural, cultural–cultural, and the natural–cultural spatial co-variances. What observations lead you to believe that the average inhabitant is, or is not, aware of the important principle of properly balancing the aesthetics with the economics in areal living?

V. Evaluation of natural and human resources in terms of (1) areal content, (2) pattern of social and economic organization of community or regional affairs. What evidence of geographic behavior points to an intelligent and dedicated stewardship in the management of areal resources—or the lack of it?

VI. Analysis of (or suggestions for) Master Planning and Zoning for the future geography of the area. Does the existing Master Plan reflect an understanding of the basic geographic processes that "make the community or region tick," as we say; and is the programming of the future realistically projected? If there is no such plan, briefly suggest planning policies to be considered for such development, and the role the geography-trained person is uniquely prepared to assume in an areal planning program.

References

1 Stamp, L. Dudley, *The Land of Britain—Its Use and Misuse,* Longmans, Green and Co., Ltd., London, 1950, in conjunction with Geographic Publications Ltd., pp. 129, 222.

2 Jones, Clarence F., and Picó, Rafael, *Symposium on the Geography of Puerto Rico,* University of Puerto Rico Press, Rio Piedras, P. R., pp. 6, 18.

3 Clapp, Gordon R., *The TVA—An Approach to the Development of a Region,* The University of Chicago Press, 1955, pp. vi-vii.

4 *Regional Planning,* Part I, Pacific Northwest, National Resources Committee, U. S. Government Printing Office, Washington, D. C., May, 1936.

5 *Regional Factors in National Planning,* National Resources Committee, U. S. Government Printing Office, Washington, D. C., December, 1935, p. 223.

6 Stamp, L. Dudley, *Our Underdeveloped World,* Faber and Faber, Ltd., London, 1952.

7 Stamp, L. Dudley, *Our Developing World,* Faber and Faber, Ltd., London, 1960.

8 Aurousseau, M., "The Distribution of Population: A Constructive Problem," *The Geographical Review,* Vol. XI, No. 4, October, 1921, pp. 569-572.

9 Harris, Chauncy D., "A Functional Classification of Cities in the United States," *Readings in Urban Geography,* Harold M. Mayer and Clyde F. Kohn, Editors, The University of Chicago Press, 1959, p. 138.

10 Nelson, Howard J., "A Service Classification of American Cities, *Readings in Urban Geography,* Harold M. Mayer and Clyde F. Kohn, editors, The University of Chicago Press, 1959, p. 139.

11 *Data Sources for Plant Location Analysis,* Office of Area Development, U. S. Department of Commerce, U. S. Government Printing Office, Washington, D. C., 1959, p. 42.

12 Dickinson, Robert E., "The Scope and Status of Urban Geography: An Assessment," *Readings in Urban Geography,* Harold M. Mayer and Clyde F. Kohn, Editors, The University of Chicago Press, 1959, pp. 18, 24, 25.

13 Mayer, Harold M., "Geography and Urbanism," *Readings in Urban Geography,* The University of Chicago Press, 1959, pp. 8-9.

14 Miller, Harold V., "Training Geographers for Planning," *Journal of Geography,* Vol. XLVII, May, 1948, p. 179.

15 Cooper, Gary M., "Geography as a Foundation for City Planning," *Journal of Geography,* Vol. LVIII, No. 9, December, 1959, p. 436.

16 Herman, Theodore, "Undergraduate Preparation for a Planning Career," *The Professional Geographer,* Vol. XII, No. 2, March, 1960, pp. 10-11.

17 "Professional Planning Education in the United States and Canada," American Institute of Planning, Washington, D. C., and American Society of Planning Officials, Chicago, Ill., 1959, p. 6.

18 Reith, John W., Chairman, "The Nontraditional Jobs of Geographers," *Report of Geographers in Business Committee,* Association of American Geographers, March, 1960, pp. 18, 19.

19 Fair, T. J. D., "Geographers and Regional Planning," *Tydskrif vir Aardrykskunde (Journal for Geography),* Published by The Society for the Teaching of Geography, Department of Geography, University of Stellenbosch, Union of South Africa, Vol. I, No. 1, September, 1957, p. 31.

20 Meyer, Alfred H., "College Geography and Community Planning: A Case Study in Applied Geography," *The Journal of Geography,* Vol. LII, No. 4, April, 1953.

21 Meyer, Alfred H., "Social and Economic Factors Giving Rise to Planning and Zoning, with a Focus on Planning Education," (program sponsored by the Valparaiso School of Law, and the Indiana Bar Association) *Proceedings, 1956 Legal Institute on Planning and Zoning,* Indiana Department of Commerce, Division of Planning, Indianapolis, June, 1959.

22 *Raumforschung Und Raumordnung,* Institut fur Raumforschung, Bad Godesburg and Akadamie fur Raumforschung und Landesplanung, Hanover, Carl Heymanns Verlag, KG, Köln, Berlin.

Significance of climatic identification-classification and its application to geographic understandings

Unlike landscape phenomena generally, weather and climate, because of their ephemerality and changeability, are not readily mapped and comprehended either as to their systematic organization or mappable and comprehensible evaluation in correlation with other areal phenomena, natural or cultural. And the very fact that statistics (pressure, temperature, precipitation, wind direction, and the like) must be used in meteorological analysis creates an initial aversion on the part of some students, while others build up the illusion that geographers are interested in such statistics for their own sake—or perhaps just to have the student engage in some busy work identifying or classifying climatic station data. It should be made very clear that the mere memorization of Köppen or other criteria, their climatic symbolism, and the ability to classify "stations" correctly have of themselves no end value, unless we understand how the climatic types are generically and genetically related to one another. And what is even more important is to comprehend how the combined cartography and classification of climates generate areal associations of seasonal and annual data with other environmental phenomena (natural and cultural) to which the elements of climate are cogently, if not directly coherently, related.

The Chorograph-Climograph principle developed in Part IV is designed to help meet this goal. Another approach is the Taxonomic Key here presented. Following the general pattern of taxonomic principles used by biologists in classifying and identifying plants and animals, the key arranges in parallel positions the criteria and identifying symbols co-ordinately related. By way of further clarification, each type is illustrated by example. Note that the sequence of major types—*E*, *B*, *A*, *C*, *D*—follows the order of textual chapter treatment.

Following the key is a suggested pattern to guide the student in systematic classification procedure. Since *E* and *B* criteria take priority over the other types, station classification should start with these two types, and in the order given. A list of unidentified stations is appended to serve the purpose of drill and testing.

And finally, some representative questions are added to indicate several types of geographic thinking involved in climate-landscape analysis.

TAXONOMIC KEY

	Type and Subtype	Symbol
1. Warmest month below 50.	HIGH LATITUDE OR HIGH ALTITUDE	E
Warmest month below 32	Frigid	EF

EISMITTE, GREENLAND *

J	F	M	A	M	J	J	A	S	O	N	D	Year
–43	–53	–40	–26	–6	2	10	–1	–8	–33	–45	–37	–23
0.6	0.2	0.3	0.2	0.1	0.1	0.1	0.4	0.3	0.5	0.5	1.0	4.3

2. Warmest month above 32 .... Tundra — ET

TIKSI BAY, U.S.S.R.

J	F	M	A	M	J	J	A	S	O	N	D	Year
–18	–18	–25	–5	19	36	45	45	36	12	–16	–30	7
0.1	0.1	0.1	0	0.1	0.5	1.7	0.8	0.8	0.2	0.2	0.1	4.7

1. Warmest month above 50 .... MIDDLE OR LOW LATITUDE — B, A, C, or D
   2. Annual rainfall less than the following applicable formula indicates:
      .44 (t-32), where rainfall of cooler six-month period is 70 per cent or more of the total; or
      .44 (t-7), where rainfall of warmer six-month period is 70 per cent or more of the total; or
      .44 (t-19.5), where rainfall is less unequally distributed ...... DRY — B
      3. Annual rainfall more than one-half of that shown in the formulae given .... *Semiarid Steppe* — BS
         4. Mean temperature below 64; warmest month above 64 — Cool Steppe — BSk
            5. At least 70 per cent of the rainfall in warmer six-month period .... — BSkw

PIERRE, U.S.A.

J	F	M	A	M	J	J	A	S	O	N	D	Year
17	20	33	48	59	69	75	74	64	51	35	22	47
0.5	0.5	1.0	1.8	2.5	2.7	2.4	2.1	1.2	1.0	0.5	0.5	16.7

5. At least 70 per cent of the rainfall in cooler six-month period .... — BSks

SAN DIEGO, U.S.A.

J	F	M	A	M	J	J	A	S	O	N	D	Year
55	56	57	60	62	64	68	69	68	64	61	57	62
1.9	2.1	1.5	0.7	0.3	0.1	0.1	0.1	0.1	0.4	0.9	2.0	10.2

4. Mean temperature below 64; warmest month below 64 — Cold Steppe — BSk′
   5. At least 70 per cent of the rainfall in warmer six-month period .... — BSk′w
4. Mean temperature above 64 .... Hot Steppe — BSh
   5. At least 70 per cent of the rainfall in warmer six-month period .... — BShw

*All meteorological data in this appendix are from Air Ministry, Meteorological Office, H. M. Stationery Office, London, 1958. By permission of the Controller of Her Majesty's Stationery Office. Temperature data are in Fahrenheit (monthly averages derived from maximum and minimum readings); precipitation, in inches of rainfall.

Type and Subtype — *Symbol*

CLONCURRY, AUSTRALIA

J	F	M	A	M	J	J	A	S	O	N	D	Year
88	86	84	79	72	66	64	69	75	82	86	88	78
4.4	4.2	2.4	0.7	0.5	0.6	0.3	0.1	0.3	0.5	1.3	2.7	18.0

5. At least 70 per cent of the rainfall in cooler six-month period .... BShs

BUSHIRE, IRAN

J	F	M	A	M	J	J	A	S	O	N	D	Year
58	59	66	74	83	87	90	91	87	80	71	62	76
2.9	1.8	0.8	0.4	0	0	0	0	0	0.1	1.6	3.2	10.8

3. Annual rainfall less than one-half of that shown in the formulae given .... *True Desert* — BW
   4. Mean temperature below 64; warmest month above 64 Cool Desert — BWk
      5. At least 70 per cent of the rainfall in warmer six-month period .... BWkw

CHIU-CH'UAN, CHINA

J	F	M	A	M	J	J	A	S	O	N	D	Year
17	26	36	49	61	69	75	71	61	51	31	20	47
0	0.1	0.1	0.1	0.1	0.5	0.5	1.1	0.3	0	0.1	0.1	3.0

5. At least 70 per cent of the rainfall in cooler six-month period .... BWks

4. Mean temperature below 64; warmest month below 64 Cold Desert — BWk'

SANTA CRUZ, ARGENTINA

J	F	M	A	M	J	J	A	S	O	N	D	Year
59	59	55	48	42	36	35	39	44	49	52	56	48
0.6	0.3	0.3	0.6	0.4	0.5	0.4	0.5	0.3	0.3	0.4	0.7	5.3

5. At least 70 per cent of the rainfall in warmer six-month period .... BWk'w

4. Mean temperature above 64 .... Hot Desert — BWh

PHOENIX, U.S.A.

J	F	M	A	M	J	J	A	S	O	N	D	Year
52	56	61	68	76	85	91	89	83	71	60	53	70
0.8	0.8	0.7	0.4	0.1	0.1	1.0	1.0	0.7	0.4	0.6	0.9	7.5

5. At least 70 per cent of the rainfall in warmer six-month period .... BWhw

ALICE SPRINGS, AUSTRALIA

J	F	M	A	M	J	J	A	S	O	N	D	Year
89	82	77	68	60	54	53	58	65	73	79	82	69
1.7	1.3	1.1	0.4	0.6	0.5	0.3	0.3	0.3	0.7	1.2	1.5	9.9

5. At least 70 per cent of the rainfall in cooler six-month period .... BWhs

	Type and Subtype	*Symbol*

CAIRO, EGYPT

J	F	M	A	M	J	J	A	S	O	N	D	Year
56	59	64	70	77	82	83	83	69	76	68	59	72
0.2	0.2	0.2	0.1	0.1	0	0	0	0	0	0.1	0.2	1.1

	Type and Subtype	Symbol
2. Annual rainfall more than the formula value for the B boundary	HUMID	A, C, or D
3. Coldest month above 64	*Tropical*	A
4. Rainfall of driest month at least 2.4	Rainforest	Af(i)*

SINGAPORE, MALAYA

J	F	M	A	M	J	J	A	S	O	N	D	Year
80	81	82	82	82	82	82	81	81	81	81	81	81
9.9	6.8	7.6	7.4	6.8	6.8	6.7	7.7	7.0	8.2	10.0	10.1	95.0

	Type and Subtype	Symbol
4. Rainfall of driest month less than 2.4, but more than the formula value .04(98.5-r)†	Rainforest Monsoon	Am(i)

MIAMI, U.S.A.

J	F	M	A	M	J	J	A	S	O	N	D	Year
68	68	71	74	78	80	82	82	81	78	72	69	75
2.8	2.1	2.5	3.2	6.8	7.0	6.1	6.3	8.0	9.2	2.8	2.0	59.7

	Type and Subtype	Symbol
4. Rainfall of the driest month less than .04(98.5-r)...	Savannah	Aw(i) or As(i)
5. Maximum rainfall in high-sun period		Aw(i)
6. Maximum temperature before high-sun solstice		Awg(i)

CALCUTTA, INDIA

J	F	M	A	M	J	J	A	S	O	N	D	Year
68	72	81	86	87	86	84	84	84	82	74	67	80
0.4	1.2	1.4	1.7	5.5	11.7	12.8	12.9	9.9	4.5	0.8	0.2	63.0

	Type and Subtype	Symbol
5. Maximum rainfall in low-sun period		As(i)
3. Coldest month between 27 and 64...	*Mid-Latitude; Mild Winter*	C
4. Rainfall of the rainiest month of winter at least three times the rainfall of the driest month of summer; driest month less than 1.6	Summer-Dry	Cs
5. Warmest month above 72	Interior	Csa

ROME, ITALY

J	F	M	A	M	J	J	A	S	O	N	D	Year
47	48	52	57	65	71	76	76	72	63	55	49	61
2.7	2.3	1.5	1.7	2.0	1.0	0.6	0.9	2.7	3.7	3.8	2.8	25.7

	Type and Subtype	Symbol
5. Warmest month below 72	West Coast	Csb
6. Hottest month in fall		Csbt′

* The letter "i" is added without parentheses where there is a temperature range of less than 9 degrees between the coolest and the warmest month. This may occur also in other categories, such as in Am, Aw, ET, Cfb, and Cwb types.

† The letter "r" stands for "annual rainfall"; if the annual rainfall is 98.5 or more, and the rainfall of the driest month less than 2.4, the station is Am.

Type and Subtype — *Symbol*

SAN FRANCISCO, U.S.A.

J	F	M	A	M	J	J	A	S	O	N	D	Year
50	53	55	56	57	59	59	59	62	61	60	52	57
4.7	3.8	3.1	1.5	0.7	0.1	0	0	0.3	1.0	2.5	4.4	22.1

4. Rainfall of the rainiest month of summer at least ten times the rainfall of the driest month of winter........Winter-Dry — Cw
   5. Warmest month above 72 .... Cwa

HONG KONG, CHINA

J	F	M	A	M	J	J	A	S	O	N	D	Year
60	59	64	71	78	82	83	83	81	77	70	64	73
1.3	1.8	2.9	5.4	11.5	15.5	15.0	14.2	10.1	4.5	1.7	1.2	85.1

5. Warmest month below 72 .... Cwb

JOHANNESBURG, REPUBLIC OF SOUTH AFRICA

J	F	M	A	M	J	J	A	S	O	N	D	Year
68	68	65	66	55	51	51	56	61	65	66	68	61
4.5	4.3	3.5	1.5	1.0	0.3	0.3	0.3	0.9	2.2	4.2	4.9	27.9

4. Rainfall less unequally distributed....Continuously Humid — Cf
   5. Warmest month above 72 ....Interior; East Coast — Cfa
      6. Maximum rainfall in spring .... Cfax

ST. LOUIS, U.S.A.

J	F	M	A	M	J	J	A	S	O	N	D	Year
32	35	45	56	66	75	80	78	71	59	56	36	57
2.3	2.5	3.5	3.8	4.5	4.5	3.5	3.4	3.2	2.9	2.8	2.5	39.4

5. Warmest month below 72; at least 4 months above 50 West Coast; (East Coast) — Cfb

PARIS, FRANCE

J	F	M	A	M	J	J	A	S	O	N	D	Year
37	39	44	51	57	63	66	65	60	52	44	38	51
1.5	1.3	1.5	1.7	2.0	2.1	2.1	2.0	2.0	2.2	2.0	1.9	22.3

SITKA, U.S.A.

J	F	M	A	M	J	J	A	S	O	N	D	Year
33	34	37	41	47	52	55	56	52	46	39	35	44
7.8	6.7	6.1	5.5	4.2	3.3	4.3	7.2	10.4	12.8	10.2	9.1	87.4

LOS EVANGELISTAS, CHILE

J	F	M	A	M	J	J	A	S	O	N	D	Year
47	46	44	44	43	40	38	39	40	41	42	44	44
11.7	10.0	11.3	11.4	9.6	9.4	9.4	8.6	9.2	8.8	9.9	10.1	119.4

5. Warmest month below 72; less than 4 months above 50 West Coast — Cfc

Type and Subtype — *Symbol*

REYKJAVIK, ICELAND

J	F	M	A	M	J	J	A	S	O	N	D	Year
32	33	35	38	45	50	53	52	47	40	36	34	42
4.0	3.1	3.0	2.1	1.6	1.7	2.0	2.6	3.1	3.4	3.6	3.7	33.9

3. Coldest month below 27 ....*Mid-Latitude; Severe Winter* — D
   4. Rainfall of the rainiest month of winter at least three times the rainfall of the driest month of summer; driest month less than 1.6 ....Summer-Dry — Ds
      5. Warmest month above 72 .... — Dsa

YEREVAN, U.S.S.R.

J	F	M	A	M	J	J	A	S	O	N	D	Year
22	26	40	54	63	72	78	78	69	57	42	32	53
0.9	1.0	1.1	1.9	2.1	0.9	0.6	0.3	0.5	0.9	1.2	1.1	12.5

5. Warmest month below 72 .... — Dsb

VAN, TURKEY

J	F	M	A	M	J	J	A	S	O	N	D	Year
26	26	32	43	54	63	70	70	63	52	43	30	48
2.2	1.6	2.0	2.3	1.4	0.6	0.2	0.1	0.3	2.0	1.5	1.3	15.5

4. Rainfall of the rainiest month of summer at least ten times the rainfall of the driest month of winter ......Winter-Dry — Dw
   5. Warmest month above 72 .... — Dwa

MUKDEN, MANCHURIA

J	F	M	A	M	J	J	A	S	O	N	D	Year
11	17	32	49	62	73	78	71	64	50	32	15	47
0.3	0.3	0.7	1.1	2.7	3.3	7.2	6.7	2.5	1.4	1.1	0.6	27.9

5. Warmest month below 72; at least 4 months above 50.... — Dwb

VLADIVOSTOK, U.S.S.R.

J	F	M	A	M	J	J	A	S	O	N	D	Year
7	14	26	40	49	58	68	70	62	48	30	14	40
0.3	0.4	0.7	1.2	2.1	2.9	3.3	4.7	4.3	1.9	1.2	0.6	23.6

5. Less than 4 months above 50; coldest month above –36.. — Dwc

IRKUTSK, U.S.S.R.

J	F	M	A	M	J	J	A	S	O	N	D	Year
–6	–2	14	31	45	56	60	58	46	31	11	–4	29
0.5	0.4	0.3	0.6	1.3	2.2	3.1	2.8	1.7	0.7	0.6	0.6	14.9

5. Coldest month below –36 .... — Dwd

VERKHOYANSK, U.S.S.R.

J	F	M	A	M	J	J	A	S	O	N	D	Year
–59	–49	–26	5	33	54	57	49	35	5	–27	–54	1
0.2	0.2	0.1	0.2	0.3	0.9	1.1	1.0	0.5	0.3	0.3	0.2	5.3

4. Rainfall less unequally distributed.....Continuously Humid — Df
   5. Warmest month above 72.......................... — Dfa

Type and Subtype — *Symbol*

CHICAGO, U.S.A.

J	F	M	A	M	J	J	A	S	O	N	D	Year
25	27	36	48	58	68	74	72	66	54	41	30	50
2.0	2.0	2.6	2.8	3.4	3.5	3.3	3.2	2.1	2.6	2.4	2.0	32.9

5. Warmest month below 72; at least 4 months above 50. . . Dfb

MONTREAL, CANADA

J	F	M	A	M	J	J	A	S	O	N	D	Year
14	16	26	42	56	66	70	67	54	47	33	20	43
3.8	3.0	3.5	2.6	3.1	3.4	3.7	3.5	3.7	3.4	3.5	3.6	40.8

5. Less than 4 months above 50; coldest month above –36. . Dfc

DAWSON, CANADA

J	F	M	A	M	J	J	A	S	O	N	D	Year
–21	–12	4	29	47	57	60	55	42	26	2	–14	23
0.9	0.7	0.5	0.5	1.0	1.2	1.5	1.5	1.4	1.2	1.1	1.0	12.6

5. Coldest month below –36. . . . . Dfd

VILYUYSK, U.S.S.R.

J	F	M	A	M	J	J	A	S	O	N	D	Year
–41	–24	–6	14	36	54	61	55	40	17	–16	–39	13
0.3	0.3	0.3	0.2	0.8	1.4	1.4	1.6	1.2	0.6	0.5	0.4	9.0

EXAMPLES ILLUSTRATING STEPS IN IDENTIFICATION

Type and Subtype — *Symbol*

TIKSI BAY, U.S.S.R.

J	F	M	A	M	J	J	A	S	O	N	D	Year
–18	–18	–25	–5	19	36	45	45	36	12	–16	–30	7
0.1	0.1	0.1	0	0.1	0.5	1.7	0.8	0.8	0.2	0.2	0.1	4.7

1. Warmest month below 50. HIGH LATITUDE OR HIGH ALTITUDE — E
   2. Warmest month above 32 . . . . Tundra — ET

CAIRO, EGYPT

J	F	M	A	M	J	J	A	S	O	N	D	Year
56	59	64	70	77	82	83	83	69	76	68	59	72
0.2	0.2	0.2	0.1	0.1	0	0	0	0	0	0.1	0.2	1.1

1. Warmest month above 50. . . . . MIDDLE OR LOW LATITUDE — B, A, C, or D
   2. Annual rainfall less than .44 (t-32). . . . . DRY — B
      3. Annual rainfall less than one-half of .44 (t-32). . . . *True Desert* — BW
         4. Mean temperature above 64. . . . . Hot Desert — BWh
            5. At least 70 per cent of the rainfall in cooler six-month period . . . . — BWhs

CALCUTTA, INDIA

J	F	M	A	M	J	J	A	S	O	N	D	Year
68	72	81	86	87	86	84	84	84	82	74	67	80
0.4	1.2	1.4	1.7	5.5	11.7	12.8	12.9	9.9	4.5	0.8	0.2	63.0

	Type and Subtype	*Symbol*
1. Warmest month above 50	MIDDLE OR LOW LATITUDE	B, A, C, or D
2. Annual rainfall more than .44 (t-7)	HUMID	A, C, or D
3. Coldest month above 64	*Tropical*	A
4. Rainfall of the driest month less than .04(98.5-r)	Savannah	Aw
5. Maximum rainfall in high-sun period		Aw
6. Maximum temperature before high-sun solstice		Awg

SAN FRANCISCO, U.S.A.

J	F	M	A	M	J	J	A	S	O	N	D	Year
50	53	55	56	57	59	59	59	62	61	60	52	57
4.7	3.8	3.1	1.5	0.7	0.1	0	0	0.3	1.0	2.5	4.4	22.1

	Type and Subtype	*Symbol*
1. Warmest month above 50	MIDDLE OR LOW LATITUDE	B, A, C, or D
2. Annual rainfall more than .44 (t-32)	HUMID	A, C, or D
3. Coldest month between 27 and 64	*Mid-Latitude; Mild Winter*	C
4. Rainfall of the rainiest month of winter at least three times the rainfall of the driest month of the summer; driest month less than 1.6	Summer-Dry	Cs
5. Warmest month below 72		Csb
6. Hottest month in fall		Csbt′

IRKUTSK, U.S.S.R.

J	F	M	A	M	J	J	A	S	O	N	D	Year
–6	–2	14	31	45	56	60	58	46	31	11	–4	29
0.5	0.4	0.3	0.6	1.3	2.2	3.1	2.8	1.7	0.7	0.6	0.6	14.9

	Type and Subtype	*Symbol*
1. Warmest month above 50	MIDDLE OR LOW LATITUDE	B, A, C, or D
2. Annual rainfall more than .44 (t-7)	HUMID	A, C, or D
3. Coldest month below 27	*Mid-Latitude; Severe Winter*	D
4. Rainfall of the rainiest month of summer at least ten times the rainfall of the driest month of winter	Winter-Dry	Dw
5. Less than 4 months above 50; coldest month above –36		Dwc

LIST OF CLIMATIC STATIONS FOR CLASSIFICATION DRILL AND TESTS

	J	F	M	A	M	J	J	A	S	O	N	D	Year
1.	21	24	37	51	61	71	76	74	66	54	39	26	50
	1.1	1.1	1.8	2.9	4.4	4.8	3.4	3.6	3.6	2.5	1.5	1.2	31.9
2.	–42	–35	–18	1	22	44	52	48	34	10	–23	–35	5
	0.3	0.2	0.3	0.3	0.5	1.0	1.5	1.6	1.5	0.9	0.4	0.3	8.8
3.	10	26	45	56	65	71	76	73	65	54	35	19	49
	0.1	0.1	0.2	0.1	0.1	1.3	0.7	0.3	0.2	0	0	0.3	3.4
4.	75	75	79	83	86	84	81	81	81	83	81	78	81
	0.1	0.1	0.1	0	0.7	19.1	24.3	13.4	10.4	2.5	0.5	0.1	71.2
5.	45	48	54	63	75	84	91	90	82	70	59	48	67
	2.8	3.1	2.1	1.9	0.7	0	0	0	0	0.2	1.9	2.4	15.0

	J	F	M	A	M	J	J	A	S	O	N	D	Year
6.	81	82	84	86	84	80	79	80	80	81	82	81	82
	0.9	0.8	2.0	4.9	11.7	28.5	23.3	13.9	7.7	13.4	6.7	1.6	115.3
7.	39	42	47	52	57	63	67	67	62	55	47	42	53
	6.1	5.2	4.6	2.8	2.1	1.6	0.5	0.6	1.8	3.3	6.2	7.0	41.8
8.	58	60	67	74	82	84	84	84	82	75	67	64	74
	0.8	1.4	1.9	3.2	7.0	8.5	9.0	9.1	5.6	2.5	1.2	0.8	51.0
9.	59	59	59	59	59	58	58	59	59	59	59	59	59
	3.9	4.4	5.6	6.9	5.4	1.7	0.8	1.2	2.7	4.4	3.8	3.1	43.9
10.	–49	–34	–10	17	40	58	64	58	42	17	–20	–43	12
	0.3	0.2	0.1	0.3	0.4	1.1	1.6	1.3	1.0	0.5	0.4	0.3	7.4
11.	69	68	65	60	53	48	48	51	54	59	63	67	59
	0.1	0.1	0.2	0.5	2.5	3.3	3.0	2.2	1.2	0.6	0.3	0.2	14.1
12.	–33	–19	–1	22	40	57	64	57	44	23	–7	–29	18
	0.3	0.2	0.2	0.3	0.6	1.5	1.6	2.0	1.1	0.6	0.5	0.4	9.3
13.	–10	–1	35	37	52	64	71	69	54	37	11	–8	33
	0.1	0.1	0.3	0.9	1.6	3.3	4.4	4.5	2.7	0.7	0.3	0.1	19.0
14.	–16	–19	–15	–1	19	34	40	39	31	17	1	–11	10
	0.2	0.1	0.1	0.1	0.1	0.3	0.9	0.8	0.5	0.5	0.3	0.2	4.1
15.	55	58	63	69	76	81	83	83	80	72	63	56	70
	4.6	4.2	4.7	4.8	4.5	5.5	6.6	5.8	4.8	3.5	3.8	4.6	57.4
16.	24	29	38	52	62	71	77	79	69	56	42	29	52
	1.2	0.8	1.5	3.0	3.2	5.1	14.8	10.5	4.7	1.6	1.8	1.0	49.2
17.	75	77	83	89	92	93	89	87	90	90	83	77	85
	0	0	0	0	0.1	0.3	2.1	2.8	0.7	0.2	0	0	6.2
18.	77	76	73	69	62	57	57	62	69	76	77	77	70
	4.1	3.6	3.6	1.5	0.3	0	0	0	0.1	0.9	1.7	2.6	18.4
19.	78	76	71	65	57	51	51	56	62	68	72	75	65
	2.4	2.5	3.1	1.5	0.7	0.2	0.2	0.3	0.6	1.0	1.6	2.0	16.1
20.	–11	1	10	30	47	59	60	55	44	27	4	–8	27
	0.9	0.5	0.7	0.3	0.6	1.3	1.9	2.1	1.3	0.8	0.7	0.6	11.7
21.	8	12	24	37	47	58	64	63	55	44	30	16	38
	1.0	1.0	1.5	2.0	3.2	4.1	3.8	3.2	3.5	2.4	1.5	1.1	28.3
22.	6	12	23	40	51	58	62	56	50	41	25	13	37
	0.9	0.6	0.8	0.9	1.9	3.1	3.3	2.3	1.3	0.7	0.7	0.8	17.3
23.	79	80	80	81	80	80	81	82	83	83	82	80	81
	14.4	12.3	15.8	18.9	21.7	15.5	6.9	2.8	1.2	1.3	4.6	10.7	126.4
24.	37	37	42	48	56	60	64	63	59	51	42	38	50
	2.6	2.0	2.4	2.5	2.5	2.6	3.5	3.0	2.6	3.0	3.1	3.2	33.0
25.	53	57	63	71	78	83	83	82	79	72	65	57	70
	0.2	0	0	0.2	0.4	0.1	0.1	0.4	0.1	0	0	0	1.5

	J	F	M	A	M	J	J	A	S	O	N	D	Year
26.	–8	–13	–11	–1	22	36	41	38	27	16	5	–9	12
	0.1	0.1	0.1	0.1	0.1	0.2	0.5	0.5	0.4	0.1	0.1	0.2	2.5
27.	47	49	57	63	71	79	82	81	77	69	60	49	65
	0.8	1.0	0.9	0.5	0.2	0.1	0	0	0.1	0.4	0.6	0.7	5.3
28.	35	36	37	39	44	48	52	51	47	41	38	47	42
	6.2	4.8	4.6	3.7	3.3	3.0	3.1	3.8	5.5	6.1	5.4	5.8	55.3
29.	79	79	79	79	78	78	76	76	77	77	77	77	78
	2.1	3.3	7.0	6.2	5.4	4.5	5.2	6.5	7.2	8.6	7.8	3.3	67.1
30.	57	57	60	65	71	76	80	82	80	75	67	60	69
	7.5	6.2	3.7	2.2	0.7	0.1	0	0	0.2	2.0	5.2	7.3	35.1
31.	80	80	81	83	83	82	82	82	82	82	81	80	81
	19.0	10.9	8.6	4.5	6.2	7.4	6.7	7.9	9.3	10.2	14.5	18.5	123.7
32.	71	71	68	63	56	52	52	57	63	68	69	71	63
	5.0	4.3	4.5	1.7	0.9	0.6	0.3	0.2	0.8	2.2	5.2	5.2	30.9
33.	77	77	77	79	80	82	82	82	81	81	79	78	80
	0.9	0.6	0.9	1.2	4.0	3.5	1.5	3.6	3.9	7.1	2.9	1.4	31.5
34.	62	64	69	76	82	85	85	84	82	78	71	66	76
	0.7	1.1	1.5	3.2	7.7	9.4	12.7	13.5	10.0	3.9	1.7	0.8	66.2
35.	25	25	35	56	58	68	73	71	64	52	40	30	49
	2.1	2.1	2.5	2.5	3.3	3.6	3.3	2.7	2.8	2.4	2.4	2.3	32.0
36.	6	6	16	30	41	51	58	55	45	33	20	10	31
	1.2	1.1	1.1	0.7	1.3	1.9	2.6	2.7	2.2	1.9	1.6	1.3	19.8
37.	31	31	38	50	61	69	74	70	70	59	44	35	48
	3.7	3.8	3.6	3.2	3.2	3.3	4.2	4.3	3.4	3.5	3.0	3.6	43.0
38.	32	37	42	48	55	63	71	70	61	52	42	34	51
	1.5	1.1	0.8	0.5	0.5	0.3	0.2	0.2	0.2	0.3	0.6	0.9	7.1
39.	41	42	50	56	59	61	62	61	60	56	48	43	53
	0.5	1.1	1.7	4.1	8.5	23.2	31.4	25.1	17.6	5.1	0.9	0.3	119.5
40.	48	49	53	60	69	76	81	81	75	67	58	52	64
	2.2	1.6	1.4	0.8	0.8	0.6	0.2	0.4	0.6	1.7	2.8	2.8	15.8

SELF-TESTING EXERCISE IN CHARACTERISTIC CLIMATE-LANDSCAPE ASSOCIATIONS

I. Analyze as many of the above listed stations as is necessary to acquire facility (i.e., instant inspection) in identifying the types of climates they represent.

II. Compose a set of hypothetical temperature and rainfall data representative of each of the three- or four-symbol climatic types. This is probably the best test for climatic classification competence.

	J	F	M	A	M	J	J	A	S	O	N	D	Year
T.													
Rf.													

III. Select any one of the above published list of stations and "locate" its position in the world (i.e., the probable or possible countries, provinces, states, or important islands where one may expect to find a seasonal and annual situation with this type of climate). ....

....

IV. Areal Coherent Relationships: In blanks provided below, supply the symbol which, in your judgment, identifies the climate *most generally* associated with the feature indicated, in genetic or economic terms:

A. Landsurface—Soils Associations

1. mesa ....; 2. muskeg ....; 3. erg ....; 4. laterite ....;

5. chernozem ....; 6. podsol ....

In terms of both the length of the frost-free season and the amount of seasonal and annual rainfall, what type of station suggests excessive (a) soil leaching? ....; (b) soil erosion? ....; (c) floods? .... What landscape factors, other than climate, must be considered for each distinctive environmental situation? ....

B. Vegetation Associations

1. mixed deciduous and conifer, with the former predominating ....;

2. with the latter predominating ....; 3. rainforest..........;

4. taiga ....; 5. the greatest expanse of coniferous forest ....;

6. selva ....; 7. savannah ....; 8. steppe grass ....; 9. steppe shrub ....; 10. prairie ....; 11. the hottest and most desolate of deserts ....; 12. heath and moor ....; 13. tundra ....

C. Animal Life Associations

1. tsetse fly (sleeping sickness) ....; 2. "big game" hunting ....;

3. fox-fur trapping or farming ....; 4. camel caravan ....

D. Population—Settlement Associations (supply both climatic realm symbol, and specific area):

1. sparsest population ....

2. densest population ....

3. highest material standard of living ....

4. How do you account for disparate densities of population—often most markedly—in different areas of essentially the same type of climate? ....

....

....

5. Select at least two different station types and indicate the probable settlement pattern and house types. ....

....

....

E. Agricultural Associations

1. nomadism ....; 2. milpa ....; 3. climax pastoral and dairying ....; 4. fox-fur farming ....; 5. summer-irrigated crops ....; 6. winter-irrigated crops ....; 7. dried fruits ....; 8. spring wheat ....; 9. rye and buckwheat ....; 10. cotton ....; 11. corn ....; 12. floriculture ....; 13. sugar cane ....; 14. beet sugar ....; 15. coffee ....; 16. rubber ....

F. Industrial Associations

1. most intense complex manufacturing ....; 2. lumbering ....; 3. fishing ....; 4. recreation industry ....; 5. movie industry ....; 6. perfume industry ....

G. National Viability (Economic-Political-Military) Associations

1. As far as climate or climates are concerned, which of the major world powers seems to have the best set-up? ....; which, the most challenging? .... 2. Evaluate the U.S. and the U.S.S.R. in terms of "problem" climates, using the appropriate numbered stations above to illustrate. ....

....

....

....

....

....

....

....

....

....

....

....

POPULATION MAP

HAWAII
LINE ISLANDS
MARQUESAS IS
COOK IS
SOCIETY IS
TUAMOTU ARCH
C A N A D
UNITED STATES
GREENLAND
ICELAND
NEWFOUNDLAND
GUATEMALA
BR HOND
EL SALVADOR
HONDURAS
CUBA
BAHAMA IS
NICARAGUA
JAMAICA
COSTA RICA
HAITI
DOMINICAN REPUBLIC
PANAMA
PUERTO RICO
ECUADOR
COLOMBIA
VENEZUELA
TRINIDAD
BR GUIANA
SURINAM
FR. GUIANA
BOLIVIA
BRAZIL
ARGENTINA
FALKLAND IS
AZORES
EIRE
PORTUGAL
CANARY IS
SPANISH SAHARA
CAPE VERDE IS
GAMBIA
PORT GUINEA
SIERRA LEONE
LIBERIA
GOLD COAST

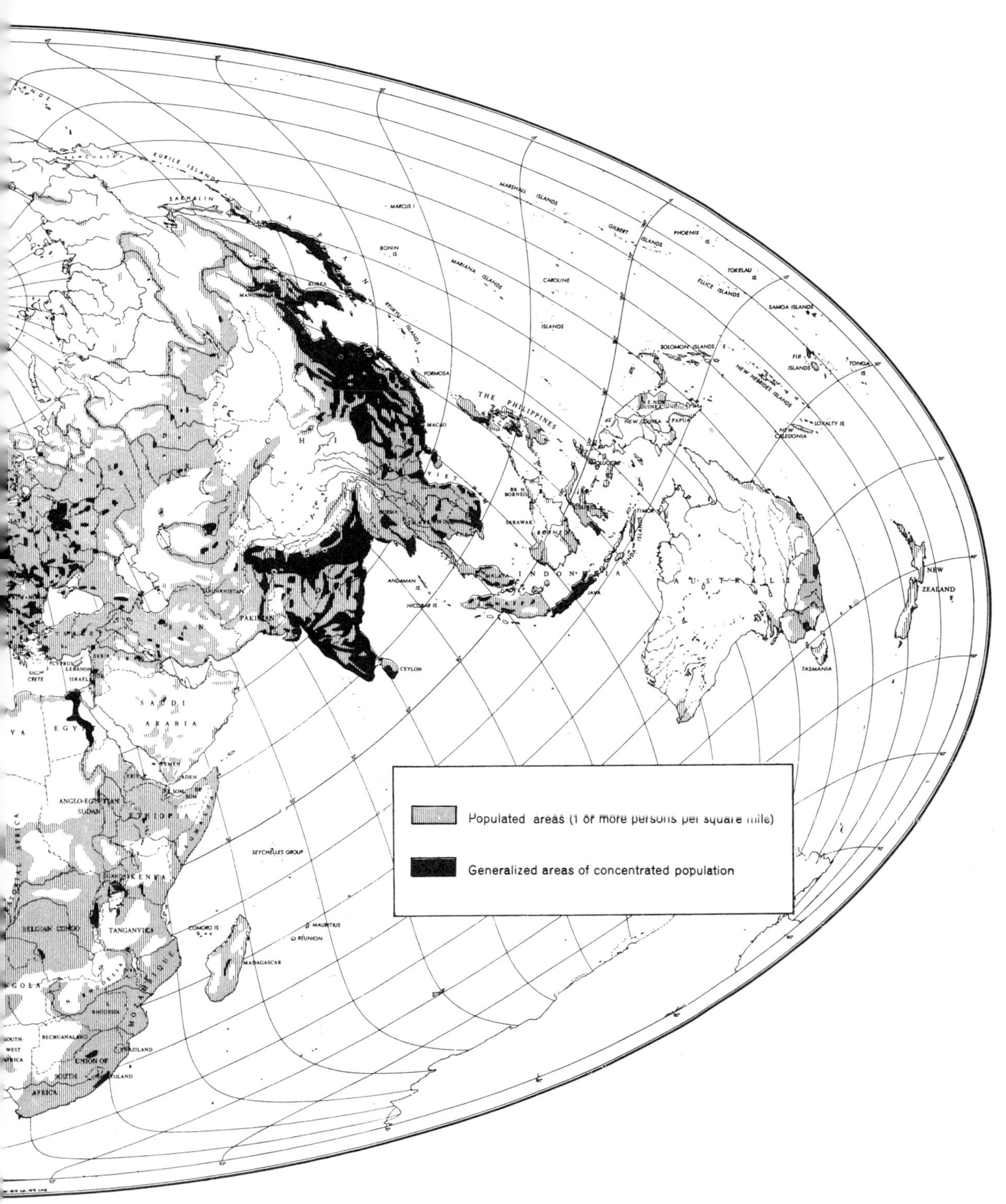

Courtesy *The Geographical Review*, The American Geographical Society

Index

DATE DUE
ÉCHEANCE

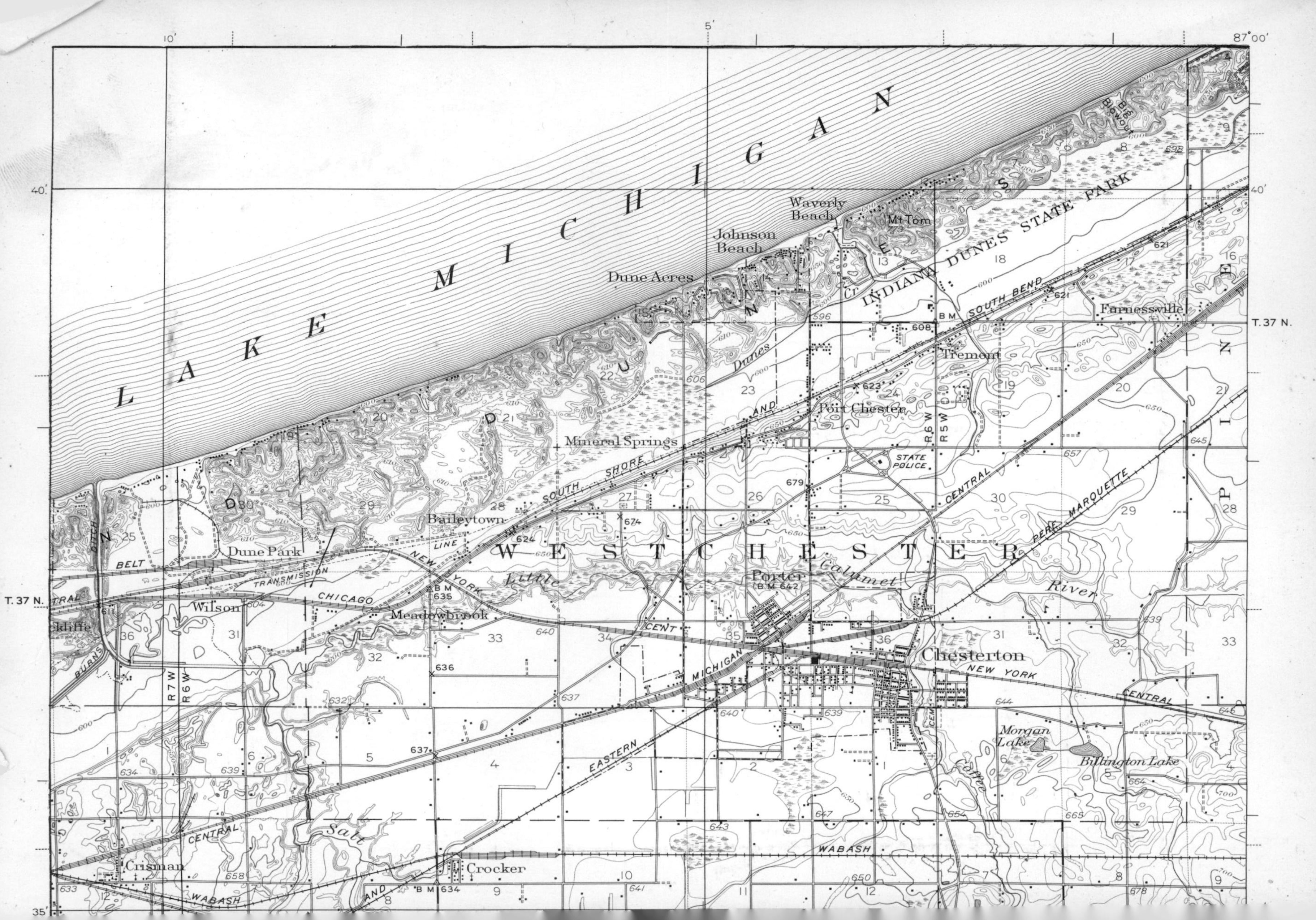

LAKE MICHIGAN
INDIANA DUNES STATE PARK
DUNES
WESTCHESTER
Chesterton
Porter
B M 642
Port Chester
Tremont
Furnessville
Waverly Beach
Johnson Beach
Dune Acres
Mt Tom
Big Blowout
Mineral Springs
Baileytown
Dune Park
Wilson
Meadowbrook
Crocker
Crisman
Morgan Lake
Billington Lake
Little Calumet River
Coffee Cr
Salt Cr
Burns Ditch
STATE POLICE
SOUTH SHORE AND SOUTH BEND
NEW YORK CENTRAL
MICHIGAN CENTRAL
PERE MARQUETTE
WABASH
EASTERN
CHICAGO
BELT LINE
TRANSMISSION LINE
T. 37 N.
R 7 W
R 6 W
R 5 W
87°00′
40′
35′
10′
5′